THIRD EDITION

OPERATIONS MANAGEMENT

Strategy and Analysis

LEE J. KRAJEWSKI   and   **LARRY P. RITZMAN**
The Ohio State University   *Boston College*

ADDISON-WESLEY PUBLISHING COMPANY

Reading, Massachusetts • Menlo Park, California • New York • Don Mills, Ontario • Wokingham, England
Amsterdam • Bonn • Sydney • Singapore • Tokyo • Madrid • San Juan • Milan ■ Paris

Sponsoring Editor   *Mac Mendelsohn*
Text Development Editor   *Sue Gleason*
Art Development Editor   *Meredith Nightingale*
Senior Production Supervisor   *Jim Rigney*
Editorial-Production Service   *Woodstock Publishers' Services*
Copyeditor   *Joyce Grandy*
Text Designer   *Karen Mason*
Cover Designer   *Peter Blaiwas*
Layout Artist   *Woodstock Publishers' Services*
Illustrators   *Network Graphics and Jim Bryant*
Art Coordinator   *Geri Davis, Quadrata, Inc.*
Photo Researcher   *Laurel Anderson, Photosynthesis*
Senior Marketing Manager   *Dave Theisen*
Prepress Services Manager   *Sarah McCracken*
Senior Manufacturing Manager   *Roy Logan*

PHOTO CREDITS

p. 11, Courtesy of Honda of America Manufacturing, Inc.; p. 19, Courtesy of Precision, Tune, Inc.; p. 20, © 1992 Bechtel Corporation/photo by Philip Jones Griffiths/Magnum; p. 32, Courtesy of Zoom Telephonics, Inc.; p. 39, Courtesy of Pizza Hut, Inc.; p. 53, Courtesy of Motorola Corporation; p. 57, Courtesy of Borden, Inc.; p. 70, Photos courtesy of Chaparral Steel Company; p. 110, Courtesy of General Motors, Inc.; p. 111, Courtesy of AT&T Archives; p. 112, Courtesy of NCR Corporation; p. 135, Courtesy of Motorola, Inc.; p. 139, Courtesy of Harley-Davidson, Inc.; p. 160, Courtesy of Hay and Forage Industries, Inc.; p. 181, Courtesy of K2 Corporation; p. 192, Courtesy of Wendy's International, Inc.; p. 217, H.P. Merten/The Stock Market; p. 222, Stephen Frisch/Stock Boston; p. 224, Courtesy of Motorola, Inc.; p. 228, Peter Vadnai/The Stock

(credits continued on page iv)

Library of Congress Cataloging-in-Publication Data

Krajewski, Lee J.
    Operations management : strategy and analysis / Lee J. Krajewski,
Larry P. Ritzman.—3rd ed.
        p.   cm.
    Includes bibliographical references and index.
    ISBN 0-201-56630-3
    1. Production management.   I. Ritzman, Larry P.   II. Title.
    TS155.K788   1992   92-12241
    658.5—dc20   CIP

ISBN 0-201-56630-3

1 2 3 4 5 6 7 8 9 10 DO 979695949392

Dedicated with love
to our families

Judie Krajewski

Gary, Jeff, Dan, and Jon

Virginia and Jerry;
Virginia and Larry

Barbara Ritzman

Todd, Karen, and Matt

Kathryn and Paul;
Mildred and Ray

Computer Solved Problems contributed by Owen P. Hall, Jr. Pepperdine University.

PREFACE

Our firm belief is that, to gain a competitive edge, organizations need a sound operations strategy. This conviction is particularly true today, considering the pressures from international competition, environmental concerns, and complicated ethical issues. The third edition of *Operations Management* reaffirms that view in light of the current issues facing operations managers. We approach the operations function as a potentially powerful tool for achieving organizational objectives and strategies.

The aim of our text is to help students become effective managers in today's competitive environment. With this in mind, we have several goals for the third edition. First, as many students taking the introductory course will go on to become managers in service or manufacturing organizations, we have made the challenge of managing this function the focus of our text. Second, we want students to discover the excitement to be found in the dynamic field of operations management by making the subject matter as lively and real as possible. Third, we want students to have an understanding of what operations managers do and to learn more about the tools they use to make better operating decisions.

The Textbook

The third edition of *Operations Management* contains comprehensive coverage of the basic concepts and issues taught in an introductory operations management course. It also provides comprehensive coverage of the material tested on the American Production and Inventory Control Society certification exams for the Certified Production and Inventory Management and the Certified Integrated Resource Management programs.

Philosophy. This revision reflects our philosophy that OM texts should address both the strategic importance and the analytic tools of operations management. We have woven strategic/managerial issues into the fabric of each chapter to emphasize that the decisions managers make in each topical area also relate to a common operations strategy. We present the tools and techniques for solving problems in the context of achieving a firm's overall goals and objectives. This philosophy is reflected in the organization of the text.

Organization. We have chosen a chronological organization that moves from strategic choices to design decisions to operating decisions. Chapters 1 and 2 explore how organizations use the operations function to gain a competitive edge. Discussion centers on strategic issues related to ethics, the environment, product planning, and competitive priorities and then solidifies these concepts with detailed tours of two real organizations: a hospital and a steel company. These introductory chapters are followed by Chapters 3 and 4, dealing with quality. In the third edition we have moved the chapter on statistical quality control to the front of the text, right after the chapter on quality management. The text now has a powerful two-chapter sequence on quality at its forefront, giving it the importance and visibility it deserves in the design of operating systems.

Chapters 5 through 10 address the trade-offs managers make in creating an operating system that will meet their firms' needs. Issues covered include process design, technology management, job design, capacity, location, and layout.

Having determined the appropriate design for their operations, managers must make successful operating decisions. Chapters 11 through 19 examine the issues managers face as they coordinate day-to-day activities consistent with an overall operations strategy. Topics covered include forecasting; materials management; independent-demand inventory systems; aggregate planning; master production scheduling; material requirements planning; just-in-time systems; and work force, operations, and project scheduling. Finally, Chapter 20 summarizes our broad view of operations as a competitive weapon.

If students are to gain a better understanding of the importance of operations management, an emphasis of its use in the real world is vital. Our general approach is to paint concepts in broad strokes, then to follow up with real-world applications whenever possible.

Flexibility. One of our goals was to write a textbook that offered considerable flexibility in order and depth of coverage, as well as in level (undergraduate or graduate). Thus instructors will find that our table of contents adapts smoothly to various course syllabi. Once Chapters 1 and 2 have been covered, instructors can easily rearrange chapters to suit their individual teaching needs. Those who wish to give more emphasis to applying quantitative methods to operations can assign any of the five supplements (Financial Analysis, Linear Programming, and so on) collected at the back of the book. These supplements are connected to earlier chapters through the advanced end-of-chapter problems.

Approach. The third edition contains expanded coverage of real companies addressing the issues of operations management. The two tours in Chapter 2 provide a closeup view of real operating systems. The managerial practices throughout the text emphasize the practicality of the topics discussed. Even our textbook applications of the methods and techniques presented in each chapter are realistic. The message to the student is clear: This text presents practical approaches to operations problems, and the solution to those problems can make a significant difference in the competitiveness of the firm.

For the third edition we made a special effort to provide a balanced treatment of manufacturing and services throughout the text. This approach helps the student view the field of operations management as a cohesive whole. In some chapters we have included a separate section addressing services, when sufficient differences between it and manufacturing so warrant. Likewise, we have provided a variety of service and manufacturing company examples throughout the text.

New Coverage. The bottom-line measure of success in the textbook business is acceptance in the marketplace. We are pleased that our first two editions were so well received. Thus a challenge in creating the new edition was deciding what to retain and what to change. To resolve that challenge we asked those who use the book, both instructors and students, what improvements they wanted to see and what new material they thought was necessary. We were able to incorporate most of their suggestions in the third edition.

To this edition we added the following new material to enhance our coverage of the ever-changing field of operations management:

- *Ethics and the environment.* Chapter 1 introduces the various issues of ethics and the environment facing operations managers today. This material is further reinforced in the discussion of process design in Chapter 5.
- *International operations.* The importance of understanding the nature of the globalization of operations is introduced in Chapter 1 and expanded upon in Chapter 9, on location decisions, and in Chapter 17, on just-in-time systems. The international dimension is also brought out in many other chapters featuring firms from around the globe.
- *Real-world tours.* Chapter 2 contains two new tours of real operations in considerable detail, enabling a good understanding of the operations of a hospital and a steel company.
- *Statistical quality control.* Chapter 4, at the end of the text in the second edition, has been moved to the front of this text and expanded to cover the basics of the sources of variability in outputs and the concept of process capability. The material on statistical process control has been moved forward in the chapter to reflect its relative importance to acceptance sampling.
- *Work team approaches.* Material on problem-solving teams, special-purpose teams, and self-managing teams has been added to Chapter 7 to address three current approaches to employee involvement.
- *Just-in-time systems.* A complete chapter has been devoted to just-in-time systems in the third edition. New material has been added to give a complete discussion of the elements of JIT systems and implementation issues.
- *Decision analysis.* A discussion of decision trees and their applications to capacity has been added to Chapter 8.
- *Service operations.* New material has been added to Chapter 6 on the new technologies available in the service sector. Additionally, more Managerial Practices, Applications, and discussion have been devoted to service operations throughout the text.

Teaching and Learning Aids

The third edition includes numerous features—some new to this edition—designed to motivate students and make this textbook a better teaching and learning tool. In addition, our goal throughout has been to present concepts as clearly as possible, in simplified language. Some of the teaching and learning aids we have used include the following.

Full-Color Art. The excitement of full-color art and photography has been used throughout the third edition to maximize the learning experience of the student. Rather than merely using color just for the sake of color, we have planned the use of color carefully to enhance the pedagogy of the text. Complex diagrams are now easier to understand because key elements are color-coded in a consistent manner and real objects are used to make concepts more concrete. Full-color photographs are used to support the text discussion when they complement and enhance the topic.

Chapter Outlines and Key Questions from Managers. Chapter outlines provide a quick overview of the topics covered in each chapter. In this edition the Key Questions from Managers—voices from the real world of operations management—are linked to the section of the chapter outline that addresses them.

Opening Vignettes. Each chapter opens with a real-life example of how a company coped with the problems addressed in the chapter.

"The Big Picture." Full-color, two-page renditions of the layouts of a hospital, a steel manufacturer, and a bakery can be found in Chapters 2 and 5 where each of these real applications are discussed.

Managerial Practices. Boxed cases, prominently displayed in the text, contain real-world applications of operations management. We replaced most of the cases from the second edition with new ones. Many of them are more detailed than earlier cases.

Applications. We have retained the popular feature of in-text applications, designed to help the students understand the quantitative material. Whenever we present a new technique, we immediately apply it to a problem and walk the reader through the solution.

Key Terms. Key terms are boldfaced and defined where they first appear in the text; these terms are also gathered at the end of the chapter and page-referenced for easy review.

Solved Problems and Formula Reviews. These special sections review key formulas and demonstrate in detail how to solve problems with the techniques presented in the text. The solved problems serve as models for students manually working homework problems and reinforce basic concepts.

Computer Solved Problems. New to the third edition are the Computer Solved Problems at the end of selected chapters. These problems provided by Owen Hall (Pepperdine University), demonstrate the power of the computer in analyzing operations problems. All were solved using Computer Models for Operations Management, which is also available packaged with the text.

Cases. Also new to the third edition is the inclusion of 12 cases at the end of selected chapters. These cases are more challenging than the typical problems at the end of the chapter and relate directly to the chapter content.

End-of-Chapter Problems. We added 20 percent more problems to the end of each chapter and updated at least 80 percent of the problems from the second edition. In addition, we divided the problems according to the level of difficulty to assist instructors in preparing assignments. In the advanced problem section, we reference the supplements containing background information useful for the analysis of certain problems.

Quantitative Supplements. The text contains five separate supplements: Financial Analysis, Linear Programming, Transportation Method of Linear Programming, Queuing Models, and Simulation Analysis. They are grouped at the end of the text to emphasize their multiple applications and to maximize flexibility of use. The problems associated with these supplements appear at the end of the appropriate chapter in the text, emphasizing the link between technique and problem area.

Ancillary Materials

From an instructor's perspective, having a good textbook to work with is only half the battle. We are committed to creating a total package that will maximize students' learning potential and ease the instructor's burden. To this end, the following ancillary materials are available.

Instructor's Manual. The *Instructor's Manual* includes extensive lecture notes and teaching tips for each chapter. Also included are a listing of useful videos and films and where to find them and a cross-referencing guide that indicates which problems in the third edition can be solved using various software packages.

Solutions Manual. We provide complete answers to all discussion questions, problems, and cases. Special attention is given to the art to allow easy conversion to transparency masters.

Test Item File and Computerized Test Item File. We have compiled approximately 1500 multiple-choice questions, complete with answers that have been checked carefully for accuracy. The questions are coded according to level of difficulty and include an equal number of conceptual and technique questions.

Both a printed version and a computerized version for the IBM PC® and compatibles are available at no cost to adopters. The computerized version, consisting of a program disk and several data disks, enables instrutors to custom-design their own quizzes and examinations.

Transparency Masters. More than 500 transparency masters feature key figures, diagrams, and problems. In excess of 250 of these masters are new visuals that do not appear in the text. Many of the new transparency masters are lists or partial solutions designed to complement the lecture notes in the *Instructor's Manual*.

Study Guide. Prepared by Nile R. Leach of Colorado State University, the *Study Guide* is an extremely useful tool that contains an overview of each chapter's contents, chapter highlights, key figures and tables from the book, self-testing material, and sidebars of helpful hints and interesting anecdotes.

Computer Models for Operations Management (CMOM). CMOM is a user-friendly, stand-alone package developed and newly updated by Owen P. Hall of Pepperdine University. CMOM was used to solve the Computer Solved Problems found at the end of various chapters. Basic requirements include an IBM PC® with 256K memory and DOS 2.1 or above. Designed to expand undergraduate and graduate students' learning horizons beyond the problems in the text, the software offers a potpourri of analytical tools for solving many of the quantitative problems encountered in an operations management course.

Videos. A number of video options are available for the third edition. *OM in Action*, produced, written, and directed by Jeff Heyl (DePaul University), provides a series of plant tours that actually teach operations management concepts. These tours include process choice at a large commercial bakery (illustrated in Chapter 5 as a "Big Picture"), capacity and queuing at a bank, and independent demand inventory at the newly automated Addison-Wesley warehouse. A series of MacNeil/Lehrer Business Reports are available, as is a video from Chaparral Steel, one of the plant tours included in Chapter 2. We will also continue to provide the Hewlett-Packard Just-in-Time video to adopters. Likewise, we continue to include a guide to outside video sources in the *Instructor's Manual*.

The Production Game™. Prepared by D. Keith Denton (Southwest Missouri State University). An operations management classroom simulation where students form their own company, produce products and services, and then seek ways to improve their performance. It is not a computer based game. An instructor's manual is available.

Full-Color Overhead Acetates. Approximately 100 full-color overhead acetates, depicting key figures and diagrams in the text, will be available for adoptors of the third edition.

The Student Edition of @RISK. This Lotus 1,2,3 add-in can be used to solve Monte Carlo simulation problems.

The Student Edition of WHAT-IF-SOLVER. This Lotus 1,2,3 add-in can be used to solve optimization problems.

The Student Edition of ForeCalc. This Lotus 1,2,3 add-in can be used to calculate time series forecasts.

Acknowledgments

This textbook could not have been revised without the help of a great many people. The entire Addison-Wesley publishing team has been a constant source of support and encouragement. Those most closely involved with the project and for whom we hold the greatest of admiration include Mac Mendelsohn, our executive editor, whose editorial judgment and ability to manage the many aspects of this project helped to create a quality product; Sue Gleason, our development editor, whose creativity and good humor helped all of us keep our sanity; Chere Bemelmans, who made sure that every paragraph was completely understandable; Joyce Grandy, whose ability as a copy editor turned rough copy into a polished gem; Jim Rigney, our production supervisor, who used methods of due-date scheduling and capacity planning to keep us on schedule; Barbara Gracia, production coordinator, who transformed raw manuscript into actual text pages; and Sheila Bendikian, supplements production coordinator, and Kim Kramer, Assistant Editor, who knew how to tactfully pour coals on a fire in the right places.

Reviewers. We also wish to thank a distinguished group of colleagues who provided extremely useful guidance for the third edition. They include R.C. Bunger, Cameron University; James A. Fitzsimmons, University of Texas at Austin; Tim Ireland, Oklahoma State University; Peter Kelly, Louisiana State University; J. Neves, Trenton State University; Mike Pesch, St. Cloud State University; Michael Pohlen, University of Delaware; Fred Raafat, San Diego State University; R. Daniel Reid, University of New Hampshire; S. Samaddar, Bryant College; Kathryn Stecke, University of Michigan; Sam Wathen, University of Georgia; and Jack Yurkiewicz, Pace University. We also would like to thank Edward A. Silver, University of Calgary, for his detailed suggestions for improvement, many of which we were able to incorporate in this edition.

We also wish to thank colleagues on the Faculty of Management Sciences, especially W.C. Benton, David Collier, Jim Hutchison, Keong Leong, David Synder, and Peter Ward, for their helpful suggestions. The Ohio State University Ph.D. students, including Tim Baker, Ken Boyer, Donavon Favre, Linda Katunich, Abe Kucukarslan, Ling Li, John McCreery, Seungwook Park, and Darryl Wilson, have provided many valuable inputs. We also want to thank Barry Kay, Boston College and Mark Miskie, Ohio State University, for their help with the problem sections and cases. This support considerably lightened our burden.

Finally, we wish to thank our families for putting up with us during the long periods of solitude. Judie and Barb were 100 percent supportive of our efforts and even pretended that they did not know the third revision was about to start as we began our traditional elegant dinner the previous evening.

L.J.K.
Westerville, Ohio

L.P.R.
Medfield, Massachusetts

CONTENTS

PART TWO / DESIGN DECISIONS

PART THREE / OPERATING DECISIONS

Chapter 1

A FOCUS ON OPERATIONS

Key Questions from Managers

What are the implications of recent employment and productivity trends in the service sector?

How can we identify and deal with environmental change when formulating corporate strategy?

What is industry doing to meet various competitive challenges?

What are the causes of recent productivity trends and shifts in shares of world markets?

How does operations strategy relate to corporate strategy?

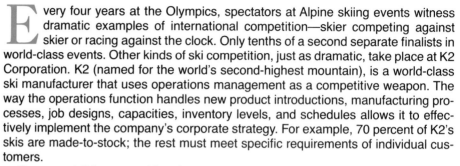

Every four years at the Olympics, spectators at Alpine skiing events witness dramatic examples of international competition—skier competing against skier or racing against the clock. Only tenths of a second separate finalists in world-class events. Other kinds of ski competition, just as dramatic, take place at K2 Corporation. K2 (named for the world's second-highest mountain), is a world-class ski manufacturer that uses operations management as a competitive weapon. The way the operations function handles new product introductions, manufacturing processes, job designs, capacities, inventory levels, and schedules allows it to effectively implement the company's corporate strategy. For example, 70 percent of K2's skis are made-to-stock; the rest must meet specific requirements of individual customers.

To support this competitive thrust, operations devotes some facilities to high-volume stock items and others to low-volume specials. Quality consistency, an important basis on which K2 competes, is achieved in part by having operators responsible for quality at their own work stations. They are trained to monitor critical quality measures. To handle product variety, K2 installed general-purpose machinery that allowed easy changeovers from one product to another. It also invested in a triaxial braiding process, which gave designers greater control over longitudinal and torsional flexes in the skis. Machine maintenance is carefully managed because the plant runs at full capacity. K2 prepares for heavy seasonal sales with a production plan that calls for building finished goods inventories from January to May. It develops schedules for specific products that take into account tight molding press capacities.

As a result of such choices, K2 is winning the race against its competitors. It is the largest domestic manufacturer of skis, selling over 300,000 pairs per year and employing about 400 people worldwide. As is the case with so many real company examples described in this text, operations management is a key weapon in the arsenal of world-class competitors.

Operations management deals with the production of goods and services that we buy and use every day. It is the process that enables organizations to achieve their goals through efficient acquisition and utilization of resources. Every organization, whether public or private, manufacturing or service, has an operations function. The management of that function is the focus of this book. We explore with you the role of operations within the total organization. We explain what operations managers do, as well as some of the latest tools and concepts they use to support key decisions. We show how, by selecting appropriate techniques and strategies, successful operations managers can give their companies a competitive edge. We hope that as you discover the full impact of operations on our standard of living and way of life, you will agree that operations management is one of the most exciting challenges the modern business world offers.

WHAT IS OPERATIONS MANAGEMENT?

Like other industrial societies, the United States is a society of organizations, ranging from sports teams, schools, and churches to hospitals, legal institutions, military complexes, and large and small businesses. These formal groups enable people to produce a vast range of products and services that would be beyond the capabilities of the individual. Operations management is crucial to each type of organization because only through successful management of people, capital, and materials can an organization meet its goals. Thus every organization has an operations function.

At one time, operations management referred primarily to manufacturing production. The emergence of a wide range of nonmanufacturing business activities, however, broadened the scope of the operations management function. Today, the term **operations management** refers to the systematic direction and control of the processes that transform inputs into finished goods and services. This function is essential to systems producing goods and services in both profit and nonprofit organizations.

As Fig. 1.1 illustrates, operations management is part of a production system. Inputs include human resources (workers and managers), capital (equipment and facilities), materials, land, and energy. The circles in the center of the figure represent the operations through which products, services, or customers may pass during the transformation process. Because operations encompass a variety of different situations, the types of transformations vary as well.

FIGURE 1.1

The Operations Management System

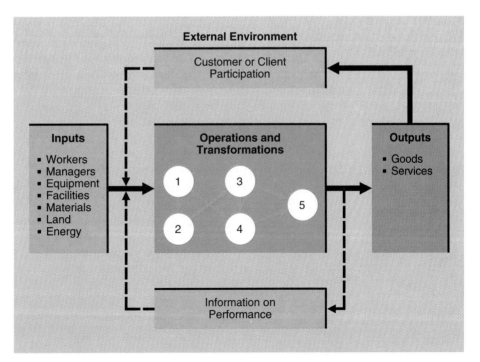

TABLE 1.1 / Examples of Inputs and Outputs

Organization	Input	Output
Jewelry store	Merchandise Store building Sales clerks Registers Jeweler Customers	Customer sales
Manufacturing plant	Machines Plant Raw materials Workers Managers	Consumer goods Materials for purchase by other firms
University	Faculty and staff Classrooms Library Supplies Students	Graduates Research Public service

For example, in a factory the transformation would be physical or chemical. At an airline it would be locational. At a school it would be educational. And at a hospital it would be physiological. The operations vary accordingly: a machine center, two or more airport terminals, a classroom, and a hospital room.

The dashed lines in Fig. 1.1 represent two special types of input: participation by customers or clients and information from internal and external sources. Participation by customers or clients occurs when they not only receive the outputs but also take an active part in the transformation process itself, such as students participating in a class discussion. Information from both internal and external sources includes internal reports on customer service or inventory management, government reports on economic trends, or telephone calls from suppliers concerning past-due shipments. The operations manager needs all types of information to manage the production system.

Outputs from manufacturing operations include goods and auxiliary services. Outputs from service operations range from delivered mail (the post office) to a recovered patient (a hospital). Even though inputs and outputs vary among different industries, the underlying transformation process holds true for all production systems. Table 1.1 shows specific inputs and outputs for operations systems in three different types of organizations.

DIFFERENCES BETWEEN MANUFACTURING AND SERVICES

Operations management initially focused on manufacturing organizations and was thus called *industrial management* or *production management*. Service organization operations were largely ignored and were performed almost at handicraft levels. Times have changed. Today's managers can apply concepts of job design, facility location, capacity, layout, inventory, and scheduling to both service organizations and manufacturing firms.

The differences between manufacturing and service organizations are real, but they also are a matter of degree. For example, more and more, manufacturing firms offer services and a decreasing proportion of their value added is due strictly to the transformation of materials. For the sake of discussion, we've organized these differences into eight categories, shown in Table 1.2. Because there are exceptions to every rule, these distinctions actually represent the ends of a continuum.

The first distinction arises from the physical nature of the product. Manufactured goods are *physical, durable* products. Services are *intangible* and *perishable*—often ideas, concepts, or information. The distinction between a goods producer and a service producer is cloudy. Service organizations normally provide a package of goods and services. For example, customers expect service as well as food at a restaurant and service as well as quality goods from a retailer.

Durable goods are outputs that can be *inventoried*. They can be stored and transported in anticipation of future demand. Thus with durable goods operations, managers can cope with peaks and valleys in demand by creating inventories and smoothing output levels. By contrast, services cannot be preproduced. Without inventories as a cushion against erratic customer demand, service organizations are more constrained by time. This constraint doesn't mean that inventories are of no importance to service systems. Hospitals, for example, must maintain an appropriate supply of medications. The difference is that these inventories are inputs, not outputs. As inputs, they must undergo further transformations during provision of the service.

A third distinction is *customer contact*. Most customers for manufactured products have little or no contact with the production system. Primary customer contact is left to distributors and retailers. However, in many service organizations the customers themselves are inputs. For example, at a college the student studies, attends lectures, takes exams, and finally receives a diploma. Hospitals, jails, and entertainment centers are other places where the customer is present during most of the service operations. Some service operations have low customer contact at one level of the organization and high customer contact at other levels. For example, the branch offices of postal, banking, and insurance organizations deal with customers daily, but their home offices have little

TABLE 1.2 / *Continuum of Characteristics of Goods and Services Producers*

More Like a Goods Producer ← →	More Like a Services Producer
Physical, durable product	Intangible, perishable product
Output can be inventoried	Output cannot be inventoried
Low customer contact	High customer contact
Long response time	Short response time
Regional, national, or international markets	Local markets
Large facilities	Small facilities
Capital intensive	Labor intensive
Quality easily measured	Quality not easily measured

direct customer contact. Similarly, the backroom operations of a jewelry store require little customer contact, whereas the sales counter involves a high degree of contact.

A related distinction is *response time* to customer demand. Manufacturers generally offer lead times measured in days or weeks. Many services, on the other hand, must be offered within minutes of customer arrival. The purchaser of a forklift truck may be willing to wait 16 weeks for delivery. By contrast, shoppers at the local supermarket grow impatient if they must wait more than five minutes in a checkout line. Since customers usually arrive at a time of their choosing, service operations may have difficulty matching capacity with demand. Furthermore, arrival patterns may fluctuate on a daily or even hourly basis—creating even more short-term demand uncertainty.

Market volume and availability of transportation and distribution facilities all affect the *location* and *size* of an operation. Manufacturing facilities often serve regional, national, or even international markets. This generally means larger facilities, more automation, and greater capital investment than for service facilities. In general, services cannot be shipped to distant locations. Thus service organizations requiring direct customer contact must locate relatively near their customers.

A final distinction is *quality*. As manufacturing systems tend to have tangible products and less customer contact, quality is easier to measure. Service systems, on the other hand, generally produce a mixture of tangibles and intangibles. Moreover, individual preferences affect assessments of quality, making objective measurement difficult. For example, one customer might value a friendly chat with the sales clerk during a purchase, whereas another might assess quality by the speed and efficiency of a transaction.

TRENDS IN OPERATIONS MANAGEMENT

Several trends—a growing service sector; productivity changes; global competitiveness; quality, time, and technological change; and other, wider issues—are focusing attention on operations. In this section we look at these trends and their implications for operations managers.

A Growing Service Sector

There is a significant service sector of the economy that breaks down into roughly three components:

1. Local, state, and federal governments
2. Wholesale and retail firms
3. Transportation, public utilities, communication, health, financial service, real estate, insurance, repair service, business service, and personal service firms

Between 1950 and 1990 the number of U.S. jobs in service-producing industries rose from 59 to 77 percent of total nonfarm jobs. This means that goods-producing industries, of which manufacturing is the major component, currently account for the remaining 23 percent. Although the absolute number of manufacturing jobs has increased, the percentage of manufacturing jobs in the total economy has dropped. Similar increases are taking place in every one of the 19 industrial countries for which data are available. In fact, the U.S. work force is moving into services less rapidly than most of its trading partners, including Germany and Japan.

The growing service sector should not lead you to conclude that manufacturing is becoming an insignificant part of the U.S. economy. Consumer expenditures and jobs have increased steadily in manufacturing over the years. In real dollars, the value of manufacturing output has risen 33 percent in just the last decade. Many experts argue convincingly that U.S. firms must keep their mastery over manufacturing because "you can't control what you can't produce." (See Cohen and Zysman, 1987.) Moreover, the service and manufacturing sectors of the economy are complementary. For example, the output of many firms is purchased by other firms as inputs. More than 25 percent of these intermediate outputs, such as express mail or consulting services, are classified as services but go to companies in the nonservice sector. Therefore, our discussion of operations management spans both manufacturing and services.

Productivity Changes

Productivity is the value of outputs (goods and services) produced divided by the values of input resources (wages, cost of equipment, and the like) used:

$$\text{Productivity} = \frac{\text{Output}}{\text{Input}}$$

Many measures of productivity are possible. For example, a manager at an insurance firm might measure office productivity as the number of insurance policies processed per employee each week. A manager at a carpet company might measure the productivity of installers as the yards installed per hour. Operations managers play a key role in determining productivity. Their challenge is to increase the value of output relative to the cost of input. If they can generate more output or output of better quality using the same amount of input, productivity increases. If they maintain the same level of output while reducing the expenditure of resources, productivity also increases.

At the national level, productivity is typically measured as the dollar value of output per unit of labor. This measure depends on the quality of the products and services generated by the firms and organizations in a nation and on the efficiency with which they are produced. Productivity is the prime determinant of a nation's standard of living (see Porter, 1990). If the value of output per work hour goes up, the nation benefits from higher overall income levels. The reason is that productivity of human resources determines employee wages. Conversely, lagging or decreasing productivity lowers the standard of living. Wage or price increases that are not accompanied by productivity increases lead to inflationary pressures rather than real increases in the standard of living.

FIGURE 1.2

Percentage Changes
in Productivity

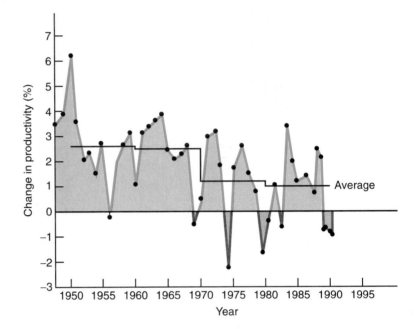

Source: Economic
Report of the
President, February
1991, p. 339.

Figure 1.2 shows the change in productivity for the business sector of the U.S. economy for the period between 1948 and 1990. (The graph reflects both manufacturing and services combined but excludes farms, which represent less than 5 percent of U.S. output and employment.) In the figure, productivity is measured as the dollar value of output per hour worked, and percentage changes are reported. For example, in 1950 productivity increased by more than 6 percent over 1949's level, in 1951 it increased 3.5 percent above the level set in 1950, and so on. Points on the graph below zero mean that productivity got worse rather than better compared to the prior year. The "Average" line represents the average percentage change for each decade. It was 2.6 percent for the 1950s, 2.5 percent for the 1960s, 1.2 percent for the 1970s, and 1.0 percent for the 1980s. This downward trend is real cause for concern.

Looking at productivity improvement for the whole economy does not tell the full story. Productivity increases in manufacturing during the 1980s averaged 3.3 percent per year, well ahead of the 1.0 percent for the whole economy. In fact, this was the best showing for the entire post–World War II era. The story was the opposite for the service sector, where the average productivity of the increasing number of employees was basically flat. It barely grew at all, despite the billions of dollars spent on computers and office technology. One recent study (see Adams and Siwaraksa, 1987) projects that this trend will continue for the rest of the 1990s, with service productivity rising only 0.5 percent per year. Conclusions on the service sector's low productivity increases must be qualified, however: Statistical data on it are less reliable. The real value (as opposed to cost) of outputs from some parts of the service sector, such as the government, health services, or education, is difficult to quantify. Furthermore, productivity advances vary greatly by industry within the service sector.

In software development and telecommunications, for example, U.S. industry is preeminent. Distribution systems, sophisticated health care, and advanced education are other bright spots. There is one indisputable conclusion: A vital service sector is crucial to the U.S. economy, and thus its productivity growth remains an ongoing concern.

Global Competitiveness

To prosper, a firm must more and more treat the world as its stage. It must view its customers, suppliers, facility locations, and competitors in global terms. Two decades ago, imports of products and services were equivalent to just over 5 percent of the total U.S. output; now they are over 13 percent. In Japan, using the same yardstick, imports climbed from 10 percent in 1970 to 14 percent today. Domestic markets no longer mean domestic competitors. Foreign competition is coming not just from Japan but from such sources as a more united European economy and East Asian countries such as Hong Kong, Taiwan, Singapore, and South Korea.

While manufactured products still account for roughly 80 percent of U.S. and world trade, foreign competition is becoming a fact of life in services as well. In 1990 the world trade in services grew to $600 billion. Firms in banking, law, data processing, airlines, and consulting are beginning to face many of the same international pressures as American manufacturers. For example, more than 260 foreign banks are now operating in the United States, and their slice of the domestic banking pie has grown from 14 percent in 1982 to more than 21 percent today.

Some Productivity Comparisons. Figure 1.3 compares the annual growth of productivity in manufacturing for seven industrial countries. Between 1960 and

FIGURE 1.3

Annual Percentage Change in Manufacturing Productivity

Note: The graph indicates average output per hour worked.
Source: Monthly Labor Review, U.S. Department of Labor, Bureau of Labor Statistics, July 1991, p. 92.

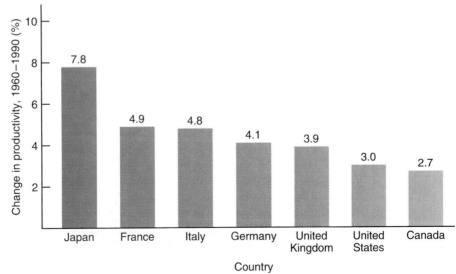

1990, the United States posted one of the lowest annual productivity increases (3.0 percent) of any country shown. Canada did even worse at 2.7 percent growth per year. By contrast, Japan is the leader at 7.8 percent. As a result, U.S. firms have experienced declining shares of the world market in aircraft, plastics, pharmaceuticals, agricultural machinery, railway vehicles, and housing fixtures. At the same time, Japanese manufacturers have penetrated U.S. markets. Examples include the automobile, semiconductor, computer, steel, machine tools, consumer electronics, shipbuilding, and telecommunications industries. Japan's share of the U.S. automobile market was 0.2 percent in 1965, 20 percent in 1980, and almost 30 percent today. Fortunately, there are signs of U.S. revitalization since 1983, with the U.S. manufacturing sector posting productivity gains averaging 4.6 percent per year. In addition, it remains a world leader in many of these industries, such as aircraft and pharmaceuticals.

Causative Factors. Analysts have offered many explanations for lagging U.S. productivity. Federal and state regulations governing occupational safety and health and environmental protection have increased costs, but government statistics don't reflect the impact of safer jobs and cleaner air on the value of output. Also, net investment in new equipment and facilities by U.S. industry during the past decade was only 6 percent of total output. No other major industrial country devotes such a small share of total output to new capital investment. (Japan's net investment over the same period was 18 percent.) Some experts point to the changing composition of the work force and changing attitudes toward work. Others argue that, as the level of U.S. productivity is already high, further improvements are difficult to achieve. Moreover, high wages and stringent union contracts are sometimes identified as obstacles to productivity increases.

Explanations such as these are incomplete. For example, Japanese firms operate successfully in the United States—using U.S. workers and paying U.S. costs. Managerial Practice 1.1 describes two Japanese-owned facilities that are achieving higher productivity than their U.S. counterparts. They can even achieve the same levels of quality and productivity that they can in Japan. The lesson is clear: Despite the multiple causes of productivity differences, the managers and employees of individual organizations ultimately are responsible for gaining a competitive advantage. How operations are managed is a key to increased productivity and the maintenance of high wages, salaries, and living standards.

Quality, Time, and Technological Change

Productivity measures more than efficiency and cost. The numerator in the productivity ratio is the value of output, which therefore introduces *quality* as a key variable. Part of the success of foreign competitors has been their ability to provide products and services of high quality at reasonable prices. Without quality, a firm loses its ability to compete in the marketplace, and its cost structure can also become uncompetitive. Operations managers, in conjunction with

Managerial Practice 1.1

Successful Japanese-Owned Facilities in the United States

Toyota Motor Corporation

In setting up New United Motor Manufacturing, Inc. (NUMMI), Toyota Motor Corporation joined forces with General Motors to revamp a mothballed GM plant in Fremont, California. Even though NUMMI is operating with GM's work force, in GM's building, and with much of GM's technology, productivity has skyrocketed because of how managers organized and operate the plant: The NUMMI managers set up a typical Toyota production system with just-in-time delivery and a flexible production line run by teams of workers in charge of their own jobs. Other benefits are that NUMMI now operates with 3100 employees, compared with 5000 at some GM factories, and production costs are comparable to Toyota's costs in Japan. GM executives are making extended visits to learn how the Toyota-managed factory achieves its high quality and productivity.

Honda of America

Honda of America Manufacturing Company now makes Accords in Marysville, Ohio, at approximately the same cost and almost the same quality as its parent in Japan. Dealers had originally pleaded with Honda not to build cars in the United States, believing that American workers could not build them as well as the Japanese. Time has shown that the key factor instead is with Honda's management style. They have a hands-on approach attuned to correcting problems, to simplifying product de-

signs, to limiting inventories, to simplifying layouts, and to passing on to workers and lower management responsibility for improvements in production techniques. Flexible teams, just-in-time delivery, attention to quality, and employee loyalty are hallmarks of their approach.

Source: "Crisis Is Galvanizing Detroit's Big Three," *Wall Street Journal,* May 2, 1991.

*A*t Honda's Marysville, Ohio, plant, employees conduct a final inspection of Accords.

the managers of other functional areas of the organization, are giving more attention to quality than ever. Total quality control (see Chapter 3) is a way of involving everyone in the organization with continuous improvement of quality. Statistical quality control (see Chapter 4) is a set of useful statistical tools for monitoring quality performance.

Another important trend is that more firms are competing on the basis of *time.* Filling orders earlier than the competition does is but one dimension. Equally important is the ability to introduce new products or services quickly and reach the market first. For example, Honda used this ability to thwart Yamaha's attempt to replace Honda as the world's largest motorcycle manufacturer. Honda's strategy was to introduce a wide variety of products so quickly that Yamaha would be unable to keep up. When the process began, Honda had 60 models of motorcycles. Eighteen months later it had introduced or replaced 113 models. Yamaha was unable to keep up and its sales all but dried up.

Another increasingly important factor in operations management is accelerating *technological change*. It affects the design of new products and services, and also the production processes themselves. Many new opportunities are coming from advances in computer technology. Robots and various forms of information technology are just two examples. U.S. firms alone spend $200 billion each year on information technology. The stakes are high, and employee attitudes depend on how technological change is managed. The right choices can give a firm a competitive advantage.

Wider Perspectives

Business challenges are always changing, and so must management education. Two recent studies, the Porter–McKibbin Report and the Graduate Management Admission Council Report, offer criticisms applicable to both U.S. and European business schools. These reports encourage business schools to turn out future managers versed in the roles that the environment, ethics, technological change, and workplace diversity play in practice. They are concerned that too many business students, at both the undergraduate and graduate levels, are well prepared for the important analytical side of their future jobs but less equipped for the hard-to-define "soft" issues facing managers in a fast-changing global marketplace.

A more ethical approach to business (see Buchholz, 1991) suggests that firms:

- Have responsibilities that go beyond producing goods and services at a profit
- Help solve important social problems
- Respond to a broader constituency than stockholders alone
- Have impacts beyond simple marketplace transactions
- Serve a range of human values that go beyond economic values

Business ethicists argue that managers' decisions on the design and operation of production systems should take into account such social issues as unsafe workplaces, discrimination against minorities and women, toxic wastes, poisoned drinking water, poverty, air quality, and global warming. Environmental problems were seen in the past as quality of life issues, and now many people see them as survival issues. As a result, the 1990s are being called the "decade of the environment." (See Post, 1991.) There is an increasing interest in a clean, healthy environment. The United States and some European nations now spend 2 percent of their gross national product on environmental protection. Managerial Practice 1.2 highlights the approaches some companies are taking on the issues of ethics and the environment.

THREE VIEWS OF OPERATIONS MANAGEMENT

We have mentioned the importance of operations in achieving organizational goals. We have also described how operations management affects competitive advantage in both the manufacturing and service sectors. In this section we

Managerial Practice 1.2

Ethics and the Environment

Nice firms, say the business ethicists, are profitable ones—a view with which companies like Britain's Marks and Spencers and America's Levi Strauss would cheerfully agree. Both firms practice, as well as preach, an ethical approach to business. Cummins Engine Company, located in Columbus, Indiana, also adheres to the notion that private industry should do social good. It has built a homeless shelter there and financed drug counseling in the public schools. It has long paid the fees of distinguished architects for public buildings, and has even lobbied for a higher state tax so that it could pay more of what it considered its fair share. In 1979 Cummins earned $57.9 million, its forty-third straight year in the black. Unfortunately, the last decade has left Cummins struggling for its very survival. The recession, stiff competition from foreign rivals, and pressure from Wall Street–backed corporate raiders have been particularly damaging. Cummins has had to close factories and eliminate thousands of jobs as it modernized its production processes, upsetting events to just about everybody at the company in one way or another. Still, it refuses to chop its charitable spending and refuses to leave Columbus for a lower-cost site.

The rise of environmental awareness among consumers poses tough challenges for operations managers as they make decisions on product designs and manufacturing processes. One recent survey showed that 50 percent of French and 80 percent of German consumers choose environmentally friendly goods when shopping at supermarkets. The first phosphate-free detergent sold in Germany gained 80 percent of the market in just three years.

Source: "With Its Spirit Shaken But Unbent, Cummins Shows Decade's Scars," *Wall Street Journal*, December 13, 1989.

explore operations management from three different perspectives: as a function, as a profession, and as a set of decisions.

As a Function

Figure 1.4 shows that operations can be identified in every organization and is but one of several functions within an organization. Large companies generally assign each function to a separate department, which assumes responsibility

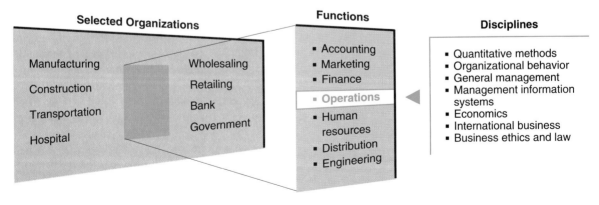

FIGURE 1.4   Operations Management as a Function

for certain activities. However, many of these functions are interrelated. Thus it is essential that top management coordinate them and establish an effective communication network to achieve organizational goals. (Owners of small businesses might choose to eliminate separate departments and manage one or more functions, such as marketing or operations, themselves.)

In large organizations an operations or production department is usually responsible for the operations function, or for the actual transformation of inputs into finished products or services. The *accounting* function collects, summarizes, and interprets financial information. *Marketing* is responsible for generating demand for the company's output. *Finance* secures and invests the company's capital assets. *Human resources* (or personnel) hires and trains employees. *Distribution* transports inputs and outputs. *Engineering* develops product and service designs and production methods. Some organizations, however, never need to perform certain functions. Other organizations find it economical to contract for a function, such as engineering, when they need it, rather than maintain an in-house department.

Operations managers draw on many disciplines and techniques (see right side of Fig. 1.4). Quantitative analysis provides modeling techniques to help solve production problems. Computers and other electronic information systems help manage vast quantities of data. Concepts of organizational behavior aid in designing jobs and managing the work force. Studies of international business methods provide useful ideas about facility location, technology, and inventory management. Thus most operations managers must be generalists. They must also be able to communicate with specialists and be comfortable with a variety of complex concepts and analytic techniques.

As a Profession

Operations has emerged as an excellent career path to upper management positions in many organizations. In 1984, biographies of 237 chief executive officers showed that 36 percent learned the ropes in production. This proportion compares favorably with those for chief executives with backgrounds in finance (22 percent), marketing (21 percent), research (10 percent), and law (9 percent). A more recent survey of manufacturing firms showed similar results, with more than 45 percent of the chief executives appointed in 1987 having an operations background and only 15 percent coming up through finance. Such statistics may be one reason why it is becoming more fashionable for business students to join a firm that makes a tangible product. The upward mobility of skilled operations managers is closely linked to the current challenge of global competition. Promotions tend to go to managers who have successfully met challenging problems.

Figure 1.5 shows a typical organization chart for a manufacturing firm. Each major business function reports to the chief executive officer (CEO). The operations function is further broken down in the figure to show the wide range of job opportunities there. In manufacturing firms, the head of operations usually holds the title vice president of manufacturing (or production or opera-

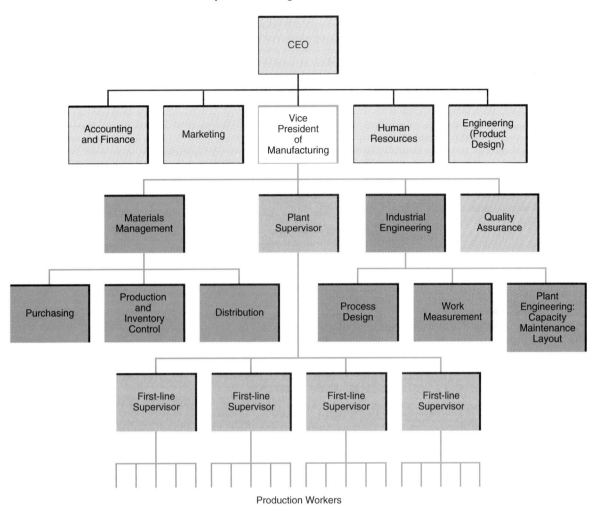

FIGURE 1.5   A Typical Organization Chart

tions). The corresponding title in a service organization might be vice president (or director) of operations. Reporting to the vice president are the managers of other production departments, such as materials, industrial engineering, quality assurance, and plant supervision. Managerial Practice 1.3 offers a glimpse of the experience required and the accountabilities for these various positions, in both manufacturing and services.

Lower management and entry-level positions in manufacturing carry titles such as inventory control supervisor, first-line supervisor, buyer, scheduler, production control analyst, time standard analyst, and facilities planner. Corresponding titles in the service sector might be department supervisor (insurance), office supervisor (contractor), section head (government), flight scheduler (airlines), operations analyst (bank), and scheduler (trucking).

Managerial Practice 1.3

Want Ads for Operations Managers

Director of Manufacturing
A rapidly growing medium-sized high technology manufacturing concern seeks the expertise of an experienced manufacturing professional. The candidate should have a minimum of five years' experience in management, including production planning and control, materials management, MRP, and facilities management.

Operations Manager
Large brokerage firm seeks experienced back office manager. Position involves all daily executing and settlement functions of a self-clearing NYSE member.

Plant Manager
An immediate position is available at our medium-sized manufacturing plant in the Chicago suburbs. Assembly, metal stamping, rubber molding, and flat surface lapping are all part of our process. Specific experience in these operations is not necessary, but a background in industrial management is. This is not a desk job. On-the-floor management of the work force and total responsibility for the manufacturing facilities will be yours.

Assistant Vice President, Materials Management
We operate two hospitals, four industrial medicine/ urgent care facilities, and a retirement community. The basic function for the assistant vice president is to plan, implement, and control all phases of pharmacy; purchasing; stores; receiving, distribution, and transportation; central processing; laundry; and printing services. Bachelor's degree in business preferred, master's degree a plus. Must have 5–10 years in materials management. Hospital experience is a plus.

Production Control Manager
An exciting opportunity for a results-oriented individual with a degree and proven track record. Responsible for controlling work-in-process to achieve on-time delivery and minimum inventory. Demands a self-starter who can coordinate major projects. The ability to interact with all levels of management is essential. A strong appreciation for systems development is needed.

Corporate Director of Purchasing
In this position you will service, select, and interface with a variety of suppliers on a national and international basis. You will personally negotiate contracts, providing timely procurement of systems, equipment, materials, and services specified by company managers.

Professional associations offer operations managers opportunities for professional growth by meeting their counterparts in other organizations and exchanging ideas about problems and their solutions. Key associations are the American Production and Inventory Control Society (APICS), American Society for Quality Control (ASQC), Association of Manufacturing Excellence (AME), National Association of Purchasing Managers (NAPM), and Operations Management Association (OMA).

As a Set of Decisions

Decision making is an essential aspect of all management activity. Although the specifics of each situation vary, decision making generally involves the same basic steps: (1) recognize and clearly define the problem, (2) collect the information needed to analyze possible alternatives, and (3) choose and implement the most feasible alternative. What sets operations managers apart, however, are the *types* of decisions they participate in with others in top management or actually make themselves. Table 1.3 lists several key decision

TABLE 1.3 / Decisions in Operations Management

Decision Area	Sample Questions
Strategic Choices	
Product and service plans (2)	What products and services should we offer?
Competitive priorities (2)	Should we excel on the basis of cost, quality, or flexibility?
Positioning strategy (2)	Should we organize resources around products or processes?
Quality management (3)	How do we get the whole organization committed to quality improvement?
Quality control (4)	How do we best achieve our quality goals?
Design Decisions	
Process design (5)	What processes should we use to make our products?
Technology management (6)	Is it time to automate some of our processes?
Job design (7)	Should our jobs be specialized or enlarged?
Capacity (8)	What is the maximum reasonable size for our facility?
Location (9)	Should we be followers or leaders in picking new store locations?
Layout (10)	How should we physically arrange desks and equipment?
Operating Decisions	
Forecasting (11)	How do we design the best forecasting system for our needs?
Materials management (12)	Who should be our suppliers? How do we evaluate and support them?
Inventory (13)	How much inventory do we need in our store? How should we control it?
Aggregate plans (14)	What should be our output rates and staffing levels for this quarter?
Master production scheduling (15)	Should we make to stock or make to order?
Production control systems (16,17)	When should we release new orders for production? In what quantities?
Scheduling (18,19)	What customers or jobs should receive top priority?

areas, along with chapter numbers in parentheses and a sample question about each. These questions correspond to major topics covered in other chapters of this book. Therefore they provide a good preview of things to come.

Table 1.3 begins with the *strategic choices* that affect the future direction of the company. For example, operations managers must help decide which products or services to offer, what the company's competitive priorities will be, what the quality objectives and control methods will be, and whether to organize resources around products or processes.

Next are the *design decisions* concerning the production system. Here the operations manager's recommendations and decisions often require long-term commitments. For example, the manager must help determine what the system's capacity should be and then decide what equipment and technologies to purchase, where to locate facilities, and how to organize departments and plan the facility's physical layout.

Operating decisions, sometimes called the operations infrastructure, deal with operating the facility once it is in place. At this stage, the operations manager decides how to manage inventory, when to release purchase or production orders, which suppliers to deal with, how to schedule resources and maintain quality, and how to increase output levels over shorter periods of time.

CORPORATE AND OPERATIONS STRATEGIES

Business and government leaders increasingly are recognizing the importance of the whole organization's—and the operations function's in particular—involvement in strategic issues. Global competition, and its link to the standard of living, are reasons. We hope that as you read this book, your appreciation of the strategic issues in operations management will increase. Let's begin by exploring some basic concepts of strategy, starting at the organization, or corporate, level.

Corporate Strategy

Whatever the type of organization, top management is responsible for relating the organization's efforts to its long-term future. Sometimes called *long-range planning,* setting **corporate strategy** (or organizational strategy) is the process of determining the organization's mission, of monitoring and adjusting to changes in the environment, and of identifying the organization's distinctive competencies. These strategic choices affect the future direction of the company.

The Mission. Determining an organization's mission requires answers to fundamental questions such as:

- What business are we in? Where should we be ten years from now?
- Who are our customers or clients?
- What are our basic concepts and beliefs?
- What are the key performance objectives, such as growth or profits, by which we measure our success?

The Environment. An organization needs to adapt continually to its changing external environment. Adaptation begins with **environmental scanning,** the process by which managers monitor the environment for potential opportunities or threats. As General Electric's chairman, John F. Welch, Jr., says, "Strategy is trying to understand where you sit in today's world. It's assessing with everything in your head the competitive changes, the market changes that you can capitalize on or ward off" ("The New Breed of Strategic Planners," 1984).

One crucial factor is competition. Competitors may be gaining an edge by broadening product lines, improving quality, or lowering costs. New entrants into the market or product substitutes may threaten continued profitability. Other important environmental elements include economic trends, technological changes, political conditions, social changes (such as attitudes toward work), and the availability of vital resources. The bargaining power of suppliers and customers can become either a threat or an opportunity. The impact of such changes on current strategies can reveal shortcomings in planning and product development—leading to adjustments in corporate strategy. In the past decade, businesses have faced a particularly turbulent environment: Some markets grow more slowly, automation is more complicated and expensive, product life cycles seem shorter, and foreign competition is intense. Managerial Practice 1.4 describes the role of environmental scanning at Precision Tune.

Distinctive Competencies. Environmental impacts cannot be managed away. Corporate strategies must change to meet them, which means taking into account the organization's unique strengths and weaknesses. An important concept is that few firms succeed by meeting competition head on but instead take advantage of what they do particularly well.

Managerial Practice 1.4

Environmental Scanning

The trend toward quality cars that rarely need tuneups and don't rust was a threat to the survival of some companies, including Precision Tune. Located in Sterling, Virginia, it was the largest U.S. tuneup franchiser and basked in a rewarding niche. After scanning its environment and noting the threat, Precision Tune responded. With automakers dropping carburetors in favor of fuel-injection systems that rarely require adjusting, Precision Tune now services all parts related to engine performance. It also offers a 12-month/12,000-mile warranty on most service and repairs, as well as several customer incentives. The new strategy has allowed sales to surge 78 percent in the last five years. Other companies haven't fared as well. Rusty Jones, of Chicago, once a major player in rustproofing, filed in 1989 for protection from creditors under Chapter 11 of the federal bankruptcy code. The reason: Fewer people wanted to pay for additional protection after U.S. automakers extended corrosion protection guarantees to 100,000 miles.

Source: "Repair Industry Struggles to Survive Cars' High Quality," *Wall Street Journal,* January 5, 1990.

*U*sing computer-aided diagnostics, Precision Tune services all facets of engine performance.

Distinctive competencies are the unique resources and strengths that management considers when formulating strategy. These competencies include:

1. *An available and competent work force.* Although skilled employees gravitate to good jobs, there is often a significant lag between demand and supply. Having the right employees when you need them is a strength.
2. *An efficient and advantageous location of facilities.* The availability of facilities, such as offices, stores, and plants, is a major advantage because of the long lead time required to build new ones.
3. *The ability to meet and create demand.* An organization that can easily change output levels, attract capital from stock sales, market and distribute its products, or differentiate its products from similar products on the market has a competitive edge.

A recent study shows that companies achieving international leadership employ various strategies, depending on their distinctive competencies (see Porter, 1990). However, their underlying character is fundamentally the same. They achieve competitive advantage through acts of innovation and new ways of doing things, such as new product designs, production technologies, training programs, quality control techniques, or new ways to manage supplier relationships. They find a new basis for competing or better ways of doing things. Some innovation in strategy is revolutionary, and other innovation is mundane and incremental, depending more on accumulation of small insights and advances than on a single major breakthrough. These innovations anticipate environmental changes at both the domestic and the foreign level. For example, Swedish companies like Volvo, Atlas Copco, and AGA took advantage of a new market opportunity by anticipating the growing international concern for product safety. Such innovations can give a firm a competitive advantage for a

*B*echtel Group Inc. designs and manages heavy construction projects. In response to a worldwide slump, it diversified into smaller projects, entered new lines of business, and decentralized. It was awarded the contract from Kuwait to help manage reconstruction of the oil facilities devastated by Iraq. To extinguish the oil fires, it directed the completion of more than 200 lagoons. Here a bulldozer excavates a lagoon.

TABLE 1.4 / The Planning Continuum

Strategic Planning ⟵ ⟶	Tactical Planning
Long time horizon	Short time horizon
Less certainty	More certainty
Less structured	More structured
More ends oriented	More means oriented
Poorly defined information requirements	Well-defined information requirements
Tends to have irreversible impact	Tends to have reversible impact
Focuses on the whole	Focuses on parts

while, but relentless improvement is also required to sustain this advantage. Competitors will eventually overtake a company that stops innovating and upgrading. Korean companies have already matched the ability of Japanese competitors to mass produce standard color televisions and VCRs, and Brazilian companies assembled technologies comparable to those of Italian rivals in casual leather footwear.

Strategies Versus Tactics. Managers make decisions today about tomorrow. This future-oriented process is called **planning**. There are differences between plans—some plans are more strategic and some are more tactical. For one thing, plans developed high up in the organization tend to be more strategic. For another, tactical plans are intended to implement strategic plans. Learning more about such differences sharpens your understanding of strategy, which must be formulated at both the corporate and functional levels. Table 1.4 shows that every planning activity lies somewhere between the two ends of a continuum, with strategy at one end and tactics at the other.

Strategic planning has a relatively longer time horizon than tactical planning. Of course, what is considered a long time depends on the specific operations involved. Because forests take so long to grow, strategic plans in the forest-products industry must look ahead as far as 100 years. A public utility that generates and distributes electric power might plan 30 years ahead. But to a firm competing in a very volatile environment with short lead times for product development and resource acquisition, a long time horizon may be only five years.

Because of their longer time horizons, strategic plans are made with little certainty about what the future holds. Accurately forecasting what will happen far into the future is difficult. Strategic plans also are less structured than tactical plans for two reasons. First, they are more ends oriented. Strategic planning establishes corporate ends (or performance objectives). By contrast, tactical planning focuses on the means by which these previously established ends can be achieved. Second, strategic planning is less structured because its information requirements are poorly defined. Managers can be less clear about information they need now to make a strategic choice that may not have an impact for five years. Tactical planning, which is more routine and repetitive, requires very specific information. Thus it must be based on more formal, well-defined information systems. These systems are often computerized because of the amount of data involved and the rapid rate at which data change.

Strategic plans lead to decisions that are major commitments of present and future resources. As a result, they tend to have an irreversible impact. For example, a strategic decision to build a new warehouse has a much greater impact than a tactical choice to order more machine parts this month from a certain supplier. Finally, strategic planning focuses more on the organization as a whole, cutting across functions and departments. This view of strategic planning recognizes that plans and decisions made in one area affect the plans and decisions made in others.

Operations Strategy

Operations strategy specifies how operations can achieve the organization's overall goals, within the framework of corporate strategy. Managers determine operational shortcomings by comparing corporate strategy requirements with the production system's current and projected capabilities. Managers then try to overcome any shortcomings by taking advantage of the operation's available resources and distinctive competencies. Or they may change operational strategies regarding automation, facility location, capacity, suppliers, and inventories. If none of these approaches is sufficient, the operations manager must alert top management, so that corporate strategy may be reviewed and, if necessary, revised.

Later in this book we examine the strategic issues of operations management within the context of individual decision areas. For now, we need to emphasize only three points:

1. Operations can be a competitive weapon or a millstone.
2. Managers should link decisions in operations.
3. Although management must first address strategic choices, success also depends on tactical choices based on careful analysis of specific alternatives.

A Competitive Weapon. Operations concentrates on the resource side of corporate strategy, where the organization usually commits the bulk of its human and financial assets. Almost 25 years ago, Wickham Skinner suggested that the production system could be either a competitive weapon or a millstone (see Skinner, 1969). He concluded that all too often it has become a millstone—or burden—with top management unknowingly giving up large portions of corporate strategy to operations managers. As a result, operations policies on such issues as inventory levels, schedules, and capacity reflect incorrect assumptions about corporate strategy and may actually work against a firm's strategic goals. This lack of understanding can commit the firm to inappropriate resources for years.

Largely because of foreign competition and the technological explosion, there is a growing recognition that a firm competes not only with new products, creative marketing, and skillful finance, but also with unique competencies in operations. The organization that can offer superior products and services at lower prices is a formidable competitor.

Linking Decision Areas. The operations manager must link various decision areas in operations in the way that best complements corporate strategy. Plans, policies, and actions within operations should focus in the same direction and be mutually supportive. Quality, automation, capacity, and inventory decisions must not be made independently. Even though individual choices may make sense on their own, collectively they might not add up to the best result.

Strategy and Analysis. Strategic planning dictates that *first-order questions* are the manager's first concern. For example, the manager must decide whether even to hold an item in inventory at all (as opposed to buying material as needed with each new customer order) before deciding how low inventory should get before reordering. Similarly, the manager must decide whether to expand on the same site or relocate before deciding how large the new parking lot will be. To help you focus on first-order questions, we introduce each chapter with several key questions from managers. Answers to these questions have a major impact on overall performance.

If you look back at Table 1.3, you'll see more long-range (or strategic) decisions listed at the top. We address them in the first few chapters of this book. The tactical questions covered in later chapters are also important. In fact, tactical decisions have a major cumulative effect. Take, for example, scheduling, shown at the bottom of the table. Scheduling is a decision area requiring detailed analysis and numerous interrelated, cumulative decisions. Just consider the millions of dollars at stake in completing a power plant or a hotel on time.

Much of tactical planning depends on careful analysis. Operations managers have a wide variety of analytic techniques at their disposal. These techniques range from simple lists of pros and cons jotted on a scrap of paper to sophisticated linear programming models, simulation models, and computer-based information systems. Strategy and analysis are both necessary and should complement one another. Although you can view each separately, they are actually part of a whole.

WHAT INDUSTRY IS DOING

To conclude this chapter, we tie together several of the topics we have covered: a growing service sector, lagging productivity, global competition, the kinds of decisions operations managers face, and how management can use operations as a competitive weapon. Managerial Practice 1.5 shows what some manufacturing and service companies are doing to improve productivity. The decision areas on which they are focusing—which are covered separately in subsequent chapters—appear in parentheses. These examples offer insight into the role operations managers play in an organization.

J.C. Penney Company

J.C. Penney is modernizing 550 of its largest stores. The $1 billion price tag aims at renovating existing stores, rather than opening new ones (*capacity* and *location*). There is a more stylish look, ranging from potted plants to striking graphics (*layout*). Penney is dropping some lines and expanding others (*product and service plans*), with an increased emphasis on quality (*competitive priority*). Sales at one of the first renovated stores rose almost 40 percent.

International Business Machines Corporation

Managers at IBM's Austin, Texas, factory that supplies circuit boards for personal computers received estimates that they could save $60 million by buying boards rather than making them (*process design*). To avoid layoffs and keep the work in-house, they found ways to produce the boards more efficiently. The key change was upgrading worker skills (*job design*). Workers were organized into teams, with each responsible for its own inspection, repairs, and materials ordering. Job classifications were changed to reflect this so-called employee empowerment approach, reorganizing manufacturing slots into categories with higher skill levels. The plant spends 5 percent of its payroll on worker training, but the benefit is that far fewer employees are needed to perform such indirect tasks as inspection, repair, and ordering. The $60 million gap between buying and making the circuit boards has been closed, with productivity up by more than 200 percent, quality five times better (*quality management*), and inventory cut by 40 percent (*inventory*). Total output has increased by 600 percent, and the work force is larger than ever.

Dillard Stores

Dillard Department Stores sells the latest fashions in gleaming, marble-inlaid stores (*layout*), succeeding in a deeply troubled industry. It continues to show double-digit returns even as its competitors falter. Dillard disproves the conventional wisdom that moderate-priced department stores are dead. It does so by offering a combination of upscale merchandise, a wide selection, and decent prices (*competitive priorities*). Aiming at baby-boomer shoppers of the 1990s, who tend to head to the closest mall, Dillard operates only four downtown stores (*location*). Its low overhead means that its operating costs are 2 percentage points lower than competitors'. One reason why Dillard can hold down costs is its sophisticated data collection system (*new technologies*). Management keeps tabs on sales at every cash register in every store. They can see, for example, whether Hickey-Freeman suits are selling as fast as expected in Kansas City or how Estée Lauder's latest line is doing nationwide. This information helps manage inventory levels (*inventory*) and also makes it possible to track the productivity of every sales clerk. Clerks have a quota to meet; those who exceed it get raises (*work measurement*). When Dillard recently acquired the J.C. Ivey chain of 22 department stores, it installed over the weekend new point-of-sale registers that tie in to the company's Arkansas headquarters. By Monday morning, the Dillard managers were tracking what was and wasn't selling. Dillard also has a quick response program that allows it to get merchandise into stores at breakneck speed (*materials management*). Goods from 187 of its suppliers are restocked in 12 days or less.

Insurance Companies

Shenandoah Life Insurance installed a new computer system (*technology management*) to help issue new life insurance policies to customers who were replacing old ones. The Roanoke, Virginia, company also revamped its procedures so that clerks were less specialized (*process design*) and worked in teams (*job design*). Over a three-year period, the number of transactions processed rose by 28 percent, while the number of workers handling them fell 15 percent. Capital Holding Corporation, also in the insurance business, used office automation (*technology management*) to reduce the work force in its data entry department by 75 percent. A new computer system is used to record and transmit claim information, replacing the typewriters and file cabinets used before.

Litton Industries

Litton Industries' industrial automation plant in Flemington, New Jersey, recently installed a computerized materials-handling system (*technology management*). The system doubled the plant's capacity without adding bricks and mortar (*capacity*). Operations is paying considerable attention to quality, and the number of defect-free units shipped has risen from 87 to 99.5 percent (*quality management*). The number of suppliers has been reduced from 750 to 107 (*materials management*), and the plant divisions work more closely with each on quality and delivery. Statistical process control helps ensure that each step in production is performed correctly (*quality control*). Computerized production planning (*production plans*) and electronic communication with customers (*master production scheduling*) have eliminated the need for big stockpiles of inventory. Combining just-in-time inventory management with faster process time has pared inventories to only a 1.3-month supply, down from a seven-month supply in earlier years (*inventory*). A team approach offers more resource flexibility and job variety (*job design*).

Marriott Corporation

J. Willard Marriott, Jr., chief executive officer of Marriott Corporation, logged 200,000 miles in one year to visit more than 100 of the chain's hotels and resorts. He believes that productivity improvement comes from direct contact with customers and employees (*job design*). He even makes spot checks at all hours (*quality management*) of conditions ranging from dishes to laundry facilities to lobby appearance. This attention to detail communicates the importance he places on each person's role in the organization.

Cincinnati Milacron

Cincinnati Milacron faces a real challenge as it seeks to reestablish itself as a world-class manufacturer of factory machinery. It has not earned an acceptable profit since 1981. Milacron got ahead of the market: Not enough companies were willing to spend the $10 million to $20 million for the new robots and flexible manufacturing systems that it offered. Meanwhile, aggressive Japanese producers seized half of the U.S. market for machine tools. Milacron executives aim to rebuild the company's capability to manufacture quality products more cheaply than competitors. Part of their strategy has been to drop the line of heavy robots (*product planning*), selling this part of the business to Asea Brown Boveri AG, which is based in Zurich, Switzerland. Milacron will concentrate on three basic product lines: machine tools, plastics machinery, and consumable industrial products such as grinding wheels. Another part of its strategy is to create so-called focus factories (*capacity* and *layout*), each of which specializes in one type of product, such as lathes or machining centers. The goal is to bring people who design, manufacture, and service machines into closer contact with the buyer. Each factory is a profit center, which helps avoid unnecessary spending on product development. The last phase of the strategy is to redesign many machines to make them more efficient to manufacture and more reliable (*product design*). The minimum goal: a 30 percent cost reduction on each machine. One division has already slashed manufacturing costs by 40 percent, partly by halving the number of parts required (*materials management*). It is now going after an additional 15 percent of cost by automating parts making and streamlining assembly (*process design*).

Sources: "Workplace Panel Is Urging Changes in Schools, on Job," *Wall Street Journal*, June 19, 1990; "Two Disparate Firms Find Keys to Success in Troubled Industries," *Wall Street Journal*, May 29, 1991; "The Service Industry: A Special Report," *Wall Street Journal*, March 28, 1989; "Upgrading of Factories Replaces the Concept of Total Automation," *Wall Street Journal*, November 30, 1987; "Milacron Wolfpack Goes in for the Kill," *Wall Street Journal*, August 14, 1990.

The steps taken by J.C. Penney Company remind us that reducing costs is not the only way to increase productivity. Productivity can be improved when the value of inputs rises, so long as the value of outputs rises even faster. The steps taken by the other companies cited cover almost every decision area in operations management. We see that each decision area in operations management is important and that each plays a vital role in the attempt to gain competitive advantage. Organizations have found that there are many roads to success within operations. It would be a mistake to look for a single cure or magic formula.

CHAPTER HIGHLIGHTS

● This book addresses the strategic issues of operations, without sacrificing the analytical side of decision making.

● Production processes transform inputs (workers, managers, equipment, facilities, materials, land, and energy) into outputs (goods and services).

● Service systems, in contrast to manufacturing systems, tend to have intangible products that cannot be inventoried, more direct contact with the customer, shorter response times, local markets, labor-intensive operations, and less measurable quality. Nonetheless, the distinctions are relative.

● Several trends are at work in operations management. Service sector employment is growing. Productivity is lagging, particularly in the service sector, and global competition is intensifying. The relentless pursuit of better quality, competing on the basis of time, and rapid technological change are also important trends. So is the increasing awareness in business education of issues such as ethics and environmental concerns.

● Operations management can be viewed as a function, a profession, and a set of decisions; it is concerned with the strategic positioning, design, and operation of production systems.

● Decision areas in which operations managers are involved include product and service plans, competitive priorities, positioning strategy, qual-

ity management and control, process design, new technologies, job design, capacity, location, layout, materials management, production and staffing plans, master production scheduling, inventory, and scheduling. Each succeeding type of decision has a shorter time horizon and is more tactical but has an important cumulative effect on system performance.

● Corporate strategy is the process of determining the organization's mission, monitoring and adjusting to changes in the external environment, and exploiting distinctive competencies. Key ingredients of successful strategy are innovation and continual improvement.

● Strategic planning, in contrast to tactical planning, has a longer time horizon, less certainty, less structure, an ends orientation, poorly defined information requirements, and a focus on the whole organization.

● Operations strategy is a natural extension of corporate strategy and involves three important concepts: (1) operations can be a formidable competitive weapon, (2) the various decisions in operations must be linked, and (3) first-order decisions are paramount, even though tactical decisions have a major cumulative effect.

● Companies are responding to the competitive challenge by dealing with the full range of decision areas in operations management.

KEY TERMS

corporate strategy **18**
distinctive competencies **20**
environmental scanning **18**

operations management **3**
operations strategy **22**
planning **21**

productivity **7**

STUDY QUESTIONS

1. Identify the inputs and outputs for four of the following types of firms.
   a. hotel
   b. public warehouse
   c. paper mill
   d. newspaper company
   e. supermarket
   f. home office of bank

2. Identify the largest firm in your hometown or county. What are its inputs, outputs, and transformation processes?

3. Do the employment shifts to the service sector mean that the demand for goods is declining? Do you expect these employment trends to continue at the same pace? Explain.

4. What are the usual distinctions between goods producers and service producers? Identify at least two types of firms that do not fit the pattern, explaining the reasons for your choices.

5. What does the productivity trend in Fig. 1.2 mean? Do you expect it to continue? Explain.

6. Why is productivity of particular interest to operations managers?

7. Describe an industry, for a country and time interval of your choice, in terms of such statistics as employment, total output, and productivity. Do you detect any trend in the data?

8. Which disciplines contribute significantly to the field of operations management? What does this imply about the skills needed by operations managers?

9. What types of jobs are available in operations management?

10. List at least three types of decisions that deal with the design of a production system, along with a sample question for each one. Do the same for three types of decisions that deal with the operation of the production system.

11. What questions does an organizational mission statement answer?

12. How are environmental scanning, adjusting to environmental change, and distinctive competencies related?

13. What are the differences between strategic and tactical planning?

14. How can linking decisions better help make operations a competitive weapon? Can tactical decisions be ignored? Explain.

15. Kathryn Shoemaker established Grandmother's Chicken Restaurant in Middlesburg five years ago. It features a unique recipe for chicken: "Just like grandmother used to make." The facility is homey, with relaxed and friendly service. Business has been very good during the past two years, for both lunch and dinner. Customers normally must wait about 15 minutes to be served, although complaints about service delays have increased. Kathryn is currently considering whether to expand the current facility or open a similar restaurant in neighboring Uniontown, which has been growing rapidly.
    a. What types of strategic and tactical plans must Kathryn make?
    b. What environmental forces could be at work at Middlesburg and Uniontown that Kathryn should consider?
    c. What are the possible distinctive competencies of Grandmother's?

SELECTED REFERENCES

Adams, F. Gerard, and Subhak Siwaraksa. "A Disaggregated Study of the Service Sector," Discussion Paper 28. The Wharton School, University of Pennsylvania, November 1987.

Bowen, David E., Richard B. Chase, Thomas G. Cummings, and Associates. *Service Management Effectiveness.* San Francisco: Jossey–Bass Publishers, 1990.

Buchholz, Rogene A. "Corporate Responsibility and the Good Society: From Economics to Ecology." *Business Horizons* (July–August 1991), pp. 19–31.

Cohen, Stephen S., and John Zysman. *Manufacturing Matters: The Myth of the Post-Industrial Economy.* New York: Basic Books, 1987.

Collier, David A. "Managing a Service Firm: A Different Management Game." *National Productivity Review* (Winter 1983–1984), pp. 36–45.

Collier, David A. *Service Management: Operating Decisions.* Englewood Cliffs, N.J.: Prentice–Hall, 1987.

Commission on Admission to Graduate Management Education. *Leadership for a Changing World: The Future Role of Graduate Management Education.* Los Angeles: Graduate Management Admission Council (GMAC), 1990, pp. 1–43.

Faulhaber, Gerald, Eli Noam, and Roberta Tasley. *Services in Transition: The Impact of Information Technology on the Service Sector.* Cambridge, Mass.: Ballinger Publishing Company, 1986.

Fitzsimmons, James A., and Robert S. Sullivan. *Service Operations Management.* New York: McGraw–Hill, 1982.

Guile, Bruce R., and James Brian Quinn. *Technology in Services: Policies for Growth, Trade, and Employment.* Washington, D.C.: National Academy Press, 1988.

"Hard Times Push B-Schools into Basics." *Business Week* (August 30, 1982), pp. 23–24.

Hax, Arnoldo C., and Nicolas S. Majluf. "The Corporate Strategic Planning Process." *Interfaces,* vol. 14, no. 1 (January–February 1984), pp. 47–60.

Hayes, Robert H., and William J. Abernathy. "Managing Our Way to Economic Decline." *Harvard Business Review* (July–August 1980), pp. 67–77.

Hayes, Robert H., Steven C. Wheelwright, and Kim B. Clark. *Dynamic Manufacturing.* London: Collier Macmillan Publishers, 1988.

Heskett, James L., W. Earl Sasser, Jr., and Christopher Hart. *Service Breakthroughs: Changing the Rules of the Game.* New York: The Free Press, 1990.

Mabert, Vincent A., and Michael J. Showalter. *Cases in Operations Management.* Plano, Texas: Business Publications, 1984.

Magaziner, Ira C., and Mark Patinkin. *The Silent War.* New York: Random House, 1989.

"Management Education." *The Economist* (March 2, 1991), pp. 2–26.

Marucheck, Ann, Ronald Pannesi, and Carl Anderson. "An Exploratory Study of the Manufacturing Strategy Process in Practice." *Journal of Operations Management,* vol. 9, no. 1 (January 1990), pp. 101–123.

"The New Breed of Strategic Planner." *Business Week,* September 17, 1984.

Porter, Lyman W., and Lawrence E. McKibbin. *Management Education and Development: Drift or Thrust into 21st Century?* New York: McGraw-Hill, 1988.

Porter, Michael E. *Competitive Advantage: Creating and Sustaining Superior Performance.* New York: The Free Press, 1985.

Porter, Michael E. "The Competitive Advantage of Nations." *Harvard Business Review* (March–April 1990), pp. 73–93.

Post, James E. "Managing As If the Earth Mattered." *Business Horizons* (July–August 1991), pp. 32–38.

Roach, Stephen S. "Services Under Siege—The Restructuring Imperative." *Harvard Business Review* (September–October 1991), pp. 82–91.

Skinner, Wickham. "Manufacturing—Missing Link in Corporate Strategy." *Harvard Business Review* (May–June 1969), pp. 136–145.

Skinner, Wickham. *Manufacturing: The Formidable Competitive Weapon.* New York: John Wiley and Sons, 1985.

Stanbeck, Thomas M., Jr., P.J. Bearse, T.J. Noyelle, and R.A. Karasek. *Services: The New Economy.* Totowa, N.J.: Allanheld, Osmun and Co., 1981.

Starr, Martin. "The Performance of Japanese-Owned Firms in America: A Survey Report." Center for Operations, Columbia Business School, 1985.

Steiner, George A. *Top Management Planning.* New York: Macmillan, 1983.

"Under Pressure, Business Schools Devise Changes." *Wall Street Journal* (April 23, 1991), p. 15.

Wheelwright, Steven C. "Manufacturing Strategy: Defining the Missing Link." *Strategic Management Journal,* vol. 5 (1984), pp. 71–91.

Chapter 2

INTRODUCING NEW PRODUCTS AND SERVICES

Key Questions from Managers

When should we add or drop products or services?

What products and services should we offer?

Where are the longest time delays between when a new product or service is conceived and when it is delivered?

What is the best positioning strategy for our production system?

When should we enter and exit the market during the life cycle of a product or service?

Should we emphasize price, quality, time, or flexibility?

What impact does this choice have on our other decisions in operations?

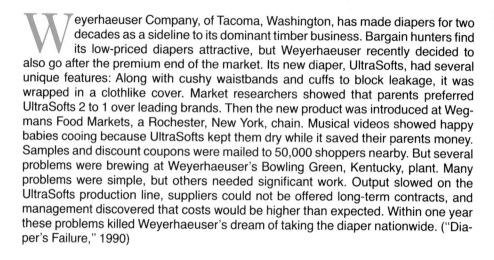

Weyerhaeuser Company, of Tacoma, Washington, has made diapers for two decades as a sideline to its dominant timber business. Bargain hunters find its low-priced diapers attractive, but Weyerhaeuser recently decided to also go after the premium end of the market. Its new diaper, UltraSofts, had several unique features: Along with cushy waistbands and cuffs to block leakage, it was wrapped in a clothlike cover. Market researchers showed that parents preferred UltraSofts 2 to 1 over leading brands. Then the new product was introduced at Wegmans Food Markets, a Rochester, New York, chain. Musical videos showed happy babies cooing because UltraSofts kept them dry while it saved their parents money. Samples and discount coupons were mailed to 50,000 shoppers nearby. But several problems were brewing at Weyerhaeuser's Bowling Green, Kentucky, plant. Many problems were simple, but others needed significant work. Output slowed on the UltraSofts production line, suppliers could not be offered long-term contracts, and management discovered that costs would be higher than expected. Within one year these problems killed Weyerhaeuser's dream of taking the diaper nationwide. ("Diaper's Failure," 1990)

No business activity attracts so much attention and optimism, and is so fundamental to corporate strategy, as introducing a new product or service. It is a chance for renewal, redirection, and getting a step on the competition. Yet such promises are seldom fully realized. Weyerhaeuser's experience shows how even the best innovations for new products and services can die from poor planning and unexpected problems. Preliminary market studies sometimes misjudge what the customers really want. And what works in a pilot plant can flop miserably in full-scale production.

Chapter 1 explained how corporate strategy defines a firm's mission and answers questions such as, What business are we in? What should it be ten years from now? Who are our customers? The answers define the products and services that the firm will offer. Although planning in this area takes place primarily at the corporate strategy level, it is the logical starting point for formulating operations strategy. Knowing the characteristics of the products and services, the operations manager can effectively design and operate the production system.

Our coverage begins with a discussion of life cycles, entrance–exit strategies, planning steps, and decision-making tools. And we present competitive priorities, or the ways in which operations must excel to make the offered products or services competitive. We then describe what some firms are doing to compete better on the basis of time. Next we take you on two tours, one at a service facility and one at a manufacturing plant, to illustrate the organization of actual operations around their competitive priorities. Finally, we use the tours to show how an organization's positioning strategy, or choice of either a process focus or a product focus, links decisions throughout the operations function.

PLANNING NEW PRODUCTS AND SERVICES

Product and service planning encompasses all the activities leading to the introduction, revision, or dropping of products and services. The planning process is ongoing—it's a job that's never completed. Intense competition, expiration of patents, and rapid technological innovations are all factors that challenge an organization's ability to produce a quality product or deliver a quality service that meets market demand and is timely. Corporate strategy guides the process because the planning must be compatible with a firm's overall goals.

More than $50 billion are spent each year designing new products or improving old ones. In fact, more than half a firm's sales dollar volume typically comes from products or services introduced within the last ten years. Large firms often spend vast sums of money assessing the market, appraising the competition, and designing products and services. Many small companies, such as Zoom Telephonics, profiled in Managerial Practice 2.1, start with a limited number of products. These products are often based on the founding entrepreneur's own special process or product innovation. As time passes, however, these firms usually must add new products or services, either to replace those being phased out or to expand their market penetration.

Here is a roadmap for the following sections on planning new products and services. We begin with life cycles and describe what's required of the operations function as a product or service goes through the various stages of its life. A firm can enter a product's life cycle in any of these stages, which introduces entrance–exit strategies and how the strategy chosen affects the way a production system is designed and operated. Next, we describe the four basic steps involved in planning new products and services. We conclude with three decision-making tools that are particularly relevant to this planning process: the preference matrix, break-even analysis, and reliability analysis.

Life Cycles

A firm that neglects to introduce new products or services periodically will eventually decline. Sales and profits from any given product decrease over time, so the pressure is on management to introduce new products before existing ones hit their peak. In the service sector, for example, Bank One Corp. is both innovative and profitable. It was the first to help securities firms offer banklike services, to install automated teller machines, and to issue a bank credit card—BankAmericard, the forerunner of Visa. It soon will introduce a bank credit card that offers S&H Green Stamps and assistance in planning an overseas vacation, at several redesigned branches that will resemble small

Managerial Practice 2.1

New Products at Zoom Telephonics Incorporated

Frank Manning designed a little speed-dialer while in college and used it to call repeatably the busy phone line that booked reservations for the tennis courts at MIT. With a little more tinkering, it became the first hit product for Zoom Telephonics Incorporated. He co-founded the company in 1977 and introduced the "Demon Dialer" in 1981. Annual sales shot up to $6 million by 1984.

But within a year, Zoom was on the ropes. Regulators changed the way long-distance telephone customers reached carriers like MCI and Sprint, eliminating the need to dial a long string of digits before a call. Three quarters of Zoom's sales volume disappeared. Manning's response was to see a new opening in the market and dash through it. He switched to producing modems, a new product to Zoom that converts computer data to sound for transmission over phone lines. By 1991 sales

Zoom Telephonics' modem, shown here, converts computer data to sound for transmission over phone lines.

hit $20 million, giving Zoom about 10 percent of shipments in the dial-up personal computer modem market. In the same year, *PC Magazine* awarded Zoom's new 9600-bps model its "Editor's Choice" award, citing its "speed, features and flawless performance."

Zoom's strategy of pricing well below the market leader is an important part of its success. The production system is designed to keep assembly costs low without going outside the United States. It keeps its inventory tight, runs a lean operation, and contracts out some work.

At the same time, the long-term outlook for modems is uncertain: If telephone transmission lines become fully digital, as planned, models will go out of style as fast as the Demon Dialer disappeared years ago. (Computers process data as digital information, so digital transmission lines wouldn't require the signal translation provided by a modem.) Furthermore, some computer makers are beginning to install modems into their machines at the factory, draining sales from independents like Zoom.

So Zoom is hedging its bets. It's building a voice synthesizer circuit board, designed for use with personal computers and inside corporate voice-mail systems. And it is designing an interface device, called an ISDN adapter, for the day when personal computers don't need modems to send and receive data over the phone.

Source: "In Niches, Necessity Can Be the Mother of Reinvention," *Wall Street Journal*, April 30, 1991.

shopping malls with separate storefronts for banking services, brokerage sales, travel planning, and insurance. Bank One also has become a leading financier of health club memberships and consumer appliances.

Let's now look at the stages in the life of such products or services.

Life-Cycle Stages. A **life cycle** consists of five stages through which a product or service passes: product or service planning, introduction, growth, maturity, and decline. Figure 2.1 depicts sales and profits associated with each stage.

1. **Product or Service Planning.** During this stage, ideas for new goods or services are generated, screened, and translated into final designs. Profits attributed to a product or service are negative at this point, as sales

FIGURE 2.1

Life Cycle of Product
or Service

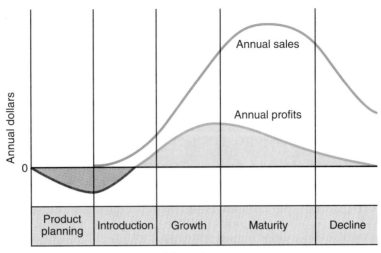

have not yet begun. Although no revenues are coming, development costs are being incurred. Operations must be involved to ensure that the new product or service is in sync with production capabilities.

2. **Introduction.** At this stage, sales begin and profits go from negative to positive. Operations is still refining production efforts, which can best be characterized as fluid and evolving. Marketing efforts may be modest (as when introducing new prescription drugs) or nearing their peak (as with new textbooks). As sales volumes have not reached their high point, annual profits are small, even though unit profit margins may be large.

3. **Growth.** The product or service next enters a stage of rapid growth. Early in this stage, sales jump dramatically and profits rise. The mandate for operations is to somehow keep up with demand; efficiency is less of a concern. Managerial Practice 2.2 demonstrates that the growth stage can be particularly difficult for a new business.

4. **Maturity.** During this stage, sales level off and profits have begun to decline. New competitors create pressures to cut costs and slow the squeeze on unit profit margins. Now operations must stress efficiency, although marketing can ease the pressure by intensifying efforts to differentiate the product or service.

    For example, computers (except for the biggest machines) have entered the maturity stage and are becoming commodities that customers buy as cheaply as possible. Analysts predict that the computer industry will never be the same again and that commodity pricing will keep plaguing the companies until more and more of them give up and drop out of the industry.

5. **Decline.** At last the product or service enters a decline stage and ultimately becomes obsolete. Either demand disappears or a better, less expensive product or service takes its place. Sales and profits decrease to the point where the firm finally drops it.

Managerial Practice 2.2

Growth-Stage Problems in the Service Sector

Hollywood makeup artist Bob Sidell first formulated his own cosmetics to deal with teenage acne on "The Waltons" and then began selling out of his home to other makeup artists. He did makeup work on science-fiction creations such as *E.T.*, helping to make them come alive. In 1985 Sidell started his own mail-order company, California Cosmetics Incorporated, with a $4000 investment. In just three years the company grew into a $10-million-a-year business. It was an entrepreneur's dream ride, but it started careening out of control. The company suffered from a common ailment of new businesses: rapid but unsustainable growth. Operations couldn't handle the volume of business. Orders were being botched. Complaints were mounting. Total returns and nondeliveries of products climbed to 17 percent. After operating debt-free since its inception, the company faced the prospect of having to borrow $100,000 to keep enough inventory on hand.

Sidell and his partner decided that the only way to survive was to stunt the company's short-term growth. The tempered growth allowed California Cosmetics to set up its operating procedures and to continue promoting from within, rather than rushing to hire an outside expert. "You bring in a purchasing manager at an inflated salary and it takes 90 days to convert them to our operations, and then you spend the next six months correcting the problems they brought with them because they're continuing to do what they did at the old company," Sidell said.

Source: "Dream to Nightmare: When Growth Gets Out of Hand," *Wall Street Journal,* January 23, 1990.

Life cycles vary greatly from one product or service to another. For example, Coleco Industries, a Connecticut toymaker, sought ways to avoid bankruptcy and court protection just three years after riding high on the huge success of its Cabbage Patch Kids line. The Ninja Turtles line of Playmates Toys is following the same pattern. The turtles were a surprise sensation in 1988, their sales peaked in 1990, and sales are already on their way down.

Looking only at the time required for the product or service planning stage, or the time between idea generation and product introduction, we find that it took Eversharp only eight months to introduce ballpoint pens. By contrast, it took Gillette 13 years, $300 million, and 18 patents to introduce its new high-tech Sensor razor. In the high-tech computer and microchip industry, products can become obsolete in months. Thus companies such as Atari and Intel Corporation generally favor a management style characterized by quick, independent action more than do companies producing products or services that have longer life cycles. Hewlett-Packard's tiny presence in PCs is a legacy from the mid-1980s when its management moved too late into this market.

Managing Life Cycles. A **life-cycle audit** evaluates which stage a product or service is in, based on how changes in sales and profits compare with those of prior years. For example, when both sales and profits are dropping, Fig. 2.1 suggests that the product is in either the late maturity stage or the decline stage. Life-cycle audits spot needs to revitalize or eliminate existing products and to introduce new ones.

When a life-cycle audit indicates that a product or service has reached maturity or entered decline, management has several options. The firm can stay

Application 2.1   *Conducting a Life-Cycle Analysis*

Management has collected the following data in preparation for a life-cycle audit of one of its products, a packaging material sold to industrial buyers.

Performance Measure	This Year's Performance	Change Over Last Year	Average Annual Change Over Last Four Years
Annual sales	$30.8 million	+1.0%	+15.8%
Unit price	1.12/lb	+2.2	+ 8.5
Unit profit Margin	0.16/lb	−0.3	+ 3.2
Total profits	4.4 million	+1.5	+22.5

In what stage of the life cycle is the product?

Solution   Sales are stabilizing, having grown only 1 percent over the past year. Average annual growth had been much higher during prior years, at 15.8 percent. Unit-price growth has slowed, and unit profit margins are beginning to shrink. Total profit is also leveling off. All of these signs suggest the *early maturity stage.*

with the product or service for a few more years, find ways to squeeze costs still more, or revise and rejuvenate it. Table 2.1 shows how companies in five industries (drugs, major appliances, food, clothing, and minor appliances) ranked various product planning activities. Adding new products ranked first, followed closely by revising existing products.

Revision might mean improving the performance of the product, such as a mix for a faster rising cake. Or it could be an update of an old standby, as with Mattel's revamp of the Barbie doll. Barbie, Mattel's 33-year-old best-seller, had been showing her age. In response to competition from Hasbro's new rock-star doll, Jem, Mattel gave Barbie an after-hours wardrobe of miniskirts, a modern hairdo, and a rock band. Barbie is now flourishing more than any time since her birth, and management hopes her worldwide sales will reach $1 billion by 1995. The latest version is making her debut in Japan, and Mattel is counting on overseas markets for much of its growth over the next several years.

TABLE 2.1 / Importance of Various Product Planning Activities

Activity	Importance*
Adding new products	41
Revising existing products	31
Finding new uses of existing products	15
Eliminating products	13

Source: Data from James T. Rothe, "The Product Elimination Decision," *MSU Business Topics,* Michigan State University, Autumn 1970, pp. 45–52.

*Average score assigned by firms surveyed, where the highest possible score was 100.

Entrance–Exit Strategies

The life cycle of a product within a company can be quite different from its cycle within an industry. For example, a firm might decide to pull out of a particular market although the industry will be producing these products or services for years to come. An **entrance–exit strategy** is a firm's choice of when to enter a market and when to leave it. Choosing one of the three basic strategies shown in Table 2.2 has important implications for the operations function.

Enter Early and Exit Late. The most natural strategy is for a firm to enter the market when a product or service is first introduced by the industry and stay with it until the end of its life cycle. Polaroid and Xerox are examples of companies that developed a new product and grew with it throughout its life cycle. By entering the market early, the firm gets a head start. This added experience may allow the early entrant to produce a better product at a lower cost than late entrants can produce initially.

This strategy requires operations to evolve from a low-volume, flexible production system into a high-volume, low-cost system. Such a shift is always a challenge because it means changing over to a whole new way of doing things. Several companies in the personal computer industry, including Apple, Atari, and Commodore International, experienced similar growing pains when they moved from a small, freewheeling venture to a large corporation.

Enter Early and Exit Early. Small, product-innovative firms often choose to stay in a low-volume, customized business. This strategy requires no painful transition. When the product reaches the maturity stage and profit margins begin to shrink, the firm drops the product and introduces new ones. Throughout the life cycle, operations management maintains a small, flexible production system that can be adapted readily to changing products or services.

Quarterdeck Office Systems Incorporated, a small computer software company in Redmond, Washington, is a good example. The company's president tries to live with Microsoft's market domination by offering additional software to users of DOS, the basic operating program for most personal computers. Her company's products give a computer more memory capacity and the ability—known as multitasking—to run more than one program at once. Quarterdeck's narrow focus and fast reflexes help it combat an aggressive and far larger rival.

TABLE 2.2 / Entrance–Exit Strategies

Strategy	Stage to Enter	Stage to Exit	Implications for Operations
Enter early and exit late	Introduction	Decline	Transition from low-volume, flexible producer to high-volume, low-cost producer
Enter early and exit early	Introduction	Maturity	Low-volume, flexible producer
Enter late and exit late	Growth	Decline	High-volume, low-cost producer

Source: Adapted from Robert H. Hayes and Steven C. Wheelwright, "The Dynamics of Process-Product Life Cycles," *Harvard Business Review* (March–April 1979), pp. 127–136.

Although its products are doing well, Quarterdeck is already developing new products, such as a program that allows personal computers to communicate with larger computers that don't use DOS.

Enter Late and Exit Late. A firm waits in the wings until other, innovative firms introduce a new product. After it is clear that the product has significant market appeal and will achieve high sales volumes, the firm enters the market with an automated, efficient production facility. Large firms, in particular, may accompany their entry with **preemptive pricing,** that is, setting their prices considerably lower than those of their competitors to ensure the high-volume sales necessary for low unit costs and to avoid a transition from low to high volumes. They can exploit their mass-marketing capabilities, establish distribution channels, and gain access to capital markets to finance the massive investment needed for top efficiency. A good example in the service sector is United Parcel Service, the package-delivery giant with 237,000 employees and $12.4 billion in revenues, which is muscling into the overnight-express business to compete head-to-head with Federal Express, the innovator in overnight express mail. UPS has made $1.5 billion in improvements to its system of tracking and scheduling deliveries and now guarantees 10:30 A.M. next-day delivery in more locations than Federal Express. It also is offering large discounts to large-volume customers.

The Planning Process

The planning process for new products and services is most active during the first stage of the life cycle. As Fig. 2.2 illustrates, it is a four-step process, guided by corporate strategy. An essential part of strategic planning, the firm's mission plays a key role in the conceptualization and design of new products

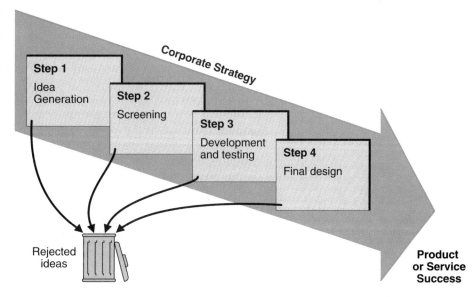

FIGURE 2.2

Steps in Planning New Products and Services

and services. If its mission is too broad, the firm could enter areas in which it has no distinctive competencies. If the mission is too narrow, promising growth opportunities will be missed. Managerial Practice 2.3 shows how four firms are each either broadening or narrowing their missions.

Step 1: Idea Generation. Ideas for new products or services often come from within the firm—from managers, employees, or research and development (R&D) laboratories. They also come from the outside—from distributors, licensers, and inventors. You may be surprised to learn that Du Pont, known for its innovative products, gets two-thirds of its new product ideas from outside sources.

New ideas are either *market oriented* or *technology oriented*. The most obvious source of new ideas is marketing, the department responsible for keeping in touch with customer and client needs. Market studies discover better ways to serve established markets, as well as opportunities to enter new ones. Examples of successful market-oriented ideas are dial-a-call services by psychologists, fast-food delivery service to students living in dormitories, low-cost news summary transmissions to radio stations via facsimile machines, and McDonald's low-fat hamburgers.

Technological advances can affect either the product or the process. Consider the innovations in the electronics and computer industries that are spawning many new products. Other inventions improve the production process, which in turn creates opportunities for more new products. For example, automatic teller machines have allowed banks to offer their customers 24-hour service. Large firms do most of the industrial R&D work, with some 80 percent of R&D being done by firms employing more than 5000 persons. Many of the new product ideas are generated by the half million scientists whose industrial research costs billions of dollars each year. Some successful technology-oriented ideas include lasers for specialized surgery, Du Pont's super-tough Kevlar fiber, AT&T's SmartPhone (which a customer can program to place an order for his usual pizza at the touch of one button), and Tandy's compact disc recorders.

Step 2: Screening. There is never a dearth of new product or service ideas. NBC estimates that it wades through 250,000 suggestions or ideas every year. The real question is, Which ideas are worth pursuing? By one estimate, only 8 of every 60 ideas make it past the screening step, and only one is actually commercialized. Some ideas do not fit the company's mission. Others fail to meet marketing, operations, or financial criteria.

Marketing criteria help managers measure the potential impact of a new product or service on the competition and on the firm's existing product line. Criteria include competitiveness, responsiveness to market needs, the idea's patent status, promotional requirements, need for after-market services, and fit with existing distribution channels. *Operations criteria* include the technical feasibility of producing a product or service and its compatibility with the firm's current processes, work force, equipment, facility locations, and supplier capabilities. *Financial criteria* include the size of the corporation, investment re-

Managerial Practice 2.3

A Broad or Narrow Mission?

- Pizza Hut, which has focused on eat-in and take-out pizza, is testing whether to broaden its mission. The chain opened a beige stucco restaurant in its headquarters city, Wichita, Kansas. Except for the red roof, it is a far cry from its other 6725 units across the country. The new restaurant, called Pizza Hut Cafe, is such a departure because the firm, so strongly associated with pizza, will feature a full-dinner house. Its menu will include minestrone, pasta, chicken, Caesar salad, and chocolate-drenched desserts, as well as pizza. The dine-in setting has higher margins, and the chain doesn't want to miss the opportunity to sell pizza to those customers.

- Apple Computer, a large personal computer maker, is planning to diversify into consumer electronics, entertainment, and mobile communications. "We have a new agenda," says Apple's chief executive officer. "The vision still is empowering individuals. But we're expanding that vision to a lot of other emerging markets." Experts expect Apple to begin introducing products outside the realm of personal computing by 1995. For example, Apple is considering a home "playstation" that would have the company's Macintosh and Hypercard software at its core, include a compact disk player, and sell for roughly $600. It is also considering a pocket-size computer that would send and receive data via cellular phone networks. Among other things, these devices might be outfitted with electronic travel guides.

- GTE Corporation, based in Stamford, Connecticut, says that it will quit the lighting business and narrow the company's focus solely on telecommunications for the first time since it began diversifying in 1959. The chairman said that GTE must continually reassess the business environment and that its telecommunications businesses, which also include AirFone, a telephone service for airline passengers, will benefit from a more focused orientation. As one telecommunications analyst pointed out, "lighting has nothing to do with the phone business."

- N.V. Philips, an electronics company with headquarters in Einhoven, the Netherlands, makes a huge array of products, including television sets, electric shavers, light bulbs, compact disks, medical scanners, toasters, hearing aids, and printed circuit boards. With units in nearly every country, the company employs 285,000. To get back on a profitable footing, Philips is making a long-term effort to narrow its focus. It has already sold U.S. companies that make toothbrushes and garage-door openers. It also heavily pruned its unprofitable computer and semiconductor operations.

Sources: "Pizza Hut Cooks Up an Italian Theme," *Wall Street Journal*, August 15, 1991; "Apple Expands Its Ambitions to Diversify," *Wall Street Journal*, September 27, 1991; "GTE to Switch Out of Lighting, Electrical Sector," *Wall Street Journal*, October 1, 1991; "Philips to Eliminate 35,000 to 45,000 Jobs by End of '91," *Wall Street Journal*, October 26, 1990.

*T*he inviting decor of the Pizza Hut Cafe, in Wichita, Kansas, should strengthen the appeal of Pizza Hut's new marketing strategy.

quired, degree of risk, predicted annual sales, profit margin per unit, and anticipated length of a product's or service's life cycle. Marketing criteria relate mainly to future revenues, whereas operations criteria relate directly to cost. In a sense, the financial tests bring marketing and operations together. Managerial Practice 2.4 demonstrates that important nonfinancial considerations—ethics and the environment—also should be part of the decision process.

Although most ideas are discarded during screening, there is no guarantee that an optimal decision will be made, as the history of the following ill-fated products suggests:

- After painstaking market research, Ford launched the Edsel car with much fanfare. One enthusiastic dealer even unfurled a huge Edsel sign above San Francisco Bay. But the company's high expectations went unmet, as Ford sold only about 100,000 of the cars.
- Extensive taste tests convinced Coca-Cola executives that customers would prefer a new flavor of the world's best-selling soft drink. They were surprised by consumer response, however, so we can now buy the new Coke and "Classic" Coke.
- RJR Nabisco's "smokeless cigarette" Premier, General Mill's Benefit cereal, and Anheuser-Busch's LA Beer were all tabled after ambitious plans to make them national brands.

There are two reasons for such failures. First, a great deal of uncertainty surrounds the choice. Making accurate forecasts of future sales, costs, and com-

Managerial Practice 2.4

Ethics and the Environment in Screening

- Following its extensive environmental audit, McDonald's Corporation is redesigning its products and services to cut the huge waste stream at its 11,000 restaurants by more than 80 percent within a few years. The program goes far beyond the decision to abandon the polystyrene "clamshell" box for hamburgers and sandwiches. Restaurant crews are now expected to give waste reduction "equal weight" with such operating priorities as quickness, cleanliness, and quality service. The urgency is clear: Americans discard about 40 million tons a year of packaging and containers of all kinds, a volume that now exceeds 30 percent of the country's municipal solid-waste stream.
- McDonnell Douglas Corporation had 410 employee-volunteers participate in evacuation drills to test its new MD-11 model. When the volunteers surged forward on command toward the exits of the pitch-black plane, chaos resulted and 50 people were hurt. The aircraft makers are now clamoring for government permission to use computer simulations in many of their product tests. But the ill-fated drills still question whether any use of employees in product testing—still fairly common practice among many consumer-product companies—makes sense and is an ethical practice. Safety issues aside, critics suggest that asking employees to raise their hands for product tests implies subtle pressure. When it comes time for promotion, employees often believe it will be taken into consideration.

Sources: "McDonald's Launches Plan to Cut Waste," *Wall Street Journal*, April 17, 1991; "Use of Staff Guinea Pigs Causes Squeals About Safety of Firms' Product Testing," *Wall Street Journal*, December 31, 1991.

petitor reactions is difficult, if not perilous. Historical data for totally new products are nonexistent. Second, multiple criteria cannot be naturally merged into a single measure (such as dollars). Managers are hard pressed to estimate the dollar equivalent of intangibles such as operations compatibility or project risk. Later in this chapter, we discuss tools managers use in decision making.

Step 3: Development and Testing. Next, the firm must test the idea's technical feasibility by considering a variety of factors. In manufacturing industries, engineers may design prototypes for testing and analyzing a product's features. Operations assesses process, facility, and material needs. Finally, marketing conducts tests in limited markets or with customer panels to gauge consumer response to the product's features, packaging, and promotional campaign. The end result of testing should be a product that is technically and economically feasible and that has customer appeal.

The U.K. firm British Aerospace estimates that decisions made during the first 5 percent of step 3 determine 85 percent of a product's eventual quality, cost, and ease of manufacture. Historically, engineering designed the product first and only then would manufacturing get involved. Engineers worked in virtual isolation. Their prototypes were not designed for efficient production and assembly, costly changes and retooling were common, and often the development process was delayed. Today, increased market segmentation and declining life cycles make short development cycles critical.

This realization has prompted many firms to involve operations in development and testing from the outset. In a process called **concurrent engineering** (and sometimes "simultaneous engineering" or "interactive design"), design engineers, manufacturing specialists, marketers, buyers, and quality specialists work jointly to design the product or service and to select the production process. Firms implement concurrent engineering in somewhat different ways. Following the precedent established by its Taurus/Sable program, Ford now gives full responsibility for each new product to a program manager. The program manager forms a product team representing every major part of the organization—including manufacturing. Thus each department can express its views while there is still time to alter the product. Changes at this step are much simpler and less costly than after the product or service has been introduced to the market. Motorola Lighting Incorporated brought together teams from engineering, marketing, and manufacturing to design its electronic ballasts (the transformers that run fluorescent lighting systems). During 1989, 22 employees worked in a single room at Motorola headquarters, where "everybody's business was everybody's business." This concept of working together is also a tradition at Honda, where animated discussions among representatives of all departments have earned the nickname *waigaya*, which loosely translates into "hubbub."

In service industries, firms must define and assess three components of the "service bundle" (see Sasser, Olsen, and Wyckoff, 1978): (1) facilitating goods, (2) explicit services, and (3) implicit services. To illustrate, in a restaurant, facilitating goods include food, drink, tables, chairs, and tableware. Explicit services include speed and quality of service and less tangible characteristics such as taste, aroma, and atmosphere. Implicit services are harder to define because they depend on customer preferences. They could include perceptions of status, comfort, or a general sense of well-being.

Restaurant chains generally begin with a carefully designed prototype. R. David Thomas founded Wendy's Old-Fashioned Hamburgers in 1969. For the first site, in Columbus, Ohio, he defined the details of product features such as menu, interior decor, and order processing service. Only after finishing the development and testing stage did Wendy's begin to expand and sell franchises. Managerial Practice 2.5 describes a similar process followed by the Olive Garden restaurant chain.

Stage 4: Final Design. During this step, the firm finalizes the details of product or service characteristics, often by lists of specifications, process formulas, and drawings. For example, engineering drawings for an electric utility boiler would specify types of material and dimensions for each component. This is the stage at which firms commit substantial financial and human resources to the project. Then production begins. Marketing starts its promotional program with kickoff sales meetings and presentations at trade exhibits. In services, a supermarket would establish maximum customer delay times. Multisite service firms such as Olive Garden restaurants might add a limited number of facilities. If they prove successful, expansion to many new sites could proceed rapidly. In just one decade

- McDonald's went from 738 to 3750 units (it now has 11,000 units).
- Holiday Inns grew from 587 to 1750 inns.
- Manpower, Inc., a temporary employment agency, increased its annual revenues from $47.3 to $161.2 million.

Decision-Making Tools

Managers must decide which new products and services to introduce and then select their particular design features. Sometimes hard thinking in a quiet room is sufficient. At other times decision makers rely on more formal procedures. We present only three of these formal procedures: a preference matrix, break-even analysis, and reliability analysis. The preference matrix helps a manager deal with the multiple criteria that are always part of decisions on which new products or services to introduce. Break-even analysis helps the manager identify the level of sales necessary to make a new product or service a profitable venture. Reliability analysis is particularly relevant for the development and testing step, when different product or service designs are being evaluated. We discuss two more-advanced techniques, financial analysis and linear programming, in Supplements 1 and 2, respectively, at the end of this book.

Preference Matrix. A **preference matrix** is a table that allows the manager to rate an alternative according to several performance criteria. The criteria can be scored on any scale, such as from 1 (worst possible) to 10 (best possible), as long as the same scale is applied to all the alternatives being compared. Each

Managerial Practice 2.5

Refining the Service Bundle at Olive Garden Restaurants

General Mills opened the prototype for Olive Garden restaurants at a failed steakhouse in Orlando, Florida, in 1982. Since then the company has spent considerable time and money creating an Italian ambience and cuisine—its restaurants serve some spaghetti but also include other dishes that appeal to the American mass market. General Mills canvassed 1000 restaurants for recipes, interviewed 5000 consumers, and tried more than 80 pots of spaghetti sauce before selecting a final service bundle. An important goal of the development and testing stage was a tomato sauce that would cling to pasta rather than run to the plate's edge. All new employees watched videotapes instructing them on the details of their jobs. Even the singing waiters' lyrics were carefully crafted. Five years after General Mills opened its prototype's doors, there were 58 Olive Garden restaurants. The firm hopes eventually to operate 500 across the country.

Source: "General Mills Risks Millions Starting Chain of Italian Restaurants," *Wall Street Journal*, September 21, 1987.

score is weighted according to its perceived importance, with the total of these weights typically equaling 100. The total score is the sum of the weighted scores (weight times score) for all the criteria. By rating various alternatives, the manager can compare the scores for new product ideas against one another or against a predetermined threshold.

Application 2.2   Evaluating an Alternative with a Preference Matrix

The following table shows the performance criteria, weights, and scores (1 = worst, 10 = best) for a new product, a thermal storage air conditioner. If management wants to introduce just one new product, and the highest total score of any of the other product ideas is 800, should the firm pursue the air conditioner?

Performance Criterion	Weight (A)	Score (B)	Weighted Score (A × B)
Market potential	30	8	
Unit profit margin	20	10	
Operations compatibility	20	6	
Competitive advantage	15	10	
Investment requirement	10	2	
Project risk	5	4	———
		Weighted score =	═══

Solution   We calculate the first weighted score in the last column of the table as 240 (30 × 8). Continuing down the column, the results are 200, 120, 150, 20, and 20. Next we sum these weighted scores, for a total of 750. This score falls short of the 800 threshold, so we would not pursue the thermal storage air conditioner idea at this time.

Not all managers are comfortable with the preference matrix technique. It requires the manager to state criterion weights before examining the alternatives, although the proper weights may not be readily apparent. Only after seeing the scores for several alternatives can the manager decide what is important and what is not. The preference matrix also allows a low score on one criterion to be compensated for or overriden by high scores on others, which may or may not be realistic. For example, the investment required for a new manufacturing process might exceed the firm's financial capability. In that case the new product or service idea must be dropped, no matter how high the scores were for the other criteria.

Break-Even Analysis. When used for product or service planning, **break-even analysis** is a technique for determining the volume at which total revenues are equal to total costs. When used to compare production methods, it finds the volume at which two different processes have equal total costs. Here we use it for the first purpose: to evaluate the profit potential of a new product or service. This technique helps the manager answer questions such as:

1. Is the predicted sales volume of the product or service sufficient to break even (neither earning a profit nor sustaining a loss)?
2. How low must the variable cost per unit be to break even, based on forecasts of sales and prices?
3. How low must the fixed cost be to break even?
4. How do price levels affect the break-even volume?

Break-even analysis assumes that all costs related to the production of a specific product or service can be divided into fixed costs and variable costs. Let

p = price charged per unit sold
c = variable cost of each unit produced
F = fixed cost per year
Q = number of units produced and sold per year

The **variable cost,** c, is the portion of the total cost that varies directly with volume of output. This cost includes costs per unit for materials, labor, and usually some variable part of overhead. The **fixed cost,** F, is the portion of the total cost that remains constant regardless of changes in levels of output. This cost represents the annual cost of new equipment and facilities purchased (or rented) for the new product or service, including depreciation, interest, taxes, and insurance. The fixed cost can also cover salaries, utilities, and portions of the sales or advertising budget. The difference between the price and the variable cost of each unit is often called the unit profit margin ($p - c$) because it contributes both to profits and to meeting fixed costs.

Let's assume that the cost function is linear and consists of the fixed cost plus total variable costs ($F + cQ$). If we set total annual revenues (pQ) equal to the total cost and solve for Q, we get the break-even quantity:

$$pQ = F + cQ$$

$$(p - c)Q = F$$

$$Q = \frac{F}{p - c}$$

We can also find this break-even quantity graphically, as shown in the following application. It is the point where the total revenue line crosses the total cost line.

Application 2.3   *Finding the Break-Even Quantity*

A hospital is considering a new procedure to be offered at $200 per patient. Fixed cost per year would be $100,000, with total variable costs set at $100 per patient. What is the break-even quantity for this service? Use both the algebraic and graphic approaches to get your answer.

Solution   For the hospital to break even, the number of patients (Q) must equal the fixed cost per year (F) divided by the unit profit margin ($p - c$). Thus, using the formula for the break-even quantity, we get

$$Q = \frac{F}{p - c} = \frac{100,000}{200 - 100} = 1000 \text{ patients}$$

The graphic approach requires that we plot two lines—one for costs and one for revenues. We begin by calculating costs and revenues for two different output levels. The following table uses $Q = 0$ and $Q = 2000$, although any two reasonably spread out output levels are equally good.

Quantity (patients) (Q)	Total Annual Cost ($) (100,000 + 100Q)	Total Annual Revenues ($) (200Q)
0	100,000	0
2000	300,000	400,000

Since two points define a line, we can now draw the cost line through points (0, 100,000) and (2000, 300,000). The revenue line goes between (0, 0) and (2000, 400,000). As Fig. 2.3 indicates, these two lines intersect at 1000 patients, the break-even quantity.

FIGURE 2.3

Graphic Approach to
Break-Even Analysis

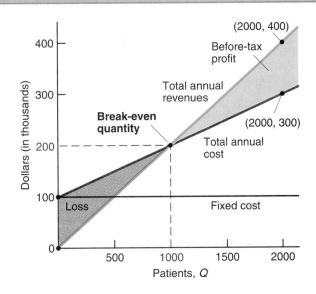

Break-even analysis cannot tell a manager whether to pursue or drop a new product or service idea. The technique can only show what is likely to happen for various forecasts of costs and sales volumes. Fortunately, we can go beyond simple break-even analysis and work directly with the underlying cost and revenue equations to evaluate a variety of "what if" questions. This approach is called **sensitivity analysis,** a technique for systematically changing the critical parameters in a model to determine their effects. With product and service planning, we can assess the sensitivity of total profit to different pricing strategies, sales volumes forecasts, or cost estimates.

Application 2.4	Sensitivity Analysis on the Sales Forecasts

If the most pessimistic sales forecast for the proposed service in Fig. 2.3 were 1500 patients, what would be the procedure's total profit contribution per year?

Solution　　The graph shows that even the pessimistic forecast lies above the break-even volume, which is encouraging. The product's total profit contribution, found by subtracting total costs from total revenues, is

$$pQ - (F + cQ) = 200(1500) - [100,000 + 100(1500)]$$
$$= \$50,000$$

Reliability Analysis. Products or services often consist of a system of components that must all be operative to be effective. Sometimes products or services can be designed with extra components (or subsystems) so that if one component fails, another can be activated. This type of design increases the **reliability** of the product or service, which is the probability that the system or one of its components will work at any time. Without backups, all components must work for the entire system to work. The reliability of a system with n different components is

$$r_s = (r_1)(r_2) \cdots (r_j) \cdots (r_n)$$

where

r_s = reliability of the system
r_j = reliability of the jth component

When there is backup for one of the components, say the jth component, or the probability that it will work at any time, then r_j must be replaced in the preceding equation by a larger number r_j':

$$r_j' = 1.0 - (1.0 - r_j)^m$$

where

r_j' = probability that at least one of the m components of type j will work at any time

$(1.0 - r_j)^m$ = joint probability that all m components of type j will fail

m = total number of components of type j designed in the product or service

| Application 2.5 | *Calculating a Product's Reliability* |

A new machine being designed has three basic components, with individual reliabilities of 0.78, 0.99, and 0.95, respectively. What is the machine's reliability with no backups? What is its reliability with two backups (a total of three units) of the first component?

Solution   The machine's reliability without backups is only 0.73, or significantly less than that of the individual components:

$$r_s = (0.78)(0.99)(0.95) = 0.73$$

When two backups are added for the first component, the machine's reliability increases to 0.93:

$$r_s = [1.0 - (1.0 - 0.78)](0.99)(0.95) = 0.93$$

COMPETITIVE PRIORITIES

As important as choosing a product or service is deciding how to excel in producing or delivering it. For example, it is not enough to decide which types of food to offer at a new restaurant. The owner must also determine the restaurant's distinctive competencies, such as its location or distinctive cuisine. By taking advantage of them, the owner can set the restaurant apart from its competitors. **Competitive priorities** are the dimensions that a firm's production system must possess to support the demands of the markets the firm wishes to compete in. There are eight dimensions, which fall into four groups:

Cost
　　1. Low cost
Quality
　　2. High-performance design
　　3. Consistent quality
Time
　　4. Fast delivery time
　　5. On-time delivery
　　6. Development speed
Flexibility
　　7. Customization
　　8. Volume flexibility

A firm gains an advantage by outperforming competitors on one or more of these dimensions with the support of its production system.

Cost

Often firms compete on the basis of low prices. Lowering prices reduces unit profit margins, an outcome that can be partially offset by the higher volumes that may follow. The firm's operations function must attempt to lower the cost of labor, materials, scrap, and overhead. But the ability to lower costs often requires additional investment in more automated facilities and equipment.

Lowering prices to maintain or increase market share, and reducing costs without jeopardizing quality, usually occurs with undifferentiated products in the maturity stage of their life cycles. At that stage output levels tend to be high, equipment is specialized, and efficiency is likely to be at a peak. In the context of break-even analysis, the fixed cost, F, is increased to achieve a sharply reduced variable cost, c.

Quality

Two competitive priorities deal with quality. The first one, **high-performance design,** can mean superior features, close tolerances, and greater durability. It also includes the helpfulness and skill of the work force, whether sales clerks or service station attendants. After-sale support and financing may also be part of the design specifications. For example, IBM now offers installment payment plans, credit cards, and equipment leasing. It leases more than $1.5 billion worth of new equipment, a big boost to sales.

The second competitive priority is **consistent quality.** It measures the frequency with which the product or service meets design specifications. A foundry might measure the percent of castings falling within the tolerances allowed for length, diameter, and surface finish. A bank might measure the number of errors made recording customer account numbers by its booking services department.

Time

Three competitive priorities deal with time. The first, **fast delivery time,** is the elapsed time between receiving a customer's order and filling it. Industrial buyers often call this *lead time.* An acceptable delivery time can be a year for a major customized machine, several weeks for scheduling elective surgery, and minutes for an ambulance. Firms can shorten delivery times by producing to inventory or having slack capacity.

The second time priority reflects variability in delivery time, rather than its average. **On-time delivery** measures the frequency of meeting delivery-time promises. Manufacturers measure on-time delivery as the percentage of customer orders shipped when promised, with 95 percent often considered the goal. A supermarket might measure on-time delivery as the percentage of customers who must wait in the checkout line for less than three minutes.

The third time priority, **development speed,** measures how quickly a new product or service is introduced, covering the elapsed time from idea generation through final design and production. In industries where life cycles are short, development time becomes critical. Companies have to respond quickly to each new product or service that enters the market. Getting the new product or service to market first gives the firm an edge on the competition, which is difficult to overcome when the business environment changes so rapidly. But one size does not fit all. Development speed is less important when R&D costs are high and technology and customer preferences are highly uncertain.

Flexibility

Some firms give top priority to one of two types of flexibility. **Customization** is the flexibility of the firm to accommodate the unique needs of each customer and ever-changing product designs. Products or services are tailored to individual preferences or have very short life cycles. Volumes for any given product or service are low because the firm competes on the basis of its ability to produce difficult, nonstandard items. The extreme case is one-of-a kind production, where each new order is unique.

Volume flexibility, on the other hand, is the ability to quickly accelerate or decelerate the rate of production to handle large fluctuations in demand. The time between peaks can be years, as with the cycles in the home-building industry or political campaigns. It can be months, as with a ski resort. It even can be hours, as with the systematic swings in demand from hour to hour at a major postal facility where mail is sorted and dispatched. Managerial Practice 2.6 (on the next page) illustrates each of the competitive priorities by referring to the practices of actual firms.

Trade-Offs

Sometimes a firm can improve cost, quality, and flexibility simultaneously. For example, scrap and rework sometimes account for 20–30 percent of a product's cost. By reducing scrap and rework the firm can sharply reduce costs, improve productivity, and reduce delivery time. Improving the quality of products and services can help stimulate sales to the point where high-volume production is possible. An underlying factor here is **repeatability,** the degree to which the same work can be repeated through job specialization or by producing standardized products and services. Increased repeatability reduces unit costs, permitting production of a higher-quality product or services at lower prices. Thus improved quality might actually be cost free.

Unfortunately, at some point further improvements on one dimension are accompanied by setbacks on one or more of the others. For example, research shows that high customization leads to both higher costs and prices (Wood, 1991). This trade-off with costs, however, doesn't always occur. For example, broader product lines and extensive variety through standard options can be achieved without sacrificing high-volume production (Kekre and Srinivasan, 1990). Another example of trade-offs is the top-of-the-line specifications of Rolls Royce, which make premium prices necessary. And delivery times are also slower because the painstaking hand assembly process means it still takes six months to build a car.

Thus managers must recognize the trade-offs that exist among the eight competitive priority dimensions. Because much depends on the exact situation, managers must judge trade-off outcomes when deciding which dimensions need particular emphasis. For example, it is easy for Earl Scheib, Inc., with its high repeatability and standard services, to emphasize not only low cost but also quick (one-day) delivery times. Low customization like that at McDonald's allows a fast, mass-production process. C. Hoare & Company en-

Managerial Practice 2.6

Competitive Priorities of Various Firms

Low Cost

Earl Scheib, Inc., of Beverly Hills, California, operates 275 shops that offer a "no-frills" face-lift to cars at rock-bottom prices. Unit profit margins are protected by pinching every penny through low-cost operations. Sales have increased at an annual rate of 15 percent, and earnings are increasing at almost 50 percent per year.

High-Performance Design

C. Hoare & Company, a bank founded in London in 1672, treats clients like royalty but charges a stiff price. Six descendants of the founder still run the family business. At least one is no more than an hour away, day or night. Customers are ushered in by a doorman in a frock coat. Teller counters are rimmed to accommodate umbrellas, with a drip gully carved below in the granite floor. The waiting room is lined with gold-rimmed ledgers in glass cases. Money is no object to the 8000 customers, whom most employees know by sight.

Consistent Quality

McDonald's restaurants are known for uniform design specifications. Eating at McDonald's is definitely a different experience from dining at a five-star restaurant. However, you can count on the same menu and standards of quality from one order to the next and from one restaurant to the next.

Fast Delivery Times

By automating its analysis and trading functions, Batterymarch, the Boston-based equity fund manager, collapsed the time it takes to decide on a portfolio change for a customer and complete the transaction. The customer gets into rising stocks and out of falling ones faster than before. Batterymarch has lower costs and high profits: Revenues per employee are triple the industry average.

On-Time Delivery

Federal Express not only offers fast delivery time (overnight delivery) but also promises that parcels will be "absolutely, positively" delivered on time. Meeting delivery promises comes at a cost. A two-day delivery by the U.S. Postal Service, priced at $2.90, can cost as much as $25 if sent overnight by Federal Express.

Development Speed

Motorola's new MicroTac Lite is a portable telephone that is tiny and light. It looks a lot like its 1989 predecessor, the original MicroTac, which broke the one-pound barrier. This cutting-edge product was developed quickly and became the first entry in a new category of very small phones. The phone's price is high, but it will tumble later once competitors can introduce their own versions. In the meantime, Motorola's quick product introduction gives it a competitive edge and healthy profit margins.

Customization

When hit by an industrywide slump, National Semiconductor Corporation decided to enter the growing market for custom-designed computer chips. Rather than mass produce the product and sell it through a catalog, the company designs each chip to suit the customer's specific requirements. A custom-made chip can cost as much as $1 million. While Japan dominates the market for commodity memory chips, U.S. producers such as National Semiconductor lead in the vital market of specialized, design-intensive chips.

Volume Flexibility

Nicholas St. George runs Oakwood Homes Corp., a North Carolina company that sells factory-built homes. In 1987, following loan defaults by home buyers, its profits plunged. Convinced that financing for his customers would dry up, St. George built up a subsidiary to supply investment money himself. He overhauled operations by cutting costs, trimming the break-even point from 300 to 225 homes sales a month, and expanded into the faster-growing luxury-home segment. Knowing when to quickly change directions in the ups and downs of the housing market allowed his firm to contend better than most of his competitors.

Sources: "Earl Scheib Is Still King of the No-Frills Paint Job," *Business Week*, May 27, 1985; "Bored with Queues? Some London Banks Let You Skip Them," *Wall Street Journal*, October 26, 1984; Joseph L. Bower and Thomas M. Hout, "Fast-Cycle Capability for Competitive Power," *Harvard Business Review* (November–December 1988), pp. 110–118; "Tiny, Light Phone Can Empty Pockets But Fits Them, Too," *Wall Street Journal*, February 2, 1992; "Don't Renew the Semiconductor Cartel," *Wall Street Journal*, May 20, 1991; "Tale of Two Prefab-Home Firms Is Darwinian Lesson," *Wall Street Journal*, April 4, 1991.

hances its top-quality image by also having fast delivery times, as by answering loan inquiries the day they are received. Moreover, the resulting increase in the price of the service provided is of little concern to the bank's customers.

Setting Competitive Priorities

It is intriguing to see how executives in the United States rate the competitive priorities for their businesses. In a 1990 survey, executives judged the importance of each competitive priority to their firms. As expected, each priority was rated by the average respondent to be quite important. To focus on the relative rankings, however, Fig. 2.4 shows the difference between a priority's average and the grand average calculated for all eight priorities. Positive values mean that the priority is more important, and negative values mean the priority is less important. On-time delivery and consistent quality emerged at the top, with high-performance design placing third and price next. The last two dimensions of time and the two flexibility priorities came in last. The most marked shift, compared to a 1988 survey, was in low price, made possible by low-cost operations. Price increased by almost 10 percent in importance. As customers seek the best value for their dollar outlays, price increasingly enters their purchasing decision.

Effective operations strategy begins with periodic reviews of competitive priorities. Managers should assess the firm's current performance in terms of the desired level on all eight dimensions. Performance should also be judged against the industry norm. Finally, the managers set specific, measurable stan-

FIGURE 2.4

Competitive Priorities
of U.S.
Manufacturers

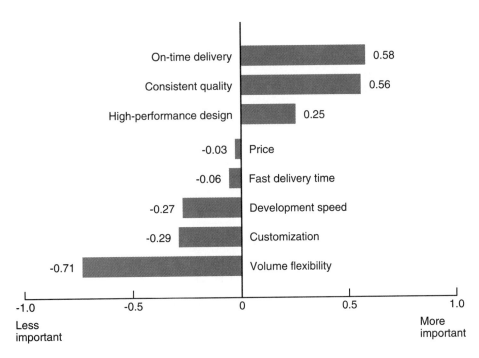

Source: Jay S. Kim and Jeffrey G. Miller, "The Manufacturing Futures Factbook: 1990 U.S. Manufacturing Futures Survey," Boston University, 1990.

dards. Examples of such standards for each competitive priority include the following:

- Reduce the cost to $10 per unit.
- Decrease scrap losses by 10 percent.
- Maintain the current tolerances for product weight.
- Promise deliveries within three weeks after receiving an order.
- Improve on-time delivery to 95 percent.
- Cut the development and testing time for a new service by six months.
- Increase the number of product options by 50 percent.
- Be able to double the production rate in just two months.

TIME-BASED COMPETITION

Quality, cost, and flexibility get considerable attention in subsequent chapters. For example, Chapters 3 and 4 focus on quality, and flexibility is a major concern in Chapter 5. We therefore give special attention here to the competitive priorities dealing with time. As Fig. 2.4 suggests, managers rank on-time delivery as one of the most important competitive priorities. Indeed, three of the top five competitive priorities are related to time-based competition. Life cycles are shrinking quickly—especially in Japan. A European car has a model-life of 12 years, while a Japanese car's life is less than 5 years and falling. By some estimates, the Japanese bring out a new product in half the time as it takes their U.S. competitors and one-third the time it takes the Europeans. This ability allows a firm to abandon today's new product or service more quickly, making it stronger and more profitable tomorrow. In response, many companies are putting particular focus on the competitive priorities of development speed and fast delivery time. With **time-based competition,** managers carefully define the steps and time involved to deliver a product or service and then critically analyze each step to see whether time can be saved without compromising quality. Managers seek fundamental changes that save time—from product or service development, order entry, production, and distribution. Significant time reductions in operations can often be achieved by changing the way current technologies are used or by turning to automation. Concurrent engineering can also speed up the development time because of everybody's early involvement and simultaneous ownership of the product or service design.

Reducing Response Time

Atlas Door gained the number one competitive position in an industry previously dominated by large, established firms by focusing on fast delivery times. Atlas makes industrial doors, a product with limitless options in width, height, and material. It reorganized its factories to allow for a uniform flow of products, thereby reducing the manufacturing time of each product. It also streamlined and automated order-entry, engineering, pricing, and scheduling processes. Today, Atlas can schedule and price 95 percent of telephoned orders while the caller is still on the line. Finally, Atlas developed a system to ensure that all parts necessary for shipment to a construction site would be available at the same time. As a result, Atlas can respond to an order in a few weeks; the industry average is four months. This quicker response time allows Atlas to charge premium prices. Because its time-efficient processes yield lower manufacturing costs, it also enjoys big profits. Atlas's competitors did not recognize the thrust of the time-based strategy and still think it will gravitate toward the industry averages as volume increases. However, the enormous lead that Atlas presently enjoys will be very difficult, perhaps impossible, to overcome.

More Products in Less Time

Firms can also use time-based competition by focusing on development speed rather than fast delivery times—but with equally devastating results. Motorola Incorporated introduced its MicroTac pocket-sized cellular phone in 1989 ("Pushing Design," 1991). By the time its competitors entered the market almost two years later, Motorola had sold over $1 billion of the 10.7-ounce phones. The new product even won two of the highest Japanese awards for top quality. Motorola was able to rush the new design into production by using new 3-D computer-aided design software (developed by Toronto-based Alias Research), which is much faster than traditional design methods. Using the software compresses the design process and electronically links every step from sketching to creating molds. Another example of time-based competition is Honda's response to Yamaha's attempt to take over a larger share of the motorcycle market (Stalk, 1988). Honda changed its methods for developing, manufacturing, and introducing new products to enable it to speed up execution of new product plans. Within 18 months it introduced or replaced 113 models, while Yamaha could manage only 37 changes in its product line. Honda's strategy caused its sales to soar. The devastating defeat of Yamaha was a clear warning to Suzuki and Kawasaki not to challenge Honda's leadership. Clearly, Motorola and Honda had used time to their competitive advantage.

A businessman uses his MicroTac cellular phone while en route to a meeting. Motorola beat the competition to the market with this 10.7-ounce phone by using innovative design software.

POSITIONING STRATEGIES

For given product and service plans, and their accompanying competitive priorities, the operations manager must select a **positioning strategy.** This choice determines whether the production system will be organized by grouping resources around the process or around the product or service.

Firms using a **process-focused strategy** tend to produce a wide range of customized products or services. The operations manager sets aside a single area for each process (such as drilling or welding in manufacturing or accounts payable in a service firm's accounting department), and various products move from one process to another. Different types of machines or workers are grouped together to handle all products or services requiring a specific function. All products (services) needing that function are then routed to it, rather than to separate processing areas created for each one. In other words, the equipment and work force are organized around the process. With this type of strategy, products (customers) may have to compete for resources; as shown in Fig. 2.5(a), products 1 and 3 must compete for the same resources at operation A, and products 2 and 3 must do the same at operation E. Note that product 1 follows an A–B–D routing pattern, product 2 follows a D–E–C pattern, and product 3 follows an E–F–A pattern. Firms typically using a process-focused

FIGURE 2.5

Two Different
Positioning Strategies

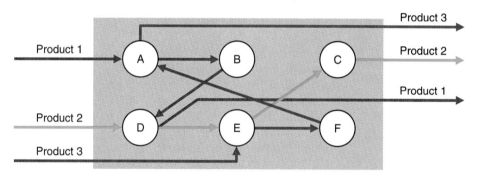

(a) Process focused

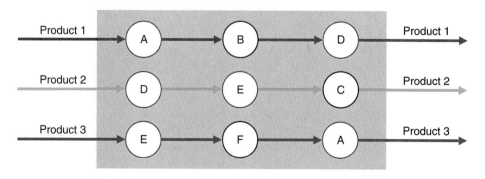

(b) Product focused

strategy include building contractors, law firms, architectural firms, and general medical practices.

In the **product-focused strategy,** illustrated in Fig. 2.5(b), the equipment and work force are organized around the product or service. This system creates duplication of operations, but products and services don't have to compete for limited resources. For example, there are two operations A in the facility, one dedicated to product 1 and one to product 3. The routing pattern for each of the three products is straightforward, with several sequential operations devoted to the same product or service. Firms typically using a product-focused strategy include automobile assembly plants, car washes, and electronic product manufacturers.

A Continuum of Strategies

Actually, a firm's strategy can vary from one of its facilities to another, depending on the product or service produced at each one. Further, numerous strategies exist between the two extremes of process focus and product focus. This continuum of choices is represented in Fig. 2.6 by the diagonal from the process focus to the product focus. The figure also shows how a manager's choice relates to volume (left to right) and flow pattern (top to bottom). The most frequently occupied positions have the most intense color. Few firms position themselves too far outside the diagonal, the white area.

FIGURE 2.6

A Continuum of Positioning Strategies

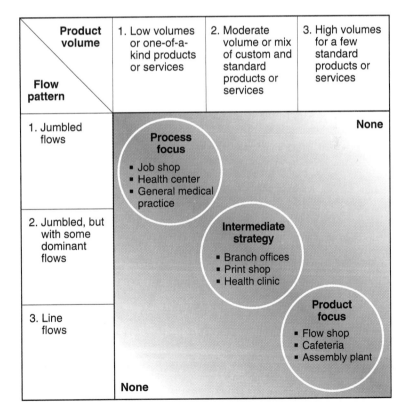

Source: After Robert H. Hayes and Steven C. Wheelwright, "Link Manufacturing Process and Product Life Cycles," *Harvard Business Review,* January–February 1979, pp. 133–140.

An even more vivid depiction of choices is the Big Picture on King Soopers Bakery (pages 186–187), a division of Kroger Company with headquarters in Colorado, which illustrates three choices at work under one roof.

Process Focus. A process-focused strategy is appropriate to a firm offering a wide range of customized (made-to-order) products, *such as King Soopers' custom cake department.* In such situations product volume tends to be low, *as shown by the bar graph on relative volume in the King Soopers picture.* If the operations manager were to dedicate resources to individual products, many operations would be duplicated and resources would often be idle. It is far more efficient to organize resources around similar processes. Because each product is unique, routings vary considerably from one order to the next. The resulting flow pattern is jumbled and unpredictable. *Compare, for instance, the complex flow in the King Soopers cake department with the linear flow in the bread line.*

A production system with a process focus is often called a **job shop,** as it takes on many types of small jobs and competes on the basis of resource flexibility. The more than 100,000 small job shops in the United States supply an estimated 75 percent of all machined metal parts used in products made by larger companies. Job shops employ the bulk of all blue-collar workers.

Intermediate Strategy. Halfway between a process focus and product focus lies an intermediate strategy. Product volumes are relatively high, and batch operations can handle several customer orders at the same time. If demand is sufficiently predictable, operations can produce some standardized products or components in advance of receiving actual customer orders. The flow pattern is still jumbled, but dominant paths emerge. For example, in some parts of the facility, the manager may dedicate resources to one product or a group of similar parts. Types of businesses that utilize this strategy include heavy equipment manufacturers, garment manufacturers, caterers, automobile repair shops, and small branch offices of service facilities such as brokerage firms and advertising agencies. *At King Soopers, the pastry line is an example of an intermediate strategy.*

Product Focus. A product-focused strategy fits high-volume production of a few standard products, *such as bread at King Soopers.* Packaging and assembly options often make products appear more diverse than they really are. For example, the same soft drink might be packaged in a bottle or a can. Cars on an assembly line might pass through the same basic operations, except for a blackwall or whitewall tire option. This type of production system is often called a **flow shop** because all products follow a linear routing pattern.

High volumes and product standardization allow product-focused operations to be both specialized and efficient. Each task is designed with painstaking detail, and the resulting process moves along at a brisk pace. For example, a fast-food restaurant takes your order, prepares and serves your meal, and processes your payment much more quickly than does a large, expensive restaurant. Other product-focused businesses include automobile manufacturers, car washes, and electronic product manufacturers.

Line flows and high volumes lend themselves to highly automated facilities. *Notice, at King Soopers, how many more machines and fewer people the bread line uses.* Such facilities can operate round the clock to offset the huge capital investment required. Borden's new pasta-making plant in St. Louis is a good example ("Borden Uses Its Noodle," 1991). It is the nation's largest pasta plant, making 250 million pounds of pasta annually. The 300,000-square-foot plant is a marvel of simplicity. Grain is milled into flour at an adjacent mill and sped to the plant a few hundred yards away via giant pneumatic tubes. The flour is then distributed to one of eight pasta-making machines, each costing $5 million and capable of producing 6000 pounds of pasta per hour. A sophisticated touch screen computer system schedules the machines. The next step is the pressing and drying operations. The mixture finally takes shape as it is forced through large dies, some weighing more than 200 pounds. What comes out is one of 65 different shapes of pasta. The product goes on to storage bins, each capable of holding 10,000 pounds of pasta until it is ready for packaging. The plant employs only 230 workers, but at no point need the product be touched by them. Packaging is computerized, sorting 1200 different shapes and brands, putting them in the right boxes, and automatically storing them. The plant operates 24 hours a day, 363 days a year.

Positioning Strategies for Services. In the service sector, customer contact is another factor for a manager to consider when choosing a positioning strategy. Some service facilities have more face-to-face customer contact than others. When service complexity is high and customer knowledge is low, services must be tailored to each customer's needs. The result is customized, low-volume production, more appropriate to a process-focused strategy. An intermediate strategy fits better when face-to-face contact and back-room work are balanced. For example, in the front office of a bank, customers and employees interact frequently with one another. By contrast, there is little or no customer contact in the back office, where automation and batching of work increases repeatability. Other service facilities, such as home offices, distribution centers, and power plants, involve virtually no face-to-face contact, resulting in standardized services and high volume.

*B*orden's new pasta-making plant in St. Louis exemplifies a successful product focus and precise flow lines. Shown here is part of the plant's packaging and storage operations.

TABLE 2.3 / *Linking Positioning Strategy with Competitive Priorities*

High-Level Decision	Positioning Strategy	
	Process Focus	Product Focus
Product and service planning	More customized products and services, with low volumes	More standardized products and services, with high volumes
	Shorter life cycles	Longer life cycles
	Products and services in earlier stages of life cycle	Products and services in later stages of life cycle
	An entrance–exit strategy favoring early exit	An entrance–exit strategy favoring late exit
Competitive priorities	High-performance design quality	Consistent quality
	More emphasis on customization and volume flexibility	More emphasis on low cost
	Long delivery times	Short delivery times

Pulling It All Together

Management must link positioning strategy to competitive priorities. In process-focused plants, the emphasis is on high-performance design (quality), customization (see Sharma, 1987), and volume flexibility. Low cost and quick delivery times are less important as competitive priorities. Thus a process focus meshes well with product or service plans favoring customization, short life cycles, or early exit from the life cycle. A product focus, on the other hand, is appropriate when product plans call for standard products or services and long life cycles. Low cost, quick delivery times, and consistent quality are the top competitive priorities. Table 2.3 summarizes these comparisons.

As Fig. 2.7 shows, operations managers use positioning strategy to translate product plans and competitive priorities into decisions throughout the operations function. To give you a better idea of how process design, inventory, scheduling, and other operations decisions mesh, let's take a tour of two very different facilities: Lower Florida Keys Health System and Chaparral Steel Company. Each firm has a different positioning strategy, which has a far-reaching effect on how each facility is designed and operated. As you read, note how decisions are linked at each facility.

TOURING A PROCESS-FOCUSED FACILITY: LOWER FLORIDA KEYS HEALTH SYSTEM*

The Lower Florida Keys Health System (LFKHS) is a full-service acute care community hospital. LFKHS patients are primarily the residents from Marathon to Key West, Florida. Some services, such as chemical dependency and eating disorders, can draw from a larger market area. Though the patient pop-

---

*We are indebted to Jeff E. Heyl (De Paul University) and Linda Stone for the background information on this tour.

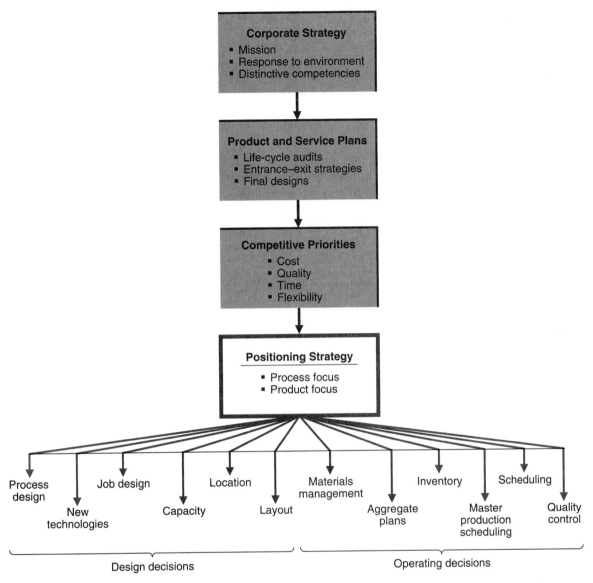

FIGURE 2.7 Positioning Strategy: The Linchpin in Operations Decisions

ulation seems fairly stable, with no significant growth, the population may be shifting north due to the cost of living in Key West. If relations with Cuba continue to thaw, however, this could change, with LFKHS providing some care to that market. The Keys have a normal population of about 75,000, about 30,000 of which are in the LFKHS service area.

The hospital is typical of relatively small facilities, with 550 employees, 420 of them full-time. This total does not include the 55 doctors who practice at the hospital and who are not strictly hospital employees. The emergency room

(ER) typically sees 50 to 60 people per day. Inpatients stay in the hospital an average of 5.4 days. LFKHS's gross revenue for the last fiscal year was $34 million, which generated a surplus of $0.7 million.

Service Plans, Competitive Priorities, and Quality

This general-purpose hospital offers a broad range of services to its patients, from treating cuts in the emergency room to obstetrics to major surgery. Its service capabilities stop just short of full trauma care. Given its small size and low volumes, it cannot offer standardized services at cut-rate prices. The services and procedures given to a patient tend to be "customized" with little opportunity for batching. Volume flexibility, and easily changing staffing levels to match daily workload requirements, is also a priority. Insufficient staffing means that service quality is jeopardized, whereas excessive staffing hurts the hospital's financial performance.

Management also emphasizes quality as a competitive priority. While quality is the responsibility of everyone, a quality assurance (QA) coordinator designs, develops, and implements policies and procedures that enhance quality performance. Accreditation and third-party payers (insurance) are requiring ever more sophisticated quality programs. The hospital has put most of its emphasis to date on after-the-fact inspection and corrective action. A "utilization review" is done for every patient when service is completed. All charts and records are reviewed to make sure that hospital personnel did what they were supposed to do. Little has been done yet in the way of continuous quality improvement or forming quality teams to find ways to continuously improve quality performance.

Process Design, Technology, and Job Design

Hospitals can be quite capital intensive, owing to the advanced technology that is now available and expected by patients. For example, a CAT scan machine can cost $2 million, and intensive-care monitoring equipment can have a $250,000 price tag. The investment in equipment and in the facilities is $12 million or $28,571 per full-time employee. This total may seem high, but it is less than some larger hospitals that enjoy higher patient volumes.

Owing to its small size, LFKHS acquires certain services from other organizations, rather than perform them in-house. For example, pharmacy operations are subcontracted. The contractors handle all orders and procure themselves whatever materials they need to provide their services. Larger hospitals, on the other hand, have sufficiently high volumes and repeatability to justify performing these services in-house.

Some areas in the hospital, such as the emergency room, insist on very broad education and experience in their employees, so that they will have the greatest possible flexibility in meeting patient needs. Accreditation standards require at least one registered nurse (RN) on duty at all times on each floor. Employee cross training is a hospital-wide approach, even for areas where services are more standardized. Salaries and wages are comparable with the Miami area, where nurses are paid $15 to $16 per hour. There is not a lot of variation within classes of employment, although experience and merit do affect wages within job classifications.

The procedures performed throughout the hospital are rigidly specified by traditional health care approaches, with little employee involvement in methods improvement. A patient's "routing" through the hospital is highly individualized. Very few patients have exactly the same routing through the hospital. Scheduled admissions have a basic routing determined at the time of their arrival, depending on the reason for their hospitalization. Different surgical procedures will have slightly different routings. Patients admitted from the emergency room have less well defined routings because there has been no advance planning. As actual work is performed on the patient, cost data are collected. The materials area uses individual stickers for items to affix to charts for later posting. Employee hours are recorded in less detail, but some basic linkage is made between time and task.

Capacity and Location

LFKHS is a relatively small facility with a total capacity of 149 beds. On the average, about 75 percent of the beds are occupied. During the peak season (December through April) occupancy (called the *hospital census*) is 90 percent; for the rest of the year it falls to slightly below 70 percent. Occasionally the emergency room runs out of beds, and surgery can schedule only three operating rooms at a time. Regular admissions are scheduled around bed availability. The facility and equipment tend to be the key limiting factor because there is no shortage of talented nurses and doctors in the area.

The hospital's location is quite rural with only one road serving the island. The nearest major hospital is in Miami, 130 miles away. The Key West location brings with it some other specific problems. There are a significant number of AIDS cases, unusual for a rural setting. The emergency room also gets a considerable number of moped bike and head-on car accidents, and there is a fairly large homeless population.

THE BIG PICTURE

Layout and Flow at LFKHS

The Big Picture, on pages 62–63, shows the layout of the LFKHS main hospital facility. Activities are grouped according to function. Volumes are too low and unpredictable to set aside many human and capital resources exclusively for a particular type of patient—except for a maternity patient. The first floor thus houses such overall functional departments as the emergency room, labs, administrative offices, radiology, materials receiving, and the operating rooms.

Lower Florida Keys Hospital

Lee is a typical emergency room admission, who has twisted his ankle while jogging on the beach. He hobbles into the Emergency Room (ER) entrance **(1)** and sits down to fill out a patient history while he waits **(2)**. Soon a nurse escorts him to an ER triage room **(3)**, where she checks the severity of his injury. He returns to a seat in the waiting room **(4)**, until an ER bed **(5)** opens up for him.

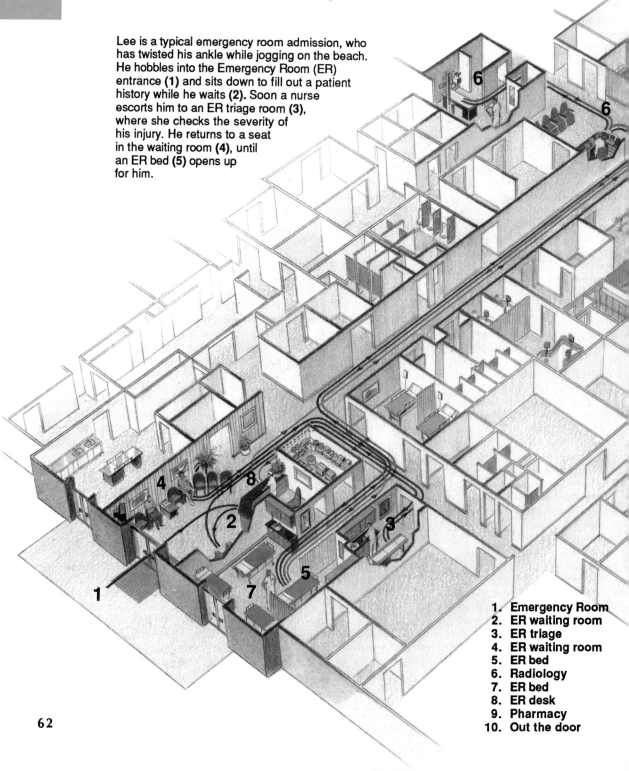

1. **Emergency Room**
2. **ER waiting room**
3. **ER triage**
4. **ER waiting room**
5. **ER bed**
6. **Radiology**
7. **ER bed**
8. **ER desk**
9. **Pharmacy**
10. **Out the door**

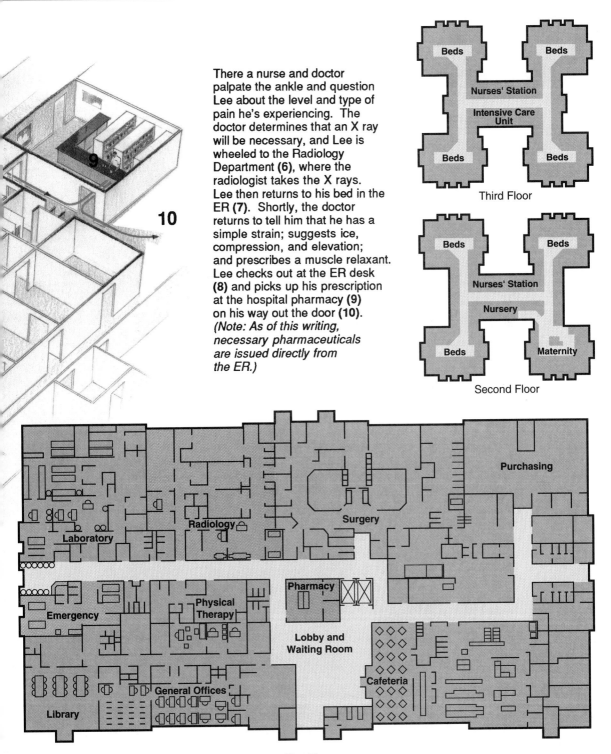

There a nurse and doctor palpate the ankle and question Lee about the level and type of pain he's experiencing. The doctor determines that an X ray will be necessary, and Lee is wheeled to the Radiology Department **(6)**, where the radiologist takes the X rays. Lee then returns to his bed in the ER **(7)**. Shortly, the doctor returns to tell him that he has a simple strain; suggests ice, compression, and elevation; and prescribes a muscle relaxant. Lee checks out at the ER desk **(8)** and picks up his prescription at the hospital pharmacy **(9)** on his way out the door **(10)**. *(Note: As of this writing, necessary pharmaceuticals are issued directly from the ER.)*

9

10

Third Floor

Beds

Beds

Nurses' Station

Intensive Care Unit

Beds

Beds

Second Floor

Beds

Beds

Nurses' Station

Nursery

Beds

Maternity

Purchasing

Radiology

Surgery

Laboratory

Pharmacy

Physical Therapy

Emergency

Lobby and Waiting Room

Cafeteria

General Offices

Library

First Floor

The second floor has three wards devoted to patient care, including maternity. The third floor has four more wards, as well as the intensive care unit. Nurses' stations are centrally located on each patient-care floor.

Due to the customized services provided to any given patient, patient flows are jumbled, with lots of individual handling. For simplicity, only one patient's path is shown in the figure. The number of stops patients make during their stay is highly variable. Some patients will make only three or four stops, and others may require twenty or more.

Materials Management, Staffing Plans, Inventory, and Scheduling

There are about 6300 items held in inventory, valued at $900,000. Items held in inventory include all medical and surgical supplies except drugs (which are provided by a contractor). There are two separate types of inventory: (1) surgical inventory maintained by and in surgical services to support only their activities and (2) supplies to support the patient wards. The former contains about 3500 items, valued at $600,000.

Typical items in the latter category are dressings, IV supplies, hypodermics, and maintenance materials. Each day much of the inventory is put in standard "kits" on carts and distributed to the wards. The carts are different, depending on the ward. Returned carts are exchanged, typically daily, for new ones.

Supplier relationships are unique. Owing to the hospital's small size and rural location, it has limited clout with its suppliers to achieve price or delivery concessions. Suppliers are generally large centralized distributors. Delivery time can be up to two weeks for some items. A large Miami hospital, on the other hand, may get the same order in two days. LFKHS has about 45 regular suppliers and 300 specialty suppliers. The purchasing policy is to monitor the inventory for the various items and place replenishment orders when the inventory gets low enough. There is some sense for how big the lot size should be, although the determination is very informal. Some specialty items, such as replacement hips, are never stocked but ordered as needed for specific patients.

Staffing plans and schedules are developed at the department level, typically to cover one month. Planning is somewhat reactive, particularly in the ER. If the hospital census and patient "acuity" (a measure of the severity of a patient's illness) increase, so does the day's staff size. At the same time, financial success depends on not having excessive staffing levels. Regular admissions are known at least one day in advance and sometimes much longer. For example, surgical procedures that require special equipment or supplies require much longer planning lead times. Schedules are developed in more detail and further ahead for departments that are more capital intensive, such as surgery, radiology, and other such specialties. However, even these schedules are very dynamic and must be changed frequently because patient loads can change unexpectedly. Coordination of schedules between departments is informal, although some effort is made for critical interfaces such as between ER and radiology.

Scheduling rules for staff, rooms, shifts, and patients vary from one department to another. Rooms and beds are often assigned on a first-come, first-served basis with some sensitivity to the nature of treatment and individual preferences. Staff schedules vary by department. Many departments use informal self-scheduling approaches once basic requirements are established. The staff make their requests and the department director adjusts them to achieve the desired staffing levels. Because of the intense customer contact of a hospital system, and the need for round-the-clock availability for many services, many employees must work anything but an 8-to-5 job on Mondays through Fridays. Per diem is the alternative of choice to handle short-term surges in work requirements. If per diem personnel are scheduled and turn out not to be needed, the extra staff is sent home early.

TOURING A PRODUCT-FOCUSED FACILITY: CHAPARRAL STEEL*

Chaparral Steel started in 1973 as a joint venture between Texas Industries, Inc. (TXI), of Dallas, Texas, and Co-Steel, Inc., of Toronto, Canada. Groundbreaking in Midlothian, just outside of Dallas, took place in the fall of 1973. The first heat (batch of steel) was melted in May 1975. The Rolling Mill started running three months later. And Chaparral went public in 1988. TXI owns approximately 80 percent of the stock, while the rest is traded on the New York Stock Exchange. Co-Steel, however, is hardly out of the picture. It is now the largest shareholder of TXI, and its president is on the TXI board of directors.

Gordon Forward, the president, seeks to keep the company innovative and on the leading edge of technology. Further, Chaparral is clearly an international producer and marketer, having received Japanese Industrial Standard certification in 1989, which approves the company's selling steel in Japan. In 1991, 7 percent of Chaparral's shipments went to Europe and Asia, and Canada and Mexico are included as home market in the company's domestic figures. Within the United States, most sales are shipped to the Sunbelt region.

Needless to say, Chaparral's facilities and operating philosophy reflect the latest advances in worldwide steelmaking. A customer orientation runs throughout the organization; a team concept blurs the lines between marketing and the other functional areas; and decision making is pushed down to the lowest levels of the organization, with an emphasis on action rather than on bureaucratic procedures. For instance, it is not at all unusual for production workers to be included in the selection, purchase, and installation of major pieces of production equipment.

Chaparral's customers are large steel buyers, who are evaluated by the sales department before the company takes on new business. For example, a customer should have the potential of purchasing at least 600 tons per year to qualify as a purchaser from the mill. This assures continuity and stable demand for Chaparral's high-volume operation. The company's sales totaled $420 million in 1991.

---

*We are indebted to Jeff E. Heyl (De Paul University) and Linda Stone for the background information on this tour.

Product Plans, Competitive Priorities, and Quality

Chaparral prides itself on providing good prices, fast delivery, and consistent quality. As for "customer orientation," Chaparral intends to be the easiest company from which to buy steel. Initially, the plant was able to produce 250,000 tons of steel per year; now it can produce 2 million. With the exception of certain specialty steels, it is a high-volume producer of standardized products.

There are three rolling mills at Chaparral—the Bar Mill, the Medium Section Mill, and the Large Section Mill—which determine the range of hot-rolled products the mill can produce. The standard products currently available are given in the following list; customers can order them in different lengths and sizes within these limitations. The standard product is made to stock and can be cut to length as needed.

Product	Bar Mill	Medium Section Mill	Large Section Mill
Reinforcing bar	3/8" to 2¼"		
Angles	1½" to 3"	3" to 6"	
Channels	3" and 4"	3" to 12"	
Flats	2" to 4"	5" to 12"	
Rounds	5/8" to 2½"	1¾" to 4¹/₁₆"	
Wide flange beams		4" to 14"	8" to 24"
Standard beams		3" to 8"	
Junior beams		5", 8", 10", 12"	

In addition to three standard mixes of steel, Chaparral produces a variety of special carbon and alloy steel bars for demanding applications in the forging and cold finishing industries. The construction industry consumes 60 to 70 percent of the products using the standard mix. Special bar quality (SBQ) sales (sales of customized product) account for about 15 percent of all sales dollars. The remainder requires a slightly richer mixture than the standard, but is not nearly as specialized as for SBQ.

In response to customer requests, Chaparral is trying to reduce the number of sections (sizes of beams) that it offers. It is also increasing the quality of the grade of steel. The large steel companies have refused to upgrade their standard because they sell by the ton, not by the grade. The 50 grade is a higher grade than the normal A36, and many large mills have a difficult time achieving this grade. By making a 50 grade the standard and totally eliminating A36, Chaparral can make one class of billet to satisfy the majority of customer needs. Chaparral's low-cost position allows it to make 50 grade for less than most mills can make A36.

Quality assurance is strictly maintained throughout the manufacturing process. Chaparral has a policy of building quality into its products at the source, rather than depending on inspections at the end of the process. The quality control department trains all employees to recognize and remove questionable products as soon as they are discovered. The quality control lab will do any necessary chemical testing to determine quality problems and how to fix them. During the process, a front and a back sample are drawn from each heat (batch).

For construction materials, the lab tests only for tensile strength. For SBQ sales, the lab may perform a variety of tests, depending on the customer's specifications. Among these are the Rockwell hardness test, the bend test, the turn-down test, magnafluxing, and the Sharpie impact test—all of which have specific standards and procedures. In addition, SBQ material is hot bed-inspected (on the cooling bed after rolling) for seams and cracks.

Quality control personnel also travel frequently to assist customers in the use of Chaparral products and to gather information for development of new products. Several people from quality control have even been integrated into the sales department to sell SBQ steel to customers.

Process Design

Historically, the steel industry has been labor and energy intensive. Chaparral Steel, on the other hand, is much more capital intensive and innovative in its choice of technologies. The manufacturing process is capital intensive, with total property, plant, and equipment costing about $292.3 million at the end of 1991. Plant investment was just over $314,000 per employee in 1991. The average labor content ran at 1.6 worker hours per ton produced.

The main production stages at Chaparral are melting, continuous casting, and rolling. First, *melting* is done by the high-powered electric arc furnace method, using computer-assisted furnaces. The melt charge, or raw material, consists exclusively of scrap metal, in contrast to steelmaking operations that begin with iron ore. Chaparral's automobile shredder alone supplies more than 200,000 tons of prepared scrap per year. The shredder has both ferrous and nonferrous separators, as well as a wet scrubber, to assure that the charge is of acceptable quality. It takes two hours for a furnace to melt a batch of metal, which is called the charge-to-tap time.

The next stage is *continuous casting*, which converts the molten metal into long steel bars called billets. Continuous casting eliminates several steps in the traditional steelmaking process of pouring ingots. Chaparral has casters dedicated to each of its rolling mills. The four-strand curved mold caster supplies 5" × 7" billets up to 49 feet in length to the Bar Mill, the smallest of the rolling mills. The five-strand caster supplies somewhat larger and shorter billets to the Medium Section Mill. The average yield of both these casters is more than 90 percent, which is the percentage of the melt poured from the ladle that is converted to finished product. The newest mill, the Large Section Mill, has been built to apply an internally developed "near net shape" caster. Instead of casting a rectangular billet, it casts one that is closer to the desired end shape of the beam. The casters have been carefully analyzed to improve quality. For example, electromagnetic stirring goes on within the molds, giving the billets superior surface and interior quality characteristics.

The billets go next to one of the *rolling* mills, where they must be heated to 2200° Fahrenheit in gas-fired reheat furnaces. At this temperature the billet becomes pliable and can be easily deformed. The heated billets are fed into a vertical reducing unit, by a set of pinch rolls. The hot steel then moves untouched through 16 in-line stands, which progressively roll it into the desired product shape. In the Large Section Mill, the product has to be rolled fewer times to get the desired end shape. An old-style mill might call for 50 passes through rollers to accomplish what the Large Section Mill can do in 8 to 12. The result: considerable savings in processing costs across the board. Energy costs are cut about 55 percent. Labor costs are down as well, with only 0.25 hour per ton required in this mill.

The rolling mills are continuous in design, with a sophisticated computerized control system assisting production personnel in maintaining precise roll speed at each stand. The computer automatically prints out metal bundle tags, which include the heat number, theoretical weight, and piece count.

The formed bars next travel to an automatic cooling bed. The cooled bars are then transferred to the cold shear, where they are cut to standard lengths from 20 to 60 feet. The sheared bars are automatically collected, strapped in bundles of 2 to 5 tons each, and tagged. Finally, they are moved to the warehouse for storage or to the shipping yard to await distribution. Angle and channel products are processed slightly differently. They are bulk-bundled, stored in the yard, and then restraightened off line at the Bar Mill Straightener.

A special shop machines the mill rolls, which are installed on the in-line stands to create the desired product shapes. The rolls are massive, weighing between 5 and 7 tons each and costing from $8000 to $19,000. Three in-shop lathes, each costing about $500,000, machine the rolls from raw materials. The 1300 different rolls needed to make different products are stored in the ⅛-mile-long shop, from which they can be rolled into place to set up the line for the next product to be rolled.

Technology and Job Design

Chaparral has found especially innovative ways to transfer state-of-the-art technologies—in particular, the computer—directly to its own production. New technology is introduced frequently, even if it means replacing equipment that is not yet fully depreciated.

Everyone on the nonunionized work force is encouraged to be innovative and to seek better ways to do his or her job. The culture at Chaparral encourages all employees to acquire new knowledge and then provides them with the freedom to apply what they have learned.

Lloyd Schmelzle, vice president of operations, expects first-line supervisors not only to run their operations but also to keep their processes on the leading edge. The new bar gauge system in the Bar Mill, spearheaded by two first-line supervisors and installed by the plant's maintenance department, is a good example. The system shows on a computer screen, both graphically and numerically, the shape of the steel bar being formed. This capability gives the floor operator instant feedback while he or she modifies the bar's shape—while safely enclosed in an observation pulpit. This particular innovation allowed the process to keep up with the mill's expanding capacity, which has increased to 200,000 tons per year. It also cut labor to 0.8 labor hour per ton, in contrast to the 6 labor hours per ton for most producers.

The educational process never ends for the Chaparral worker. A 3½-year-long program, covering mechanical, electrical, and statistical fundamentals, as well as the safe operation of plant equipment, is mandatory for all employees. Beyond this, a wide variety of classes are available on site to help employees develop a broad range of skills to further their careers. Additional classes can be taken at local colleges. While the educational program applies primarily to job-related skills, Chaparral will support classes in a variety of subjects. The company believes in the development of its employees in all areas. Teams of managers and workers, drawn from a mix of departments and functional areas, have been sent on numerous occasions to observe electrical furnace operations at other plants to learn new ideas.

The manager of the Bar Mill encourages workers to find ways to automate themselves out of their own jobs, so that productivity can be increased and employees can move on to improving other jobs. Chaparral people are prepared for change and do not resist it. All employees are expected to prepare someone else to do their jobs and to grow on the job themselves. There is considerable cross training throughout the organization. This type of job enlargement is coupled with financial incentives: Chaparral treats employees as partners, providing them with profit sharing and stock ownership plans.

Capacity and Location

Due to economies of scale, Chaparral has just a single steel plant. It is located on 300 acres of land, and its plant covers about 75 acres. The plant operates 24 hours a day, 7 days a week. In 1974 there was one furnace, and the plant's capacity was 250,000 tons per year. It was then expanded to 500,000 tons through the use of computers, larger ladles and transformers, and more efficient operating procedures. In 1983 there was a $200 million expansion, featuring a second furnace that immediately boosted capacity by another 300,000 tons per year. Today, with the opening of the Large Section Mill, the plant's capacity is 2 million tons per year.

Capacity is well understood and a top management concern. The shredder is a good example. Its total capacity, when operated over three shifts, is 500,000 tons per year. It is possible to exceed this output rate for short periods of time. For example, the record daily production was 2664 tons. Maintenance on the shredder is extensive, averaging 30 to 40 percent of the total hours worked.

THE BIG PICTURE

Layout and Flow at Chaparral Steel

The Big Picture on pages 70–71 shows that the process flow through the Bar Mill is linear, following a one-directional route from the reheat furnace to storage of finished product. An overhead crane is used to change the mill rolls on

Layout and Flow at Chaparral Steel

The Chaparral Steel plant covers some 75 acres. In the aerial view below, one sees the sites of the Bar Mill (A), the Medium Section Mill (B), the Large Section Mill (C), and the melt shop and continuous caster (D). The entire process is continuous in design, with a sophisticated computerized control system assisting personnel. At lower right is a floor plan of the Bar Mill, with an expanded cutaway on the opposite page highlighting the linear flow of the steel as it passes through operations.

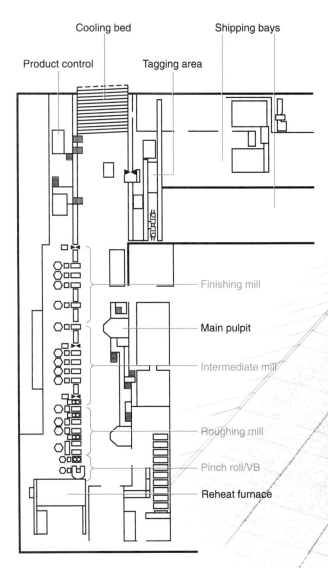

Cooling bed

Product control

Tagging area

Shipping bays

Finishing mill

Main pulpit

Intermediate mill

Roughing mill

Pinch roll/VB

Reheat furnace

Computer consoles in the control pulpit.

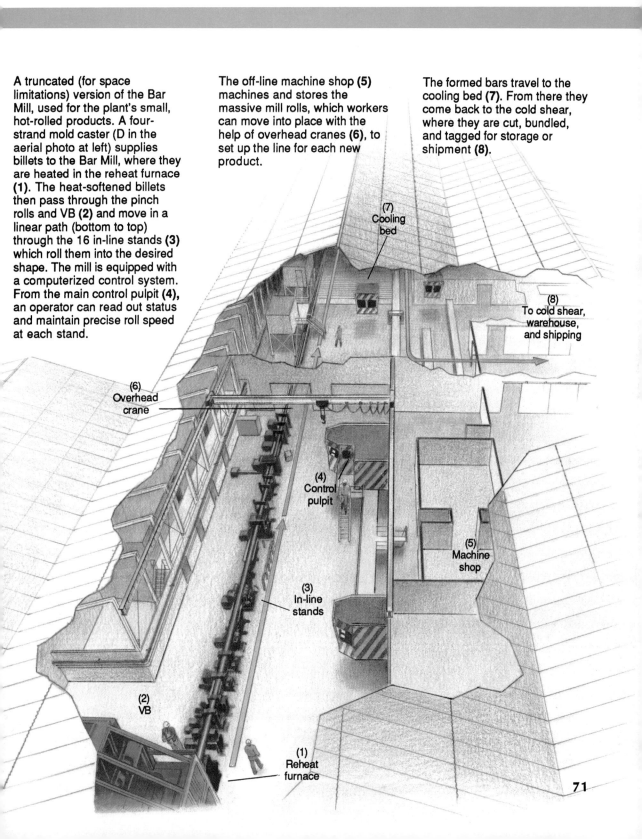

A truncated (for space limitations) version of the Bar Mill, used for the plant's small, hot-rolled products. A four-strand mold caster (D in the aerial photo at left) supplies billets to the Bar Mill, where they are heated in the reheat furnace **(1)**. The heat-softened billets then pass through the pinch rolls and VB **(2)** and move in a linear path (bottom to top) through the 16 in-line stands **(3)** which roll them into the desired shape. The mill is equipped with a computerized control system. From the main control pulpit **(4)**, an operator can read out status and maintain precise roll speed at each stand.

The off-line machine shop **(5)** machines and stores the massive mill rolls, which workers can move into place with the help of overhead cranes **(6)**, to set up the line for each new product.

The formed bars travel to the cooling bed **(7)**. From there they come back to the cold shear, where they are cut, bundled, and tagged for storage or shipment **(8)**.

(7)
Cooling bed

(8)
To cold shear, warehouse, and shipping

(6)
Overhead crane

(4)
Control pulpit

(5)
Machine shop

(3)
In-line stands

(2)
VB

(1)
Reheat furnace

71

the line. At the end of the process, electromagnetic cranes and forklifts move material off the mill to storage. With these exceptions, material handling tends to be automated and to follow fixed paths. For example, the steel flows down through the rolling mills automatically. Compare this linear, high-volume flow with the jumbled, customized flows at Lower Florida Keys.

Materials Management, Production Plans, Scheduling, and Inventory

Chaparral recognizes the value of long-term relationships with its suppliers. In the past, it has allowed each department to do its own buying, because it was felt that they knew best what they needed. Currently, Chaparral is pursuing a new strategy of centralized purchasing, in hopes of achieving economies of scale. It recruited the former general manager of steel production to assist in the acquisition of raw materials. Whereas the company had been operating on a JIT delivery basis, it is now investigating nearby warehousing of some of the raw materials necessary for production, as well as barter with Russia for some materials.

Chaparral does not buy in large quantities just to gain quantity discounts. Much of the material it buys can be had in spot markets, and the purchasing people watch these very closely, to buy quantities when the spot prices are low. They do not use blanket orders or long-term contracts because of the volatile nature of their raw material prices.

Most steel companies use a broker to get their scrap for them, who in turn receives a percentage of the job. Chaparral's vice president of raw materials negotiates with each and every supplier individually every month. This gives Chaparral a very competitive price advantage. Sources of scrap metal include crushed cars, which are then put through the shredder; turnings from machine shop operations; home scrap (leftover material from Chaparral processes); and plant and structural materials. Chaparral tends to deal with the same scrap suppliers, thus forming long-term but somewhat informal relationships.

Chaparral develops production plans three months into the future. This forward planning is essential to maximize facility utilization and to establish accurate due dates for customer orders. Because of its high volumes, broad geographic area, and fairly standardized products, Chaparral can respond to unexpected demand shifts by swapping production between various product groups to meet customer demands.

The Bar Mill sets up for 5 to 7 days of a product at a time. It makes different sizes of a product there during the week. For example, it might set up for reinforcing bar ("rebar") and make ⅜", ½", and ⅝" sizes. The Bar Mill tends to run one size for several days, then switch over to the next. Setup times range from 1 to 3 hours. A change from a ⅝" round to a 2¹⁄₁₆" round takes one hour. Changing from round to rebar takes about 2 hours. Changes tend to go from smaller to larger sizes.

The Medium Section Mill also sets up for 5 to 7 days of beams. It will make several different sizes during the week, say, 8", 12", and 10". By and large, the setups are, like this one, independent of size. Most changeovers take about 5 or 6 hours.

The three-month production schedule is done by the production scheduler. It is reviewed at a weekly production meeting, where small revisions are made. The basic schedule comes from firm orders and requests from marketing. If the actual demand is less than capacity, additional production is scheduled (for which there is no stated demand), to ensure that the mills run at full capacity. Demand is considered seasonal, because much of the demand for construction materials is in the summer.

Finished goods inventory is maintained at the mill for a variety of bundle sizes, grades, and lengths. It is stored in either the 80-foot-wide or the 100-foot-wide warehouse or out in the shipping yard to await distribution. Chaparral recently opened a remote inventory warehouse in Pittsburgh, for even timelier delivery to the Northeast. The normal amount of crushed car inventory kept to feed the shredder is 25,000 tons, or approximately 6.5 weeks' supply. Finished goods inventory amounted to $45,230,000 in 1991. Of that amount, work in process was $6,282,000. Raw materials, including scrap and crushed cars, totaled $10,193,000.

The new computerized order system allows customers direct access, to check inventory levels, open orders, and pricing, and eventually to place orders. The quick response time allows customers to get by with lower inventory levels, which gives Chaparral a competitive edge. Chaparral ships from its steel mill by common carrier, customer truck, and rail car, at a rate of about 30 rail cars, or 120 truck loads, per day.

In terms of performance measures, Chaparral monitors production per hour, yield, alloys used per ton, electricity per ton, and tons per hour per employee. But tons shipped (produced) is the bottom line—the number that matters the most. When you drive into the plant, there is a sign right by the entrance that shows yesterday's tonnage. Like any similar type of facility, running at near-full capacity is the best way for Chaparral to make money.

LINKAGES AT LFKHS AND CHAPARRAL STEEL

The sharp contrast between LFKHS and Chaparral Steel, summarized in Table 2.4, gives a sense of how decisions in operations must mesh. Clearly, the two firms utilize different positioning strategies. Product or service plans and competitive priorities on which these strategies are based differ as well. LFKHS has a process focus. The hospital's service plans call for low-volume, customized services. Chaparral Steel has a product focus. The product volumes at Chaparral are huge: 2 million tons of steel per year. Most of its volume is for standardized products. Its dominant competitive priorities are low cost, fast delivery, and consistent quality. The opposite is true at LFKHS, where competitive priorities center on a broad variety of services customized to individual patients. LFKHS also has considerable volume flexibility, being able to adjust its capacity with overtime and part-time help to closely match work requirements that vary with patient census and acuity.

While LFKHS has advanced and expensive technologies in certain areas, it is also very labor intensive. Its financial health depends heavily on its being

TABLE 2.4 / Linkages at LFKHS and Chaparral

Decision Area	Process Focus at LFKHS	Product Focus at Chaparral
Product or service plan	Low-volume, customized service	High-volume, standardized products
Competitive priorities	Customized services, consistent quality, and volume flexibility	Low cost, fast delivery, and consistent quality
Process design	Labor intensive	Capital intensive
Capacity	Lower utilization	Higher utilization
Materials management	Informal supplier relationships	Formal supplier relationships
Scheduling	Fluid	Planned far ahead

able to manage its labor costs. Chaparral Steel is quite different. To be cost competitive, it must use automation and technology to the fullest.

Capacity policies at the two organizations are also quite different. The facility utilization is much lower at LFKHS, which is equipped to handle the demand of the peak season from December through April. Operating at a 75 percent capacity utilization level also allows the hospital to handle unexpected surges in patient demand. Such a big capacity cushion would be too expensive for capital-intense Chaparral.

Materials management at LFKHS is only informally related to its suppliers; its volumes are too small to give it much clout. By contrast, Chaparral tends to deal long term, though informally, with its suppliers of scrap metal. It also has more control over customer demands. Finished goods inventory is maintained at the mill, which protects it much more than LFKHS from variations in customer demands.

Finally, scheduling procedures are quite different. The process focus, and amount of customer contact at LFKHS, requires more fluid scheduling procedures. Detailed plans are not made very far ahead because of the uncertainties involved. This reactive scheduling process is not found at Chaparral. There, the concern for top efficiency and the simplicity of line flows demand elaborate scheduling and day-to-day monitoring of performance.

SOLVED PROBLEMS

1. A company is screening three new product ideas. Resource constraints allow only one of them to be commercialized. Given the performance criteria and ratings in Table 2.5, and assuming equal weights for each performance criterion, which product should management choose?

Solution   Each criterion receives 20 points (arbitrarily).

Product	Calculation	Total Score
A	20(0.3) + 20(0.7) + 20(1.0) + 20(0.4) + 20(0.4)	= 56
B	20(0.9) + 20(0.8) + 20(0.4) + 20(0.7) + 20(0.6)	= 68
C	20(0.2) + 20(0.6) + 20(0.8) + 20(0.6) + 20(0.5)	= 54

TABLE 2.5

	Rating		
Performance Criterion	Product A	Product B	Product C
1. Demand uncertainty and project risk	0.3	0.9	0.2
2. Similarity to present products	0.7	0.8	0.6
3. Expected return on investment (ROI)	1.0	0.4	0.8
4. Compatibility with current manufacturing process	0.4	0.7	0.6
5. Competitive advantage	0.4	0.6	0.5

The best choice is product B. Products A and C are will behind in terms of total weighted score.

2. The owner of a small manufacturing business has patented a new device for washing dishes and cleaning dirty kitchen sinks. Before trying to commercialize the device and add it to her existing product line, she wants reasonable assurance of success. Variable cost is estimated at $7 per unit produced and sold and fixed costs per year at $56,000.

a. If the selling price is set at $25, how many units must be produced and sold to break even? Use both the algebraic and graphic approaches.

b. Forecasted sales for the first year are 10,000 units if the price is reduced to $15. What would be the product's total contribution to profits in the first year, with this pricing strategy?

Solution   a. Beginning with the algebraic approach, we get:

$$Q = \frac{F}{p - c} = \frac{56,000}{25 - 7} = 3111 \text{ units}$$

Using the graphic approach, shown in Fig. 2.8, we first draw two lines:

$$\text{Total revenue} = 25Q$$

$$\text{Total cost} = 56,000 + 7Q$$

The two lines intersect at $Q = 3111$ units, the break-even quantity.

b. Total profit contribution $=$ Total revenue $-$ Total cost

$$= pQ - (F + cQ)$$

$$= 15(10,000) - [56,000 + 7(10,000)]$$

$$= \$24,000$$

FIGURE 2.8

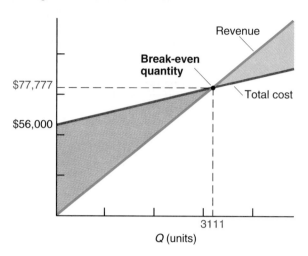

3. A rocket has two different components that can fail. The reliability of the first component is 0.80, and 0.70 for the second component. What is the reliability of the rocket if the designer provides redundancy with a backup for each component?

Solution

The reliability of the first component, when enhanced with a backup, becomes

$$r_1' = 1.0 - (1.0 - 0.80)^2 = 0.96$$

Similarly,

$$r_2' = 1.0 - (1.0 - 0.70)^2 = 0.91$$

Therefore the whole rocket's reliability is 0.87:

$$r_s = (r_1')(r_2') = (0.96)(0.91) = 0.87$$

FORMULA REVIEW

1. Break-even quantity:

$$Q = \frac{F}{p - c}$$

2. Total profit contribution:

$$pQ - (F + cQ)$$

3. Reliability:

$$r_s = (r_1)(r_2) \cdots (r_j) \cdots (r_n)$$

$$r_j' = 1.0 - (1.0 - r_j)^m$$

CHAPTER HIGHLIGHTS

● Product and service planning is an ongoing activity that is the starting point for designing and operating a production system.

● A life cycle consists of five stages: product and service planning, introduction, growth, maturity, and decline.

● There are three strategies for when to enter and exit the life cycle of a product or service. Each places a different demand on the production system. Entering early and exiting late forces a transition from flexibility to low cost.

● The planning steps are idea generation, screening, development and testing, and final design. These steps must fit the firm's mission, which may prove to be too narrow or too broad and have to be modified.

● Concurrent engineering involves operations and other functions in developing and testing a new product or service.

● The preference matrix and break-even analysis, while not limited to product planning, are two techniques used to screen new product lines. Reliability analysis is a third technique, but its purpose is to assess how the system as a whole will perform.

● Competitive priorities state the dimensions on which the firm's production system should excel. There are eight priorities: low cost, high-performance design, consistent quality, fast delivery time, on-time delivery, development speed, customization, and volume flexibility. Trade-offs among them are often necessary. Management must judge which trade-offs are

best, along with the firm's distinctive competencies, when establishing desired levels for each dimension.

● With time-based competition, managers seek to save time on the various steps taken to deliver a new or existing product or service.

● The positioning strategy that meshes best with product plans and competitive priorities should be selected. The continuum of choices ranges from a process focus to a product focus.

● A process focus organizes resources around the process. This focus fits low volumes and jumbled flow patterns. A product focus organizes resources around specific products, resulting in straightforward flow patterns. It fits high volumes and standardized products.

● The more the customer contact at a service facility, the greater is the tendency toward a process focus.

● Tours of two companies, Lower Florida Keys Health System and Chaparral Steel Company, demonstrate how positioning strategy acts as a linchpin in operations decisions. Positioning strategy helps managers to translate corporate decisions into operations decisions.

● A process focus fits with low volumes, high flexibility, general-purpose equipment, labor-intensive technologies, lower capacity utilization, informal relationships with suppliers and customers, large work-in-process inventories, and fluid schedules. The opposite is true of a product focus.

KEY TERMS

STUDY QUESTIONS

1. A sign on the way to an abandoned mine reads: "Choose your ruts carefully; you will be in them for the next 15 miles." How does this caution apply to product and service planning and choosing competitive priorities?

2. How does the concept of life cycles illustrate the ongoing need for product and service planning?

3. How does the decision on when to enter and exit the life cycle of a product or service affect the operations function? With which entrance–exit strategy would a product focus make most sense?

4. The Sealtight Company is a well-diversified manufacturer in the packaging business. It makes a variety of packaging materials and sells them to industrial buyers. Management is currently conducting a life-cycle audit to identify the current stage of each product in its life cycle. The profiles for two products are shown in Table 2.6.

   a. In which stage is product A? Product B? Explain your answers.
   b. For which product would low price be a higher competitive priority? Why?

5. Give an example of each component of the "service bundle" for each of the following products.

   a. An insurance policy
   b. An airline trip
   c. Dental work

6. A Gallup Organization poll published in the January 1991 issue of *Advertising Age* magazine ranked Procter & Gamble Company as the most "environmentally conscious" corporation in the United States. The consumer products company earns high marks for condensing bulky bottles of Downy fabric softener into compact concentrates that use 80 percent less packaging. Its Liquid Tide and other detergent containers use recycled plastics, keeping 190 million soda bottles and milk jugs out of landfills each year. But some environmentalists say that there's another side to P&G. To protect established businesses, it spends millions of dollars to fight certain environmental measures in statehouses from New York to California. Discuss the ethical and environmental issues of this situation.

7. Eight in ten Americans regard themselves as "environmentalists" and half of them say they are "strong" ones. But when it comes to making concrete buying decisions, many aren't the environmentalists they claim to be. Have such concerns actually led *you* to buy something—or not buy something—in the last six months? Discuss.

TABLE 2.6

Product	Performance Measure	This Year's Performance	Change over Last Year	Average Annual Change over Last Four Years
A	Annual sales	$42.1 million	−3.1%	+1.2%
	Unit price	1.53/lb	+0.0	+0.5
	Unit profit margin	0.22/lb	−2.1	−0.5
	Total profit contribution	6.0 million	−7.4	+0.2
B	Annual sales	5.4 million	+72.1	+35.0
	Unit price	1.30/lb	+7.0	+6.8
	Unit profit margin	0.70/lb	+12.1	+15.1
	Total profit contribution	2.9 million	+80.1	+37.2

8. What dimensions of competitive priorities seem to be the most important for each of the following companies?
   a. McDonald's
   b. Toyota
   c. A manufacturer of specialty glues tailored to the needs of industrial buyers in the furniture and mobile-home industries

9. Explain how time-based competition can be used to gain a market niche.

10. What positioning strategy (process focus or product focus) seems best for each of the following types of companies? Briefly defend your choice.
    a. A builder of skyscrapers and bridges
    b. A paper mill
    c. A microwave manufacturer
    d. A manufacturer of a wide variety of men's suits

11. Why do firms offering more customized, low-volume products tend to
    a. compete less on short customer delivery times and low costs?
    b. be less capital intensive?
    c. maintain larger capacity cushions?

12. Why do firms with a product focus tend to
    a. plan production and inventory levels further into the future?
    b. have more formalized supplier relationships?
    c. concentrate inventory less at the work-in-process level?

13. Two forces are at work in the health-care industry. First, there is pressure to make heavy investments in new equipment to keep up with rapid advances in technology. Second, there is pressure for shorter patient stays and more outpatient treatment, thereby helping curb escalating health costs. Use break-even analysis to describe how these forces change fixed costs, break-even inpatient volumes, and the financial position of the typical hospital.

14. Is volume flexibility needed more by LFKHS or by Chaparral Steel? How is it achieved and what is the impact on the predictability of an employee's upcoming work schedule? What is the impact on facility utilization?

15. Where is extensive customer contact most needed—at LFKHS or at Chaparral Steel? How does this requirement influence the location of customers for each facility? How does it affect the amount of inventory held by each one?

PROBLEMS

Review Problems

1. The Forsite Company is screening three ideas for new services. Resource constraints allow only one idea to be commercialized at the present time. The following estimates have been made for the five performance criteria that management feels are most important.

Performance Criterion	Rating		
	Service A	Service B	Service C
1. Capital equipment investment required	0.6	0.8	0.3
2. Expected return on investment (ROI)	0.4	0.6	0.9
3. Compatibility with current work-force skills	0.4	0.7	0.4
4. Competitive advantage	1.0	0.4	0.6
5. Compatibility with current EPA requirements	0.2	1.0	0.2

   a. Calculate a total weighted score for each alternative, using a preference matrix and assuming equal weights for each performance criterion. Which alternative is best? Worst?

b. Suppose that the expected ROI is given twice the weight assigned to each of the remaining criteria. [Sum of weights should remain the same as in part (a).] Does this affect the ranking of the three candidate services?

2. You are in charge of analyzing five new product ideas and have been given the information shown in Table 2.7.

- Management has decided that criterion 2 and criterion 3 are equally important, criterion 1 is five times as important as criterion 2, and criterion 4 is three times as important as criterion 2.
- Only two new products can be introduced.
- A product can be introduced only if it exceeds 70 percent of the total possible points.

a. What are the weights on the criteria if they must sum to 100?

b. What is the threshold on weighted scores?

c. Which product ideas do you recommend?

3. Buzzrite Corporation is considering the introduction of a new lightweight chain saw to broaden its line of home-use products. The R&D department has developed two prototypes—a gasoline-powered model A and an electrically powered model B. Due to constraints, Buzzrite can introduce only one of the models, and management is debating which model to bring to market. The following performance criteria have been estimated to evaluate the two products.

Performance Criteria	Rating	
	A	B
1. Capital equipment investment required	0.5	0.6
2. Expected return on investment (ROI)	0.7	0.5
3. Similarity to present products	0.4	0.3
4. Competitive advantage	0.3	0.6
5. Energy efficiency	0.6	0.4

a. Calculate a total weighted score for each alternative, using a preference matrix and assuming equal weights for each performance criterion except ROI, which is twice the weight of any of the others.

b. If ROI is 3 times and competitive advantage is 2 times the weights of the other criteria, what will be the total weighted score for the two products?

4. Mary Williams, owner of Williams Products, is evaluating whether to introduce a new product line. After thinking through the production process and the cost of raw materials and new equipment, Williams estimates the variable cost of each unit produced and sold at $5 and the fixed cost per year at $42,500.

a. If the selling price is set at $16, how many units must be produced and sold to break even? Use both the graphic and algebraic approaches to get your answer.

b. Williams forecasts sales of 7000 units for the first year if the selling price is set at

---

TABLE 2.7

	Rating (1 = worst; 10 = best)				
Performance Criterion	Product A	Product B	Product C	Product D	Product E
1. Compatibility with current manufacturing processes	8	7	3	6	8
2. Project risk	3	8	4	7	7
3. Market potential	7	5	7	6	2
4. Unit project margin	7	6	9	1	6

$12.50. What would be the total contribution to profits from this new product during the first year?

c. If the selling price is set at $11, Williams forecasts that first-year sales would increase to 10,000 units. Which pricing strategy ($11 or $12.50) would result in the greatest total contribution to profits?

d. What other considerations would be crucial to the final decision about making and marketing the new product?

5. A product at the Jennings Company has enjoyed reasonable sales volumes, but its contributions to profits have been disappointing. In 1992, 17,500 units were produced and sold. The selling price is $22 per unit, c is $18, and F is $80,000.

a. What is the break-even quantity for this product? Use both the graphic and algebraic approaches to get your answer.

b. Jennings is considering ways to either stimulate sales volumes or decrease variable costs. He feels it is possible to increase sales by 30 percent or reduce c to 85 percent of its current level. Which alternative leads to higher contributions to profits, assuming that each is equally costly to implement? *Hint:* Calculate profits for both alternatives and identify the one having the greatest profits.

c. What is the percentage change in the unit profit margin generated by each alternative in part (b)? How does this explain the result you obtained in part (b)?

6. The Franklin Electronics Company is a small manufacturer of electronic products. Its executive committee is considering the possibility of introducing a novelty tape recorder. The production department estimates that buying the necessary equipment would increase fixed cost per year by $20,000. The accounting department projects that the product would have to absorb another $20,000 for the additional costs of executive salaries, rent, and taxes. The marketing department believes that the initial

advertising budget would have to be $35,000 per year and that its sales budget would increase by another $40,000 per year. The new product would be priced at $30 F.O.B. factory with no quantity discounts. The various operating departments expect the variable cost for labor and materials to be $20 per unit.

a. How many units must be produced and sold for the company to break even?

b. If the advertising budget were increased to $45,000, what would be the break-even quantity?

c. A more automated production process could be used. It would double production's fixed cost, while reducing the total variable cost per unit from $20 to $14. Would this more advanced technology decrease or increase the break-even quantity? Must this always be the case?

7. John Anderson, vice president of Tri-Arrow Enterprises, has the following estimates of production and sales for the upcoming year for one of Tri-Arrow's products.

$$\text{Expected sales} = 15,000 \text{ units}$$
$$\text{Fixed cost} = \$280,000/\text{year}$$
$$\text{Variable cost} = \$100/\text{unit}$$
$$\text{Selling price} = \$125/\text{unit}$$

a. What is the expected contribution to profits of this product for the upcoming year?

b. Anderson believes that variable costs may increase because of an increase in raw-material costs. By how much can variable costs increase and still allow this product to positively contribute to profits for the next year?

c. Anderson believes that fixed cost can be reduced by decreasing the projected marketing budget (with no ill effect on expected sales). If variable costs increase by the amount calculated in part (b), by how much would fixed cost have to decrease to achieve the contribution to profits originally projected?

8. Tron Audio Products is planning to introduce a new model cassette recorder. To produce the new recorder, Tron will have variable manufacturing costs of $72 per unit, fixed costs of $225,000 per year, and a one-time initial investment cost of $110,000 for new manufacturing equipment, with no salvage value at the end of the product cycle. Tron predicts a four-year life cycle for the new recorder. The selling price to distributors will be $145.

   a. How many recorders must be sold the first year to reach the break-even point if the initial cost of the new manufacturing equipment is to be fully recovered during the first year? Use both the algebraic and graphic approaches to obtain your answer.

   b. Tron believes it will sell 4000 units the first year, 7000 units yearly for the second and third years, and 3500 units the fourth year. If sales and fixed costs are constant throughout each year, how long will it take before Tron begins to show a profit from the new recorder? Use the algebraic approach to obtain your answer. (For this problem, ignore the time value of money.)

   c. Based on the above information, should Tron introduce this new model?

9. Clips, Inc., a retail office-supply products chain, is planning to open retail computer centers in each of its ten stores. While they will carry several models selling at different prices, the average model will cost them $1800 and will sell for $2295. Additional fixed costs incurred by each store will be $114,000 yearly, and Clips estimates that it will spend an additional $250,000 at the corporate level for marketing and other activities related to the computer centers.

   a. Using both the graphic and the algebraic methods, calculate the break-even point for Clips, Inc., based on the average cost and sales price.

   b. What will be the average number of computers sold per store for each store to realize a $100,000 profit after all store and pro rata share of corporate costs have been accounted for?

10. The Medfield Bike and Ski Company is introducing a new service at its store. The owner estimates that the variable cost of each customer serviced will be $30 and annual fixed costs, $15,000. Sales for three different pricing strategies are forecasted as follows.

Pricing Strategy	Sales Price ($/customer)	Demand (customers per year)
A	75	2000
B	100	1250
C	125	1000

   What pricing strategy would make the greatest contribution to profits?

11. A new service can be sold for $12 per client. It costs $7 (unit variable cost) to provide this service on a new piece of equipment. If the break-even quantity is 10,000 clients per year, what must be the annual fixed cost to acquire the equipment?

12. A restaurant is considering adding to its menu a new item that will require $45,000 in fixed costs per year. Variable costs are estimated to be $12.75. The firm wants to break even if 8000 units are produced and sold per year. What should be the price of the new item?

13. A semiconductor has three components. Component 1 has a reliability of 0.98, component 2, 0.95; and component 3, 0.85.

   a. What is the reliability of the semiconductor?

   b. If two backups are provided for component 2, and three backups for component 3, what is the reliability of the new system?

14. An intricate part on an amusement park ride has a reliability of only 0.70, despite all engineering efforts to increase it. If redundancy is provided with four backups, giving a total of five replicates, what is the part's reliability?

Advanced Problems

Supplement Connections: Problems 16–20 and 26 require reading of Supplement 1 (Financial Analysis), and Problems 21–27 require prior reading of Supplement 2 (Linear Programming). A computer package is helpful for Problems 16–22, one is mandatory for Problems 23–27.

15. Melissa Graham has the following data concerning the production of one of her company's best-selling products, the Electrotype typewriter. All dollar amounts are in 1989 dollars (to adjust for inflation).

Year	Total Cost	Units Sold	Selling Price per Unit
1989	$100,000	950	$120
1990	$110,000	1100	$122.50
1991	$130,000	1250	$125
1992	$110,000	1200	$125

   a. Determine the break-even quantity using the graphic approach.
   b. Assume that the data from 1989 and 1990 are most representative of the Electrotype operation. What are the annual fixed cost and the variable cost per unit? *Hint:* Solve the following two linear equations for the two unknowns.

$$F + c(1000) = \$100,000$$
$$F + c(1500) = \$140,000$$

16. The following information is available about a service that Highlife Company wishes to introduce.

   - The expected life span of the service is five years. The projected annual demand (in customers) for the next five years is 11,000, 16,000, 17,000, 24,000, and 10,000, respectively.
   - The selling price is $8 and the variable cost per unit is $6.
   - The tax rate is 40 percent.
   - The desired rate of return is 13 percent. The initial equipment investment for this product is $40,000 and the salvage value of the equipment is $5000.

   - Assume straight-line depreciation.
   a. Determine the incremental after-tax cash flows attributable to this service over its life.
   b. Should this service be accepted using the NPV method of analysis?
   c. If management has set a payback period of three years, should the service be accepted?
   d. What does your answer in part (c) tell you about using the payback period as a method of evaluation?

17. Joan Ruiz designs and makes custom pottery, which she sells at upscale gift shops. If Joan purchases a new high-pressure sprayer, she can add new high-gloss plateware to her product line. Based on previous experience, she could produce the high-gloss plates for only about four years before she or her customers tire of it. The sprayer she wants costs $4800, and Joan estimates that it would be worth $1200 in salvage value at the end of four years. If she buys the sprayer, she will also have to invest $1000 in used ventilation equipment, for a total investment of $5800. At the end of four years, she would sell the ventilation equipment for the same amount she bought it. Joan thinks she can sell the plates for $15 apiece. She estimates her variable cost at $10 per plate; her fixed costs to run the sprayer unit and ventilation are $500 per year.

   Joan believes that she can sell 40 plates to each of the 18 shops that carry her products. Joan wants this investment to earn at least 15 percent. Assume that her tax rate is 35 percent. Calculate the following and make a recommendation concerning her potential investment.
   a. Annual after-tax income
   b. Incremental after-tax cash flows attributable to this expansion of her product line for four years.
   c. Net present value of this investment
   d. Payback period

18. Suppose that Joan's plateware (Problem 17)

becomes extremely popular and she is able to sell 75 plates at each gift shop (instead of 40). Recalculate your answers in Problem 17. Do these new figures change your recommendation? Explain.

19. The expected product life of Mass Media's new miniature television is ten years. Annual demand forecasts (units) are as follows:

Year 1	125	Year 6	300
Year 2	145	Year 7	340
Year 3	165	Year 8	200
Year 4	180	Year 9	110
Year 5	240	Year 10	60

- The selling price is expected to be $300 for the first three years, $260 for the next four years, and $200 for the remaining three years. The variable cost per unit is $150 for all years.
- The fixed costs are $5000 for the first year and increase 4 percent each remaining year.
- Mass Media's tax rate is 35 percent.
- Mass Media's desired rate of return is 16 percent.
- The initial capital investment is $35,000, and the salvage value at the end of ten years is $9000.
- Assume straight-line depreciation.

a. Determine the after-tax cash flows for this product.
b. Based on an NPV analysis, should this product be introduced?
c. If the payback period for Mass Media is five years, should this product be introduced?

20. The vice president for research and development at IBM is considering funding a voice interactive computer system. The initial capital investment is estimated at $200 million. The projected net earnings over the next ten years are $50 million/year. The appropriate tax rate is 25 percent, and the company's discount factor is 10 percent. The salvage value of the project at the end of 10 years is $150 million; assume straight-line depreciation. If this project is not funded, the company will invest the $200 million in a CD that will earn 8 percent annually.

a. What is the net present value for the two alternatives? Should the project be funded?
b. At what discount factor will the decision change?
c. What is the impact if the project's net earnings increase at a rate of 5 percent per year starting after the first year?

21. The Trim-Look Company makes several lines of skirts, dresses, and sport coats for women. Recently it was suggested that the company reevaluate its South Islander line and allocate its resources to those products that would maximize contribution to profits and overhead. Each product must pass through the cutting and sewing departments. In addition, each product in the South Islander line requires the same polyester fabric. The following data were collected for the study.

	Processing Time (hr)		Material
Product	Cutting	Sewing	(yd)
Skirt	1	1	1
Dress	3	4	1
Sport coat	4	6	4

The cutting department has 100 hours of capacity, sewing has 180 hours, and 60 yards of material are available. Each skirt contributes $5 to profits and overhead; each dress, $17; and each sport coat, $30.

a. Specify the objective function and constraints for this problem.
b. Solve the problem using the simplex method.

22. Consider Problem 21 further.
a. How much would you be willing to pay
   i. for an extra hour of cutting time?
   ii. for an extra hour of sewing time?
   iii. for an extra yard of material?
   Explain your responses to each question.
b. Determine the range of right-hand-side

values over which the shadow price would be valid for each of the following constraints.

   i. Cutting

   ii. Material

23. The Big-n-Tall Company makes fine clothing for large men. A few years ago it entered the sportswear market with its "Sunset" line of shorts, pants, and shirts. Management wants to know now how much to make of each product, so as to maximize profits. Each type of clothing is routed through two departments, A and B. The following are the relevant data for each product.

Processing Time (hr)

Product	Department A	Department B	Material (yd)
Shirt	2	1	2
Shorts	2	3	1
Pants	3	4	4

Department A has 120 hours of capacity, department B has 160, and 90 yards of material are available. Each shirt contributes $10 to profits and overhead; each pair of shorts, $10; and each pair of pants, $23.

a. Specify the objective function and constraints for this problem.

b. Solve the problem using a computer package.

c. How much would you be willing to pay for an extra hour of capacity at department A? Department B? Over what range of right-hand values are these shadow prices valid?

24. The Butterfield Company makes a variety of hunting knives. Each knife is processed on four machines. The following are the processing times required and machine capacities.

Processing Time (hr)

Knife	Machine 1	Machine 2	Machine 3.	Machine 4
A	0.05	0.10	0.15	0.05
B	0.15	0.10	0.05	0.05
C	0.20	0.05	0.10	0.20
D	0.15	0.10	0.10	0.10
E	0.05	0.10	0.10	0.05
Capacity (hr)	1500	1400	1600	1500

Each product contains a different amount of two basic raw materials. Raw material 1 costs $0.50 per ounce, and raw material 2 costs $1.50 per ounce. There are 75,000 ounces of raw material 1 and 100,000 ounces of raw material 2 available.

Knife	Raw Material 1 (oz/unit)	Raw Material 2 (oz/unit)
A	4	2
B	6	8
C	1	3
D	2	5
E	6	10

The selling price of each knife is:

Knife	Selling Price (per unit)
A	$15.00
B	25.50
C	14.00
D	19.50
E	27.00

a. If the objective is to maximize profit, specify the objective function and constraints for the problem. Assume that labor costs are negligible.

b. Solve the problem using the simplex method, with a computer package.

25. A small fabrication firm makes three basic types of components for use by other companies. Each component is processed on three machines. The following are the processing times and machine capacities.

Processing Time (hr)

Component	Machine 1	Machine 2	Machine 3
A	0.25	0.10	0.05
B	0.20	0.15	0.10
C	0.10	0.05	0.15
Capacity	1600	1400	1500

Each component contains a different amount of two basic raw materials. Raw material 1 costs $0.20 per ounce, and raw material 2 costs $0.35 per ounce. There are 200,000 ounces of raw material 1 and 85,000 ounces of raw material 2 available.

Component	Raw Material 1 (oz/unit)	Raw Material 2 (oz/unit)
A	32	12
B	26	16
C	19	9

The selling price of each component is:

Component	Selling Price (per unit)
A	$40
B	28
C	24

a. Assuming that the company must make at least 1200 units of component B, labor costs are negligible, and the objective is to maximize profits, specify the objective function and constraints for the problem.

b. Solve the problem using a computer package.

26. The firm in Problem 25 is considering expansion of its capacity to cover an expected demand surge over the next four years. With the completion of the expansion, the new annual capacities of its three machines will be as follows.

Machine	Capacity (hr)
1	3000
2	3500
3	3200

The following information has been gathered on the expansion.

- The initial investment in the equipment expansion is $250,000, and there is no salvage value at the end of four years.
- The fixed costs associated with the expansion are $25,000 per year.
- The desired rate of return is 18 percent, and the tax rate is 30 percent.
- Assume straight-line depreciation (over four years).

- At least 2400 units of component B must be produced annually.
- There are 400,000 ounces of raw material 1 and 170,000 ounces of raw material 2 available.

The rest of the data from Problem 25 still applies.

a. Specify the objective function and constraints that would maximize annual profits given the new machine capacities. Assume that labor costs are negligible.

b. Solve the problem using a computer package.

c. Using your answer to part (b), determine the annual after-tax cash flows for the next four years resulting from the increased capacities.

d. Using the NPV method, should the firm expand?

27. The Nutmeg Corporation produces five different nut and nut mix products: almond pack, walnut pack, gourmet pack, fancy pack, and thrifty pack. Each product (individual or mix) comes in a one-pound can. The firm can purchase almonds at $0.80/pound, walnuts at $0.60/pound, and peanuts at $0.35/pound. Peanuts are used to complete each mix, and the company has an unlimited supply of them. The supply of almonds and walnuts is limited. The company can buy up to 3000 pounds of almonds and 2000 pounds of walnuts. The resource requirements and forecasted demand for the products follow. Solve this problem using a computer package.

Product	Minimum Requirements (%)		Demand (cans)
	Almonds	Walnuts	
Almonds	100	—	1250
Walnuts	—	100	750
Gourmet	45	45	1000
Fancy	30	30	500
Thrifty	20	20	1500

a. What mix minimizes the cost of meeting the demand for all five products?

b. What is the impact on the product mix if only 2000 pounds of peanuts are available?

c. What is the impact on the product mix if the gourmet pack requires 50 percent almonds and 50 percent walnuts?

d. What is the impact on the product mix if the demand for the fancy pack is doubled?

SELECTED REFERENCES

Blackburn, Joseph. *Time-Based Competition: The Next Battleground in American Manufacturing.* Homewood, Ill.: Business One Irwin, 1991.

"Borden Uses Its Noodle to Build Largest U.S. Pasta-Making Plant." *The Columbus Dispatch,* August 14, 1991.

Bower, Joseph L., and Thomas M. Hout. "Fast-Cycle Capability for Competitive Power." *Harvard Business Review* (November–December 1988), pp. 110–118.

Burgelman, Robert A., and Modesto A. Maidique. *Strategic Management of Technology and Innovation.* Homewood, Ill.: Irwin, 1988.

Chase, Richard B., and David A. Tansik. "Customer Contact Model for Organization Design." *Management Science,* vol. 29, no. 9 (September 1983), pp. 1037–1050.

Clark, Kim B., and Takahiro Fujimoto. "The Power of Product Integrity." *Harvard Business Review* (November–December 1990), pp. 107–118.

Dean, James W., Jr., and Gerald I. Susman. "Organizing for Manufacturable Design." *Harvard Business Review* (January–February 1989), pp. 28–36.

"Diaper's Failure Shows How Poor Plans, Unexpected Woes Can Kill New Products." *Wall Street Journal,* October 4, 1990.

Ferdows, Kasra, and Arnoud De Meyer. "Lasting Improvements in Manufacturing Performance: In Search of a New Theory." *Journal of Operations Management,* vol. 9, no. 2 (April 1990), pp. 168–184.

Giffi, Craig A., Aleda V. Roth, and Gregory M. Seal. *Competing in World-Class Manufacturing: America's 21st Century Challenge.* Homewood, Ill.: Business One Irwin, 1991.

Guile, Bruce R., and James Brian Quinn. *Technology in Services: Policies for Growth, Trade, and Employment.* Washington, D.C.: National Academy Press, 1988.

Harrigan, Kathryn R. *Strategic Flexibility.* Lexington, Mass.: Lexington Books, 1985.

Hayes, Robert H., and Roger W. Schmenner. "How Should You Organize Manufacturing?" *Harvard Business Review* (January–February 1978), pp. 105–108.

Hayes, Robert H., and Steven C. Wheelwright. "Link Manufacturing Process and Product Life Cycles." *Harvard Business Review* (January–February 1979), pp. 133–140.

Heskett, James L., and Leonard A. Schlesenger. "The Service-Driven Service Company." *Harvard Business Review* (September–October 1991), pp. 71–81.

Hill, Terry. *Manufacturing Strategy: Text and Cases.* Homewood, Ill.: Irwin, 1989.

Kekre, Sunder, and Kannan Srinivasan. "Broader Product Line: A Necessity to Achieve Success?" *Management Science,* vol. 36, no. 10 (October 1990), pp. 1216–1231.

Kim, Jay S., and Jeffrey G. Miller. "The Manufacturing Futures Factbook: 1990 U.S. Manufacturing Futures Survey." Boston University, 1990.

Krubasik, Edward G. "Customize Your Product Development." *Harvard Business Review* (November–December 1988), pp. 46–52.

Leavitt, Theodore. "The Industrialization of Service." *Harvard Business Review* (September–October 1976), pp. 63–74.

Merrills, Roy. "How Northern Telecom Competes on Time." *Harvard Business Review* (July–August 1989), pp. 108–114.

Powell, Gary N., and George A. Johnson. "An Expectancy-Equity Model of Productive System Performance." *Journal of Operations Management,* vol. 1, no. 1 (August 1980), pp. 47–56.

"Pushing Design to Dizzying Speed." *Business Week,* October 21, 1991, p. 64.

Roth, Aleda V., and Marjolijn van der Velde. *The Future of Retail Banking Delivery Systems.* Rolling Meadows, Ill.: Bank Administration Institute, 1988.

Sasser, W. Earl, R. Paul Olsen, and D. Daryl Wyckoff. *Management of Service Operations.* Boston: Allyn and Bacon, 1978.

Schmenner, Roger W. *Plant Tours and Service Tours in Operations Management,* 3rd ed. New York: Macmillan, 1991.

Sharma, Deven. "Manufacturing Strategy: An Empirical Analysis." Unpublished dissertation, Ohio State University, 1987.

Skinner, Wickham. *Manufacturing in the Corporate Strategy.* New York: John Wiley and Sons, 1978.

Stalk, George Jr. "Time—The Next Source of Competitive Advantage." *Harvard Business Review* (July–August 1988), pp. 41–51.

Swamidass, Paul M., and W.T. Newell. "Manufacturing Strategy, Environmental Uncertainty and Performance: A Path Analytic Model." *Management Science*, vol. 33, no. 4 (April 1987), pp. 509–524.

Taylor, S.G., S.M. Seward, and S.F. Bolander, "Why the Process Industries Are Different." *Production and Inventory Management* (Fourth Quarter 1981), pp. 9–24.

Taylor, S.G., S.M. Seward, S.F. Bolander, and R.C. Heard. "Process Industry Production and Inventory Framework: A Summary." *Production and Inventory Management* (First Quarter 1981), pp. 15–32.

Wheelwright, Steven C. "Reflecting Corporate Strategy in Manufacturing Decisions." *Business Horizons* (February 1978), pp. 57–65.

Wheelwright, Steven C., and Robert H. Hayes. "Competing Through Manufacturing." *Harvard Business Review* (January–February 1985), pp. 99–109.

Wheelwright, Steven C., and W. Earl Sasser, Jr. "The New Product Development Map." *Harvard Business Review* (May–June 1989), pp. 112–125.

Wood, Craig H. "Operations Strategy: Decision Patterns and Measurement." Unpublished dissertation, Ohio State University, 1991.

Chapter 3

QUALITY MANAGEMENT

How do consumers perceive the quality of our products or services?

How can we include employees in the quality improvement process?

How can we best meet the quality levels dictated by our competitive strategies?

What are the high costs of poor quality?

What factors in our operations system are causing major quality problems?

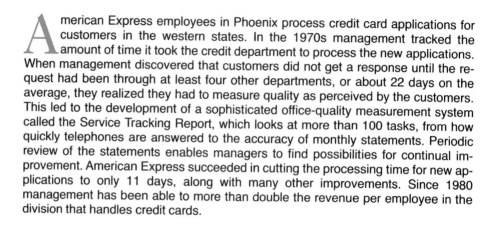

American Express employees in Phoenix process credit card applications for customers in the western states. In the 1970s management tracked the amount of time it took the credit department to process the new applications. When management discovered that customers did not get a response until the request had been through at least four other departments, or about 22 days on the average, they realized they had to measure quality as perceived by the customers. This led to the development of a sophisticated office-quality measurement system called the Service Tracking Report, which looks at more than 100 tasks, from how quickly telephones are answered to the accuracy of monthly statements. Periodic review of the statements enables managers to find possibilities for continual improvement. American Express succeeded in cutting the processing time for new applications to only 11 days, along with many other improvements. Since 1980 management has been able to more than double the revenue per employee in the division that handles credit cards.

The challenge for top managers today is to produce quality products or services efficiently. Quality management puts operations managers squarely in the middle of top-management goal setting and policy making because it is operations—in conjunction with the other functional areas in the organization—that must meet the challenge. American Express is just one example of a company that has met the challenge and is using quality as a competitive weapon. This chapter is the first of two that address the topic of quality. Here we explore the competitive implications of quality, focusing on quality improvement and the costs associated with quality failures. We conclude with some prescriptions for quality excellence from respected consultants in the field. In Chapter 4 we address quality control, which consists of the statistical techniques useful for appraising and monitoring quality in an operating system.

WHAT IS QUALITY?

In Chapter 2 we identified two competitive priorities that deal with quality: high-performance design and consistent quality. These priorities are not definitions of quality. Rather, they characterize an organization's competitive thrust. Strategic plans that recognize quality as an essential competitive priority must be based on some operational definition of quality. This task is complicated by the fact that producer and consumer definitions of quality often differ. In this section we briefly discuss these definitions of quality and emphasize the importance of bridging the gap between consumer expectations of quality and operating capabilities.

Producer Definitions of Quality

Within an organization, **quality** typically means *conformance to specifications*. Managers specify quality standards for their products or services and measure quality performance by how closely they conform to those specifications. The specifications can be used to define high-performance design to the operating system. In manufacturing systems a tolerance is specified for the critical dimensions of every part produced. Parts that fail to fall within the tolerances are either reworked or scrapped, resulting in consistent quality. Seagate, for example, emphasizes the high-performance design of its disk drives by advertising that the drives have a "mean time between failures" of 30,000 hours. All the components of the disk drive must conform to their individual specifications to achieve the performance of the complete product. In service systems, conformance to specifications is also important, even though tangible products are not produced. For example, Bell Canada measures the performance of their operators in Ontario as a group. If the group average time to process a call (called "handle time") exceeds the standard of 23 seconds, managers ask the operators if they know the cause and work with them to get it back down.

Consumer Definitions of Quality

Customers typically define **quality** as *value*, that is, how well the product or service serves its intended purpose at a price they are willing to pay. Another definition is *fitness for use*, or how well the product performs. These definitions are similar and involve the customer's expectations of the product or service. In assessing value or fitness for use, the customer may consider various aspects of quality, as shown in Table 3.1.

TABLE 3.1 / Examples of Consumer Definitions of Quality

Quality Aspect	In Services	In Manufacturing
Hardware	Style and appearance of tableware at a restaurant Age of equipment in a dentist's office	Visible appearance of the product Ease of installation and use of the product
Product or service support	Number of errors in bank statements Responsiveness to expressed or implied warranties	Accuracy of billing procedures and ease of correcting errors Truthfulness in advertising
Psychological impressions	Courtesy of the bellman at a hotel Sympathy of the clerk at the customer complaints desk of a retail store	Knowledge of the salesperson regarding product performance Reputation of the brand name

Hardware. In service industries, hardware quality relates to the interior and exterior aesthetics of the location where a service is provided and to the condition of the equipment used to provide the service. In manufacturing industries, hardware quality refers to product characteristics such as appearance, style, durability, reliability, craftsmanship, and serviceability. Thus both workmanship and product design are judged by the consumer.

Support. Often the product or service support provided by the company is just as important as the quality of the product or service itself. Customers can get very upset with a company if financial statements are incorrect, responses to warranty claims are delayed, or advertising is misleading. Often, good product support can partially offset deficiencies in hardware quality. For example, a customer who just had a brake job understandably would be upset if the brakes began squealing again a week later. A reputable brake shop will give a warranty to redo the work at no additional charge. If it also has a policy of following up with a call to find out whether the customer is satisfied, the company makes very clear its intent to satisfy the customer.

Psychological Impressions. Not to be overlooked is the psychological aspect of quality. In the provision of services, where the customer is in close contact with the provider, the appearance and actions of the provider are very important. Nicely dressed, courteous, friendly, and sympathetic employees can affect the customer's perception of service quality. For example, rumpled, discourteous, or grumpy bellhops can undermine a hotel's best efforts to provide high-quality service; the guests who encounter them may form lasting negative impressions of the hotel from such encounters.

In manufacturing, product quality is often judged on the basis of contact with salespersons or advertisements. The knowledge and personality of salespersons, as well as the product image presented in advertisements, convey an impression of product quality in customers.

Implications for Producers. From this discussion of the consumer's definitions of quality, it should be apparent that defining quality is no easy task. To make things worse, consumers change their perceptions of quality. Take automobiles for instance: Consumer preferences shifted from power and styling in 1970 to fuel economy in 1975 to quality of design and performance in the 1980s. Changes in consumer life-styles and values in response to changing economic conditions during that time drastically altered customer perceptions of automobile quality. Today, a buyer is more inclined to invest in a long-lasting, safe product, even if it means paying more for it at the outset. By not identifying these trends and responding to them quickly, U.S. automakers lost opportunities to maintain or increase their market shares relative to foreign competition. In general, business success depends on the accuracy of management's perceptions of customer expectations and the degree to which it can bridge the gap between consumer expectations and operating capabilities. Poor quality erodes the firm's ability to compete in the marketplace and increases the costs of producing its product or service. By improving quality, a firm can increase its market share as well as reduce the cost of its products or services.

Malcolm Baldrige National Quality Award

Before closing this segment on the definitions of quality, it is important to point out that quality has become a national priority and that defining quality for a firm is a critical activity. That isn't to say that other priorities are not important to create a market niche for a company. Rather, it is becoming more apparent that good quality will be required of all businesses and organizations. To emphasize that point, in August 1987, the Malcolm Baldrige National Quality Improvement Act was signed into effect, creating the Malcolm Baldrige National Quality Award. The award is named for the late Secretary of Commerce Malcolm Baldrige, who was a strong proponent of enhancing quality as a means to reduce the trade deficit. The purpose of the award program is to promote quality awareness and practices, recognize quality achievements, and publicize quality strategies and achievements.

A maximum of two awards can be made each year in each of three categories: large manufacturers, large service companies, and small businesses in either manufacturing or services. As of 1991, twelve companies have received this prestigious award: Marlow Industries, Motorola, Commercial Nuclear Fuel Division of Westinghouse, Globe Metallurgical, Milliken & Company, Xerox Business Products and Systems, Solectron, Cadillac Motor Car Division of General Motors, IBM Rochester, Federal Express Corporation, Zytec, and Wallace Company.

The Federal Express Corporation was the first service company to receive the award. Starting in 1973 with a fleet of eight small aircraft, the company has grown to 90,000 employees at more than 1600 sites that process 1.5 million shipments daily. Since 1987, overall customer satisfaction with Federal Express's domestic service has averaged better than 95 percent and its international service has averaged 94 percent. There are several key reasons for Fed Ex's success. First, a well-developed and thoroughly employed management evaluation system called SFA (Survey/Feedback/Action) involves employees in the development of action plans for improvement. Second, employees are provided extensive training to improve the quality of service. They are encouraged to be innovative and to make their own decisions. Federal Express provides the information and the technology employees need to continuously improve their performance. Finally, Federal Express replaced its old measure of quality performance—percentage of on-time deliveries—with a 12-component index that comprehensively describes how performance is viewed by customers. Measures such as the numbers of invoice adjustments, damaged packages, lost packages, and missed pickups are included. The index is tracked to detect weekly, monthly, and annual trends and provides an important source of information for quality action teams searching for the root causes of problems in service quality.

For firms competing for the Malcolm Baldrige Quality Award, the application and review process is rigorous. Going through the process often helps companies define what quality means for them. Companies must answer 192 questions that address the seven major criteria for the award:

1. *Leadership* in creating and sustaining a visible quality culture
2. Effectiveness in *collecting and analyzing information* for quality improvement and planning
3. Effectiveness in integrating quality requirements into the *strategic planning process*
4. Success in utilizing the full potential of the *work force* for quality improvement
5. Effectiveness of the company's systems for *assuring quality control*
6. *Results* of quality achievement and improvement, as demonstrated by quantitative measures
7. Effectiveness of *customer satisfaction* systems to determine customer requirements and meet them

Customer satisfaction is an underpinning aspect of these seven criteria. Managerial Practice 3.1 depicts the efforts of IBM Rochester, winner in the manufacturing category, to achieve customer satisfaction.

The application that companies must submit represents many hours of work. Xerox budgeted $800,000 for the examination process, excluding the salaries of the 20 employees assigned full time to the project. Federal Express involved hundreds of employees and devoted seven executives full time for several months. None of this ensures that a company will be selected. In 1991, 106 companies applied and only 3 won.

There are four stages to the review process. In the first stage at least four members of the board of examiners review the application. Second, there is a consensus review to determine which companies will receive site visits. Third, at least five members of the examination board make a site visit to each company selected. Finally, the judges review all site-visit reports to make final recommendations to the National Institute of Standards and Technology for presentation to the Secretary of Commerce.

More than 100,000 award application packets were sent to inquiring companies in 1991. Each year this figure increases. This is good news for consumers, for it implies that more and more producers of products and services see that quality provides a competitive edge.

MARKET IMPLICATIONS

In the past, price was considered to be the key factor in a firm's gaining market share, but today this is not a hard and fast rule. Consumers are much more quality-minded and in many cases would prefer to spend more for a product that lasts longer or a service that is delivered promptly and thoroughly. A survey of 2000 business units conducted by the Strategic Planning Institute of Cambridge, Massachusetts, indicated that the degree of product quality affects

Managerial Practice 3.1

Customer Satisfaction at IBM Rochester

The Rochester, Minnesota, site of the International Business Machines Corporation employs more than 8100 people in the manufacture of computer hardware and software. More than 400,000 IBM Rochester systems have been installed worldwide. One of the ingredients of its success has been careful attention to customer satisfaction. Customers are involved in every aspect of the product, from design to delivery. For example, customers and IBM business partners representing 4500 businesses worldwide participated on advisory councils during product development of the AS/Entry Systems and the Application System/400. Customers also participated in testing product prototypes.

While customer involvement in the product design and development phase is important, the product must be produced with high quality if customer satisfaction is to be maintained. IBM Rochester has invested more than $300 million since 1986 to improve its processes and information systems. Many of these improvements were aimed at *preventing* quality defects, and they shortly paid for themselves. Capital spending for defect *detection* devices decreased 75 percent in the 1980s, and losses as a proportion of manufacturing output dropped 55 percent. Nonetheless, improved processes and information systems were not enough. IBM Rochester invested heavily in quality education and job training, which increased employees' skills and made them more flexible for other job assignments. Management also increased their recognition of employees who contributed to quality improvements, thereby increasing morale.

Suppliers are also important. IBM Rochester has 700 suppliers, each expected to ship defect-free products and keep up with new developments in quality production. While the requirements are high, so, too, is the support suppliers receive. IBM Rochester has trained more than 1000 of the suppliers' employees in IBM manufacturing and quality control techniques (as in Chapter 4). Also, the suppliers have access to state-of-the-art technology in exchange for their expertise in resolving production problems with new products.

Because of IBM's attention to quality, product reliability increased 300 percent over a six-year period, enabling IBM to increase its warranty period from 2 to 12 months. Its customers enjoy one of the lowest costs of ownership in the industry. IBM Rochester has gone a long way toward using quality management to improve customer satisfaction.

Source: 1990 Award Winner: IBM Rochester, brochure distributed by The Commerce Department, 1990.

a firm's chances of increasing its market share. If quality is stable, a high-quality product or service stands a much better chance of gaining market share than does one of low quality. If customers perceive improvements in quality, the chances of increasing market share are better, regardless of the level of quality.

Good quality can also pay off in higher profits. High-quality products and services can be priced higher than comparable but lower-quality ones and yield a greater return for the same sales dollar. In addition, as you will see later in this chapter, high quality can reduce costs, which in turn increases profits. Management is more able to compete on price as well as on quality.

COST IMPLICATIONS

In a recent poll by the American Society for Quality Control, executives seemed to underestimate the cost to their companies of poor quality. A majority claimed that the costs of poor quality accounted for less than 10 percent of gross sales. But most experts on the costs of poor quality estimate losses in the range of 20 to 30 percent for defective or unsatisfactory products because the costs of poor quality often go beyond the obvious cost of scrap or rework. For example, the Hubble Space Telescope, a $1.5 billion orbiting observatory, was launched in April 1990, and engineers discovered two months later that a mirror had been incorrectly manufactured. The telescope's view of the stars was blurred, severely reducing its value to astronomers. Experts determined that a device called a null corrector was incorrectly positioned by 1 millimeter, causing the incorrect grinding and polishing of the mirror. Apparently the mirror was not properly checked before it was attached to the telescope. A simple test, costing a few hundred thousand dollars, could have been performed years earlier to detect the defect.

But manufacturing systems do not hold a monopoly on creating costly quality problems. "Dirty" electric power supplied by utility companies to manufacturers is becoming a big problem. Tiny power surges, sags, and outages, often less than a millisecond long, rarely faze old manufacturing equipment but wreak havoc on new equipment that relies heavily on delicate computer chips. General Motors couldn't figure out why the computer running its minivan assembly line in Baltimore kept shutting down for hours at a time. Finally the problem was traced to the local utility's faulty underground wiring. When the robots on the assembly line kicked in, the power drain caused spikes and outages that shut down the computer. Blackouts like this can cost a manufacturer as much as $500,000 per hour.

For many years consultants such as J.M. Juran and W. Edwards Deming have demonstrated the costs of poor quality to managers in Japan and the United States. But only recently have U.S. managers begun to take action. The result is a conscious effort to reduce the level of defective products and services.

Four major categories of cost are associated with quality management and are summarized in Table 3.2. **Prevention costs** are associated with preventing

TABLE 3.2 / Costs Associated with Quality Management

Cost Category	As Quality Increases, Costs . . .	Comments
Prevention	Increase	Costs are associated with preventing defects before they happen. Included are the costs of process design, product and service design, employee training, and supplier programs.
Appraisal	Decrease	Costs are incurred in assessing the level of quality attained by the operating system. Included are the costs of quality audits and statistical quality control programs.
Internal failure	Decrease	Costs result from yield losses and the need to rework products or services because of defective workmanship.
External failure	Decrease	Costs include those of warranty repairs, loss of market share, and lawsuits arising from injury or property damage from use of the product or service.

defects before they happen. These costs increase as the quality level (as measured by product or service design) or quality consistency (as measured by conformance to specifications) increases. That is, improving quality requires the expenditure of time, effort, and money. Prevention costs include the costs of process design, product design, employee training, and supplier programs. The "Improving Quality" section later in this chapter will give you more detail on these costs.

Appraisal costs are incurred in assessing the level of quality attained by the operating system. These costs decrease as quality level or quality consistency increases. Quality appraisal helps management identify quality problems. As preventive measures improve quality, fewer resources are needed for quality inspections and the subsequent search for causes of any problems that are detected. Appraisal costs, which include the costs of quality audits and statistical quality control programs, are discussed in more detail in Chapter 4.

Internal failure costs and *external failure costs* both decrease as the quality level or consistency increases. These costs are associated with the failure to control quality and are discussed in detail in the next two sections.

Internal Failure Costs

Internal failure costs result from defects generated during production of a product or service and fall into two major cost categories: **yield losses,** which are incurred if a defective item must be scrapped, and **rework costs.** With rework, the item is rerouted to some previous operation(s) to correct the defect. In the case of a service, the customer calls or returns in person if further work is needed.

Yield Losses. Your first thought about yield losses may be the cost of the material lost. Although that is only a fraction of the total cost involved, it is a good place to start. Suppose that you wanted to determine how many units of a specific raw material you would need to ensure a given number of nondefective product units from the production process. Let

$$d_i = \text{average proportion of defective units generated at operation } i \text{ of the process}$$

$$n = \text{number of operations in the production process for the product}$$

$$M = \text{desired number of units of finished product}$$

$$B = \text{average number of units of the raw material needed at the start of the production process—the decision variable}$$

The output from the first operation is $B(1 - d_1)$. This quantity is then processed by the second operation, which produces a proportion of d_2 defectives.

Consequently, the output from the second operation is $B(1 - d_1)(1 - d_2)$. The output from the other operations is similarly determined. In the end, we want the total output from the production process to equal M, the desired number of units of finished product. The equation becomes

$$B(1 - d_1)(1 - d_2) \cdots (1 - d_n) = M$$

or

$$B = \frac{M}{(1 - d_1)(1 - d_2) \cdots (1 - d_n)}$$

Application 3.1 **Estimating Yield Losses**

Manufacturing the head of a fireplace shovel requires four steps, as depicted in Fig. 3.1. The raw material input to the process is a shank and a steel blank for the blade, one of each per shovel. Each operation generates the following average proportion of defects:

Operation		Proportion Defective
1	Cut off blade	0.01
2	Weld shank to blade	0.04
3	Heat and roll blade	0.02
4	Stamp blade	0.06

How many units of the raw material (shanks and steel blanks), on the average, are needed at operation 1 to ensure 100 nondefective shovel heads after operation 4?

Solution Let B be the number of shanks required. We would need an equal number of steel blanks. The output of each operation is the input for the next operation. The input for operation 2 is B multiplied by the proportion of nondefective shovels generated by operation 1, or $B(1 - 0.01)$. The input for operation 3 is $B(1 - 0.01)(1 - 0.04)$, and so on. Consequently,

$$B(1 - 0.01)(1 - 0.04)(1 - 0.02)(1 - 0.06) = 100$$

and

$$B = \frac{100}{0.8755} = 114$$

Thus 114 shanks and 114 steel blanks are needed at the start.

FIGURE 3.1

A Four-Operation Production Process for Manufacturing Fireplace Shovel Heads

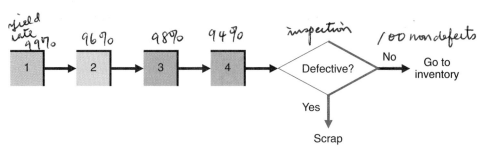

In the preceding application, the 14 extra units of each input required because of the defectives generated at each operation increase raw-material costs by 14 percent. However, other costs are hidden from the casual view of the unwary manager. Suppose that all 114 shovels are moved from one operation to the next and finally checked for quality after the last operation, a common practice in many firms. What are the hidden costs? More labor and machine hours are required to produce the same quantity of product than for a defect-free process. For example, each operation must process 114 shovels per day. If no defectives were generated, each operation would only have to process 100 shovels per day. Thus the firm must spend 14 percent more for labor and machine costs because of yield losses. The increase in machine hours could cause additional failures and further increase machine downtime. In addition, because more material must be processed in order to get the required daily quantity, product manufacturing time will increase. The implications for customer service are an increase in the percentage of back orders and the potential loss of future sales. In-process and end-of-production inspections are based on the assumption that inspectors will catch all the defects generated by the process. If the inspectors fail to do so, downstream operations incur additional costs such as those already discussed. Finally, work-in-process costs rise because more material must flow between operations.

Rework Costs. Sometimes when a defective part or production lot is discovered or a service is improperly delivered, it can be corrected by reworking it. Suppose that an operations manager wants to estimate the average daily number of units of a certain product that must be reworked at a certain operation where, if the production lot is defective, every unit must be inspected and reworked. In this case,

P_j = probability that a lot (or batch) of product j will be defective and have to be reworked

Q_j = lot size of product j

N_j = average number of defect-free lots of product j required per day

M_j = average number of units of product j produced at the rework operation per day

Consider a single production lot of item j passing through the production process. Suppose that an inspection station immediately follows an operation known to produce defects, such as operation 3 in Fig. 3.2. After operation 3

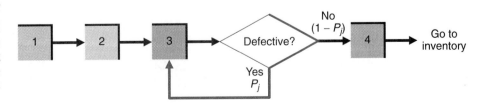

processes the production lot the first time, there is a probability of P_j that it will come back. After it is processed a second time, it could return again. The probability of a production lot returning twice is P_j^2. In theory, this can happen over and over again. The expected number of times operation 3 will have to process the lot is $(1 + P_j + P_j^2 + P_j^3 + \cdots) = 1/(1 - P_j)$. The expected number of units processed per lot is $Q_j[1/(1 - P_j)]$. Consequently,

$$M_j = \frac{Q_j N_j}{1 - P_j}$$

Application 3.2 | *Estimating the Amount of Rework*

Let's consider our fireplace shovel application again, except that this time there is no scrap. Instead, let's suppose that the shovel is produced in lots of 10, that an entire lot can be defective, and that 100 defect-free shovels are still required at the end of the day. Units are inspected after operation 3, and there is a 10 percent chance that operation 3 will produce a defective lot; if it does, the lot must be sent back for rework. This situation is that shown in Fig. 3.2, where P_j is now 0.10. How many shovels per day can be expected to require reworking because of operation 3?

Solution

The accompanying table shows how this situation affects the operation of the system. Processing 10 lots per day would, on average, result in 1 lot that needs rework. This means that operation 3 and inspection would be expected to process at least 110 shovels per day. *The lot that has to be reworked, however, has a 10 percent chance of being defective again.* If the chances of rework are independent of whether the lot has already been reworked, there is a 1 percent chance $[0.10(0.10) = 0.01]$ that the lot will have to be reworked twice. Consequently, the average number of shovels processed per lot is $10[1.0 + 0.1 + (0.1)^2 + (0.1)^3 + \cdots] = 10/(1 - 0.10)$, or approximately 11.1 shovels, including the first time every lot must be processed. Thus the expected number of shovels per day worked by operation 3 and inspection is 111 $[10(10)/(1 - 0.10)]$ over an extended period of time.

The Effects of Rework on a Four-Operation Production Process

Operation	Probability of Rework per Lot	Operation to Route to	Average Number of Shovels Processed per Lot*	Average Number of Shovels Processed per Day†
1	0	—	10	100
2	0	—	10	100
3	0	—	11.1	111
Inspection	0.10	3	11.1	111
4	0	—	10	100

*The average number of units processed per lot equals $10[1.0 + 0.1 + (0.1)^2 + (0.1)^3 + \cdots]$, or approximately 11.1.

†Since 10 lots per day are required, the average number of units processed per day equals 10 times the average number of units processed per lot.

Let's consider each of the costs associated with rework in the preceding application. Obviously, more labor, machine, and inspection hours would be needed at operation 3—in this case, 11 percent more than in the case of no rework. In addition, most situations involving rework involve an increase in the number of setups, even if only a portion of a lot must be reworked. Furthermore, work-in-process inventory levels increase because the units to be reworked stay in a semifinished state longer. The value of that inventory also increases because of the added labor and machine costs needed to produce it correctly. Finally, the manufacturing time for the average production lot increases because of the possibility that it may have to be rerouted for rework. Consequently, promised due dates may not be met, or the lead time for customer delivery may have to be increased to such an extent that the company can no longer compete in the marketplace.

Rework problems are not restricted to manufacturing processes. For example, the claims department of a medical insurance company must deal with a wide variety of reimbursement requests from its customers. If the company fails to pay the correct amount, or sends the check to the wrong doctor, the customer must contact the claims manager to get the matter straightened out. Before checks are mailed, the claims department manager must check the authorizations for payment. If errors are found, the claim must be rechecked and additional paperwork is usually required. Another example is the operation at National Tire Wholesale, where a quality examiner compares the actual work done on a car to the work order authorized by the customer. This is done just before the customer drives the car out of the garage. If some items have not been done to the customer's satisfaction, the car is sent back to the mechanic who worked on it.

External Failure Costs

External failure costs arise from product or service failures at the customer level. We differentiate them from internal failure costs because they are incurred to correct defective products or services that somehow escaped internal checks and controls. When a customer—as opposed to a firm's production worker or quality inspector—finds a defect, there are several implications for the producer. The most obvious is the loss of market share and future profits because bad news travels fast: Dissatisfied customers tell their friends, who in turn tell others; consumer protection groups alert the media. The potential impact on future profits is difficult to assess, but without doubt poor quality erodes market share and profits. These aren't the only external failure costs. There are also warranty service and litigation costs.

Warranty Costs. A **warranty** is a written guarantee of the integrity of a product or service and of the producer's responsibility to replace or repair defective parts or to reperform the service to the customer's satisfaction. Usually, a warranty is given for some specified time period. For example, television repairs are usually guaranteed for 90 days and new automobiles for three years or 36,000 miles, whichever comes first. Warranty costs must be considered in the

FIGURE 3.3

The Costs of
Detecting a Defect

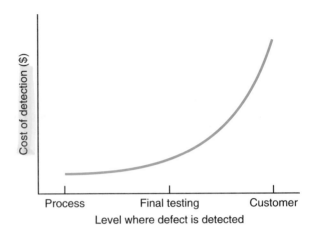

design of new products or services, particularly as they relate to reliability (see Chapter 2).

Encountering defects and correcting them after the product is in the customer's hands is costly. As Fig. 3.3 shows, the place to catch the defect is where it occurs: in the production process. The closer a product is to its finished state, the costlier it is to find defects and correct them. When the product has finally been shipped to the customer, the cost to fix a defect skyrockets. It is very expensive to send a customer engineer from IBM to a remote computer installation to find out what is wrong and fix it. Even more expensive is the cost of sending a team of electrical engineers to India to diagnose and repair a problem with a switch gear in an electric power station.

Litigation Costs. Unfortunately, defective products can injure and even kill consumers who purchase them. Such a defect could arise from poor product design and/or nonconformance to specifications. An increasing number of states are adopting strict liability laws that force companies to pay damages—often large amounts—to injured plaintiffs or heirs, even when they have not proved that the manufacturer was negligent in designing the product. All that needs to be shown is that a product was defective and that it caused the injury or death. At present, there is no nationwide uniform code on product liability. Each state can have its own set of rules, which creates a chaotic situation for companies that sell their products in more than one state.

Chaotic as the situation may be, its one common element is the high cost of litigation. For example, the Ford Motor Company, whose 23 million automatic transmissions manufactured from 1968 to 1980 were alleged to slip from park into reverse if the engine were left running, at one time faced more than 1000 lawsuits exceeding $500 million in claims for injuries and deaths supposedly caused by the transmissions. The Firestone Tire and Rubber Company, whose Firestone 500 tire allegedly had defects in construction causing premature wear, resolved nearly 8000 lawsuits arising from these allegations and spent $180 million, including recalls, to solve the problem.

Litigation is costly not only in terms of legal fees but also in terms of bad publicity. More and more frequently, lawsuits brought on behalf of injured plaintiffs are spotlighted by the news media. Procter & Gamble's Rely tampon, allegedly a cause of toxic shock syndrome, and Merrell–Dow Pharmaceuticals' Bendectin, allegedly a cause of birth defects, are examples of costly litigation and media notoriety. Rely and Bendectin were eventually taken off the market because of bad press. Regardless of whether the company is judged to be at fault in a court of law, the cost of litigation is enormous.

From this discussion it is clear that internal and external failure costs can be substantial. The implication of all this is that improving quality by spending more on preventive measures is a good investment for any organization. However, it depends on whether management is talking about high-performance design or quality consistency. If it is trying to increase the *quality level* by higher-performance design, for example, management is actually addressing business objectives and trade-offs among the competitive priorities of price (cost), quality, time, and flexibility in the hope of doing better in the marketplace. In this situation, reductions in other costs of poor quality may not completely offset increased prevention costs. As a result, management may have to raise the price of the product or service, moving closer to a competitive priority of high-performance design rather than price. For example, Honda's competitive priorities are price and consistent quality, whereas Mercedes–Benz's is high-performance design, which costs a great deal more.

Alternatively, if management is trying to increase quality consistency by better conformance to specifications, the added prevention costs may be more than offset by the reduced appraisal, internal failure, and external failure costs. For the same set of product or service specifications, less waste is generated, and savings can be enormous. This is why many firms are spending large sums of money to improve quality consistency. The overwhelming evidence is that improving quality consistency makes worthwhile the trade-off between prevention costs and other costs of poor quality.

After a discussion of total quality control, we discuss methods for improving quality in more detail.

TOTAL QUALITY CONTROL

Total quality control (TQC) is a concept that makes quality a responsibility to be shared by all the people in an organization, but especially the workers who actually make the product or service. Total quality control was first introduced by Armand Feigenbaum, but it was the Japanese who made it work at the level of the individual worker. In Japan, the foreman and the workers, not a quality control department, have primary responsibility for quality consistency. Everyone else is expected to contribute to the overall improvement of quality—from the secretary who avoids typing errors, to the salesperson who presents the product properly, to the engineer who builds automatic error-detecting devices, to the manager who approves funding for quality improvement projects. In other words, TQC involves all the functions that relate to a product or service.

In TQC, all personnel share the view that quality control is an end in itself. Errors or defects should be caught and corrected (if possible) at the source. Quality at the source becomes a way of life, and workers even have the authority to stop a production line if they see quality problems. At Kawasaki's U.S. plant, lights of different colors strung along the assembly lines indicate the severity of the quality problem detected. Workers activate a yellow light to indicate that a problem has been detected and a red light when the problem is serious enough to stop the line. If the line is stopped, the problem must be resolved quickly because each lost minute results in less output and costs money. In TQC, quality consistency has a higher priority than the level of output.

Rather than trying to "inspect quality into the product" by using inspectors to weed out defective products, the TQC approach is to ensure that an employee does not pass defective units to the next operation. To demonstrate some of the advantages of quality at the source, consider Table 3.3, Fig. 3.1, and Application 3.1 from our earlier discussion. Suppose that each operator passed only nondefective shovels to the next operation. That is, operator 1 passes only 113 shovels to operator 2, who passes 108 shovels to operator 3, and so on. The operations manager still needs capacity for 114 shovels per day at operation 1, but capacity only for 113 shovels at operation 2, 108 at operation 3, and 106 at operation 4. Consequently, fewer machine and labor hours (regular and overtime) are required to produce the 100 units needed. Figure 3.4 compares the labor and machine hours required for the same amount of defect-free output using the "inspect quality into the product" and "quality at the source" approaches to quality assurance.

Also, assuming no delays for machine or worker availability, ensuring quality at the source reduces manufacturing lead time because the process times per batch at operations 2, 3, and 4 are shorter. Moreover, there is less wear and tear

TABLE 3.3 / The Effects of Yield Loss on a Four-Operation Production Process

Operation	Percentage of Defective Shovels	Shovels Processed*	Number of Defective Shovels Added by Operation[†]	Number of Good Shovels Passed to Next Operation
1	1	114	1	113
2	4	114	5	108
3	2	114	2	106
4	6	114	6	100
Total number of defective shovels produced			14	

*Number of shovels each operation must process if defects are passed along.

[†]Rounded to the nearest number of whole shovels. The number of defective shovels is equal to the number of nondefective shovels passed to the operation by the previous operation multiplied by the percentage of defectives generated at the operation. For operation 2, for example, 113(0.04) = 5 defective shovels.

FIGURE 3.4

Implications of
Yield Losses
in a Four-Operation
Production Process
for Fireplace Shovels

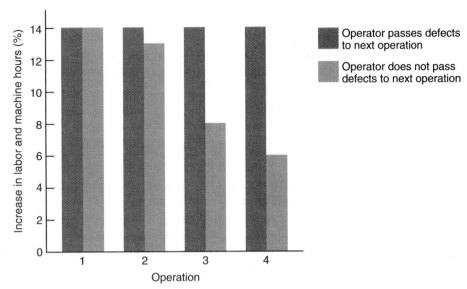

on the equipment, which reduces maintenance and downtime costs. Even though the cost of scrap is the same, there is a savings in the work-in-process inventory investment; no value is added to materials made defective at an early operation only to be scrapped at the end of the production line. In total, the savings can be significant. Similar arguments can be made for the case of re-work.

Obviously, the ideal solution is to produce no defective units because this quality level can significantly reduce operating costs. Recognizing that this condition may not be practical or economical in many instances, we contend that ensuring quality at the source can result in significant savings, regardless of the percentage of defective units generated at each operation. This approach can also decrease the need for inspectors and thereby reduce appraisal costs.

TQC is a philosophy which, if it is to be successful, must pervade the entire organization. Table 3.4 contains some TQC guidelines that have been catego-rized into three general areas. The equipment guidelines emphasize good equipment design and sound maintenance programs. The quality process guidelines focus on where and how often the quality checks should be made. The organizational guidelines deal with employee authority and responsibility as well as how human resources should be organized and trained. In the next section we will address more organizational approaches to quality improve-ment.

IMPROVING QUALITY

Efforts to improve quality require the support of top management, as improv-ing quality involves the entire organization. Some of the ways that organi-zations are improving quality are: breaking down organizational barriers,

TABLE 3.4 / TQC Guidelines

Equipment

Design error-proof processes or machines with automatic checking devices.

Keep machines in excellent working order.

Quality Process

Make every station a quality control point.

When feasible, inspect every item or service immediately after it has been produced.

When it is not feasible to inspect an item or service immediately, enable fast feedback on quality performance directly to the producer.

Organizational

Give each employee the authority to stop producing when quality problems appear, even if it means shutting down a costly assembly line.

Each work group should be responsible for correcting its own defects.

Send defective but correctable problems back to the producer of the item or service rather than to someone else assigned to do rework.

Provide enough time to do the job right.

Where feasible, organize employees and equipment the way work flows. (See Chapter 10 for a description of product layouts.)

Organize employees into quality circles or work teams.

Train supervisors and operators to use statistical process control methods.

---

motivating employees to improve product or service quality, developing quality circles, considering quality in both product and process design, and controlling supplier quality.

Organizational Barriers

One of the ways to improve quality is to demolish the organizational barriers among departments and encourage managers in different functional areas to work together to design and produce more reliable products or services. Although this is easier said than done, several efforts at moving organizations in this direction are being tried.

Quality Assurance Groups. Sometimes organizational barriers among departments encourage the development and testing of products or services in a vacuum, without interaction with other departments. This may lead to premature introduction of products or services into the market. One way to increase the likelihood of a rational approach to the design and testing of new products is to have a quality assurance group.

Quality assurance is broader than quality control. **Quality assurance** is any activity concerned with maintaining quality at the desired level. It also deals with the detection of quality problems if they do occur. In such cases, a quality assurance group conducts rigorous tests to make sure that the problems have been corrected. Management thus can be assured that the firm is marketing a high-quality product or service. The quality assurance group should be staffed by people who have the confidence of the various departmental managers. The group determines the cause of actual problems encountered by the consumer, identifies potential problems, and initiates corrective actions. To help the group discover design or workmanship problems, management may even include a budget allotment to buy back products that have been in service a long time or products that have failed prematurely. In service organizations as well as manufacturing companies, the quality assurance group assists management in establishing and updating quality standards, developing information feedback systems, developing quality cost data, and performing quality improvement studies.

Marketing Interface. Marketing managers must provide information about customers' perceptions of quality if management is to develop reasonable quality goals. In addition, marketing can help improve product quality by not pressuring for premature release of new products. For example, Gillette had advertised its introduction of a new shaving cream. Just before the first shipments were to be made, the firm discovered that the cans averaged slightly less product weight than was printed on the label. Considerable pressure to ship the slightly defective product could have developed. Instead, Gillette's top management focused on correcting the defect. The shipments were late, but customers received all they paid for.

Employee Considerations

The challenge of quality management is to instill an awareness of the importance of good quality in all employees and to motivate employees to improve product quality. All too often it takes a crisis to effect changes. For example, in 1979 the Scandinavian Airline System (SAS) was operating in the red as a result of deregulation and rapidly rising fuel prices. Jan Carlzon, president of SAS, decided that SAS should be a customer-driven company, based on service quality. He set out to reshape the corporate culture to influence the norms and values of the people who deliver the service. His most important step was to introduce the concept of the "moment of truth," or the moment when a customer directly encounters an SAS representative. SAS carried 12 million passengers in 1986. Each passenger meets an average of five SAS front-line employees. Therefore, customers encountered SAS services on 60 million different occasions in 1986. This concept drove home the importance of the employee in the delivery of quality services. The company went into the black in 1980 and earned a profit margin of about 10 percent by 1986. Managerial Practice 3.2 depicts two other organizations whose managements believe that employees are the key to quality improvements.

Individual Development. On-the-job training programs can help improve quality. Programs aimed at new work methods for experienced workers and short courses in current practices for new employees can increase productivity and

Employees: The Key to Quality
Improvements

Xerox Corporation

According to Paul A. Allaire, president and chief executive officer of Xerox, the 1970s and 1980s were challenging times because of tough foreign competition. Xerox wilted under the attack, but then fought back by adopting a total quality strategy in 1983. All employees underwent quality training, and Xerox reversed the trend of declining profitability and market share. The focus became one of producing quality goods and services.

Xerox learned some valuable lessons. First, the trust and support of employees and the commitment of top management are essential to success. Second, everyone must realize that quality improvement is a continual effort. Finally, the company must be willing to commit the time and resources to get the job done. Allaire believes that there will be turmoil and uncertainty as Xerox continues its quest for total quality, but that not to do it would be tantamount to surrendering the future.

Internal Revenue Service

By April 8, 1988, the Internal Revenue Service (IRS) had processed 52.7 million tax returns. Unfortunately, the General Accounting Office reported that 20.7 percent contained errors and that the IRS was responsible for about half. Although these error rates were lower than expected because of sweeping changes in the tax law, IRS commissioner Larry Gibbs and senior IRS management initiated a program that would make fundamental changes to the organization's culture.

Currently 85 percent of the top 11,000 managers have completed a quality management course taught by J.M. Juran, a well-respected consultant in the area of quality improvement. These managers will, in turn, train others within the 100,000-plus work force scattered throughout the country. The general theme is that quality goes at the front end (customer service) and involves everyone.

Sources: "Success in Global Marketplace Requires Corporate Commitment to Total Quality," *P&IM Review with APICS News,* January 1991; "Little Improvement Seen in Error Rate of IRS," *New York Times,* April 14, 1988.

reduce the number of product defects. Some companies train workers on related jobs to help them understand how defects in their own work can cause problems for others. They may even be encouraged to propose remedial action when defects occur. Top management can also benefit from training programs. Texas Instruments initiated a quality improvement program in which 300 top executives attended an outside training program on quality management. Later, 20,000 other employees attended a 16-hour, in-house course.

Monetary Incentives. Some of the incentive for improving quality comes from merit pay and bonuses. Companies may tie monetary incentives directly to quality improvements. The Marriott Corporation, for example, has a profit-sharing plan whereby employees can elect to contribute at least 5 percent of their earnings, and the company makes a contribution from profits. Presumably, as quality of service increases, profits increase and employees are rewarded. Texas Instruments takes a more direct approach. Top managers are ranked by the quality of the products they produce and receive pay increases and bonuses based on this ranking.

Quality Circles

Another way to promote employee participation and improve quality is to develop quality circles, a concept originated by Kaoru Ishikawa. A **quality circle** is a small group of supervisors and employees who meet to identify, analyze, and solve production and quality problems. The philosophy behind quality circles is that most employees take more pride and interest in their work if they are allowed to help shape it. Typically, participation in a quality circle is voluntary, and the group sometimes meets after normal working hours. Groups are kept small (between six and ten employees), to let all members interact freely. Consequently, a company may have a large number of quality circles. For example, one IBM facility has 800 quality circles.

One quality circle can generate hundreds of ideas for improvements in a year. Many may be minor, and some may not prove feasible. However, management must seriously consider all these ideas if quality circles are to work. Benefits in the form of improved quality, productivity, and cost savings can be substantial. Managerial Practice 3.3 highlights the experiences of two large companies with quality circles.

Process Design Implications

Preventing quality problems involves more than solving people problems. The design of service or product and the process used to make it are crucial.

Product and Service Design. Typically, the more design changes there are, the greater the defect rates. Thus stable product and service designs can help reduce quality problems. If design changes are called for because of customer considerations, there is no easy answer. If the company tries to minimize such changes it might become less competitive in the marketplace. If changes are a response to the introduction of new products, the firm could imitate Japanese manufacturers by emphasizing reliability engineering and careful shakedowns of new designs.

Often a firm redesigns a product or service to better conform to the capabilities of its operations. The trade-off here is higher quality and increased competitiveness in exchange for added time and cost to test the product thoroughly before introducing it. Ashton–Tate, producer of dBase software, experienced the penalties of inadequate planning and testing when it introduced its latest offering, dBase IV. The program had bugs that caused it to crash even when doing simple routines, and it was issued to customers long after it was promised. As a result, the product's U.S. market share plunged from 68 percent in 1985 to 48 percent in 1988. The sales Ashton–Tate lost as a result of these coding errors and delays could have been salvaged by more thorough planning and checking during the design and testing stages. Since 1988, dBase product developers have performed extensive testing of 45,000 functions to weed out glitches. Nonetheless, the effect on profitability was devastating. In 1991, Ashton–Tate was acquired by Borland International.

Managerial Practice 3.3

Quality Teams in Action

Paul Revere Insurance

At the urging of executives of Paul Revere's parent company, President Aubrey Reid initiated the Quality Has Value program to improve performance in quality and create a culture in quality at the company. A steering committee of vice presidents of insurance operations and human resources decided to pursue two approaches: Quality Teams and Value Analysis Workshops.

Quality Teams averaged ten people from a department and included every one of the Paul Revere home office staff of 1200 employees. The teams were authorized to identify and implement their ideas for improvement immediately and then tell management what they did. According to Peter Townsend, a former Marine major hired to oversee the Quality Has Value program, "A decision to institute a quality team process is, if you will, a decision to allow a revolution. Revolutions come from the bottom up. If there is to be a new American revolution—a service industrial revolution—all the troops must be enlisted."

The Value Analysis Workshops focused on the question "Are we doing the right things?" and the Quality Teams focused on the question "Are we doing things right?" The Quality Has Value program was a big success. By 1986 annual savings were estimated at $13 million. Quality Teams were averaging 40 ideas per year, an impressive figure in light of the experiences of quality circles in Japan, which averaged only about 5 ideas per year and included only 15 percent of the employees.

Sources: James L. Heskett, W. Earl Sasser, Jr., and Christopher W. L. Hart, *Service Breakthroughs: Changing the Rules of the Game* (New York: The Free Press, 1990), pp. 129–132; *General Motors Public Interest Report*, 1988, pp. 1–12.

General Motors

General Motors is attempting a significant cultural change, although change in an organization the size of GM comes slowly. The firm is encouraging employees to participate in the decision-making process in areas that deeply affect the workplace. The concept is particularly emphasized in the new UAW/GM Quality Network, a program emphasizing teamwork and continuous quality improvement. One important aspect of this program is the quality audit and review. In this daily event, groups of managers and production employees at GM assembly plants meet to review the quality of the cars they have built. Quality measurements closely related to customer perceptions of quality are emphasized.

*A*t GM's Saturn facility, this quality group meets to conduct a quality and audit review.

Process Design. The design of the process used to produce the product or service greatly affects its quality. For example, managers at the First National Bank of Chicago noticed that customers of its letter-of-credit department were bounced around from person to person when they called. In 1985, a customer's request would take four days to go through dozens of steps involving nine employees before a letter of credit would be issued. The solution was to train the letter-of-credit issuers so that the customer dealt with just one person. In addition, customers were given the same employee each time they ordered a letter. Today, First Chicago issues credit letters in less than a day.

Process design is closely related to product or service quality and quality management. The approach taken to quality management depends on the organization's positioning strategy, as described in Chapter 2. Firms with a process focus are more likely to compete on the basis of high-performance design and rely largely on employee involvement to ensure quality. However, firms with a product focus are more likely to compete on the basis of consistent quality, utilize quality specialists, and have more formal controls. Automated inspection becomes more likely. In some cases, such as at breweries, much of the quality is designed into the process itself, and periodic sampling is used to check quality levels. Managerial Practice 3.4 reveals the lengths to which companies in the semiconductor industry must go to compete in a market where high quality and low price are vital.

Managerial Practice 3.4

Semiconductors Require a Clean Environment

Semiconductors, or "chips," are the things that let computers "think." They are packed with thousands of transistors whose features are measured in microns. One micron is one hundredth of the width of a human hair. A particle one tenth of the size of a semiconductor's smallest feature can destroy it by causing a short circuit or leakage of the tiny charges stored in the chip. With such a requirement for cleanliness, chips are difficult to manufacture. Why? Because the people who make them are filthy. At rest, a person sheds at least 100,000 particles a minute of flaking flesh, saliva, hair spray, dandruff, lint, and other things. Head movement releases 500,000 particles, slow walking five million, and exercise 30 million. Breathing is bad and a sneeze is disastrous. One particle is enough to destroy a chip.

Companies have gone to great lengths to build "clean rooms" with strictly controlled air flows and temperatures. Employees must wear bunny suits with hoods, breathing apparatus, boots, and gloves. Some companies even require an air shower after suiting up. Even with all this, touching a chip is forbidden because a glove print can damage the chip. Special suction devices must be used to handle the chips at each step of the process.

Source: "Why You Shouldn't Sing 'La Marseillaise' in Computer Factory," *Wall Street Journal*, December 28, 1984.

A semiconductor "clean room" at an AT&T facility.

The purchase of new machinery can help prevent or overcome quality problems. Suppose that the design specification for the distance between two holes in a metal plate is 3.000 in. ± 0.0005 in. Suppose also that too many plates are defective; that is, the space between holes falls outside the design specification. One way to reduce the percentage of defective parts produced by the process would be to purchase new machinery with the capability to produce metal plates with holes 3.000 in. ± 0.0003 in. apart. Reducing the percentage of defective parts would increase conformance to the design specifications. The trade-off would be greater process costs.

Linking Product or Service Design to Process Design. One of the keys to obtaining high quality is to make sure the product or service is designed to fit the firm's capability to produce it. World-class firms are using a concept called concurrent engineering, in which operations managers and designers work closely together in the initial phases of product or service design to ensure that the production requirements are synchronized with the process capabilities. The result is much better quality and shorter development times. For example, NCR, in Atlanta, makes terminals for checkout counters. In 1987 the company

A quality control employee at NCR, in Atlanta, inspects terminals for checkout counters. NCR has been able to reduce engineering changes and quality rejects significantly through concurrent engineering.

tried concurrent engineering for its latest machine. The new product rolled off the assembly line 22 months later, half the usual time. In addition, the terminal had 85 percent fewer parts and could be assembled in only two minutes. Quality rejects and engineering changes dropped significantly. The National Institute of Standards and Technology estimates that manufacturing firms using concurrent engineering experience 30 to 70 percent less development time, 20 to 90 percent less time to market, and 200 to 600 percent better quality.

Management should be concerned with linking each aspect of quality prized by the customer to the inputs, methods, and process steps that build a particular attribute into the product. Design drawings show how products or services should be produced. However, they cannot pinpoint a problem in design that needs to be corrected in order to satisfy a customer's particular quality concern. One way to identify such problems is to develop a **fishbone diagram,** which is a method first developed by Kaoru Ishikawa, that relates a product or service defect to potential contributing factors. The diagram helps management trace customer complaints directly to the operations involved. Operations that have no bearing on a particular defect aren't shown on the fishbone diagram for that defect.

For example, Fig. 3.5 shows a fishbone diagram for one quality problem related to airline operations: delayed flight departures (identified as the main arrow of the diagram). Five factors are considered critical: personnel, equipment, material, procedure, and other factors out of management's control. These factors are identified as the main connecting arrows of the fishbone. Subfactors are identified by secondary arrows. The relevant subfactors should be checked if a critical factor is suspected of causing the quality problem. Thus, if material is suspected, the subfactors checked would be food service, fueling, and baggage—to see whether any of these operations is causing the problem. However, the benefits of fishbone diagrams go beyond identifying potential causes of a problem. The process of constructing a fishbone diagram itself calls to managerial and worker attention the critical factors affecting product quality.

Purchasing Considerations

Since the production of most goods and services requires the input of some raw materials or purchased items, the operations manager must pay attention to the quality of these inputs. Large companies have hundreds and even thousands of suppliers, some of which supply the same parts. Quality assurance for the items they supply is an enormous task. Purchased parts of poor quality can have a devastating effect on a company with a product focus. For example, one day, the Ford Motor Company halted Tempo and Topaz production at its Kansas City, Missouri, and Oakville, Ontario, plants. A faulty engine part purchased from an outside supplier apparently caused some gears in the engine to lose a few teeth during a test run. Approximately 5500 hourly workers were temporarily laid off. In addition, Ford lost about 2000 cars each day that production was stopped.

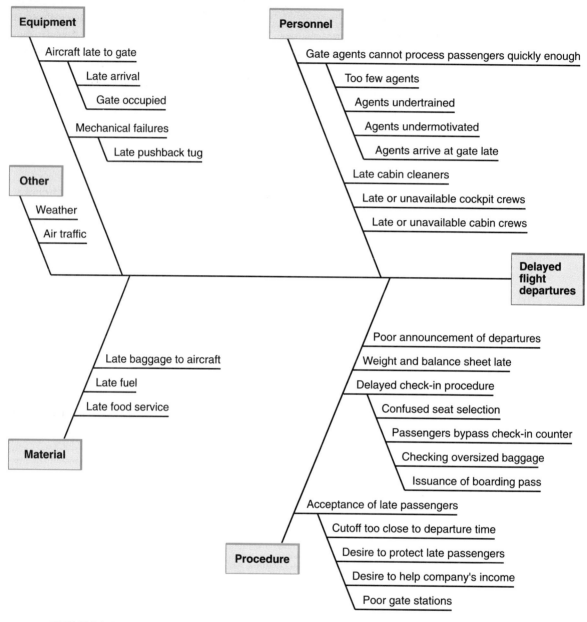

FIGURE 3.5 Fishbone Analysis of Causes of Flight Departure Delays

Source: D. Daryl Wyckoff, "New Tools for Achieving Service Quality," *The Cornell Hotel and Restaurant Administration Quarterly*, November 1984, p. 89. © 1984 Cornell H.R.A. Quarterly. Used by permission. All rights reserved.

Regardless of the number of suppliers involved, both the buyer's approach and specification management are keys to controlling supplier quality. The firm's buyer may emphasize positive reports of money saved, orders placed, and on-time delivery performance of suppliers, overriding negative reports on quality performance unless top management places a high priority on quality. Operating under such a priority, a competent buyer will identify supplier capabilities. The buyer will then concentrate on those suppliers and products that offer an opportunity for quality improvement at a reasonable cost. From a technical standpoint, this is no easy task. After such suppliers have been identified, however, the buyer should work with the supplier to obtain essentially defect-free parts. The buyer can do so by examining and evaluating trade-offs, handling problems of off-specification materials firmly but diplomatically, and participating in corrective actions. Thus patience, understanding, and trust are qualities needed in a buyer.

Specification management is also important. The specifications for purchased parts and materials must be clear and *realistic*. Sometimes specifications are set arbitrarily to a tight limit to protect the designer in case something goes wrong. In other cases, the specifications make the product uneconomical to produce or service later. Specifications have implications for the buyer, who is trying to identify quality standards for the firm's suppliers and at the same time keep costs down. As a check on specifications, buyers in some companies initiate *process capability studies* for important products. These studies amount to trial runs of small product samples to ensure that all components, including the raw materials and purchased parts, work together to form a product that has the desired quality level. Analysis of study results may identify unrealistic specifications and lead to changes.

Top management also has some responsibilities regarding supplier quality. If it wants the purchasing department to identify several low-cost, qualified suppliers, top management must allow purchasing enough time to obtain and analyze the information. An unrealistic deadline can lead to poor selections based on incomplete information about supplier qualifications. In addition, top management can help tear down organizational barriers that hamper communication between purchasing and other departments, such as engineering and quality control. Some of the information needed to assess supplier qualifications requires sampling products and analyzing in detail the supplier's manufacturing process, a task usually performed by quality control personnel and engineers in cooperation with the supplier's technical staff. This effort requires cooperation between purchasing and other departments that have the technical capabilities to do these analyses.

PRESCRIPTIONS FOR EXCELLENCE IN QUALITY

In this chapter we have described companies in both the manufacturing and service sectors that are making significant improvements in the quality of their products and, in so doing, increasing their competitive advantage. Where did they find the keys to their success? Many of them, after having been thrashed in the marketplace by their international competitors, sought the help of one of a small group of respected consultants in the area of quality management. We have already discussed the ideas of Armand Feigenbaum and total quality control. We conclude this chapter with a brief summary of the general philosophies of several other consultants.

Edwards Deming: Quality Is Management's Responsibility

Quality improvement has far-reaching, long-lasting effects on an organization. W. Edwards Deming (1986), considered to be the father of quality control in Japan, summarized the importance of improving quality with his five-step chain reaction: (1) Costs decrease because of less rework, fewer mistakes, fewer delays, and better use of time and materials; (2) productivity improves; (3) market share increases with better quality and prices; (4) company increases profitability and stays in business; and (5) number of jobs increases.

Deming's 14 points to quality, shown in Table 3.5, summarize his philosophy of quality improvement. Deming urges a company to have a definite strategic plan for where it is going and how it will get there. Management should embrace the philosophy that mistakes, defects, and unsuitable materials are no longer acceptable and should be eliminated. The quality of supervision should be improved by allowing more time for supervisors to work with employees and providing them with the tools they need to do the job. Management should also create an environment in which employees will not fear reporting problems or recommending improvements. This fear usually results from imagined retaliation that will affect the reporting worker or fellow workers. For example, a quality assurance inspector may incorrectly report the result of an inspection to avoid exceeding the quota of allowable defectives for the work force. Work standards (see Chapter 7) should not be defined only as numbers or quotas but should include some notion of quality to promote the production of defect-free output. Management also has the responsibility to train (or retrain) employees in new skills to keep pace with changes in the workplace.

TABLE 3.5 / Deming's 14 Points to Quality

1. Create constancy of purpose: allocate resources for long-term planning, research, education, and maintenance.
2. Learn the new philosophy: We can no longer live with defective materials and poor workmanship.
3. Require statistical evidence of process control from suppliers.
4. Reduce the number of suppliers.
5. Use statistical methods to detect the sources of problems.
6. Institute modern aids to training on the job.
7. Improve supervision.
8. Drive out the fear to express ideas and report problems.
9. Break down barriers between departments.
10. Eliminate production quotas.
11. Create work standards that account for quality.
12. Institute a training program in statistical methods.
13. Institute a program for retraining people in new skills.
14. Emphasize the above 13 points every day.

Source: W. Edwards Deming, "Improvement of Quality and Productivity Through Action by Management," *National Productivity Review*, vol. 1, no. 1 (Winter 1981–1982), pp. 12–22.

Management must develop the proper tools to manage quality. Such tools are not only the machines or hand tools that help to gauge the quality of a produced item, but also statistical methods to control processes or incoming materials and to help identify the sources of quality problems. Statistical methods can even be used to determine whether more worker training is needed. Deming believes that statistical methods are the backbone of management's arsenal of tools for managing quality. We explore some of these methods in Chapter 4.

J.M. Juran: A Quality Trilogy

Juran, like Deming, pioneered the education of the Japanese in quality management and significantly affected the staggering quality improvement demonstrated by Japanese manufacturers over the past 40 years. He is a well-respected author and consultant, but like Deming, he was not discovered by American business until the early 1980s. Juran's experience indicates that over 80 percent of quality defects are caused by factors controllable by management. Consequently, management continually needs to seek improvements through sound quality management, which Juran defines as the trilogy of quality planning, control, and improvement.

Quality planning involves deciding the proper quality level and reliability and linking product and service design to process design to achieve the quality characteristics desired. Quality control compares products or services to standards and acts to correct discrepancies. This part of the trilogy, treated in detail in Chapter 4, provides the information to identify needed improvements. Juran's prescription for the final part of the trilogy is to get into the habit of making significant annual improvements. Select an area with chronic quality problems, convince others that a breakthrough solution is needed, analyze alternatives to the problem, select an alternative and implement it. Make sure that proper controls are put in place to monitor the results. Juran believes that annual improvement, hands-on management, and training are fundamental to achieving excellence in quality.

Kaoru Ishikawa: Total Company Involvement

Admittedly influenced by the thinking of Deming, Juran, and Feigenbaum, Kaoru Ishikawa has made significant contributions of his own to the thought and practice of quality management. He is credited with originating the concept of quality control circles and their use. He also developed the fishbone diagram, which, as you saw earlier, helps to identify causes of quality problems.

Ishikawa concluded that, in the West, quality control is generally relegated to only a few staff specialists—and usually only in response to a serious problem. By contrast, his studies of Japanese managers revealed them to be totally committed to quality, a commitment that lasts the life of the organization. He favors total company involvement relative to inputs for quality improvement and believes that even nonspecialists in quality improvement should provide suggestions. This view is similar to Feigenbaum's.

Phillip B. Crosby: Quality Is Free

Because he was a corporate vice president and director of quality at ITT for fourteen years, it is no wonder that Phillip B. Crosby gained a lot of attention when he published his book *Quality Is Free* in 1979. Then the conventional wisdom was that each level of quality had some price. An 8 percent level of defects cost so much. Reducing that level to 3 percent defects would cost a lot more. Why? Improved machines would have to be purchased or better materials used in the products or more skilled labor hired. Crosby points out that managers were forgetting the cost reductions due to performing the job right the first time. He is referring to the hidden costs of poor quality: increased labor and machine hours, increased machine failures and downtime, customer delivery delays and lost future sales, and even increased warranty costs. All these costs are over and above the loss of materials to scrap. Crosby believes that these costs typically dwarf the cost of machines, materials and training needed to create an environment that fosters achievement of high quality. The savings in the reduction of hidden costs can offset the costs incurred to create the proper environment.

Crosby, now a consultant, advocates a goal of zero defects. To have any other goal is tantamount to declaring a commitment to producing a certain amount of defective material. Continuous improvement should be the means that management uses to achieve zero defects.

Genichi Taguchi: Quality Engineering

The major tenet behind Genichi Taguchi's approach to quality is developing high-quality products in a way that reduces costs. He calls it "quality engineering," which involves combining engineering and statistical methods to achieve improvements in cost and quality by optimizing product design and manufacturing processes. In team interaction sessions, employees and managers hypothesize critical factors affecting the quality of a selected product. An experimental design is set up and an experiment conducted to gather data. Statistical techniques are then used to determine the factor(s) contributing most to the product's quality problems and the settings that would optimize their performance. A follow-up experiment is conducted at the optimal settings to verify the results.

Taguchi's contributions go beyond statistical procedures. He believes that there are unwelcome costs associated with *any* deviation from a quality characteristic's target value. Managers often assume that the goal in achieving good quality is to produce products or services that fall within the tolerances engineers designed for them, and that the cost is the same regardless of whether they are close to the tolerance limits or right on the target value. Taguchi's view is that customers have their own tolerance limits and there is a quality loss function that is zero when the quality characteristic of the product or service is exactly on the target value. The quality loss function exponentially increases as the quality characteristic gets closer to the customer's tolerance limits. This notion of social cost leads Taguchi to the conclusion that managers should constantly be searching for ways to reduce all variability from the target value in the production process.

Users believe that Taguchi's methods aid communication among functional groups. His methods also permit efficient fine tuning of processes, permitting fewer adjustments with more predictable effects from each adjustment.

At this point you are probably thinking that all these people are saying just about the same thing. To a large extent you're right. While each has his own niche, or points of emphasis, they all propose total management commitment to quality. Anything less perpetuates status-quo behavior which, for most companies today, is not good enough.

SOLVED PROBLEMS

1. The Crampton Electric Company manufactures semiconductors for the electronics industry. Although the company produces many types of semiconductors, one of its products requires only four operations. The raw material is a silicone bar, 3 inches in diameter. The bar is sliced on the first operation, and the slices are processed on three more machines to complete the product. However, each of the four machines generates a certain percentage of defective units.

Operation	Machine	Defectives
1	Saw	2%
2	Scrubber	1
3	Edge grinder	5
4	KOH	3

a. Demand for the product is 1000 slices per day. How many slices must the saw cut in order to ensure 1000 units of acceptable output from KOH?

b. Assume that all defects are discovered after each operation. What is the implication for the quantity of silicone bar needed?

c. What is the percentage of extra capacity required at each machine owing to the defect rates of the machines?

a. Let d_i be the proportion of yield loss at operation i, and B be the raw-material input in units. To produce 1000 units of defect-free product at the end of the process, the total number of units required is

$$B(1 - d_1)(1 - d_2)(1 - d_3)(1 - d_4) = 1000$$
$$B(0.98)(0.99)(0.95)(0.97) = 1000$$

or

$$B = \frac{1000}{0.8940} = 1118.5 \quad \text{or} \quad 1119 \text{ units}$$

The saw, being the first operation, must cut 1119 pieces on the average to ensure that 1000 pieces come from KOH.

b. The operations require 11.9 percent more silicon bar than if there were no yield losses.

c. Each machine must process the following number of slices:

Operation	Defective	Units Processed	Defect-free Output*
Saw	2%	1119	1097
Scrubber	1	1097	1086
Edge grinder	5	1086	1031
KOH	3	1031	1000

*Final answers rounded to the nearest whole number.

Based on these data, the saw requires 11.9 percent more capacity, the scrubber 9.7 percent, the edge grinder 8.6 percent, and KOH 3.1 percent. All are based on the defect-free rate of 1000 slices per day.

2. After the last operation in a three-operation production process, an inspector determines whether an entire lot must be reworked. Historically, 20 percent of the lots have to be reworked. If rework is required, the entire lot is moved back to operation 2, and the lot must also go through operation 3 again. The size of each production lot is 50 units, and the daily requirement is 200 units. Estimate the average extra capacity per day required at operation 2, operation 3, and inspection.

Solution As the daily requirement is 200 units, there is no need to determine Q and N individually. Because the defective units must pass through operations 2 and 3 and inspection every time, only the average number of units processed per day for any one of the operations has to be determined; they will all be the same. Let's use operation 2 and $P_j = 0.20$. Then,

$$M_j = \frac{Q_j N_j}{1 - P_j} = \frac{200}{1 - 0.20} = 250 \text{ units}$$

Operation 2 must process 250 units per day as opposed to the defect-free rate of 200 units per day—a 25 percent increase. Thus operation 3 and the inspection station must also handle 250 units per day.

FORMULA REVIEW

1. Number of units of raw material required at the start of a production process:

$$B = \frac{M}{(1 - d_1)(1 - d_2) \cdots (1 - d_n)}$$

2. Average number of units processed at a rework operation:

$$M_j = \frac{Q_j N_j}{1 - P_j}$$

CHAPTER HIGHLIGHTS

● Quality is a competitive weapon. The challenge for operations managers is how to produce products or services both efficiently and to meet the quality demanded by customers.

● Quality can be defined from the producer's perspective as conformance to specifications and from the consumer's perspective as value or fitness for use. Value, or fitness for use, may be judged on the basis of hardware quality, product or service support, and psychological impressions.

● Quality management is important because of the impact on market share, price and profits, and the costs of poor quality. The four major categories of cost associated with quality management are prevention, appraisal, internal failure, and external failure.

● Prevention costs increase as quality reliability and level increase. Appraisal, internal failure, and external failure costs all decrease as quality is improved through preventive measures.

● The costs of internal failure arise from yield losses and rework. In addition to the cost of scrapped material, yield losses and rework increase the costs of labor hours, machine hours, machine failure, and work-in-process inventory. Lead times also increase, which has an impact on future sales.

● External failure costs consist of warranty and litigation costs. These costs can be extremely large but can be significantly reduced with effective quality management.

● Increasing prevention expenditures to increase quality level through better product or service and process design may involve trade-offs among the competitive priorities of price (cost), quality, time, and flexibility. Increasing prevention expenditures to obtain better conformance to specifications may be offset by savings in appraisal, internal failure, and external failure costs. Better quality reliability and a reduction in total costs may be possible.

● Total quality control (TQC) is a concept which states that the responsibility for quality is shared by all employees in the organization. At the heart of the concept is the "quality at the source" approach, which dramatically reduces yield loss and rework costs.

● Quality improvement can be addressed organizationally by using quality assurance groups and fostering close cooperation between operations and marketing.

● Employee-related strategies for improving quality include employee training, adequate monetary incentives, and quality circles. Quality problems can also be prevented by having product or service and process designs that are stable and that foster quality reliability. Linking product and service design to process design can increase quality reliability. One useful analytic technique is the fishbone diagram, which identifies possible causes of a particular quality problem.

● The role of the buyer in identifying supplier capabilities and working with suppliers to achieve higher levels of quality is as important as comparing purchased parts and materials against specifications.

KEY TERMS

appraisal costs **97**
external failure costs **101**
fishbone diagram **113**
internal failure costs **97**

prevention costs **96**
quality **91**
quality assurance **106**
quality circle **109**

rework costs **97**
total quality control (TQC) **103**
warranty **101**
yield losses **97**

STUDY QUESTIONS

1. Your company makes Christmas tree lights. Define *quality* from both the producer's and the consumer's perspective by giving examples of conformance to specifications and factors that influence the consumer's perceptions of product quality.

2. You own a small company that provides an income-tax preparation service. Define *quality* from both the producer's and the consumer's perspective by giving examples of conformance to specifications and factors that influence the consumer's perceptions of service quality.

3. Suppose that you are the proprietor of an independently owned motel located at the intersection of two interstate highways. Give an example of each of the three aspects of quality (Table 3.1) for your motel service.

4. What are the implications of quality management for the marketing function of an organization?

5. Explain why poor quality can be expensive for companies manufacturing a product or producing a service.

6. What roles does a quality assurance group play in the improvement of quality?

7. As a manager, what can you do for your employees to improve the quality of output?

8. What are the implications of *product* and *service* design for quality management? Of *process* design?

9. Suppose that you are the purchasing manager of a company that buys raw materials from hundreds of suppliers, some of which supply the same raw materials. You are convinced that the quality of these materials, as measured by conformance to specifications, can be improved. Disregarding sampling plans, what can you do to improve the quality of the raw materials your company needs? Do the engineering group and top management also have some responsibilities? Explain.

10. Why are internal failure costs so expensive?

11. Explain why the costs of detecting quality problems increase dramatically with the distance from the source of the problem.

12. What is the essence of the total quality control concept? Do you think that it can be easily applied in the United States?

PROBLEMS

Review Problems

1. Wyandotte Manufacturing is a producer of women's apparel. One of its products requires five operations. The raw material is a bolt of cloth 60 inches wide. The first operation cuts the bolt of material in 36-inch lengths. Each piece of material is then processed by four more machines in order to produce the final garment. The following data are available concerning this process.

Operation	Machine	Defective
1	Bolt cutter	3%
2	Pattern cutter	2
3	Stitcher 1	1
4	Stitcher 2	1
5	Presser	2

a. Demand is 700 garments per day. How many cuts must the bolt cutter make in order to produce 700 finished units?

b. If all defects are found after each individual operation, what can be said about the amount of material needed?

c. How much extra capacity (in garments/day) is required at each machine because of the defect rates? Assume that quality at the source is being practiced.

d. Compute the percentage of extra capacity required at each machine and compare it to the percentage of defects generated by the machine. Why is the former greater than the latter at the bolt cutter? The pattern cutter? The stitchers?

e. Besides extra capacity costs, what other costs are higher because of poor quality in this case?

2. The following data apply to a four-operation production process.

Operation	Machine	Defective
1	A	3%
2	C	6
3	G	2
4	F	1

For each unit of raw material, R100, introduced into this process, one unit of final product, X123, is produced. There are currently 455 units of R100 available. A customer wishes to place an order for 400 units of X123. Should the order be accepted? Assume that the customer will not accept a partial shipment.

3. The service department of a car dealership has three stages of service: order taking, shop repair, and billing. Customers arrive at the service department and describe their problems to an associate at the order-taking desk. The car proceeds to the shop for repair. Finally, the customer goes to the billing window to pay for the service and get the keys to the car. If the customer finds that the problem has not been solved, the car is returned to the order-taking desk and subsequently proceeds through the shop and billing.

The service manager expects 200 customers per day. There is a 10 percent chance that a customer will return a car because it had not been repaired properly.

a. If a mechanic can service 10 cars per day, how many mechanics are needed in the shop? Assume the "lot size" is 1 for this problem.

b. If a mechanic's salary is $20,000 per year,

how much is the rework problem costing in terms of mechanics' salaries?

4. A product is made in a four-operation process, with a final inspection at the end of the fourth operation. The inspector determines whether the entire batch must be reworked. If it does, the batch must be reprocessed through operations 3 and 4. Typically, 20 percent of the batches must be reworked. The size of each batch is 300 units, and 10 batches are required each day. Additional information about this process is as follows:

Operation	Capacity (units/day)
1	3100
2	3100
3	3400
4	3375
Inspection	3700

a. Is it possible to meet the requirement of 10 batches per day? If not, how many batches per day can be produced?

b. What effect does the percentage of rework have on cost?

5. The manager of the claims department of an insurance company must decide on a training proposal for employees in his department. Customers file claims which must be evaluated for completeness and legitimacy. Sometimes employees make errors such as authorizing checks in the wrong amount, sending checks to the wrong address, or denying a legitimate claim. The department receives 100 new claims per day and each clerk can process 5 claims. Errors, however, cause customers to call back, and their files must be accessed and reprocessed. Presently 8 percent of the claims need reprocessing, so the manager has 22 employees on duty.

The training program will reduce the error rate to only 2 percent but will cost $20,000. Each employee in the department earns $18,000 per year. If the manager only considers salary expenses, should the proposal be accepted?

Advanced Problems

6. Westwood Company produces two different products using four different operations. Product A is processed at operations 1, 2, and 4, and then inspected for quality (1–2–4–I). The routing of product B is 1–2–3–4–I. The percentage of defective products at each operation (excluding inspection) is 2 percent. If the inspector determines that rework is necessary, each product is returned to operation 2. Historically, the rework rate has been 15 percent for product A and 20 percent for product B. If after rework the inspector rejects the product, it is scrapped without further rework. The following information is available about the processing times (min/unit) of each product at each operation.

	Product	
Operation	A	B
1	0.20	0.20
2	0.10	0.08
3	—	0.10
4	0.15	0.20

a. If 1000 units of each product are required each day, how many units of raw material are needed for each product?

b. What is the expected daily load for operation 4 from these two products if 1000 units of each are required?

7. (A computer spreadsheet package is helpful for this problem.) A product goes through five operations and a final inspection during man-ufacture. If the product is rejected at final inspection after initial processing, it is returned to operation 3 for reprocessing. If it is rejected at final inspection after rework, it is scrapped. Historically, 25 percent of the product has been returned for rework. The following is the rate of defectives produced at each operation.

Operation	Defective
1	8%
2	5
3	6
4	4
5	7

a. If one unit of raw material produces one unit of final product, how many units of defect-free product can be produced by 5000 units of raw material?

b. Suppose that management has the opportunity to reduce the defective rate of operation 3. Illustrate graphically the effect of decreasing d_3 on final output levels.

c. Suppose that management has the opportunity to reduce the rework rate of the entire production process by utilizing more effective final inspection techniques. Graphically illustrate the effect on final output levels of reducing the rework rate.

d. What costs must be considered before management implements either reduction program?

CASE   CRANSTON NISSAN

Steve Jackson, General Manager of Cranston Nissan, slowly sifted through his usual Monday morning stack of mail. The following letter was one he would not soon forget.

Dear Mr. Jackson:

I am writing this letter so that you will be aware of a nightmare I have experienced recently regarding the repair of my 300ZX in your body shop and subse-quently in your service department. I feel you do not know about this case because too many actors played minor roles in two departments. Since this is so bizarre, I will detail the events in chronological order.

August 28

I dropped the car off for repair of rust damage in the following areas:

• Roof—along the top of the windshield area

- Left rocker panel—under driver's door
- Left quarter panel—near end of bumper
- Rear body panel—under license plate

I was told it would take three or four days.

September 1

I called to inquire about the status of the car since this was the fifth day the car was in the shop. I was told that I could pick up the car anytime after 2 P.M. My wife and I arrived at 5 P.M. (we have to take two cars each time we come because we come from Turnerville). The car was still not ready. In the meantime, I paid the bill of $443.17 and waited. At 6 P.M. the car was driven up dripping wet (presumably from a wash to make it look good). I got into the car and noticed the courtesy light in the driver's door would not turn off when the door was closed. I asked for help and Jim Boyd, body shop manager, could not figure out what was wrong. His solution was to remove the bulb and have me return after the Labor Day holiday to have the mechanic look at it. I agreed and began to drive off. However, the voice warning, "Left door is open," repeatedly sounded. Without leaving the premises I returned to Mr. Boyd, advising him to retain the car until it was fixed—there was no way I could drive the car with that repeated recording. Mr. Boyd then suggested I call back the next day (Saturday) to see if the mechanic could find the problem. I must emphasize, I brought the car to the body shop on August 28 in perfect mechanical working condition—the repair work was for body rust. This point will become important as the story unfolds.

September 2

I called Jim Boyd at 10:30 A.M. and was told that the car had not been looked at yet. He promised to call back before the shop closed for the holiday, but he never did. I later learned that he did not call because "there was nothing to report." The car sat in the shop Saturday, Sunday, and Monday.

September 5

I called Jim Boyd to check on the status of the car. It was 4 P.M. and Mr. Boyd told me nothing had been done, but that it should be ready by the next day. At this point it was becoming obvious that my car did not have priority in the service department.

September 6

I called Jim Boyd again (about 4 P.M.) and was told that work had halted on the car because the service department needed authorization and they didn't know how much it would run. At the hint that I would have to pay for this mess I became very upset and demanded that the car be brought immediately to the mechanical condition it was in when it was dropped off August 28. At this point Ted Simon, service department manager, was summoned, and he assured me that if the problem was caused by some action of the body shop, I would not be financially responsible. I had not driven the car since I dropped it off, and I could not fathom the evidence anyone could produce to prove otherwise.

September 7

Again late in the day, I called Mr. Simon, who said that Larry (in the service department) knew about the problem and switched me over to him. Larry said that they narrowed it down to a wire that passed several spots where body work was performed. He said the work was very time consuming and that the car should be ready sometime tomorrow.

September 8

I called Mr. Simon to check on the status of the car once more. He told me that the wiring problem was fixed, but now the speedometer didn't work. The short in the wires was caused by the body work. Larry got on the phone and said I could pick up the car, but they would send the car out to a subcontractor on Monday to repair the speedometer. He said that when the mechanic test-drove the car he noticed the speedometer pinned itself at the top end, and Larry thought that someone must have done something while searching for the other problem. I asked him if there would be charges for this and he said there would not. My wife and I arrived to pick up the car at 5 P.M. I clarified the next steps with Larry and was again assured that the speedometer would be repaired at no charge to me.

The car was brought to me, and as I walked up to it I noticed that the rubber molding beneath the driver's door was hanging down. I asked for some help and Mr. Simon came out to look at it. He said it must have been left that way after the search process for the bad wire. He took the car back into the shop to screw it on. When it finally came out again, he said that he would replace the molding because it was actually damaged.

When I arrived home I discovered that the anti-theft light on the dash would not stop blinking when the doors were closed. Attempting to activate the security system did not help. The only way I could get the light to stop flashing was to remove the fuse. In other words, now my security system was damaged. Needless to say, I was very upset.

September 11

On Sunday evening I dropped off the car and left a note with my keys in the "early bird" slot. The note listed the two items that needed to be done from the agreement of last Friday—the molding and the speedometer. In addition, I mentioned the security system problem and suggested that "Somebody must have forgotten to hook something back up while looking for the wire problem." On Monday I received a call from someone in the service department (I think his name was John) who said that the problem in the security system was in two places—the hatchback lock and "some wires in the driver's door." The lock would cost me $76 and the cost for the rest was unknown. The verbal estimate was for a total of $110. I asked him why he did not consider this problem a derivative of the other problems. He said that both the body shop and the mechanic who worked on the wire problem said they could see no way that they could have caused this to happen.

I told the fellow on the phone to forget fixing the security system because I was not going to pay for it. At this point I was getting tired of this whole problem, and too many characters were involved. I just wanted the car back home, thinking I could address the problem later with someone such as yourself. I told him to have the speedometer fixed and again asked about charges for it. I was assured there would be none.

September 13

The service department called to say I could pick up the car anytime before 8 P.M. He also said that the molding had to be ordered because it was not in stock. The need for the part was known on September 8, and NOW the part must be ordered. This will cause me another trip to the shop.

When I went to the service department to pick up the car I was presented a bill for $126. I asked what the bill was for and I was shown an itemized listing which included speedometer repair and searching for the security problem. I said my understanding was that there would be no charges. Somebody at the service desk was apprised of the problem and released the car to me with the understanding that the service manager would review the situation the next day.

My car was brought around to me by the same person who brought it to me September 8. As I got into the driver's seat, I noticed there was no rear view mirror—it was lying in the passenger's seat, broken off from its mounting. I was too shocked to even get mad. I got out of the car and asked how something like this could happen without anyone noticing. Jim Boyd said someone probably did not want to own up to it. He requisitioned a part and repaired the mirror mounting.

Mr. Jackson, I realize this is a long letter but I have been so frustrated and upset over the past three weeks that I had to be sure that you understood the basis for that frustration. I am hoping you can look into this matter and let me know what you think.

Sincerely,

Sam Monahan

Sam Monahan
555 South Main
Turnerville

QUESTIONS

1. Categorize the quality problems in this case.
2. What are the probable causes of so many mishaps?
3. Prepare a fishbone chart for "Failure to remedy repair problem to customer satisfaction."
4. What are the specific actions Jackson should take immediately? What should some of his longer-term goals be?

SELECTED REFERENCES

Aubrey, C.A., and L.A. Eldridge. "Banking on High Quality." *Quality Progress*, vol. 14, no. 12 (December 1981), pp. 14–19.

Barker, Thomas R. "Quality Engineering by Design: Taguchi's Philosophy." *Quality Progress*, vol. 19, no. 12 (December 1986), pp. 32–42.

Crosby, Phillip B. *Quality Is Free*. New York: McGraw–Hill, 1979.

Deming, W. Edwards. "Improvement of Quality and Productivity Through Action by Management." *National Productivity Review*, vol. 1, no. 1 (Winter 1981–1982), pp. 12–22.

Deming, W. Edwards. *Out of the Crisis*. Cambridge, Mass.: Massachusetts Institute of Technology Center for Advanced Engineering Study, 1986.

Feigenbaum, A.V. *Total Quality Control: Engineering and Management*, 3rd ed. New York: McGraw–Hill, 1983.

Garvin, David A. "How the Baldrige Award Really Works." *Harvard Business Review* (November–December 1991), pp. 80–93.

Garvin, David A. "Quality on the Line." *Harvard Business Review* (September–October 1983), pp. 65–75.

Heskett, James L., W. Earl Sasser, Jr., and Christopher W.L. Hart. *Service Breakthroughs: Changing the Rules of the Game*. New York: The Free Press, 1990.

Hostage, G.M. "Quality Control in a Service Business." *Harvard Business Review* (July–August 1975), pp. 89–106.

Ishikawa, Kaoru. *Guide to Quality Control*. Tokyo: Asian Productivity Organization, 1972.

Juran, J.M., and Frank Gryna, Jr. *Quality Planning and Analysis*, 2nd ed. New York: McGraw–Hill, 1980.

Reddy, Jack, and Abe Berger. "Three Essentials of Product Quality." *Harvard Business Review* (July–August 1983), pp. 153–159.

Schonberger, Richard J. *Japanese Manufacturing Techniques*. New York: The Free Press, 1982.

Sullivan, Lawrence P. "The Power of Taguchi Methods." *Quality Progress*, vol. 20, no. 6 (June 1987), pp. 76–79.

Takeuchi, Hirotaka, and John A. Quelch. "Quality Is More Than Making a Good Product." *Harvard Business Review* (November–December 1981), pp. 14–19.

Chapter 4

STATISTICAL QUALITY CONTROL

What trade-offs are involved if we use attribute measurements instead of variable measurements of quality?

What are the implications of our narrowing the control limits in a process control chart?

How can we devise a system to monitor quality consistency and to help us identify the sources of problems?

Where should we put our inspection stations?

Of the various acceptance sampling methods available, which one can we best use in a given situation?

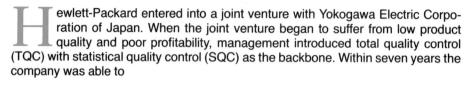

Hewlett-Packard entered into a joint venture with Yokogawa Electric Corporation of Japan. When the joint venture began to suffer from low product quality and poor profitability, management introduced total quality control (TQC) with statistical quality control (SQC) as the backbone. Within seven years the company was able to

- Reduce defects 79 percent.
- Reduce costs 42 percent.
- Increase revenues per employee 120 percent.
- Increase market share 193 percent.
- Increase profits 244 percent.

In Chapter 3 we explored the philosophy of total quality control as a method for improving quality. Quality improvement, however, relies on the continual monitoring of the inputs and outputs of the processes producing the products or services. Statistical quality control (SQC) methods are useful tools for appraising and monitoring quality performance and are key ingredients to successful application of TQC.

What is SQC and how can it be used? **Statistical quality control (SQC)** is the application of statistical techniques to ensure satisfactory quality. There are three major subgroups of techniques. **Statistical process control (SPC)** is the application of statistical techniques to the control of processes. In SPC, tools called control charts are used primarily to prevent or detect production of defective products (finished goods, assemblies, components) or services. **Acceptance sampling** is the application of statistical techniques to determine whether a quantity of material should be accepted or rejected, based on the inspection or test of a sample. Finally, **traditional statistical techniques** such as frequency distributions, measures of central tendency and dispersion, regression, correlation, and tests of significance can also be used to judge the quality of products or services. Table 4.1 shows examples of problems that can be detected through the use of SQC.

SQC can be used to assist managers in decision making. Statistical methods operate on an *exception* basis, alerting management when something is wrong and needs correction. For example, the manager of the accounts payable department of an insurance company would like to know when the proportion of claimants receiving late payment (30 or more days after the request) exceeds 0.05. Suppose that one month the proportion is 0.08. This would cause the manager to seek the source of the poor performance. Perhaps the number of claims significantly increased, causing an overload on the employees in the department. The decision might be to hire more personnel. Alternatively, the manager might find out that the procedures being used are ineffective or that more training is needed. Whatever the conclusion, SQC is a useful set of techniques to apply to decision making for quality improvement.

TABLE 4.1 / *Problems That Can Be Detected with the Use of SQC*

Problems		Problem Sources
In Manufacturing Systems	In Service Systems	
Diameters on a crankshaft consistently too low	Salt content of IV solutions too low at a medical lab	Machine needs resetting or replacement
Sudden increase in the proportion of defective gear boxes	Increase in the average number of complaints per day at a hotel	Employees need training or work methods have changed
Too many plastic bottles with rough edges in a purchased lot	Too many bloated cans of dog food purchased by a supermarket	Supplier's process out of control

In this chapter we will explore the techniques of statistical process control and acceptance sampling and indicate the role they play in decision making. Before we get into the specifics, however, we need to get a better understanding of the inspection process.

THE INSPECTION PROCESS

Many companies use quality inspection improperly, merely to weed out the defectives before they reach the customer. This approach is doomed to failure because of the internal and external failure costs we discussed in Chapter 3. World-class companies use inspection in a different way, to monitor and detect abnormalities in quality so they can be corrected early. They promote "quality at the source." SQC is used to gather the needed information. In this section we will first discuss output variation, the primary culprit behind the need for inspection. Then we will address the issues of measurement, sampling, and inspection station location.

Variation

No two products or services are exactly alike because the processes that produce them contain many sources of variation. The differences may be small, but they are there nonetheless. A crankshaft diameter is susceptible to variation from machine wear, tool wear, material hardness, operator skill, and temperature. Likewise, the time it takes to process a credit card application varies because of the load on the credit department, the financial background of the applicant, and the skills and attitudes of the employees. Inspection is concerned with the *causes* of the variation.

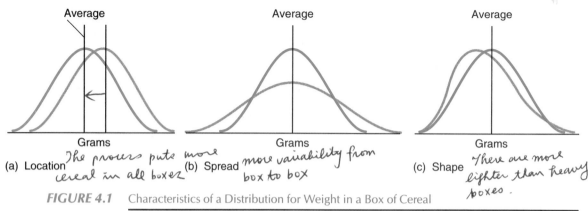

(a) Location *The process puts more cereal in all boxes*   (b) Spread *more variability from box to box*   (c) Shape *There are more lighter than heavy boxes.*

FIGURE 4.1   Characteristics of a Distribution for Weight in a Box of Cereal

Adapted from Ross Johnson and William O. Winchell, *Production and Quality*, Milwaukee: American Society for Quality Control, 1989. Reprinted with permission of ASQC.

Causes of Variation. There are two basic categories of variation in output. **Common causes of variation** refer to the purely random, chance sources of variation within a process. Whereas individually measured values of a quality characteristic, such as weight, are all different, when viewed as a group they tend to form a pattern that can be described as a *distribution*. For example, a machine that fills cereal boxes will not put exactly the same weight in each box. The actual individual weights of a group of cereal boxes form a distribution. Such a distribution can be characterized by location (typical value or weight of a box), spread (range of values or weights), and shape (symmetric or skewed). Figure 4.1 shows how these distributions can differ. The purple lines depict a change in the distribution for weight in a box of cereal. In Fig. 4.1(a), the purple line shows the results of a process that has put more cereal in all the boxes, thereby increasing the average weight. In Fig. 4.1(b), weight in the boxes has more variability from box to box, affecting the spread of the distribution. Finally, in Fig. 4.1(c), the purple line represents a process that has produced a distribution of box weight that is no longer symmetric to the average value. That is, there are now more lighter than heavier boxes, whereas there were previously equal amounts of light and heavy boxes around the average.

Assignable causes of variation, the second category of variation, refer to any factors causing variation, such as an employee needing training or a machine needing repair, that cannot be explained as purely random causes. These causes must be identified and eliminated or they will continue to affect the process output. SPC procedures can be used to detect assignable causes. **Process control** is achieved when all assignable causes of variation are eliminated. Figure 4.2 shows the differences between a process that is in control and one that is not. In Fig. 4.2(a), the process is generating different distributions of cereal box weight over time. Assignable causes must be present. In Fig. 4.2(b), the distributions of weight are stable over time. This allows the managers to assess the process capability.

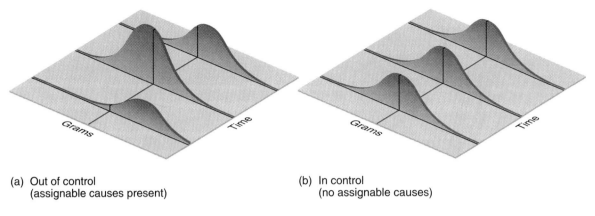

(a) Out of control
(assignable causes present)

(b) In control
(no assignable causes)

FIGURE 4.2   The Effects of Assignable Causes on Process Control

Adapted from Ross Johnson and William O. Winchell, *Production and Quality*, Milwaukee: American Society for Quality Control, 1989. Reprinted with permission of ASQC.

Process Control and Process Capability. A process must first be brought into statistical control before its capability can be assessed, because only then do we have predictable performance. **Process capability** refers to the ability of the process to meet a product's or service's design specifications. Design specifications are often expressed as a **nominal value** (or target) and a **tolerance** (an allowance above or below the nominal value). For example, the weight of cereal in a box might have a nominal value of 425 grams and a tolerance of ±5 grams. Thus we have an *upper specification limit* of 430 grams and a *lower specification limit* of 420 grams. The machine filling the box must be capable of producing within the design specifications, otherwise it will produce a certain proportion of defective boxes.

Figure 4.3 shows how a process can be in statistical control but not have the capability to produce all its output within the design specifications. In Fig. 4.3(a), the machine filling the boxes cannot stay within the specifications of 425 ± 5 grams, yet the distribution of weight is stable. The process is in statistical control, but the machine is not capable of doing the job. In Fig. 4.3(b), the machine is capable of staying within the specifications.

It is clear that reducing variability in output reduces defective products or services. Managerial Practice 4.1 highlights Motorola's plan to reduce variability in the manufacture of its products.

Quality Measurement

To detect abnormal variations in output, inspectors must be able to measure the quality characteristics. There are two ways quality can be evaluated. One way is to measure **variables,** that is, characteristics of a product or service such as weight, length, volume, or time that can be measured on a continuous scale.

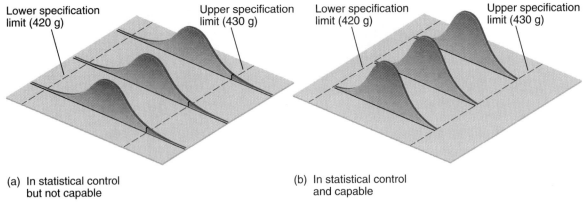

(a) In statistical control
     but not capable

(b) In statistical control
     and capable

FIGURE 4.3   Process Capability

Adapted from Ross Johnson and William O. Winchell, *Production and Quality*, Milwaukee: American Society for Quality Control, 1989. Reprinted with permission of ASQC.

For example, inspectors at Harley–Davidson can measure the diameter of a piston and plot the results to determine whether the product adheres to the specifications (within the allowable tolerance) and identify differences in diameter over time. Similarly, United Parcel Service managers monitor the length of time drivers spend delivering packages. The advantage of measuring a quality characteristic on a continuous scale is that if a product or service misses its quality specifications, you know by how much. The disadvantage is that you must take measurements that typically involve special equipment, employee skills, procedures, and more time and effort.

Another way to evaluate quality is to measure a product's or service's **attributes,** the characteristics that can be quickly checked for acceptable quality. The method allows inspectors to make a simple yes–no decision for a product or service. Attributes are often measured when quality specifications are complex and measuring by variables is difficult or costly. Some examples of attributes that can be measured are the number of insurance forms containing errors causing underpayments or overpayments, the proportion of radios inoperative at the final test, the proportion of airline flights arriving within 15 minutes of scheduled times, and the number of stove-top subassemblies with spotted paint. The advantage of attributes measures is that relatively less effort and fewer resources are needed to make the measurements. These measures can simply be counted. The disadvantage is that they tell you that quality performance has changed, but may not be of much use in telling you by how much. For example, we may know that the proportion of airline flights arriving within 15 minutes of their scheduled times has decreased, but we do not know by how much beyond the 15-minute tolerance the flights are arriving. Measuring the actual deviation from the scheduled arrival, a variables measure, would be needed.

Motorola's Six-Sigma Quality Program

In 1986, after discussing quality issues with customers, Motorola's management recognized the need to improve its products and customer services. These meetings prompted a change to the Motorola Quality Goal and resulted in the following statement: "Improve product and service quality ten times by 1989, and at least 100-fold by 1991. Achieve six-sigma capability by 1992."

Sigma refers to one standard deviation, a statistical measure of variability. For Motorola, *six-sigma capability* means that all processes should produce parts, assemblies, and products with quality dimensions that fall within the design specifications 99.9999998 percent of the time. This percentage is the portion of the normal curve that is covered by a spread of 12 standard deviations, 6 above the nominal value and 6 below. Putting the six-sigma goal in perspective, even if the average value for a quality characteristic of a part unexpectedly shifted by 1.5 standard deviations from the nominal value, the probability of producing the part within the design specifications is 0.9999966. This implies that no more than 3.4 defects would be produced in 1 million operations.

The importance of this stringent goal becomes obvious when one looks at the manufacture of a complete product. The MicroTac cellular phone has 400 parts assembled by robots and workers in only two hours. Suppose the process average shifts by 1.5 standard deviations and the processes producing the parts are only achieving four-sigma capability. That is, 99.379 percent of the time each process produces a part within its specifications even after the shift in the process average. The probability that 400 parts will be nondefective is 0.99379 times 0.99379, 400 times, or 0.08276. That is, there is only an 8.276 percent chance that a complete MicroTac will not require repair after final assembly. With six-sigma capability, the chances are so remote that any part will be defective that the probability of assembling a nondefective MicroTac increases to 0.99864, or $(0.9999966)^{400}$. This computation is analogous to the reliability analysis we discussed in Chapter 2.

By 1989 Motorola had reduced defective production to less than 200 parts per million. This performance helped Motorola win the coveted Malcolm Baldrige National Quality Award in 1988. The company continues to make significant progress toward its goal of six-sigma capability. The experience of a team involved with the electrical component insertion line for a portable radio is a case in point. As of December 1990 they achieved

- 370 percent reduction in defects per million parts.
- 500 percent increase in quality, to 5.1-sigma capability.
- 40 percent reduction in manufacturing cycle time.
- 60 percent increase in production with no additional personnel.

Sources: Sam Tomas, "Six Sigma: Motorola's Quest for Zero Defects," *APICS—The Performance Advantage*, July 1991, pp. 36–41; "The Rival Japan Respects," *Business Week*, November 13, 1989, pp. 108–118.

A Motorola employee conducts a computer analysis on a cellular phone prior to its distribution.

Sampling

It would seem that the ultimate approach to inspection is to inspect each product or service for quality. This is called *complete inspection* and is used when the inspection costs are far outweighed by the costs of passing a defect to the next work station or customer. For example, suppliers of components for the space shuttles check each component many times before shipping them to a contractor. In such a situation, the cost of failure—injury and death—greatly exceeds the cost of inspection. Complete inspection almost guarantees that an employee does not pass defective units to the next operation or the customer, a policy consistent with the principle of "quality at the source" discussed in Chapter 3. Nonetheless, when human inspectors are involved, even complete inspection may not uncover all defects. Inspector fatigue or imperfect testing methods may allow some defects to pass unnoticed. Manufacturing firms can overcome these failings by using automated inspection equipment, such as a computer-controlled pneumatic reject device that deflects products not meeting specifications off the production line. Detailed data on product parameters can be recorded and summarized in control reports. Many companies have found that automated inspection equipment can pay for itself in a reasonably short time.

A well-conceived sampling plan can often approach the same degree of protection as complete inspection. Sampling is appropriate when inspection costs are a major concern, as they are in many firms. These costs may be high because of the special knowledge, skills, procedures, and expensive equipment required to perform the inspections. Moreover, sampling is necessary *regardless of inspection costs* when tests are destructive. For example, at its Milford, Michigan, Proving Ground, GM's Safety Research and Development Laboratory crash-tests as many as 400 full-scale vehicles each year to learn more about what happens to vehicles and occupants in crashes. An average of 1200 crash tests are also performed each year on components using the laboratory's two impact sleds. In this chapter we focus on the SQC methods that involve taking samples.

Inspection Station Location

Before management can decide where to locate inspection stations, it must identify the aspects of quality important to the consumer and the key steps in the process that affect those characteristics. A fishbone diagram (see Chapter 3) is a good way of identifying these steps. Inspection stations occur in three different stages of the total process: raw-material inputs, work-in-process, and finished goods or services.

The inspection of purchased materials is important to ensure the proper quality of the inputs to the production process. At this stage of the production process, various acceptance-sampling plans could be used. We will address these plans later in this chapter.

Inspection is usually more complicated at the work-in-process stage. Conceivably, the operations manager could put an inspection station after each step in the process. However, this approach could be very costly if testing requires highly skilled inspectors and/or expensive technology. A TQC program, which has the goal of not passing defective materials from one step in the process to the next, requires discipline in the work force but greatly reduces the need for inspection stations. In deciding on the number and location of inspection stations, the operations manager must remember that quality cannot be inspected into the product; inspection can only detect that the process is not operating according to specifications and identify the need for corrective action. Thus even with a TQC program, some inspection stations would be needed. Using a fishbone diagram, an analyst can identify the steps in the process at which important quality characteristics should be checked. Quality should also be checked just prior to costly operations. The cost of inspecting materials at any location should be balanced against the cost of passing defective materials to the next step.

Final inspections are made after the product or service has been finished. In the case of manufacturing systems, the inspections are made just prior to stocking finished goods or shipping them to the customer. Product failures discovered at this point result in (1) scrapping the defective items or batch, (2) routing the defective items or batch to a previous step in the process for rework, or (3) routing the defective items or batch to a special area for diagnosis and correction of the defects. Final inspections in service systems involve similar considerations; however, in many cases, the customer plays a major role in the inspection process. Table 4.2 contains some examples of final inspection procedures used in manufacturing and service processes.

TABLE 4.2 / Examples of Final Inspection Procedures

Semiconductor manufacturing	Semiconductors are tested for their conformance to specifications. Those that do not meet the specifications but are above some minimal performance level can be sold as a different, lower grade product. Those that fall below the minimal performance level are scrapped.
Plastic bottle manufacturing	Plastic bottles that do not conform to specifications on wall thickness or neck diameter are shredded and reused as raw material in the production of new bottles.
Glue manufacturing	Batches of glue are pumped from the reactor to holding vessels where they are checked for viscosity, percentage solids, pH level, and amount of grit. A chemist checks the batch and may order adding water, removing water, or filtering the batch in the holding vessel.
Automotive repair	The mechanic test-drives the car before returning it to the customer. If problems remain, previous repair procedures may have to be repeated. The customer may also request some rework.
TV repair	The TV repairperson tests the TV before returning it to the customer. Premature failure of replaced components results in the customer returning the set for more repair.
Hair styling	The hair stylist works with the customer until the customer is satisfied.
Hotels	Most hotels have customer-survey cards in each room, allowing the customer to grade the quality of service provided by the hotel.

STATISTICAL PROCESS CONTROL METHODS

As we've said, statistical process control (SPC) is used to monitor quality characteristics during the production process. SPC methods are useful for both measuring the current quality of products or services and detecting whether the process itself has changed in a way that will affect quality. The basic procedure for determining whether a process is in control is as follows: A random sample is taken of the product or service, and the quality characteristic is measured. If the sample measurement is found to be outside the *upper control limit (UCL)* or the *lower control limit (LCL)*, the process is checked to determine the assignable cause of variation (such as a faulty engine lathe setting, an inexperienced credit manager, or low-quality materials).*

Figure 4.4 contains four examples of control charts used to track series of samples. What action would you recommend in each case? Chart (a) shows a process that is in control. In chart (b) the process has suddenly increased in variation after eight points near the nominal value. You should be concerned with such sudden changes even though the control limits have not been exceeded. Chart (c) shows a trend pattern. Even though the control limits have not been exceeded, you should take action because it won't be long before the process will be generating defects. In a manufacturing company the cause may be gradual tool wear, and you should either replace the tool or reset the ma-

---

*Process industries such as paper, chemical, and oil refining use process control equipment that continuously monitors the production process. We discuss sampling methods only in this chapter.

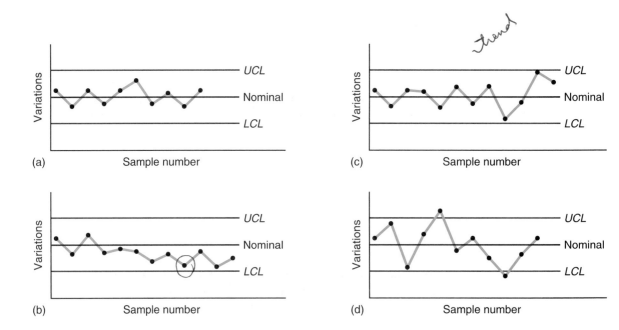

FIGURE 4.4   Control Chart Examples

*H*arley-Davidson makes extensive use of statistical process control methods. Here an employee measures the dimensions of a part and posts the data on a control chart.

chine to some value between the nominal value and the upper control limit to extend tool life. In a service system such as an airline company concerned with on-time performance, the cause may be a slow buildup of air traffic at the airport at the scheduled arrival times of its flights. Schedule changes may be in order. Finally, chart (d) indicates that the process went out of control twice. The process should have been stopped or checked when the upper control limit was exceeded. The question addressed by SPC is whether observed variations are abnormal or normal. Setting a UCL and an LCL allows detection of abnormal variation. This in turn can lead to finding the assignable causes (people, procedures, machines, materials) and correction of the problem.

C → observed → UCL → abnormal variation → finding assignable causes variation LCL → correction of problems

Control Charts for Attributes

***p*-Charts.** A commonly used control chart for attributes is the ***p*-chart** for the population proportion defective. The method involves selecting a random sample and inspecting each item in it. The sample proportion defective is equal to the number of defective units divided by the sample size. The analyst plots the sample proportion defective on a chart and compares it to the upper and lower control limits to determine whether the process is out of control. Table 4.3 shows some attributes used in the banking industry for which *p*-charts have been used.

Because sampling with attributes involves a yes–no decision, the underlying statistical distribution is the binomial distribution. However, for large sample

TABLE 4.3 / *Attributes in the Banking Industry*

Attribute	Population
Wrong account number recorded	Total number of deposits
Nonendorsed deposits	Total number of deposits
Missing items	Total number of statements
Stop-payment transaction incorrect	Total stop-payment transactions
Misfiled items	Total checks and debits
Wrong statement sent	Total number of statements
Incorrect adjustments	Total number of statements

Source: C. A. Aubrey and L. A. Eldridge, "Banking on High Quality," *Quality Progress*, vol. 14, no. 12, December 1981, pp. 14–19.

sizes, the normal distribution provides a good approximation to it. The standard deviation of the distribution of proportion defectives is

$$\sigma_p = \sqrt{\frac{\bar{p}(1 - \bar{p})}{n}}$$

where n is the sample size and $\bar{p}$ is the historical average population proportion defective. We can use this measure of the variation to arrive at the following upper and lower control limits for a p-chart.

$$UCL = \bar{p} + z \sqrt{\frac{\bar{p}(1 - \bar{p})}{n}} \quad \text{and} \quad LCL = \bar{p} - z \sqrt{\frac{\bar{p}(1 - \bar{p})}{n}}$$

where $\bar{p}$ is the average proportion defective, or central line of the chart, and z is the number of standard deviations from that average. Typically, the upper and lower control limits are set at ± 3 standard deviations (or three-sigma limits), allowing 99.74 percent of the variation to fall within the control limits. (See the normal probability table in Appendix 3.) Thus the probability is very small (approximately 1 chance in 400) that a sample proportion defective that falls outside these limits will have come from a population with a mean proportion defective equal to $\bar{p}$. When a sample proportion defective does fall outside the control limits, the analyst concludes that there has been a change in the process to a different process average and the assignable cause is corrected. If that sample was used to compute the $\bar{p}$ for the control chart, the sample data are discarded and new control limits are calculated.

$z = 3$

Application 4.1 | *Using a p-Chart to Monitor a Process*

The operations manager of the booking services department of Hometown Bank is concerned about the number of wrong customer account numbers recorded by Hometown personnel. Each week a random sample of 2500 deposits is taken, and the number of incorrect account numbers is recorded. The results for the past 12 weeks are shown in the following table. Is the process out of control? Use three-sigma control limits.

Observed Number of Wrong Account Numbers Recorded in 12 Samples of 2500 Each

Sample Number	Wrong Account Numbers	Proportion of Sample
1	15	0.0060
2	12	0.0048
3	19	0.0076
4	2	0.0008
5	19	0.0076
6	4	0.0016
7	24	0.0096
8	7	0.0028
9	10	0.0040
10	17	0.0068
11	15	0.0060
12	3	0.0012
Total	147	

Solution   In our example, $\bar{p} = 147/[12(2500)] = 0.0049$

$$UCL = 0.0049 + 3\sqrt{\frac{0.0049(0.9951)}{2500}} = 0.00909$$

and

$$LCL = 0.0049 - 3\sqrt{\frac{0.0049(0.9951)}{2500}} = 0.00071$$

The control chart and the results obtained for the 12 samples are shown in Fig. 4.5. The manager can see that sample 7 exceeded the upper control limit. Thus she can say that the process is out of control and that the reasons for the poor performance that week should be determined. She might find that the account numbers were incorrectly entered into the computer by a trainee or that an encoding machine was defective. She would then correct the problem and recalculate the control limits after discarding sample 7. The new $\bar{p}$ is 0.00447, the UCL is 0.00847, and the LCL is 0.00047. Now all data points fall within the control limits, so the manager can assume the process is in statistical control. Thus the p-chart provides a tool not only to measure product quality, but also to indicate when the process needs adjustment.

c-Charts. Sometimes quality characteristics cannot be measured as a proportion. For example, on a decorative adhesive nameplate for a vacuum cleaner, there could be countless scratches or blemishes on the multicolored surface that would serve to make the nameplate defective. That is, one defective item could have many defects on it. It would be impossible to compute the proportion of defects found on a nameplate because we do not know how many de-

FIGURE 4.5

Control Chart for
Wrong Account
Numbers

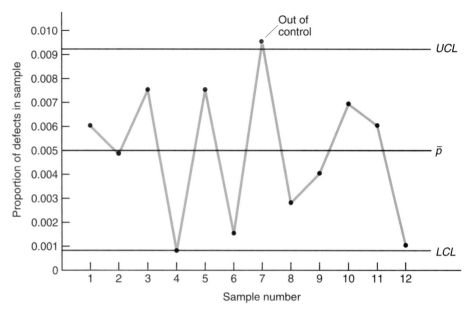

fects are possible. We can count the number of blemishes and scratches, but we cannot count the number of blemishes or scratches that did not occur. Consequently, management would be interested in a control chart for the number of defects per unit, rather than a proportion of items that have some sort of defect in a sample of items. Such charts are called *c*-**charts.**

The underlying sampling distribution is the Poisson distribution. We assume that defects occur over a continuous region and the probability of two or more defects at any one location is negligible. The mean of the distribution is $\bar{c}$ and the standard deviation is $\sqrt{\bar{c}}$. For control chart purposes, a useful tactic is to use the normal approximation to the Poisson, which yields the following control limits:

$$UCL = \bar{c} + z\sqrt{\bar{c}}$$

$$LCL = \bar{c} - z\sqrt{\bar{c}}$$

The *c*-chart is useful in manufacturing as well as service industries. Defects such as the number of air bubbles per television picture tube face panel, accidents per month at a particular intersection, complaints per week at a hotel, and ink blotches per square yard of wallpaper can all be measured.

| Application 4.2 | *Using a c-Chart to Monitor Defects per Unit* |

The Woodland Paper Company produces paper for the newspaper industry. As a final step, the paper passes through a machine that measures various quality characteristics. When the process is in control, it averages 20 defects per roll.

1. Set up a control chart for the number of defects per roll. Use two-sigma control limits.
2. If the latest roll sampled contained 27 defects, is the process in control?
3. Suppose the latest roll contained only 5 defects. Is the process in control?

Solution

1. The average number of defects per roll is 20. Therefore,

$$UCL = 20 + 2\sqrt{20} = 28.94$$

$$LCL = 20 - 2\sqrt{20} = 11.05$$

2. Because the latest roll had only 27 defects, which is less than the upper control limit, the process is still in control.
3. Five defects is less than the lower control limit, and therefore the process is technically "out of control." However, the control chart has indicated that something good has happened. Management should find the assignable cause and exploit it so that the average number of defects can be reduced.

Control Charts for Variables

Two control charts for variables frequently used in tandem are the *range chart*, or **R-chart**, and the *average chart*, or **$\bar{x}$-chart**. Recall that the term *variables* means that the quality characteristic to be controlled (such as distance, weight, or response time) is measured on a continuous scale. A sample is taken and two values are calculated: the sample mean of the quality characteristic and the range. The range is calculated by subtracting the smallest from the largest measurement in each sample. These values are used to develop an R-chart for the process variability and an $\bar{x}$-chart for the process average. Both the process variability and the process average must be in control before we can say that the process is in control.

Range Chart. The process variability must be in control before the analyst can construct a valid chart for the process average. The reason is that a measure of process variability is required to determine the control limits for the $\bar{x}$-chart. If the process variability is out of control, the control limits for the $\bar{x}$-chart will be incorrect.

The control limits for the R-chart are

$$UCL_R = D_4\bar{R} \quad \text{and} \quad LCL_R = D_3\bar{R}$$

where $\bar{R}$ is the average of several past R values (and the central line of the control chart), and D_3 and D_4 are constants that provide three standard deviation (three-sigma) limits for the range for a given sample size. Values for D_3 and D_4 are contained in Table 4.4.

Average Chart. When the process variability is in control, the analyst can construct an $\bar{x}$-chart to control the process average. The control limits for the $\bar{x}$-chart are

$$UCL_{\bar{x}} = \bar{\bar{x}} + A_2\bar{R} \quad \text{and} \quad LCL_{\bar{x}} = \bar{\bar{x}} - A_2\bar{R}$$

TABLE 4.4 / *Factors for Calculating Three-Sigma Limits for*
x̄-Chart and R-Chart

Size of Sample (n)	Factor for UCL and LCL for x̄-Charts (A₂)	Factor for LCL for R-Charts (D₃)	Factor for UCL for R-Charts (D₄)
2	1.880	0	3.267
3	1.023	0	2.575
4	0.729	0	2.282
5	0.577	0	2.115
6	0.483	0	2.004
7	0.419	0.076	1.924
8	0.373	0.136	1.864
9	0.337	0.184	1.816
10	0.308	0.223	1.777

Source: 1950 *ASTM Manual on Quality Control of Materials,* copyright © American Society for Testing Materials. Reprinted with permission.

where $\bar{\bar{x}}$ is the average of several past sample averages (and the central line of the control chart) or a target value that management has set for the process. The values for the constant A_2 provide three standard deviation (three-sigma) limits for the process average and are also contained in Table 4.4. Note that the control limits use the value of $\bar{R}$, which again is the reason for constructing the x̄-chart *after* the process variability is in control.

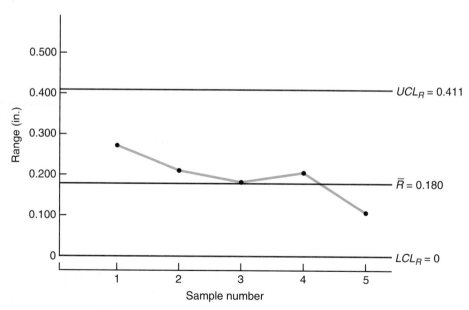

FIGURE 4.6   Range Chart for the Metal Screw

Application 4.3	Using $\bar{x}$- and R-Charts to Monitor a Process

The management of West Allis Industries is concerned about the production of a special metal screw used by several of the company's largest customers. The diameter of the screw is critical. Historically, the process average $\bar{x}$ has been 0.500 in. and the average range has been 0.18 in. Data from the last five samples are shown in the accompanying table. The sample size is 4. Is the process in control?

$n = 4$

Data for the R-Chart and $\bar{x}$-Chart

Sample Number	Observations of Screw Diameter in Sample (in.)				Sample Average $\bar{x}$*	Sample Range $R^\dagger$
	1	2	3	4		
1	0.51	0.63	0.39	0.35	0.47	0.28
2	0.50	0.56	0.42	0.64	0.53	0.22
3	0.68	0.49	0.53	0.62	0.58	0.19
4	0.45	0.33	0.47	0.55	0.45	0.22
5	0.70	0.58	0.64	0.68	0.65	0.12

*The value of $\bar{x}$ is the sum of the observations in each sample divided by 4.

$\dagger$The value of R is the difference between the largest and smallest observation in a sample. In sample 1, for example, $R = 0.63 - 0.35 = 0.28$.

Solution   The firm's analyst constructs the R-chart. Because the sample size is four, Table 4.4 gives him the control-limit factors to use in calculating the control limits for the R-chart:

$$UCL_R = D_4\bar{R} = 2.282(0.18) = 0.411 \text{ in.}$$

and

$$LCL_R = D_3\bar{R} = 0(0.18) = 0 \text{ in.}$$

The value of the range for each sample in the data table is then plotted on the R-chart, as shown in Fig. 4.6. None of the sample ranges falls outside the control limits. Consequently, the analyst can say that process variability is in control. Only random causes of variation are present. If any of the sample ranges had fallen outside the limits (the range can never be negative, of course), the analyst would have had to search for the cause of the excessive variability.

The analyst can now proceed to construct the $\bar{x}$-chart for the process average. Using $\bar{x} = 0.500$ and Table 4.4, the control limits for the $\bar{x}$-chart are

$$UCL_{\bar{x}} = \bar{\bar{x}} + A_2\bar{R} = 0.500 + 0.729(0.18) = 0.631 \text{ in.}$$

and

$$LCL_{\bar{x}} = \bar{\bar{x}} - A_2\bar{R} = 0.500 - 0.729(0.18) = 0.369 \text{ in.}$$

The values for $\bar{x}$ for the last five samples (from the data table) are shown on the $\bar{x}$-chart in Fig. 4.7. The value of sample 5 falls above the upper control limit, indicating that the process average is out of control and that the analyst should look for assignable causes. Perhaps a fishbone diagram (as shown in Chapter 3) could help determine whether machines, operators, or materials are at fault.

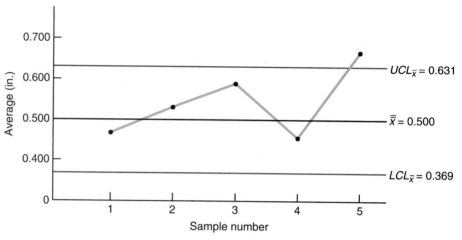

FIGURE 4.7   Average Chart for the Metal Screw

MANAGERIAL CONSIDERATIONS IN STATISTICAL PROCESS CONTROL

Two major decisions needed to implement statistical process control are sample size choice and control limit spread. We now turn to some of the managerial considerations involved in making these decisions.

Sample Size

The ultimate in process control is to test each item (raw material, component, product, or service) to make sure that it satisfies design specifications. Often this is not possible, particularly when the test involves the destruction of the item or the test is very technical and time consuming. Consequently, the choice of sample size has economic as well as control implications.

***p*-Charts Versus *x̄*-Charts.** Earlier we said that *p*-charts are based on attributes and are useful in situations where quality can be easily checked and the acceptance decision is a simple yes or no. The ease of measuring quality attributes (compared to variables) is accompanied by the requirement for larger sample sizes. The magnitude of the difference varies, but an attribute control chart may require 4 to 100 times the sample size of that required for a variable control chart. Typical *x̄*-charts require sample sizes of 4 or 5, whereas the sample size for a *p*-chart must be large enough to detect at least one defective item on the average. For example, the population proportion defective in our banking services example was 0.005, requiring a bare minimum sample size of 200. The reason that we can use smaller sample sizes for *x̄*-charts is that we can derive much more information from the variables. Consequently, unless measuring variables takes far more effort than measuring attributes, variable control charts are usually less expensive to utilize.

Degree of Control. Another consideration is the effect of sample size on degree of control or our ability to detect a shift in the process average. Recall that the standard deviation for the p-chart has n in the denominator. Also note that in Table 4.4 the value of A_2 decreases as the sample size increases. The relationship implies that, as the sample size increases, the control *limits* on the control charts move closer to the central line, or target process average. Thus the analyst is more likely to detect a shift in the process average. For example, when we use an $\bar{x}$-chart, sample sizes of 4 or 5 are usually sufficient to detect a relatively large shift in the process average (say, two standard deviations). However, we would need a sample size three to five times larger to detect shifts of only one standard deviation. Here again, management must balance the cost of inspection against the cost of not detecting a shift in the process average.

Homogeneity. The sample should represent subgroups of output that are as homogeneous as possible. When significant deviations occur and assignable causes can be identified, the causes should show up as differences between subgroups and not as differences between members of a subgroup. Consider, for example, a two-shift operation, with each shift capable of producing 500 units. Choosing a sample size of 2000 could mask one of the assignable causes of quality problems: differences in output quality by shift. It might be better in this case to take samples that are homogeneous by shift, so that management can determine whether the problems occur during one particular shift.

Control Limit Spread

In our examples of control charts we used control limits that were three standard deviations from the central line. However, we could have chosen other control limits. Figure 4.8 shows the effects of changing the number of standard deviations from the process average in a p-chart. As you can see from this figure, a change from $z = 3$ to $z = 2$ increases the probability of detecting a shift in the process average. But it also increases the probability of searching for an assignable cause when none exists. The choice of z would depend on the cost of looking for assignable causes where none exist versus the cost of not detecting a shift. In general, charts with $z = 1.5$ or $z = 2$ are more economical than those with $z = 3$, if the operations manager can determine inexpensively and quickly whether something is wrong. If the cost of looking for the cause of a problem is high, charts with $z = 3$ or $z = 4$ might be more useful and more economical.

ACCEPTANCE SAMPLING

As we have seen, statistical process control techniques are used to monitor and control the processes that produce products and services. Acceptance sampling techniques, however, are used to determine whether to accept or reject a specific quantity of material. Manufacturing and service firms use acceptance sampling to screen purchased items used in the manufacture of their products and services. Some manufacturing firms use it to provide a final check on their prod-

FIGURE 4.8

Effects of Changing z
in a p-Chart

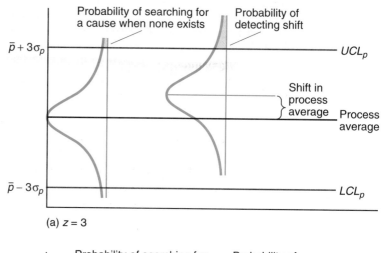

(a) z = 3

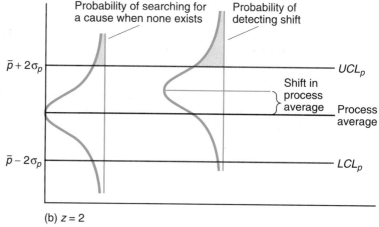

(b) z = 2

ucts before shipping them to their customers. The basic procedure is straightforward: A random sample is taken from a large quantity of items and tested or
measured relative to the quality characteristic of interest. If the sample passes
the test, the entire quantity of items is accepted. If not, either the items may
be subjected to complete inspection and all defective items repaired or replaced, or the entire quantity is returned to the supplier. In this section we will
first discuss the managerial parameters that must be specified when devising
acceptance sampling plans and then address several attribute-sampling plans.
We conclude this chapter with a discussion of the use of the computer in acceptance sampling.

Managerial Parameters

Acceptance sampling involves two parties: the producer (or supplier) and the
consumer (or buyer). Acceptance-sampling plans provide the consumer with
decision guidelines that limit the risk of rejecting good quality materials or

accepting bad quality materials. Consequently, it is the consumer, sometimes in conjunction with the producer, who specifies the parameters of the plan.*

Management should specify two levels of quality when designing an acceptance-sampling plan. The first is the **acceptable quality level (AQL)**, the quality level acceptable to the *consumer*. This is the quality level that the producer of the item aims for and the consumer typically states in a contract or purchase order. For example, a contract might call for a quality level of one defective unit in 10,000, or an AQL of 0.0001. The probability of rejecting a lot with AQL quality is called the **producer's risk (α),** or the risk the sampling plan will fail to verify an acceptable lot's quality and thus reject it. Most often the producer's risk is set at 0.05, or 5 percent.

Although producers are interested in low risk, they often have no control over the consumer's acceptance-sampling plan. Fortunately, the consumer is also interested in a low producer's risk because sending good materials back to the producer (1) disrupts the consumer's production process and increases the likelihood of shortages in materials, (2) adds unnecessarily to the lead time for finished products, and (3) creates poor relations with the producer.

The second level of quality is the **lot tolerance proportion defective (LTPD),** or the worst level of quality that the consumer will accept. Recognizing the high cost of defects, operations managers have become more cautious about accepting materials of poor quality from suppliers (see Chapter 3). Thus sampling plans now tend to have lower LTPD values than in the past. The probability of accepting a lot with LTPD quality is the **consumer's risk (β).** A common value for the consumer's risk is 0.10, or 10 percent. Table 4.5 summarizes the decisions that managers make with regard to acceptance sampling.

---

*Any company can be both a producer and a consumer. A company can produce goods that are purchased by another company, and it can consume raw materials supplied by another company.

TABLE 4.5 / *Decisions in Acceptance Sampling*

Decision	Comments
Sampling versus complete inspection	The trade-off of inspection cost versus the potential cost of passing a defective item is important. Destructive testing requires a sampling plan. Fatigue and the monotony of the testing procedure should be considered.
Attribute versus variable measures	Attribute measures involve a simple yes–no decision about a quality characteristic. Variable measures involve measurement of quality characteristics of an item on a continuous scale to quantify the amount of deviation from specifications.
If sampling is chosen: Acceptable quality level (AQL); producer's risk (α) Lot tolerance proportion defective (LTPD); consumer's risk (β)	These parameters quantify risks to the producer and the consumer. They provide the basis for determining the specifics of a sampling plan.
Design of the sampling plan	The design is derived from the specification of AQL, α, LTPD, and β.

The Single-Sampling Plan

Let's now turn to a simple attribute plan: the **single-sampling plan.***   As its name implies, this method involves a decision to accept or reject a lot based on the results of one random sample from the lot. To begin, we let

n = sample size, randomly selected from the lot to be judged

c = acceptable number of defective items in the sample

d = actual number of defective items found in the sample

The procedure is to take a random sample of size n from the lot and inspect each item. If $d \leq c$, the inspector accepts the lot; if $d > c$ the inspector rejects the lot.

Operating Characteristic Curves.   A graphic display of the performance of a sampling plan, as expressed by the probability of accepting the lot for a range of lot proportion defectives, is called an **operating characteristic (OC) curve.** It describes how well a sampling plan discriminates between good and bad lots. Undoubtedly, every manager wants a plan that accepts lots with AQL or better quality 100 percent of the time and accepts lots with worse than AQL quality 0 percent of the time. No sampling plan can guarantee this level of performance; inspection of the entire lot is the only way to guarantee it. Consequently, managers are left with choosing a sample size n and an acceptance level c to achieve a given level of performance as specified by AQL, α, LTPD, and β.

Suppose that an analyst has a sample size (n) and acceptance level (c) for a single-sampling plan. How does she draw the OC curve for that plan? In this case the sampling distribution is the binomial distribution. For each item inspected, the item is either defective (a failure) or not (a success). The probability of accepting the lot, P_a, is equal to the probability that she can take a sample of size n from a lot with a proportion defective of p and find c or fewer defective items, or

$$P_a = \sum_{r=0}^{r=c} \frac{n!}{r!(n-r)!} p^r (1 - p)^{n-r}$$

However, if n is greater than 20 and p is less than 0.05, we can ease our computational burden by using the Poisson approximation to the binomial. We set the mean of the Poisson distribution equal to np, the mean of the binomial distribution, and make use of the cumulative Poisson probability curves in Appendix 4. To compute the OC curve the analyst would compute P_a for a range of values of p. For given values of n and c, this procedure is used for each value of p:

1. Multiply p by the sample size n.
2. Find the value of np along the horizontal axis of the chart.

---

*Single-sampling plans can also be devised for variables.

3. Move up the chart to the curve for the appropriate value of c.
4. Move horizontally to the left-hand side of the chart and read the value for P_a from the vertical axis.

Application 4.4 demonstrates the construction of an OC curve for an acceptance-sampling plan used by a muffler installation service.

Application 4.4	*Constructing an OC Curve*

The Noise King Muffler Shop is a high-volume installer of replacement exhaust muffler systems. John Birns, store manager, just received word that a shipment of 1000 mufflers arrived in the receiving department yesterday. Operations must inspect these mufflers before sending them to the storage room. The sampling plan calls for a sample size n of 50 and an acceptance level c of 1. The contract with the muffler manufacturer calls for an acceptable quality level of 1 defective muffler per 100. The lot tolerance proportion defective is 6 defective mufflers per 100.

1. Calculate the OC curve for this plan.
2. Determine the producer's risk and the consumer's risk for the plan.

Solution Let $p = 0.01$. Then multiply n by p and get $50(0.01) = 0.50$. Locate 0.50 on the horizontal axis of the Poisson chart in Appendix 4. Move up to the curve for $c = 1$ and over to the vertical axis. Read $P_a = 0.91$ (approximately). You can repeat this process for a range of p values. The accompanying table contains the remaining values for the OC curve. Note that the plan provides a producer's risk of 9 percent and a consumer's risk of 20 percent. Both values are higher than the usually acceptable values for plans of this sort. Figure 4.9 shows the curve and the producer's and consumer's risks.

Values for the Operating Characteristic Curve with n = 50 and c = 1

Proportion Defective (p)	Value of np	Probability of c or less Defects (P_a)	Comments
0.01 (AQL)	0.5	0.910	$\alpha = 0.090 \ (1.000 - 0.910)$
0.02	1.0	0.740	
0.03	1.5	0.560	
0.04	2.0	0.410	
0.05	2.5	0.275	
0.06 (LTPD)	3.0	0.200	$\beta = 0.200 \ (1.00 - 0.8)$
0.07	3.5	0.130	
0.08	4.0	0.090	
0.09	4.5	0.060	
0.10	5.0	0.040	

Application 4.4 raises the question of how to change the sampling plan to avoid rejecting more good lots and accepting more bad lots than management might want. How should n and c be changed?

FIGURE 4.9

OC Curve for a
Single-Sampling Plan
with $n = 50$ and
$c = 1$

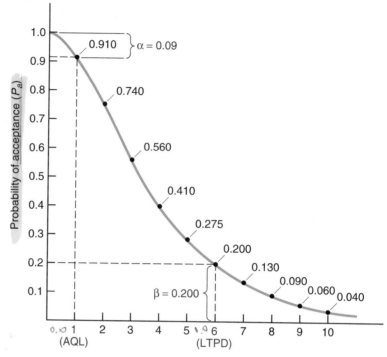

Proportion defective (in hundredths)

Let's see how n and c affect the shape of the OC curve. To aid the discussion we define the *acceptance proportion* as the ratio of c to n, or c/n. If examination of the sample reveals that the sample proportion defective is less than or equal to the acceptance proportion, the inspector accepts the lot. Now let's compare the Noise King plan of $n = 50$ and $c = 1$ to another plan in which $n = 100$ and $c = 2$. The acceptance proportion remains the same $(1/50 = 2/100 = 0.02)$, but the sample size increases. Figure 4.10 shows the OC curves for these two plans and the complete-inspection curve for purposes of comparison. As the sample size increases—holding the acceptance proportion constant—the sampling plan becomes more discriminating between good and bad lots. Note that the producer's risk (α) and the consumer's risk (β) are reduced. Thus larger samples reduce the probabilities of making the wrong decision. The ultimate, of course, is complete inspection but, as we have said, the cost of complete inspection may well outweigh its benefits. Consequently, managers are often left with sampling and the risks of making a bad decision.

Now suppose that we change the acceptance proportion. Let's compare the plan in which $n = 100$ and $c = 2$ to a plan in which $n = 100$ and $c = 4$. The acceptance proportion is 0.02 in the former and 0.04 in the latter. Figure 4.11 compares the OC curves for these two plans. Note that as we increase the acceptance proportion—holding sample size constant—the producer's risk (α) drops but the consumer's risk (β) rises. This result makes sense intuitively

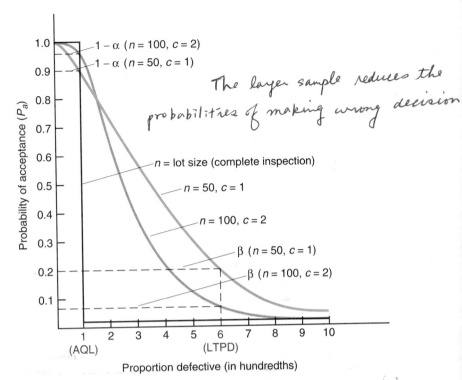

The larger sample reduces the probabilities of making wrong decision

$1-\alpha$ ($n = 100$, $c = 4$) $\quad 0.04 \Rightarrow \alpha \downarrow, \beta \uparrow$
$1-\alpha$ ($n = 100$, $c = 2$) $\quad 0.02$

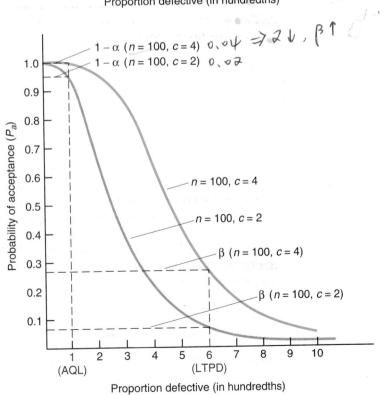

TABLE 4.6 / Effects of n and c on OC Curves

Sampling Plan Changes			OC Curve Changes	
Acceptance Proportion (c/n)	Acceptable Number of Defective Items (c)	Sample Size (n)	Producer's Risk (α)	Consumer's Risk (β)
Unchanged	Increases	Increases	Decreases	Decreases
Unchanged	Decreases	Decreases	Increases	Increases
Increases	Increases	Unchanged	Decreases	Increases
Increases	Unchanged	Decreases	Decreases	Increases
Decreases	Decreases	Unchanged	Increases	Decreases
Decreases	Unchanged	Increases	Increases	Decreases

because increasing the acceptance proportion—holding sample size constant—only makes it easier for a good lot to pass inspection. However, it makes it easier for a bad lot to pass, as well. Table 4.6 summarizes the effects of n and c on the OC curve.

Finding the Best Single-Sampling Plan. The best single-sampling plan is the one that meets the desired producer's and consumer's risk levels with the smallest sample size. Given the AQL and LTPD, we need to find values for n and c that meet the desired α and β. Because the sampling distribution is the binomial, we could use it to specify two equations for the probability of acceptance, one for the case in which the proportion defective is at the AQL level and the other for the case in which it is at the LTPD level, as shown in the following equations:

$$\sum_{r=0}^{c} \frac{n!}{r! \, (n-r)!} (AQL)^r \, (1 - AQL)^{n-r} = 1 - \alpha$$

$$\sum_{r=0}^{c} \frac{n!}{r! \, (n-r)!} (LTPD)^r \, (1 - LTPD)^{n-r} = \beta$$

Solving these two equations for n and c isn't very palatable. At the other extreme, we could find the best plan by starting with good guesses for n and c and incrementally adjusting them using the guidelines of Table 4.6. For each increment, we could calculate α and β with the help of Appendix 4 and compare them to the desired values. This approach might yield a good plan, but it also might be time consuming.

Alternatively, we could use a table such as Table 4.7 to get close (in many cases close enough) to the best plan, in which α and β take on the usual values of 5 percent and 10 percent, respectively. The upper number in each cell is the sample size (n) and the lower number is the acceptance level (c). Table 4.7

TABLE 4.7 / Single-Sampling Table for $\alpha = 0.05$ and $\beta = 0.10^*$

	LTPD (%)									
AQL (%)	1.0	2.0	3.0	4.0	5.0	6.0	7.0	8.0	9.0	10.0
0.05–0.19	532 2	195 1	130 1	97 1	78 1	65 1	33 0	29 0	26 0	23 0
0.20–0.39	1299 8	334 3	177 2	97 1	78 1	65 1	56 1	49 1	43 1	39 1
0.40–0.59		464 5	223 3	133 2	106 2	89 2	56 1	49 1	43 1	39 1
0.60–0.79		711 9	309 5	167 3	106 2	89 2	76 2	67 2	43 1	39 1
0.80–0.99			392 7	200 4	134 3	111 3	76 2	67 2	59 2	53 2
1.00–1.19			514 10	263 6	160 4	111 3	95 3	67 2	59 2	53 2
1.20–1.39			671 14	294 7	186 5	133 4	95 3	84 3	59 2	53 2
1.40–1.59				385 10	211 6	155 5	114 4	84 3	74 3	67 3
1.60–1.79				474 13	260 8	176 6	133 5	100 4	74 3	67 3
1.80–1.99					308 10	196 7	133 5	100 4	89 4	67 3
2.00–2.19					356 12	217 8	150 6	116 5	89 4	80 4
2.20–2.39					426 15	257 10	168 7	132 6	103 5	80 4
2.40–2.59						296 12	203 9	147 7	117 6	93 5
2.60–2.79						336 14	220 10	162 8	117 6	93 5
2.80–2.99							254 12	178 9	131 7	105 6
3.00–3.19							288 14	193 10	144 8	118 7
3.20–3.39								222 12	158 9	118 7
3.40–3.59								237 13	171 10	130 8
3.60–3.79								266 15	184 11	142 9
3.80–3.99									211 13	154 10
4.00–4.19									237 15	166 11
4.20–4.39										190 13
4.40–4.59										213 15

*Table values are based on the Poisson approximation to the binomial distribution. Shaded cells represent plans where c must be greater than 15 or where there is an impossible situation, such as AQL greater than LTPD.

accommodates a maximum acceptance level of only 15, although it could be expanded to any acceptance level. The Poisson approximation to the binomial distribution was used to determine the plans. The single-sampling plan in each cell is designed for the *largest* AQL in the range for that row, given the LTPD for that column. This configuration ensures that the producer's risk will not exceed 5 percent for any AQL in the range, but it may require a larger sample size than necessary for some AQLs at the lower end of the range. All tabular values meet the consumer's risk of 10 percent.

Let's return to the Noise King example. What is the best single-sampling plan? From Table 4.7, with AQL = 1 percent and LTPD = 6 percent, the plan would be to have a sample size $n = 111$ and an acceptance level $c = 3$. Note in Fig. 4.11 that the plan with $n = 100$ and $c = 4$ has a producer's risk of almost zero and a consumer's risk of approximately 28 percent. We also know from Table 4.6 that reducing the acceptance proportion—holding n constant—increases the producer's risk and reduces the consumer's risk. This is the direction we want to go. The recommended plan of $n = 111$ and $c = 3$ takes us in that direction.

Average Outgoing Quality. We have shown how to choose the best sample size and acceptance number given the AQL, α, LTPD, and β parameters, but the performance of the single-sampling plan may not yet be what we want. We still have not checked the plan's **average outgoing quality (AOQ)**, which is the expected proportion of defects that the plan will allow to pass. To calculate the AOQ, we assume that if the lot is rejected, all defective items in the lot will be replaced with good items. All defective items in the sample are replaced, as well, if the lot is accepted. This is called *rectified inspection*. With these assumptions, the equation for AOQ, expressed as the proportion defective, is

$$AOQ = \frac{p(P_a)(N - n)}{N}$$

where

$$p = \text{true proportion defective of the lot}$$

$$P_a = \text{probability of accepting the lot}$$

$$N = \text{lot size}$$

$$n = \text{sample size}$$

Not knowing the proportion defective before the inspection process begins, the analyst can use the equation for AOQ to estimate the performance of the plan over a range of possible proportion defectives. The maximum value of the average outgoing quality over all possible values of the proportion defective is called the *average outgoing quality limit (AOQL)*. If the AOQL seems too high, the parameters of the plan must be modified until an acceptable AOQL is achieved.

Application 4.5	*Calculating the AOQL*

Suppose Noise King is using rectifying inspection for its single-sampling plan. Calculate the average outgoing quality limit for the plan with $n = 111$, $c = 3$, and $N = 1000$. Use Appendix 4 to estimate the probabilities of acceptance for values of the proportion defective from 0.01 to 0.10.

Solution The following table contains the calculations for the AOQ for each value of the proportion defective. For demonstration purposes we have used only selected values for p. Based on the results shown in the table and Fig. 4.12 (on the next page), the $AOQL$ is approximately 0.0149, or 1.49 percent defectives, when the lot proportion defective is 0.03. Trying more values of p between 0.02 and 0.03 would result in a more precise estimate of $AOQL$. Note how the average outgoing quality improves dramatically as the proportion defective of the lot increases. The reason is that as p gets large the probability is high that the lot will be rejected and all the defective mufflers replaced with good ones. Management does not know the actual proportion defective of the lot of 1000 mufflers, but it does know that the worst the plan will do is allow 1.49 percent defectives. If this performance is not acceptable, the sampling plan must be revised.

Calculations for Average Outgoing Quality

(1) Proportion Defective (p)	(2) (np)*	(3) Probability of Acceptance P_a†	(4) $\dfrac{N - n}{N}$	(5) Average Outgoing Quality (AOQ) (1) × (3) × (4)
0.01	1.11	0.970	0.889	0.0086
0.02	2.22	0.820	0.889	0.0146
0.03	**3.33**	**0.560**	**0.889**	**0.0149**
0.04	4.44	0.350	0.889	0.0124
0.05	5.55	0.200	0.889	0.0089
0.06	6.66	0.100	0.889	0.0053
0.07	7.77	0.050	0.889	0.0031
0.08	8.88	0.020	0.889	0.0014
0.09	9.99	0.010	0.889	0.0008
0.10	11.10	0.004	0.889	0.0004

*Column (1) times 111.

†Column (3) is estimated from the chart in Appendix 4, with $c = 3$. First, locate the Column 2 value on the horizontal axis. Then, move up the chart to the curve for $c = 3$. Finally, move horizontally to the vertical axis on the left and read the value for P_a.

Other Attribute-Sampling Plans

The single-sampling plan is the simplest of acceptance sampling plans. Other plans that may be appropriate under certain conditions include the double-sampling plan and the sequential-sampling plan.

Double-Sampling Plan. In a **double-sampling plan** management specifies two lot sizes (n_1 and n_2) and two acceptance levels (c_1 and c_2). c_1 is the minmum number of defective items allowed in the first sample of size n_1, and c_2 is the

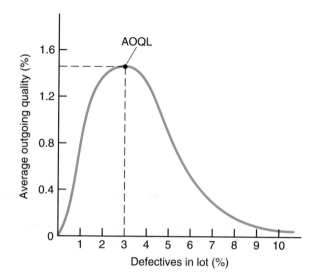

maximum number of defects allowed, either from the first sample or the combined samples of n_1 and n_2. The procedure is as follows:

1. Take a random sample of size n_1 and determine d_1, the number of defectives in the sample.
2. If $d_1 \leq c_1$, accept the lot; if $d_1 > c_2$, reject the lot.
3. If $c_1 < d_1 \leq c_2$, take another random sample of size n_2 and determine d_2, the number of defectives in the second sample.
4. If $(d_1 + d_2) \leq c_2$, accept the lot; otherwise, reject the lot.

A double-sampling plan can significantly reduce the costs of inspection relative to a single-sampling plan for lots with very low or very high proportion defectives. In these situations decisions are often based on the first sample, and n_1 is usually much smaller than the sample size in a single-sampling plan.

The Sequential-Sampling Plan. Extending the concept of the double-sampling plan to its limit yields the item-by-item **sequential-sampling plan.** Each time an item is inspected a decision is made to (1) reject the lot, (2) accept the lot, or (3) continue sampling, based on the cumulative results so far. The analyst can plot the total number of defectives against the cumulative sample size, and if the number of defectives is less than a certain acceptance number (c_1), accept the lot. If the number is greater than another acceptance number (c_2), the analyst rejects the lot. If the number is somewhere between the two, another item is inspected. Figure 4.13 illustrates a decision to reject a lot after examining the fortieth unit. Such charts can be easily designed with the help of statistical tables.*

The average number of items inspected (*ANI*) in the sequential-sampling

---

*Statistical tables can be found in a publication of the Statistical Research Group, Columbia University, *Sequential Analysis of Statistical Data: Applications* (New York: Columbia University Press, 1945).

FIGURE 4.13

Sequential-Sampling
Chart

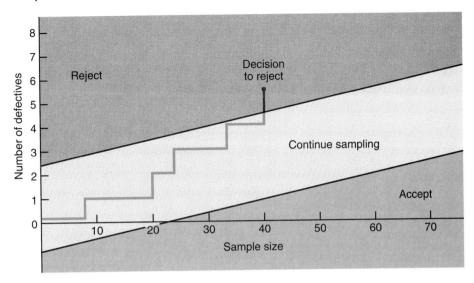

plan is generally lower than that for any other form of acceptance sampling. Achieving low levels of *ANI* is important because the fewer the items inspected, the lower the costs of inspection will be. For extreme values of the proportion defective, no other plan with a comparable OC curve will have a lower *ANI*. However, it is possible, although unlikely, that a sequential-sampling plan will have a larger *ANI* than a comparable single- or double-sampling plan for intermediate values of the proportion defective. In general, the sequential-sampling plan may reduce *ANI* to 50 percent of that required by a comparable single-sampling plan and consequently save substantial inspection costs.

COMPUTERS AND STATISTICAL QUALITY CONTROL

Can you imagine managers at United Parcel Service, American Airlines, Ford Motor Company, or Hewlett–Packard manually developing control charts or sampling plans? Not likely. Computers play a big role in implementing the techniques discussed in this chapter. Often thousands of parts, products, or services require management to monitor vast amounts of data such as quality measures; standards and inspection procedures; criteria for accepting, reworking, or rejecting materials; process control parameters; design specifications; costs; and historical quality performance of internal processes and suppliers.

Computers can link data collection activities to company databases and provide a means to access that information through on-line displays and printed reports. Computer routines can develop control charts and acceptance sampling plans, as well as provide the traditional statistical techniques such as frequency diagrams and correlations. In Chapter 3 we discussed the Service Tracking Report used by American Express to monitor 100 tasks deemed critical to quality performance. Managerial Practice 4.2 provides an example of the use of computers in a manufacturing firm.

Managerial Practice 4.2

Computerized SQC at Hay & Forage Industries

Hay & Forage Industries (HFI) produces a variety of farm equipment such as windrowers, hay handling equipment, forage harvesters, tractors, balers, mowers, rotary cutters, backhoes, and tillers. In the mid-1970s the company experienced losses because of the farm crisis, and over the next decade it suffered from intense national and global competition. Consequently, management launched an aggressive program to enhance quality in an attempt to survive, grow, and increase market share. A key element of the program is a computerized process control decision support system (PCDSS) that is capable of monitoring vast amounts of data critical to maintaining product quality as well as recommending sampling plans and control charts. For example, HFI inventories about 2000 parts from 200 suppliers and produces many more of its own. After some investigation, management determined that HFI had inadequate acceptance-sampling plans. A desirable sampling plan for one product and supplier may not be feasible at another time or for other products or suppliers. For internally manufactured parts, with PCDSS, HFI can now develop a single-sampling plan for each part and, because the proportion of defectives varies from day to day, management can use the most recent data to determine the average outgoing quality of each production lot. In addition, process control information can be shared by various departments at HFI. The actual proportion of defective products obtained from control charts is reported to the design engineering and marketing departments. As a result, design engineers can produce more meaningful product specifications and marketing managers have more reliable information on product quality.

The benefits from PCDSS and the quality program at HFI are many. Since 1987, the proportion defective for most parts decreased 30 percent, and in some cases, 60 percent. More economical sampling plans provide as good or better protection as before, and management spends 50 percent less time designing control charts and sampling plans, analyzing causes and effects, and training operators. Finally, HFI has experienced an increase in sales and increased their work force from 500 to 725, even though the farming industry is still suffering from a long-term recession.

Source: Jinoos Hosseini and Nassar S. Fard, "A System for Analyzing Information to Manage the Quality-Control Process," *Interfaces*, vol. 21, no. 2, March–April 1991, pp. 48–58.

*A*t Hay and Forage, each windrower tractor is physically inspected and test driven by a quality assurance auditor before it is released for shipment.

Assessing an Acceptance-Sampling Plan

The receiving manager at Breakthrough Technologies wishes to devise a plan with AQL = 0.02, α = 0.05, LTPD = 0.08, and β = 0.10 and assess its operating characteristics.

a. Develop the sampling plan and its OC curve.
b. What is the probability that a lot with 4 percent defectives will be accepted? With 6 percent defectives?

Solution This problem is solved using CMOM. Your output may look different if you are using another software package.

a. A graph of the OC curve is given in Printout 1. A plan with n = 116 and

Printout 1

```
               CMOM-QUALITY CONTROL
              ACCEPTANCE SAMPLING PLAN


                   DATA ENTERED

ACCEPTABLE QUALITY LEVEL (AQL) :      0.0200
PRODUCER'S RISK (ALPHA)        :      0.0500
LOT TOLERANCE DEFECTIVE (LTPD) :      0.0800
CONSUMER'S RISK (BETA)         :      0.1000



               CMOM-QUALITY CONTROL
              ACCEPTANCE SAMPLING PLAN


                    SOLUTION


          AQL BASED                LTPD BASED
```

ACCEPTANCE NUMBER	EXPECTED DEFECTIVES	SAMPLE SIZE	EXPECTED DEFECTIVES	SAMPLE SIZE
0	0.0513	3	2.3025	29
1	0.3553	18	3.8896	49
2	0.8176	41	5.3223	66
3	0.3663	69	6.6807	84
4	1.9702	99	7.9937	100
5	2.6130	131	9.2747	116
6	3.2854	164	10.5322	132
7	3.9810	199	11.7710	147
8	4.6953	235	12.9946	162
9	5.4253	271	14.2061	178
10	6.1689	308	15.4067	193

```
0.93              •


0.83


0.73        Q
            U
0.63        A
            L
0.53        I        •
            T
0.43        Y


0.33        L
            E
0.23        V
            E
0.13        L              •


0.03                    •  •  •  •  •  •  •  •  •  •  •  •  •  •
```

PROPORTION   DEFECTIVE

```
C = 5            .03 .05 .08 .10 .13 .15 .18 .20 .23 .25 .28 .30 .33 .35 .38
Sample Size = 116
```

Notes:

$c = 5$ (highlighted) provides the smallest sample size adhering to both the α and β targets.

b. An inspection of the OC curve shows that the probability of accepting a lot with 4 percent defective is approximately 68 percent and that the probability of accepting a lot with 6 percent defective is approximately 30 percent.

SOLVED PROBLEMS

1. The data processing department of the Arizona Bank has five keypunch operators. Each day their supervisor verifies the accuracy of a random sample of 250 records. A record containing one or more errors is considered defective and must be redone. The results of the last 30 samples are shown in Table 4.8. All were checked to make sure none were out of control.
   a. Based on this historical data, set up a p-chart using $z = 3$.
   b. Samples for the next four days showed:

	Number of
Sample	Defective Records
31	17
32	15
33	22
34	21

What is the supervisor's assessment of the keypunch process likely to be? Explain.

Solution　　a. From Table 4.8, the supervisor knows that the total number of defective records is 300 out of a total sample of 7500 [30(250)]. Therefore, the

TABLE 4.8

Sample	Number of Defective Records	Sample	Number of Defective Records
1	7	17	12
2	5	18	4
3	19	19	6
4	10	20	11
5	11	21	17
6	8	22	12
7	12	23	6
8	9	24	7
9	6	25	13
10	13	26	10
11	18	27	14
12	5	28	6
13	16	29	11
14	4	30	9
15	11	Total	300
16	8		

central line of the chart is

$$\bar{p} = \frac{300}{7500} = 0.04$$

The control limits are

$$UCL = \bar{p} + z\sqrt{\frac{\bar{p}(1 - \bar{p})}{n}}$$

$$= 0.04 + 3\sqrt{\frac{0.04(0.96)}{250}} = 0.077$$

and

$$LCL = \bar{p} - z\sqrt{\frac{\bar{p}(1 - \bar{p})}{n}}$$

$$= 0.04 - 3\sqrt{\frac{0.04(0.96)}{250}} = 0.003$$

b.

Sample	Defects	Proportion
31	17	0.068
32	15	0.060
33	22	0.088
34	21	0.084

Samples 33 and 34 are out of control. The supervisor should look for the problem and, finding it, take corrective action.

2. The Minnow County Highway Safety Department monitors accidents at the intersection of Routes 123 and 14. Accidents at that intersection have averaged three per month.
   a. Which type of control chart should be used? Construct a control chart with three-sigma control limits.
   b. Last month seven accidents occurred at the intersection. Is this sufficient evidence to justify a claim that something has changed at the intersection?

Solution   a. Since the safety department cannot determine the number of accidents that did *not* occur, there is no way to compute a proportion defective at the intersection. Therefore, administrators must use a *c*-chart.

$$UCL = 3 + 3\sqrt{3} = 8.20$$

$$LCL = 3 - 3\sqrt{3} = -2.196 \text{ (adjusted to zero)}$$

It does not make sense to have negative accidents, so the lower control limit in this case is set equal to zero.
   b. The number of accidents last month falls within the upper and lower control limits of the chart. We conclude that no assignable causes are present, and the increase in accidents was due to chance.

3. The Watson Electric Company produces a certain brand of incandescent light bulb. The following data on the number of lumens for each light bulb were collected when the process was in control.

Sample	Observation 1	2	3	4
1	604	612	588	600
2	597	601	607	603
3	581	570	585	592
4	620	605	595	588
5	590	614	608	604

   a. Calculate control limits for an *R*-chart and an $\bar{x}$-chart.
   b. Since those data were collected, some new employees were hired. A new sample was taken and had the following readings: 570, 603, 623, and 583. Is the process still in control?

Solution   a.

Sample	$\bar{x}$	R
1	601	24
2	602	10
3	582	22
4	602	32
5	604	24
Total	2991	112
Average	598.2	22.4

The R-chart control limits are

$$UCL_R = D_4\bar{R} = 2.282(22.4) = 51.12$$

$$LCL_R = D_3\bar{R} = 0(22.4) = 0$$

The $\bar{x}$-chart control limits are

$$UCL_{\bar{x}} = 598.2 + 0.729(22.4) = 614.53$$

$$LCL_{\bar{x}} = 598.2 - 0.729(22.4) = 581.87$$

b. The operations manager first checks to see whether the variability is still in control based on the new data. The range is 53 (623 − 570). This value is outside the upper control limit for the R-chart. Consequently, the process variability is not in control. Assignable causes must be found and corrected. Once the process variability is in control, the process average can be checked.

4. An inspection station has been installed between two production processes. The feeder process, when operating correctly, has an acceptable quality level of 0.03. The consuming process, which is expensive, has a specified lot tolerance proportion defective of 0.08. The feeding process produces in batch sizes and, if a batch is rejected by the inspector, the entire batch must be checked and the defective items reworked. Consequently, management wants no more than a 5 percent producer's risk and, because of the expensive process that follows, no more than a 10 percent chance of accepting a lot with 8 percent defectives or worse.

a. Determine the appropriate sample size (n) and acceptable number of defective items in the sample (c).

b. Calculate values and draw the OC curve for this inspection station.

c. What is the probability that a lot with 5 percent defectives will be rejected?

Solution

a. For AQL = 3 percent, LTPD = 8 percent, $\alpha = 0.05$, and $\beta = 0.10$, Table 4.7 suggests use of

$$n = 193 \quad \text{and} \quad c = 10$$

b. Table 4.9 contains the data for the OC curve. Appendix 4 was used to estimate the probability of acceptance. Figure 4.14 shows the OC curve.

c. According to Table 4.9, the probability of accepting a lot with 5 percent defectives·is 60 percent. Therefore, the probability that a lot with 5 percent defects will be rejected is 40 percent (100 − 60).

TABLE 4.9

Proportion Defective (p)	Value of np	Probability of c or Less Defects (P_a)	Comments
0.01	1.93	1.000	
0.02	3.86	0.998	
0.03 (AQL)	5.79	0.960	$\alpha = 0.04$
0.04	7.72	0.840	
0.05	9.65	0.600	
0.06	11.58	0.350	
0.07	13.51	0.230	
0.08 (LTPD)	15.44	0.100	$\beta = 0.100$
0.09	17.37	0.050	
0.10	19.30	0.010	

FIGURE 4.14

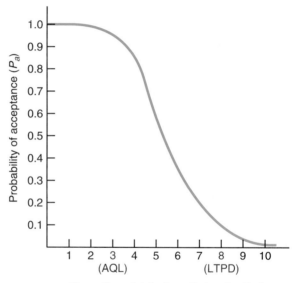

Proportion of defectives (in hundredths)

FORMULA REVIEW

1. Sample standard deviation for *p*-charts:

$$\sigma_p = \sqrt{\frac{\bar{p}(1 - \bar{p})}{n}}$$

2. Control limits for *p*-charts:

$$UCL = \bar{p} + z\sqrt{\frac{\bar{p}(1 - \bar{p})}{n}} \quad \text{and} \quad LCL = \bar{p} - z\sqrt{\frac{\bar{p}(1 - \bar{p})}{n}}$$

3. Control limits for c-charts:

$$UCL = \bar{c} + z\sqrt{\bar{c}} \quad \text{and} \quad LCL = \bar{c} - z\sqrt{\bar{c}}$$

4. Control limits for variable process control charts:

$$UCL_R = D_4\bar{R} \quad \text{and} \quad LCL_R = D_3\bar{R}$$

$$UCL_{\bar{x}} = \bar{\bar{x}} + A_2\bar{R} \quad \text{and} \quad LCL_{\bar{x}} = \bar{\bar{x}} - A_2\bar{R}$$

5. Average outgoing quality:

$$AOQ = \frac{p(P_a)(N - n)}{N}$$

CHAPTER HIGHLIGHTS

● A key to meeting design specifications in a product or service is to reduce output variability. When in a state of statistical control, output subject to common causes of variation follows a stable probability distribution. When assignable causes of variation are present, the process is out of statistical control. SQC methods are used to detect the presence of assignable causes of variation.

● A process can be in statistical control but still not be capable of producing all of its output within design specifications.

● Inspection stations should be located at the point where incoming materials are received, at selected points in the process, and at the end of the process. The cost of inspection should be weighed against the cost of passing defective items downstream in the process and defective products to the customer.

● Statistical process control charts are useful for measuring the current quality generated by the process and for detecting whether the process has changed to the detriment of quality. The use of p-charts and $\bar{x}$-charts can help management identify abnormal variations in the process average. c-charts are used when the number of defects cannot be measured as a proportion. The presence of abnormal variations triggers a search for assignable causes. The use of R-charts can help management define abnormal variations in process variability.

● Process variability should be in control before process average control charts are constructed. The reason is that the average range is used in the calculation of control limits for process average control charts. Crucial decisions in the design of control charts are sample size and control limits.

● The use of p-charts requires a larger sample size than does the use of $\bar{x}$-charts, but the measurement of attributes may be easier than the measurement of variables. Larger samples provide greater protection in detecting a shift in the process average than do smaller samples. Also, the sample should be homogeneous with respect to potential causes of quality problems.

● The central line of a control chart can be the average of past averages of the quality measurement or a management target related to product specifications. The spread in control limits affects the chances of detecting a shift in the process average or range, as well as the chances of searching for assignable causes when none exist.

● Acceptance-sampling plans and statistical process control methods are useful for appraising the degree of quality performance and identifying where problems exist in quality reliability.

● Acceptance sampling is concerned with the decision to accept or reject a certain quantity of goods. The design of the acceptance-sampling process includes decisions about sampling versus complete inspection, attribute versus variable measures, AQL, α, LTPD, β, sample size, and the acceptable number of defective items in the sample.

● Sampling using attributes can be done with single-sampling, double-sampling, or sequential-sampling plans. The latter two have an advantage over single-sampling plans because the average sample size needed to make a decision is less when the lot proportion defective is either very low or very high. Management can select the best plan (choosing sample size n and acceptance number c) by using an operating characteristic curve.

KEY TERMS

acceptable quality level
  (AQL) **149**
acceptance sampling **130**
assignable causes of
  variation **132**
attributes **134**
average outgoing quality
  (*AOQ*) **156**
c-chart **142**
common causes of
  variation **132**
consumer's risk (β) **149**

double-sampling plan **157**
lot tolerance proportion
  defective (LTPD) **149**
nominal value **133**
operating characteristic (OC)
  curve **150**
p-chart **139**
process capability **133**
process control **132**
producer's risk (α) **149**
R-chart **143**

sequential-sampling
  plan **158**
single-sampling plan **150**
statistical process control
  (SPC) **130**
statistical quality control
  (SQC) **130**
tolerance **133**
traditional statistical
  techniques **130**
variables **133**
$\bar{x}$-chart **143**

STUDY QUESTIONS

1. Explain how a process can be in statistical control but still produce bad products.

2. What is the rationale for having upper and lower control limits in process control charts?

3. What are the critical design parameters that must be specified for control charts? Are they interrelated? Explain.

4. What factors should be considered regarding inspection station location?

5. Using sampling to determine conformance to quality specifications involves certain risks. What are they?

6. Explain the trade-offs that are made in choosing the sample size n and the acceptance number c in a single-sampling plan for attributes.

7. What are the considerations involved in choosing between sampling and complete inspections? Between variables and attributes?

8. How can an operating characteristic curve help management settle on the design parameters for a single-sampling plan?

9. For a given AQL and LTPD, what is the effect on α and β in a single-sampling plan of increasing the acceptance number c while holding the sample size n constant? Explain.

10. For a given AQL and LTPD, what is the effect on α and β in a single-sampling plan of increasing the sample size n while holding the acceptance number c constant? Explain.

11. Compare and contrast single-sampling plans, double-sampling plans, and sequential-sampling plans. What are the implications for inspection costs?

PROBLEMS

Review Problems

1. The Webster Chemical Company produces mastics and caulking for the construction industry. The product is blended in large mixers and then pumped into tubes and capped. The company is concerned with the possibility of underfilling the tubes, thereby short-changing the customer. Twenty samples of 150 tubes each had the number of underfilled tubes shown in Table 4.10.

   a. Construct a p-chart for this situation. Use $z = 3$ and the historical average defective from Table 4.10 as the central line of the chart.

   b. Comment on the process average proportion defective for the samples in Table 4.10.

2. The Emerald Dormer is a luxury hotel in Key West, Florida. The manager of the hotel was interested in the overall quality of service the hotel was providing to its customers. A unique customer survey system was developed to collect data and help the manager to make a judgment. Each customer was given a survey card and a blank envelope. The survey card contained a number of specific questions about various services and asked the customer to score the overall service on a scale from 0 to 100, with 100 considered excellent. The customer could fill out the card anonymously and put it in the envelope. If it was given to the desk clerk at checkout, the customer received a 5 percent discount on the bill. The program was very successful, and only a negligible number of customers ever turned in blank cards.

   The manager of the hotel considered a score of 75 on the overall evaluation the breakpoint between acceptable and unacceptable service. Each week, 50 envelopes were picked at random, opened, and examined. If the overall score on a card was less than 75, the card was considered "defective." The manager felt that an average proportion defective of 0.10 meant that service was in control (that is, 90 percent of the customers thought that service was good or better).

   a. Specify the control limits of a p-chart for the manager of the hotel. As service is considered so important, $z = 2$ is desired. The cost of searching for service-quality problems is far outweighed by the cost of a shift in overall customer satisfaction with the service received.

TABLE 4.10

Sample Number	Number of Underfilled Tubes	Sample Number	Number of Underfilled Tubes
1	10	12	20
2	16	13	7
3	11	14	15
4	24	15	11
5	20	16	8
6	8	17	29
7	9	18	14
8	12	19	16
9	28	20	12
10	8	Total	298
11	20		

b. The following are the results of the past five weeks of sampling.

Sample	Score of < 75
March 1	12
March 8	3
March 15	18
March 22	21
March 29	8

Suppose that you are in charge of recording the results of the samples. What would you tell the manager about the overall service quality of the hotel? Would you make any recommendations?

3. The Stosh Motor Company manufactures bolts for its model X-350 high-performance racing engine. If defective, the bolts typically have damaged threads or improper diameters. A defect can be easily discovered by threading the bolt into a block of steel with a hole of correct threading and diameter. If a defective bolt is passed to the assembly line there is a chance that the threads in the engine block hole will be damaged or that the bolt may work itself loose during operation of the engine. The historical proportion defective average has been 0.015.

   a. Set up a *p*-chart for this process. Assume that management wants 99.7 percent of the normal variation to fall within the control limits. The sample size is 16.

   b. The following numbers of defects were found in the last five samples. Is there a need for concern?

Sample	Number of Bad Bolts
1	1
2	1
3	2
4	2
5	3

4. The Metropolitan Transit Company serves the town of Brandywine. Bus passengers are encouraged to comment on the service they receive by filling out postcards located in holders on the back of each seat. While the company is concerned with all comments, it is considered normal to receive 4 complaints per week. Since funding for bus service is partially provided through taxpayer-approved levies, monitoring the complaints is very important. Metropolitan uses two-sigma control limits on its *c*-chart. Over the past six weeks, the following numbers of complaints were registered: 2, 7, 3, 5, 9 and 6. Is there any reason for management to take action?

5. Your company produces plastic sheeting for use in the construction industry. The process for producing the sheeting must be controlled so as to keep the number of dimples per sheet low. Contractors do not mind a few dimples in the sheets, but they complain if there are too many. When the process was in control, the following defects were found in randomly selected sheets over an extended period of time:

Sheet	Dimples	Sheet	Dimples
1	4	6	10
2	7	7	2
3	2	8	12
4	8	9	7
5	13	10	5

   a. Construct a *c*-chart for the number of dimples per sheet. Use three-sigma limits.

   b. Suppose the next three sheets sampled had 3, 16, and 12 dimples respectively. What can you say about the process now?

6. The Canine Gourmet Company produces delicious dog treats for canines with discriminating tastes. One particular treat, Super Breath, combines chlorophyl and retsin to form a breath sweetener most appreciated by people who own large dogs. Since the primary consumers of this product get violent if the boxes of Super Breath are underfilled, management would like to closely monitor the box filling line to make sure that the pro-

cess is in control. The filling line is set for 680 grams in each box.

An inspector at the end of the filling line periodically selects a random sample of eight boxes and weighs the contents. The historical range in the weight of each sample has averaged 15 grams, which is considered normal for this process.

a. Design an R-chart and an $\bar{x}$-chart for this process.

b. The results from the last four samples are

Sample	Average Weight (g)	Range (g)
1	684.3	10.6
2	690.2	25.8
3	673.4	14.2
4	691.8	19.4

Is the process in control? Explain.

7. The Marlin Company produces plastic bottles to customer order. Management is concerned about the process that produces the Golden Hair Shampoo bottle. The quality inspector randomly selects four bottles from the bottle machine and measures the inside diameter of the bottle neck, a critical quality dimension for the producer of Golden Hair. The dimensions (inch) from the last five samples are

	Bottle			
Sample	1	2	3	4
1	0.757	0.741	0.746	0.753
2	0.751	0.753	0.742	0.755
3	0.740	0.742	0.756	0.759
4	0.753	0.740	0.748	0.760
5	0.768	0.752	0.743	0.746

a. Assuming that using only five samples is sufficient, use the data in the table to construct R- and $\bar{x}$-charts. Is the process in statistical control?

b. Suppose the specifications on the bottle are 0.750 ± 0.009 inch. Is the process capable of producing the bottle? Discuss.

8. The Mega-Byte Academy is an exclusive school for teaching the fine art of computer programming. Only those students who have impeccable scholastic records and a high aptitude for programming are admitted. In an attempt to judge and monitor the quality of instruction, the administration devised an examination to test students on the basic concepts that all should have learned.

Each year, a random sample of 10 graduating students is selected for the test. The average score is used to track the quality of the educational process. Prior experience with this exam indicates that the average range of student scores is 20. Test results for the past 10 years are

Year	Sample $\bar{x}$	Year	Sample $\bar{x}$
1983	80.31	1988	80.62
1984	74.37	1989	75.00
1985	78.12	1990	81.87
1986	80.00	1991	74.06
1987	81.25	1992	77.50

a. Set up an $\bar{x}$-chart using this historical information.

b. This year the exam was given again. Scores for individual students were

$$63 \quad 57 \quad 92 \quad 87 \quad 70$$
$$61 \quad 75 \quad 58 \quad 63 \quad 71$$

What comments would you make to the administration of the Mega-Byte Academy?

9. You are responsible for purchasing bearings for the maintenance department of a large airline. The bearings are under contract from a local supplier and you must devise an appropriate acceptance sampling plan for them. Management has stated in the contract that the acceptable quality level is 1 percent defective. In addition, the lot tolerance proportion defective is 4 percent, the producer's risk is 5 percent, and the consumer's risk is 10 percent.

a. Specify an appropriate acceptance sampling plan that meets all these criteria.

b. Draw the OC curve for your plan. What is the resultant producer's risk?

c. Determine the *AOQL* for your plan. Assume the lot size is 3000.

10. The Lustre-Potion Shampoo Company purchases the label that is pasted on each bottle of shampoo it sells. The label contains the company logo, the name of the product, and directions for the product's use. Sometimes the printing on the label is blurred or the colors are not right. The company would like to design an acceptable sampling plan for the purchased item. The acceptable quality level is 10 defectives per 1000 labels and the lot tolerance proportion defective 0.05. Management would like to find a plan in which the producer's risk is 0.05 or less and the consumer's risk is 0.10 or less.

a. Specify a plan that satisfies those directives.

b. What is the probability that a shipment with 3 percent defectives will be rejected by the plan?

c. Determine the *AOQL* for your plan. Assume the lot size is 2000 labels.

11. Your company supplies sterile syringes to a distributor of hospital supplies. The contract states that quality should be no worse than 0.20 percent defective, or 20 parts in 10,000. During negotiations, you found out that the distributor will use an acceptance sampling plan, with $n = 400$, to test quality.

a. You feel strongly that the producer's risk (that is, the probability that a good shipment will be sent back to you) should be no greater than 5 percent. What is the lowest acceptance level that should be used?

b. You realize that your system's average performance has only been 25 parts in 10,000. Given $n = 400$ and the acceptance level you suggested in (a), what is the probability that a shipment will be returned to you?

c. Given (b), suppose that you want a less than 5 percent chance that your shipment will be returned to you. What acceptance level value should you have suggested in (a)? What is the producer's risk for that plan?

12. A buyer of electronic components has a lot tolerance proportion defective of 40 parts in 10,000, with a consumer's risk of 10 percent. If the buyer will sample 2000 components out of the shipment, what acceptance level value would the buyer want? What is the producer's risk if the AQL is 10 parts per 10,000? Use Table 4.6 and the buyer's desired acceptance level to propose a compromise to the supplier. (You need not design a new sampling plan.)

13. Consider a certain raw material for which a single-sampling plan using attributes is needed. The AQL is 0.01 and the LTPD is 0.040. Two plans have been proposed:

Plan 1	Plan 2
$n = 100$	$n = 200$
$c = 3$	$c = 6$

Are the two plans equivalent? Substantiate your response by determining the producer's and consumer's risk for each plan.

14. You presently have an acceptance-sampling plan in which $n = 50$ and $c = 1$, but you are unsatisfied with its performance. The AQL is 0.01 and the LTPD is 0.05.

a. What are the producer's and consumer's risks for this plan?

b. Specify a plan that will decrease the producer's risk and the consumer's risk. Specify the producer's and consumer's new risks.

c. Compare the *AOQL*s for your plan and the old plan. Assume the lot size is 1000 units.

Advanced Problems

A computer package is recommended for solving Problems 15–20.

15. Suppose that AQL $= 0.005$, $\alpha = 0.05$, LTPD $= 0.02$, $\beta = 0.06$, and $N = 1000$.

a. Find the *AOQL* for the single-sampling plan that best fits the given parameter values.

b. For each of the following experiments, find the *AOQL* for the best single-sampling plan. Change only the parameter indicated, holding all others at their original values.

    i. Change N to 2000.

    ii. Change AQL to 0.008.

    iii. Change LTPD to 0.060.

c. Discuss the effects of changes in the design parameters on plan performance, based on the three experiments in (b).

16. Mark Edwards is the Quality Assurance Manager at an engine plant. The summer intern assigned to Edwards is a student in operations management at a local university. The intern has been assigned to calculate the following, given the SPC information at the engine plant:

$$
\begin{array}{ll}
\text{AQL} = 0.002 & \beta = 0.01 \\
\alpha = 0.02 & N = 1000 \\
\text{LTPD} = 0.025 &
\end{array}
$$

a. Find the *AOQL* for the single-sampling plan that best fits the given parameter values.

b. For each of the following experiments, find the *AOQL* for the best single-sampling plan. Change only the parameter indicated, holding all others at their original values.

    i. Change N to 2000.

    ii. Change AQL to 0.003.

    iii. Change LTPD to 0.04.

c. Discuss the effects of changes in the design parameters on plan performance, based on the three experiments in (b).

17. The Mansfield Machinery Company produces various types of hand-held tools that are manufactured on an assembly line that produces one product every minute. On one of their products, the critical quality dimension is the diameter (measured in thousandths of an inch) of a hole that is bored out in one of the subassemblies. Management would like to detect any shift in the process average diameter from 0.015 inch. Management considers the variance in the process to be in control. Historically, the average range has been 0.002 inch, regardless of the process average. You have been asked to design an $\bar{x}$-chart to control this process. The center line of the chart should be 0.015 inch and the control limits should be three-sigma from the center line. The sample size and the frequency of sampling was left to you to analyze.

To test your design, management has provided the results of 80 minutes of output from the production line. (See Table 4.11.) During this 80 minutes the process average changed once. All measurements are in thousandths of an inch.

a. Set up an $\bar{x}$-chart with $n = 4$. The frequency should be sample 4, then skip 4. Thus your first sample would be for minutes 1–4, the second would be for minutes 9–12, and so on. When would you stop the process to check for a change in the process average?

b. Set up an $\bar{x}$-chart with $n = 8$. The frequency should be sample 8, then skip 4.

    i. When would you stop the process now?

    ii. What can you say about the desirability of large samples on a frequent sampling interval?

18. Using the data from Problem 17, continue your analysis of sample size and frequency by trying the following plans.

a. Using the $\bar{x}$-chart for $n = 4$, try the frequency sample 4, then skip 8. When would you stop the process in this case?

b. Using the $\bar{x}$-chart for $n = 8$, try the frequency sample 8, then skip 8. When would you consider the process out of control?

c. Using your results from (a) and (b), what trade-offs would you consider in choosing between them?

174 *CHAPTER 4 / Statistical Quality Control*

TABLE 4.11

Minute	Diameter	Minute	Diameter	Minute	Diameter
1	15	28	17	55	14
2	16	29	18	56	16
3	18	30	15	57	15
4	14	31	16	58	17
5	16	32	15	59	18
6	17	33	14	60	14
7	15	34	15	61	15
8	14	35	16	62	16
9	14	36	17	63	17
10	13	37	18	64	18
11	16	38	16	65	13
12	17	39	15	66	15
13	15	40	16	67	14
14	16	41	16	68	14
15	17	42	14	69	16
16	16	43	17	70	15
17	14	44	18	71	17
18	14	45	19	72	18
19	13	46	15	73	16
20	14	47	16	74	16
21	15	48	15	75	17
22	16	49	12	76	18
23	15	50	17	77	16
24	17	51	16	78	15
25	14	52	14	79	14
26	13	53	15	80	17
27	15	54	17		

19. The plant manager at Northern Pines Brewery was recently fired because of a lack of control over the bottling line. No one knew what the quality of the bottling process was or what its problems were. A strong advocate of statistical process control, the new plant manager decided to gather data on the number of defective bottles generated on the line. Every day a random sample of 250 bottles was inspected for fill level, cracked bottles, bad labels, and poor seals. Any bottle failing to meet the standard for any of these criteria was counted as a reject. The study lasted 30 weeks and yielded the data in Table 4.12.

Based on these data, what can you tell the new plant manager about the quality of the bottling line? Do you see any nonrandom behavior in the bottling process? If so, what might cause this behavior?

20. Red Baron Airlines serves hundreds of cities per day, but competition is increasing from smaller companies affiliated with major

TABLE 4.12

Sample	Rejected Bottles	Sample	Rejected Bottles	Sample	Rejected Bottles
1	4	11	4	21	13
2	9	12	6	22	11
3	6	13	8	23	7
4	12	14	10	24	3
5	8	15	12	25	2
6	2	16	4	26	8
7	13	17	3	27	11
8	10	18	10	28	6
9	1	19	14	29	9
10	9	20	5	30	5

TABLE 4.13

Sample	Late Planes	Sample	Late Planes	Sample	Late Planes
1	3	11	3	21	12
2	8	12	5	22	10
3	5	13	7	23	6
4	11	14	9	24	2
5	7	15	12	25	1
6	2	16	5	26	8
7	12	17	4	27	4
8	9	18	9	28	5
9	1	19	13	29	8
10	8	20	4	30	2

carriers. One of the key competitive priorities is on-time arrivals and departures. Red Baron defines *on time* as any arrival or departure that takes place within 15 minutes of the scheduled time. To stay on top of the market, management has set the high standard of 98 percent on-time performance. The operations department was put in charge of monitoring the performance of the airline. Each week, a random sample of 300 flight arrivals and departures was checked for schedule performance. Table 4.13 contains the number of arrivals or departures over the last 30 weeks that did not meet Red Baron's definition of on-time service. What can you tell management about the quality of service? Do you see any nonrandom behavior in the process? If so, what might cause the behavior?

John Troll, chief executive officer and president of the Merry Gremlin Plastics Company, was concerned over the operating reports from the plastic bottle division. This year, the division reported more than $150,000 in scrap losses—a significant percentage of their total operating budget. Although he had heard a number of suggestions from the division personnel, he decided to hire an outside consultant to find out if anything could be done to improve the quality of production. Jane Carroway, the consultant, had a brief meeting with Troll and was given free access to the personnel and company records. Carroway realized that, given this much latitude, she had better come up with some solid suggestions for improvement.

Background

The Merry Gremlin Plastics Company has sales of $50 million and employs 200 hourly employees. Since the founding of the company 30 years ago, the major competitive weapons in the marketplace have been quality and customer service. The words of John Troll, Sr., the founder of Merry Gremlin, are still etched in a granite pillar outside the main doors to the customer lobby: "Honor your customers. Give them a high-quality product when they want it. They, in turn, will honor you."

The plastic bottle division manufactures plastic containers for companies producing a variety of products ranging from milk to shampoo. Most of the production is custom-made to customers' specifications and design, and many of the customers demand high volumes of product. The production process itself is not very complicated. Raw materials including resins, polyethylene, and coloring agents are mixed and fed to the hot-stamp machines, where air pressure is used to form the bottles in specially designed molds. If the bottles are to be decorated they are processed on either the silk-screen labeling machines or the common paper labeling machines depending on the type of decoration the customer specifies. The bottles are then packed in boxes for shipment to the customer. Defective bottles can be reground and used as raw material only if they have not been decorated.

The plastic bottle division currently operates three shifts seven days per week. The first shift starts at 6 A.M., the second at 2 P.M., and the third at 10 P.M. There are fifty hourly workers and supervisors, in-

cluding five part-time workers, in the division. The supervisors report to Sam Jenkins, the manager of the plastic bottle division, who in turn reports to Jack Holly, the director of manufacturing.

Production Perspectives

Carroway decided that she had better find out what Sam Jenkins thought about the quality problems in the plastic bottle division. After some reflection, Sam had these comments:

> We try our best to keep defects down, but we are operating at full capacity now and it's hard for our supervisors to keep track of everything that goes on. We have had a lot of machine downtime and some of our supervisors are spending a significant portion of their work hours actually repairing machines. For example, we have had trouble with some of the hot-stamp machines keeping enough air pressure. When the air pressure is too low, the bottles look like a forklift truck ran over them. We have to stop the production line and figure out what's wrong—this can take quite a while.
>
> I also wish we could get more cooperation from the sales department. We seem to be getting a lot of small, special orders with short lead times lately. It takes as much as four hours to reset the machines for the raw bottles. Each time you reset the machines you're asking for quality problems. In addition, we lose resin and polyethylene when the machines are adjusted—it actually falls to the floor and gets contaminated so that it can't be used. I figure we lose about 10 percent of these materials that way.

Quality Management Perspectives

Carroway's next interview was with Bob Summers, the quality control manager. Summers had a lot of information about the quality program at Merry Gremlin.

> I have twelve inspectors reporting to me. Only three of them are assigned to the plastic bottle division because the toy division is so much larger. They work from Monday to Friday, 8 A.M. to 5 P.M. They certainly earn their pay because of all the problems we have there.
>
> We check a number of quality characteristics on the bottles. The obvious ones are rough finish (rough

edges or threads) and bad color. We also check the height of the bottle neck, the outside diameter of the neck (including thread depth), the inside diameter of the neck, and the thickness of the walls. For a given bottle design, we have preset gauges that can tell us quickly if the bottle is within tolerance.

We did a pilot study for a high-volume product where we measured the inside diameter of the bottle. I will see that you get a copy. [See Exhibit 1.]

In general, I feel there are two problems we should address. First, I do not think that the production people are concerned enough about quality. The workers don't seem to know what good quality control is or, for that matter, what to look for. The workers should do more quality control themselves. Secondly, we don't find out that there is a quality problem quickly

enough. Then, once we see there is a problem, we don't know what the cause is in most cases. Perhaps you can help.

QUESTIONS

1. Exhibit 1 shows some recent experiences with a quality characteristic associated with the bottle for Sticky Glue. Assume the sample size is 10 bottles. The target value of the inside diameter is 0.7500 inch and the average range has been 0.012 inch. What can you say about the process average based upon the data in Exhibit 1?

2. Address the sources of quality problems brought out in the interviews. What can be done to resolve them?

EXHIBIT 1 / Pilot Study of Inside Diameter Measurements

Product Sticky Glue   **Date** September 8–10, 1992

Carton Size 10   **Dimension** Inside Diameter   **Specification** 0.7500 inch

Sample		Average Diameter*	Sample		Average Diameter*
Day	Hour		Day	Hour	
Sunday	12 noon	0.7483	Monday	6PM	0.7469
Sunday	2PM	0.7451	Monday	8PM	0.7450
Sunday	4PM	0.7502	Monday	10PM	0.7490
Sunday	6PM	0.7523	Tuesday	12 midnight	0.7482
Sunday	8PM	0.7460	Tuesday	2AM	0.7542
Sunday	10PM	0.7500	Tuesday	4AM	0.7510
Monday	12 midnight	0.7465	Tuesday	6AM	0.7498
Monday	2AM	0.7540	Tuesday	8AM	0.7530
Monday	4AM	0.7542	Tuesday	10AM	0.7481
Monday	6AM	0.7483	Tuesday	12 noon	0.7503
Monday	8AM	0.7520	Tuesday	2PM	0.7525
Monday	10AM	0.7501	Tuesday	4PM	0.7470
Monday	12 noon	0.7475	Tuesday	6PM	0.7542
Monday	2PM	0.7472	Tuesday	8PM	0.7544
Monday	4PM	0.7521	Tuesday	10PM	0.7452

*The average range of the diameters in each sample was 0.0120 inches. There was no reason to believe the process variability was out of control.

SELECTED REFERENCES

Charbonneau, Harvey C., and Gordon L. Webster. *Industrial Quality Control.* Englewood Cliffs, N.J.: Prentice–Hall, 1978.

Crosby, Philip B. *Quality Is Free: The Art of Making Quality Certain.* New York: McGraw-Hill, 1979.

Deming, W. Edwards. *Out of the Crisis.* Cambridge, Mass.: MIT Center for Advanced Engineering Study, 1986.

Dodge, Harold F., and Harry G. Romig. *Sampling Inspection Tables—Single and Double Sampling,* 2d ed. New York: John Wiley & Sons, 1959.

Duncan, Acheson J. *Quality Control and Industrial Statistics,* 4th ed. Homewood, Ill.: Richard D. Irwin, 1974.

Feigenbaum, A.V. *Total Quality Control: Engineering Management.* New York: McGraw–Hill, 1961.

Fetter, Robert B. *The Quality Control System.* Homewood, Ill.: Richard D. Irwin, 1967.

Ishikawa, Kaoru. *Guide to Quality Control.* Tokyo: Asian Productivity Organization, 1972.

Juran, J.M., and F.M. Gryna, Jr. *Quality Planning and Analysis.* New York: McGraw–Hill, 1970.

Saniga, Erwin M., and Larry E. Shirland. "Quality Control in Practice—A Survey." *Quality Progress,* May 1977, pp. 30–33.

Sullivan, L.P. "The Seven Stages in Company-Wide Quality Control." *Quality Progress,* May 1986.

Wald, A. *Sequential Analysis.* New York: John Wiley & Sons, 1947.

Chapter 5   PROCESS DESIGN

What mix of resources should we use to produce our goods and services?

Do we need general-purpose or special-purpose equipment, and how flexible should our work force be?

Can we use flow diagrams, process charts, or multiple activity charts to study and improve our operations?

How much should we depend on machinery and automated processes?

How much of our supply chain should we control?

How much should we involve our customers in the production process?

Once a firm has identified its market niche and the competitive priorities that spell success, it must design an operations system to meet its needs. K2 Corporation, the largest U.S. manufacturer of Alpine skis, chose an intermediate positioning strategy that allowed customization and high-volume production of some products. High-performance design and quality became competitive priorities. The next step was to design a manufacturing process that would deliver.

For customization, K2 installed general-purpose machinery that allowed easy changeovers from product to product. For design and quality, they invested in a triaxial braiding process that gave designers greater control over longitudinal and torsional flexes in the skis. K2's plant has five departments: parts, molding, base finishing, graphics, and finishing. Molding has 52 general-purpose presses, some dedicated to high-volume products. Within base finishing and finishing, machines are arranged to use the machine sequences common to most products.

One essential question in the design of a production system is, *How* should we make our products or provide our services? The question is obvious, but the answer involves many different choices in selecting the best mix of human resources, equipment, and materials. Process design choices are strategically important. Wrong choices can affect an organization's ability to compete over the long run. Process design directly affects productivity because much of the input of the output/input ratio is set during process design. However, process design choices are not made once and for all—process design is an ongoing activity. Its principles apply to both first-time and redesign choices.

We begin by defining and considering four facets of process design: capital intensity, resource flexibility, vertical integration, and customer involvement. We turn next to some basic techniques for analyzing new and existing processes: capital budgeting, flow diagrams, process charts, and multiple activity charts. In Chapter 6 we explore technological advances, an important aspect of process design, and the ever-widening array of choices they present. Chapter 7 covers the other critical aspect of process design: job design and work teams.

WHAT IS PROCESS DESIGN?

Process design is the selection of inputs, operations, work flows, and methods for producing goods and services. Input selection includes choosing the mix of human skills, raw materials, and equipment consistent with an organization's positioning strategy and its ability to obtain these resources. Operations managers must determine which operations will be performed by workers and which by machines. They also determine the transformations (see Fig. 1.1) that will be used to meld human beings and machines into cohesive production processes. Process design or redesign decisions must be made when:

- A new or substantially modified product or service is being offered.
- Competitive priorities have changed.
- Demand volume for a product or service is changing.
- Current performance is inadequate.

*T*he revolutionary triaxial braiding process at K2 creates a tight fiberglass casing around a wood core, producing an extremely strong and durable ski.

- Competitors are gaining by using a new process or technology.
- The cost or availability of inputs has changed.

Not all these situations lead to a change in the current process. Sometimes the costs of change clearly outweigh the benefits. Whether or not changes are made, process design must take into account other choices concerning product and service design, quality, capacity, and layout. Process design decisions also depend on where products and services are in their life cycle, on competitive priorities, and on positioning strategy. Ethics and the environment are other considerations, as Managerial Practice 5.1 shows.

FACETS OF PROCESS DESIGN

Whether considering processes for offices, service industries, or manufacturers, operations managers must weigh four common facets of process design. **Capital intensity** is the mix of equipment and human skills in a production process; the greater the relative cost of equipment, the greater is the capital intensity. **Resource flexibility** is the ease with which equipment and employees can handle a wide variety of products, output levels, duties, and functions. **Vertical integration** is the degree to which a firm's own production system handles the supply chain from raw materials to final consumer. The more a firm's production system manages the supply chain, the greater is the degree of vertical integration. **Customer involvement** reflects how much and in what ways the customer becomes a part of the production process.

181

Ethics

Wall Street has been in love with Nucor Corporation, which has transformed itself from a backwater fabricator into the seventh-largest U.S. steel company. Its minimills, which spin gleaming sheet steel out of scrapped cars and refrigerators, are efficient and profitable. Most of its 15 minimills are situated in small towns, where they employ and train people who never thought that they would make so much money. "Every manager wondering what it takes to compete in the twenty-first century needs to know the Nucor story," said Ann McLaughlin, the former U.S. secretary of labor. But there is another side of the Nucor story. Since 1980, its worker death rate has been the highest in the steel industry. Eleven employees have died as a result of accidents. Six more have died in accidents during construction of new plants. A review of court and safety documents and interviews with employees suggest that Nucor's work methods (and thus process design) and rush to maximize productivity may have a human cost. Nucor is a highly decentralized company that leaves safety up to the individual plant managers.

And the Environment

The chemical industry's record on the environment has been bad, and it still accounts for almost half of all toxic pollution produced in the United States. Things are changing, however, in part due to the legacy of Bhopal, India, where 3800 people died following the release of toxic gas at a Union Carbide Corporation subsidiary in 1984. Chemical companies are beginning to view waste as a measure of efficiency. The more unusable by-products a process creates, the less efficient it is. The Du Pont Company plant in Beaumont, Texas, used to spew out a staggering 110 million pounds of waste annually as by-products of making plastics and paint. By adjusting its process design to use less of one raw material, it slashed the waste by two thirds. Du Pont's chairman and chief executive officer sees waste reduction as a way to achieve a competitive advantage.

Sources: "Nucor Steel's Sheen Is Marred by Deaths of Workers at Plants," *Wall Street Journal*, May 10, 1991; "Chemical Firms Find That It Pays to Reduce Pollution at Source," *Wall Street Journal*, May 10, 1991.

Because the facets of process design are interrelated, a manager's choices concerning one may significantly affect choices concerning the others. Sales, as well as production costs, are affected by the manager's choices. For example, automation of GE's dishwasher plant in Louisville, Kentucky, which was an increase in capital intensity, helped increase the firm's market share from 32 to 40 percent. The state-of-the-art plant improved product quality and thus sales.

Capital Intensity

Whether designing a new process or redesigning an existing one, an operations manager must determine which tasks will be performed by human beings and which by machines. With the increased sophistication of modern computer hardware and software, process designers face an ever-widening range of choices, from operations requiring very little automation to those requiring task-specific equipment and very little human intervention. Automation is often heralded as a necessary ingredient to gaining competitive advantage. Actually there are both advantages and disadvantages: The automation decision requires careful examination.

Computers can significantly increase productivity. For example, Bailey Company, an independent Arby's franchisee based in Lakewood, Colorado, has installed computerized devices in its roast beef restaurants. Customers actually punch in their own orders on the devices, giving them more control over their orders and increasing employee efficiency amid a labor shortage. As the customer places the order, it appears on a similar screen in the kitchen area, eliminating the need for clerks to shout or walk orders back to the cooks. The system allows one clerk to handle two terminals for two lines of customers and has improved both service time (by about 20 seconds per order) and order accuracy. The system also encourages sales. For example, if a customer orders a sandwich and a salad but no soft drink, the screen illuminates a printed message suggesting a refreshing soda.

More capital intensity is not always best. A case in point is E.T. Wright's shoemaking plant, which a recent survey selected as one of the country's ten best-managed factories. The company still relies on skilled artisans and hand labor to make its arch-preserver shoes. Competitive priorities call for a unique product of high quality, even if a pair of shoes retails for more than $150. The firm has not been able to achieve these priorities with high capital intensity.

Some types of equipment can be acquired a piece at a time, allowing the user to try it out without making a large and risky initial capital investment. Examples of such equipment are new photocopy machines and stand-alone word processors and printers. However, many other technological choices involve large and costly systems—and a great deal more capital and risk.

Resource Flexibility

In Chapter 2 we discussed customization and volume flexibility as competitive priorities. Process design affects a firm's ability to achieve either one. And the choices that management makes concerning employees, facilities, and equipment determine the degree of resource flexibility. For example, when product plans call for short life cycles or high customization, equipment must be general purpose and employees need to perform a broad range of duties. Otherwise resource utilization will be too low for economical operation.

Until recently, the low production volumes associated with short life cycles and customization meant that a firm could not justify the investment dollars required to be capital intensive. The result was a strong inverse relationship between capital intensity and resource flexibility: When one was low the other was high. Figure 5.1 illustrates this relationship for two processes. Process 1 calls for inexpensive general-purpose equipment. It gets the job done but not at peak efficiency. Although fixed costs (F_1) are low, making it a less capital-intensive process, the variable unit cost (the slope of the total cost line) is high. Process 2 is more capital intensive: Although its fixed costs (F_2) are high, it is a more efficient process and therefore has a lower variable unit cost. Such efficiency often is possible only because the equipment is designed for a narrow range of products or tasks.

The break-even quantity in Fig. 5.1 is the quantity at which the total costs for the two alternatives are equal. At quantities beyond this point, the cost of process 1 exceeds that for process 2. The break-even quantity in Fig. 5.1 is well to the right on the graph. Therefore, unless the firm expects to sell more than that amount (which is unlikely with high customization), the efficiency of

FIGURE 5.1

Relationship Between
Capital Intensity and
Product Volume

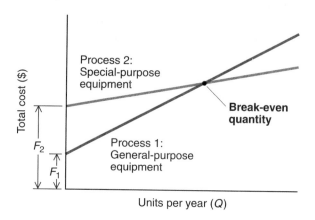

process 2 is not warranted. For example, General Electric built a plant in Lynn, Massachusetts, to make parts for T700 jet engines at extremely low variable unit costs. The $52 million plant was highly automated (high fixed costs) and custom built to make these engines. Unfortunately, the Pentagon failed to order engines in the numbers anticipated, so the plant was running at only 60 percent of capacity—too low for an efficient operation. Also, the inflexibility of the process design makes it difficult to manufacture other products. The plant was built to make T700s—or similar-sized engines—and nothing else.

Exceptions to the inverse relationship between capital intensity and flexibility are beginning to emerge. As you will see in Chapter 6, technologies allowing certain types of flexible automation (such as robots) are now available. They are capital intensive but allow for more resource flexibility than in the past.

Resource flexibility also has important implications for the work force. Operations managers must decide whether to have a **flexible work force.** Members of a flexible work force are capable of doing many tasks, either at their own work stations or as they move from one work station to another. Such flexibility often comes at a cost, requiring greater skills and thus more training and education. Nevertheless, benefits can be large. We showed in one study that worker flexibility is one of the best ways to achieve reliable customer service and alleviate capacity bottlenecks (Ritzman, King, and Krajewski, 1984). We found resource flexibility to be particularly crucial to process-focused positioning strategy. Resource flexibility helps absorb the feast-or-famine workloads at individual operations that are caused by low-volume production, jumbled routings, and fluid scheduling.

Resource flexibility is practiced by manufacturers such as Westinghouse and Corning. Westinghouse's overhaul of its Sumter, South Carolina, plant allowed employees to perform a variety of tasks and resulted in increased productivity and capacity. Corning recently opened a plant in Blacksburg, Virginia, and trained its employees to have interchangeable skills. The workers must learn three skill modules—or families of skills—within two years to keep their jobs. A multiskilled work force is one reason why the Blacksburg Corning plant turned a $2 million profit in its first eight months of production, instead of losing $2.3 million as projected for the startup period. Training has been extensive, however. In the first year of production, 25 percent of all hours worked were devoted to training, at a cost of about $750,000.

Resource flexibility is also an issue in the service sector. Administrators of large urban hospitals must make decisions about staffing and degrees of specialization. Many hospitals use all registered nurses (RNs) instead of a mix of RNs, licensed vocational nurses (LVNs), and aides. Registered nurses have a higher education level and earn more than LVNs and aides, but they are more flexible and can perform all nursing tasks. Sometimes hospitals choose the opposite extreme (worker specialization) in an attempt to hold costs down. In Russia, for example, delicate eye surgery is performed in an "assembly line" consisting of patients on stretchers that move past five work stations. A surgeon at each station has three minutes to complete a specific portion of the operation before the patient moves on to the next surgeon. Obviously, these surgeons are highly specialized. Resource flexibility has been sacrificed, but great speed and economy are attained.

The type of work force required also depends on the need for volume flexibility. When conditions allow for a smooth, steady rate of output, the likely choice is a permanent work force that expects regular full-time employment. If the process is subject to hourly, daily, or seasonal peaks and valleys in demand, the use of part-time or temporary employees to supplement a smaller core of full-time employees may be the best solution. However, this approach may not be practical if knowledge and skill requirements are too high for a temporary worker to grasp quickly.

THE BIG PICTURE

Process Design at King Soopers Bakery

Now pause for a moment and look at The Big Picture illustration on pages 186–187. We have literally lifted the roof of a multiproduct bakery, King Soopers, a division of Kroger Company, in Denver, Colorado, to show you process design at work in a real setting.

Notice that capital intensity and resource flexibility vary inversely, appropriate to the products made at King Soopers. To produce a relatively high volume of products (loaves of bread) efficiently, the bread line must be highly automated (high capital intensity), with very few people monitoring its operation. On the other hand, the line can produce only bread: It has low resource flexibility.

In stark contrast, the custom cake line produces very few cakes because it involves so much custom and hand work. Because several individual workers are required, capital intensity is low and resources are as flexible as they need to be to complete the unique custom orders.

The pastry line at King Soopers falls between the bread and cake lines in capital intensity and resource flexibility. The line is flexible enough to produce different kinds of pastries with little change in the line's resources.

Process Flow at King Soopers Bakery

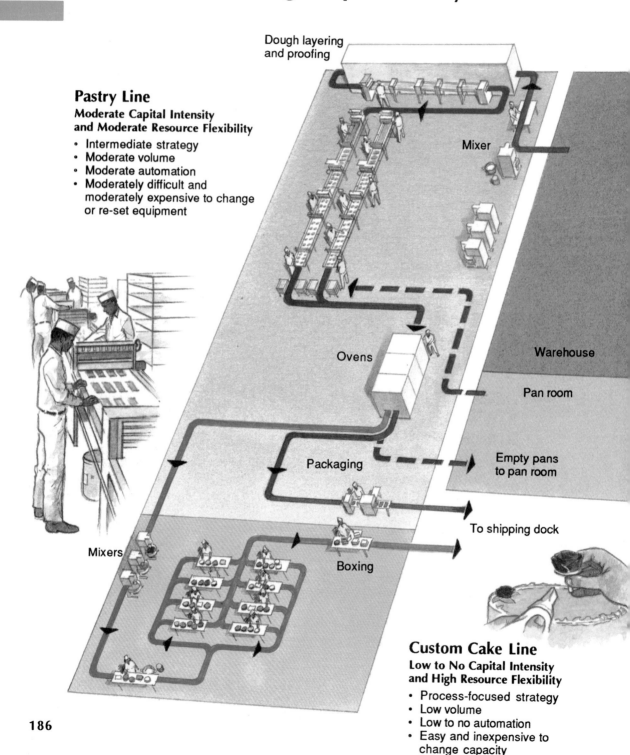

Dough layering
and proofing

Mixer

Pastry Line
Moderate Capital Intensity and Moderate Resource Flexibility

- Intermediate strategy
- Moderate volume
- Moderate automation
- Moderately difficult and moderately expensive to change or re-set equipment

Warehouse

Pan room

Ovens

Packaging

Empty pans
to pan room

To shipping dock

Mixers

Boxing

Custom Cake Line
Low to No Capital Intensity and High Resource Flexibility

- Process-focused strategy
- Low volume
- Low to no automation
- Easy and inexpensive to change capacity

Bulk storage tanks

Holding tanks

Cutting,
rolling,
and
loading
machines

Bread
mixers

Proofing
oven

Bread
oven

Cooling
conveyor

Slicing and
bagging

Bread Line
High Capital Intensity and Low Resource Flexibility

- Product-focused strategy
- High volume
- Difficult and expensive to change capacity

7000
loaves/hr

1000
pastries/hr

50
cakes/hr

Bread
line

Pastry
line

Cake
line

Vertical Integration

All businesses buy at least some inputs to their processes, such as raw materials, manufactured parts, or professional services, from other producers. Management makes decisions about vertical integration by looking at the entire supply chain—from acquisition of raw materials to delivery of finished product. The more processes in the chain the organization controls, the more vertically integrated it is. As Managerial Practice 5.2 illustrates, firms may have different strategies for procuring necessary resources.

Extensive vertical integration is generally attractive when volumes are high and task specialization and high repeatability lead to greater efficiency. It is also attractive if the firm has the relevant skills and views the industry into which it is integrating as particularly important to its future success (Porter, 1990). For example, most small restaurants and food-service operators buy precooked eggs for salad bars and sandwiches from suppliers, rather than process their own. It is hard to match the efficiency of a supplier such as Atlantic Foods, where a team of six employees can peel 10,000 eggs in one shift. Similarly, a corner grocery store lacks the sales volume and resources to operate its own trout farm, as does Kroger Company.

Vertical integration can be in two directions. *Backward integration* represents movement toward the sources of raw materials and parts. (Managerial Practice 5.2 illustrates firms choosing more or less backward integration.) *Forward integration* means that the firm owns more channels of distribution, such as its own distribution centers (warehouses) and retail stores. Village Meats, a fresh-meat supplier and the dominant source of hamburger for Wendy's International, is an example of less forward integration. When Wendy's decided to have just one company deliver all of its fresh, frozen, and dry products, Village Meats chose to end its door-to-door deliveries. It had been delivering its meat and some produce directly to restaurants. Becoming the sole distributor to Wendy's restaurants, however, would have required the company to secure more warehouse space, handle frozen products, and purchase new trucks. The necessary investment was too much for its size. It still supplies Wendy's meat, but leaves the distribution to another firm.

Another example of less forward vertical integration is IBM's decision to allow versions of its minicomputer and mainframes to be marketed in Japan under the label of Mitsubishi Electric Corporation. IBM becomes an *original-equipment manufacturer* (OEM) for this part of its market and leaves the selling to Japanese firms. This move allows it to crack tough markets, such as Japanese government agencies. Mitsubishi Electric, for example, is a big supplier to the Japanese defense forces and currently has more of a distinctive competence than IBM for selling computers in Japan.

Vertical integration can reduce resource flexibility in that a large investment in facilities and equipment may not be easy to reverse. When customers became less enthusiastic about house brands and generic (no-brand) products and turned toward national brands, Kroger found itself with idle equipment and facilities. The shift in consumer preferences created excess manufacturing capacity, which Kroger had to find a way to utilize. It did so by making ice cream

Managerial Practice 5.2

Choosing the Right Amount of Vertical Integration

More Integration

- Kroger Company, the fourth-largest food retail chain in the United States on the basis of domestic sales, operates 1300 supermarkets and has considerable vertical integration. From 38 plants it manufactures products for sale under the Kroger label, including peanut butter, crackers, coffee, and many other dry groceries. Its operations also include 15 dairies, 11 bakeries, and a trout farm. Its extensive vertical integration lets it use cost as a competitive priority.

- Dozens of U.S. corporations, frustrated with rising corporate health-care costs, are spurning the health-insurance industry to deal directly with health-care providers. They are betting that they can do it better and cheaper by applying the same management attention to health care that they do to their core businesses. For example, Baxter International, a big medical-supply company in Deerfield, Illinois, contracts directly with 350 doctors and several hospitals in a half-dozen locations. Baxter negotiates discounts and sets quality guidelines with health-care providers. Its staff regularly visit the providers to review data on trends in costs and procedures to make sure that the savings resulting from discounts aren't eroded by increased use of services. Employees submit their bills to Baxter, which subsidizes their health-care costs directly rather than rely on an insurance company to provide this service. In 1990 health-care costs rose only 12 percent among the 5000 employees who used the contract plan. This increase is much less than the 20 to 30 percent increases for Baxter's traditional plans offered through health-insurance companies. Such vertical integration requires purchasing power and a knowledgeable staff.

Less Integration

- Japanese companies operating assembly plants in the United States have less vertical integration than do GM, Ford, and Chrysler because the former rely more on their suppliers. The Japanese firms do more *outsourcing*, which means that they buy more of the parts going into their automobiles from independent subcontractors. One big reason is that the suppliers pay lower wage rates. While the Japanese firms and the Big Three pay virtually identical wages for assembly workers in their own plants, independent subcontractors pay their workers perhaps $20 an hour less. Whereas the Japanese firms can take advantage of this differential by doing more outsourcing, the Big Three are prevented from doing so by UAW union resistance and so must do more part fabrication in-house.

For example, across the street from its Lake Orion assembly plant, GM operates a small plant that makes car seats. A forklift driver who hauls crates of cushions from the receiving docks to the line that assembles the seats earned $59,000 last year, albeit by working a lot of overtime. A worker at Johnson Controls, the biggest independent U.S. maker of car seats, earns half this amount. Not surprisingly, Johnson Controls is snapping up most of the seat-making business at the U.S. assembly plants of Nissan, Honda, and Toyota. The lower-cost seats help these Japanese companies build cars at a lower cost than the Big Three can.

- LDDS Communications Inc., a long-distance carrier in Jackson, Mississippi, offers customized service to low-volume clients in 24 states. Whereas big carriers tend to sell uniform products to small businesses, LDDS tries to tailor its service to each customer's calling patterns to cut costs. LDDS is too small for much vertical integration: It owns its own switches but can't afford to build its own transmission network. Instead it leases transmission facilities from AT&T, MCI, and other larger carriers. This strategy has worked well in the past because the larger carriers cut leasing prices to LDDS to use up excess capacity. Now price cuts are abating, making the big carriers an ever-present threat to small carriers, such as LDDS, which collectively control little more than 1 percent of the total long-distance market.

Sources: "Kroger Chief Expects Asset Sale to Reap $333 Million for Bid to Stay Independent," *Wall Street Journal*, September 27, 1988; "Firms Perform Own Bypass Operations, Purchasing Health Care from the Source," *Wall Street Journal*, August 19, 1991; "UAW and Big Three Face Mutual Mistrust as Auto Talks Heat Up," *Wall Street Journal*, August 29, 1990; "LDDS Communications Wins Big by Thinking Small," *Wall Street Journal*, July 26, 1991.

and frozen pizza dough for its competitors, which in turn sold the products under their own labels. About 20 percent of the sales from its plants are now to companies outside Kroger. It also has sold some of its plants. While these may be ideal solutions, extensive vertical integration limited Kroger's resource flexibility and range of acceptable business opportunities.

Hollow corporations use a converse strategy to that of Kroger: gaining flexibility but taking a different risk. A **hollow corporation** is a small central firm that relies on other firms for most of its production—and for many of its other functions—on a contract basis. It is sometimes called a *network company* because its few employees spend most of their time on the telephone coordinating suppliers. Lewis Galoob Toys, which features trendy toys, is a good example. So are Emerson Radio (consumer electronics) and Liz Claiborne (apparel). Hollow corporations can move in and out of markets, riding the waves of fashion and technology. They are vulnerable to new competition, however, because the investment barriers to enter their businesses are low: Their suppliers can integrate forward or their customers can integrate backward. A hollow corporation's risk of losing its business to suppliers or customers increases as product volumes increase and product life cycles lengthen. For example, Conner Peripherals has been very successful since entering the hard disk drive industry in 1986. Because product life cycles are so short, often measured in months, it lets outside suppliers manufacture the parts it designs and therefore avoids investing in factories that become obsolete as technology changes. If life cycles were longer, then one of its big customers, such as Compaq Computer Corporation, might decide to make the computer drives itself and bypass Conner entirely.

Make or Buy. Backward integration is often referred to as the *make-or-buy decision*. The operations manager must study all the costs and advantages of each approach. Break-even analysis is a good starting point. However, its application differs from that for product and service planning (see Chapter 2) because it is assumed that the decision doesn't affect revenues. Rather than find the quantity where total costs equal total revenues, the analyst finds the quantity for which the total costs for two alternatives are equal. For the make-or-buy decision, this is the quantity for which the total "make" cost equals the total "buy" cost. The buy option may or may not have a fixed cost. To find the break-even quantity, equalize the two cost functions and solve for Q, as follows:

$$F_b + c_b Q = F_m + c_m Q$$

$$Q = \frac{F_m - F_b}{c_b - c_m}$$

where F_b is the fixed cost (per year) of the buy option, F_m is the fixed cost of the make option, c_b is the variable cost (per unit) of the buy option, and c_m is the variable cost of the make option.

The make option would never be considered, ignoring qualitative factors for the moment, unless its variable cost were lower than that of the buy option. The reason is that fixed costs for making the product or service are typically higher than for buying. Under these circumstances, the buy option is best if production volumes are less than the break-even quantity. Beyond that quantity, the make option becomes best.

Application 5.1 **Break-Even Analysis for Make-or-Buy Decisions**

The manager of a fast-food restaurant featuring hamburgers is adding salads to the menu. There are two options, and the price to the customer will be the same for each one. The "make" option is to install a salad bar stocked with vegetables, fruits, and toppings and let the customer assemble the salad. The salad bar would have to be leased and a part-time employee hired. The manager estimates the fixed cost at $12,000 and variable costs totaling $1.50 per salad. The "buy" option is to have preassembled salads available for sale. They would be purchased from a local supplier at $2.00 per salad. With preassembled salads it would be necessary to install and operate additional refrigeration, with a fixed cost of $2,400. The manager expects to sell 25,000 salads per year.

What is the break-even quantity?

Solution Set the fixed cost plus the variable cost $(F + cQ)$ for the buy option equal to the equivalent costs for the make option, then solve for Q:

$$\$2,400 + 2.0Q = \$12,000 + \$1.5Q$$
$$\$0.5Q = \$9,600$$
$$Q = 19,200 \text{ salads}$$

The break-even quantity is 19,200 salads. Since the 25,000-salad sales forecast exceeds this amount, the make option is preferred. Only if the restaurant expected to sell fewer than 19,200 salads would the buy option be best.

Equally important are qualitative factors. The customers of the restaurant in Application 5.1, for example, might be willing to pay more for a salad that they can make to their own tastes (that is, more customization). Or perhaps a preassembled salad doesn't fit the customers' image of the restaurant. Although some "make" decisions require sizable capital investments, they may take better advantage of the firm's human resources, equipment, and space.

Own or Lease. When a firm decides on more vertical integration, it must also decide whether to own or to lease the necessary facilities and equipment. The lease option is often favored for items affected by fairly rapid changes in technology, items that require frequent servicing, or items for which industry practices have made leasing the norm, as in the photocopier industry. Leasing is also common when a firm has a short-term need for equipment. For example, in the construction industry, where projects usually take months or years to complete, heavy equipment is often leased only as needed.

Many firms lease payroll, security, cleaning, and other types of services, rather than employ personnel and use their own resources to provide these services. Frequently, an organization can hire a firm with the desired expertise and obtain higher-quality service at lower cost than it could from a staff of its own.

*A*t Wendy's SuperBar customers assemble their own salads and make selections from Mexican and Italian dishes. Bucking a trend away from salad bars, Wendy's gets 25 percent of its sales from food bars.

Customer Involvement

The fourth facet of process design is the extent to which customers interact with the process. In many service industries, customer contact is crucial. Customers are involved in terms of self-service, product selection, and time and location, as at Wendy's SuperBar.

Self-Service. To save money, some customers prefer to do part of the process formerly performed by the manufacturer or dealer. Self-service is the process design choice of many retailers, particularly when price is a competitive priority. Some product-focused manufacturers also use self-service to advantage. Their customers become the final assemblers of toys, bicycles, furniture, and other products. Production, shipping, and inventory costs frequently are lower, as are losses from damage.

Product Selection. A business that competes on customization frequently allows customers to come up with their own product specifications or even become involved in designing the product. For example, salad bar customers have more control over portions and ingredients. Another good example of customer involvement is in custom-designed and -built homes; the customer is heavily involved in the design process and inspects the work in process at various times. Furthermore, customer involvement is not likely to end even when the owner occupies the house, because most builders guarantee their work for some extended time period.

Time and Location. For industries in which service cannot occur without the customer's presence, time and location issues affect the process design. If the service is delivered to the customer, client, or patient by appointment, decisions involving the location of such meetings become part of process design. Will customers be served only on the supplier's premises, will the supplier's employees go to the customers' premises, or will the service be provided at yet a third location? Operators of emergency ambulance services cannot provide

192

service without a patient. They cannot predict when the next call for service will come in or where the ambulance will have to go, so they must design their response processes accordingly. On the other hand, in their role as independent auditors, certified public accountants frequently work on their clients' premises, a situation in which both the time and place are likely to be known well in advance.

High customer involvement processes tend to be less capital intensive and more resource flexible than do low customer involvement processes. These conditions are particularly relevant when there is a need for full service, customized orders, unpredictable demands, and service provision at customer locations. Exceptions, such as telephone exchanges, vending machines, and automatic bank tellers, can be found, mainly because these processes require minimal personalized attention.

Relationships Between Facets

We have already identified several relationships among the four facets of process design. An underlying variable that creates these relationships is volume. High volume comes from large product or service demands, significant work content per unit made or served, standardization of parts, and task specialization. Figure 5.2 shows how the process design facets and positioning strategy are inextricably tied to volume. The solid vertical lines show the link between

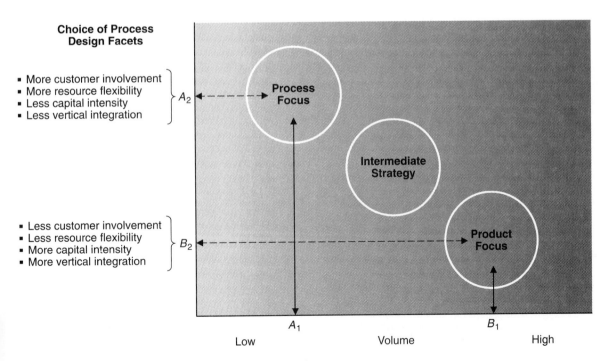

FIGURE 5.2   Volume, Positioning Strategy, and Process Design Facets

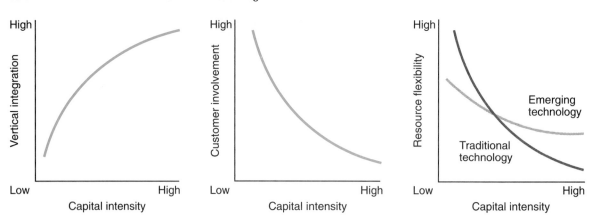

FIGURE 5.3   Relationships Between Facets

volume and positioning strategy, and the dashed horizontal lines show the subsequent link between positioning strategy and process design. For example, when volume is low (volume A_1) a process focus is the likely choice, whereby the firm is likely to have more customer involvement and opt for more resource flexibility, less capital intensity, and less vertical integration (process design choices A_2). A product-focused facility (volume B_1) opts for the opposite ends of the continuum (choices B_2). The high volumes of a product focus, which typically mean less customer involvement, justify the large fixed cost of an efficient capital-intensive operation. They also reduce the need for resource flexibility and create more opportunities for vertical integration. Kroger's large volumes encouraged it to have extensive vertical integration, while LDDS's low volumes led it to rely on others to provide the transmission network.

Given their fundamental tie with volume, it is possible to infer the relationships between all pairs of facets. Figure 5.3 shows three such pairings, with capital intensity as a common facet. For example, vertical integration and capital intensity are directly related: High volumes mean more capital intensity and more vertical integration. Resource flexibility and capital intensity are inversely related: High volumes mean more capital intensity and less need for resource flexibility. Finally, customer involvement and capital intensity are inversely related: High volumes typically go with less customer involvement and more capital intensity. Because vertical integration and customer involvement relate to volume oppositely, we can conclude that they are also inversely related; that is, when vertical integration is high, customer involvement is low. Of course, these are general tendencies rather than unbreakable laws. Exceptions can be found, but these relationships provide a way of understanding how process choices can be linked coherently.

Capital Budgeting

Capital budgeting is a method to allocate scarce funds among competing investment alternatives. Ideas for improving a process, including a change in one of the process design facets, often call for capital investment in facilities and equipment. For example, further vertical integration by a firm invariably requires more equipment and perhaps a new facility. As most of a firm's assets are usually committed to operations, many ideas originate there for capital expenditures and proposals for their inclusion in the firm's capital budget.

Operations managers are constantly looking for ways to encourage innovative ideas for improving productivity. At the same time, they must screen out ideas that don't fit with established operations strategy or generate enough benefits. Benefits can be labor savings, materials cost reduction, less scrap, better quality, lower inventory, better customer service, or higher revenues. Benefits can also be more qualitative, such as expanded opportunities for future products resulting from greater resource flexibility. The operations manager must estimate the costs, benefits, and risks involved in the proposed change. These estimates are then analyzed by means of one or more capital budgeting techniques, such as net present value, payback, or internal rate of return. A brief review of these techniques is found in Supplement 1.

The final decisions in capital budgeting are made by top management—or even the board of directors when a major capital investment is proposed. They make sure that very large investments in equipment and facilities are in line with corporate strategies, particularly with respect to product plans and competitive priorities.

PROCESS ANALYSIS

The four facets of process design represent broad, strategic issues. There is another, more tactical side to process design: the careful, detailed analysis of each process. **Process analysis,** sometimes called *methods study* or *work simplification*, is the systematic study of the activities and flows of each process to improve it.

In this section we present three basic techniques for analyzing activities and flows within processes: flow diagrams, process charts, and multiple activity charts. These techniques can be used systematically to question the process itself and each of its details. The operations manager can highlight tasks that can be simplified or indicate where productivity can otherwise be improved. Managers can use these techniques to design new processes and redesign existing ones and should use them periodically to study all operations. However, the greatest payoff is likely to come from applying them to operations having one or more of the following characteristics:

- The process involves disagreeable or dangerous working conditions.
- The process results in pollution or large amounts of waste materials.
- The process is a bottleneck. That is, work piles up waiting to go through this process, and people or machines are idle while waiting for the output of the process.
- The process consumes a great amount of time.
- The process requires a great deal of physical movement.

All three analytic techniques involve breaking a process into detailed components. To do this, the manager should ask six questions:

1. *What* is being done?
2. *When* is it being done?
3. *Who* is doing it?
4. *Where* is it being done?
5. *How* long does it take?
6. *How* is it being done?

Answers to these questions are challenged by asking still another series of questions. *Why?* Why is the process even being done? Why is it being done where it is being done? Why is it being done when it is being done? Such questioning often can lead to creative answers that can cause a breakthrough in process design. Work elements can be streamlined, whole processes eliminated entirely, raw material usage cut, or jobs made safer. Most facilities can trim labor costs by eliminating unnecessary functions—parts inspection, warehousing, materials handling, and redundant supervision, among others—and reorganizing the production process. For example, Eaton Corporation rearranged its plant in Marshall, Michigan, so that a rough forging placed on a conveyor travels automatically from machine to machine until it emerges as a polished gear for a truck differential. Computerized measuring machines, instead of human inspectors, ensure that automated turning centers cut gears to a precise size. Such changes came from a critical analysis of each process.

Flow Diagrams

When an operation involves considerable movement of materials or people, a flow diagram is a useful analytical tool. A **flow diagram** traces the flows of people, equipment, or materials through a process. To make a flow diagram, the analyst first makes a rough sketch of the area in which the process is performed. On a grid (graph paper or other paper marked off in squares) the analyst plots the path followed by the person, material, or equipment, using arrows to indicate the direction of movement, or the direction of flow.

Figure 5.4 shows a flow diagram for a car wash facility, illustrating the flows of cars and customers. Cars enter one of two lines from the street and alternate in forming a single line that rounds a sharp corner into the washing bay. Just before a car enters the bay, the customer exits the car and walks through a separate door and hallway to the office and pays for the service. The car proceeds through the washing bay, and the customer exits through the hallway and out a second door to rejoin the car after it is rolled to an open area and wiped down. The customer then gets back into the car and drives away. The facility used to have only one waiting line, but during peak periods, the line of cars would extend back into the street, blocking traffic. The owner used a flow diagram to determine that the second waiting line could be added without changing the flow of the other operations. (Queuing and simulation analysis, described in Supplements 4 and 5, are more extensive methods to study waiting lines.)

FIGURE 5.4

Flow Diagram for a
Car Wash Facility

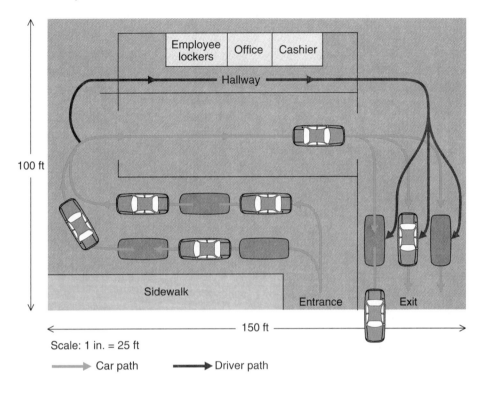

Process Charts

A **process chart** is an organized way of recording all the activities performed by a person, by a machine, at a work station, or on materials. For our purposes we group these activities into five categories:

- operation
- transportation
- inspection
- delay
- storage

An *operation* is productive work that changes, creates, or adds something. Examples are mixing tar, stone, and sand to make asphalt; drilling a hole; and serving a customer at a store. *Transportation* (sometimes called materials handling) is the movement of the study's subject from one place to another. The subject can be a person, a material, a tool, or a piece of equipment. Examples of transportation are a customer walking from one end of a counter to another, a crane hoisting a steel beam to a location, and a conveyor carrying a partially completed product from one work station to the next. An *inspection* checks or verifies something but does not change it. Checking for blemishes on a surface, weighing a product, and taking a temperature reading are examples of inspections. A *delay* occurs when the subject is held up awaiting further action. Time spent waiting for materials or equipment, time for cleanup, and time that workers, machines, or work stations are idle because there is nothing for them to do are examples of delays. *Storage* occurs when something is put away until a later time. Supplies being unloaded and placed in a storeroom as inventory, equipment put away after use, and papers put in a file cabinet are examples of storage. Depending on the situation, other activity categories can be used, such as subcontracting/outside services or distinguishing between temporary storage and permanent storage.

To complete a process chart for a new process, the analyst must identify each step performed. If the process is an existing one, the analyst can actually observe the steps, categorizing each step according to the subject being studied. Changing the subject (say, from the product being made to the worker) might also change the category to which a step is assigned. The analyst then records the distance traveled and the time taken to perform each step. (See Chapter 7 on the various ways to establish time standards.) After recording all the activities and steps, the analyst calculates summary data on the number of steps, total times, and total distance.

Application 5.2 | Completing a Process Chart

You are to analyze the process of baking a batch of brownies. The subject of the study is the baker. The process begins when the baker removes the preassembled brownie mix and ends when the large pan is placed in the oven for baking. Raw materials (the brownie mix, water, and eggs) and equipment and container (bowl, mixer, measuring container, and pan) must be assembled. The ingredients must be measured, mixed, poured in a pan, and placed in the oven.

Solution

Figure 5.5 shows the completed process chart. The process is broken into 26 steps. A summary of the times and distances traveled is shown in the upper-right hand corner of the process chart. The times add up to 27.2 minutes, and the baker travels a total of 430 feet.

After the process is charted, the analyst estimates the annual cost of the entire process. The annual cost becomes a benchmark against which other methods for performing the process can be evaluated. Annual labor cost, for example, can be estimated by finding the product of (1) time in hours to perform the process each time, (2) variable cost per hour, (3) number of times the process is performed each week, and (4) number of weeks per year in which the process is performed.

Application 5.3 | Computing the Annual Labor Cost

The baker earns $17 per hour (including fringe benefits) and makes 12 batches per week. What is the annual labor cost?

Solution

$$\text{Annual labor cost} = \frac{27.2 \text{ min}}{60 \text{ min/hr}} (\$17/\text{hr})(12/\text{wk})(52 \text{ wk/yr}) = \$4809$$

Process: *MAKING ONE BATCH OF BROWNIES* Subject charted: *BAKER* Beginning: *REMOVE BROWNIE MIX FROM BIN* Ending: *PLACE PAN IN OVEN*	Summary			
	Activity	**Number of Steps**	**Time**	**Distance**
	Operation ●	15	18.0	–
	Transport ➡	9	9.0	430
	Inspect ■	2	0.2	–
	Delay ◗	0	–	–
	Store ▼	0	–	–

Step No.	Time (min)	Distance (ft)	●	➡	■	◗	▼	Step Description
1	1.3		X					REMOVE PREASSEMBLED MIX FROM BIN
2	0.2		X					PLACE MIX ON COUNTER
3	1.2	60		X				WALK TO CABINET
4	0.4		X					REMOVE BOWL AND MIXER
5	1.2	60		X				RETURN THE BOWL AND MIXER TO COUNTER
6	0.2		X					PLACE BOWL AND MIXER ON COUNTER
7	1.3		X					OPEN BAG OF MIX AND DUMP INTO BOWL
8	1.2	60		X				WALK TO CABINET
9	0.3		X					REMOVE PAN AND MEASURING CONTAINER
10	1.2	60		X				RETURN WITH THEM TO COUNTER
11	0.2		X					PLACE THEM ON COUNTER
12	0.6	30		X				WALK TO REFRIGERATOR
13	0.8		X					REMOVE EGGS FROM REFRIGERATOR
14	0.6	30		X				WALK BACK TO COUNTER
15	0.1		X					PLACE EGGS ON COUNTER
16	3.1		X					BREAK EGGS INTO BROWNIE MIX; DISCARD SHELLS
17	2.2		X					USE MIXER TO STIR EGGS AND BROWNIE MIX
18	0.9	40		X				PICK UP MEASURING CONTAINER; WALK TO SINK
19	1.4		X					FILL MEASURING CONTAINER WITH WATER
20	0.8	40		X				WALK BACK TO COUNTER
21	0.3		X					POUR WATER INTO BROWNIE MIX
22	4.3		X					USE MIXER TO STIR INGREDIENTS IN BOWL
23	0.1				X			INSPECT MIXTURE IN BOWL
24	1.9		X					POUR MIXTURE INTO PAN
25	0.1				X			INSPECT MIXTURE IN PAN
26	1.3	50		X				PICK UP PAN; WALK TO OVEN; PLACE PAN IN OVEN

FIGURE 5.5   Process Chart for Making Brownies at a Bakery

The calculations convert minutes to hours and then multiply this figure by the hourly rate and the number of baker hours per year needed for the process. Adding in the cost of materials would yield a sizable variable cost, and brownies are but one of many products made at the bakery.

Next comes the creative part of process analysis. The analyst now asks the what, when, who, where, how long, and how questions, challenging each of the steps of the process charted. The summary of the process chart indicates which activities take the most time. To make a process more efficient, the analyst should question each delay and then analyze the operation, transport, inspection, and storage activities to see whether they can be combined, re-arranged, or eliminated. There is always a better way, but someone must think of it. Improvements in productivity can be significant.

Application 5.4   *Improving the Process*

What improvement can you make in the process in Fig. 5.5?

Solution   Your analysis should verify the following two ideas for improvement. You may also be able to come up with others.

1. **Combine the trips for equipment.** The baker walks to the cabinet twice to get tools. This is inefficient because the tools aren't heavy or large enough to require two trips. Even if they were unwieldy, he could use a cart. Combining steps 3–5 and 8–10 saves time, as the baker gathers all the tools at once and eliminates 120 feet of travel.
2. **Eliminate the first mixing.** Steps 16, 17, 21, and 22 can be rearranged to add the eggs and water to the brownie mix before mixing. This cuts out another step.

Multiple Activity Charts

A process chart describes the work being done by or on just one subject. How-ever, simultaneously tracking multiple subjects may be more revealing. A **multiple activity chart**, sometimes called a *man-machine chart*, is a record of the activities performed by or on several subjects over a given time period. The first step in preparing these charts is to determine which process to study. The analyst divides a sheet of paper into columns, with one for each person, mate-rial, or work station. The analyst next observes the process and establishes a time standard for each activity (see Chapter 7). Finally, the analyst charts the time required to perform each activity, using vertical bars having lengths that represent these times.

Application 5.5   *Completing a Multiple Activity Chart*

Dr. Wilson, an orthodontist with a large practice, sees patients biweekly for adjustment of their braces. The receptionist seats the patient in one of four chairs, and Dr. Wilson then checks the patient. After making his check and washing up, which takes about a minute, one of the two orthodontic technicians adjusts the patient's braces. The adjust-ment procedure takes the technicians about 8 minutes per patient. After the braces are adjusted, Dr. Wilson again checks the patient, makes any necessary final adjustment, and washes up again. This final step takes about 2 minutes. Dr. Wilson's objective is to get them in and out of the chair in 20 minutes or less. The technicians take about one minute between patients to wash their hands, and each technician is allowed to take a 5-minute break at the end of each hour.

Prepare a multiple activity activity chart for the first hour of a day, with columns for the orthodontist, two technicians, and four chairs. Because we are interested in only one of the receptionist's activities—seating the patients—you do not need an extra column for the receptionist. Let technician 1 work on patients in chairs A and B, and technician 2 work on patients in chairs C and D. Assume that it is a busy morning and that patients are available as soon as they can be handled.

Solution   Figure 5.6 (next page) shows the completed chart. Technician utilization (the time they are occupied divided by the period of time being studied) is a very high 88 percent. Dr. Wilson's utilization is much lower, however. He is occupied only 36 minutes of the hour, for a utilization rate of 36/60 = 60 percent. The chart also indicates the amount of time that each chair is unoccupied or is occupied by a patient waiting for the next step in the process. A patient in chair A had to spend only 2 minutes waiting, and the chair was unoccupied for 22 minutes of the hour (shown as idle time). Chair D was empty for only 15 minutes, and patients had to wait 9 minutes. As this waiting time was spread over three patients, for 3 minutes each, it was probably acceptable to them.

The next step is to find ways to improve the process. Analyzing the multiple activity chart can uncover ways to divide work among employees, reduce time required for certain activities, or rearrange activities to shorten a job's overall time. It helps managers decide how to utilize people, work stations, or machines more effectively. Managers frequently use multiple activity charts to find ways to minimize idle time. The result can be significant productivity improvements. Such is the case for dentistry, which is a much different business than it used to be. The dental profession stands out in the health-care industry as a leader in productivity improvement. These substantial gains are being studied carefully by the rest of the health-care industry.

Application 5.6   *Improving a Multiple Activity Process*

Many patients are referred to Dr. Wilson, and he would like to expand his practice without devoting more hours to routine brace adjustments. He is thinking of adding two more chairs and hiring one more technician. He would continue to spend one minute with the patients before the technicians work on them and about two minutes with them after the technicians have finished. How many more patients can he see, and what will be the utilizations and patient wait times, with the expansion?

Solution   The new chart is shown in Fig. 5.7. The orthodontist now has as little unoccupied time as the technicians. All are busy for 53 of the 60 minutes, for utilization ratios of 88 percent. Even though almost every patient has to wait before and after seeing the technician, no patient's total time in the chair exceeds 20 minutes, so that goal can be met. It appears that Dr. Wilson can add two chairs and an additional technician to his staff and see 18 patients every hour instead of 12, but he and his technicians would be very busy.

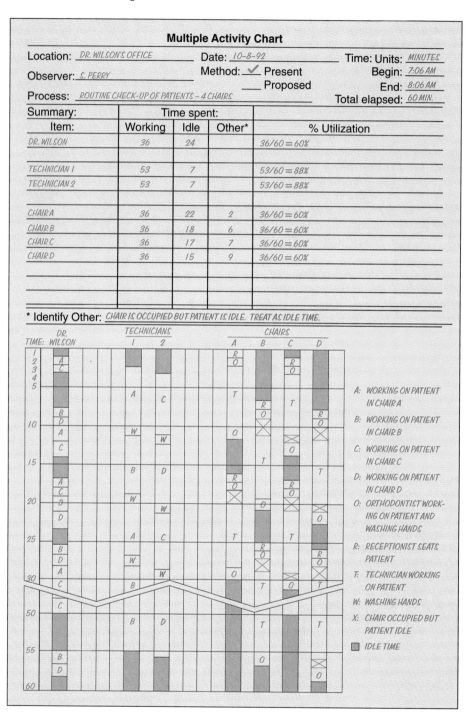

FIGURE 5.6   Multiple Activity Chart for Orthodontist: Four Chairs

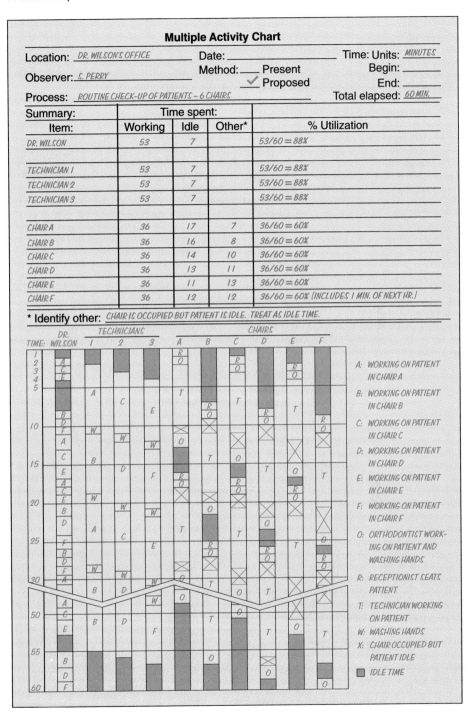

FIGURE 5.7   Multiple Activity Chart for Orthodontist: Six Chairs

SOLVED PROBLEMS

1. Two different manufacturing processes are being considered for making a new product that is to be introduced soon. The first process is less capital intensive, with a fixed cost of only $50,000 per year and a variable cost of $400 per unit. The second process has a fixed cost of $200,000 but would have a variable cost of only $150 per unit. What is the break-even quantity, beyond which the second process becomes more attractive than the first?

Solution We set fixed cost plus variable cost $(F + cQ)$ for the first process equal to the equivalent costs for the second process and solve for Q:

$$\$50,000 + \$400Q = \$200,000 + \$150Q$$
$$\$250Q = \$150,000$$
$$Q = 600 \text{ units}$$

The break-even quantity is 600 units, beyond which the second process is better.

2. Consider again the process analysis for baking a batch of brownies. Prepare a revised process chart that implements the two ideas proposed in Application 5.4. The only new information is:

- Removing the bowl, mixer, pan, and measuring container takes 0.5 minute.
- Placing the equipment on the counter takes 0.3 minute, up from 0.2 minute because the measuring container is brought along on the trip.
- The total mixing time (combining both mixings into one) is 5.0 minutes.

Solution Figure 5.8 shows the revised process chart. We eliminate five steps, 4.5 minutes, and 120 feet traveled.

FORMULA REVIEW

Break-even quantity for make or buy:

$$Q = \frac{F_m - F_b}{c_b - c_m}$$

CHAPTER HIGHLIGHTS

- Process design deals with *how* to make a product. Many choices must be made concerning the best mix of human resources, equipment, and materials.

- Process design is of strategic importance and is closely linked to the productivity levels a firm can achieve. It involves the selection of inputs, operations, work flows, and methods used to produce goods and services.

- Process design decisions are made when a new product is to be offered or an existing product modified, demand levels change, current perfor-

Process:	MAKING ONE BATCH OF BROWNIES				**Summary**				

Process: MAKING ONE BATCH OF BROWNIES Subject charted: BAKER Beginning: REMOVE BROWNIE MIX FROM BIN Ending: REMOVE BROWNIES FROM OVEN	Activity	Number of Steps	Time	Distance
	Operation ●	12	15.9	–
	Transport ⇒	7	6.6	310
	Inspect ■	2	0.2	–
	Delay D	0	–	–
	Store ▽	0	–	–

Step No.	Time (min)	Distance (ft)	●	⇒	■	D	▽	Step Description
1	1.3		X					REMOVE PREASSEMBLED MIX FROM BIN
2	0.2		X					PLACE MIX ON COUNTER
3	1.2	60		X				WALK TO CABINET
4	0.5		X					REMOVE BOWL, MIXER, PAN, AND MEASURING CONTAINER
5	1.2	60		X				RETURN TO COUNTER WITH EQUIPMENT
6	0.3		X					PLACE EQUIPMENT ON COUNTER
7	1.3		X					OPEN BAG OF MIX AND DUMP INTO BOWL
8	0.6	30		X				WALK TO REFRIGERATOR
9	0.8		X					REMOVE EGGS FROM REFRIGERATOR
10	0.6	30		X				WALK BACK TO COUNTER
11	0.1		X					PLACE EGGS ON COUNTER
12	0.9	40		X				PICK UP MEASURING CONTAINER; WALK TO SINK
13	1.4		X					FILL MEASURING CONTAINER WITH WATER
14	0.8	40		X				WALK BACK TO COUNTER
15	0.3		X					POUR WATER INTO BROWNIE MIX
16	2.8		X					BREAK EGGS INTO BROWNIE MIX; DISCARD SHELLS
17	5.0		X					USE MIXER TO STIR INGREDIENTS IN BOWL
18	0.1				X			INSPECT MIXTURE IN BOWL
19	1.9		X					POUR MIXTURE INTO PAN
20	0.1				X			INSPECT MIXTURE IN PAN
21	1.3	50		X				PICK UP PAN; WALK TO OVEN; PLACE PAN IN OVEN

FIGURE 5.8   Process Chart After Improvements

mance is inadequate, new technology is available, costs or availability of inputs change, or competitive priorities change.

● Four facets of process design are capital intensity, resource flexibility, vertical integration, and customer involvement. *Capital intensity* concerns the mix of capital equipment and human skills in a process. *Resource flexibility* reflects the degree to which equipment is general purpose and individuals can handle a wide variety of work. *Vertical integration* concerns the decisions to make or buy parts and services. Such decisions are made by looking at the entire chain of supply from acquisition of raw materials to delivery of the finished product to the consumer and then determining which processes the firm itself wants to perform. *Customer involvement* is the extent to which customers are allowed to interact with the production process. Self-service, product selection, and the timing and location of the interaction must all be considered.

- Relationships among these facets suggest how process choices can be linked coherently. For example, higher capital intensity is usually associated with lower resource flexibility, higher vertical integration, and lower customer involvement. The variable underlying these relationships is volume.

- Process design choices often require invest-

ment in new facilities or equipment. Operations managers must assess benefits and costs of each investment proposed. After the necessary estimates have been made, break-even analysis or net present value techniques can be applied.

- Three techniques for analyzing process activities and flows are flow diagrams, process charts, and multiple activity charts. All are organized ways of studying the details of a process to improve it by designing or redesigning it.

KEY TERMS

capital budgeting **194**
capital intensity **181**
customer involvement **181**
flexible work force **184**

flow diagram **196**
hollow corporation **190**
multiple activity chart **200**
process analysis **195**

process chart **197**
process design **180**
resource flexibility **181**
vertical integration **181**

STUDY QUESTIONS

1. When you registered for this course you had to go through a registration process. Think of this process from the standpoint of your university or college. Identify elements of the process for which process design or redesign is needed.

2. Compare the process of preparing and serving your own lunch at home with the process of preparing and serving lunch to others at a local pizza parlor. What inputs in terms of materials, human effort, and equipment are involved in each process? How are these inputs similar? How are they different?

3. "Process design choices cannot be isolated from decisions in other areas of operations management." Comment on this statement from the standpoint of a bookstore manager. *Hint:* Look over the table of contents to get some ideas.

4. How much capital intensity do you recommend for a business having an extremely unpredictable product demand? How much vertical integration? Explain.

5. The number of mail order businesses has increased dramatically in the United States in the last ten years. Compare the processes of a business selling ski equipment and clothing by direct mail to the processes of a retail store handling the same items. How do they differ in terms of capital intensity, resource flexibility, vertical integration, and customer involvement? How are they the same?

6. Suppose that you and a friend decide to start a business selling sandwiches and snacks in college dormitories late at night. What decisions must you make regarding vertical integration? How will your customers be involved in your process?

7. Suppose that a grocery store has decided to add an in-store bakery. The next decision to be made is whether to install a drive-in window for the bakery so that customers do not have to enter the store in order to purchase baked goods. The store manager expects that this window would do a high volume of business early in the morning, as people purchase

donuts on their way to work. How is this window likely to affect other processes in the store? What processes will bakery employees have to perform that they would not otherwise? How would customer involvement differ from that in the rest of the grocery operations?

8. King Soopers Bakery anticipates a peak demand for holiday cakes in December. What implications does this have for its use of its work force? Should part-timers be hired? Should there be more cross-training?

9. King Soopers' management is considering offering customers a "menu" of 10 different custom cake options from which to choose. How might this change affect the custom cake line?

PROBLEMS

Review Problems

1. Goliath Manufacturing must implement a manufacturing process that reduces the amount of toxic by-products. Two processes have been identified that provide the same level of toxic by-product reduction. The first process will incur $205,000 of fixed cost and $650 per unit of variable cost. The second process has a fixed cost of $145,000 and a variable cost of $800 per unit.
   a. What is the break-even quantity beyond which the first process is more attractive?
   b. What is the difference in total cost if the quantity produced is 500 units?

2. Dr. Wilson (see Applications 5.5 and 5.6) estimates that adding two new chairs will increase fixed cost by $105,000, including the annual equivalent cost of the capital investment and the salary of one more technician. Each new patient is expected to bring in $1925 per year in additional revenue, with variable cost estimated at $250 per patient. The two new chairs will allow him to expand his practice by as many as 200 patients annually. How many patients would have to be added for the new process to break even?

3. Hahn Manufacturing has been purchasing a key component of one of its products from a local supplier. The current purchase price is $1500 per unit. Efforts to standardize parts have succeeded to the point that this same component can now be used in five different products. Annual component usage should increase from 150 to 750 units. Management wonders whether it is time to make the component in-house, rather than to continue buying it from the supplier. Fixed cost would increase by about $40,000 per year for the new equipment and tooling needed. The cost of raw materials and variable overhead would be about $1100 per unit, while labor cost would go up by another $300 per unit produced.
   a. Should Hahn make rather than buy?
   b. What is the break-even quantity?
   c. What other considerations might be important?

4. A construction company is trying to decide whether to continue renting or to buy a concrete pump for its foundation and slab construction. The fixed annual cost for buying a new pump with hose and all other accessories is $8800, and annual maintenance costs would be another $2000 per year. One of the company's current employees would operate the pump, at a wage rate of $35 per hour. If the company doesn't buy the pump, it will continue to rent one for $125 per hour, including operator labor cost. The pump is normally needed for eight hours per pour.
   a. What is the break-even quantity, in number of pours?
   b. If the company expects to have 40 pours per year, should it buy or continue to rent? What is the difference in annual costs at this volume?

5. Suppose that you are in charge of a large mailing to the alumni of your college inviting them to contribute to a scholarship fund. The letters and envelopes have been individually addressed (mailing labels were not used). The letters are to be folded and stuffed into the correct envelope, the envelopes are to be sealed, and a large commemorative stamp is to be placed in the upper right-hand corner of each envelope. Make a process chart for this activity, assuming that it is a one-person operation. Estimate how long it will take to stuff, seal, and stamp 2000 envelopes. Assume that the person doing this work is paid $8.00 per hour. How much will it cost to process 2000 letters, based on your time estimate? Consider how each of the following changes individually would affect the process.

- Each letter has the greeting "Dear Alumnus or Alumna," instead of the person's name.
- Mailing labels are used and have to be put on the envelopes.
- Prestamped envelopes are used.
- Envelopes are to be stamped by a postage meter.
- Window envelopes are used.
- A preaddressed envelope is included for contributions.

a. Which of these changes would reduce the time and cost of the process?
b. Would any of these changes be likely to reduce the effectiveness of the mailing? If so, which ones? Why?
c. Would the changes that increase time and cost be likely to increase the effectiveness of the mailing? Why?
d. What other factors need to be considered for this project?

6. Prepare a multiple activity chart for a hypothetical worker whose job is to load and unload two dry cleaning machines (call them machines A and B). Use the following conditions.

- It is the beginning of the day, and all machines are empty.
- The machines are identical.
- Each machine takes 2 minutes to load and 3 minutes to unload.

The machines run for 16 minutes each time they are loaded. The worker starts by loading machine A and then machine B. The machines are close enough together that the travel time from one to the other can be ignored. After the initial loading, the worker unloads and reloads each machine as soon as the machine stops running or as soon as the worker is available. (In other words, the worker does not waste time.)

a. Complete the multiple activity chart for the two machines and for the worker for one hour. Calculate the utilization (percentage) for each.
b. Assume that the machines are not turned off until the end of the day. What is the percentage utilization of the machines and the worker for the second hour and every hour thereafter?

7. Suppose that the dry cleaning worker in Problem 6 is given three machines to tend. Complete a multiple activity chart for three machines and one worker under the same conditions.

a. What is the percentage utilization of the worker and the machines? Compare your answer to that obtained for two machines.
b. Is it possible, hypothetically, for a worker to be utilized 100 percent? Is it possible practically? What would you likely observe if you watched a person actually working at 100 percent utilization?

8. Diagrams of two self-service gasoline stations, both located on corners, are shown in Fig. 5.9(a) and (b). Both have two rows of four pumps and a booth in which an attendant receives payment for the gasoline. At neither station is it necessary for the customer to pay in advance. The exits and entrances are marked on the diagrams. Analyze

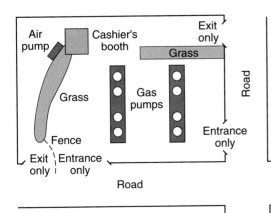

(a)

(b)

FIGURE 5.9

the flows of cars and people through each station.

a. Which station has the most efficient flows from the standpoint of the customer?

b. Which station is likely to lose the most sales from potential customers who cannot gain access to the pumps because another car is headed in the other direction?

c. At which station can a customer pay without getting out of the car?

9. You have been asked by the management of Just Like Home restaurant to analyze some of its processes. One of these processes is making a single-scoop ice cream cone. Cones can be ordered by a server (for table service) or by a customer (for take-out). Figure 5.10 (on the next page) illustrates the process chart for this operation.

- The ice cream counter server earns $10 per hour (including variable fringe benefits).
- The process is performed 10 times per hour (on average).
- The restaurant is open 363 days a year, 10 hours a day.

a. What is the total labor cost associated with the process?

b. How can this operation be made more efficient? Draw a process chart of the improved process. What are the annual labor savings if this new process is implemented?

Advanced Problems

Supplement Connections: Problems 11–17 require prior reading of Supplement 1 (Financial Analysis); Problems 18 and 19, Supplement 2 (Linear Programming); Problems 20–25, Supplement 4 (Queuing Models); and Problem 26, Supplement 5 (Simulation Analysis). A computer package is useful for all problems except 10, 18, and 26, and one is mandatory for Problem 19.

10. Make a multiple activity chart for a pizza baker who is assembling pizzas and baking them in two ovens that each hold two pizzas. Assume that demand for the pizzas is so high that all possible output will be used. Use the following conditions.

- Each pizza takes 5 minutes to assemble.
- Pizzas must bake for 17 minutes and be removed promptly.
- It takes one minute to put a pizza in the oven and one minute to take it out. Assume that this does not prolong the baking time for any other pizza in the oven.
- An oven may be opened to put in a pizza or take one out, even if another pizza is baking.

Process: MAKING ONE SINGLE-SCOOP ICE-CREAM CONE	Summary			
Subject charted: SERVER AT COUNTER	Activity	Number of Steps	Time	Distance
Beginning: WALK TO CONE STORAGE AREA	Operation ●	6	1.70	–
Ending: GIVE SERVER OR CUSTOMER THE CONE	Transport ➡	6	0.80	76
	Inspect ■	1	0.25	–
	Delay D	1	0.50	–
	Store ▼	0	–	–

Step No.	Time (min)	Distance (ft)	●	➡	■	D	▼	Step Description
1	0.20	5		X				WALK TO CONE STORAGE AREA
2	0.05		X					REMOVE EMPTY CONE
3	0.10	5		X				WALK TO COUNTER
4	0.05		X					PLACE CONE IN HOLDER
5	0.20	8		X				WALK TO SINK AREA
6	0.50					X		ASK DISHWASHER TO WASH SCOOP
7	0.15	8		X				WALK TO COUNTER WITH CLEAN SCOOP
8	0.05		X					PICK UP EMPTY CONE
9	0.10	2.5		X				WALK TO FLAVOR ORDERED
10	0.75		X					SCOOP ICE CREAM FROM CONTAINER
11	0.75		X					PLACE ICE CREAM IN CONE
12	0.25				X			CHECK FOR STABILITY
13	0.05	2.5		X				WALK TO ORDER PLACEMENT AREA
14	0.05		X					GIVE SERVER OR CUSTOMER THE CONE

FIGURE 5.10

- When a pizza is being assembled and it is time to take another out of the oven, the assembly process is interrupted. The baker then continues assembling the first pizza.

Prepare a multiple activity chart for the baker and ovens from 5:00 P.M. until 6:30 P.M. Assume that the ovens are hot but empty at 5:00 P.M.

a. How many pizzas can the baker turn out in this period of time?

b. How many pizzas are in the oven at 6:30 P.M.?

c. What is the percentage utilization of each oven shelf?

d. What percentage of the time is each oven being used (with one or two pizzas in it)?

e. What is the percentage utilization of the baker?

Hint: You will probably need a column for each shelf of each oven and one for the baker. Use any symbols that you think are appropriate.

11. John's AutoWorks specializes in major body work that requires repainting the entire automobile after the body work is complete. John's present spray booth is operated by two mechanics, each earning $25 per hour. The processing times per automobile follow:

- Sanding and preparation takes 15 minutes.
- Taping and masking takes 5 minutes.
- Spraying takes 10 minutes for one color, and 5 more minutes for a second color.
- Baking takes 10 minutes.
- Cleanup and driving to the parking area takes 5 minutes.

John is contemplating buying a new spray booth that would reduce spraying time to 5 minutes for one color and 3 minutes for a second color. Only one mechanic would be required for the spraying and baking operation, although two would still be required for the other operations. The second mechanic could help in another area while spraying and baking operations are underway.

a. Prepare a multiple activity chart to show the utilization of the old and newly proposed spray booths. Assuming that only one 2-color automobile is normally painted per day, at the beginning of the day, how many can be painted in each booth in an 8-hour day?

b. John has been offered a special price of $45,000 if he buys the new booth now. His current booth is in good shape, would last another eight years, and has a salvage value of $12,500. Assume that John's after-tax gross margin is $100 per automobile and volume is sufficient to utilize either booth to its maximum capacity during an 8-hour day. What is the net annual savings of this investment? What is its payback period?

12. A local restaurant is considering adding a salad bar. Application S1.1 (see Supplement 1) gives the related data and assumptions. Table S1.1 shows the NPV financial analysis.

   Another option (instead of the salad bar), to assemble, store, and sell preassembled salads, would require an investment outlay of $6000 to remodel the kitchen. The price and variable cost of each salad would drop to $2.25 and $1.50, respectively. Fixed cost (excluding depreciation) would be $900, since there is no longer a need to hire someone to stock the salad bar. The other assumptions about total demand, project life, tax rate, hurdle rate, salvage value, and depreciation method remain unchanged.

a. Based on the NPV method, is the salad bar or preassembled salad option best?

b. What is the payback period for each option?

c. What other factors might influence your decision?

13. Suppose that the demand estimate for salads in Problem 12 is revised upward to 36,000 salads per year.

a. Evaluate both options using the NPV method.

b. Evaluate both options using the payback method.

c. Does the higher demand estimate change any of your conclusions?

14. A restaurant is considering adding an ice cream sundae bar to allow customers to create their own desserts. The investment to remodel the dining area would be $18,000, and annual demand is estimated to be 12,000 desserts. The price and variable cost per sundae are $3.75 and $2.15, respectively. Fixed costs, other than depreciation, for the energy to operate the refrigerated unit and for a new part-time employee would be $9000. The project would last four years, with no salvage value. The tax rate is 30 percent, and management wants to earn a return of at least 16 percent.

a. Based on the NPV method, should the sundae bar project be funded?

b. Based on the payback method, should it be funded?

c. Do your conclusions change if the demand forecast is revised upward to 40,000 desserts per year?

15. Dr. Wilson, an orthodontist, is considering expanding his office from four to six chairs. Each chair requires an investment of $200,000. He will have to hire one new technician at $18,000 per year. Other additional costs are expected to be negligible. The two new chairs will allow him to expand his practice by 200 patients per year. Each new patient is expected to bring in $1500 per year in before-tax revenue. Dr. Wilson will depreciate the chairs over a five-year period, after which they are expected to have no

value. Assume that Dr. Wilson is in the 50 percent tax bracket and requires a return of 20 percent on an investment. Calculate the following:

a. The incremental after-tax cash flows attributable to the two new chairs
b. The net present value of the investment
c. The payback period
d. The number of new patients Dr. Wilson will have to add to break even (before taxes) on an annual basis

16. The owner of a bowling alley is thinking about adding pool tables, which would require an investment of $12,000. The owner expects to generate incremental after-tax cash flows of $4000 for each of the next five years by having pool tables at the bowling alley. What is the present value of the stream of expected cash flows? (Use 16 percent for the hurdle rate.)

a. What is the net present value?
b. What is the payback period?
c. What advice would you give the owner about the proposed investment?
d. What other issues should the owner consider?

17. Catherine Lerme, owner of Super Quick Car Care, is considering expanding her garage from four to six bays. Each bay requires an investment in tools and a hydraulic lift of $125,000. She will also have to hire a new mechanic for each bay at $17,000 per year. Other additional costs are expected to be negligible. The two new bays will allow her to service an additional 1800 automobiles per year. Each additional automobile serviced is expected to bring in an average of $100 in before-tax revenue. Lerme will depreciate the equipment and tools over a five-year period, after which they will have no salvage value. Super Quick Car Care has a tax rate of 30 percent and requires a 20 percent return on investment. Calculate the following:

a. The incremental after-tax cash flows attributable to the two new bays
b. The net present value of the investment

c. The payback period
d. The number of additional cars that Super Quick must service annually to break even (before taxes)

18. The manufacturer of textile dyes can use two different processing routings for a particular type of dye. Routing 1 uses drying press A, and routing 2 uses drying press B. Both routings require the same mixing vat to blend chemicals for the dye before drying. The following table shows the time requirements and capacities of these processes.

| | Hours per Kilogram | | Capacity |
Process	Routing 1	Routing 2	(hr)
Mixing	2	2	54
Dryer A	6	0	120
Dryer B	0	8	180

In addition, each kilogram of dye processed on routing 1 uses 20 liters of chemicals, whereas each kilogram of dye processed on routing 2 uses only 15 liters. The difference results from differing yield rates of the drying presses. Consequently, the profit per kilogram processed on routing 1 is $50 and on routing 2 is $65. A total of 450 liters of input chemicals is available.

a. Write the constraints and objective function for this problem to maximize profits.
b. Use the graphic method of linear programming to find the optimal solution.

19. Use the simplex method to solve Problem 18, both manually and on the computer.

20. The Howard, Smith, and Parke law firm produces many legal documents that must be typed for clients and the firm. Requests average four pages of documents per hour and arrive according to a Poisson distribution. The secretary can type five pages per hour on average according to an exponential distribution.

a. What is the average utilization rate of the secretary?
b. What is the probability that more than four pages of documents are waiting or being typed?

c. What is the average number of documents waiting to be typed?

d. What is the average waiting time for documents in queue?

21. An automobile manufacturer uses a welding robot in its assembly line. Cars arrive at the welding station at a rate of 120 per hour according to a Poisson distribution. The speed of the welding robot can be adjusted, although actual welding time depends on the particular model of car being assembled. Setting the robot too fast causes more defects, whereas setting it too slow causes bottlenecks in assembly. Regardless of the speed, the robot's average time required to weld is exponentially distributed. Answer the following questions, assuming that the single-server queuing model applies:

a. At what average service rate should the robot be set to ensure a 30 percent chance that three or more cars are in queue or being welded?

b. What is the average time a car spends at this weld station?

c. What is the average number of cars waiting to be welded?

22. Dr. Weston is a dentist who oversees the training of new dental students in a local clinic serving the needs of the general public. The clinic has three dental chairs, each manned by a student, and patients arrive at the rate of five per hour according to the Poisson distribution. The average time required for a dental checkup is 30 minutes according to an exponential distribution.

a. What is the probability that there will be no patients in the clinic?

b. What is the probability that there will be six or more patients in the clinic?

c. What is the average number of patients waiting in queue?

d. What is the average waiting time in queue?

23. The Hairy Knoll is a discount barbershop where the students from the Kingston Barber School serve their apprenticeship. The shop has only three barber chairs, each manned by an eager student. An instructor oversees the operation and gives guidance as needed. Patrons are served on a first-come, first-served basis and arrive at the rate of ten customers per hour according to a Poisson distribution. The time required for a haircut averages 15 minutes according to an exponential distribution.

a. What is the probability that there will be no customers in the shop?

b. What is the probability that there will be five or more customers in the shop?

c. What is the average number of customers waiting in queue?

d. What is the average waiting time in queue?

24. Consider further the Hairy Knoll barbershop described in Problem 23. Suppose that it is desirable to allow the students idle time so they can sweep the floor and be given additional instruction in cutting hair. The dean of the Kingston Barber School believes that the added expense of remodeling the Hairy Knoll to accommodate four barber chairs could be offset by slightly increased prices, if the average waiting time in queue per customer is less than five minutes. Assuming that the price change will not affect the rate of customer arrivals, should the Hairy Knoll be remodeled?

25. The tool crib supervisor at Ace Electronics wishes to determine the staffing policy that minimizes total operating costs. The average arrival rate at the crib, where tools are dispensed to the workers, is 8 machinists per hour; each machinist's pay is $18 per hour. The supervisor can staff the crib either with a junior attendant who is paid $5 per hour and can process 10 arrivals per hour or with a senior attendant who is paid $9 per hour and can process 12 arrivals per hour. Which type should be selected, and what is the total estimated hourly cost?

26. Eagle Dry Cleaners specializes in same-day dry cleaning. Customers drop off their gar-

ments early in the morning and expect them to be ready for pickup on their way home from work. There is a risk, however, that the work needed on a given garment cannot be done that day, depending on the type of dry cleaning required and the toughness of extraordinary stains. Historically, an average of 15 garments had to be held over to the next day. The store manager is contemplating expanding to reduce or eliminate that backlog. A simulation model was developed with the following distribution for garments per day:

Number	Probability	Random Numbers
50	0.10	00–09
60	0.25	10–34
70	0.30	35–64
80	0.25	65–89
90	0.10	90–99

With expansion, the maximum number of garments that could be dry cleaned per day is:

Number	Probability	Random Numbers
60	0.30	00–29
70	0.40	30–69
80	0.30	70–99

In the simulation for a specific day, the number of garments needing cleaning (NGNC) is determined first. Next, the maximum number of garments that could be dry cleaned (MNGD) is determined. If MNGD $\geq$ NGNC, all garments are dry cleaned for that day. If MNGD $<$ NGNC, then (NGNC $-$ MNGD) garments must be added to the number of garments arriving the next day to obtain the NGNC for the next day. The simulation continues in this manner until a specific number of days have been simulated.

a. Assuming that the store is empty at the start, simulate 15 days of operation using the following random numbers (the first determines the number of arrivals and the second the capacity):

(49, 77), (27, 53), (65, 08), (83, 12), (04, 82), (58, 44), (53, 83), (57, 72), (32, 53), (60, 79), (79, 30), (41, 48), (97, 86), (30, 25), (80, 73)

What is the average daily number of garments held overnight, based on your simulation?

b. If the cost associated with garments being held over is $25 per garment per day and the added cost of expansion is $100 per day, is the expansion a good idea?

SELECTED REFERENCES

Abernathy, William J. "Production Process Structure and Technological Change." *Decision Sciences*, vol. 7, no. 4 (October 1976), pp. 607–619.

"And Now, the Post-Industrial Corporation." *Business Week*, March 3, 1986.

Chase, Richard B. "Where Does the Customer Fit in a Service Operation?" *Harvard Business Review* (November–December 1978), pp. 137–142.

Harrigan, K. R. *Strategies for Vertical Integration.* Lexington, Mass.: D.C. Heath, 1983.

Hill, Terry. *Manufacturing Strategy: Text and Cases.* Homewood, Ill.: Irwin, 1989.

Kantrow, Alan M. "The Strategy–Technology Connection." *Harvard Business Review* (July–August 1980), pp. 6–21.

Levitt, Theodore. "The Industrialization of Service." *Harvard Business Review* (Sept.–Oct. 1976), pp. 63–74.

Lovelock, Christopher H., and Robert F. Young. "Look to Consumers to Increase Productivity." *Harvard Business Review* (May–June 1979), pp. 168–178.

Malhotra, Manoj K., and Larry P. Ritzman. "Resource Flexibility Issues in Multistage Manufacturing." *Decision Sciences*, vol. 21, no. 4 (Fall 1990), pp. 673–690.

Nadler, Gerald. *Work Design.* Homewood, Ill.: Irwin, 1970.

Niebel, Benjamin W. *Motion and Time Study.* Homewood, Ill.: Richard D. Irwin, 1976.

Porter, Michael E. "The Competitive Advantage of Nations." *Harvard Business Review* (March–April 1990), pp. 73–93.

Ritzman, Larry P., Barry E. King, and Lee J. Krajewski. "Manufacturing Performance—Pulling the Right Levers." *Harvard Business Review* (March–April 1984), pp. 143–152.

Skinner, Wickham. "Operations Technology: Blind Spot in Strategic Management. *Interfaces*, vol. 14 (January–February 1984), pp. 116–125.

Swamidass, Paul M. "Manufacturing Flexibility." *OMA* Monograph 2, January 1988.

Wheelwright, Steven C., and Robert H. Hayes. "Competing Through Manufacturing." *Harvard Business Review* (January–February 1985), pp. 99–109.

Chapter 6

TECHNOLOGY MANAGEMENT

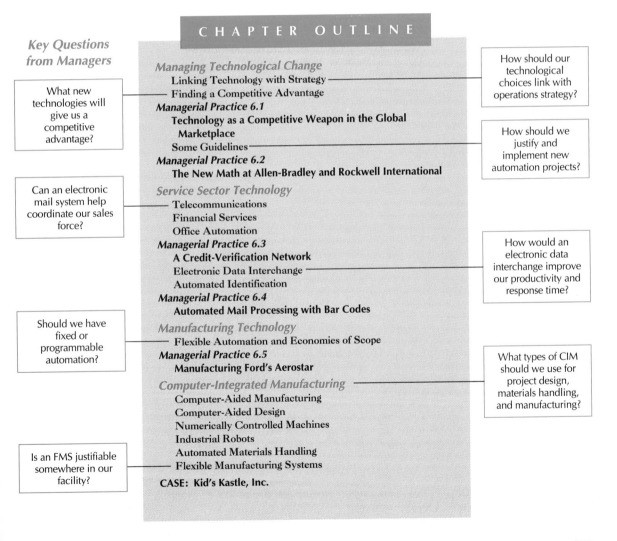

What new technologies will give us a competitive advantage?

Can an electronic mail system help coordinate our sales force?

Should we have fixed or programmable automation?

Is an FMS justifiable somewhere in our facility?

How should our technological choices link with operations strategy?

How should we justify and implement new automation projects?

How would an electronic data interchange improve our productivity and response time?

What types of CIM should we use for project design, materials handling, and manufacturing?

215

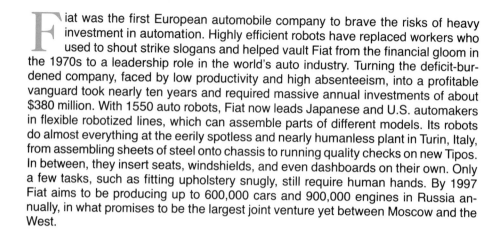

Fiat was the first European automobile company to brave the risks of heavy investment in automation. Highly efficient robots have replaced workers who used to shout strike slogans and helped vault Fiat from the financial gloom in the 1970s to a leadership role in the world's auto industry. Turning the deficit-burdened company, faced by low productivity and high absenteeism, into a profitable vanguard took nearly ten years and required massive annual investments of about $380 million. With 1550 auto robots, Fiat now leads Japanese and U.S. automakers in flexible robotized lines, which can assemble parts of different models. Its robots do almost everything at the eerily spotless and nearly humanless plant in Turin, Italy, from assembling sheets of steel onto chassis to running quality checks on new Tipos. In between, they insert seats, windshields, and even dashboards on their own. Only a few tasks, such as fitting upholstery snugly, still require human hands. By 1997 Fiat aims to be producing up to 600,000 cars and 900,000 engines in Russia annually, in what promises to be the largest joint venture yet between Moscow and the West.

Capital intensity, as you learned in Chapter 5, is an important facet of process design. In this chapter we look at some newer, often more capital-intensive, technologies. For our purposes, we define **technology** as any manual, automated, or mental process used to transform inputs into products and services. Each operation has a technology, even if it is manual. Invariably, managers have several technologies from which to choose. For example, look at the options for the simple process of sawing lumber:

1. A worker using a simple hand saw
2. A worker operating and controlling a portable power saw
3. A rigidly mounted power saw, which a worker must set up, load, and unload, but which automatically guides the lumber into the blade
4. A high-speed, continuously running power saw, which automatically feeds and unloads lumber with only infrequent worker intervention

Note that the options for sawing lumber differ in one important respect: Some are more automated than others. The word *automatic*, which comes from the Greek word for "self-acting," has been around for well over 200 years. The word **automation,** coined in the late 1940s, today means a system, process, or piece of equipment that is self-acting and self-regulating.

Because technology is changing so rapidly, it is more important than ever for operations managers to make intelligent, informed decisions about automation. Many new opportunities are the result of advances in computer technology. Deciding whether to take advantage of such opportunities is closely related to process design. The stakes are high because such choices affect the human as well as the technical aspects of operations. Job satisfaction and positive employee attitudes can be maintained only if technological change is managed well.

We begin with some principles on the management of technological change, valid for service and manufacturing organizations alike. We cover how technological choices link with operations strategy and how technology can create a competitive advantage, and conclude with some useful guidelines on managing innovation. The remainder of the chapter presents some newer technologies in the service sector and in manufacturing (including computer-integrated manufacturing). We can't possibly cover all new technologies in a single chapter, and they do not always break out cleanly between service and manufacturing. For example, robots and fax machines are used in both sectors. However, enough new technologies are sampled to give you a sense of the widening array of possibilities.

MANAGING TECHNOLOGICAL CHANGE

Management of both service and manufacturing industries is looking to emerging technologies for improvements in productivity and quality. When deciding which technologies to use, the operations manager should not assume that the best decision is more automation. In the 1970s and 1980s new technologies were held out as the cure-all for lagging U.S. productivity. Doomsayers warned of a robot gap with Japan, and companies spent billions of dollars to automate. The 1990s bring with them a more balanced view of automation: It can become a competitive weapon or a millstone (burden), depending on the situation. For example, General Motors' most automated plant is a $500 million truck factory in Hamtramck, Michigan. The plant, which operates with the help of 300 robots, has lower productivity and poorer quality performance than the organization's labor-intensive plant at Fremont, California, which GM runs as a joint venture with Japan's Toyota. As a result, GM's new Saturn plant is less capital intensive than originally planned.

General Motors has entered a joint venture with a German automaker. Shown here are computerized robots spot welding Opel auto bodies.

Linking Technology with Strategy

The right technological choices must link with operations strategy. As Fig. 5.2 demonstrates, volume is an important variable to consider in determining the amount of automation and capital intensity. Automation requires large outlays for equipment and thus increased fixed costs. Automation can also increase maintenance costs and often reduces resource flexibility. On the other hand, if volumes are high enough, the benefits of automation will overcome the drawbacks. Volume in turn derives from strategic choices made about the product or service, competitive priorities, and positioning strategy. If a firm succeeds in its priority to become the low-cost producer, it is likely to enjoy higher volumes and opt for a product focus and for more capital intensity. If sales do not materialize as expected after investing in considerable automation, the firm's production system becomes a millstone, particularly if the equipment is not adaptable to other products or services.

Finding a Competitive Advantage

Managerial Practice 6.1 describes how Obayashi and Motorola made technology a competitive weapon. Managers in the global economy must be alert to all opportunities for improvement, and the rapid changes in technology make it a particularly important area to evaluate. The potential benefits from a new technology are far-ranging. The most obvious one is reducing the *direct cost* of labor and raw materials. For example, Fiat reduced its work force from 138,000 to 72,000 in nine years with its investment in robots. *Sales* can increase, as MCI Communications found when it spent $300 million to update its computer systems. It now can offer innovative residential calling services, such as a plan offering 20 percent discounts on calls to preselected parties, which other carriers can't easily match. *Quality* can improve, as illustrated by the new magnetic resonance imaging (MRI) machines that can diagnose heart and liver diseases without using x-rays and radioactive materials; also, scanning times are reduced from about 45 to 20 minutes, which increases patient throughput, reduces costs, and increases patient comfort. In manufacturing, Giddings & Lewis makes groups of machine tools by using automated material-handling equipment and computer control. These systems are reducing human error—and thus improving product quality—and resulting in *quicker delivery times* due to reduced processing times and delays. These reductions in turn allow *reduced inventories*, with less inventory held on the shop floor. The *environment* might even improve: CSX Corporation replaced the mufflers on some of its unloading machinery with a "noise cancellation" system consisting of tiny speakers, a microphone, and a small signal processor. The new technology eliminates the engine noise completely: It analyzes the noise and then, in a fraction of a second, generates identical waves that are 180 degrees out of phase with the sound waves. Workers now need no ear protection in a workplace that used to produce 123 decibels of noise, as loud as the sound of a commercial jet during takeoff.

On the other side of the ledger, investment costs can be forbidding, particularly for complex and expensive automation projects that require extensive

Managerial Practice 6.1

Technology as a Competitive
Weapon in the Global Marketplace

- Rising seven stories above downtown Salt Lake City, Utah, the new arena to house professional basketball's Utah Jazz team was built through expertise from the other side of the world. The Tokyo-based Obayashi Corporation undertook the project as a joint venture and used a new technology by which the arena's sprawling roof could be quickly slid into place. (The older method set up the roof by crane in individual trusses.) The construction was started in June 1990 and completed in 17 months, almost a year less time than would have taken otherwise. Back home in Tokyo, Obayashi is building a mile-high skyscraper with robots, requiring as little as 10 percent of the conventional work force. Such technological advances have enabled the Japanese to cut costs and shorten construction time. The U.S. construction industry lags behind Japan and other countries in developing and implementing such new technologies. Foreign-owned firms controlled 6 percent of U.S. building contracts in 1989, compared with about 2 percent in 1982. Meanwhile, the U.S. share of major construction contracts worldwide fell from 50 percent in 1980 to 25 percent in 1988.

- Motorola uses "computer integration" instead of robots to gain a competitive manufacturing its pocket pagers. A sales representative in California types in a new customer order on a personal computer, specifying the delivery data and the unique code that will cause each pager to beep. The order zips over telephone lines to a mainframe computer in the new plant at Boynton Beach, Florida. The computer automatically schedules the pagers, orders the components, and, on the day of assembly, informs the shipping docks how best to transport them to the customer. The factory's machines and computers speak the same language as the computers in sales and shipping. The payback: The Florida plant makes pagers at the same cost as does Motorola's Singapore plant, which uses cheaper labor but is not computer integrated. And the domestic plant delivers, overnight, custom-built pagers that used to take nearly six weeks to supply.

Sources: "U.S. Contractors Trail Japan in R&D," *Wall Street Journal*, August 6, 1991; "Putting It All Together," *Wall Street Journal*, June 4, 1990.

facility overhaul. The investment can also be risky, due to uncertainties in demand and in per unit benefits. More highly trained employees may be needed to maintain and operate the new equipment, or the new technology may not work at all. Employees may resist the change or may lose their jobs. Customers may feel that service is not as good with the new technology.

The operations manager must sort out the pros and cons of different technological choices. Managing technology means more than choosing the right one: It also means implementing the technology and supporting it throughout the project startup.

Some Guidelines

Operations managers must make informed decisions with courage and vision. Although they offer no guarantees of success, four useful guidelines have emerged from recent experience.

Simplification and Initial Planning. Before considering automation, a manager should simplify and streamline current operations to eliminate duplication and waste. The "base case" against which to justify new automation should be what the current operation can achieve, *not* what it is achieving. Several showcase plants have not lived up to expectations because automation preceded streamlining.

When the time comes to automate, management should plan well, making sure that operations strategy and competitive priorities match technological choices. Operations managers should state precisely what they expect from automation. They should quantify goals and perform structured analysis, rather than settle for an undefined goal of reduced costs. When possible, consider approaching automation incrementally, as did managers at successful plants such as Allen-Bradley, Caterpillar, and Hewlett-Packard.

Justification. How to justify investment in emerging technologies is a controversial topic. Traditional techniques of financial analysis, such as the net present value method (see Supplement 1), would reject some very successful innovations. The problem is not with the technique itself but with how it is applied. Labor savings still justify most automation projects, but labor is a shrinking component of total costs. Production workers account for only 10 to 15 percent of total cost at today's factories. On the other hand, fixed costs comprise nearly 70 percent for the more capital-intensive factories. As Managerial Practice 6.2 shows, a narrow focus on labor can foreclose excellent automation projects.

Operations managers must look beyond direct costs to the impact of automation on customer service, delivery times, inventories, and resource flexibility. Although quantifying a firm's ability to move quickly into a new market may be difficult, such intangibles make the difference. The smart operations manager also realizes that the base case of doing nothing is *not* the status quo. A firm that fails to automate—while its competitors do just that—can lose its competitive advantage. The result may be declining revenues and layoffs.

Thus justification still must begin with financial analysis techniques, but it must recognize *all* quantifiable factors that can be translated into dollar values. The resulting financial measure of merit—such as net present value, payback period, or internal rate of return (see Supplement 1)—is insufficient by itself. It must be merged with the qualitative factors and intangibles, perhaps using the preference matrix approach (see Chapter 2).

The Human Side. The jobs that people actually perform are largely determined by technology—that is, when technology changes, so do the jobs. Automation affects jobs at all levels: Some are eliminated, some upgraded, and others downgraded. Even when the changes resulting from automation are small, people-related issues may become large. For example, poorly trained and poorly motivated workers can cause enormous damage, as illustrated by the nuclear accidents at Three Mile Island and Chernobyl. The operations manager must anticipate such changes and prepare for them. Transition is easiest when automation is part of capacity expansion or a new facility and thus doesn't threaten

Managerial Practice 6.2

The New Math at Allen-Bradley and Rockwell International

- Allen-Bradley's $15 million, 50-machine, flexible-assembly facility produces motor starters in 125 different configurations at a rate of 600 an hour. The company didn't justify automation with a narrow investment-driven focus. Instead, it began with a corporate strategy and then developed a manufacturing plant that would achieve the desired goals. After deciding to compete anywhere on price (corporate strategy), the company justified the facility investment (operations strategy) on the basis of quality, cost, market share, competition, and profitability. "If there is a time to ignore conventional return-on-investment calculation, it's when your long-term goals are at stake," said Tracy O'Rourke, Allen-Bradley's CEO.

- At Rockwell International's Collins Defense Communications facility, management decided to create a strategic advantage in manufacturing, rather than relocate to chase low labor rates. Its automation program is an $11 million addition to the existing plant. Labor savings did not justify the investment because employment in the assembly areas remained constant. Instead, justification came from increased flexibility; the facility now handles high and low production rates economically. Quality has improved, and skilled, experienced employees work where their expertise helps the most.

Source: "Automation and the Bottom Line," *Industry Week*, May 26, 1986.

existing jobs. In other situations early education and retraining is essential. Before Chrysler opened its automated plant in Sterling Heights, Michigan, it put its employees collectively through 900,000 labor hours of training.

Another key to successful implementation is involving employees in the design of new systems. When Ford revamped its plant to make the Aerostar minivan, management reviewed proposed methods with workers directly responsible for specific operations. Employees made 434 suggestions, about 60 percent of which were adopted. Both the number and percentage were considered quite good.

Leadership. The operations manager should identify a team to lead and coordinate new automation projects. All departments affected by the automation should be represented on the team. A "project champion" who promotes the project at every opportunity and who has contagious enthusiasm should be in charge. This leader should be respected by all team members and preferably should have had experience dealing with equipment suppliers. Top management's ongoing support of the team must be evident throughout the project. Everyone should know that the operations manager is knowledgeable about the project, stands behind it, and will give it the resources it needs to succeed.

SERVICE SECTOR TECHNOLOGY

Table 6.1 shows examples of automated processes in several service industries. Although we take many of these processes for granted, some are quite remarkable. Financial services, air transportation, communications, and health care

TABLE 6.1 / Automation in Service Industries

Industry	Automated Process
Financial services	Automated trading Electronic funds transfer
Transportation	Autopilots Bay Area Rapid Transit System
Communications	Voice-mail machines Videotex service
Health care	MRI machines Ambulance electronic dispatching
Wholesale and retail trade	EDI Point-of-sale electronic terminals
Education	Electronic library cataloguing Language translation computers
Utilities and government	Meter reading Optical mail scanners
Restaurants and food	Bar codes Vending machines that cook
Hotels and motels	Video messages Electronic key and lock systems
Leisure activities	Television games Video-disc machines

are particularly dynamic with respect to technological change, and such advances are crucial to the performance of both manufacturing and the whole economy. In the following sections, we explore a few of the innovations in service industries.

Technological advances within the service sector affect everyday concerns such as transportation. In the photo, a commuter prepares to board a Bay Area Rapid Transit (BART) train, which brings a greater level of automation to San Francisco's transportation system. The BART system also helps to alleviate traffic congestion on San Francisco's streets and offers riders low-cost, convenient service. BART passengers avoid the rush-hour gridlock and the heavy parking fees common in most major U.S. cities.

Telecommunications

Advances in telecommunications have been particularly dramatic. Most of the new technologies are computer based, which has led to the term *telematics* (computers + telecommunications).

A **voice-mail machine** is a computerized answering machine that allows users to record, store, forward, and broadcast voice messages. The simplest machines let callers leave a recorded message, just like a standard tape answering machine. But many of the systems—the so-called *automated attendants*—do much more, directing callers to select from various options by using the buttons on a touch-tone phone. The phone line is hooked to a device that converts voice signals into digital information which is then recorded on disk. In fact, some systems give the callers the option of listening to and redoing their messages. The system can be interactive because it depends on a computer that recognizes the tones generated by touch-tone phones. Such technology eliminates the need for receptionists, allows 40,000 students at Texas A&M University to register for classes by phone, protects costly employees from time-consuming outside callers, allows deluxe hotels to take messages for guests, allows callers to check on flight delays, and allows the regional telephone company to give you a wake-up call. Sales for voice-mail suppliers were $810 million in 1990, up from only $120 million in 1985.

Videotex service is an electronic information medium that gives subscribers at home or work access to various on-line databases and enables them to perform various tasks. Users access information through a special terminal or a personal computer linked to the master computer by a modem. The master computer contains an electronic library, or collection of databases, which the service updates regularly. Users can check stock prices, get electronic brokerage services, reserve airline tickets, and the like. A related technology is the **voice-response machine** by which the computer "reads" the information requested by the caller over a touch-tone phone. The caller hears digitized speech rather than see the information displayed on a screen.

A vast quantity of information is available. Some databases are built on numbers: economic indicators, stock market prices, and so forth. Others build collections of key subjects or words: weather data, ski conditions, the status of bills in Congress, and full texts of several major newspapers and magazines from around the world, to name a few. Thus computers have given decision makers instant access to vast quantities of data never before so readily available.

An **electronic mail (e-mail) system** usually consists of a host mainframe hooked up to numerous microcomputers. Special communications software allows users to contact the central computer to leave or pick up messages. Electronic mail bypasses time-consuming interoffice memos and eliminates the annoying game of "telephone tag." Additionally, the message sender can communicate with several people at the same time. For example, if several customer service representatives need information about price changes or product availability, the service manager can send this information to all of them simultaneously.

*M*otorola's cellular phone facilitates efficient use of time. Employees can communicate with their office or call ahead to clients to confirm or delay appointments.

A **facsimile (fax) machine** transmits copies of documents quickly and accurately over phone lines, with equipment needed at both the sending and receiving ends. A fax machine allows bids, reports, and legal documents to be filed at the last minute, if necessary. Faxes (and e-mail) help managers perform in today's global business environment: Managers can communicate across different time zones without working 24 hours a day. Fax services are being offered in new and innovative ways. For example, American Telephone & Telegraph is creating "portable offices" for travelers. Some of its new public pay phones will have outlets that accept portable fax machines and laptop computers and be equipped with a data screen for reading and editing text. The latest twist, the *fax-back*, is possible with phone-based information systems. Callers simply indicate what information they want—a sales brochure or map, for example—by punching keys on their phone. Then they key in their fax numbers and the information is automatically faxed to them.

The **cellular phone** is a mobile radio service that allows people in cars and trucks to talk with land-based telephone customers using ordinary telephones. Cellular systems distribute their channels among small areas, or "cells," through small, low-powered transmitters. As a vehicle travels from one cell to another, the call in progress is automatically and imperceptibly "handed-off" to the next transmitter by software-controlled switching equipment. Cellular phones allow a person to stay in touch with the office and clients while in transit and thus use time more efficiently. The system now offers a voice-recognition chip, which instantaneously dials a number after the driver says a person's name—without taking the hands off the wheel.

Financial Services

The financial sector owns almost half of all service sector computers. Financial services hold more than 25 percent of their total capital in the form of computers and other office machinery—over seven times the ratio for all other industries. Within the finance sector, securities brokers, investment holding companies, and insurance companies depend most heavily on computers, followed in turn by banks and credit agencies. We look at three examples of automation through computers: automated trading systems, electronic funds transfer, and automated teller machines.

Automated trading at the New York Stock Exchange (NYSE) involves the use of various computer and telecommunications technologies to receive orders (buy or sell), make stock exchanges, report transactions and quotes, inform the entering party of the results, and report to the clearinghouse. Technological change is particularly difficult to implement at NYSE because multiple, independent parties must be satisfied, transactions must be made more or less instantaneously, and a "price discovery" mechanism must be provided fairly and quickly. Volume variation is large: Capacity requirements may exceed 600 million shares on one day and be "only" 140 million the next. At busy times, the floor resembles "sharks in a feeding frenzy." The NYSE floor is essentially electronically automated, with orders arriving at electronic speeds at stock specialist positions. Multiple added participants (through helper terminals) can be called in for particularly hectic stocks.

One important part of the automation is the Designated Order Turnaround (DOT) system, which helps report on a transaction. A specialist on the trading floor reports the trade on a "mark sense card" (rather than fill out an ordinary ordering ticket) that is fed into an optical reader for computer entry. The specialist need not repeat any fixed information on the order but merely stroke a "turnaround number" to summon the information from the computer bank. The DOT "bunching" feature allows individual orders to be aggregated during volume surges according to parameters set by floor officials on-line, reducing the number of transactions to be handled.

Automation is an ongoing process: Cathode ray tubes are being replaced with flat screen technology, taking less space and displaying more information. Such automation allowed NYSE to keep up with the deluge of orders in mid-October 1987, which was greater than anything that occurred in the 1960s volume surges that created the major "back-office crises" of that period.

Two particularly successful technologies in banking are electronic funds transfer (EFT) systems and automatic teller machines (ATMs). The EFT systems transfer money automatically between bank accounts. ATMs are computers that allow customers to make withdrawals and deposits and check their account balances electronically—24 hours a day. Banks also benefit because ATM systems are relatively inexpensive to operate. For example, the average operating cost per ATM transaction is $0.66, compared with a teller cost of $0.90 to $1.20. The latest innovation may be ATMs with miniature cameras that allow banks to doublecheck on people who contend their accounts were debited on a day they did not use an ATM. Prior technology required expensive cameras with large lenses that revealed themselves to potential cheats. The new technology, developed in Scotland, incorporates all the circuitry needed for a video camera on a single computer chip. The price tag for the new tiny cameras, which need only a pinhole to peep through, may be as low as $40.

One survey showed that banks expect to rely even more on ATMs and home banking in the future. During the 1990s self-service technologies may handle as much as 60 percent of all withdrawals in certain markets, a dramatic increase from the current 13 percent (see Roth and Van der Velde, 1988). Forecasters expect automated deposits to grow from 9 to 53 percent and cash advances from 11 to 53 percent. Managerial Practice 6.3 describes a related technology for verifying credit at the point of sale.

Office Automation

Almost 58 percent of the 116 million U.S. workers are in the office, a segment of the work force that has grown twice as fast as any other since 1976. White collar productivity rose less than one percent during the 1980s. It is no wonder that there is such an interest in office automation, in both manufacturing and services, to help workers with repetitive activities that often are highly cognitive. Computer usage has increased rapidly even among small firms, growing at a rate of 55 percent in the past five years. About two-thirds of all small businesses now use various computer technologies.

A *word processor* is a computer system that allows documents to be created, modified, stored, and retrieved electronically. A secretary uses it to prepare a letter, a CEO to formulate a long-term plan. Most microcomputer users also have access to *electronic spreadsheets*, which have a large number of rows and columns into which data are entered and manipulated mathematically. They are also frequently linked to sophisticated *graphics* capabilities for use by managers, analysts, and clerical workers alike.

Linked communication and information systems are especially important to office automation. In 1990 alone U.S. firms hooked up 3.8 million personal computers in small office *networks,* raising the total by 48 percent in one year. Many of these networks tie into minicomputers and mainframes that control thousands of terminals and printers. The networks provide decision makers at all levels with timely information on sales, engineering, inventory, marketing, and shipping that can boost productivity and improve competitiveness. A good example is Wal-Mart Stores, which recently spent $20 million on a satellite network linking its 1182 outlets to its Bentonville headquarters.

Another example is Dayton Power and Light Company, an electric and gas utility in Ohio that uses networks to improve productivity and reduce customer errors. Its meter readers use portable computers to key in their readings right on site. If an entry falls outside normal bounds, the portable computer will beep, signaling a possible error. Each evening files from these portables are read into a network of microcomputers, which then transfer the accumulated data to the central mainframe computer. The entire process of updating customer accounts, which used to take the better part of each night, is now done

Managerial Practice 6.3

A Credit-Verification Network

A credit card point-of-sale authorization system provides a rapid and convenient service to the customer at the time of sale. An electro-optical technique for reading the card and a network of computers make it all possible. The trail of a typical Visa transaction is described:

- A customer buys diamond earrings for $795 in Chicago. The clerk passes the Visa card through a credit-verification terminal and punches in purchase data.
- The data travel by satellite, land lines, or microwave to National Data Corporation's computers in Cherry Hill, New Jersey.
- From Cherry Hill the credit query goes to NDC headquarters in Atlanta for processing. The transaction tops $50, so it needs a second opinion. The request is turned over to Visa USA minicomputers at NDC.

- The Visa minis shoot the query to mainframes in McLean, Virginia, or San Mateo, California.
- The Visa mainframe determines that the card is from a San Francisco bank and contacts the bank's computer, which checks whether $795 credit is available.
- The bank's okay retraces the path of the authorization request: from the bank to Visa USA to NDC in Atlanta to NDC in Cherry Hill to the merchant in Chicago.

Total elapsed time: 15 seconds

Source: "Taming the Wild Network," *Business Week*, October 8, 1990, pp. 143–147.

in minutes. Frito-Lay uses a similar technology for its delivery people to enter orders at each store, produce itemized invoices, and transmit sales reports to company headquarters in Dallas.

Another type of network links the supplier with its customers. *Integrated computer order systems* allow customers to place orders electronically with a supplier and, in some cases, to reserve inventory in the supplier's warehouse. For example, airlines place computer terminals in travel agencies to facilitate processing customers' reservations. American Hospital Supply has placed terminals in the purchasing agent's office at many hospitals. Rapid order and delivery capability reduces the need to stockpile supplies, thus lowering inventory carrying costs.

Electronic Data Interchange

Electronic data interchange (EDI) is the computer-to-computer exchange of routine business documents over telephone lines, using a standard format, between two or more companies. Special communications software translates documents into and out of a generic form, allowing organizations to exchange information even if they have different hardware and software components. Invoices, purchase orders, and payments are some of the routine documents EDI can handle—it replaces the phone call or mailed document. EDI saves the cost of opening mail, directing it to the right department, checking the document for accuracy, and reentering the information into a computer system. EDI also improves accuracy, shortens response times, and can even cut inventory. Cost savings, ranging from $2 to $25 per document, are considerable, with the thousands of documents a firm typically handles daily.

Super Valu Stores estimates that it saves $5000 to $6000 a week using EDI because it no longer has to manually process invoices and other documents generated by mail or phone. The food wholesaler also saves $600,000 a year as a result of cuts in the clerical staff, which checked purchase orders against invoices. Within five years, the Pentagon plans to purchase 80 percent of its goods using EDI. The new program will come into use piece by piece and is expected to sharply reduce the paperwork associated with military procurement.

EDI is not limited to the service sector. It is finding widespread adoption with manufacturers. For example, Navistar International Corporation, a truck and engine manufacturer, was an early EDI user. During the first 18 months following installation of EDI, the firm cut truck inventories by a third, or $167 million. EDI's instantaneous execution of transactions enables the company to keep better track of inventory.

Automated Identification

The most widespread technology for automated identification is bar coding. Emerging technologies include *imaging machines*, which provide an enhanced photolike image of a document and eventually will read handwriting, and *optical character readers* that can read words on a document or an envelope. A **bar code** is a pattern of wide and narrow black bands and alternating white spaces that a computer reads with the aid of an optical scanner or wand. The code can be printed directly on the product or on an attached label.

A technician at an OTIS facility uses bar coding to conduct an audit check as materials are delivered to or retrieved from storage.

Managerial Practice 6.4

Automated Mail Processing with Bar Codes

The Postal Service is the largest U.S. civilian employer: Its work force of 756,000 handles 162 billion pieces of mail per year. By 1995 it expects to trim 84,000 jobs from a peak of 787,000 in 1989. Savings in 1995 alone can be $4 billion. The reductions, made through attrition rather than layoffs, are due to increased automation. The keys to the hoped-for turnaround are bar codes, which will represent nine digits—ZIP codes plus four more numbers—to target deliveries right down to the city block. The Postal Service can spray on the codes with its own optical character readers but prefers volume mailers to put them on so that the addresses can be quickly read by automated bar code sorters. Letters with bar codes already affixed go directly to the sorters. By the end of 1992 about 61 percent of all cards and letters handled by the Postal Service will carry bar codes.

Productivity rates vary considerably by technology. A postal worker can manually sort letters into metal pigeonholes at a rate of 500 letters an hour—the way all mail was handled for 190 years. Letter sorting machines are an intermediate technology that requires a 17-member crew, including 12 on keyboards who each use three keys to sort 1600 pieces of mail an hour. The letter sorting machines have caused repetitive motion trauma to some employees, however, so the goal is to phase out these machines in favor of bar code processing, creating a safer and more productive work environment.

Source: "U.S. Postal Service Expects to Trim 47,000 Jobs by '95," *Wall Street Journal,* September 27, 1991.

Computerized checkout procedures have helped firms such as K mart and Wal-Mart dramatically increase productivity and manage inventory with greater accuracy and efficiency. As the system scans bar codes, it automatically records both price and item and updates inventory records. The customer receives a precise record of the transaction and quicker, more accurate service. And K mart uses the data it collects each day from each store to fine-tune product prices and maximize revenue. Today, bar codes are used by supermarkets, public libraries, VCR rental stores, retailers, and discount retailers. Surgical nurses also use bar codes, to read a drug's label and a patient's wrist bracelet before delivering medication. Managerial Practice 6.4 describes how the U.S. Postal Service plans to save $4 billion through the use of bar codes.

Federal Express used bar code technology as a strategic tool. Its early ability to track packages throughout the handling cycle, a capability possessed by none of its competitors, created a marketplace demand for the technology. Today, the hand-held, bar code reading computer is standard issue for every Federal Express courier worldwide. It accepts information from the courier and from bar codes placed on every Federal Express package and ensures that the information is complete and usable.

In manufacturing, bar codes allow computers to monitor labor distribution, inventory levels, quality losses, tool locations, and employee attendance. Allen-Bradley, a Milwaukee manufacturer of industrial controls, uses bar codes in its fully automated assembly line. The bar codes identify which of several products coming down the line will be assembled next. The computer then instructs each automated station to perform the appropriate operations and to select the correct parts to install from the 200 available.

MANUFACTURING TECHNOLOGY

Advances in technology can dramatically change factory operations as well as service processes. Managerial Practice 6.5 describes how Ford Motor Company uses computer-controlled machines, computer-aided design, welding robots, automated spray machines, and power-and-free conveyors to make the Aerostar minivan. Figure 6.1 goes beyond Ford's plant: It reports the experience of hundreds of automated North American manufacturing plants. For example, computer-aided design and computer numerical control are more widely applied than robots and automated materials-handling systems. In this section we explore such technologies in detail, after first differentiating them on the basis of flexibility.

Flexible Automation and Economies of Scope

There are two types of automation: fixed and flexible (or programmable). **Fixed automation** configures flow lines to produce one type of part or product in simple operations in a fixed sequence. Until the mid-1980s most U.S. automobile plants were dominated by fixed automation—and some still are. Chemical processing plants and oil refineries also utilize this kind of automation.

FIGURE 6.1

Automation in Manufacturing

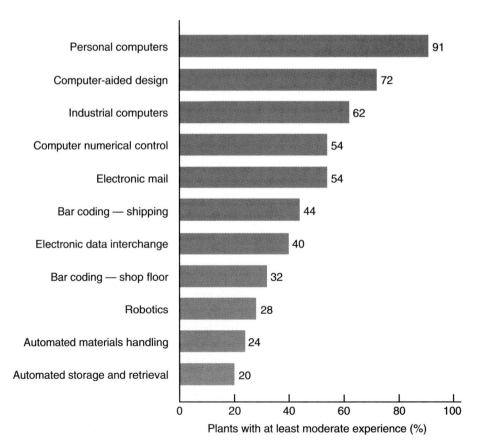

Source: Giffi, Craig, and Aleda V. Roth, "Taking Aim at World Class Manufacturing," *Annual Survey of North American Manufacturing Technology,* Deloitte & Touche, 1991, p. 15.

Managerial Practice 6.5

Manufacturing Ford's Aerostar

To produce Aerostar, Ford's most versatile entry in the mini-van market, Ford Motor Company uses some of the most sophisticated manufacturing technology in the world. The company has enlarged its St. Louis assembly plant and re-equipped it with new facilities and tooling. The new technology includes more than 550 computers linked in a network to continuously monitor the computer-controlled machines. Computers and other innovative manufacturing technologies allow Ford to build vehicles of very consistent quality.

Industrial designers use computer graphics to design Aerostar's roof panel. Electronic data are converted into computer commands that operate numerically controlled mills for machining sheet metal dies and inspection tools. Computers also compare roof panels stamped from the dies against original design data. By using computer-aided design and manufacturing techniques, production is able to ensure a uniform fit between body panels. The tight fit means less wind and road noise and better protection from the weather.

Aerostar's underbody assembly line uses 40 welding robots, including 24 gantry models—Ford's first overhead-mounted robots. The gantry robots carry up to 200 pounds of tooling and require less floor space than do side-mounted models. Robots and other automated equipment perform more than 97 percent of Aerostar's 4000 spot welds. They also apply enamel to Aerostar's interior surfaces. The robots and automatic spray machines that apply paint to the exterior produce a defect-free finish of consistent quality. The automated process eliminates repetitive operations workers found tedious.

Aerostar's chassis and trim department uses a material-handling system called *power-and-free-conveyors*. These conveyors eliminate conventional under-the-line floor pits, which separate workers from their co-workers and make it difficult to reach parts. By contrast, the new conveyors give all workers easier access to the vehicle.

Source: Ford Motor Company, "Second Quarter Report to Stockholders," Summer 1985.

Operations managers consider fixed automation when demand volumes are high, product designs are stable, and product life cycles are long. These conditions compensate for the process's two primary drawbacks: large initial investment cost and relative inflexibility. The investment cost is particularly high when a single, complex machine must be capable of handling many operations. Because the system is designed around a particular product, changing equipment to accommodate new products is difficult and costly. On the plus side, fixed automation maximizes efficiency and yields a rock-bottom variable cost per unit.

Flexible Automation. Flexible, or programmable, automation is another option for achieving repeatability when volumes are low. **Programmable automation** is an automatic process that can be reprogrammed to handle various products. The ability to reprogram machine instructions is useful in both process-focused and product-focused operations. A machine that makes a variety of products in small batches (process focus) has a program for each product, and an operator simply enters the appropriate instructions to alternate between programs. When a machine has been dedicated to a particular product (product focus) that has reached the end of its life cycle, it can simply be reprogrammed with a new sequence of operations for a new product. Cummins Engine Company, a manufacturer of diesel engines based in Columbus, Indiana, falls into the product-focused use of flexibility. In the first 18 months after introduction, the new compression brakes for its engines underwent 14 design changes. If the brakes were made on less flexible machines, these changes would have probably taken several years and many millions of dollars to incorporate and inhibited development of performance-enhancing modifications. Instead, programmable automation gave it a competitive advantage: It cut time to the market by two years, reduced annual warranty expenses by an estimated $300,000, and reduced cost to the customer by more than 30 percent.

Economies of Scope. Programmable automation breaks the traditional inverse relationship between resource flexibility and capital intensity (see Chapter 5). With programmable automation, both high capital intensity and high resource flexibility are possible. The result has been called **economies of scope,** which is the ability to produce multiple products more cheaply in combination than separately. In such situations, two conflicting competitive priorities—customization and low price—become more compatible.

Opportunities for economies of scope are not without limit. Someone must identify a family of parts or products with enough collective volume to fully utilize equipment, often in multiple shifts. Adding a product to the family results in one-time programming (and sometimes fixture) costs. *Fixtures* are reusable devices that maintain exact tolerances by holding the product firmly in position while it is processed.

COMPUTER-INTEGRATED MANUFACTURING

The popular press often writes about the factory of the future—a fully automated factory that manufactures a wide variety of products without human intervention. While some "peopleless" factories do exist and others will be built, the concept goes beyond displacing people with automation.

Computer-integrated manufacturing (CIM) is an umbrella term for the total integration of product design and engineering, process planning, and manufacturing by means of complex computer systems. Less comprehensive computerized systems for production planning, inventory control, or scheduling are often considered part of CIM. Computerized integration of all phases of manufacturing—from initial customer order to final shipment—is CIM's ultimate goal. For example, in 1989 McDonnell Douglas spent $10 million to introduce CIM to a Florida missile factory, where Tomahawk missiles once traveled through the plant accompanied by a two-inch-thick manual. The company installed computer systems that automatically schedule manufacturing tasks, keep track of labor, and send instructions to computer screens at work stations along the assembly line, thus eliminating paperwork. Workers do 30 percent more work now that they don't have to shuffle paper.

Computer-integrated manufacturing helps many manufacturing firms, even those with high wage rates, remain competitive in the global marketplace. In the following sections, we describe several technologies that make up CIM: computer-aided manufacturing, computer-aided design, numerically controlled machines, robots, automated materials handling, and flexible manufacturing systems. The purpose of using these technologies is to increase productivity, improve quality, and offer more flexibility.

Computer-Aided Manufacturing

The component of CIM that deals directly with manufacturing operations is called **computer-aided manufacturing (CAM).** It utilizes computers to design production processes and to control machine tools and materials flow. The various types of programmable automation are a basic part of CAM.

Computer-Aided Design

Computer-aided design (CAD) is a computerized design process for creating new parts or products or altering existing ones. These electronic design systems are replacing drafting traditionally done by hand. The heart of CAD is a powerful desktop computer and graphics software that allow a designer to manipulate geometric shapes. The designer creates drawings on a display monitor and instructs the computer to show several views of the subject according to specified dimensions. The computer can also simulate the reaction of a part to strength and stress tests. Using the design data stored in the computer's memory, manufacturing engineers and other users can quickly obtain printouts of plans and specifications for a part or product.

*K*2's CAD/CAM work station integrates its design and manufacturing functions. Here designers are converting numerical data into new ski designs.

Analysts can use CAD to store, retrieve, and classify data about various parts. This information is useful in creating families of parts to be manufactured by the same group of machines. Computer-aided design also helps designers avoid wasting time reinventing the wheel. Designers can quickly access and modify old designs, rather than start from scratch.

A *CAD/CAM system,* which integrates the design and manufacturing function through a computer, is the first step toward a paperless factory. The system translates final design specifications directly into detailed machine instructions for manufacturing the part. It is quicker, less error prone, and eliminates duplication between engineering and manufacturing. K2 Corporation, the largest U.S. manufacturer of Alpine skis, must constantly redesign its products to better meet customer needs. It produces about 20 different models in 12 different lengths. Its CAD/CAM work station allows its designers to convert the numerical descriptions for a new ski shape into drawings and tooling designs. It also creates machining instructions that can be used directly by the milling machines. Prototype skis are designed and produced for rapid testing, allowing K2 to respond rapidly to changing requirements in a competitive international market. An additional benefit is that K2 uses the system to make its own production machines, including a belt conveyor and an automated robotic ski topping system.

Numerically Controlled Machines

Numerically controlled (NC) machines are large machine tools programmed to produce small- to medium-sized batches of intricate parts. By following a preprogrammed sequence of instructions, NC machines can drill, turn, bore, or mill many different parts in various sizes and shapes. These machines were first developed in the early 1950s at the Massachusetts Institute of Technology through research sponsored by the U.S. Air Force. The objective was to find more efficient methods of manufacturing jet aircraft.

Numerically controlled machines are currently the most commonly used form of flexible automation. The newer models receive their instructions from a computer, not from a punched tape or card as in the past. **Computerized numerically controlled (CNC) machines** are usually stand-alone pieces of equipment, each controlled by its own microcomputer. More than 40 percent of the world's NC machines are at work in Japan. Since the early 1980s, Japanese industry has spent twice as much as North American or European industry on factory equipment, more than half on CNC machines.

Industrial Robots

Robots are more glamorous than the NC workhorses. The first industrial robot joined the GM production line in 1961. **Industrial robots** are versatile, computer-controlled machines programmed to perform various tasks. These "steel collar" workers operate independently of human control. Most are stationary and mounted on the floor, with an arm that can reach into difficult locations.

FIGURE 6.2

Robot and Its
Standard Movements

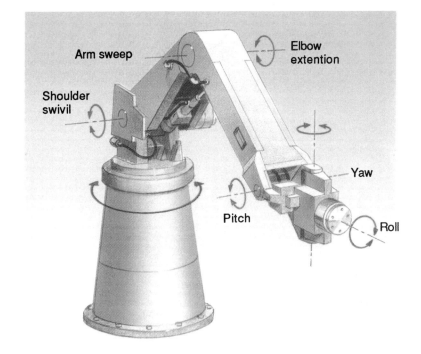

Source: Chris Voss,
"Managing New
Manufacturing
Technologies," OMA
Monograph 1,
September 1986.
Reprinted by
permission.

Figure 6.2 shows the six standard movements of a robot's arm. Not all robots have every movement.

The robot's hand, sometimes called an *end effector* or *tool*, actually does the work. The hand (not shown in Fig. 6.2) can be changed to perform different tasks, including materials handling, spot welding, spray painting, assembly, and inspection and testing. Second-generation robots equipped with sensors that simulate touch and sight have opened up new applications. For example, robots can wash windows, pick fruit from trees, mix chemicals in laboratories, and handle radioactive materials.

The initial cost of a robot depends on its size and function. Other factors include modifying both product and process to accommodate the robot, preparing the work site, installing and debugging the robot, and retraining and relocating workers. Benefits from robot installation include reduced waste materials, more consistent quality, and labor savings. Robots are the drudges of the work force, performing highly repetitive tasks without tiring, taking a lunch break, or going to the restroom. They accept zero wages and perform hazardous tasks without complaint. Table 6.2 highlights other characteristics of industrial robots.

By the late 1980s there were more than 20,000 robots in North America, 28,000 in Europe, and 80,000 in Japan. The U.S. robot market has fallen short of expectations. As Fig. 6.1 shows, less than 30 percent of the manufacturers surveyed had even moderate experience with robots, instead choosing robots for more isolated tasks—certainly not at the usage level of Fiat. One possible reason is that U.S. employers haven't faced a labor shortage, a fear in Japan

TABLE 6.2 / Robots: Current Practice

Characteristic	Actual Experience
Investment cost	From $20,000 to $100,000, depending on sophistication
Payback period	Typically less than three years
Return on investment	Typically from 12% to 18%, with some as high as 40%
Operating life	From 15,000 to 25,000 work hours
Annual maintenance cost	10% of initial investment cost; major overhaul after 10,000 hours
Best volume levels	More than 50,000 units per year and less than 500,000 units per year
Installation time	One to five days, depending on complexity

Source: Roger H. Mitchell and Vincent A. Mabert, "Robotics: Myths and Realities for Smaller American Manufacturers," *Business Horizons,* July/August 1986. Reprinted by permission.

when the government began to subsidize robots. Cincinnati Milacron, the last big U.S. robot maker, recently left the robot business and returned to making basic machine tools. Robotics, therefore, should be seen as but one of many possible technologies in gaining a competitive advantage.

Automated Materials Handling

In both manufacturing and service industries, how, when, and by whom materials are handled is an important technological choice. **Materials handling** covers the processes of moving, packaging, and storing a product. Each process costs time and money but adds no value to the product. Therefore operations managers are always looking for ways to automate the flow of materials to and from an operation.

The amount of justifiable materials-handling automation depends on positioning strategy. When operations have a process focus, job paths vary and there is little repeatability in materials handling. In such situations, automation can't be justified and workers move materials and equipment in open-top containers, carts, or lift trucks. When operations have a product focus and repeatability is high, however, handling can be automated. In addition, other types of flexible automation are now available for firms with positioning strategies that fall between these two extremes. Let's look at two such technologies: automated guided vehicles and automated storage and retrieval systems.

AGVs. An **automated guided vehicle (AGV)** is a small, driverless, battery-driven truck that moves materials between operations. Instructions are issued from either an on-board computer or a centralized computer. Most models follow a cable installed below the floor, but optical paths and free-ranging methods have extended their capabilities. They can go anywhere with aisle space and a relatively smooth floor.

The AGV's ability to route around problems such as production bottlenecks and transportation blockages helps production avoid expensive, unpredictable shutdowns. Furthermore, AGVs give just-in-time delivery of parts, thus reducing stockpiles of expensive inventories throughout the plant. The automotive industry now uses AGVs in some plants as mobile assembly stands, primarily for heavy loads. Workers prefer them to inflexible conveyors because the AGVs don't leave until the workers have done the job correctly at their own pace. NCR Corporation installed a $100,000 AGV system in one of its electronics fabrication facilities. Machines run along a 3000-foot guidepath at 1.5 miles per hour, ferrying parts between the stockroom, assembly stations, and the automated storage and retrieval system.

AS/RS. An **automated storage and retrieval system (AS/RS)** is a computer-controlled method of storing and retrieving materials and tools using racks, bins, and stackers. With support from AGVs, an AS/RS can receive and deliver materials without the aid of human hands. For example, IBM's new distribution center in Mechanicsburg, Pennsylvania, ships 105,000 spare computer parts and related publications each day—a staggering volume—using an AS/RS and 13 AGVs. Computer control assigns newly arrived materials to one of 37,240 storage locations. If optical sensors confirm that the materials will fit, the automated system moves them along to the proper location. Production at this highly automated facility has increased 20 percent and accuracy of filled orders has reached 99.8 percent.

Flexible Manufacturing Systems

A **flexible manufacturing system (FMS)** is a configuration of computer-controlled, semi-independent work stations where materials are automatically handled and machine loaded. Like NC machines and industrial robots, an FMS is a type of flexible automation and is part of CIM. Such systems require a large initial investment ($5 million to $20 million) but little direct labor to operate. There are three key components of an FMS:

1. Several computer-controlled work stations, such as CNC machines or robots, that perform a series of operations
2. A computer-controlled transport system for moving materials and parts from one machine to another and in and out of the system
3. Loading and unloading stations

Workers bring raw materials for a part family to the loading points, where the FMS takes over. Under the direction of the central computer, transporters begin delivering the materials to various work stations, where they pass through a specific sequence of operations unique to each part. The route is determined by the central computer. The goal is to synchronize activities to maximize the system's utilization. Because automatic tool interchange capabilities make it possible to switch tools quickly, setup times for machines are short. This flexibility often allows more than one machine to perform an oper-

(a)

(b)

(c)

(d)

(e)

(f)

Views of Mazak's FMS. (a) End view with CNC 1 on the immediate left. The AGV is coming down the track just left of center. In the center are pallets of stored parts. The computer control room is behind the windows on the second floor. (b) CNC 2 and an AGV that has just received a finished part from CNC 1. (c) Closeup view of a pallet and fixture for positioning a particular part the same way each time. (d) The tooling magazine (right) and the tool changer (left) assigned to each CNC. (e) An AGV at the position marked AGV 1 in Fig. 6.3. (f) View of AS/RS in the background, where finished parts are stored.

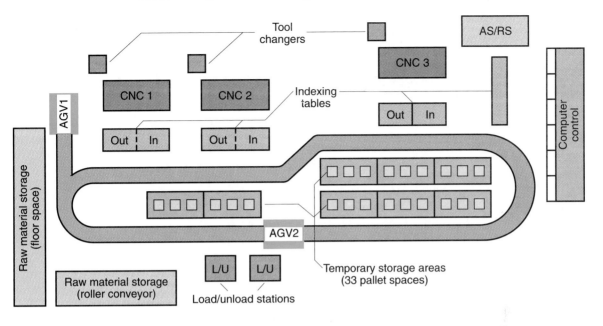

FIGURE 6.3   A Flexible Manufacturing System at Mazak Corporation

Source: Courtesy of Vincent Mabert and Mazak Corporation. Reprinted by permission.

ation. As a result, production continues even when one machine is down for maintenance and bottlenecks are avoided by routing parts to another machine when one is busy.

Figure 6.3 shows the layout of an FMS at the Mazak Corporation plant in Kentucky.* The plant produces turning and machining centers. Specific characteristics of this FMS include the following:

- The computer control room (right) housing the main computer, which controls the transporter and sequence of operations

- Three CNC machines, each with its own microprocessor, which control the details of the machining process

- Two AGVs, which travel around a 200-foot-long oval track, moving materials on pallets to and from the CNCs. When the AGVs' batteries run low, the central computer directs them to certain spots on the track for recharging.

- Indexing tables, which lie between each CNC and the track. Inbound pallets from an AGV are automatically transferred to the right side of the table. Outbound pallets holding finished parts are automatically transferred to the left side for pickup.

---

*We are indebted to Vincent Mabert for much of the information about this FMS, including Fig. 6.5 and the photos of the system.

- A tool changer located behind each CNC, which loads and unloads tool magazines. Each magazine holds an assortment of tools. A machine automatically selects tools for the next specific operation. Changing from one tool to another takes only two minutes.

- Two load/unload stations, to which workers are assigned during one of three shifts; loading takes 10 to 20 minutes

- An automatic AS/RS (upper right), where finished parts are stored. The AGV transfers parts on its pallet to an indexing table, which then transfers them to the AS/RS. The process is reversed when parts are needed for assembly into finished products elsewhere in the plant.

This particular system typifies the future that many envision for FMSs. It fits with an intermediate positioning strategy involving medium-level variety (5 to 100 parts) and volume (annual production rates of 40 to 2000 units per part). The system can simultaneously handle small batches of many products. In addition, an FMS can be used a second way: At any given time, an FMS can produce low-variety, high-volume products in much the same way that fixed automation does. However, when these products reach the end of their life cycles, the FMS can be reprogrammed to accommodate a different product. This flexibility makes FMS very appealing, even to product-focused firms where life cycles are short.

CHAPTER HIGHLIGHTS

- To achieve a competitive advantage, operations managers must pay continuing attention to technological advances. Potential benefits can be associated with direct cost, quality, delivery times, inventories, and even the workplace environment.

- The right technological choices depend on operations strategy. Volume is a particularly important variable, which depends on strategic choices with the product, competitive priorities, and positioning strategy.

- Operations managers must make informed choices about investing in new automation and how to implement them. Success is more likely if the manager first simplifies current operations, sets goals, recognizes all costs and benefits, deals with people-related issues, and provides the necessary leadership and support.

- Advances in computer technology have significantly broadened technological choices in both service and manufacturing industries.

- Voice-mail machines, videotex services, voice-response machines, e-mail, fax machines, and cellular phones are examples of newer technologies in telecommunications.

- Financial services have become particularly computer intensive, such as in automated trading, EFTs, and ATMs.

- Other technologies increasingly adopted in the service sector are personal computers, computer networks, EDI, and automated identification.

- Fixed automation maximizes efficiency for high-volume products with long life cycles, but programmable (flexible) automation provides economies of scope. Flexibility is gained and set-ups are minimized because the machines can be reprogrammed to follow new instructions. Numerically controlled (NC) machines and robots are examples of programmable automation.

- Computer-integrated manufacturing (CIM) goes beyond labor savings, by totally integrating product design, engineering, process planning, and manufacturing through complex computer systems. Computer-aided manufacturing (CAM) is the part of CIM that deals directly with manufacturing.

● A CAD/CAM system links computerized product design and production. It's the first step toward a paperless factory.

● Managers automate materials handling systems when there is enough repeatability. Two

new methods used are the automated guided vehicle (AGV) and the automated storage and retrieval system (AS/RS).

● Programmable automation includes flexible manufacturing systems (FMSs), which consist of several computer-controlled work stations, an interconnecting transport system, and areas for loading and unloading. An FMS is very expensive to acquire but is flexible enough to accommodate new product families.

KEY TERMS

automated guided vehicle
   (AGV) **236**
automated storage and retrieval
   system (AS/RS) **237**
automation **216**
bar code **228**
cellular phone **224**
computer-aided design
   (CAD) **233**
computer-aided manufacturing
   (CAM) **233**
computer-integrated
   manufacturing (CIM) **232**

computerized numerically
   controlled (CNC)
   machines **234**
economies of scope **232**
electronic data interchange
   (EDI) systems **227**
electronic mail (e-mail)
   system **223**
facsimile (fax) machine **224**
fixed automation **230**
flexible manufacturing system
   (FMS) **237**

industrial robots **234**
materials handling **236**
numerically controlled (NC)
   machines **234**
programmable automation **231**
technology **216**
videotex service **223**
voice-mail machine **223**
voice-response machine **223**

STUDY QUESTIONS

1. Fiat's widespread use of robots was an economic success, helping improve its global competitiveness. Much of the savings resulted from reducing its work force from 138,000 to 72,000. There was a human cost of displaced workers, however: Finding another job in the Turin region is particularly difficult because Fiat is the dominant employer in the area. Was Fiat's automation decision defensible on ethical grounds? What steps can a firm take to be a responsible and ethical employer when cutbacks are necessary?

2. What development over the last 20 years has contributed to greater technological choices in the service and manufacturing sectors?

3. How should technological choices link with operations strategy?

4. What are the pros and cons of more automation?

5. Why are traditional financial analysis techniques criticized when used to justify automation projects? Must these projects just be accepted as a leap of faith and an act of hope?

6. What are some newer technologies that can be used to improve office productivity?

7. Suppose that an electric utility company contracts to have its meter readers read meters for the local water company in addition to reading its own. What productivity improvements might result if the electric and

water companies were viewed as a single en-
tity? Could meter readers read as many electric meters in a day if they read water meters
too? If the electric utility uses an integrated
system of computers in meter reading, what
additional network links would be required?

8. In what ways is an automatic teller machine
(ATM) more flexible than a human bank
teller? In what ways is the human teller more
flexible? What are the advantages of an ATM
system to the bank? What are the advantages
to the customer? How does an ATM allow the
bank to increase repeatability?

9. How can bar codes improve both service and
manufacturing operations?

10. Explain the difference between fixed and
programmable automation. Give examples
of each.

11. What is computer-integrated manufacturing
(CIM)? Is it a good choice for all manufacturers?

12. What are some of the advantages of computer-aided design (CAD)?

13. What do numerically controlled (NC) machines and robots have in common?

14. What is materials handling? Why is it said
that "the best materials handling is no handling at all"? Compare materials handling in
two industries: one with a product focus and
one with a process focus.

15. In what ways do an AGV and an AS/RS qualify as flexible automation?

16. What are the elements of a flexible manufacturing system (FMS)? Why is this kind of
system flexible?

PROBLEMS

Advanced Problems

Supplement Connections: Problems 1 through 6 require prior reading of Supplement 1 (Financial
Analysis). Problem 7 requires prior reading of
Supplement 5 (Simulation Analysis). A computer
package is helpful, but not mandatory, for Problems 1 through 6.

1. Riverbend Hospital is considering two different computerized information systems to
improve pharmacy productivity. The first alternative is a portable computer system that
will require a one-time investment of $80,000
for the computer hardware, software, and
necessary employee training. After-tax cash
flows attributable to the investment are expected to be $20,000 per year for the next
eight years. Savings would accrue from increased pharmacist productivity and the value
of having timely and accurate information.
The second alternative is to install a mainframe computer linked to bedside terminals
that would allow doctors to prescribe treat-
ments directly to the pharmacy from patients'

rooms. This system would require an investment of $170,000 but is expected to generate
after-tax cash flows of $40,000 per year for
eight years. The hospital must earn 16 percent on its investments. Assume that both
systems will have no salvage value at the end
of eight years.
a. Calculate the net present value and payback periods for each alternative.
b. Based on your financial analysis, what do
you recommend?
c. Are there any valid considerations other
than financial?

2. First State Bank is considering installing a
new automatic teller machine (ATM) at either
of two locations: inside a supermarket or inside the bank itself. An initial investment of
$60,000 is required for the ATM regardless of
location. The operating costs of the supermarket ATM would be $15,000 per year, and
the ATM inside the bank $10,000 per year.
The higher costs of the supermarket ATM are
due to the additional cost of leasing super-

market space and transportation. Revenue generated from new accounts because of the installation of each ATM should also differ, with the supermarket ATM generating $55,000 per year and the bank ATM $52,000 per year. Assume a tax rate of 30 percent and a desired rate of return of 18 percent on investments. The ATMs have an expected life of 10 years with no salvage value at the end of that time.

a. Calculate the net present value and payback periods for each alternative.

b. Based on your analysis, what location do you recommend?

c. Are there other factors that must be considered when evaluating these alternatives?

3. The manager of Fun and Games, a large toy and hobby store, wants to install a computerized cash register system. The system being evaluated consists of electronic cash registers linked to an in-store computer and scanning equipment. The registers will price and track sales of all items sold, using look-up codes. The scanning equipment will read UPC product symbols at checkout stands and transmit that information to the in-store computer for inventory updating and recording of sales. The installation of the system will require an initial investment of $150,000. After-tax cash flows attributed to the system, based on a reduction in labor costs and inventories, would be $28,000 per year for the next six years. The store must earn 14 percent on its investments, and there is no salvage value at the end of six years.

a. Based on NPV analysis, should the system be implemented?

b. If the increase in labor productivity and the availability of timely and accurate inventory records are now estimated to produce $40,000 per year for the next six years, should the system be implemented?

c. What else does the manager need to consider before making this decision?

4. Underwater Recovery is a deep-sea exploration firm that recovers gold and other treasures from old shipwrecks. The owner of this small entrepreneurial company is considering purchasing an underwater robot to explore and retrieve artifacts from the ocean floor. Two types of robots are being considered: robot A, operated through soundwaves by a diver in a nearby bathysphere, and robot B, operated from the deck of the ship. Robot A requires an initial investment of $280,000 and robot B $325,000. Deep dives are dangerous and require annual diver salaries of $125,000. The robots would be able to save 70 percent of these salaries. Robot A would still require a diver to go on board the bathysphere, however, at an additional annual cost of $25,000. There are no such additional costs for robot B. Underwater Recovery expects to retrieve artifacts worth $110,000 per year with the use of robot A, and $135,000 with robot B. Both robots have an expected life of ten years, after which there is no salvage value. Underwater Recovery seeks at least a 20 percent return on its investments, and its tax rate is 35 percent.

a. Calculate the net present value for each alternative.

b. Based on your financial analysis, what do you recommend?

c. Based on other factors, should either robot be purchased?

5. New England Power and Electric, a supplier of electric power to the northeast United States, is considering the purchase of a robot to repair welds in nuclear reactors. Two types of vision system robots are being considered: a "smart" robot, whose actions in the reactor would be controlled by what it "sees," and a different kind of robot, whose actions in the reactor would be controlled by an external operator. The "smart" robot requires an initial investment of $400,000, while the operator-controlled robot requires an initial investment of $330,000. Both robots have an expected life of five years and no salvage value at the end of that time. Welds are currently repaired by a human welder. The job is hazardous, so

the welder's annual salary and fringe benefits total $120,000. Buying either robot eliminates the need for the human welder, but the operator-controlled robot requires an operator whose annual salary (and benefits) would be $40,000. The "smart" robot requires an extra $30,000 in technical support. New England Power and Electric seeks at least 18 percent on its investments, and its tax rate is 50 percent.

a. Calculate the net present value for each alternative.

b. Based on your financial analysis, what do you recommend?

c. Based on other factors, should either robot be purchased?

6. The vice president of operations at Sun Electric is considering three automation projects in different areas of the plant. The straight-line method is used for depreciation and the hurdle rate is 16 percent.

Project A
Initial investment	$5 million
Salvage value	5%
Time frame	5 years
Tax rate	25%
Annual net cash flow	$2 million/yr

Project B
Initial investment	$7 million
Salvage value	10%
Time frame	6 years
Tax rate	25%
Annual net cash flow	$3 million/yr

Project C
Initial investment	$10 million
Salvage value	0%
Time frame	6 years
Tax rate	25%
Annual net cash flow	$4 million/yr

a. Which of the projects yields the largest after-tax net present value?

b. If the company has $14 million to invest in operations, which projects should be funded?

c. What is the impact on the decision if the projected annual net cash flows are increased by 10 percent? Decreased by 10 percent?

7. The Precision Manufacturing Company is considering the purchase of an NC machine and has narrowed the possible choice to two models. The company produces 20 products, but each requires the same amount of time to manufacture. At an average shift at Precision batches of jobs arrive at the NC machine every 10 minutes that have the following discrete distribution:

Number of Jobs	Probability
3	0.1
6	0.2
8	0.3
14	0.2
18	0.2

The distributions of the processing times and setup times of the two NC machines follow. Assume that the jobs in a batch share a single setup and have equal processing times.

NC Machine 1	
Setup Time (min)	Probability
1	0.1
2	0.2
3	0.4
4	0.2
5	0.1

Processing Time (sec)	Probability
5	0.10
6	0.20
7	0.30
8	0.25
9	0.15

NC Machine 2

Setup Time (min)	Probability	Processing Time (sec)	Probability
1	0.05	3	0.20
2	0.15	4	0.25
3	0.25	5	0.30
4	0.45	6	0.15
5	0.10	7	0.10

Simulate 100 job arrivals for the two NC machines. Which one would you recommend if both machines cost the same to purchase, operate, and maintain?

CASE   KID'S KASTLE, INC.

Kid's Kastle, Inc., has a unique retailing concept known as the "toy supermarket." Just as their grocery counterparts, they provide their customers with considerable width and depth in toy selection. Kid's Kastle operates twelve toy supermarkets in the South, with its operation base in Atlanta. All warehousing operations for these supermarkets are consolidated at one 180,000-square-foot facility. Its large size can be attributed partially to the seasonal aspect of the toy industry: Almost 60 percent of Kid Kastle's business occurs during the six weeks just prior to Christmas. Toy manufacturers have evolved an "early purchase plan," whereby the wholesaler or retailer accepts merchandise from the manufacturer early in the calendar year, even though the actual payment occurs much later. This plan allows manufacturers to level production, in exchange for lower prices to the wholesaler or retailer.

This arrangement, plus the very strong growth experienced in sales, is forcing Kid's Kastle to expand its current warehouse to 300,000 square feet. Management is simultaneously looking for more efficient stockpicking methods. At the present time, stockpickers go through the warehouse, gathering items listed on computerized order sheets. All items on a sheet are destined for a particular store. When all items on a list are gathered or the cart is filled (whichever happens first), the stockpicker takes the items to a truck earmarked to go to that particular store. When one list is finished, a picker starts on another list. Pickers spend a large percentage of their time simply walking from one part of the warehouse to another. Primarily to save on walking time, management is considering a proposal to use an automated conveyor picking system for at least half the warehouse. The other half would continue operating much as it does now. Exhibit 1 shows the proposed system.

A powered conveyor line, consisting of five feeder lines and one trunk line, would run through part of the warehouse. Pickers would be assigned to zones and work from new computerized order sheets showing the destination store for each item. After locating the desired merchandise, the stockpicker would mark on each carton its destination and then place it manually on the feeder line adjacent to the storage bins. The carton would travel on the feeder line to the final trunk line and continue on until reaching the backlog in front of a control station. The operator of the control station would determine the destination of each carton (already marked on it by a stockpicker) and then direct it to the appropriate trailer by remote control operation of mechanical pushers. These pushers would send the cartons down non-powered conveyor lines into waiting tractor trailers.

Management expects that the same level of output can be achieved with a much smaller cadre of stockpickers because travel time would be eliminated and because unnecessary chatting and social contact would be reduced, as workers must stay in their zones when the system is running. Management also hopes that quality would improve as pickers became familiar with the items stocked in their zone. At the same time, the new system seems more vulnerable to surges in volume or to breakdowns in the powered conveyor during the peak time of the year. There is also the issue of which employees to lay off or transfer.

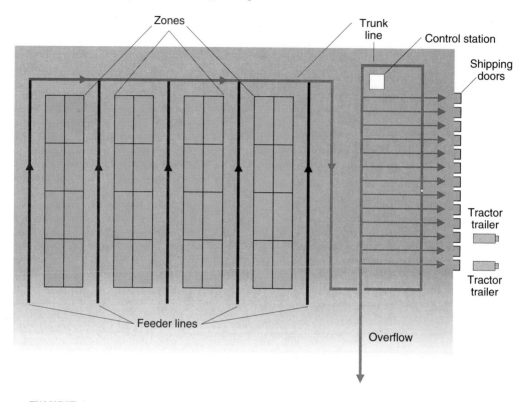

EXHIBIT 1

QUESTIONS

1. Do you think the new technology will work? What happens to the feeder lines and stockpickers if the queue in front of the control station gets too large? Can anything be done in how the line is designed or operated to handle this problem?
2. What will be the likely reaction of the stockpickers to this change? Will they like their new jobs more or less? Will they need more or less job knowledge to operate effectively?
3. What are the advantages and disadvantages of the proposed technology? What data should management collect on its estimated savings and costs?
4. What other technologies might you suggest for consideration?
5. If management decides to adopt the new technology, what steps should it take to help assure successful implementation?

SELECTED REFERENCES

Amstead, B.J., P.F. Oswald, and M.L. Bregman. *Manufacturing Processes*, 7th ed. New York: John Wiley & Sons, 1977.

Bowen, David E., Richard B. Chase, Thomas G. Cummings, and Associates. *Service Management Effectiveness*. San Francisco: Jossey-Bass, 1990.

Bylinsky, Gene. "The Race to the Automatic Factory." *Fortune*, February 21, 1983, pp. 52–60.

Collier, David A. *Service Management: The Automation of Services*. Reston, Va.: Reston Publishing Company, 1985.

Collier, David A. "The Service Sector Revolution: The Automation of Services." *Long Range Planning*, vol. 16, no. 6 (December 1983), pp. 11–13.

Doyle, Lawrence E., Carl A. Keyser, James L. Leach, George F. Schrader, and Morse B. Singer. *Manufacturing Processes and Materials for Engineers*, 3rd ed. Englewood Cliffs, N.J.: Prentice-Hall, 1985.

Faulhaber, Gerald, Eli Noam, and Roberta Tasley. *Services in Transition: The Impact of Information Technology on the Service Sector*. Cambridge, Mass.: Ballinger, 1986.

"Flexible Manufacturing Systems." *Modern Materials Handling*, September 7, 1982.

Gaimon, Cheryl. "The Optimal Acquisition of Automation to Enhance the Productivity of Labor." *Management Science*, vol. 31, no. 9 (1985), pp. 1175–1190.

Gerwin, Donald. "Do's and Don'ts of Computerized Manufacturing." *Harvard Business Review* (March–April 1982), pp. 107–116.

Giffi, Craig A., Aleda V. Roth, and Gregory M. Seal. *Competing in World-Class Manufacturing: America's 21st Century Challenge*. Homewood, Ill.: Business One Irwin, 1991.

Gold, Bela. "CAM Sets New Rules for Production." *Harvard Business Review* (November–December 1982), pp. 88–94.

Goldhat, J.D., and Mariann Jelinek. "Plan for Economies of Scope." *Harvard Business Review* (November–December 1983), pp. 141–148.

Green, Timothy J., and Randall P. Sadowski. "A Review of Cellular Manufacturing Assumptions, Advantages and Design Techniques." *Journal of Operations Management*, vol. 4, no. 2 (February 1984), pp. 85–97.

Groover, Mikell P., and E. W. Zimmers, Jr. *CAD/CAM: Computer-Aided Design and Manufacturing*. Englewood Cliffs, N.J.: Prentice-Hall, 1984.

Guile, Bruce R., and James Brian Quinn. *Managing Innovation: Cases from the Services Industries*. Washington, D.C.: National Academy Press, 1988.

Hausman, W.H., L.B. Schwartz, and S.C. Graves. "Optimal Storage Assignment in Automatic Warehousing Systems." *Management Science*, vol. 22, no. 6 (1976), pp. 629–638.

Hyer, Nancy, and Urban Wemmerlov. "Group Technology and Productivity." *Harvard Business Review* (July–August 1984), pp. 140–149.

"IBM's Automated Factory—A Giant Step Forward." *Modern Materials Handling*, March 1985.

Jaikumar, Jay. "The Boundaries of Business: The Impact of Technology." *Harvard Business Review* (September–October 1991), pp. 100–101.

Jaikumar, Ramchandran. "Postindustrial Manufacturing." *Harvard Business Review* (November–December 1986), pp. 69–76.

Jenkins, K.M., and A.R. Raedels. "The Robot Revolution: Strategic Considerations for Managers." *Production and Inventory Management* (Third Quarter 1982), pp. 107–116.

Kaplan, Robert S. "Must CIM Be Justified by Faith Alone?" *Harvard Business Review* (March–April 1986), pp. 87–95.

Levitt, Theodore. "The Industrialization of Service." *Harvard Business Review* (September–October 1976), pp. 63–74.

Mertes, Louis H. "Doing Your Office Over—Electronically." *Harvard Business Review* (March–April 1981), pp. 127–135.

Norri, Hamid. *Managing the Dynamics of New Technology: Issues in Manufacturing Management*. Englewood Cliffs, N.J.: Prentice-Hall, 1990.

Poppel, Harvey L. "Who Needs the Office of the Future?" *Harvard Business Review* (November–December 1982), pp. 146–155.

Rosenthal, Stephen. "Progress Toward the Factory of the Future." *Journal of Operations Management*, vol. 4, no. 3 (May 1984), pp. 203–229.

Roth, Aleda V., and Marjolijn van der Velde. *The Future of Retail Banking Delivery Systems*. Rolling Meadows, Ill.: Bank Administration Institute, 1988.

Seligman, Daniel. "Life Will Be Different When We're All On-Line." *Fortune*, February 4, 1985, pp. 68–72.

Skinner, Wickham. "Operations Technology: Blind Spot in Strategic Management." *Interfaces*, vol. 14, no. 1 (January–February 1984), pp. 116–125.

Starr, Martin K., and Alan J. Biloski. "The Decision to Adopt New Technology—Effects on Organizational Size." *Omega*, vol. 12, no. 4 (1984), pp. 353–361.

Stecke, Kathryn E., and James J. Solberg. "Loading and Control Policies for a Flexible Manufacturing System." *International Journal of Production Research*, vol. 19, no. 5 (1981), pp. 481–490.

Stone, Philip J., and Robert Luchetti. "Your Office Is Where You Are." *Harvard Business Review* (March–April 1985), pp. 102–117.

Suresh, Nallan C., and Jack R. Meredith. "A Generic Approach to Justifying Flexible Manufacturing Systems." In *Proceedings of the First ORSA/TIMS Special Interest Conference*, August 15–17, 1984.

Thomas, Dan R.E. "Strategy Is Different in Service Businesses." *Harvard Business Review* (July–August 1978), pp. 158–165.

White, Robert B. "A Prototype for the Automated Office." *Datamation* (April 1977), pp. 83–90.

Chapter 7

JOB DESIGN AND WORK MEASUREMENT

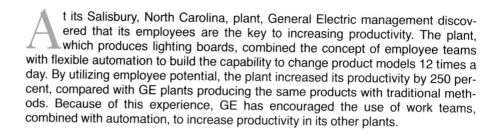

At its Salisbury, North Carolina, plant, General Electric management discovered that its employees are the key to increasing productivity. The plant, which produces lighting boards, combined the concept of employee teams with flexible automation to build the capability to change product models 12 times a day. By utilizing employee potential, the plant increased its productivity by 250 percent, compared with GE plants producing the same products with traditional methods. Because of this experience, GE has encouraged the use of work teams, combined with automation, to increase productivity in its other plants.

As we discussed in Chapters 5 and 6, linking process design to competitive priorities, coupled with the appropriate technology, is important to maintaining or improving a firm's competitive position. There is one more important ingredient to that success, however: the employee. In the 1980s we saw the introduction of powerful technologies and systems that gave us the capability to do things unthinkable 20 years ago. Now, in the 1990s, managers are faced with the problems of taking advantage of that capability. As General Electric discovered, the employee is the key.

This chapter explores two important aspects of work-force management: job design and work measurement. **Job design** is the specification of job content and of the employee skills and training needed to perform that job. **Work measurement** is the task of estimating operating system output, taking into account the effects of learning. It involves estimating the time necessary to complete the job. Both job design and work measurement are critical to the effective utilization of a firm's human resources. We begin the chapter with current issues in job design and then discuss various methods useful for measuring work outputs. We conclude with the topic of learning curves and their implications for operations strategy and planning.

JOB DESIGN

Traditional job design got its start more than 100 years ago when Frederick Taylor proposed an approach known as scientific management. **Scientific management** is the philosophy that any operation can be improved by breaking it into components, measuring the work content of the components, and finding ways to improve work methods. Flow diagrams, process charts, and multiple activity charts (see Chapter 5) align closely with this philosophy. Taylor believed that managers should study jobs scientifically, using careful analysis and experimentation, to find the most economic way to perform a task.

The manager should choose workers and train them in the new method and then install it in operations. Taylor stressed the need for teamwork between management and workers. He believed that management must accept the responsibility for coordinating work so that output is not restricted by poor planning and timing. Taylor also believed that scientific management would work only if the economic benefits of increased output were shared by both management and workers.

Taylor's methods dealt primarily with the technical aspects of job design. His "engineering approach" was concerned primarily with ways to best reach, grasp, and move objects; the number of repetitions to be performed before a rest was needed; and the best physical position for the worker. Taylor began his work in the steel industry, but his theories spread throughout many industries and were widely practiced by the early 1900s. Undoubtedly, scientific management techniques practiced by industrial engineers contributed greatly to the rise in U.S. productivity between 1900 and 1950. Even today, many of Taylor's concepts continue to be the first that managers apply when seeking to increase productivity. Nonetheless, new approaches to job design are being used by some firms. In this section we address two job design aspects of concern to managers—the degree of job specialization and the work team approach.

Job Specialization

Whether to design a job in narrow or broad terms is one of the toughest decisions in job design. A job with a high degree of specialization involves a narrow range of tasks, which enables a high degree of repetition and, presumably, greater efficiency. Engineers, sociologists, psychologists, economists, managers, and workers all have different opinions on the merits of high degrees of specialization. Table 7.1 contains some of the arguments. The actual choices vary considerably. Many U.S. industries have achieved tremendous success with highly specialized jobs for their employees. This is particularly true for firms with a product focus. However, there are firms in traditionally product-focused industries using broader job designs.

TABLE 7.1 / Considerations for Job Specialization

Arguments in Favor of Job Specialization	Arguments Against Narrowly Defined Jobs
Workers need less time to learn highly specialized methods and procedures.	The inability to divide tasks perfectly creates an imbalance of work. Consequently, some workers have idle time and others do not.
The work pace is faster, leading to more output in less time.	The need for coordination and materials handling increases.
The education and skill requirements of the work force are much lower, so workers may be easier to find and the wages paid can be lower.	Highly repetitive work may have adverse behavioral consequences, such as costly employee turnover, low output rates, and poor quality.

*T*wo employees, part of a Volvo work team at its Uddevalla plant, complete one phase of the assembly process for a Volvo sedan. The sedan is tipped on its side for easy access to the underbody.

Volvo, for example, employs teams of seven to ten hourly employees at its Uddevalla plant, each trained to handle all assembly jobs. Each employee works an average of three hours before repeating the same task, compared to work cycles of one or two minutes on conventional assembly lines. One team can assemble four cars per shift. Volvo management believes the major benefits are lower absenteeism (8 percent versus the typical 20 percent) and better quality; Swedish workers are highly educated and typically do not like to perform boring and routine tasks. Volvo claims that Uddevalla produces cars with fewer labor hours and better quality than its three other Swedish plants. The Volvo experience brings up the need to link the behavioral dimensions of job design with the technology to produce the product or service.

Sociotechnical Theory. In the early 1950s Eric Trist's studies in the coal fields of Great Britain led to a theory of job design that combined technical elements with behavioral considerations. This theory holds that the job designer needs to recognize two dimensions in any production system: the technical subsystem and the social subsystem. If one is emphasized and the other neglected, inefficiency will result. Work organizations are viewed as sociotechnical systems in which people use technology to carry out sets of tasks related to a specified purpose. People and equipment are inputs to the system. (This is the approach GE took at its Salisbury plant.) The fit of people and equipment determines the levels of economic performance and job satisfaction, which are the output (Trist, 1981). Thus the entire work system, rather than its individual tasks, becomes the basic unit for analysis. Similarly, the work group becomes more important than the individual.

Behavioral Considerations. People work for a variety of reasons. Economic needs, social needs (needs to be recognized, to belong to a group), and individual needs (to feel important, to feel in control) influence how people perform their jobs. In narrowly designed jobs, workers have fewer opportunities to control the pace of work, receive gratification from the work itself, advance to a better position, show initiative, and communicate with fellow workers.

Sociologists and psychologists contend that highly repetitive jobs lead to monotony, which in turn leads to boredom and sometimes to poor job performance. Some symptoms of poor job performance exhibited by blue-collar workers include high turnover rates, absenteeism, grievances, and intentional disruption of production. White-collar workers may exhibit many of the same behaviors. Other behaviors, such as excessive personal illness and incomplete work assignments, are more subtle and difficult to detect.

Several remedies are suggested to overcome the boredom of highly specialized jobs: job enlargement, job rotation, and job enrichment. **Job enlargement** increases the number of tasks assigned to each employee, thereby enabling the employee to complete a larger proportion of the total work required for the product or service. Typically, this approach requires that workers have a greater number of skills. Besides reducing boredom, job enlargement has the potential to increase employee satisfaction. If the number of tasks assigned to each worker is large enough, the worker can identify with the finished product or service and feel a greater sense of pride in the customer satisfaction it generates. Job enlargement represents the *horizontal* expansion of a job; it does not involve prework planning or postwork inspection.

Job rotation allows workers to exchange jobs periodically. This approach provides more diversity for the worker and is more likely to be effective when the jobs are not all equally boring. Job rotation increases the skills of the work force through on-the-job training. This approach allows management the flexibility to replace absentee workers or to add capacity at backlogged work stations. In addition, moving workers to other jobs is associated with total quality control (TQC) and the concept of "quality at the source," as discussed in Chapter 3. When the output of one worker is passed along to another worker, and the workers' jobs require similar skills, rotating jobs can give each worker a better appreciation for the production problems of the other and the value of passing only good quality downstream.

The most comprehensive approach to job design is **job enrichment,** which entails a *vertical* expansion of job duties and more worker responsibility. For example, a worker may be given the responsibility for operating several machines, inspecting the output, deciding when machines need maintenance, and even performing some types of maintenance. Job enrichment embraces the factors that Frederick Herzberg (1987), a proponent of this approach, believes increase job satisfaction: achievement, recognition, and responsibility. Workers feel a sense of achievement when they learn the additional tasks required in an enriched job. They receive recognition by way of direct feedback from users of their output. Finally, the responsibility comes from the need to schedule work, plan for the resources needed, and be held accountable for the consequences.

Sometimes work teams are formed to achieve the benefits of job enlargement, job rotation, or job enrichment. Work teams provide opportunities for communication and a greater sense of accomplishment. We shall discuss this approach next.

Work Team Approaches

Employee involvement has its basis in the formation of work teams. It is also called *worker participation*, a term familiar to firms in the United States since the 1920s, or *labor–management jointness*. The three approaches to employee involvement most often used in the United States are problem-solving teams, special-purpose teams, and self-managing teams.

Problem-Solving Teams. These teams first were introduced in the 1920s and enjoyed more widespread use in the late 1970s following the success of the Japanese quality circles (see Chapter 3). The teams typically consist of five to twelve volunteers, sometimes drawn from different areas of a department, but often involving employees assigned to a particular task, such as automobile assembly or credit application processing. The teams meet several hours a week to work out quality and productivity problems and make suggestions to management, but they have no power to actually implement the ideas. Such teams are used extensively by Japanese-managed firms in the United States, in that they parallel the Japanese philosophy of encouraging and implementing employee inputs but maintaining close control over their job activities. Although problem-solving teams are successful in reducing costs and improving quality, they die off if management does not implement a good proportion of the suggestions generated.

Special-Purpose Teams. An outgrowth of the problem-solving teams, special-purpose teams address particular issues of paramount concern to management, labor, or both. For example, the assignment might be to design and introduce new work policies and new technologies or to bridge several functional areas when addressing customer service problems. When unions are involved, problems at all operational levels can be addressed by special-purpose teams consisting of labor and management representatives. Essentially, this approach gives workers a voice in higher-level decisions. Special-purpose teams, which first appeared in the United States in the early 1980s, are beginning to increase in popularity.

Self-Managing Teams. This approach takes worker participation to its highest level and is associated with two related activities: employee empowerment and organizational restructuring. **Employee empowerment** places the responsibility for decisions further and further down the organizational chart, to the level of the employee actually doing the job. For self-managing teams, this usually means allowing from 2 to 15 employees to produce a major portion, if not all, of a product or service. Members learn all tasks and rotate from job to job. The teams take over managerial duties such as work and vacation scheduling, or-

Using Self-Managing Teams at AT&T Credit Corporation

AT&T Credit Corporation (ATTCC), a subsidiary of American Telephone and Telegraph Company, was formed to process equipment lease applications that had previously been processed by an independent bank. The bank could not keep up with the demand because it designed its employees' jobs with a high degree of specialization. One department handled applications and checked credit ratings, a second drew up contracts, and a third collected payments. Employees had no sense of how their job contributed to the total service because no one had complete responsibility for it. The bank could process only 400 applications per day, and it usually took several days to make a decision.

ATTCC President Thomas C. Wajnert had a better idea. He set up 11 teams of 10 to 15 workers in a high-volume division serving small businesses. Each team could perform all three major leasing functions. Employees are responsible for completely solving a customer's problem. They coined the slogan: "Whoever gets the call owns the problem."

The teams manage themselves in that they make decisions regarding work schedules, employee assignments, and new-hire interviews. Managers act only as advisers to the teams. With this new job design, ATTCC can process up to 800 applications per day, with an average time of 24 to 48 hours to make a decision. Largely due to this capability, ATTCC is growing at a 40 to 50 percent compound annual rate.

Source: "The Payoff from Teamwork," *Business Week*, July 10, 1989, pp. 56–62.

dering supplies, and new-hire decision making. This is the approach Volvo took at Uddevalla.

Organizational restructuring, in this case meaning creating a "flatter" organization by eliminating some supervisors and middle managers, is a natural result of employee empowerment. Because employees actually take the role of supervisors, there is less need for the supervisors and their middle-management bosses. Self-managing teams essentially change the way work is organized because employees have control over their jobs. Self-managing teams have only recently begun to catch hold in the United States, and some have increased productivity by 30 percent or more in many applications. Managerial Practice 7.1 explains how AT&T Credit Corporation applies self-managing teams in its equipment leasing department.

Worker participation may seem to be a panacea for maintaining or improving a firm's competitiveness, but not everyone thinks it's a good idea. Some United Auto Workers leaders, for example, view worker participation as just another ploy to motivate employees to work harder for the same pay. They fear that it is merely an attempt to undermine the authority of the union. Interestingly, some companies that move to self-managing teams initially experience high turnover rates because some employees do not want to accept the additional responsibilities and switch from job to job. This was the experience of GE at its Salisbury plant, where it experienced a 14 percent turnover rate for two years after it went to team-based production. In addition, organizational restructuring involving reductions in managerial positions is often resisted by first-line supervisors who would lose their jobs and by other managers who do not like giving workers decision-making authority. Even employees on self-managing teams do not like the prospects for advancement because there are fewer managerial positions to fill. Nonetheless, most managers and employees are favorably inclined to worker participation in some form. Studies show that about 25 percent of the workers volunteer for problem-solving teams in plants where such action is voluntary. Another 70 percent are passive supporters, and only 5 percent are opposed ("The Payoff from Teamwork," 1989).

It is important to note that not all firms utilizing work teams use self-managing teams. In fact, most companies utilize the problem-solving approach, or quality circles. The teams are used only to help discover problems, not to provide more autonomy for the employees. Workers still perform minutely subdivided tasks on a highly repetitive basis. This is the approach used at New United Motors Manufacturing Incorporated (NUMMI), the joint venture between GM and Toyota.

Now that we have explored some of the issues posing challenges in job design for managers, we turn to the issue of measuring the output rates expected of the system that result from choices in process design, technology, and job design.

WORK STANDARDS

A **standard** is a commonly accepted basis for comparison. With respect to work measurement, we usually refer to either labor standards or machine standards. A **labor standard** is the time required for a trained worker to perform a given task following a prescribed method with normal effort and skill. Labor standards are more difficult to develop than are machine standards because factors such as skill, effort, and stamina vary from one employee to another. By contrast, machines of the same type, such as robots, perform the same repetitive tasks with little variation from unit to unit.

The key to creating a labor standard is defining "normal" performance. Suppose, for example, that you are the manager of a fast-growing company that manufactures frozen pizza. You want to create a standard for pizza assembly. You observe as a worker spreads sauce over the pizza shell, adds pepperoni and cheese, places the pizza in a box, and puts the assembled product on a cart for fast freezing. The entire process takes 20 seconds. You calculate that at this pace a worker could assemble 1440 pizzas in an eight-hour day.

Before settling on 20 seconds as the standard, however, you have to take some tangible factors into consideration. For example, the worker you observed may be exceptionally energetic and efficient. If she had considerable experience, her skills might be well above average. Moreover, your estimate of 20 seconds per pizza should also take into account fluctuations in pace and rest periods scheduled during the workday. Generally, you cannot use the time per unit observed over a short period of time for one employee as a standard for an extended period of time for all employees. Creating labor standards requires some modification of observed times, based on the judgment of skilled observers.

*P*izzas are assembled to order at a Domino's restaurant before being placed in the oven.

Work Standards as a Management Tool

Managers use work standards in a variety of ways:

1. **Motivating workers.** Standards can be used to define a day's work or to motivate workers to improve their performance. For example, under an incentive compensation plan, workers can earn a bonus for output that exceeds the standard.

2. **Comparing alternative process designs.** Time standards are used to compare different routings for an item. The manager can also use time standards to evaluate new work methods and to estimate the advantages of utilizing new equipment.

3. **Scheduling.** Managers need time standards to assign tasks to workers and machines in ways that effectively utilize resources.

4. **Capacity planning.** With the aid of time standards for tasks, managers can determine current and projected capacity requirements for given demand requirements. Long-term capital investment and work-force staffing decisions also can require these time estimates.

5. **Establishing prices and costs.** Using labor and machine time standards as a base, managers can develop cost standards for current and new products. Cost standards also can be used to develop budgets, determine prices, and reach make-or-buy decisions.

6. Performance appraisal. A worker's output can be compared to the standard output over a period of time to determine how well the worker is performing. Time standards can also be used to estimate the proportion of time workers are idle or otherwise unproductive.

Work measurement is used more for some of these purposes than for others. A survey of 1500 firms indicated that the most frequent use of work measurement was for estimating and costing (89 percent of the firms), followed by incentive compensation plans (59 percent), scheduling (51 percent), and performance appraisal (41 percent). Only 2 percent of the firms used work measurement for staffing and capacity planning (Rice, 1977).

Areas of Controversy

Work standards is one of the most controversial areas of operations management because of the conflicts that often arise between management and labor. When an organization uses output standards as the basis for pay, unions object if they believe that standards are set "too high" and management objects if they believe that standards are set "too low." Of course, setting output standards at either extreme makes it difficult to plan for appropriate capacity levels, increases costs, and reduces profits.

The controversy is not confined to differences between labor and management. Managers often disagree among themselves over the use of engineered work standards to increase productivity. Some believe that employee involvement should be used and that time studies are dehumanizing to workers. The United Parcel Service (UPS) feels otherwise. UPS has work standards for all operations, from drivers to package sorters. Managers at UPS believe the key to success is being able to manage labor and hold it accountable ("United Parcel Service," 1986). Some managers believe that the costs of large industrial engineering staffs and the hidden costs of labor–management conflicts outweigh the benefits of elaborate standards. Others believe using engineered standards for piecework incentives actually defeats their purpose, which is to increase worker productivity. To keep management from raising standards, employees may be secretive about new work methods that they devise to increase output. There is also the threat that workers will lose sight of quality.

METHODS OF WORK MEASUREMENT

Various methods of work measurement are available to the manager, but the method of choice often depends on the purpose of the data. For example, managers might need a high degree of precision when comparing actual work method results to standards. A stopwatch study or predetermined times might be required. Alternatively, estimating the percentage of time that an employee is idle while waiting for materials requires a method such as work sampling. Consequently, a manager may use more than one approach to obtain needed work measurement information. We present and discuss four of the more commonly used methods in this section: time study method, elemental standard data approach, predetermined data approach, and work sampling method.

Time Study Method

The method used most often for setting time standards for a task is **time study.** A job is divided into a series of smaller work elements representing the accepted work method for the job. Using a stopwatch, an analyst performs a *pilot study* by timing a trained worker performing the work elements for a number of work cycles, then calculates the average time for each element. Given the information from the pilot study, the analyst determines whether the sample size was adequate to provide the desired precision in the average time estimate. If not, additional observations must be made. Once the sample size is deemed sufficient, the analyst proceeds to develop a time standard for the task by using additional information such as judgment-based performance ratings and allowances for fatigue.

Step 1: Selecting Work Elements. The first step in a time study is to select the work elements. Figure 7.1 shows an observation sheet used in a time study of packaging ceramic coffee cups. This particular operation requires only four

Operation: COFFEE CUP PACKAGING				Date: 1/23			Operator: B. LARSON Clock no.: 43-6205				
Observer: S. JOHNSON		Start: 9:00	A.M. P.M.	Stop: 9:22	A.M. P.M.	Elapsed study time: 21.68				Time per piece: 21.68/10 = 2.168	

Element Description		Observations										$\bar{t}$	F	RF
		1	2	3	4	5	6	7	8	9	10			
1. Get two cartons*	t	0.48		0.46		0.54		0.49		0.51		0.50	0.50	1.05
	r	0.48		0.85		9.14		0.53		0.83				
2. Put liner into carton	t	0.11	0.13	0.09	0.10	0.11	0.13	0.08	0.12	0.10	0.09	0.11	1.00	0.95
	r	0.59	0.56	0.94	0.82	0.25	0.23	0.61	0.50	0.93	0.83			
3. Place cups into carton	t	0.74	0.68	0.71	0.69	0.73	0.70	0.68	0.74	0.71	0.72	0.71	1.00	1.10
	r	1.33	3.24	5.65	7.51	0.98	0.93	14.29	16.24	18.64	20.55			
4. Seal carton and set aside	t	1.10	1.15	1.07	1.09	1.12	1.11	1.09	1.08	1.10	1.13	1.10	1.00	0.90
	r	2.43	4.39	6.72	8.60	11.10	13.04	15.38	17.32	19.74	21.68			

Normal time for cycle	
Allowances (% of normal time) _____ 15% _____	Standard time _____ Min/piece

* This element occurs only on every other cycle.

Legend: t = elapsed element time; r = stopwatch reading on completion of element; $\bar{t}$ = select time; F = frequency of occurrence; RF = performance rating factor.

FIGURE 7.1   Time Study Observation Sheet

work elements. Several considerations are involved in selecting the work elements for a time study. First, each work element should have definite starting and stopping points to facilitate taking the stopwatch readings. Second, work elements that take less than three seconds to complete should be avoided because they are difficult to time. For example, work element 2 in Fig. 7.1 could have been divided into three detailed elements: (1) pick up liner with left hand, (2) expand liner to open the holes for each cup, and (3) insert liner into carton. Because each of these activities is done very quickly, it is difficult to obtain accurate times for each one. Finally, the work elements should correspond to the standard work method that has been running smoothly for a period of time in a standard work environment. Incidental operations not normally involved in the task should be identified and separated from the repetitive work.

Step 2: Timing the Elements. After the work elements have been identified, a worker trained in the work method is selected for study. The analyst then times the worker on each element to get an initial set of observations. Figure 7.1 shows the results of the *continuous method* of timing. Using this method, the analyst enters the stopwatch reading for each work element on completion of that element in the r row. To get the observed time for a work element, the analyst records in row t the difference between two successive continuous watch readings after completing the timing part of the study. For example, in observation 1, the clock read 0.48 minute after element 1 and 0.59 minute after element 2. Thus the difference, 0.11 minute, appears in the t row of element 2. (Note that the numerals after the decimal refer to *hundredths* of a minute, not seconds. For example, 0.48 minute equals 28.8 seconds.) To avoid unnecessary writing, whole numbers are shown only when they change from the last observation. For example, the stopwatch reading on completion of the second observation of the element "put liner into carton" was actually 2.56, but only 0.56 was written on the form. (The t and r rows for the second observation of element 1, "Get two cartons," are blank because this element occurs only on every other cycle.)

An alternative timing technique, called the *snap-back method*, involves resetting the watch to zero after each work element has been completed. Although this technique gives work element times directly for each observation, it requires the observer to read and record the times and to reset the watch at the end of each element. Sometimes, two watches are used, one for recording the previous work element and the other for timing the present work element. However, if some work elements are done quickly, noting accurate times may be difficult.

Frequently, a review of the sample data will reveal a single, isolated time that differs greatly from other times recorded for the same element. The cause of such variation should be investigated. If it is an "irregular occurrence," such as a dropped tool or a machine failure, the analyst should not include it in calculating the average time for the work element. Sometimes, the decision to include an observed time must be made in consultation with the union. The average observed time based only on representative times is called the **select time** ($\bar{t}$). In Fig. 7.1 no irregular occurrences were noted. Therefore, the select time is the simple average of all observed times.

Step 3: Determining Sample Size. Figure 7.1 shows that the analyst observed only 10 cycles of the packaging operation. Was this number enough? Typically, those who use the time study to set standards want an average time estimate that is very close to the true long-range average 95 percent of the time. A formula, based on the normal distribution, allows us to determine the sample size, n, required:

$$n = \left[\left(\frac{1.96}{p} \right) \left(\frac{s}{\bar{t}} \right) \right]^2$$

where

$n = $ required sample size

$p = $ precision of the estimate as a proportion of the true value

$\bar{t} = $ select time for a work element

$s = $ sample standard deviation of representative observed times for a work element

The constant 1.96 represents the ± 1.96 standard deviations from the mean that leave a total of 5 percent in the tails of the normal curve. The term $s/\bar{t}$ is called the **sample coefficient of variation**. The precision of the estimate, p, is expressed as a proportion of the true (but unknown) average time for the work element.

Application 7.1   *Estimating the Sample Size in a Time Study*

Consider the coffee cup example in Fig. 7.1. Determine the appropriate sample size if the estimate of the select time for any work element is to be within 4 percent of the true mean 95 percent of the time.

Solution   The sample sizes for the work elements will differ from one another because their sample coefficients of variation differ. The largest required sample size should be used for the study so that all estimates will achieve the desired precision. To determine the coefficients of variation, the sample standard deviations must be calculated using the formula

$$s = \sqrt{\frac{\sum_{j=1}^{\hat{n}} (t_j - \bar{t})^2}{\hat{n} - 1}}$$

where t_j is the recorded time on the *j*th cycle for a work element and $\hat{n}$ is the size of the pilot sample. In this problem, $\hat{n} = 5$ for work element 1, and 10 for work elements 2, 3, and 4. The following table contains the calculations for determining the appropriate sample size for each work element:

Work Element	s	$\bar{t}$	$\dfrac{s}{\bar{t}}$	$n = \left[\left(\dfrac{1.96}{0.04}\right)\left(\dfrac{s}{\bar{t}}\right)\right]^2$
1	0.0305	0.50	0.0610	9
2	0.0171	0.11	0.1554	58
3	0.0226	0.71	0.0318	3
4	0.0241	1.10	0.0219	2

All fractional calculations for n were rounded to the next largest integer. If we want to be sure that all select times are within 4 percent of the true mean 95 percent of the time, we will need to have a total of 58 observations because of work element 2. Consequently, we will need 48 (58 − 10) more observations.

Step 4: Setting the Standard. The final step is to set the standard. The analyst first determines the **normal time (*NT*)** for each work element by judging the pace of the observed worker. The analyst must assess not only whether the worker's pace is above or below average but also *how much* above or below average. The analyst assigns a **performance rating factor (*RF*)** to the worker's performance on each work element. For example, in Fig. 7.1 the performance rating factor for work element 3 is 1.10. A performance rating factor greater than 1.0 means that in the subjective evaluation of the observer, the worker performed at a faster pace than he or she would in normal conditions (that is, produced more output in a given amount of time). In other instances, the worker performed at a slower pace than he or she would in normal conditions. The rating factor is solely a judgment call made by the analyst, based on experience. We will return to the issue of judgment in time studies later in the chapter.

Another factor the analyst must recognize is the frequency of occurrence (*F*) of a particular work element in a work cycle. As mentioned previously, a work element may not be performed on every cycle. For example, in Fig. 7.1, the work element "get two cartons" is performed only once every two cycles. That is why *F* equals 0.5 for that element.

The analyst multiplies the select time ($\bar{t}_i$), the frequency (F_i) of the work element per cycle, and the rating factor (RF_i) to obtain the normal time for work element i and the **normal time for the cycle (*NTC*)**; that is,

$$NT_i = \bar{t}_i(F_i)(RF_i)$$

$$NTC = \sum_i NT_i$$

Application 7.2	*Determining the Normal Time*

Refer again to the coffee cup packaging problem. Suppose that 48 additional observations were taken and the following data were recorded:

Work Element	$\bar{t}_i$	F_i	RF_i
1	0.53	0.50	1.05
2	0.10	1.00	0.95
3	0.75	1.00	1.10
4	1.08	1.00	0.90

What are the normal times for each work element and for the complete cycle?

Solution   The normal times are calculated as follows:

$$\text{Element 1: } NT_1 = 0.53(0.50)(1.05) = 0.28 \text{ min}$$
$$\text{Element 2: } NT_2 = 0.10(1.00)(0.95) = 0.10 \text{ min}$$
$$\text{Element 3: } NT_3 = 0.75(1.00)(1.10) = 0.83 \text{ min}$$
$$\text{Element 4: } NT_4 = 1.08(1.00)(0.90) = 0.97 \text{ min}$$
$$\text{Total} = 2.18 \text{ min}$$

Because element 1 occurs only every other cycle, its average time per cycle must be half its average observed time. That's why $F_1 = 0.50$ for that element. All others occur every cycle. The normal time for the complete cycle is 2.18 minutes.

The normal time for the cycle (*NTC*) is 2.18 minutes in the preceding application, but we cannot use that time as a standard. It does not account for fatigue, rest periods, or unavoidable delays that occur during an average workday. Consequently, we must add some **allowance time** to the normal time to adjust for these factors. Thus the **standard time (*ST*)** is

$$ST = NTC(1 + A)$$

where A is the proportion of the normal time to be added for allowances.*

Application 7.3	*Determining the Standard Time*

Suppose that the proportion of the normal time to be added for allowances is 0.15. What is the standard time for the coffee cup packaging operation, and how many cartons can be expected per 8-hour day?

Solution   Since $A = 0.15$,

$$ST = 2.18(1 + 0.15) = 2.51 \text{ minutes/carton}$$

For an 8-hour day, this translates into a standard of

$$\frac{480 \text{ minutes/day}}{2.51 \text{ minutes/carton}} = 191 \text{ cartons/day}$$

---

*Another formula for the standard time is given by $ST = NTC/(1 - A)$. In this formula, A represents the proportion of the *total time* to be added for allowances.

Judgment in Time Study. Several aspects of a time study require the use of judgment by the analyst. First, the analyst must take care when defining the work elements to be included in the study. As we have pointed out, these work elements must not be too short and must have definite starting and stopping points. Also, some work elements may occur infrequently and irregularly. The analyst must be sure to include times for these work elements as well.

Second, the analyst may have to eliminate some observed times because the elements are nonrepresentative of the work. An obvious case would be a worker accidentally dropping a tool, although nonrepresentative elements are not always that obvious. In some cases a chance happening such as a machine malfunction can distort the results. If these nonrepresentative times aren't excluded, the standard will be incorrect. However, the analyst must use judgment in deciding which times, if any, to exclude.

Another area where judgment plays a role is in the amount of allowance time to be used. Most allowances range from 10 to 20 percent of normal time. They are intended to account for factors such as fatigue or unexpected delays that are difficult to measure. As you will see later in this chapter, work sampling can be used to estimate some of the factors in allowance time.

Finally, the aspect of time study requiring the greatest amount of judgment is that of performance rating. Usually only a few workers are observed during a study, and their performance will seldom conform to the notion of normal used in the definition of standard. Thus the analyst has to make an adjustment in the average observed time to estimate the time it would take a trained operator to do the task at a normal pace.

Unfortunately, the analyst cannot avoid the use of judgment or the need to arrive at a performance rating by studying all the workers and using their average time as normal. If the workers are fast, it would not be fair to set the standard based on their average time, particularly if a wage incentive plan is involved. Conversely, if the workers are slow, basing the standard on their normal time would be unfair to the company. Further, the possibility that workers will slow their pace when they are being observed in a time study is very real. Consequently, the use of judgment in assigning performance rates seems to be a necessary, but often controversial, aspect of conducting a time study. Many analysts, however, go through training programs to ensure consistency of ratings over many analysts and within a company.

Overall Assessment of Time Study. Time study is the most frequently used method for setting time standards. Qualified analysts can typically set reasonable standards using this method, and workers understand the process. The method has some limitations, however. Its use is not appropriate, for example, when setting standards for "thinking" jobs, such as a mathematician solving a problem, a professor preparing a lecture, or an automobile mechanic diagnosing the cause of a problem. Nor is it appropriate for nonrepetitive jobs, such as nonroutine maintenance repair, in which the nature of the task differs each time. In addition, the use of a stopwatch is an art, and an inexperienced person should not conduct time studies. Obviously, errors in recording information can result in unreasonable standards. Similarly, an inexperienced person may not include all the work elements. Finally, unions may object to time study on the basis of the subjectivity involved. Nonetheless, time study conducted by an experienced observer is usually a satisfactory, although imperfect, tool for setting equitable time standards.

Elemental Standard Data Approach

If thousands of work standards are needed in a plant, the time and cost of the time study method may be excessive. In such cases analysts often use **elemental standard data** to derive standards for various jobs. This approach is based on the notion that a high degree of similarity exists in the work elements of certain jobs. The time standards for work elements common to a class of jobs can be stored in a database for future use. A work measurement approach, such as time study, can be used to compile standards for these common elements. Sometimes, the time required for a work element depends on certain variable characteristics of the jobs. In these situations an equation that relates these characteristics to the time required for the work element can also be stored in the database. Once established, the database can provide the data needed to estimate the normal times for jobs requiring these work elements. However, allowances still must be added to arrive at standard times for the jobs.

The elemental standard data approach can reduce the number of time studies needed. In addition, the database can develop standards for new work before production begins, a feature helpful in product costing, pricing, and production planning. When an element's work methods change, moreover, its normal time can be determined easily. With the time stored in the database, it can be applied easily and quickly to each job requiring that work element.

This approach also has some disadvantages, however. Although the need for time studies is reduced, they probably can't be eliminated. In general, the analyst should develop the normal times for the database, using the time study method. Also, companies like to use time studies periodically to check the standards developed by the elemental standard data approach. Another consideration is that specifying all the job variables that affect times for each work element may be difficult. Consequently, equations attempting to relate these variables to the time for that work element may not be very good.

Predetermined Data Approach

The predetermined data approach carries the elemental standard data approach one step further. The analyst divides each work element into a series of micromotions common to a wide variety of tasks. The normal times for these micromotions are stored in a database, along with modifications for job variables, so that the normal time for any task can be developed by accessing the database.

One of the most commonly used predetermined data systems is **methods time measurement (MTM)**. Actually, there are a variety of MTM databases, but we focus on the most accurate, MTM-1. In MTM-1 the basic micromotions are reach, move, disengage, apply pressure, grasp, position, release, and turn. The normal times for these micromotions, modified for job variables, were developed from motion picture studies of a sample of workers in various industrial settings. Trained observers applied performance ratings to the observations.

Table 7.2 shows the *move* motion from the MTM-1 data. A time measurement unit (TMU) is 0.0006 minute (1/0.0006 = 1667 TMUs per minute). The table allows for differences in weight, distance moved, and circumstances of the move. For example, suppose a worker must move an 18-pound object with both hands to an exact location 20 inches away. The hands are not in motion prior to the move. To find the TMU value for this action, we first go to the case description column on the far right of the table. Note that case C describes the circumstances of this move. We then go to column C of the TMU columns and find the entry for 20 inches, which is 22.1 TMUs. Now make adjustments for the weight of the object. Since the worker is using two hands, the weight *per hand* in our example is 9 pounds, which is greater than 7.5 pounds and less than 12.5 pounds in the weight allowance columns. The dynamic factor is 1.11, and the static factor is 3.9 TMUs. To find the final TMU value for this move activity, we multiply the tabular TMU value for the distance moved by the dynamic factor and add the static factor. In our example, we have 22.1(1.11) + 3.9 = 28 TMUs. There are similar tables for other motions.

Setting standards using predetermined data involves several steps. First, each work element must be broken down into its basic micromotions. Then, the mitigating factors of each motion must be determined so that the proper tabular value is used. These factors include weight, distance, size of object, and degree of difficulty. Next, the normal times for each motion from the tables are added to get the normal time for the task. Finally, the normal time is adjusted for allowances to give the standard time.

The predetermined data approach offers some advantages over the other approaches we have discussed. First, standards can be set for new jobs before production begins, which cannot be done with the time study method. Second, new work methods can be compared without conducting a time study. Third, a greater degree of consistency in the setting of time standards is provided because the sources of error in time studies, such as data recording errors, are reduced. Finally, this approach defuses the objection of biased judgment in performance rating. Performance ratings are no longer needed in the derivation of a standard.

The predetermined data approach also has its drawbacks. Work must be broken down into micromotions, making this method impractical for firms with a process focus and low repeatability. Moreover, the data may not reflect the situation in any specific plant: What is normal for one plant may not be for another plant. The sample of workers used to develop the predetermined data may not be representative of the workers in a particular facility. Further, performance time variations can result from many factors—too many to publish in tables such as Table 7.2. In some circumstances, the time needed to move an object may depend on the shape of the object, but the MTM-1 charts do not recognize this factor. Then, the method is based on the assumption that the times associated with the micromotions simply can be summed to get the total time for a task. This assumption disregards the possibility that the actual time

TABLE 7.2 / *MTM Predetermined Data for the Move Micromotion*

| Distance Moved (in.) | Time TMU | | | | Wt. Allowance | | | Case and Description |
	A	B	C	Hand in Motion B	Wt. (lb) Up to	Dynamic Factor	Static Constant (TMU)	
¾ or less	2.0	2.0	2.0	1.7				
1	2.5	2.9	3.4	2.3	2.5	1.00	0	
2	3.6	4.6	5.2	2.9				A Move object to other hand or against stop.
3	4.9	5.7	6.7	3.6	7.5	1.06	2.2	
4	6.1	6.9	8.0	4.3				
5	7.3	8.0	9.2	5.0	12.5	1.11	3.9	
6	8.1	8.9	10.3	5.7				
7	8.9	9.7	11.1	6.5	17.5	1.17	5.6	
8	9.7	10.6	11.8	7.2				
9	10.5	11.5	12.7	7.9	22.5	1.22	7.4	
10	11.3	12.2	13.5	8.6				B Move object to approximate or indefinite location.
12	12.9	13.4	15.2	10.0	27.5	1.28	9.1	
14	14.4	14.6	16.9	11.4				
16	16.0	15.8	18.7	12.8	32.5	1.33	10.8	
18	17.6	17.0	20.4	14.2				
20	19.2	18.2	22.1	15.6	37.5	1.39	12.5	
22	20.8	19.4	23.8	17.0				
24	22.4	20.6	25.5	18.4	42.5	1.44	14.3	
26	24.0	21.8	27.3	19.8				C Move object to exact location.
28	25.5	23.1	29.0	21.2	47.5	1.50	16.0	
30	27.1	24.3	30.7	22.7				
Additional	0.8	0.6	0.85		TMU per inch over 30 inches			

Source: Copyright © by the MTM Association for Standards and Research. No reprint permission without written consent from the MTM Association, 16–01 Broadway, Fair Lawn, N.J. 07410.

may depend on the specific *sequence* of motions. Finally, there is a danger that the approach will be misused because, on the surface, it appears easy to use. Actually, considerable skill is needed to identify all the micromotions and accurately judge the mitigating factors of the motion. Training and experience are required; an inexperienced person will come up with poor standards.

Work Sampling Method

Work sampling is a broad approach to work measurement, not concerned with timing detailed motions but with estimating the proportions of time spent by people and machines on activities such as producing a product or service, doing paperwork, waiting for instructions, waiting for maintenance, or being idle. These estimates are based on a large number of observations. The underlying assumption is that the proportion of time the activity is observed in the sample will be the proportion of time spent on the activity in general. The sample size affects the degree of precision that can be expected from estimates for a given level of statistical confidence. Data from work sampling also can estimate machine or labor utilization percentages and the allowances needed to set standards for use with the other methods already discussed, to determine job content, and to help assess the cost of jobs or activities.

Work Sampling Procedure. Conducting a work sampling study involves the following steps:

1. Define the activities.
2. Design the observation form.
3. Determine the length of the study.
4. Determine the initial sample size.
5. Select random observation times.
6. Determine the observer schedule.
7. Observe the activities and record the data.
8. Check to see whether additional sampling is required.

Application 7.4	*Designing a Work Sampling Observation Form*

The hospital administrator at a private hospital is considering a proposal for installing an automated medical records storage and retrieval system. To determine the advisability of purchasing such a system, the administrator needs to know the proportion of time that registered nurses (RNs) and licensed vocational nurses (LVNs) spend accessing records. Presently these nurses must either retrieve the records manually or have them copied and sent to their wards. Define the activities for a work sampling study and design the observation form.

Solution   Figure 7.2 shows an observation form for the work sampling study at the hospital. More detailed activities could be shown, but the hospital administrator is interested mainly in the proportion of time that RNs and LVNs spend accessing records. The other data can be useful for planning purposes and are included to provide a representative example of an observation form. Information on RNs and LVNs is recorded separately because they spend different amounts of time with medical records at this hospital. The form should provide enough space to record the observations as they are made. They can be summarized later for analysis.

FIGURE 7.2

Observation Form for
a Nursing Work
Sampling Study

	Activity				
	Accessing records	Attending to patients	Other support activities	Idle or break	Total observations
RN					
LVN					

A work sampling study should be conducted over a representative period of time. Each activity must be given a chance to occur a representative number of times. For example, if an activity occurs only once a week, it wouldn't make sense to conduct a one-day study because there is a good chance that the activity would not be observed. In such a case, the study should probably span several months. In Application 7.4, accessing records occurs continuously throughout the week and from week to week throughout the year. Consequently, the study should cover several weeks.

Initially, the analyst may have to make a reasonable guess for the proportion of time an activity takes and then take a number of observations to provide a desired degree of precision. Later, once the sample proportion has been determined, additional sampling may be required. Table 7.3 can be used to determine appropriate sample sizes.

Application 7.5   *Determining the Sample Size*

The hospital administrator in Application 7.4 suspects that accessing records takes about 20 percent of RNs' time and about 5 percent of LVNs' time. A typical ward, staffed by eight RNs and four LVNs, is selected for the study. The administrator wants 95 percent confidence that the estimates for each category of nurses fall within ±0.03 of their true proportions. Use Table 7.3 to determine how many trips the observer will have to take through the ward.

Solution   The administrator's original estimate for the proportion of time spent accessing records is 0.20 for RNs and 0.05 for LVNs, and the administrator is willing to accept an error of ±0.03 (0.20 ± 0.03 for LVNs and 0.05 ± 0.03 for RNs). Table 7.3 indicates that the sample size should be 683 observations for RNs and 203 for LVNs. However, there are eight RNs and four LVNs that can be observed on each trip, implying we need 86 (683/8) trips for the observations of RNs and only 51 (203/4) trips for the LVNs. Thus an observer schedule that provides for 86 trips through the ward will be sufficient for both nurse groups. This number of trips will generate more observations than needed for the LVNs, but as the observer will be going through the ward anyway, he or she might as well record the data.

TABLE 7.3 / Sample Size Requirements for Work Sampling Studies for Various Values of P and Absolute Error*

Proportion of Time for Activity or Delay, P	Absolute Error					Proportion of Time for Activity or Delay, P	Absolute Error				
	±0.01	±0.02	±0.03	±0.04	±0.05		±0.01	±0.02	±0.03	±0.04	±0.05
0.01 or 0.99	380	95	42	24	15	0.26 or 0.74	7388	1847	821	462	296
0.02 or 0.98	753	188	84	47	30	0.27 or 0.73	7569	1892	841	473	303
0.03 or 0.97	1117	279	124	70	45	0.28 or 0.72	7741	1935	860	484	310
0.04 or 0.96	1475	369	164	92	59	0.29 or 0.71	7907	1977	879	494	316
0.05 or 0.95	1824	456	203	114	73	0.30 or 0.70	8064	2016	896	504	323
0.06 or 0.94	2166	541	241	135	87	0.31 or 0.69	8214	2053	913	513	329
0.07 or 0.93	2500	625	278	156	100	0.32 or 0.68	8356	2089	928	522	334
0.08 or 0.92	2826	707	314	177	113	0.33 or 0.67	8490	2123	943	531	340
0.09 or 0.91	3145	786	349	197	126	0.34 or 0.66	8617	2154	957	539	345
0.10 or 0.90	3456	864	384	216	138	0.35 or 0.65	8736	2184	971	546	349
0.11 or 0.89	3759	940	418	235	150	0.36 or 0.64	8847	2212	983	553	354
0.12 or 0.88	4055	1014	451	253	162	0.37 or 0.63	8951	2238	995	559	358
0.13 or 0.87	4343	1086	483	271	174	0.38 or 0.62	9047	2262	1005	565	362
0.14 or 0.86	4623	1156	514	289	185	0.39 or 0.61	9135	2284	1015	571	365
0.15 or 0.85	4896	1224	544	306	196	0.40 or 0.60	9216	2304	1024	576	369
0.16 or 0.84	5161	1290	573	323	206	0.41 or 0.59	9289	2322	1032	581	372
0.17 or 0.83	5418	1355	602	339	217	0.42 or 0.58	9354	2339	1039	585	374
0.18 or 0.82	5668	1417	630	354	227	0.43 or 0.57	9412	2353	1046	588	376
0.19 or 0.81	5910	1477	657	369	236	0.44 or 0.56	9462	2365	1051	591	378
0.20 or 0.80	6144	1536	683	384	246	0.45 or 0.55	9504	2376	1056	594	380
0.21 or 0.79	6371	1593	708	398	255	0.46 or 0.54	9539	2385	1060	596	382
0.22 or 0.78	6589	1647	732	412	264	0.47 or 0.53	9565	2391	1063	598	383
0.23 or 0.77	6801	1700	756	425	272	0.48 or 0.52	9585	2396	1065	599	383
0.24 or 0.76	7004	1751	778	438	280	0.49 or 0.51	9596	2399	1066	600	384
0.25 or 0.75	7200	1800	800	450	288	0.50	9600	2400	1067	600	384

*These sample sizes yield a 95 percent confidence that the estimate for P is within a specific absolute error of the population average.

The times of day the observer makes the trips to gather data should be selected at random over the length of the study. This approach reduces the amount of bias in the data. For example, if employees know that they will be observed each day at 2:30 P.M., they may alter their behavior from normal patterns. If that happens, the data won't represent actual performance. After the observation times have been determined, a schedule for the observer can be developed.

Application 7.6   Using Work Sampling Data for Decision Making

The hospital administrator in Applications 7.4 and 7.5 estimates that the annual amortization cost and expenses for maintaining the new automated medical records storage and retrieval system will be $150,000. The supplier of the new system estimates that the system will reduce the amount of time the nurses spend accessing records by 25 percent. The total annual salary expense for RNs in the hospital is $3,628,000, and for LVNs it is $2,375,000. The hospital administrator is willing to assume that nurses could productively use any time saved by the new system.

The pilot work sampling study resulted in the data shown in Fig. 7.3. Should the administrator purchase the new system?

Solution   Let

$$P_1 = \text{proportion of time spent by RNs with records}$$
$$P_2 = \text{proportion of time spent by LVNs with records}$$

From Fig. 7.3, $P_1 = 0.18$ (124/688) and $P_2 = 0.08$ (28/344). Thus the original estimates were off the mark. However, the sample results fall within the allowable error range for each proportion, and the sample sizes were adequate for the values obtained (see Table 7.3 for $P_1 = 0.18$ and $P_2 = 0.08$). If the sample sizes were too small for the proportions found, additional sampling would have to be performed.

Estimated annual net savings from the purchase of the automatic medical records storage and retrieval system are

$$\text{Net savings} = 0.25(\$3,628,000P_1 + \$2,375,000P_2) - \$150,000$$
$$= 0.25[\$3,628,000(0.18) + \$2,375,000(0.08)] - \$150,000$$
$$= \$60,760$$

Based on the results of the work sampling study, the new system appears to be a good investment.

Overall Assessment of Work Sampling. The work sampling method is used frequently in practice because it offers certain advantages over other approaches. No special training is required for the observers, no stopwatches are needed, and several studies can be conducted simultaneously. It is more economical for studying jobs having long cycle times because less observer time is required; observations are made only at random times. Importantly, workers themselves often prefer this method of work measurement to other approaches.

The major disadvantage to work sampling is the large number of observations required. Even though each is short, many observations are needed to provide a reasonable degree of precision for the estimate. This method is usually not as economical for setting standards for repetitive, well-defined jobs as the other approaches we have discussed.

FIGURE 7.3

Results of the Initial Study

	Activity				
	Accessing records	Attending to patients	Other support activities	Idle or break	Total observations
RN	124	258	223	83	688
LVN	28	251	46	19	344

LEARNING CURVES

The work measurement methods presented so far are based on the assumption that the effects of future learning are negligible. The implication is that the workplace is a stable environment where change does not take place. However, that assumption and its implication are rarely true in today's workplace. Change *does* occur, and where there is change, there is also learning. The two major types of learning are individual and organizational.

With instruction and repetition, workers learn to perform jobs more efficiently and thereby reduce the number of direct labor hours per unit. Such may be the case for the process illustrated in Fig. 7.4. It shows the process time per unit continually decreases until the 140th unit is produced. At that point learning is negligible and a standard time for the operation can be developed.

Organizational learning, in general, and management learning, in particular, involve gaining experience in product and process design, automation and other capital investments, and changes in administrative methods or personnel to improve the efficiency of operations. The process time improvement shown in Fig. 7.4 could have resulted from better work methods, tools, product design, or supervision, as well as from individual worker learning. Changes such as these in the workplace create the need for continually reevaluating existing standards and setting new ones, as necessary. Managerial Practice 7.2 shows how organizational learning paid off for Samsung, the world's leading microwave oven producer.

The Learning Effect

The learning effect can be represented by a line called a **learning curve,** which displays the relationship between the total direct labor per unit and the cumulative quantity of a product produced. The curve in Fig. 7.4 is an exam-

FIGURE 7.4

Relationship Between
Learning Curve and
Standard Time per
Cycle

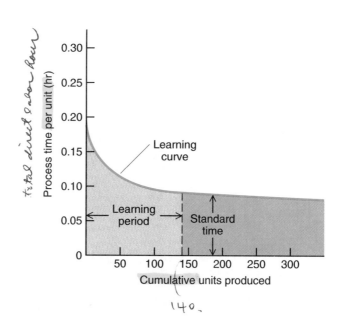

total direct labor hour

140.

Managerial Practice 7.2

The Learning Curve Effect at Samsung

In 1976 Yun Soo Chu, a young engineer at Korean giant Samsung, received an unexpected assignment—design a microwave oven. While visiting the United States, J.U. Chung, a vice president at Samsung, became intrigued with a new kind of oven, one that was not heated by electricity or gas but by microwaves. His goal was to penetrate the market early and produce a low-cost product for export. He asked Chu to head up a team to design a microwave oven for Samsung. Chu began by buying leading microwave ovens and studying how they were made. He had to purchase equipment and materials he didn't have, such as presses and magnetron tubes, the heart of the oven. Chu spent one year of 80-hour workweeks to complete the first prototype, only to have it melt when he turned it on. It wasn't until June 1978 that Chu and his team produced a prototype that worked.

The production team, on a makeshift assembly line, began making one oven a day, then two, and then five as employees began to learn how to assemble the ovens. However, by mid-1979 Samsung had finished making only 1460 ovens. Convinced that Samsung could compete in the world microwave market, and buoyed by a few initial orders, Samsung decided to improve the production efficiency of the microwave line. I.J. Jang, a production engineer, immersed himself in learning the product and visiting leading Japanese manufacturers of microwave ovens. Despite his long hours redesigning the assembly line, some bugs remained. Samsung operated the line during the day, and Jang studied it at night to work out the problems. Production improved to 10 ovens a day, then 15. Soon they were making 1500 per month.

By the end of 1981 Samsung had increased annual production a hundredfold, from little more than 1000 the year before to over 100,000, by improving methods and adding assembly lines. By 1982 annual production was 200,000. In 1983 it was 750,000 and in 1984, over 1 million. With each milestone, management celebrated the achievement—but only briefly. The next day they were back to work, looking for ways to increase production and quality while reducing costs.

Source: Ira C. Magaziner and Mark Patinkin, "Fast Heat: How Korea Won the Microwave War," *Harvard Business Review* (January–February 1989), pp. 83–92.

A microwave production line at a Samsung plant.

ple of a learning curve for one process. The terms *manufacturing progress function* and *experience curve* have also been used to describe this relationship, although the experience curve typically refers to total value-added costs per unit rather than labor hours. The principles underlying these curves are identical to those of the learning curve, however. Here we use the term *learning curve* to depict reductions in either total direct labor per unit or total value-added costs per unit.

Background. The learning curve was first developed in the aircraft industry prior to World War II, when it was discovered that the direct labor input per airplane declined with considerable regularity as the cumulative number of planes produced increased. A survey of major airplane manufacturers revealed that a series of learning curves could be developed to represent the average experience for various categories of airframes (fighters, bombers, and so on). The unique aspect of these curves was their similarity despite the differing times required to produce the first unit of each type of airframe. For example, once production started, the direct labor for the eighth unit was only 80 percent that of the fourth unit, and the twelfth was only 80 percent of the sixth, and so on. In each case, each doubling of quantities reduced production time by 20 percent. Because of the consistency in the rate of improvement, it was concluded that the aircraft industry's rate of learning was 80 percent between doubled quantities of airframes. Of course, for any given product and company, the rate of learning can be different.

Learning Curves and Competitive Strategy. Learning curves enable managers to project the manufacturing cost per unit for a given cumulative production quantity. Firms that choose to emphasize low price in their competitive strategy rely on high volumes to maintain profit margins. These firms strive to move down the learning curve (lower labor hours per unit or lower costs per unit) by increasing volume. This tactic makes entry into a market by competitors difficult. For example, in the electronics component industry, the cost of developing an integrated circuit is so large that the first units produced must be priced high. As cumulative production increases, costs (and prices) fall. The first companies in the market have a big advantage because newcomers, such as Korean firms, must start selling at lower prices and suffer large initial losses.

Projecting learning effects with learning curves or experience curves can be risky. Managers all too easily forget the dynamics of the environment, in which disturbances (such as new products or market changes) can disrupt the expected benefits of increased production. For example, Douglas Aircraft was forced to merge with McDonnell Company because of financial problems. Douglas assumed that it could reduce the costs of its new jet aircraft by following a learning curve formula and committing to fixed delivery dates and prices. Continued modification of its planes disrupted the learning curve, and the cost reductions were not realized. Nonetheless, the learning curve has many useful applications. Let's now turn to the problem of formulating a learning curve.

Developing Learning Curves

In the following discussion and applications we focus on direct labor hours per unit, although we could have used costs just as easily. When we develop a learning curve we make the following assumptions:

- The direct labor required to produce the $n + 1$st unit will always be less than the direct labor required for the nth unit.
- Direct labor requirements will decrease at a declining rate as cumulative production increases.
- The reduction in time will follow an exponential curve.

0.03798   0.00347   0.0212   0.00252
4.83%   0.7%   2.39%   0.39%

TABLE 7.4 / Conversion Factors for the Cumulative Average Number of Direct Labor Hours per Unit

	80 Percent Learning Rate (n = Cumulative Production)					90 Percent Learning Rate (n = Cumulative Production)				
n		n		n		n		n		n
1	1.00000	19	0.53178	37	0.43976	1	1.00000	19	0.73545	37	0.67091
2	0.90000	20	0.52425	38	0.43634	2	0.95000	20	0.73039	38	0.66839
3	0.83403	21	0.51715	39	0.43304	3	0.91540	21	0.72559	39	0.66595
4	0.78553	22	0.51045	40	0.42984	4	0.88905	22	0.72102	40	0.66357
5	0.74755	23	0.50410	64	0.37382	5	0.86784	23	0.71666	64	0.62043
6	0.71657	24	0.49808	128	0.30269	6	0.85013	24	0.71251	128	0.56069
7	0.69056	25	0.49234	256	0.24405	7	0.83496	25	0.70853	256	0.50586
8	0.66824	26	0.48688	512	0.19622	8	0.82172	26	0.70472	512	0.45594
9	0.64876	27	0.48167	600	0.18661	9	0.80998	27	0.70106	600	0.44519
10	0.63154	28	0.47668	700	0.17771	10	0.79945	28	0.69754	700	0.43496
11	0.61613	29	0.47191	800	0.17034	11	0.78991	29	0.69416	800	0.42629
12	0.60224	30	0.46733	900	0.16408	12	0.78120	30	0.69090	900	0.41878
13	0.58960	31	0.46293	1000	0.15867	13	0.77320	31	0.68775	1000	0.41217
14	0.57802	32	0.45871	1200	0.14972	14	0.76580	32	0.68471	1200	0.40097
15	0.56737	33	0.45464	1400	0.14254	15	0.75891	33	0.68177	1400	0.39173
16	0.55751	34	0.45072	1600	0.13660	16	0.75249	34	0.67893	1600	0.38390
17	0.54834	35	0.44694	1800	0.13155	17	0.74646	35	0.67617	1800	0.37711
18	0.53979	36	0.44329	2000	0.12720	18	0.74080	36	0.67350	2000	0.37114

Collectively, these assumptions comprise the basic premise of learning curves: The production time per unit is reduced by a fixed percentage each time production is doubled. Given these assumptions, the labor hours for the first unit produced, and the learning rate, we can draw a learning curve using a logarithmic model. The direct labor required for the nth unit, k_n, is

$$k_n = k_1 n^b$$

where

k_1 = direct labor hours for the first unit
n = cumulative number of units produced
b = log r/log 2
r = learning rate

We can also calculate the cumulative average number of hours per unit for the first n units with the help of Table 7.4. It contains conversion factors that, when multiplied by the direct labor hours for the first unit, yield the average time per unit for selected cumulative production quantities.

Application 7.7 | *Using Learning Curves to Estimate Direct Labor Requirements*

It takes a manufacturer of diesel locomotives 50,000 hours to produce the first unit and, based on past experience with products of this sort, the rate of learning is 80 percent. Use the logarithmic model to estimate the direct labor required for the fortieth diesel locomotive and the cumulative average number of labor hours per unit for the first 40 units. Draw a learning curve for this situation.

Solution   The estimated number of direct labor hours required to produce the fortieth unit is

$$k_{40} = 50{,}000(40)^{\log 0.8/\log 2} = 50{,}000(40)^{-0.322} = 50{,}000(0.30488) = 15{,}244 \text{ hr}$$

We calculate the cumulative average number of direct labor hours per unit for the first 40 units with the help of Table 7.4. For a cumulative production of 40 units and an 80 percent learning rate, the factor is 0.42984. The cumulative average direct labor hours per unit is 50,000(0.42984) = 21,492 hours.

We utilized the logarithmic model to calculate the points for plotting the learning curve in Fig. 7.5, using selected values for the cumulative units produced. We can also calculate the curve by using the basic premise of learning curves. For example, the second unit's labor time is 80 percent of the first, the fourth is 80 percent of the second, and so on.

Estimating the Rate of Learning

If historical data are available, the rate of learning can be estimated with the logarithmic model. In this case, the time required to produce the first unit and the time required to produce the nth unit are known. The solution involves two steps:

1. Estimate the value of b, using the logarithmic model.

$$k_n = k_1 n^b$$

We know k_n, k_1, and n, so we need to solve for b.

$$n^b = \frac{k_n}{k_1}$$

$$b \log n = \log \left(\frac{k_n}{k_1}\right)$$

$$b = \frac{\log(k_n/k_1)}{\log n}$$

FIGURE 7.5

80 Percent Learning Curve

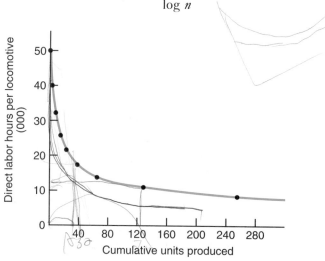

2. Use the definition of b to estimate the learning rate, r.

$$\frac{\log r}{\log 2} = b$$

$$\log r = b \log 2$$

$$r = 10^{(b \log 2)}$$

Application 7.8	*Calculating the Learning Rate*

A company produces landing flap assemblies for a large aircraft manufacturer. Suppose that it takes 2500 hours to produce the first assembly and 402 hours to produce the 165th assembly. What is the learning rate for producing a landing flap assembly?

Solution

$$b = \frac{\log (402/2500)}{\log 165}$$

$$= \frac{-0.7937}{2.2175} = -0.35793$$

$$r = 10^{(-0.35793 \log 2)} = 10^{(-0.10775)} = 0.78$$

Consequently, the learning rate is 78 percent. This rate means that when production is doubled, the direct labor per unit is reduced by 22 percent.

Estimates have to be more subjective before production has begun. The analyst can assume either that the learning rate will be the same as that in the past for similar goods produced by the company or that the learning rate will equal that of the industry as a whole for similar applications. In either case, actual performance should be monitored and revisions should be made in the learning rate as data are accumulated.

Blindly accepting the industry learning rate is dangerous because it can be quite different for a specific company. One factor involved is the mix of labor-paced and machine-paced operations. The opportunity to reduce direct labor hours on machine-paced operations is limited because the output rate is controlled by the capability of the machines, not the workers. The greater the ratio of labor-paced to machine-paced operations, the greater is the effect of learning on direct labor requirements.

Another factor affecting the rate of learning is degree of product complexity. The learning rate for simple products is not as pronounced as it is for complex products. Complex products offer more opportunity to improve work methods, materials, and process design over the product's life. Closely associated with this factor is the experience of the organization with similar products. The greater the difference in the product relative to anything the company has manufactured in the past, the greater is the expected learning rate.

The rate of capital inputs also affects the learning rate. Here we are referring to the overall reduction of direct labor hours by automation or general improvements in plant and equipment. Capital improvements are introduced at specific points in time and typically have a significant effect. Thus they tend to make the actual learning curve uneven in contrast to a theoretical curve, such as the one shown in Fig. 7.5. Consequently, when estimating the learning rate based on previous experience or industry averages, an analyst must consider anticipated capital inputs.

Using Learning Curves

Learning curves can be used in a variety of ways. Let's look briefly at their use in bid preparation, financial planning, and labor requirement estimation.

Bid Preparation. Estimating labor costs is an important part of preparing bids for large jobs. Knowing the learning rate, the number of units to be produced, and wage rates, the estimator can arrive at the cost of labor by using a learning curve. After calculating expected labor and materials costs, the estimator adds the desired profit to obtain the total bid amount.

Financial Planning. Learning curves can also be used in financial planning to help the financial planner determine the amount of cash needed to finance operations. Learning curves provide a basis for comparing prices and costs and can be used to project periods of financial drain, when expenditures exceed receipts. A contract price is determined, in part, by the average direct labor costs per unit for the number of contracted units. In the early stages of production, the direct labor costs will exceed that average, whereas in the later stages of production the reverse will be true. This information enables the financial planner to arrange in advance with customers and banks to finance certain phases of operations.

Labor Requirement Estimation. Given a production schedule, the analyst can use learning curves to project direct labor requirements. This information can be used to estimate training requirements and develop hiring plans. We will show how such information is used in production and staffing plans in Chapter 14.

Application 7.9   *Using Learning Curves to Estimate Labor Requirements*

The manager of a custom manufacturer just received a production schedule for an order for 64 large turbines. Over the next seven months, the company is to produce 2, 3, 5, 8, 12, 20, and 14 turbines, respectively. The first unit took 30,000 direct labor hours, and experience on past projects indicates that a 90 percent learning curve is appropriate; therefore the second unit will require only 27,000 hours. If each employee works an average of 150 hours per month, estimate the total number of full-time employees needed each month for the next seven months.

Estimating Labor Requirements Using a 90% Learning Curve

	Production Schedule		Estimates of Labor Requirements			
Month	Units per Month (1)	Cumulative Units (2)	Cumulative Average Time (3)	Cumulative Total Hours (4)	Total Hours/Month (5)	Total Full-Time Employees/Month* (6)
1	2	2	28,500	57,000	57,000	380
2	3	5	26,035	130,175	73,175	488
3	5	10	23,983	239,830	109,655	731
4	8	18	22,224	400,032	160,202	1068
5	12	30	20,727	621,810	221,778	1479
6	20	50	19,368	968,400	346,590	2311
7	14	64	18,613	1,191,232	222,832	1486

*Based on an assumed 150 labor hours in each month.

Solution The table above shows the production schedule and estimates of labor requirements. Columns 1 and 2 show the units per month and cumulative units. Column 3 shows the cumulative average time per unit, which is calculated using the cumulative units in column 2 and factors from Table 7.4. The calculations for months 1 and 2 are:

$$\text{Month 1} \qquad 30,000(0.95000) = 28,500$$
$$\text{Month 2} \qquad 30,000(0.86784) = 26,035$$

and so on. The factor for month 6 had to be interpolated from the factors for 40 units and 64 units in Table 7.4 as follows:

$$0.66357 - \left(\frac{50 - 40}{64 - 40}\right)(0.66357 - 0.62043) = 0.64560$$

The cumulative average time per unit after 50 units is $30,000(0.64560) = 19,368$ hours. The manager calculated cumulative total hours by multiplying column 2 by column 3. He obtained the total hours per month, shown in column 5, by subtracting the successive monthly cumulative totals in column 4. (For example, for month 2, 130,175 − 57,000 = 73,175 hours.) Finally, he calculated column 6 by dividing the number of work hours per month into column 5. This calculation gave the manager the estimated number of full-time production employees needed.

MANAGERIAL CONSIDERATIONS IN JOB DESIGN AND WORK MEASUREMENT

Our discussion of job design and work measurement would not be complete without mentioning compensation plans based on work measurement and the ever-growing role of automation and its effect on work measurement in the future.

Compensation Plans

Compensation plans based on work measurement typically involve incentive schemes. Those used most often are piece rate and individual incentive plans.

Piece Rate Plans. Piece rate is a compensation plan based on the number of units processed during a day or week. Machine operators are often paid on the basis of output: The faster the operator, the higher the pay. Similarly, workers performing a telephone survey may be paid on the basis of the number of positive contacts they make. To set the pay rates for piece rate plans such as these, management must specify what constitutes a fair day's work. As we have shown, work measurement methods can be used to determine standard times for estimating daily output. Pay rates can be based on these estimates.

Individual Incentive Plans. Sometimes, incentive plans are used to motivate workers. Such plans reward output that exceeds a predetermined base level. The base level can be set after work measurement methods have established the expected rate of output for an average worker. One plan is the 100 percent premium plan. Suppose that the base level is set at 50 units of output. Under the plan, a worker who produces 60 units would receive an additional 10/50, or 20 percent, of the base pay rate. If the incentive plan is a 50 percent premium plan, the worker would get a bonus equal to 50 percent of 10/50, or 10 percent, of the base pay rate.

Quality and Compensation Plans. The purpose of incentive pay is to encourage high levels of output from employees. However, a high rate of output may be achieved at the expense of quality. Where is the advantage to a company if a worker produces at 115 percent of standard but has a 20 percent defective rate?

In Chapter 3 when we discussed total quality control, we argued that quality at the source is critical for achieving world-class quality performance. Incentive plans that do not recognize and reward quality may not motivate the worker to produce high-quality goods.

Two basic approaches are used to recognize quality in incentive plans. The first is the autocratic approach, which docks the worker's pay for defective production or requires the worker to repair all defects at a lower rate of pay. The latter is not popular with workers because in many cases the defects are not repairable or were not the fault of the worker.

The second is the motivational approach, which is based on the concept of extra pay for extra effort. The following example uses two standards: one for daily production and the other for quality. Suppose that the daily production standard for an item is 1000 units. The daily wage rate is $80, but the operator gets an additional $0.30 for each unit produced over 1000 units. A daily production total of 1040 units would net the operator a bonus of $12.00, bringing daily earnings to $92.00. However, there is also a quality standard of 95 percent defect-free production. If the operator does better than that, a bonus of $0.10 is added for each defect-free unit produced beyond the standard. Suppose that the operator produces 1009 acceptable items. The quality bonus is 1009 − 0.95(1040) = 21 units. This adds a bonus of $2.10, raising the total daily wage to $94.10.

Many variants of the motivational approach of including quality in work measurement are used in practice. The important point is that quality should be clearly recognized when compensation plans are being developed.

Impact of Automation

When a firm increases its level of automation, its application of work measurement changes, and traditional values for allowance factors may no longer be appropriate. In an automated facility there is less need to actually observe an operation and rate performance because machines increasingly control processing cycles. Many cycle times are determined by digital control devices and therefore do not have to be observed. And although there is still a need to determine allowances for fatigue, its nature shifts from physical to mental fatigue.

Automation also affects the methods used for work measurement. The method of work sampling is simplified in automated facilities, as the state of many work units can be electronically monitored. Predetermined data systems focus instead on analyzing robotic motions and the activities of knowledge workers. Systems such as robot time and motion (RTM) are useful for evaluating alternative robotic work methods. The emphasis shifts to measuring the work of knowledge workers because they comprise a greater proportion of the automated facility's work force.

Looking to the future, standard data will be developed for major segments of the automated manufacturing system, as opposed to separate operations in an item's processing cycle. The times required for major manufacturing segments would be put into a database for use in simulating alternative work methods and estimating product costs before production actually starts.

Our discussion of the impact of automation holds equally well for service industries. In manufacturing or services, the major objective of work measurement will remain unchanged. Management then, as well as now, will still be interested in increasing productivity, improving quality, and reducing costs.

COMPUTER SOLVED PROBLEM
Determining Production Standard

The packing manager at Lamps-"R"-Us is interested in setting production standards for the company's lamp packing line. The current production target calls for a minimum of 60 units per day. The production process consists of the following eight steps:

1. Get lamp components.
2. Assemble lamp.
3. Test lamp.
4. Get carton.
5. Place lamp in carton.
6. Insert two liners in carton.
7. Seal carton.
8. Place carton in storage.

The total operating time per day is 480 minutes (8 × 60), and the time allowance factor is 15 percent. The manager has performed a time study of the production process using a sample size of 10 observations. The raw time data (t), frequency of work element per cycle (F), and estimated performance rating factor (RF) are reported below.

Observations (min)

Element	1	2	3	4	5	6	7	8	9	10	F	RF
1	1.27	1.27	1.24	1.25	1.20	1.26	1.24	1.27	1.26	1.24	1	1.05
2	2.10	2.09	2.18	2.17	2.09	2.08	2.15	2.18	2.14	2.12	1	0.95
3	0.60	0.59	0.64	0.67	0.65	0.68	0.61	0.62	0.64	0.60	1	1.00
4	0.39	0.42	0.32	0.40	0.34	0.36	0.37	0.38	0.40	0.32	1	0.90
5	0.51	0.53	0.45	0.44	0.47	0.49	0.45	0.50	0.46	0.50	1	0.95
6	0.26		0.29		0.30		0.27		0.28		0.5	1.00
7	0.86	0.91	0.89	0.86	0.84	0.85	0.91	0.88	0.86	0.84	1	1.10
8	1.19	1.18	1.20	1.16	1.21	1.15	1.16	1.20	1.18	1.17	1	1.00

a. What is the production standard?
b. Does the production standard meet the current target?
c. Provide an interpretation of the total normal and standard times.
d. What is the impact on the production standard if the total operating time is increased to 500 minutes?

Solution   This problem is solved using CMOM (Work Measurement module). Your output may look different if you are using another software package.

a. Printout 1 shows selected input data and solution. The production standard is 59 units per day. This is determined by dividing the total operating time by the standard time per unit (480/8.0869).

b. The production standard does not meet the target (59 units per day versus 60 units per day).

PRINTOUT 1

CMOM–WORK MEASUREMENT–TIME STUDY

DATA ENTERED

NUMBER OF WORK ELEMENTS: 8
ALLOWANCE FACTOR   :   0.1500
TIME PER PERIOD   :   480

	T–BAR	RF	FREQ
WE1	1.25	1.05	1
WE2	2.13	0.95	1
WE3	0.63	1	1
WE4	0.37	0.90	1
WE5	0.48	0.95	1
WE6	0.28	1	0.50
WE7	0.87	1.10	1
WE8	1.18	1	1

CMOM—WORK MEASUREMENT—TIME STUDY

SOLUTION

WORK ELEMENT	NORMAL TIME	STANDARD TIME
WE1	1.3125	1.5094
WE2	2.0235	2.3270
WE3	0.6300	0.7245
WE4	0.3330	0.3830
WE5	0.4560	0.5244
WE6	0.1400	0.1610
WE7	0.9570	1.1006
WE8	1.1800	1.3570
TOTAL	7.0320	8.0869

PRODUCTION STANDARD (UNITS/PERIOD) :   59

c. The total normal time represents the average time to complete the eight steps. The standard time is the normal time multiplied by 1.0 plus the allowance factor (in this case, 0.15). The results given in Printout 1 suggest that it takes 7.03 minutes to complete one work cycle (normal time).

d. An increase in the operating time from 480 to 500 minutes, an approximate 5 percent change, results in a production standard of 62 units per day. The production standard is now above the current company target of 60 units per day. This change was implemented through the use of the CMOM edit option.

SOLVED PROBLEMS

1. A time analyst observed a job for which the work methods have just been changed. The job is divided into four work elements. The element times for the first five cycles, recorded on a continuous basis, are shown in the following table with a performance rating (RF) for each element.

Element	1	2	3	4	5	RF
			Cycle Times (min)			
1	0.50	3.30	5.70	8.20	10.85	1.10
2	0.70	3.45	5.95	8.55	11.10	1.20
3	1.45	4.05	6.50	9.25	11.75	1.20
4	2.75	5.25	7.60	10.35	13.00	0.90

a. Calculate the normal time for this job.
b. Calculate the standard time for this job, assuming that the allowance is 20 percent.
c. What is the appropriate sample size for estimating the time for element 2 within ±10 percent of the true mean with 95 percent confidence?
d. What sample size is needed for a precision of ±5 percent?

TABLE 7.5

Work Element	Observation 1	2	3	4	5	$\bar{t}$	F	RF	NT
1	0.50	0.55	0.45	0.60	0.50	0.52	1	1.1	0.572
2	0.20	0.15	0.25	0.35	0.25	0.24	1	1.2	0.288
3	0.75	0.60	0.55	0.70	0.65	0.65	1	1.2	0.780
4	1.30	1.20	1.10	1.10	1.25	1.19	1	0.9	1.071

Normal time per cycle (*NTC*) = 2.711 min

Solution

a. To get the normal time for this job, we must first determine the observed times for each work element for each cycle. We do so by subtracting successive continuous clock readings. Table 7.5 contains the data we need to compute the normal time per cycle; all times are representative.

b. Standard time = (Normal time per cycle)(1.0 + Allowances)

$$ST = NTC(1.0 + A) = 2.711(1.0 + 0.2)$$
$$= 3.25 \text{ minutes}$$

c. For work element 2, we have:

$$p = 0.10$$

$$s = \sqrt{\Sigma\,(t_i - 0.24)^2/(n - 1)} = 0.0742$$
$$\bar{t} = 0.24$$

The sample coefficient of variation = $s/\bar{t} = 0.3092$, so

$$n = \left[\left(\frac{1.96}{p}\right)\left(\frac{s}{\bar{t}}\right)\right]^2 = \left[\left(\frac{1.96}{0.10}\right)(0.3092)\right]^2$$

$$= 36.7 \quad \text{or} \quad 37 \text{ observations}$$

d. For precision of ±5 percent, the appropriate sample size is

$$n = \left[\left(\frac{1.96}{0.05}\right)(0.3092)\right]^2$$

$$= 146.9 \quad \text{or} \quad 147 \text{ observations}$$

2. A library administrator wants to determine the proportion of time the circulation clerk is idle. The following information was gathered on a random basis using work sampling:

Day	No. Times Clerk Busy	No. Times Clerk Idle	Total No. Observations
Monday	8	2	10
Tuesday	7	1	8
Wednesday	9	3	12
Thursday	7	3	10
Friday	8	2	10
Saturday	6	4	10

If the administrator wants a 95 percent confidence level and a degree of precision of ± 0.04, how many more observations are needed?

Solution

The total number of observations made equals 60. The clerk was observed to be idle 15 times. The initial estimate of the proportion is $P = 15/60 = 0.25$. From Table 7.3, the required sample size for a precision of ± 0.04 is 450. As 60 observations have already been made, an additional 390 are needed.

3. The Compton Company is manufacturing a new product that requires methods and materials never before used by the company. The order is for 80 units. The first unit took 46 direct labor hours, whereas the tenth unit took only 24.
   a. What is the rate of learning on this product?
   b. Estimate direct labor hours for the eightieth unit.

Solution

a.

$$b = \frac{\log (24/46)}{\log (10)} = -0.2825$$

$$r = 10^{(-0.2825 \ \log \ 2)} = 10^{(-0.08504)} = 0.82$$

The learning rate is 82 percent for this product.

b.

$$k_{80} = 46(80)^{(-0.2825)} = 13.34 \text{ hours}$$

4. You have just been given the following production schedule for a new product. This product is considerably different from any others your company has purchased. Historically, the learning rate has been 80 percent on projects such as this.

Month	Units
1	3
2	7
3	10
4	12
5	4
6	2

The first unit took 1000 hours to produce. If your budget only provides for a maximum of 30 direct labor employees in any month and a total of 15,000 direct labor hours for the entire schedule, will your budget be adequate? Assume 150 work hours in each month.

Solution

The first unit took 1000 hours to produce, and there is an 80 percent learning curve. We can use Table 7.4 to get the data we need for Table 7.6.

The schedule is feasible in terms of maximum direct labor required in any month because it never exceeds 29 employees. However, the total cumulative hours is 16,568, which exceeds the budgeted amount by 1568 hours. Therefore the budget will not be adequate.

TABLE 7.6

Month	Units Scheduled	Cumulative Production	Cumulative Avg. Time[1]	Cumulative Total Hr[2]	Total Hr/month[3]	Employees per Month[4]
1	3	3	834	2,502	2,502	17
2	7	10	632	6,320	3,818	26
3	10	20	524	10,480	4,160	28
4	12	32	459	14,688	4,208	29
5	4	36	443	15,948	1,260	9
6	2	38	436	16,568	620	5

[1]Values from Table 7.4 multiplied by 1000 and rounded to the nearest whole number.
[2]Cumulative production multiplied by cumulative average time per unit.
[3]Difference between successive total cumulative hours. For example, 6,320 − 2,502 = 3,818 for month 2.
[4]Total hours per month divided by 150 and rounded to the next largest integer.

FORMULA REVIEW

1. Required sample size in a time study:

$$n = \left[\left(\frac{1.96}{p} \right) \left(\frac{s}{\bar{t}} \right) \right]^2$$

2. Normal time:

$$NT_i = \bar{t}_i(F_i)(RF_i)$$

3. Normal time for the cycle:

$$NTC = \sum_i NT_i$$

4. Standard time:

$$ST = NTC(1 + A)$$

5. Direct labor required for the nth unit:

$$k_n = k_1 n^b$$

where

$$b = \frac{\log r}{\log 2}$$

6. Learning rate:

$$r = 10^{(b \log 2)}$$

where

$$b = \frac{\log (k_n/k_1)}{\log n}$$

CHAPTER HIGHLIGHTS

● Scientific management is an engineering approach to job design that is concerned with the most economical way to perform the job.

● Managers must decide whether jobs are to be narrowly or broadly defined. Advantages of narrowly defined jobs are short learning time, fast work pace, and low labor costs. Disadvantages are creation of more idle time for some workers, increased materials handling and coordination, and adverse behavioral consequences.

● Job enlargement, job rotation, and job enrichment are three remedies suggested for overcoming the boredom of highly specialized jobs.

● The sociotechnical theory of job design considers both the technical and the social requirements of the job. The focus is on the work group instead of the individual worker.

● Problem-solving teams, special-purpose teams, and self-managing teams are three ways firms are implementing worker-participation or employee involvement programs. Problem-solving teams analyze productivity or quality problems and make suggestions to management. Special-purpose teams address problems of concern involving various functions of the firm. Self-managing teams manage many of their own affairs and involve the concepts of employee empowerment and organizational restructuring.

● Work measurement results are useful for comparing alternative process designs, scheduling, capacity planning, pricing and costing, appraising performance, and developing incentive plans. Work measurement data are used most often for estimating and costing, followed by incentive plan development, scheduling, and performance appraisal.

● The most commonly used method of setting time standards for a job is time study. The job is divided into a series of smaller work elements. A stopwatch is used to time a trained worker using the prescribed work method for a number of cycles. The worker's pace is rated, and allowances are added to arrive at a standard.

● The elemental standard data approach attempts to limit the number of standards that must be derived and used. The time standards for work elements common to a class of jobs can be stored in a database for future use in compiling time standards for jobs having the same elements.

● The predetermined data approach further divides each work element into a series of micromotions. The normal times for these micromotions are stored in a database. Standards can be developed without a stopwatch by adding the micromotion times for work elements.

● Work sampling is used most often to estimate the proportion of time spent on various broader activities associated with the production of goods or services. A large number of random observations are needed to make the estimates.

● In situations when significant learning takes place as production increases, learning curves can be used to prepare bids, decide whether to make or buy a component, estimate financial requirements over the life of a contract, and estimate the amount of direct labor needed to meet a production schedule. If the learning rate is 90 percent, for example, each doubling of production volume reduces the direct labor required per unit by 10 percent.

● Firms using a low-price strategy strive to move down the learning curve to reduce labor hours and costs per unit by increasing volume. This approach makes entry into a market by competitors very costly.

● Labor standards used for incentive pay plans should include recognition for product quality.

● The advent of automated factories will facilitate the process of work measurement because much of the work will be machine paced and monitored by computers. However, allowances will have to be made for worker mental fatigue, and there will be greater need to develop predetermined time systems for knowledge workers.

KEY TERMS

allowance time 263
elemental standard data 265
employee empowerment 254
job design 250
job enlargement 253
job enrichment 253
job rotation 253
labor standard 256
learning curve 272

methods time measurement
  (MTM) 265
normal time (*NT*) 262
normal time for the cycle
  (*NTC*) 262
organizational
  restructuring 255
performance rating factor
  (*RF*) 262

sample coefficient of variation
  (*s/t̄*) 261
scientific management 250
select time (*t̄*) 261
standard 256
standard time (*ST*) 263
time study 259
work measurement 250
work sampling 268

STUDY QUESTIONS

1. What are the arguments for and against narrowly defined jobs?

2. What is the difference between job enlargement and job enrichment? How do they relate to the arguments for and against narrowly defined jobs?

3. What opportunities do workers lack in some work environments? Compare an assembly line worker in a highly automated plant to a secretary in a busy law office. Which opportunities is each likely to have? Which is each worker likely to lack?

4. What is sociotechnical theory? How does it differ from scientific management?

5. An instructor for an introductory class in operations management positions all her students on the 50-yard line of the football field. She declares that anyone who does not reach the goal line in five seconds will fail the course. Discuss this intriguing way of grading a class from the perspective of the definition of a standard.

6. The Italian Maiden Pizza Company produces pizza for resale in the frozen food section of large supermarkets. Recently, product designs for a new deep-dish product were finalized. Which work measurement technique should be used to develop time standards for this product before production actually begins?

7. What role does the sample coefficient of variation play in work measurement studies? If management introduces new work methods or tools at a work station and in so doing reduces the variance of the time per cycle, what will be the impact on work measurement studies of that operation?

8. A colleague of yours comments that a time study with the use of a standard stopwatch is a precise method for determining work standards. What is your reply?

9. Your company builds concrete patio floors to customer specifications. The activities are (1) consulting with the customer to get the specifications, (2) drawing the plans, (3) digging the foundation, (4) building the forms, and (5) laying the concrete. How would you develop a time standard for installing patio floors?

10. Two of your assistants are arguing over the precision required for a work sampling study. The proportion of time spent by a group of your employees manually filling out forms for customer orders turned out to be 0.28 in a recent pilot study. There is a proposal to bring in a network of microcomputers to speed this process. One assistant believes that the estimate should be within ±0.01 of the true proportion, and the other thinks

that a precision of ± 0.05 is sufficient. The pilot study had a sample size of 100. What would you consider in choosing a sample size here?

11. In Chapter 2, Fig. 2.6 depicts the continuum of positioning strategies. Relate what Fig. 2.6 shows to the concepts of learning curves and competitive strategy.

12. Which results in a lower number of direct labor hours per unit: an 80 percent learning curve or a 90 percent learning curve? Explain.

13. A friend of yours firmly believes that if the "factory of the future" is ever realized, there will be no need for work measurement. Comment.

PROBLEMS

Review Problems

1. A worker assembled 10 parts in 50 minutes during a time study. The analyst rated the worker at 95 percent. The allowance for fatigue, personal time, and other contingencies is 20 percent. Calculate:
   a. Normal time for this job.
   b. Standard time for this job.

2. The manager of Swifty Car Lube wants a labor standard for oil changes. Sandy Johnson completed 20 oil changes in a total of 178 minutes. Sandy is considered an above-average worker and was rated at 110 percent. The allowance is 10 percent. Calculate:
   a. Normal time for oil changes.
   b. Standard time for oil changes.

3. You have just received the data in Table 7.7 involving the assembly of hamburgers in a fast-food restaurant. The data are expressed in minutes. Allowances typically constitute 15 percent of the normal time. You have also been told that the schedule calls for 300 hamburgers per day for the foreseeable future. If each part-time employee works 225 minutes per day, how many employees will you need?

4. The information shown in Table 7.8 pertains to a particular operation. The data are expressed in minutes. What is the normal time for this operation?

TABLE 7.7

Work Element	Observation				RF
	1	2	3	4	
1	0.45	0.41	0.50	0.48	1.0
2	0.85	0.81	0.77	0.89	0.9
3	0.31	0.24	0.27	0.26	0.8
4	0.60	0.55	0.59	0.58	1.1

TABLE 7.8

Work Element	Observation												F	RF
	1	2	3	4	5	6	7	8	9	10	11	12		
1	0.20	0.22	0.24	0.18	0.20	0.21	0.22	0.19	0.24	0.18	0.19	0.25	1.0	1.2
2	0.82			0.84			0.73			0.85			0.33	1.1
3	0.40	0.38	0.37	0.41	0.41	0.40	0.36	0.37	0.41	0.42	0.39	0.36	1.0	0.8

TABLE 7.9

| | Cycle Times | | | | | | |
Element	1	2	3	4	5	F	RF
1	0.10	1.67	2.99	4.68	6.04	1.0	0.9
2	0.40		3.30		6.31	0.5	1.1
3	1.30	2.62	4.34	5.70	7.31	1.0	0.8
4	1.55	2.88	4.59	5.94	7.57	1.0	1.2

5. A time analyst observed a job for which work methods had just been changed. The job is divided into four work elements. The element times (in minutes) for the first five cycles, recorded on a continuous basis, are shown in Table 7.9.
   a. Calculate the normal time for this job.
   b. Calculate the standard time for the job, assuming that the allowance is 15 percent.
   c. What sample size is appropriate for estimating the time for element 1 within ± 5 percent of the true mean with 95 percent confidence?

6. A pilot time study has been conducted on a new assembly operation. The data shown in Table 7.10 (in minutes) were obtained. How many additional observations are needed if the estimate of time for element 3 is to be within ± 3 percent of the true mean with 95 percent confidence?

7. Consider the recorded observations of 10 cycles of the cup packaging operation shown in Fig. 7.1.
   a. Suppose that we want a sample size that gives an average time within ± 5 percent of the true average 95 percent of the time. Did we make enough observations? If not, how many more should we make?
   b. Suppose that all we wanted was a precision of ± 10 percent. How many additional observations would we need?

8. The information systems department of Evergreen Life Insurance Company wants to determine the proportion of time that the data entry operator is idle. The following information was gathered randomly using work sampling.

Date	No. Times Clerk Busy	No. Times Clerk Idle	Total No. Observations
8/22	11	2	13
8/23	12	3	15
8/24	11	3	14
8/25	12	4	16
8/26	13	1	14
8/27	13	3	16
8/28	6	6	12

If the department wants a 95 percent confidence level and a degree of precision of ± 0.05, how many more observations are needed?

TABLE 7.10

| | Observation | | | | | | | | | |
Element	1	2	3	4	5	6	7	8	F	RF
1	0.78	0.70	0.75	0.80	0.79	0.82	0.81	0.80	1.0	1.2
2	0.20	0.21	0.16	0.19	0.23	0.25	0.24	0.26	1.0	1.0
3	0.41	0.36	0.45	0.37	0.39	0.40	0.43	0.44	1.0	1.1
4	0.61	0.60	0.55	0.57	0.63	0.61	0.62	0.60	1.0	0.9

9. The manager of the Twin-Fork post office is interested in the amount of time window clerks spend on ancillary services such as selling special-issue stamp sets or commemorative T-shirts and helping customers with passport applications. Three clerks, each earning $25,000 per year, staff the windows. When they are not needed at the window, they are sorting mail for the mail carriers. The results of a preliminary work sampling study are shown in the table below.
   a. Assuming a degree of precision of ± 0.05, is the sample size adequate for special stamp sets? For T-shirts? For passports? What proportion of time do the clerks spend in each activity?
   b. If a stamp machine could be purchased outright for $3500, would you recommend buying it? Discuss.

10. Mass Balance Company is manufacturing a new digital scale for use by a large chemical company. The order is for 40 units. The first scale took 60 hours of direct labor while the third unit took only 45.
   a. What is the rate of learning?
   b. What is the estimated time for the fortieth unit?

11. Cambridge Instruments is an aircraft instrumentation manufacturer. It has received a contract from the Department of Defense to produce 30 radar units for a military fighter. The first unit took 85 hours to produce.

Based on past experience with manufacturing similar units, Cambridge estimates that the learning rate is 93 percent. How long will it take to produce the fifth unit? The tenth? The fifteenth? The final unit?

12. The following production schedule has been developed for a new product.

Week	Units
1	20
2	65
3	100
4	140
5	120

Historically, the learning rate has been 90 percent on such projects. Your budget allows for a maximum of 40 direct labor employees per week and a total of 7000 direct labor hours for the entire schedule. Assume 40 work hours per week. If the first unit took 30 hours to assemble, is this production schedule feasible? If not, how can it be altered? Are there additional costs?

Advanced Problems

Supplement Connections: A computer package is helpful for Problems 13–16. Problem 16 requires prior reading of Supplement 1 (Financial Analysis).

13. You have been asked by management to explain the method of work sampling at its

Number of Occurrences

Day	Selling Postage	Priority Mail	Special Stamp Sets	T-shirt Sales	Passports	Other	Total
1	6	1	1			2	10
2	6	1		1	1	1	10
3	9			1			10
4	6	1	1		1	1	10
5	8			1		1	10
6	7	2	1				10
7	7	1		1	1		10
8	6	1	1			2	10
9	8	1				1	10
10	6	3		1			10

weekly meeting. A consultant has recommended this approach to determine the proportion of unproductive time on one of the production lines, and management wants an "insider" to fill them in on the method. To prepare your presentation you had an assistant observe one of the typists from the typing pool for an entire week, categorizing activities as filing, typing, coffee breaks, or idle. The actual times spent on these activities during that week are shown in Fig. 7.6.

You intend to use this chart to simulate work sampling, rather than sampling in real time. In this way a simple schedule normally requiring a week to execute can be simulated in a few minutes. Later, the estimates from the sample can be compared to the actual amount of time spent on each activity.

a. Use a random number table to select 20 times during the week you will "observe" the typist. Use a random number first to determine the day, and then use another to determine the time of day. Omit the time period 12 to 1 P.M. each day because this is the standard lunch time. Put these 20 times into an observation schedule.

b. Using your observation schedule, determine what the typist is doing, using Fig. 7.6 at these times. Determine the sample

proportion of time spent on each activity.

c. What are the actual proportions of time spent on each activity from Fig. 7.6? How do the estimates compare? Determine the sample size needed to ensure accuracy within ±0.04 with 95 percent confidence. Based on your experiment, what can you tell management about sample sizes and accuracy?

14. The Bovine Products Company recently introduced a new automatic milking system for cows of all shapes and sizes. The company just completed an order for 16 units. The last unit (number 16) required 15 hours of labor, and the learning rate is estimated to be 90 percent on systems such as this. Another customer has just placed an order for the same system. This company, which owns many farms in the Midwest, wants 46 units. How many total labor hours will be needed to satisfy this order?

15. Suppose that you are bidding on a project and need to know how much to charge per unit. Assume that the product has an 80 percent learning rate. The contract calls for 100 units. You estimate that the first unit will cost $3500.

a. What is the total cost of the contract quantity?

FIGURE 7.6

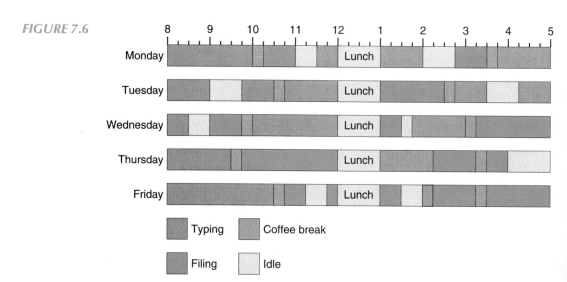

b. At what point during production will the company begin to make a profit on each unit of the contract if you bid $1200 per unit?

16. As manager of an encoding department in a bank, you are concerned about the amount of time your encoder clerks have to spend cleaning their machines because of malfunctions. You were handed a proposal to modify the design of the machines for a price of $70,000. The modification will reduce the amount of time spent cleaning the machines by 75 percent. You employ 25 encoder clerks at an annual salary of $15,000 each. Any time saved from cleaning the machines can be used to process more checks. By reducing costs the bank will be able to raise the interest rate it pays to savings account customers. To help decide whether the proposal is worth considering, you had a pilot work sampling study made, which provided the following results:

Activity	Observations
Processing checks	52
Cleaning machine	15
Waiting for checks	25
Breaks	8
Total	100

a. If the life of the modification is 10 years and the bank's tax rate is 50 percent, what is the simple payback period for the proposal based on your sample estimate? (Use straight-line depreciation.)

b. Construct a 95 percent confidence interval for your estimate. Would you suggest a larger sample size? Why? *Hint:* Base your confidence interval on the normal approximation to the binomial distribution where the standard error is

$$\sigma_P = \sqrt{\frac{P(1 - P)}{n}}$$

SELECTED REFERENCES

Abernathy, William J., and Kenneth Wayne. "Limits of the Learning Curve." *Harvard Business Review* (September–October 1974), pp. 109–119.

Andress, Frank J. "The Learning Curve as a Production Tool." *Harvard Business Review* (January–February 1954), pp. 1–11.

Barnes, Ralph. *Motion and Time Study: Design and Measurement of Work*, 7th ed. New York: John Wiley & Sons, 1980.

Caruth, Donald L. *Work Measurement in Commercial Banks*. Boston: Bankers Publishing, 1971.

Graves, Clare W. "Deterioration of Work Standards." *Harvard Business Review* (September–October 1966), pp. 118–126.

Hackman, J. Richard, Jone L. Pearce, and Jane Camins Wolfe. "Effects of Changes in Job Characteristics on Work Attitudes and Behaviors." *Organizational Behavior and Human Performance*, vol. 21 (1978), pp. 298–304.

Hauck, Warren C. *Motivating People to Work: The Key to Improving Productivity.* Atlanta: Industrial Engineering and Management Press, 1984.

Herzberg, F., B. Mausner, and B. Snyderman. *The Motivation to Work*. New York: John Wiley & Sons, 1959.

Herzberg, F. "One More Time: How Do You Motivate Employees?" *Harvard Business Review* (September–October 1987), pp. 109–120.

Kilbridge, Maurice, and Leon Wester. "An Economic Model for the Division of Labor." *Management Science*, vol. 12, no. 6 (February 1966), pp. B255–B269.

Knights, David, Hugh Willmott, and David Collison, eds. *Job Redesign*. Hants, England: Gower Publishing, 1985.

Moore, Franklin G. *Manufacturing Management*. Homewood, Ill.: Richard D. Irwin, 1969.

Nadler, Gerald. *Work Design*. Homewood, Ill.: Richard D. Irwin, 1970.

Niebel, Richard W. *Motion and Time Study*, 8th ed. Homewood, Ill.: Richard D. Irwin, 1988.

Paul, William J., Keith B. Robertson, and Frederick Herzberg. "Job Enrichment Pays Off." *Harvard Business Review* (March–April 1969), pp. 61–78.

"The Payoff from Teamwork." *Business Week*, July 10, 1989, p. 58.

Pierce, Jon L., and Randall B. Dunham. "Task Design: A Literature Review." *Academy of Management Review* (October 1976), pp. 83–96.

Rice, Robert S. "Survey of Work Measurement and Wage Incentives." *Industrial Engineering*, vol. 9, no. 7 (July 1977), pp. 18–31.

Shell, Richard L. "The Impact of Automation on Work Measurement." *1982 Fall Industrial Engineering Conference Proceedings*, Institute of Industrial Engineers (November 1982), Cincinnati, pp. 348–353.

Sirota, David. "Productivity Management." *Harvard Business Review* (September–October 1966), pp. 111–116.

Steers, Richard M., and Richard T. Mowday. "The Motivational Properties of Tasks." *Academy of Management Review* (October 1977), pp. 645–658.

Trist, Eric L. "The Sociotechnical Perspective." In A.H. Van de Ven and W.F. Joyce, eds., *Perspectives on Organization Design*. New York: John Wiley & Sons, 1981.

"United Parcel Service Gets Deliveries Done by Driving Its Workers." *Wall Street Journal*, April 22, 1986.

Walker, Charles R. "The Problem of the Repetitive Job." *Harvard Business Review*, vol. 28 (May 1950), pp. 54–58.

Yelle, Louis E. "The Learning Curve: Historical Review and Comprehensive Survey." *Decision Sciences*, vol. 10, no. 2 (April 1979), pp. 302–328.

Chapter 8

CAPACITY

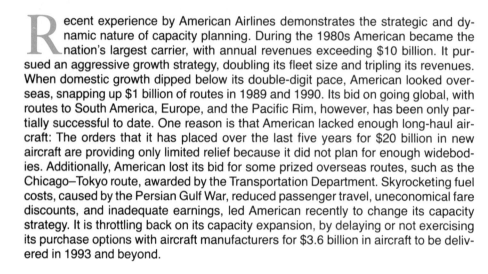

R ecent experience by American Airlines demonstrates the strategic and dynamic nature of capacity planning. During the 1980s American became the nation's largest carrier, with annual revenues exceeding $10 billion. It pursued an aggressive growth strategy, doubling its fleet size and tripling its revenues. When domestic growth dipped below its double-digit pace, American looked overseas, snapping up $1 billion of routes in 1989 and 1990. Its bid on going global, with routes to South America, Europe, and the Pacific Rim, however, has been only partially successful to date. One reason is that American lacked enough long-haul aircraft: The orders that it has placed over the last five years for $20 billion in new aircraft are providing only limited relief because it did not plan for enough widebodies. Additionally, American lost its bid for some prized overseas routes, such as the Chicago–Tokyo route, awarded by the Transportation Department. Skyrocketing fuel costs, caused by the Persian Gulf War, reduced passenger travel, uneconomical fare discounts, and inadequate earnings, led American recently to change its capacity strategy. It is throttling back on its capacity expansion, by delaying or not exercising its purchase options with aircraft manufacturers for $3.6 billion in aircraft to be delivered in 1993 and beyond.

After deciding what products or services should be offered (product planning in Chapter 2) and how they should be made (process design in Chapter 5), managerial attention turns to capacity. **Capacity** is the maximum rate of output for a facility. The facility can be a work station or an entire organization. The operations manager must provide the capacity to meet current and future demand or suffer the consequences of missed opportunities.

Capacity plans are made at two levels. Long-term capacity plans, which we describe in this chapter, deal with investments in new facilities and equipment. These plans look at least two years into the future, but construction lead

*P*art of the American Airlines fleet at its hub in the Dallas/ Fort Worth International Airport. Aggressive expansion in the 1980s gave it the youngest fleet in the industry. It recently switched to a wait-and-see capacity strategy and curbed its equipment purchases until business conditions become more favorable.

times alone can force much longer time horizons. Currently, U.S. investment in *new* plant and equipment is $550 billion annually. Service industries account for more than 64 percent of the total. Such sizable investments require top-management participation and approval because they are not easily reversed. Short-term capacity plans, which we discuss in later chapters, are constrained by long-term plans. Short-term plans focus on work-force size, overtime budgets, inventories, and the like, rather than on capital investment decisions.

CAPACITY PLANNING

Capacity planning is central to the long-term success of an organization. Too much capacity can be as agonizing as too little, as Managerial Practice 8.1 demonstrates. When choosing a capacity strategy, managers have to consider ques-

---

Managerial Practice 8.1

The Agony of Too Much—And Too Little—Capacity

Too Much Capacity

The commercial real estate market in most major U.S. cities is sick, caused in part by the recession in the early 1990s. At the same time many tenants, especially those in the financial industry, are undergoing restructurings expected to cut demand for office space for years to come. The vacancy rate of office space is 26 percent in Miami, Oklahoma City, Phoenix, and Dallas alike; it is 20 percent nationwide. Values have declined as much as 30 percent in some markets, and the capacity glut hurts everyone. For example, the CenTrust Tower in Miami, a 47-tower building built by a failed thrift for $165 million, was recently sold for only $38 million.

To make matters worse, the real estate industry is suffering from a virus becoming known as the "rollover risk." Tenants from well-planned and pricey buildings are being lured to cheaper, empty buildings. With the exception of the credit squeeze, rollover risk may be the single greatest obstacle to the recovery of the real estate market. "There isn't a tenant in Washington who pays the rent who isn't getting two calls a week from brokers asking the tenant to break the lease and move into cheap space elsewhere," says a banking consultant in Washington, D.C. "The entire market is being cannibalized."

Too Little Capacity

In the late 1980s the world's airlines reequipped their fleets and vied to buy a record number of commercial passenger jets. Orders for Boeing, Airbus, and Mc-

Donnell Douglas surged to more than 2600 planes. Douglas alone had a backlog of some $18 billion in firm orders for its MD-80 and new MD-11 wide-body. That's enough to keep its plant fully utilized for more than three years. Despite the number of orders, Douglas' commercial aircraft division announced a startling loss, Airbus had yet to make money, and even the mighty Boeing fought to improve subpar margins.

The large number of orders caused many problems. For one, Douglas' suppliers in the metal forging industry were unable to keep pace with sales. Another problem was with its own work force: In two years Douglas' work force doubled, but training periods were abbreviated and the new hires were much less productive than seasoned employees. Plant managers tried to keep on schedule by pushing planes along the assembly process, even if all the work at one particular station had not been completed. Work was also subcontracted to other plants, including a sister plant that makes combat planes and a leased plant owned by the U.S. Air Force. Because of the capacity shortage, costs skyrocketed and profits plummeted. By the start of the 1990s the capacity pressure was relieved because American had cut back on the hypergrowth strategy that had set the pace for the entire airline industry in the 1980s.

Sources: "Office Buildings, Under Pressure Already, Face Threat to Their Leases," *Wall Street Journal,* September 27, 1991; "Planemakers Have It So Good, It's Bad," *Business Week,* May 8, 1989.

tions such as, Should we have one large facility or several small ones? Should we expand capacity before the demand is there or wait until demand is more certain? A systematic approach is needed to answer these and similar questions and to develop a capacity strategy appropriate for each situation.

Measuring Capacity

Capacity planning requires a knowledge of current capacity and its utilization. A statistic often used to indicate the degree to which equipment, space, or labor is currently being utilized is the **average utilization rate,** calculated as follows:

$$\text{Average utilization rate} = \frac{\text{Average output rate}}{\text{Capacity}}$$

and expressed as a percentage. The average output rate and the capacity must be measured in the same terms, that is, time, customers, units, or even dollars. As you will see later in this chapter, the utilization rate is an indicator of the need for adding extra capacity or eliminating capacity no longer needed. However, to plan for proper utilization rates, management first needs to measure capacity.

Basic Capacity Measures. No single capacity measure is applicable to all types of situations. Table 8.1 lists some commonly used measures of capacity. A reasonable capacity measure might be the number of patients that can be treated per day at a hospital, annual sales dollars generated by a retailer, available seat-miles (ASMs) per month of an airline, or number of machines at a job shop. In general, capacity can be expressed in terms of outputs or inputs.

Output measures are the usual choice of product-focused firms. Nissan Motor Company confidently states its capacity to be 450,000 vehicles per year at its Tennessee plant. Capacity is well understood as an output rate because customization is low. For multiple products, however, the capacity measure must recognize the product mix. For example, a restaurant may be able to handle

TABLE 8.1 / Examples of Capacity Measures

Type of Organization	Measures of Capacity	
	Inputs	Outputs
Truck manufacturer	Machine hours per shift	Number of trucks per shift
Hospital	Number of beds	Number of patients treated per day
Airline	Number of planes	Seat-miles flown per week
Restaurant	Number of seats	Customers served per day
Retailer	Size of display area	Sales dollars per year
Theater	Number of seats	Number of customers per week

100 take-out customers *or* 50 sit-down customers per hour. It might also handle 50 take-out *and* 25 sit-down customers or many other combinations of the two types of customers.

Input measures are the usual choice of process-focused firms. For example, managers of a job shop think of capacity as machine hours or number of machines. Just as product mix can complicate output capacity measures, so also can demand complicate input measures. Demand, which invariably is expressed as an output rate, must be converted to an input measure. Only after making the conversion can a manager compare demand requirements and capacity on an equivalent basis.

Defining Maximum. One last complication lies with the meaning of *maximum*, as it does not have a precise definition. When capacity is measured relative to equipment alone, the appropriate measure is **rated capacity**: It is an engineering assessment of maximum annual output, assuming continuous operation except for an allowance for normal maintenance and repair downtime. However, managers must deal with economic capacity levels that can be sustained. In some organizations, economic capacity implies a one-shift operation; in others it implies a three-shift operation. For this reason, the Census Bureau defines capacity in its surveys as the greatest level of output the firm can *reasonably sustain* using realistic employee work schedules and the equipment currently in place. Of course, a firm can expand capacity temporarily beyond this sustainable level by using extraordinary measures, such as excessive overtime, extra shifts, temporarily reduced maintenance activities, overstaffing, and subcontracting. While helping with temporary peaks, these options cannot be sustained for long. Employees do not want to work excessive overtime for extended periods, and overtime and night shift premiums drive up costs. Thus measures for both *peak* and *sustained* capacity levels are needed.

When operating at peak capacity a firm can make minimal profits or even lose money when sales are at a record high. Such was the case with the aircraft manufacturers mentioned in Managerial Practice 8.1 and at Cummins Engine Company in Columbus, Indiana. In reacting to an unexpected demand surge

A bus, powered by a Cummins engine, drives by Big Ben in London. Cummins Engine recently experienced a quarterly loss of $6.2 million, despite record high sales, because of inadequate production capacity and having to operate at peak capacity.

caused by the weakened dollar, the plant operated three shifts, often seven days a week. Overtime soared and exhausted workers dragged down productivity. So did calling back less skilled workers, laid off during an earlier slump. Cummins reported a quarterly loss of $6.2 million, at the very time when sales stretched capacity.

Economies of Scale

Now that you have an idea of how to measure capacity, let's turn to the issues relating to facility size. Historically, many organizations have subscribed to the concept of **economies of scale.** The concept seems simple: Increasing a facility's size (or scale) decreases the average unit cost. But in reality, it's not at all simple. At some point, a facility becomes so large that **diseconomies of scale** set in. Excessive size can bring complexity, loss of focus, and inefficiencies, which raise the average unit cost. In Fig. 8.1 the 500-bed hospital shows economies of scale because the average unit cost at its "best operating level" is less than that of the 250-bed hospital. However, further expansion to a 750-bed hospital leads to higher average unit costs and diseconomies of scale.

Figure 8.1 also shows a second dimension to the concept. Not only is there an optimal size for a facility but also an optimal operating level for a facility of a given size. Economies (and diseconomies) of scale are represented not just *between* cost curves but also *within* each one. As the output rate approaches a facility's best operating level, economies of scale are realized. Beyond that level, diseconomies set in.

Although finding the best size and operating level is elusive, managers often set policies regarding the maximum size for any one facility. Employee ceilings of 300 are common for industries such as metal working or apparel (Schmenner, 1982). The limits are as large as 6000 employees for industries such as transportation equipment or electronics. The real challenge in setting such limits is predicting how costs will change for different output rates and facility sizes.

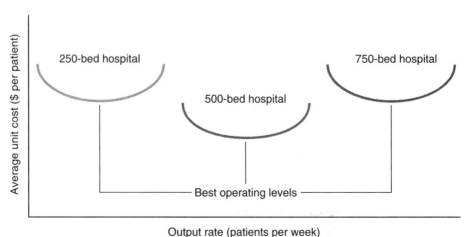

FIGURE 8.1

Economies and Diseconomies of Scale

Sources: "Rival Operations," *Wall Street Journal*, June 6, 1990; "Coke Still Searching for Bottling Formula," *Wall Street Journal*, September 6, 1991.

Managerial Practice 8.2

Economies of Scale at Work

- The two archrival hospitals in Kalamazoo, Michigan, are not getting the full benefit from economies of scale. Borgess Medical Center and Bronson Methodist Hospital each have their own heart programs, maternity wards, state-of-the-art emergency rooms, and radiology services. They even have their own helicopter ambulances. There are only 90 in the whole country and Kalamazoo has two of them. Operating both helicopter units costs a total of $5 million a year, and combining their operations would save at least $1 million, even while keeping both choppers running. Hospital bills in Kalamazoo, a metropolitan area of only 200,000, are the second highest in Michigan and among the highest in the nation. In general, hospital costs in two-hospital towns like Kalamazoo are 30 percent higher than in one-hospital communities, where consolidated volumes allow the hospital to enjoy greater economies of scale.

- Coca-Cola Enterprises, one of Coca-Cola Company's biggest bottlers, has been consolidating many of Coke's smaller, disparate bottlers. The strategy is to cut production costs significantly below the rest of the industry. It bought 34 bottlers for about $3.6 billion and then molded them into a single operation. It cut its work force by 20 percent, to 20,000, and cut costs by merging distribution and raw materials buying. Even more recently, its merger with Johnston Coca-Cola Bottling Group, executives say, will consolidate operations still more and reap the benefits of even bigger, better economies of scale.

This assessment requires careful attention to the different causes of economies of scale for each situation. (See Managerial Practice 8.2.)

Spreading Fixed Costs. In the short term, certain costs do not vary with changes in the output rate. These fixed costs include heating costs, debt service, and management salaries (see Chapter 2). Depreciation of plant and equipment already owned is also a fixed cost in the accounting sense. When the output rate—and therefore the facility's utilization rate—increases, the average unit cost drops because fixed costs are spread over more units. Because increments of capacity are often rather large, a firm initially might have to buy more capacity than it needs. However, a fairly wide range of demand increases in subsequent years can then be absorbed without adding fixed costs.

Construction Costs. A second reason that the 500-bed hospital enjoys greater economies of scale than the 250-bed hospital in Fig. 8.1 is that it costs less to build than twice the cost of the smaller hospital. The 750-bed facility would enjoy similar savings. Its higher average unit costs in Fig. 8.1 can be explained only by diseconomies of scale, which outweigh the savings realized in construction costs. Another example is the construction cost of an oil tanker, which does not increase at the same rate as its capacity. The hauling volume increases at a faster rate than the amount of steel needed to build a vessel.

Process Advantages. High-volume production provides many opportunities for cost reduction. A more efficient process technology may be possible and its capital intensity justified at a higher output rate. The process shifts toward a product-focused strategy, with resources dedicated to individual products. More-specialized equipment replaces general-purpose machinery. The benefits from dedicating resources to individual products or services may include learning curve effects, lower inventory, and a greater ability to improve process and job designs. It can also reduce changeovers and setups. For example, higher volumes allow James River Corporation's paper mill in Louisiana to optimize its mix and run lengths. With strong demand, the plant might have orders for 10,000 tons of a certain grade of paper, compared with 5000 tons in less busy times. The mill can set the machine for one long run and not have to halt it as often to adjust for different grades.

Focused Facilities

Prior to 1970 many firms were willing to endure the managerial headaches that went with size. The nature of competition changed, however, and economies of scale no longer could guarantee an advantage. Quality and flexibility gained importance as rapid technological change shortened life cycles and managers of large facilities found it increasingly difficult to maintain high production volumes. For many companies the time had come to reevaluate the usefulness of large facilities.

The concept of **focused facilities** holds that narrowing the range of demands on a facility will lead to better performance because the operations manager can concentrate on fewer tasks and motivate a work force toward a single goal. First proposed in the early 1970s, this concept persuaded many firms to move away from large facilities trying to do everything (Skinner, 1974). For example, one plant attempting to produce all of its products at one location may give way to several smaller plants, called product plants, each specializing in a certain product or line of products. Or one plant producing all the components and assembling the final product may split into two plants, one producing the components and one assembling the final product. Thus each can focus on its own individual process technology. Even within a large facility, focus can be gained by having *plants within plants* (PWPs). The competitive priorities, technology, and work force are individualized at each PWP. Boundaries may be established by physically separating subunits, even within the same building. The separation can be less tangible, as by revised organizational relationships.

The focused facilities concept has led some firms to tout the virtues of smallness. The General Electric Aircraft Engine Group once concentrated production in two large complexes but now has eight smaller satellite plants. Hewlett-Packard, S. C. Johnson and Sons, and American Telephone and Telegraph, to name but a few, have also gone to smaller facilities and focused operations. There are fewer layers of management, team approaches to problem solving are easier to use, and lines of communication between departments are shorter. The message is clear: Do not let the facility get too large and make sure that it has enough focus.

The concept of focused facilities also applies to service industries. Specialty retailers, such as The Gap and The Limited, opened stores that have smaller, more accessible spaces and chipped away at the large department stores throughout the 1980s. To avoid second-tier status, some department stores are emphasizing their own specialties and focusing on specific customers or products. For example, Federated Department Stores wants to capitalize on its furniture departments, while J.C. Penney is pushing hard to boost its apparel image.

Capacity Strategy

Before we look at a systematic approach to capacity decisions, let's consider three dimensions of capacity strategy: capacity cushions, timing and sizing of expansion, and links.

Capacity Cushions. Average utilization rates should not get too close to 100 percent. When they do, it is usually a signal to increase capacity or lose orders or endure declining productivity. The amount by which the average utilization rate falls below 100 percent is called the **capacity cushion**. Specifically,

$$\text{Capacity cushion} = 100 - \text{Average utilization rate}$$

expressed as a percentage. From 1948 to 1990 U.S. manufacturers maintained an average cushion of 18 percent, with a 9 percent low in 1966 and a 27 percent high in 1982. The average cushion is now 18 percent. The best-sized cushion varies by industry and firm. In the capital-intensive paper industry, where machines can cost hundreds of millions of dollars each, cushions well under 10 percent are preferred. Electrical utilities are also capital intensive but consider cushions of 15 to 20 percent in electric generating capacity to be optimal to avoid brownouts and loss of service to customers. Clearly, managers must carefully weigh the arguments for both large and small cushions.

We begin with arguments for large cushions. For example, a clerk in the human services department of a state government, one that prizes itself on customer service, can handle as many as 50 clients per day. Demand is not evenly paced, however. Some days of the week (such as Mondays) have predictably higher demands than other days, and there can even be an hour-to-hour pattern. Such peaks cannot be smoothed with inventories or long customer wait times. Prompt customer service requires a capacity cushion large enough to handle peak demand, particularly in service industries. Customers grow impatient if they have to wait in a supermarket checkout line for more than a few minutes.

Large cushions are also necessary when future demand is uncertain, particularly when resource flexibility (see Chapter 5) is low. One large bank operated its computer for six months at an average 77 percent load on the central processing unit (CPU) during peak demand. Top management believed that the capacity cushion was more than ample and rejected a proposal to expand capacity. During the next six months, however, the average CPU utilization during peaks surged to 83 percent. Totally unexpected was the dramatic decline in customer service and missed due dates. Because of unexpectedly large, uncontrollable hour-to-hour variations around the demand average, the sizable 17 percent capacity cushion proved to be too small to meet the bank's customer service objectives.

Another type of demand uncertainty is a changing product mix. Though total demand might remain stable, the load can shift unpredictably from one work center to another as the mix changes. Feast-or-famine conditions go along with high customization. An example is a municipal court system, where the capacity (courtroom hours) varies with the nature of the trials and whether a jury is needed. The mix varies from one month to the next. Similarly, uncertainty in the product mix caused American Airlines to estimate incorrectly how much of its capacity to devote to widebodies for international travel.

Other reasons for large capacity cushions lie on the supply (rather than the demand) side. Capacity often comes in large increments, so that expanding even by the minimum amount possible may create a large cushion. Allowances must be made for absenteeism, vacations, holidays, and any other delays not already accounted for by time standards (see Chapter 7). Penalty costs for overtime and subcontracting can create the need for further increases in capacity cushions.

The motivation for small cushions is simple: Unused capacity costs money. For capital-intensive firms, minimizing the capacity cushion is vital. The survey results presented in Table 8.2 show that businesses with high capital investment achieved a disappointing 7 percent return on investment (ROI) when the capacity cushion was high. The ROI increased to a more respectable 17 percent when the capacity cushion was low. This strong correlation does not exist for labor-intensive firms, however: The ROI was about the same, regardless of utilization, because the lower investment in equipment made high utilization less critical. Small cushions also avoid another cost of large cushions, that of hiding inefficiencies. Problems with absenteeism or unreliable suppliers do not surface as customer service problems if they are masked by capacity excesses. Once managers and workers identify such problems, they often can find ways to correct them.

Since the recession of the early 1980s many companies have downscaled their own capacity and cut their capacity cushions. They rely more heavily on subcontractors to handle demand peaks, a strategy to avoid layoffs in times of slow demand. Of course, relying on subcontractors has its downside: Layoffs and job insecurity may be shifted from the company to the subcontractors.

TABLE 8.2 / Return on Investment for Capital-Intensive Businesses

Capacity Cushion	Return on Investment (ROI)*
Low (less than 15%)	17%
Medium (between 15% and 30%)	11
High (above 30%)	7

Source: Derek F. Abell and John S. Hammond, *Strategic Market Planning: Problems and Analytical Approaches* (Englewood Cliffs, N.J.: Prentice-Hall), 1979.

*ROI measured as pretax income divided by average investment.

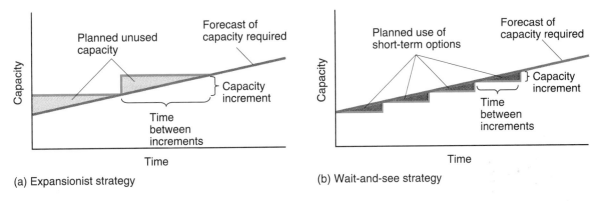

FIGURE 8.2 *Two Capacity Strategies*

Timing and Sizing of Expansion. The second issue of capacity strategy is when to expand and by how much. Figure 8.2 illustrates two extreme strategies: the *expansionist strategy*, which involves large, infrequent jumps in capacity, and the *wait-and-see strategy*, which involves smaller, more frequent jumps. For example, American Airlines followed an expansionist strategy in the 1980s, when it aggressively pursued overseas routes. After several setbacks, including lack of proper equipment and rising fuel costs because of the Persian Gulf War, it adopted a less risky wait-and-see strategy.

The timing and sizing of expansion are related. That is, when the time between increments increases, the size of the increments must also increase. The expansionist strategy stays ahead of demand. Even though this approach creates a large capacity cushion, it minimizes the chance of lost sales due to insufficient capacity. (See Managerial Practice 8.3.) The wait-and-see strategy lags behind demand, relying on short-term options to fill any shortfalls. Short-term options, including authorizing overtime, hiring temporary workers, subcontracting work, allowing stockouts (see Chapter 14), and postponing preventive maintenance, have their drawbacks. For example, overtime means time-and-a-half wages for nonexempt employees, and maybe lower productivity during overtime hours. And union agreements can limit the amount of allowable overtime. Nonetheless, some mix of short-term options might make the wait-and-see strategy best in certain situations.

Several factors favor the expansionist strategy. When economies of scale and learning effects are strong, a firm can reduce its costs and compete on price. This strategy might increase its market share. The expansionist strategy becomes a form of preemptive marketing when a firm makes a large capacity expansion or perhaps just announces that one is imminent. By making it clear that it will do whatever is necessary to compete on cost, the firm is using capacity as a competitive weapon, preempting expansion by others who must sacrifice some of their market share or risk glutting the industry with overcapacity. To be successful, the preempting firm must have credibility that it will carry out its plans and signal them before competition can act.

The Limited's Leslie H. Wexner plans to more than double sales volume, to increase it to $10 billion by the mid-1990s. To help reach that goal, he plans to increase total selling space in The Limited's seven specialty apparel store divisions by opening new outlets and expanding existing ones. Wexner, the founder and owner of The Limited, took on this expansion drive while his company was reeling from the women's apparel slump in 1987 and 1988. At first, he says, he found himself "literally begging" shopping mall developers to try his larger formats at a time when they were particularly loath to devote more space to clothing. But a 50-store test proved that shoppers preferred his large superstores, with their white marble floors, black walls, and expanded lines of women's wear, accessories, and children's and men's clothing. With sales per square foot nearing $400—about twice the average of most department stores—the bigger stores are already as productive as the smaller ones.

As a result of the store expansions and the clustering of stores from The Limited's seven divisions, Wexner became the largest specialty store tenant in hundreds of malls. In a shopping center in Columbus, Ohio, The Limited divisions account for 125,000 square feet, or 25 percent of the total. That kind of space gets such concessions as prime locations, cheaper rents, and even money from developers to help with construction costs. By 1990 The Limited's holdings grew by 27 percent, to 3419 stores; its sales grew by 68 percent, to $5.2 billion. Economists expect apparel sales to grow no faster than 5 percent annually in the next few years—yet The Limited is counting on double-digit gains.

Source: "Is There No Limit to The Limited's Growth?" *Business Week*, November 6, 1989.

The wait-and-see strategy is conservative and minimizes risk. When a firm does expand, it might be to renovate existing facilities rather than build new ones. The more a firm invests in any one facility, the more it depends on that facility's success. The wait-and-see strategy reduces the risks of overly optimistic demand forecasts, technological change that would make the facility obsolete, and unpredictable competitive reactions. The wait-and-see strategy has been criticized as a short-term strategy typical of some U.S. management styles. Some U.S. managers tend to take fewer risks. They are on the fast track of corporate advancement, spending only a few years in each succeeding job. They earn promotions by avoiding the big mistake and maximizing short-term profit and ROI. The wait-and-see strategy fits this style but can erode market share over the long run.

Management may choose one of these two strategies or one of the many between these extremes. The choice could even be a *follow-the-leader strategy* of expanding when others do. If others are right, so are you, and nobody gains a competitive advantage. If they make a mistake and overexpand, so have you, but everyone shares in the agony of overcapacity.

Links. Capacity is closely linked to strategies and operations throughout the organization. When managers make decisions in areas such as location, resource flexibility, and inventory, capacity cushions often must be changed as well. Table 8.3 lists how some of the strategic and operations decisions are linked to capacity cushions, and this section discusses three additional areas that affect capacity decisions.

TABLE 8.3 / *Linking Capacity Cushions with Other Strategic and Operations Decisions*

Decision Area	Change to	Needed Change in Capacity Cushion
Competitive priorities	More emphasis on fast delivery	Larger cushion provides quicker response, even when demand is uneven or uncertain.
Quality management	Smaller yield losses	Smaller cushion is needed, as there will be fewer unpredictable output losses.
Capital intensity	More capital-intensive process design	Smaller cushion increases equipment utilization and achieves acceptable ROI.
Resource flexibility	Less worker flexibility	Larger cushion helps reduce the operation overloads that are more likely to occur with a less flexible work force.
Inventory	Less reliance on inventory to smooth production rate	Larger cushion helps meet increased production during peak periods.
Scheduling	More stable environment	Smaller cushion is needed, as production can be scheduled with more assurance.

First, capacity and a firm's competitive priorities are linked. As an example, consider the subsidiary of a large goods manufacturer that sold 85 percent of its output to other divisions in the company, with the remaining 15 percent going to outside customers. The capacity of one of its processes was being squeezed. One option was to expand, enabling the subsidiary to attract more outside customers. However, this approach would shift competitive priorities: Rather than being a low-cost supplier to the other divisions, the subsidiary would have to place higher priority on customization and quality. Management decided against the expansion because of poor coupling with other policies.

A survey gives us a second example of how managers link capacity with other decisions. Managers were asked which of eight broad categories of processes (such as packaging, changing shapes of metals, and assembling) were performed in their plants. As Fig. 8.3 shows, managers opt for a less focused facility (more processes in the same facility) when a more customized product is being produced.

Capacity and location decisions are also closely linked. A firm that is expanding eventually must add new facilities and find good locations for them. Conversely, a multisite firm that is "restructuring" often must identify which locations to eliminate. General Motors, in cutting back its capacity to stop large losses in its North American automobile operation, had to shut down several

Source: Deven Shama,
"Manufacturing
Strategy: An Empirical
Analysis," Unpublished
dissertation, Ohio State
University, 1987.

FIGURE 8.3

Customization Links
with Facility Focus

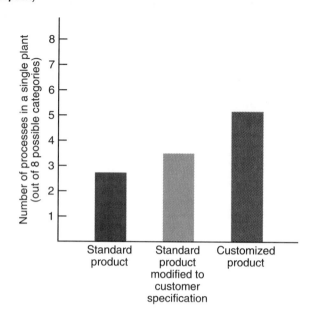

factories. GM faced tough choices between closing older factories with cooperative and productive work forces and abandoning expensive, modern plants where labor relations are poor. The UAW contract also made closing a facility quite costly, so some plants remained open which otherwise should have been closed.

A SYSTEMATIC APPROACH TO CAPACITY DECISIONS

Although each situation is somewhat different, a four-step procedure can, in general, help managers make sound capacity decisions:

1. Estimate future capacity requirements.
2. Identify gaps by comparing requirements with available capacity.
3. Develop alternative plans for filling the gaps.
4. Evaluate each alternative, both quantitatively and qualitatively, and make a final choice.

Step 1: Estimate Capacity Requirements

The beginning point is a demand forecast. Because long-term decisions are involved, forecasts of demand, productivity, competition, and technological changes must extend well into the future. Unfortunately, forecast errors enlarge as forecast time horizons grow. (See Chapter 11 for a more detailed discussion of quantitative and qualitative forecasting methods.)

As we have mentioned, the demand forecast has to be converted to a number that can be compared directly with the capacity measure being used. Suppose that capacity is expressed as the number of available machines at a machining operation. With this particular measure, the analyst must convert the demand rate to the number of machines required. The number of machine hours required per year is found by summing the processing times and setup times required to produce all products (or services) to accommodate production:

$$R = \sum_{i=1}^{P} D_i p_i + \sum_{i=1}^{P} \frac{D_i}{Q_i} s_i$$

where

R = total machine hours required per year

D_i = number of units of product or service i forecasted per year

p_i = processing time per unit of product or service i

Q_i = number of units in each lot (or batch) of product or service i

s_i = standard setup time per lot

P = number of products made or services produced at the operation

The next step is to calculate the number of hours that one machine can provide. This calculation begins with the total number of hours during which the facility is open, found by multiplying the number of work hours per day by the number of workdays per year. This total is then deflated to a more realistic number by multiplying a proportion that allows for the desired utilization rate. The proportion is simply 1.0 minus the desired capacity cushion (translated from a percent to a proportion by dividing by 100). The calculation is

$$H = N\left(1 - \frac{C}{100}\right)$$

where

H = hours provided per year by one machine, allowing for capacity cushion

N = number of hours operated on all shifts and all workdays in a year

C = capacity cushion (as a percent)

Knowing the total hours required (R) and the amount provided per machine (H), the analyst obtains the number of machines required from the ratio

$$M = \frac{R}{H}$$

Always round up, unless short-term options such as overtime or stockouts are used to cover any shortfalls.

This conversion process isn't limited to machines. The input unit could just as easily be seats in a theater, teller stations in a bank, or any other capacity measure.

Application 8.1	Estimating Requirements

A copy center in an office building prepares bound reports for two clients. The center makes multiple copies (the lot size) of each report. The processing time to run, collate, and bind each copy depends, among other factors, on the number of pages. The following table gives the necessary information for each client. The center operates 250 days per year, with one 8-hour shift. Management believes that a capacity cushion of 15 percent (beyond the allowance built into time standards) is best. How many machines are needed at the copy center?

Item	Client X	Client Y
Annual demand forecast (reports)	50	100
Lot size (copies per report)	40	60
Annual demand forecast (copies)	2000	6000
Standard processing time (hr/copy)	0.5	0.7
Standard setup time (hr/report)	5	8

Solution Summing machine hour requirements for both clients, we get

$$R = \left[2000(0.5) + \left(\frac{2000}{40} \right)(5) \right] + \left[6000(0.7) + \left(\frac{6000}{60} \right)(8) \right]$$

$$= 6250 \text{ hours}$$

The remaining calculations are

$$H = [(250 \text{ days/year})(1 \text{ shift/day})(8 \text{ hours/shift})]\left(1.0 - \frac{15}{100} \right) = 1700 \text{ hours}$$

$$M = \frac{6250}{1700} = 3.68 \quad \text{or} \quad 4 \text{ machines}$$

Rounding up to the next integer, four machines are needed.

Step 2: Identify Gaps

Any positive difference, or shortfall, between projected demand and current capacity is a capacity gap. The correct capacity must be used, however, and complications arise when multiple operations and several resource inputs are involved. For example, when studying market-share statistics in the early 1970s, many executives concluded that airlines having the larger share of seats flown attract a larger share of the total passengers. In other words, fly more seats to get more passengers. Many airlines responded by buying more jumbo jets. It soon became evident that competitors flying smaller planes enjoyed more success, the key factor being the number of departures rather than the number of seats. Thus several airlines had to adjust the capacity imbalance between small and large planes by selling or mothballing jumbo jets. Capacity balance also applies to manufacturing. Expanding the capacity of some operations in a plant may increase overall capacity very little if other bottleneck operations are not also expanded.

Identifying Capacity Gaps

Grandmother's Chicken Restaurant is known throughout Middlesburg for its unique chicken recipe and homey atmosphere. Business is booming. Kathryn Shoemaker, the owner, expects total sales for this year (1993) to be $800,000, straining the kitchen's capacity to its limit. Although the kitchen is operating at 100 percent capacity, the dining room can handle a sales volume of up to $1,050,000. Demand is expected to increase $100,000 per year for the next five years. Using annual dollar sales as the capacity measure, what are the capacity gaps through 1998?

Solution The accompanying table shows the results. For example, demand in 1996 should reach $1,100,000. As the kitchen's capacity is $800,000, there is a $300,000 capacity gap ($1,100,000 − $800,000). The dining room's 1996 gap is only $50,000 because its current capacity is $1,050,000. For the restaurant as a whole in 1996, the gap is $300,000 because the kitchen is the limiting resource.

Capacity Gaps at Grandmother's Chicken Restaurant

Projections	Annual Estimates ($000)				
	1994	1995	1996	1997	1998
Demand	900	1000	1100	1200	1300
Capacity gaps					
Kitchen (current capacity, $800,000)	100	200	300	400	500
Dining (current capacity, $1,050,000)	—	—	50	150	250

Step 3: Develop Alternatives

The next step is to develop alternative plans to cope with projected gaps. One alternative, called the **base case,** is to do nothing and simply lose orders from any demand that exceeds current capacity. Other alternatives are various timing/sizing options for adding new capacity, including the expansionist and wait-and-see strategies illustrated in Fig. 8.2. Additional possibilities include expanding at a different location or using short-term options such as overtime, temporary workers, and subcontracting.

Step 4: Evaluate the Alternatives

In this final step, the manager evaluates each alternative, both quantitatively and qualitatively. Quantitatively, the manager estimates the change in cash flows over the forecast time horizon, compared to the base case. **Cash flow** is the difference between the flow of funds into (inflow) and out of (outflow) an organization over a period of time, including revenues, costs, and changes in assets and liabilities. The manager is concerned here only with calculating the cash flows really attributable to the project. Because these cash flows extend over several years, the net present value technique should be used to reflect the time value of money. (See Supplement 1.)

Qualitatively, the manager has to look at how each alternative fits the overall capacity strategy and other aspects of the business not well expressed by financial analysis. Of particular concern might be uncertainties about demand, competitive reaction, technological change, and cost estimates. Some of these factors cannot be quantified and have to be assessed on the basis of judgment and experience. Others can be quantified, and the manager can analyze each alternative, using different assumptions about the future. One set of assumptions could represent a worst case, where demand is less, competition is greater, and construction costs are higher than expected. Another set of assumptions could represent the most optimistic view of the future. This type of "what-if" analysis gives the manager an idea of each alternative's implications before making a final choice.

Application 8.3   *Evaluating the Alternatives*

One alternative for Grandmother's Chicken Restaurant is to expand both the kitchen and dining room now, bringing their capacities up to $1,300,000 of sales per year. The initial investment required would be $200,000, made at the end of 1993. Kathryn estimates that her before-tax profit is 20 percent. She arrived at that figure by determining that, for each $100 of sales, $60 is required to cover variable costs and $20 to cover fixed costs (other than depreciation).

What are the before-tax cash flows from this project for the next five years, compared to those of the base case of doing nothing?

Solution   The following table shows the incremental cash inflows and outflows through 1998. The inflows are the profits from added sales made possible by expansion. For example, compared to the base case of losing all sales over $800,000, the expansion adds $300,000 in sales in 1996. To convert added sales into cash inflows, simply multiply added sales by the profit margin (20 percent). The only cash outflow through 1998 is the $200,000 initial investment.

Before-Tax Cash Flows for Expanding to $1,300,000 Capacity

| Projections | 1993 | Annual Estimates ($000) | | | | |
		1994	1995	1996	1997	1998
Added sales	—	100	200	300	400	500
Cash inflow	—	20	40	60	80	100
Cash outflow	−200	—	—	—	—	—
Combined cash flow	−200	20	40	60	80	100

Because we are evaluating an alternative that provides enough capacity to meet all demand through 1998, the added sales are identical to the capacity gaps in Application 8.2. That wouldn't be true if the new capacity were smaller than expected demand in any year. To find the added sales in that case, we subtract the base-case capacity from the new capacity (rather than the demand). The result is smaller than the capacity gap.

TOOLS FOR CAPACITY PLANNING

Long-term capacity planning requires demand forecasts for an extended period of time. Unfortunately, forecast accuracy decreases as the forecasting horizon lengthens. In addition, anticipating what competitors will do increases the uncertainty of demand forecasts. Finally, demand for any one period (say a year) is not evenly distributed within the year: There can be peaks and valleys of demand within the time period. These realities necessitate the use of capacity cushions. In this section we introduce two decision tools that more formally deal with the uncertainty and variability in demand: queuing models and decision trees. Queuing models account for the random, independent behavior of many customers, both in terms of their time of arrival and their processing needs. Decision trees account for major events such as competitor actions.

Queuing Models

Queuing models often are useful in capacity planning. Waiting lines tend to develop in front of a work center, such as an airport ticket counter, a machine center, or a central computer, because the time between jobs or customers varies according to a probability distribution and the processing time varies from one customer to the next. Queuing models provide estimates of average customer delay time, average length of waiting lines, and utilization of the work center. Managers can use this information to choose the best cost-effective capacity to balance customer service and the cost of adding that capacity.

Supplement 4 provides a fuller treatment of queuing models. It provides formulas for estimating important characteristics of a waiting line, such as the average customer wait time or the average facility utilization, for different kinds of production systems. For example, a facility might be designed to have one or multiple lines at each operation and to route customers through one or

A successful queuing model, such as for the airline terminal counter shown here, can eliminate bottlenecks not only at its own station but at subsequent service areas, such as the adjacent boarding gate on the right.

multiple operations. Given the estimating capability of these formulas, and cost estimates for waiting and idle time, managers can select cost-effective designs and capacity levels that also provide the desired level of customer service. More complex queuing problems must be analyzed with simulation (see Supplement 5).

Decision Trees

A decision tree is a general approach to a wide range of decisions in operations management, such as product planning, process design, technological choices, and location. It is particularly valuable for evaluating different capacity expansion alternatives when demand is uncertain and sequential decisions are involved. For example, the owner of Grandmother's Chicken Restaurant (see Application 8.3) may expand the restaurant in 1993 only to discover in 1996 that demand is much higher than forecasted. In that case, she may need to make a second decision on whether to expand once again or possibly build a second restaurant.

A **decision tree** is a schematic model of alternatives available, and their possible consequences, to the decision maker. The name derives from the treelike appearance of the model (see Fig. 8.4). It consists of a number of *nodes* with emanating *branches* and should be read from left to right. Square nodes represent decision points, and branches leaving them, the alternatives. Branches leaving circular nodes represent *chance events*, sometimes called "states of nature," not under the manager's control. The probability of each chance event, $P(E_i)$, is shown above each branch. The sum of the probabilities for all branches leaving a chance node must sum to 1.0. The conditional payoffs are shown at the end of each possible alternative–event combination. Payoffs are given only at the outset, before the analysis begins, for the end points of each alternative–event combination. In Fig. 8.4, for example, payoff 1 is the financial outcome the manager expects if alternative 1 is chosen and then chance event 1 occurs. No payoff can be associated yet with any branches further to the left, such as alternative 1 as a whole, because it is followed by a chance event and is not an end point. Payoffs are expressed as the present value (see Supplement 1) of net profits. If revenues are not affected by the decision, the payoff is expressed as net costs.

After drawing a decision tree, solve it by working from right to left. Calculate the *expected payoff* for each node as follows:

1. For an event node, multiply the payoff of each event branch by the event's probability. Sum these products to get the event node's expected payoff.
2. For a decision node, pick the alternative that has the best expected payoff. If an alternative leads to an event node, its payoff is equal to that node's expected payoff (already calculated). "Saw off," or "prune," the other branches not chosen, marking two short lines through them. The decision node's expected payoff is the one associated with the single remaining unpruned branch.

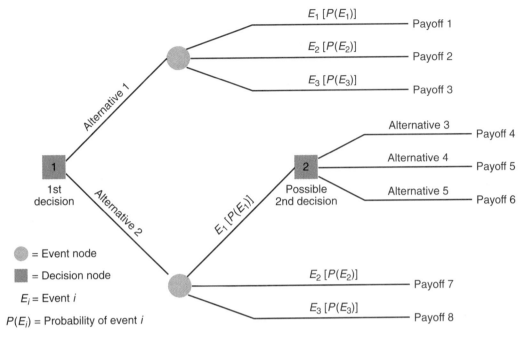

- = Event node
- = Decision node
- E_i = Event i
- $P(E_i)$ = Probability of event i

FIGURE 8.4 A Decision Tree Model

This process continues until the leftmost decision node is reached. The unpruned branch emanating from it is the best alternative to pursue. If multistage decisions are involved, the manager must await subsequent events before deciding what to do next. If new probability or payoff estimates are obtained, the manager should reapply the process.

Application 8.4 | *Analyzing a Decision Tree*

A retailer must decide whether to build a small or a large facility at a new location. Demand at the location can be either small or large, with probabilities estimated to be 0.4 and 0.6, respectively. If a small facility is built and demand proves to be large, the manager may choose to maintain the current size or to expand. The payoff (present value of net profits) is $223,000 for the first alternative–event combination (not expanding) and $270,000 for the second (expanding). If a small facility is built and demand is small, there is no reason to expand and the payoff is $200,000. If a large facility is built and demand proves to be small, the choice is to do nothing ($40,000) or to stimulate demand through local advertising. The response to advertising can be either modest or sizable, with their probabilities estimated to be 0.3 and 0.7, respectively. If it is modest, the payoff is estimated to be only $20,000; the payoff grows to $220,000 if the response is sizable. Finally, the best possible alternative–event combination is the scenario where a large facility is built and demand turns out to be large. There is no reason for expansion, and the payoff is $800,000.

Draw a decision tree. Then analyze it to determine the expected payoff for each decision and event node. Which alternative—building a small facility or building a large facility—has the highest expected payoff?

Solution   The decision tree in Fig. 8.5 shows the event probabilities and the payoff (present value of net profits in $000) for each of the seven alternative–event combinations. Ignore for now the expected payoffs shown in red beneath the event and decision nodes; we will calculate them once the analysis begins in the next step. The first decision node in the decision tree is whether to build a small or a large facility. It is shown first, to the left, because it is the decision the retailer must make now. The second decision node, whether to expand at a later date, is reached only if a small facility is built and demand turns out to be large. Finally the third decision point, whether to advertise, is reached only if the retailer builds a large facility and demand turns out to be small.

Now we can begin the analysis of the decision tree, calculating the expected payoffs from right to left. As they are calculated they are posted to Fig. 8.5 in red beneath the appropriate event and decision nodes.

1. For the event node dealing with advertising, the expected payoff is 160, or the sum of each event's payoff weighted by its probability [0.3(20) + 0.7(220)].

2. The expected payoff for decision node 3 is 160 because *Advertise* (160) is better than *Do nothing* (40). Prune the *Do nothing* alternative by putting a double slash through it.

3. The payoff for decision node 2 is 270 because *Expand* (270) is better than *Don't expand* (223). Prune *Don't expand*.

4. The expected payoff for the event node dealing with demand, assuming a small facility is built, is 242 [0.4(200) + 0.6(270)].

5. The expected payoff for the event node dealing with demand, assuming a large facility is built, is 544 [0.4(160) + 0.6(800)].

6. The expected payoff for decision node 1 is 544 because the large facility's expected payoff is largest. Prune the small facility alternative.

The best alternative is to build the large facility.

SOLVED PROBLEMS

1. You have been asked to put together a capacity plan for a critical bottleneck operation at the Surefoot Sandal Company. Your capacity measure is number of machines. Three products (men's, women's, and children's sandals) are manufactured. The time standards (processing and setup), lot sizes, and demand forecasts are given in Table 8.4. The firm operates two 8-hour shifts, 5 days per week, for 50 weeks per year. Experience shows that a capacity cushion of 5 percent will suffice.

   a. How many machines are needed?

   b. If the operation currently has two machines, what is the capacity gap?

Solution   a. Summing up the machine hour requirements for all three products, we have:

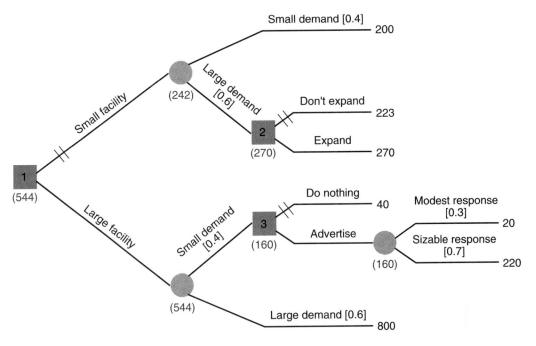

FIGURE 8.5 Decision Tree for Retailer

$$R = [80,000(0.05) + (80,000/240)(0.5)] + [60,000(0.10)$$
$$+ (60,000/180)(2.2)] + [120,000(0.02) + (120,000/360)(3.8)]$$
$$= 14,567$$

The number of hours provided per machine is

$$H = (2 \text{ shifts/day} \times 8 \text{ hours/shift} \times 250 \text{ days/year})\left(1.0 - \frac{5}{100}\right)$$
$$= 3800$$

The capacity requirement is 3.8 machines, which rounds up to 4 machines:

$$M = \frac{14567}{3800} = 3.8 \quad \text{or} \quad 4 \text{ machines}$$

TABLE 8.4

| Product | Time Standards | | | |
	Processing (hr/pair)	Setup (hr/lot)	Lot Size (pairs/lot)	Demand Forecast (000 pairs/yr)
Men's	0.05	0.5	240	80
Women's	0.10	2.2	180	60
Children's	0.02	3.8	360	120

b. The capacity gap is 1.8 machines (3.8 − 2). Two more machines should be purchased, unless management decides on short-term options to fill the gap.

2. Another capacity alternative for Grandmother's Chicken Restaurant (see Application 8.3) is a two-stage expansion. This alternative expands only the kitchen now, bringing its capacity up to that of the dining area ($1,050,000 in sales per year). If sales in 1994 and 1995 live up to expectations, both the kitchen and the dining room will be expanded at the *end* of 1996 up to the $1,300,000 sales level. The initial investment would be $80,000 at the end of 1993 and an additional investment of $170,000 at the end of 1996. What are the before-tax cash flows for this alternative through 1998, compared with the base case of no expansion?

Solution Table 8.5 shows the cash inflows and outflows. The 1996 cash flow is unusual in two respects. First, the added sales is only $250,000 ($1,050,000 − $800,000) instead of $300,000 ($1,100,000 − $800,000) because the restaurant's capacity falls somewhat short of demand. Second, an outflow occurs at the end of 1996, when the second-stage expansion occurs.

3. White Valley Ski Resort is planning the ski lift operation for its new ski resort. Management is trying to determine whether one or two lifts will be necessary; one lift can accommodate 250 people per day. Skiing normally occurs in the 14-week period from December to April, during which the lift will operate seven days per week. The first lift will operate at 90 percent capacity if economic conditions are bad, which is believed to be about 0.3 likely. During normal times the first lift will be utilized at 100 percent capacity, and the excess crowd will provide 50 percent utilization of the second lift. The probability of normal times is 0.5. Finally, if times are really good, a probability of 0.2, the utilization of the second lift will increase to 90 percent. The equivalent annual cost of installing a new lift, recognizing the time value of money and its economic life (see *annuities* in Supplement 1), is $50,000. The annual cost of installing two lifts is only $90,000 if both are purchased at the same time. If used at all, each lift costs $200,000 to operate, no matter how low or high its utilization rate. Lift tickets cost $20 per customer per day. Should the resort purchase one lift or two?

TABLE 8.5

	Annual Estimate ($000)					
Projection	1993	1994	1995	1996	1997	1998
Added sales	—	100	200	250	400	500
Cash inflow	—	20	40	50	80	100
Cash outflow	− 80	—	—	− 170	—	—
Combined cash flow	− 80	20	40	− 120	80	100

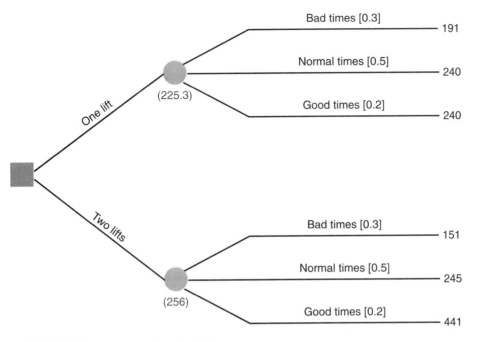

FIGURE 8.6   Decision Tree for Ski Resort

Solution   The decision tree is shown in Fig. 8.6. The payoffs (in $000) for each alter-
native–event branch are calculated below, where the total revenues from
one lift operating at 100 percent capacity are $490,000 (250 customers/day
× 98 days × $20/customer).

Alternative	Economic Condition	Payoff Calculation (Revenue − Cost)
One lift	Bad times	0.9(490) − (50 + 200) = 191
	Normal times	1.0(490) − (50 + 200) = 240
	Good times	1.0(490) − (50 + 200) = 240
Two lifts	Bad times	0.9(490) − (90 + 200) = 151
	Normal times	1.5(490) − (90 + 400) = 245
	Good times	1.9(490) − (90 + 400) = 441

Calculate the expected profits from right to left:

1. For the event node on economic conditions, when one ski lift is installed
   the expected payoff is $225.3 [0.3(191) + 0.5(240) + 0.2(240)].
2. For the event node on economic conditions, when two ski lifts are installed the expected payoff is $256 [0.3(151) + 0.5(245) + 0.2(441)].
3. The expected payoff for the decision node is $256,000 because the two-
   lift alternative has the largest expected payoff. Prune the one-lift alternative.

The best alternative is to build two lifts.

FORMULA REVIEW

Capacity requirements:

$$R = \sum_{i=1}^{P} D_i p_i + \sum_{i=1}^{P} \frac{D_i}{Q_i} s_i$$

$$H = N\left(1 - \frac{C}{100}\right)$$

$$M = \frac{R}{H}$$

CHAPTER HIGHLIGHTS

- Operations managers must plan for timely acquisition of additional capacity.

- Long-term capacity planning involves investment in new facilities and equipment and is crucial to an organization's long-term success.

- Capacity can be stated in terms of either input or output measures. Complications in measuring capacity arise from changes in product mix and differentiation of peak and sustained capacity levels.

- Economies of scale derive from spreading fixed costs, reduced construction costs, and process advantages. Diseconomies of scale have forced many firms to focus their operations and move to smaller, rather than larger, facilities.

- Capacity cushions can be small or large, depending on the cost of unused capacity, required delivery times, supply uncertainties, and uneven or uncertain demand.

- Three capacity strategies are expansionist, wait-and-see, and follow-the-leader. The expansionist strategy is attractive when there are economies of scale, learning effects, and a chance for preemptive marketing. The wait-and-see strategy minimizes risk by relying more on short-term options. The follow-the-leader strategy maintains the current balance between competitors.

- Capacity choices must be linked to other operations management choices, ranging from competitive priorities to scheduling.

- The four steps in capacity planning are (1) estimate capacity requirements, (2) identify gaps, (3) develop alternatives, and (4) evaluate the alternatives.

- Queuing models and decision trees are particularly helpful for capacity decisions, but they also can be applied to a wide range of operations management problems.

- Queuing models help the manager choose the capacity level that best balances customer service and the cost of adding more capacity.

- Decision trees are schematic models that can represent chance events and sequential decision points over time. They are solved by calculating expected payoffs for nodes from right to left. The unpruned alternative that emanates from the first decision point is the best alternative, based on expected payoffs.

KEY TERMS

STUDY QUESTIONS

1. What factors make capacity planning a particular challenge?

2. What are the different ways of responding to capacity gaps?

3. What capacity measure would you recommend for a drive-in window at a bank? For an entire toy manufacturing plant? What complications might you run into when using these measures?

4. What types of estimates and forecasts are needed for capacity planning?

5. A young boy has set up a lemonade stand on the corner of Speedway and Park. Temperatures climb to 110° during the summer. The intersection is near a major university and a large construction site. Explain to this young entrepreneur how his business might benefit from economies of scale.

6. Explain to the young entrepreneur in Question 5 the sorts of conditions that might lead to diseconomies of scale.

7. You are the manager of a small messenger service. Currently your average messenger utilization rate is 96 percent. Adding another messenger would reduce your average utilization rate to 85 percent. What factors would you consider in making a decision about this capacity increase?

8. Application 8.3 describes a one-stage expansion for Grandmother's Chicken Restaurant, whereas Solved Problem 2 describes a two-stage expansion. Which alternative resembles the expansionist strategy? The wait-and-see strategy? Qualitatively, what factors favor the wait-and-see strategy?

PROBLEMS

Review Problems

1. An automobile brake supplier makes three components of a brake. Table 8.6 shows the time standards, lot sizes, and demand forecasts for the components. Because of demand uncertainties, the operations manager obtained three demand forecasts (pessimistic, expected, and optimistic). The brake supplier operates on two 8-hour shifts, 5 days per week, for 52 weeks per year. The manager believes that a 20-percent capacity cushion is best.

   a. What is the minimum number of machines needed? The expected number? The maximum number?

   b. If the operation currently has three machines and the manager is willing to expand capacity by 20 percent through short-term options, what is the capacity gap?

2. Up, Up and Away is a producer of kites and windsocks. Relevant data on a bottleneck

TABLE 8.6

	Time Standards		Lot Size (units/ lot)	Demand Forecast (000 units/yr)		
Component	Processing (hr/unit)	Setup (hr/lot)		Pessimistic	Expected	Optimistic
A	0.05	1.0	60	15	18	25
B	0.20	4.5	80	10	13	17
C	0.05	8.2	120	17	25	40

operation in the shop for the upcoming fiscal year are given in the following table.

Item	Kites	Windsocks
Demand forecast (units/yr)	30,000	12,000
Lot size (units)	20	70
Standard processing time (hr/unit)	0.30	1.0
Standard setup time (hr/lot)	3	4

The shop works two shifts per day, 8 hours per shift, 200 days per year. There currently are four machines, and a 25-percent capacity cushion is desired. How many machines should be purchased to meet the upcoming year's demand, without resorting to any short-term capacity solutions?

3. Trak, Inc., is a manufacturer of high-quality bicycles. One production facility manufactures ten-speed touring bikes and the increasingly popular mountain bikes. The projected demand for the upcoming year follows.

Item	Touring	Mountain
Demand forecast (units/year)	10,000	8,000
Lot size (units)	100	100
Standard processing time (hr/unit)	1/2	2/3
Standard setup time (hr/lot)	1	1

The shop currently works 8 hours a day, 5 days a week, for 50 weeks a year. Trak currently has five work stations, each producing one bicycle in the time given in the table. The shop now maintains a 20 percent capacity cushion. How many work stations will Trak require next year to meet the expected demand without using overtime and without decreasing its current capacity cushion?

4. The lock box department at Bank 21 handles the processing of monthly loan payments to the bank, monthly and quarterly premium payments to a local insurance company, and bill payments for 85 of the bank's largest commercial customers. The payments are processed by machine operators, with one operator per machine. An operator can process one payment in 0.25 minute; setup times are negligible in this situation. The operation requires a capacity cushion of 20 percent. The average monthly (not annual) volume of payments processed through the department currently is 400,000 but is expected to increase by 20 percent. The department operates 8 hours per shift, two shifts per year, 260 days per year. How many machines (not operators) are needed to satisfy the new total processing volume? (Round up to the next whole integer.)

5. Worchester Athletic Club is considering expanding its facility to include two adjacent suites. This expansion would increase its current yearly sales from $500,000 to $550,000. Its before-tax profit is 20 percent of sales. Based on the following demand forecasts, what before-tax cash inflows will the expansion produce for the next several years?

Year	Annual Demand ($000)	Year	Annual Demand ($000)
1993	450	1997	530
1994	480	1998	550
1995	510	1999	600
1996	515		

6. Karen Herron is considering expanding the capacity of her retail clothing store from $20,000 in sales per quarter to $30,000 per quarter. The before-tax profit from additional sales is 20 percent. Sales are seasonal, with peaks in the spring and summer quarters. Demand forecasts expressed in sales per quarter follow.

Year	Quarter	Sales per Quarter ($000)
1994	1	10
	2	15
	3	22
	4	17

Year	Quarter	Sales per Quarter ($000)
1995	1	27
	2	31
	3	34
	4	19

Demand in 1996 and beyond is expected to exceed $30,000 per quarter. If Karen expands toward the end of 1993, the slowest part of the year, how much will her quarterly before-tax cash flow increase through 1995? Beyond 1995?

7. Magic World, an amusement park, has the opportunity to expand its size now, the end of 1993, by purchasing adjacent property for $150,000 and adding attractions at a cost of $350,000. This expansion is expected to increase attendance by 20 percent a year. Additional operating costs are expected to be $100,000. Estimated gross receipts for the next five years, *without expansion*, follow.

Year	Gross Receipts ($000)
1994	1000
1995	1100
1996	1175
1997	1250
1998	1350

a. What are the before-tax combined cash flows for 1993 through 1998 that are attributable to the park's expansion?

b. Ignoring tax and the time value of money, how long will it take to recover the investment?

8. Jeffrey Ringuest owns a drugstore that is experiencing significant growth. He is trying to decide whether to expand its capacity, which currently is at $200,000 in sales per quarter. Sales are seasonal. Forecasts of capacity requirements, expressed in sales per quarter, for next year follow.

Quarter	($000)
1	240
2	180
3	220
4	260

Ringuest is considering expanding capacity to $250,000 in sales per quarter. The before-tax profit from additional sales is 15 percent. How much would before-tax profit increase next year because of this expansion?

9. Roche Brothers is considering a capacity expansion of its supermarket. The annual sales projected through 1998 follow. The current capacity is equivalent to $300,000 in sales. Assume a 20 percent pretax profit on sales.

Year	Annual Sales ($000)
1994	310
1995	320
1996	340
1997	370
1998	400

a. If Roche expands capacity to $360,000 sales now (1993), how much will pretax profits increase for each of the next five years?

b. If Roche expands the capacity to an equivalent of $360,000 sales now and then expands the capacity to an equivalent of $400,000 sales at the beginning of 1997, how much would pretax profit increase in total for all years (1994–1998)?

10. Analyze the decision tree in Fig. 8.7. What is the expected payoff for the best alternative?

11. A manager is trying to decide whether to buy one machine or two. If only one is purchased and demand proves to be excessive, the second machine can be purchased later. Some sales will be lost, however, since the lead time on this kind of machine is six months. In addition, the cost per machine will be lower if both are purchased at the same time. The probability of low demand is estimated to be 0.25, of high demand, 0.75. The after-tax net present value of the benefits from purchasing the two machines together is $94,000 if demand is low and $165,000 if demand is high.

If one machine is purchased and demand is low, the net present value is $115,000.

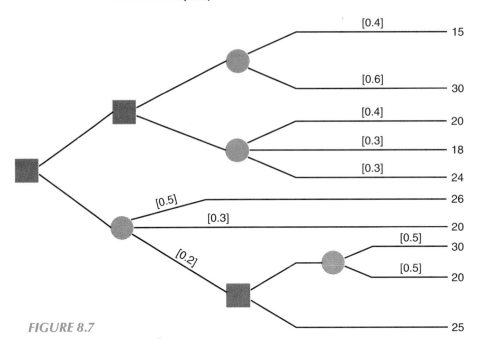

FIGURE 8.7

If demand proves to be high, the manager has three options. Doing nothing has a net present value of $115,000; subcontracting, $140,000; and buying the second machine, $126,000.

a. Draw a decision tree for this problem.
b. How many machines should the manager initially buy? What is the expected payoff for this alternative?

12. A manager is trying to decide whether to build a small, medium, or large facility. Demand can be either low, average, or high, with the estimated probabilities being 0.25 for low, 0.40 for average, and 0.35 for high.

A small facility is estimated to earn an after-tax net present value of just $18,000 if demand is low. If demand is average, the small facility earns $75,000; the facility can be increased to average size to earn a net present value of $60,000. If demand is high, the small facility earns $75,000 and can be expanded to average size and earn $60,000 or to large size and earn $125,000.

A medium-sized facility will lose an estimated $25,000 if demand is low and earn $140,000 if demand is average. If demand is high, the medium-sized facility earns a net present value of $150,000 or can be expanded to a large size for a net payoff of $145,000.

If a large facility is built and demand is high, earnings are estimated to be $220,000. If demand is average for the large facility, the present value will be $125,000; if demand is low the facility will lose $60,000.

a. Draw a decision tree for this problem.
b. What should management do to achieve the highest expected payoff?

13. A manufacturer has reached full capacity of its current plant and must build a second plant at a nearby location. The new plant can be either small or large. The probabilities are 0.40 for low demand and 0.60 for high demand.

If demand is low, the large plant has a present value of $5 million, and the small plant $8 million. If demand is high, the large plant pays off with a present value of $17 million, and the small plant only $10 million.

However, the small plant can be expanded later if demand proves to be high, for a present value of $15 million.

a. Draw a decision tree for this problem.
b. What should management do to achieve the highest expected payoff?

14. A firm is adding a new product line and so must build a new plant. Demand will be either favorable or unfavorable, with probabilities of 0.60 and 0.40, respectively. If a large plant is built and demand is favorable, the after-tax net present value of benefits is estimated at $1,520,000. If demand is unfavorable, the loss with the large plant will be $20,000.

If a small plant is built and demand is unfavorable, the net present value is $760,000, after deducting the costs to build and equip the plant. If demand proves to be favorable, the firm can maintain the small facility or expand it. Maintaining the small facility has a present value of $95,000, and expanding, $570,000.

a. Draw a decision tree for this problem.
b. What should management do to achieve the highest expected payoff?

Advanced Problems

Supplement Connections: Problems 15–21 require prior reading of Supplement 1 (Financial Analysis); Problem 22, Supplement 2 (Linear Programming); Problems 23–26, Supplement 4 (Queuing Models); and Problems 27–29, Supplement 5 (Simulation Analysis). A computer package is helpful for Problems 15–26.

15. Acme Steel Fabricators has experienced booming business for the past five years. The company fabricates a wide range of steel products, such as railings, ladders, and light structural steel framing. Acme owns a forklift to move materials from one department to another within the plant. The facility is used to its fullest capacity, and the current method of materials handling is causing excessive inventories and congestion.

Acme is considering the purchase of an overhead rail-mounted hoist system to increase capacity and improve manufacturing efficiency. The entire cost of the hoist system is $65,000, including all installation costs. The economic life of the system is 10 years, when its salvage value would be $15,000. The lowest desired rate of return on investments at Acme is 16 percent, and it uses straight-line depreciation. The tax rate is 50 percent. The annual before-tax payoff from the system depends on future demand. If it stays at the current level, which has a probability of 0.40, annual savings will be $10,000. If the demand increase is moderate, the annual benefit will be $25,000 because of operating efficiencies in addition to new sales. Finally, if the demand increase is high, the annual benefit is estimated to be $40,000. The probability is estimated to be 0.50 for moderate demand, and 0.10 for high demand. Assume that the current forklift has no salvage value.

a. Draw a decision tree for this problem, and compute the after-tax net present value of the payoff for each alternative–event combination.
b. What is the best alternative, based on the expected net present values?

16. A few years ago, River City built a water purification plant to remove toxins and filter the city's drinking water. Due to population growth, the demand for water next year will be more than the plant's capacity of 120 million gallons per year. Therefore, the city must expand the facility. The estimated demand over the next 20 years is given in Table 8.7.

The city planning commission is considering three alternatives:

- *Alternative 1:* Expand enough at the end of year 0 to last for 20 years. This means an 80 million gallon increase (200 − 120).
- *Alternative 2:* Expand at the end of year 0 and at the end of year 10.
- *Alternative 3:* Expand at the end of years 0, 5, 10, and 15.

TABLE 8.7

Year	Capacity	Year	Capacity	Year	Capacity
0	120	7	148	14	176
1	124	8	152	15	180
2	128	9	156	16	184
3	132	10	160	17	188
4	136	11	164	18	192
5	140	12	168	19	196
6	144	13	172	20	200

Each alternative would provide the needed 200 million gallons at the end of 20 years, when the value of the plant would be the same regardless of the alternative chosen. There are significant economies of scale in construction costs: A 20 million gallon expansion would cost $18 million; a 40 million gallon expansion, $30 million; and an 80 million gallon expansion, only $50 million. The level of future interest rates is uncertain, leading to uncertainty about the hurdle rate. The city believes it could be as low as 12 percent and as high as 16 percent. (See Supplement 1.)

a. Compute the cash flows for each alternative, compared to a base case of doing nothing. (*Note:* As a municipal utility, the operation pays no taxes.)

b. Which of the three alternatives minimizes the present value of construction costs over the next 20 years if the discount rate is 12 percent? 16 percent?

c. Since the decision involves public policy and compromise, what political considerations does the planning commission face?

17. Complete the financial analysis begun in Problem 6. Karen estimates construction costs at $20,000 and the investment life at 20 years. She uses straight-line depreciation ($1000 per year), pays taxes of 30 percent, and expects a return on her investment of at least 16 percent. Salvage value is assumed to be negligible.

a. How much do 1994 after-tax profits increase if Karen expands at the end of 1993? Does this benefit exceed the $3200 opportunity cost [$20,000 × (0.16)] of investing at that time?

b. Repeat part (a) for an expansion at the end of 1994, calculating the after-tax cash inflow in 1995.

c. Calculate the net present value of the 1994 expansion, recognizing the cash inflows for 1995 through 2014 (20 years). Should Karen plan to expand at all? Explain.

18. Calculate the net present value for the single-stage expansion in Application 8.3 and two-stage expansion in Solved Problem 2. Which expansion possibility is best? Assume that federal and state taxes are 50 percent of profits and use a discount rate of 0.16. Other assumptions are shown in Table 8.8.

TABLE 8.8

Single-Stage Expansion	Two-Stage Expansion
Initial investment of $200,000 at the end of 1993	Initial investment of $80,000 at the end of 1993 and an additional investment of $170,000 at the end of 1996
20-year life	20-year life for initial investment and 17-year life for the additional investment
Depreciation of $10,000 per year with no salvage value	Depreciation of $4000 per year through 1996 and $14,000 ($4,000 + $10,000) per year thereafter, with no salvage value

19. Two new alternatives have come up for expanding Grandmother's Chicken Restaurant (see Problem 18). They would involve more automation in the kitchen and feature a special cooking process that retains the original recipe taste of the chicken. Although the process is more capital intensive, it also drives down labor cost, so that the before-tax profit for *all* sales (not just the sales from the capacity added) goes up, from 25 to 28 percent. This increases the pre-tax profit by 3 percent of each sales dollar through $800,000 and by 28 percent of each sales dollar between $800,000 and the new capacity limit. Otherwise, the new alternatives are much the same as the original two. The two new alternatives follow:

- Expand both the kitchen and dining area now (at the end of 1993), bringing capacity up to $1,300,000 of sales per year. The construction cost, including the new automation, would be $336,000 (rather than the earlier $200,000). Assume a 20-year life, straight-line depreciation of $16,800 per year, and the same tax rate (50 percent).

- Expand only the kitchen now, bringing its capacity up to $1,050,000 of annual sales. At the end of 1996, expand both the kitchen and dining area up to the $1,300,000 volume. Construction and equipment costs would be $424,000, with $220,000 at the end of 1993 and the remainder at the end of 1996. The initial investment has a 20-year life, and the subsequent investment has a 17-year life. As with the first new alternative, the contribution margin goes up to 28 percent. Annual depreciation would be $11,000 through 1996 and $23,000 thereafter.

With both new alternatives, the salvage value will be negligible at the end of 2013 (20 years from now).

a. Calculate the net present value for each

alternative, keeping the 16 percent discount rate. Which alternative is best?

b. Should Grandmother's Chicken Restaurant expand with the new or the old technology?

20. A new kidney dialysis machine costs $80,000 and has a life of ten years. Riverside Hospital currently has a six-year-old machine. Annual maintenance and operating costs vary with the age of such a machine. The following information was gathered. The salvage values are after-tax inflows.

Age (yr)	Maintenance and Operating Costs ($000)	Salvage Value ($000)
1	14	72
2	16	64
3	18	56
4	20	48
5	22	40
6	24	32
7	26	24
8	28	16
9	30	8
10	32	0

Management is currently evaluating three policies:

- Keep the current machine for another four years, when its salvage value reaches zero.
- Buy a new machine now and every four years thereafter.
- Buy a new machine now and every two years thereafter.

Under all three policies, a new machine is bought at the end of year 4, so cash flows need to be projected only that far. The salvage value, but not a new investment outlay, should be included in year 4.

Using the first policy as the "base case," an analyst calculated the following cash flows ($000) for the policy of replacing the machine every four years.

Year	Investment	Salvage Value	Annual Cost Savings
0	80	32	—
1			26 − 14 = 12
2			28 − 16 = 12
3			30 − 18 = 12
4		48	32 − 20 = 12

a. What are the cash flows from replacing the machine every two years? The annual cost savings will be higher in the last two years, as maintenance and operating costs drop back to only $12,000 in the third year with the new machine.

b. Calculate the net present value for replacing the machine every two or four years, compared to the base case. Use straight-line depreciation, a discount rate of 14 percent, and a tax rate of 25 percent. Since the annual depreciation in this example will be the same for all three policies, depreciation does not shield the cost savings from taxes. Should the machine be replaced now? If so, is it better to wait two years or four years until the next replacement?

21. Truck-Tuff, a producer of bed liners for pickup trucks, is currently operating at its capacity of 2000 liners per day. Daily demand has picked up to the rate of 2500 liners; thus Truck-Tuff is losing potential business due to lack of capacity. The contribution to profit is $20 per liner. An expansion to produce another 1000 liners per day would cost $8 million.

a. Using a payback period of four years, should Truck-Tuff expand? (Assume no taxes.)

b. What is the lowest demand per day that would satisfy the payback period requirement of four years?

22. The following is a linear programming model for analyzing the product mix of Maxine's Hat Company, which produces three hat styles:

$$\text{Max } z: \$7x_1 + \$5x_2 + \$2x_3$$

subject to:

$$3x_1 + 5x_2 + x_3 \leq 150 \text{ (machine A time)}$$
$$5x_1 + 3x_2 + 2x_3 \leq 100 \text{ (machine B time)}$$
$$x_1 + 2x_2 + x_3 \leq 160 \text{ (machine C time)}$$
$$x_1, x_2, x_3 \geq 0$$

Printout 1 shows the optimal solution to the problem. Consider each of the following statements independently, state whether it is true or false, and explain.

a. If the price of hat 3 were increased to $2.50, it would be part of the optimal product mix.

b. The capacity of machine C can be reduced to 65 hours without affecting profits.

c. If machine A had a capacity of 170 hours, the production output would remain unchanged.

23. The son of a local hamburger magnate is preparing to open a new fast-food restaurant called Hasty Burgers. He is presently designing the drive-in window operation. Based on the arrival rates at his father's outlets, customers are expected to arrive according to a Poisson distribution with a mean of 20 customers per hour. The service rate is flexible, as the work methods are yet to be designed; however, the service times are expected to follow an exponential distribution. The drive-in window is a single-server operation.

a. What service rate is needed to keep the average number of customers in the service system (line plus being served) to four?

b. For the service rate found in part (a), what is the probability that more than four customers are in line and being served?

c. For the service rate found in part (a), what is the average waiting time in queue for each customer? Does this seem satisfactory for a fast-food business? Explain.

24. The manager of the Pinball Palace, a video arcade, is concerned about the number of

PRINTOUT 1

LINEAR PROGRAMMING
MAXIMIZATION

SOLUTION

VARIABLE LABEL	VARIABLE VALUE	ORIGINAL COEFFICIENT	COEFFICIENT SENSITIVITY
X1	3.1250	7	0
X2	28.1250	5	0
X3	0	2	0.7500

CONSTRAINT LABEL	ORIGINAL RHV	SLACK OR SURPLUS	SHADOW PRICE
C1	150	0	0.2500
C2	100	0	1.2500
C3	160	100.6250	0

OBJECTIVE FUNCTION VALUE: 162.5000

SENSITIVITY ANALYSIS
OBJECTIVE FUNCTION COEFFICIENTS

VARIABLE LABEL	LOWER LIMIT	ORIGINAL COEFFICIENT	UPPER LIMIT
X1	5.2857	7	8.3333
X2	4.2000	5	11.6667
X3	NO LIMIT	2	2.7500

RIGHT-HAND-SIDE VALUES

CONSTRAINT LABEL	LOWER LIMIT	ORIGINAL VALUE	UPPER LIMIT
C1	60	150	166.6667
C2	90	100	250.0000
C3	59.3750	160	NO LIMIT

video games down for repair. Three employees in the maintenance department are responsible for repairing the games. A maintenance worker can fix one video game machine every eight hours on average, with an exponential distribution. A recent study revealed that an average of one video game machine failed every three hours according to a Poisson distribution. Each down machine costs the Palace $10 per hour in lost profits. A new maintenance worker would cost $8 per hour.

The manager is not sure whether any new personnel should be hired. If so, he must determine how many. Since you had written on your résumé that you are familiar with the multiple-server model, the manager has asked you to analyze the situation. What would you recommend to the manager, based on your analysis?

25. The College of Business and Public Administration at Benton University has a copy machine on each floor for faculty use. Heavy use of the five copy machines causes frequent failures. Maintenance records show that a machine fails every 2.5 days (or $\lambda_0 = 0.40$ failure/day). The college has a maintenance contract with the authorized dealer of the copy machines. Since the copy machines fail so frequently, the dealer has assigned one person to the college to repair them. This person can repair an average of 2.5 machines per day. Answer the following questions using the finite-source model.
    a. What is the average utilization of the maintenance person?
    b. On average, how many copy machines are being repaired or waiting to be repaired?
    c. What is the average time spent by a copy machine in the repair system (queue plus repair)?

26. Bryant Manufacturing has six critical machines in its plant that fail frequently. On the average, a machine fails every four days. The repair person assigned full time to maintain the machines can fix an average of two machines per day. Answer the following questions using the finite-source model.
    a. What is the repair person's average utilization?
    b. How many machines are being repaired or waiting to be repaired, on average?
    c. What is the average time spent by a machine in the repair system (queue plus repair)?

27. The Capital City Shuttle takes people from the downtown business district to the airport. The shuttle bus has a capacity of 12 people and takes exactly one hour to make the round trip to and from the airport. If more than 12 people arrive during the hour, the excess must wait until the next trip

and the service charge to them is discounted 15 percent. The arrival distribution at the downtown depot follows.

People Arriving per Hour

Number	Probability	RN
10	0.20	00–19
11	0.35	20–54
12	0.20	55–74
13	0.15	75–89
14	0.05	90–94
15	0.05	95–99

a. Suppose the owner of the shuttle charges $10 per person. Disregarding any revenues that might be generated on the trip from the airport, estimate the average hourly revenue for the trip from downtown to the airport. Base your estimate on a simulation of 8 hours using the following random numbers.

87, 44, 29, 02, 97, 20, 71, 15

b. What is the average utilization of the shuttle bus from downtown to the airport?

28. Swift Airlines has a large service center to overhaul and maintain its fleet of passenger jets. A maximum of two jets per day can be serviced by the maintenance crew employed by Swift. However, the aircraft arrive at the service center to be overhauled according to the following distribution.

Aircraft Arriving per Day

Number	Probability	RN
1	0.33	00–32
2	0.34	33–66
3	0.33	67–99

If a jet arrives at the service center but cannot receive any maintenance the same day, it must wait overnight in the hanger for service the next day. Using the following random numbers:

24, 05, 19, 53, 20, 80, 58, 32, 93, 77

a. Simulate the arrival and service of aircraft for ten days.

b. Determine the maximum number of aircraft held overnight in any one day.

29. A machine center handles four types of clients: A, B, C, and D. The manager wants to assess the number of machines required to handle these clients. Setup times for changeover from one client to another are negligible. There is considerable uncertainty on the annual demand and processing times; demand can be either low, normal, or high. The probabilities for these three events are shown in the following table for each type of client.

Low Demand

Client	(Units/Yr)	Probability
A	3000	0.10
B	500	0.30
C	1500	0.10
D	600	0.40

Normal Demand

Client	(Units/Yr)	Probability
A	3500	0.60
B	800	0.50
C	3000	0.50
D	650	0.50

High Demand

Client	(Units/Yr)	Probability
A	4200	0.30
B	900	0.20
C	4500	0.40
D	700	0.10

Processing times can be long, average, or short and are distributed, in machine hours per unit, as follows.

Short

Client	(Hr/Unit)	Probability
A	10	0.35
B	60	0.25
C	12	0.25
D	60	0.30

Average

Client	(Hr/Unit)	Probability
A	20	0.45
B	90	0.50
C	15	0.60
D	70	0.65

Long

Client	(Hr/Unit)	Probability
A	30	0.20
B	100	0.25
C	20	0.15
D	80	0.05

a. Explain how simulation could be used to generate a probability distribution on the total number of machine hours, R, required per year to service the clients.

b. Simulate one year using the following random numbers. For example, use random number 78 for client A's demand and 10 for client A's processing time.

$$78, 10, 62, 72, 11, 28, 16, 99$$

CASE SOUTH SHORE MACHINE SHOP

Roger Ream started his own machine shop in 1982. Despite two difficult years, the firm grew steadily, and in 1992 sales exceeded $1,500,000. South Shore produces a wide variety of small metal parts for sale to other manufacturers in the region. Some 50 percent of customer orders are one of a kind. The average order size is 35 pieces, but order quantities range from 1 to 500 pieces. South Shore competes for orders through the bidding process, with the lowest bidder usually winning the job.

The plant is process focused, housing 32 machines valued at $350,000. The work force is flexible, and most workers are trained to operate several different machines. Hourly wages, starting at $7 per hour and ranging up to $14 for the most highly skilled workers, are competitive. The plant is not unionized and currently operates on a single-shift basis, five days per week. It closes for vacation during two weeks in the summer. Equipment capacity is the main limitation, with work overloads handled with overtime.

One bottleneck work center in the shop has four machines, each requiring a worker in attendance when running. An operator earns $10 per hour. Due to the high utilization of these machines, Ream has an operator assigned on a permanent basis to each one. Productivity is probably higher because of this specialization, but the workers do have less variety on the job. Ream believes that the requirements for this type of machining will grow. Next year's requirements for the work center, expressed in terms of machines operating on a one-shift basis of 2000 hours per year, could range anywhere from 4 to 10 machines. Intuitive estimates of the following probability distributions are based on Ream's sense for sales trends and economic conditions:

Machines	Probability
4	0.10
6	0.25
8	0.50
10	0.15

Ream must decide now how many new machines (if any) to buy for next year because the lead time for buying the machines from the supplier is more than six months. The cost to buy and install a machine is $31,000. Ream uses straight-line depreciation, and the tax rate is 25 percent. The hurdle rate that he uses for the cost of capital is 14 percent. Each machine has an economic life of 10 years and has no scrap value after 8 years.

The least expensive way to operate the work center is to use regular time. The standard time per piece produced on the equipment is 10 hours, which means that 200 pieces can be produced per year from one machine on a single-shift basis. In addition to direct labor costs, the cost of materials and variable overhead is another $120 per piece produced.

If regular-time capacity proves to be insufficient because not enough machines were ordered, Ream must decide how best to proceed. One possibility is to use overtime, his preferred policy in the past, at time-and-a-half pay. The maximum sustainable amount, however, is 15 hours per week because employees like some level of overtime to supplement their income but do not want it to be excessive. Furthermore,

Ream suspects that worker productivity drops off when overtime becomes the norm. Perhaps the time per piece grows to 11 hours, although he has no data to support this belief.

Ream also can subcontract work to a competitor, at a cost of $310 per piece for an order of 100 pieces or less, and $295 apiece for larger orders. The competitor's capacity is sufficiently large to absorb whatever work Ream chooses to offload, although Ream prefers to keep the work in-house. A third possibility is not to bid on work when capacity is reached. Not only would the immediate profit be forgone (average sales price per piece made at the work center is $350), but customers may be less likely to turn to South Shore for future orders.

The last option for covering a capacity shortage is to start a second or even third shift. Ream has resisted this idea in the past. A supervisor for each new shift probably would have to be hired, and finding good employees for night shifts is more difficult. Not only might productivity be lower, but quality might not be controlled as well. There would also be some sort of shift premium involved. Finally, Ream wants to be a good employer and not hire and train new workers only to lay them off if demand doesn't reach expected levels.

If Ream buys more equipment than needed for next year, he must confront a different set of issues. If all machines are not fully utilized, he probably will change his current policy of assigning a worker permanently to each machine and instead reassign them to other parts of the shop to be more fully utilized. However, there is a limit to how labor hours can be absorbed by the rest of the shop: If demand falls too short, some of the newly hired and trained employees must be curtailed. There is also the question of what to do with the excess equipment capacity. One option is to sell some of the excess machines. Another is to stand fast, hoping that the demand will pick up in the following year.

QUESTIONS

1. Prepare a capacity plan for South Shore. How many (if any) machines should South Shore buy at the bottleneck work center? State any assumptions that you make and justify your recommendations.

2. For the number recommended, what should be done if demand exceeds capacity? If capacity exceeds demand?

SELECTED REFERENCES

"America's Best Managed Factories." *Fortune*, May 28, 1984, pp. 16–24.

"Avoiding Plant Failures Grows More Difficult for Many Industries." *Wall Street Journal*, January 8, 1981.

Bott, Kevin, and Larry P. Ritzman. "Irregular Workloads with MRP Systems." *Journal of Operations Management*, vol. 3, no. 4, 1983, pp. 169–182.

Bowman, Edward H. "Scale of Operations—An Empirical Study." *Operations Research* (June 1958), pp. 320–328.

Buffa, Elwood S. *Meeting the Competitive Challenge: Manufacturing Strategy for U.S. Companies*. Homewood, Ill.: Dow Jones–Irwin, 1984.

Hayes, Robert H., and Steven C. Wheelwright. *Restoring Our Competitive Edge: Competing Through Manufacturing*. New York: John Wiley & Sons, 1984.

Miller, Jeffrey G., and Jay S. Kim. *Executive Summary of the 1990 North American Manufacturing Futures Survey*. Research report, School of Management, Boston University, 1990.

Sassar, W. Earl. "Match Supply and Demand in Service Industries." *Harvard Business Review* (November–December 1976), pp. 133–140.

Schmenner, Roger W. *Making Business Location Decisions*. Englewood Cliffs, N.J.: Prentice-Hall, 1982.

Skinner, Wickham. "The Focused Factory." *Harvard Business Review* (May–June 1974), pp. 113–121.

"Small Is Beautiful Now in Manufacturing." *Business Week*, October 22, 1984, pp. 152–156.

Chapter 9

LOCATION

Should our new facility be located in the Sunbelt?

Should we open facilities overseas? If so, how should they be managed?

What factors should we consider to be dominant in picking a new location? Secondary?

How does the quality of life enter our location decision?

Should we be leaders or followers in picking locations for new retail outlets?

Should we expand on site, add a new facility, or relocate the existing facility?

Should we locate near suppliers, the work force, or customers?

Should we organize multiple plants by product line, market area, or process? What about flexibility?

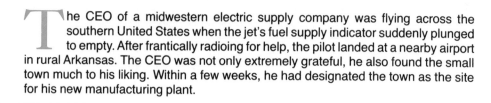

The CEO of a midwestern electric supply company was flying across the southern United States when the jet's fuel supply indicator suddenly plunged to empty. After frantically radioing for help, the pilot landed at a nearby airport in rural Arkansas. The CEO was not only extremely grateful, he also found the small town much to his liking. Within a few weeks, he had designated the town as the site for his new manufacturing plant.

Although one CEO made his location decision this way, you should not conclude that location decisions usually are based on executive whim. On the contrary, such decisions have a significant impact on other issues such as operating costs, the price at which goods and services can be offered, and a company's ability to compete in the marketplace. Thus location decisions have many strategic implications. For example, have you ever wondered why White Castle restaurants often locate near manufacturing plants? Or why many competing new-car sales showrooms locate near one another? In the first case, White Castle's strategy is to achieve market segmentation by catering to blue-collar workers. As a result they tend to locate near the target population and away from competitors such as Wendy's and McDonald's. In contrast, managers of new-car showrooms deliberately locate near one another because customers prefer to do their comparative shopping in one area. In each case, management's location decision reflects a different strategy.

Recognizing the strategic impact of location decisions, we first examine overall trends in location patterns and then consider factors that influence location choices. Consideration of strategic issues only may not indicate the best location for a facility. Depending on whether management is planning a single facility or multiple facilities, there may be two very different sets of variables to assess. We will discuss both types of situations.

SIGNIFICANT U.S. TRENDS

In a typical year in the United States, manufacturing firms build more than 3000 new plants and expand 7500 others. When we also take into account the construction and remodeling of numerous stores, office buildings, warehouses, and other facilities in the service industries, the impact of location decisions becomes readily apparent. Analyzing location patterns to discover the various underlying strategies is fascinating. In the United States three location trends stand out: geographic diversity, movement to the growing Sunbelt, and movement out of urban areas. Let's look briefly at these trends before examining a very important fourth trend: the globalization of operations.

Geographic Diversity

Today the tendency of industries to concentrate in certain geographic regions is lessening. Although electric machinery and electronics remain key industries in New England, as do fabricated metals in the Mid-Eastern part of the country, these industries are relatively less important in those regions than they were just a decade ago. Geography and distance are becoming increasingly irrelevant. (An important exception are the just-in-time systems described in Chapter 17, which rely on supplier proximity.) The trend of separating operations and putting thousands of miles between them applies not just to big corporations but increasingly to small and medium-sized companies. They place warehouses in Ohio because its location is central, customer-service toll-free numbers in Des Moines because Iowans speak with an all-American accent, and data-processing offices in North Dakota because people in the Farmbelt are skilled and eager to work.

The trend toward geographic dispersion has two primary causes. The first, *improved transportation and communication technology*, reduces transportation costs and facilitates supervision and coordination. For example, air transportation can move goods quickly from, say, Kansas City to New York or even from Osaka, Japan, to Kansas City. Telecommunications (voice and data) technology—including electronic mail, facsimile machines, and sophisticated toll-free telephone arrangements—allows facilities to service larger market areas. For example, in service industries, home offices centralize more back-room operations and provide support to branches located near the customer.

The second factor behind geographic dispersion is the *narrowing of regional wage differentials*. The Pacific region (California, Oregon, Washington, Alaska, and Hawaii) still enjoys one of the higher incomes per capita, at $20,200. However, this lead slipped from 120 percent of the national average in 1960 to only 108 percent in 1990. The Southeastern part of the United States (Virginia south to Florida and west to Texas) has the lowest income per capita, but it has moved up from 78 to 90 percent of the national average over the same three decades.

These two factors have expanded considerably the number of attractive locations. In fact, many industries now find that the exact location of a new facility is not so critical. Nevertheless, managers must avoid "the big mistake." For example, the National Seating and Dimensional Company relocated to West Virginia for low labor rates but went bankrupt trying to achieve the necessary worker skill levels. Other firms, such as most textile firms that decided to remain in New England, went bankrupt for *not* relocating. Clearly, a poor location decision can negate sound decisions that a manager may make in other areas.

The Move to the Sunbelt

The map in Fig. 9.1 divides the United States into the Sunbelt (Southern and lower Pacific regions, indicated by gold) and the Frostbelt (North Central, Great Lakes, Mid-Eastern, upper Pacific, and New England Regions). The relatively mild climate of the Sunbelt has enticed many industries, both in ser-

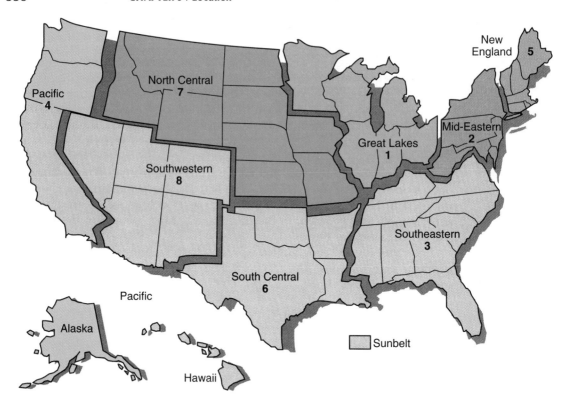

FIGURE 9.1   The Migration to the Sunbelt

both in services and in manufacturing, from the Frostbelt. But climate is not the only incentive. The Sunbelt also offers lower labor costs, less unionism, and possibly a stronger work ethic. As a result, many firms formerly entrenched in the industrial heartland of the Great Lakes and Mid-Eastern regions have opened facilities in the Sunbelt. This migration south and west has been accelerated by declining transportation and communication costs.

The Sunbelt accounts for 48 percent of the U.S. population and for more than 40 percent of the nation's manufacturing employment, up from 34 percent in 1967. Nevertheless, the Mid-Eastern and Great Lakes regions still lead in *sales density*, which is dollars of retail sales per square mile. Because service organizations need people with purchasing power, these regions will remain strong locations for service industries.

Decline of Urban Areas

Many firms in services and manufacturing alike have relocated from crowded, older cities to suburban and rural areas. In fact, during the past two decades more than 50 percent of new industrial jobs in the United States went to non-urban regions. A similar shift is taking place in Japan and the industrialized

European countries. Moreover, organizations such as IBM and J.C. Penney have recently relocated their corporate offices. Reasons for these movements include the high cost of living, the high crime rate, and the general decline of the quality of life in many large cities.

GLOBALIZATION OF OPERATIONS

Globalization is an umbrella term describing businesses' treatment of the world as their stage. One important dimension of globalization is the deployment of facilities and operations in foreign countries. For years U.S. firms have built production facilities overseas. That trend continues, and for the first time, foreign businesses are building facilities in this country in a big way. Michigan now has nearly 300 Japanese companies, a sixfold increase in eight years. Mostly auto-related, they have located near Detroit to buy from or sell to the Big Three automakers (General Motors, Ford, and Chrysler) and to hire American engineers for their own growing U.S. operations. In the service sector there have been high-profile Japanese acquisitions: Columbia Pictures, CBS Records, Universal Studios, and a majority interest in New York's Rockefeller Center. By 1990 other countries had increased their total investment in U.S. service and manufacturing industries to $404 billion. Europe accounts for 64 percent of the total, with the United Kingdom leading the way at 29 percent. Japanese firms are the major investors from Asia and the Pacific, accounting for another 21 percent.

Globalization also means more sales to and imports from other countries, often called "offshore" sales and imports. U.S. manufacturers report increased offshore sales and purchases, to 14 percent of total sales and 10 percent of total purchases. And corporate voice, data, and teleconferencing traffic volume between countries is growing at an annual rate of 15 to 20 percent, about double the corporate domestic rate. It is no wonder that Robert E. Mercer, chairman of the Goodyear Tire and Rubber Company, concludes that "to compete effectively in the industry today, you have to be a global player" ("A Global Fight," 1988).

Causes of Globalization

Globalization is spurred by three factors. First, the world's financial systems became more open in the last decade, making it easier to locate where capital, supplies, and resources are cheapest. Second, improved transportation and communication technologies are breaking down the barriers of time and space between countries—communication and travel between countries is easy today. Third, import penetration in the major economies is increasing, which expands foreign markets. Imports of goods and services now account for about 13 percent of total output in the United States and 14 percent in Japan, up considerably from earlier decades. Penetration is often easier if a firm produces its products or services where they are sold. This local presence can increase sales by reducing customer aversion to buying imports. It can also help decrease the threat of import quotas or other kinds of trade barriers, such as India's restrictions on certain imports or the U.S. voluntary quotas imposed on Japan's automobiles. Of course, there can also be disadvantages to overseas manufacturing, such as relinquishing proprietary technology, being exploited by a foreign government once a plant is built (nationalization being one extreme possibility), alienating customers back home, and reducing response times.

Hot Spots of Global Activity

Globalization creates a more interconnected world economy, which means that countries are becoming increasingly dependent on each other. Let's look at a few areas where globalization is particularly visible.

Mexico. American, Japanese, South Korean, and European firms have opened nearly 2000 plants employing almost 500,000 in **maquiladoras,** or industrial parks, along the northern border of Mexico. The *maquilas*, or plants in the maquiladoras, assemble foreign parts and reexport the finished product to the United States. For example, Ford opened a new plant in Hermosillo to make the Escort and is spending $700 million to expand its engine plant in Chihuahua to build multivalve four-cylinder engines, which will increase capacity from 270,000 to 500,000 engines per year by 1995. The massive devaluation of the peso in 1982 put Mexico's wages in the ballpark with those of newly industrialized Asian countries. A firm facing a $10 per hour average payroll cost can save $15,000 yearly per employee by moving to Mexico. The incentive of inexpensive labor must be balanced, however, against lower productivity, less workforce stability, an inefficient rail system, dusty roads, and considerable training requirements, among other disadvantages. For example, the setup costs to connect to Mexico's underdeveloped electric grid can be as high as $200,000 for a new plant. The maquiladoras are the main reason Mexico has experienced massive recovery after the collapse of its economy a decade ago.

Western European Community. The European Community (EC) is becoming a united market, having dropped most internal trade barriers. Significant economic expansion is expected in Western Europe over the next two decades. Multinational firms are positioning themselves to be treated as *EC corporations*, with the ability to trade freely within the EC's prospective single market. One important qualifier in getting this preferred status, and avoiding import quotas or duties, is locating local production facilities in Europe. "Local-content" rules require more than locating assembly operations in the EC: A product's core parts must also be manufactured there to qualify as an EC corporation. For example, Whirlpool Corporation acquired Philips' European appliance business and is streamlining its production operations there. Whirlpool expects European appliance sales to grow 4 percent per year, compared to just 2 percent in the United States: Only 14 percent of European households own clothes dryers and 19 percent have dishwashers. Japanese multinationals—Toyota, Honda, Nissan, Sony, Matsushita, Fujitsu, and the Mitsubishi companies—are also pouring staggering amounts of money in manufacturing plants in Europe.

Nissan, Toyota, and Honda have committed $2.6 billion to major manufacturing investments in Britain alone. They hope to capture a larger share of the $180 billion automobile market, the largest one in the world.

East Europe and the Former Soviet Union. With the fall of the Berlin Wall and the changes in the former Soviet Union, many firms began looking increasingly to East Europe and the former Soviet republics. Although the pace of growth may be more uncertain than in other regions due to the enormous political and economic turmoil, the population of 410 million promises huge expansion opportunities later in the decade. Foreign companies are establishing joint ventures in local manufacturing at an accelerating pace. For example, General Motors may be investing up to $400 million by 1996 in a joint venture in Poland to produce a mid-sized Opel in Warsaw and $150 million in two Hungarian ventures to make various automobile parts. It also won a five-year agreement to supply nearly $1 billion of pollution-control and engine-control parts to Volga Auto Works, the largest automaker in the former Soviet Union. In the computer business, IBM is setting up joint ventures in Russia, Czechoslovakia, and the former East Germany.

East Asia. While attention has focused on Japan because of its manufacturing capability, another force in Asia is playing an increasingly important role in the world economy. The *East Asian tigers* (Hong Kong, Taiwan, Singapore, and South Korea) are rapidly industrializing nations with growing economic strength. Their economies depend heavily on export of their manufactured goods. Taiwan exports 70 percent of its total output to other countries; it started in garments and is working into other areas such as electronics, software, and steel. For example, it makes 20 percent of the world's IBM-compatible PCs. Hong Kong, a British crown colony until it reverts to the jurisdiction of the People's Republic of China in 1997, exports 90 percent of its manufac-

*G*lobalization at work in East Asia. Shown here are students in a school in Hong Kong that uses IBM equipment and networking software developed at Waterloo University in Canada.

turing output. Due to its small size, this city-state concentrates on light industries such as electronics, garments, and printing.

The East Asian tigers have attracted large investments from foreign firms and share in many joint ventures. Apple, Texas Instruments, and General Electric, as well as Matsushita of Japan, are among the 170 foreign firms with plants in Singapore, which are collectively responsible for 60 percent of all manufacturing output. Four major domestic conglomerates in South Korea (Daewoo, Samsung, Hyundai, and Lucky-Goldstar), known as the *chaebol*, account for 40 percent of the country's total output. The Korean economy has internationalized and attracts foreign investment, particularly from the United States and Japan. Daewoo has a joint venture with Suzuki to build Japanese minicars and trucks. Kia Motors, another South Korean firm, is partly owned by Ford and Mazda, and builds the Ford Festiva for the U.S. market.

Globalization of Services. In 1990 world trade in services reached $600 billion, or roughly 20 percent of total world trade. Banking, law, information services, airlines, education, consulting, and restaurant services are particularly active in global operations. For example, McDonald's joined the international trend and opened a record 220 restaurants offshore in just one year. Small companies are also beginning to export their services overseas. For example, the Tokyo city government gave a New York architect a $50 million contract to design and build its $1 billion International Forum complex on a 6.7-acre downtown site, and India's Steel Authority of India Ltd. hired a firm in Silver Spring, Maryland, to design and implement quality systems for its five major steel plants.

Managing Global Operations

Setting up facilities abroad entails adapting to the norms and customs of various ethnic communities. For example, more than two thirds of the managers surveyed in Japan believe that business should take an active role in environmental protection; only 25 percent of the Mexican managers agree (see Kanter, 1991). Managers often must reevaluate their on-the-job behavior (such as superior–subordinate relationships), worker attitudes, and hiring and promotion practices, to name a few. Unfortunately, many managers are poorly equipped to handle such differences, as exemplified by the low numbers of U.S. managers who speak a foreign language. There are currently more English teachers in the former Soviet Union than students studying Russian in the United States. Several U.S. franchisers, such as Century 21 Real Estate, Levi Strauss, and Quality Inns International, found that the problems of penetrating British markets went beyond language. Although the language is basically the same, the British conduct business differently.

As Managerial Practice 9.1 illustrates, the general economic and political climates of other countries may also introduce challenges in managing multinational operations. Managers in charge of overseas plants must deal with unfamiliar labor laws, tax laws, and regulatory requirements. A different economic environment can mean that a seemingly sound policy on automation is actually inappropriate because of an unexpected cost mix.

Managerial Practice 9.1

Managerial Challenges with Global Operations

- **Mexico.** Doing business in countries with different traditions and cultures can be difficult for small firms. In this respect the maquiladoras make a valued contribution. They provide what other industrial parks across the globe provide, such as plants built to the clients' specifications and construction and maintenance of roads, sewers, power lines, and other physical facilities. But they also do much more. The maquiladora manager acts as a co-manager and helps the foreign firm recruit, train, and pay all the Mexicans in the work force—including supervisors and engineers. The maquiladora manager also guides the maquila's relationships with the local governments, local community, tax collector, and so on. The foreigner runs the business part, and the maquiladora manager leads the social tasks.

- **Western European Community.** More managers are crossing borders, particularly from one European country to another, often at critical stages of their careers. Responsibilities of these "Euromanagers" are shifting from national to regional, or pan-European, units. At the same time, companies must stay in touch with local conditions. They need managers who can think big while understanding local nuances, who can deal with a variety of cultures skillfully and bring a diverse team together. And that means hiring and promoting more foreigners. The best kind of manager in an international setting must be flexible—not always go by the book. Getting along with colleagues is important in a foreign setting, where extra effort is needed to build understanding and trust.

- **East Europe and the Former Soviet Union.** U S West, a Denver-based phone company, found itself in a jam in August 1991. The August coup attempt in Russia unfolded just two weeks before a scheduled ceremony to officially switch on St. Petersburg's (formerly Leningrad) new cellular telephone system. Fortunately, the coup unraveled and the ceremony went on as scheduled. The incident illustrates the politics and pitfalls associated with operations there. U S West's experience in such projects provides several lessons, such as getting into a country early, understanding how its power structure works, establishing relationships with several layers of officials, and being willing to change plans on short notice. The company also learned to sidestep potential conflicts of interest in dealing with foreign officials.

- **East Asia.** It is tough for small businesses to find executives with international experience—and tougher still to check their credentials. Concord Camera opened a Chinese assembly plant 15 miles north of Hong Kong, where the going wage is $8 a week instead of $8 an hour as at its New Jersey home base. The new operation turned out to be a nightmare. Distance and language differences handicapped its ability to work with its new overseas managers. Feedback to Concord's home office was minimal, almost all of it coming through one manager whom the company wound up suing for "wrongful actions."

- **Services.** Federal Express is finding that its pioneering approach to overnight package deliveries is not easily transplanted. Its international operations, after almost a decade of expansion, fine-tuning, and promises of success, are on the ropes. Problems cropped up immediately in Europe, with Federal arriving well after competitors such as DHL and TNT. Setting up the hub-and-spoke system, which permits standardized sorting, tracking, and arrival of parcels, has proved very difficult. Local regulators saw Federal Express as foreign competition and acted accordingly. There were delays and roadblocks to getting permission for making certain flights. To speed up the process, Federal tried to grow through acquisitions, buying a total of 21 European transportation firms between 1983 and 1990. But the strategy was costly and often left the company with decidedly "unexpresslike" operations. Finally Federal's obsession with tight central control became a drawback. Until recently, all shipping bills and sales brochures were printed in English. To keep arrival times constant, it also cut off pickups after 5 P.M. throughout Europe, even though the Spanish work as late as 8 P.M.

Sources: "Mexico's Ugly Duckling—the Maquiladora," *Wall Street Journal*, October 4, 1990; "Firms in Europe Try to Find Executives Who Can Cross Borders in a Single Bound," *Wall Street Journal*, January 25, 1991; "Playing Politics," *Wall Street Journal*, October 4, 1991; "Small Firms Face Big Headaches in Far-Flung Ventures," *Wall Street Journal*, July 1, 1991; "Innocents Abroad," *Wall Street Journal*, April 15, 1991.

Managers must decide to what degree to transplant their corporation's production methods overseas and how much control the home offices should retain. Four distinct approaches are possible (see Bartlett and Ghoshal, 1989) to managing international operations. A *global* firm relies on its home offices for strategic direction and is more centralized. *International* firms are more decentralized but still depend heavily on the abilities of the home office. *Multinational* firms are highly decentralized, with each company subsidiary operating relatively autonomously. *Transnational* firms, the ideal according to Bartlett and Ghoshal, think globally but act locally as conditions mandate. They have a worldwide vision but allow for local differences. A transnational manager must be able to manage highly decentralized organizations with a wide mix of product strategies, cultures, and consumer needs.

FACTORS AFFECTING LOCATION DECISIONS

Facility location is the determination of a geographic site on which to locate a firm's operations. Managers must weigh many factors when assessing the desirability of a particular site. In fact, there are comprehensive checklists covering the myriad factors that could be important in any given situation. As Managerial Practice 9.2 suggests, when GM decided on the location of its Saturn facility, it gave particular weight to union attitudes, outbound transportation costs, quality of life, and the availability of utilities. To pare the checklist to a reasonable size, managers generally disregard those factors that do not meet at least one of two conditions:

1. The factor must be sensitive to location. A factor will influence choice only if management is convinced that the degree of factor achievement will vary among the locations under consideration.
2. Management must consider the difference in degree of factor achievement to be significant. Even a 50 percent differential is not important when applied to a minor cost category.

*A*n aerial view of GM's Saturn plant in Tennessee.

Managerial Practice 9.2

GM's Saturn Plant in Tennessee

General Motors Corporation needed a location for its new Saturn manufacturing complex for small cars. The facility would be the most integrated car operation in the United States, with many parts made by one of several feeder plants located on site. After considering 60 different location factors and more than 1000 possible sites in two dozen states, GM concluded that Spring Hill, Tennessee, offered the "best balance." Saturn Corporation headquarters and the engineering staff would remain in Michigan near Detroit.

Spring Hill is near Nashville, a metropolitan area offering a variety of educational and cultural activities. Major rail and highway routes provide access to most customers within a 500-mile radius. The state offers a stable economic climate, with adequate water and electric power. Although a Michigan site would be closer to existing suppliers, the Spring Hill facility would make most major parts on site.

Although Tennessee historically is an antiunion state, the Saturn facility is operated by a UAW work force. The contract is quite innovative, providing for an unprecedented degree of worker flexibility and more of a "consensus decision-making" structure.

Source: "GM Is Expected to Put Saturn Complex in Tennessee as UAW Board Votes Pact," *Wall Street Journal*, January 29, 1985.

Managers can divide location factors into dominant and secondary factors. Dominant factors are derived from competitive priorities (cost, quality, time, and flexibility) and have a particularly strong impact on sales or costs. For example, a labor-intensive plant might require low wage costs to remain competitive. Secondary factors are also important, but management may downplay or even ignore some of them if others are relatively more important. Thus for GM's Saturn plant, which makes many parts on site, inbound transportation costs were not a location requirement or even an important secondary factor.

Dominant Factors in Manufacturing

According to interviews and survey data, five groups of factors dominate location decisions for new U.S. manufacturing plants (Schmenner, 1982a). The percentage shown for each group represents the proportion of respondents who picked it as a "must" when considering a new location.

1. Favorable labor climate (76 percent)
2. Proximity to markets (55 percent)
3. Quality of life (35 percent)
4. Proximity to suppliers and resources (31 percent)
5. Proximity to company's other facilities (25 percent)

Favorable Labor Climate. For 76 percent of the respondents, a favorable labor climate was a dominant factor in making location decisions. Labor climate is a function of wage rates, training requirements, attitudes toward work, worker productivity, and union strength. Many executives believe that weak unions or a low probability of union organizing efforts is a major advantage. One indicator of this attitude is that, although 50 percent of U.S. industry is unionized, only 20 percent of new plants being opened have unions. Labor-intensive firms that give strong consideration to labor climate include manufacturers of textiles, furniture, and consumer electronics.

Proximity to Markets. After determining where the demand for goods and services is greatest, management must select a location for the facility that will supply that demand. Locating near markets is particularly important when goods are bulky or heavy and outbound transportation rates are high. For example, manufacturers of products that are relatively inexpensive to produce, such as paper, plastic pipe, and heavy metals, all emphasize proximity to their markets.

Quality of Life. Respondents from all but one of the industrial groups gave quality of life a relatively low rating. The lone exception was high-tech executives, who rated it at the top of their lists. For them, attracting and keeping a good engineering staff is more important than labor environment or transportation costs. Quality schools, recreational facilities, and an attractive life-style can make the difference in their location decisions.

Proximity to Suppliers and Resources. Most respondents rated proximity to suppliers and resources of relatively low importance. The exception was industries dependent on bulky or heavy raw materials. In such cases inbound transportation costs become a dominant factor, forcing these firms to locate facilities near suppliers. For example, it is practical to locate paper mills near forests and food processing facilities near farms. Another advantage of locating near suppliers is the ability to maintain lower inventories. (See JIT principles in Chapter 17.)

Proximity to the Parent Company's Facilities. In many companies, plants supply parts to other facilities or rely on other facilities for management and staff support. These ties require frequent coordination and communication, activities that can become more difficult as distance increases.

Other important factors may emerge, depending on the situation. They include the cost of shuffling people and materials between plants, utility costs (telephone, energy, water), local and state taxes, financing incentives offered by local or state governments, relocation costs, and land costs. For example, companies building new facilities in California are concerned about the high cost of land, about $100,000 an acre, in San Francisco, Los Angeles, and San Diego. Many are finding refuge in the state's Central Valley communities, long considered less desirable than the more glamorous coastal cities. Florestone Products, a maker of bath and shower products, decided to build its new plant in the Central Valley, 150 miles from the company's headquarters and existing plant, and bought 15 acres for only $150,000 for its $4.2 million plant. The same acreage in the San Francisco area would have cost $1.5 million.

After management narrows the location choice to a specific site, still other factors arise: room for expansion, construction costs, accessibility to multiple modes of transportation, insurance costs, competition from other firms for the work force, local ordinances (such as pollution or noise control), community attitudes, and many others.

Dominant Factors in Services

For service industries, location is a key factor in determining how conveniently customers can carry on business with a firm. For example, few people would patronize a dry cleaner or a supermarket if they had to travel for miles from their homes to a remote location. Thus the influence of location on revenues tends to dominate the other important factors we already identified for manufacturing. Residential density, traffic volumes, and income levels are all important aspects of estimating sales and revenue.

Warehouse location is another example. As with locating manufacturing plants, low transportation costs are a requirement. The difference is that proximity to markets takes on greater importance for warehousing and distribution operations. With a warehouse close by, many firms can hold inventory closer to the customer, thus reducing delivery time and promoting sales. For example, Invacare Corporation of Elyria, Ohio, gained a competitive edge in the distribution of home health-care products by going from one to 32 warehouses across the country. The products include wheelchairs, hospital beds, and other patient aids aimed at the trend toward administering more health care at home. Invacare sells its products, some of which it produces and some of which it buys from other firms, to small dealers located throughout the country, who in turn sell them to the ultimate consumers. Previously the dealers, often small mom-and-pop operations, had to wait three weeks for deliveries, which meant a lot of their cash tied up in excess inventory. With Invacare's new distribution network, the dealers get daily deliveries. Instead of going to 30 different sources for their purchases, they are now coming to Invacare. Invacare's location strategy is another example of time-based competition (see Chapter 2).

One complication in estimating the sales potential at different locations is the impact of competitors. Management must not only consider the current location of competitors but also try to anticipate their reaction to the firm's new location. Because customers often shop at the nearest stores, firms find it often pays to avoid areas where competitors are already well established. In other cases, locating near competitors is actually more advantageous. This is clearly the case for new-car sales showrooms, as noted earlier, and for fast-food chains, as described in Managerial Practice 9.3. The strategy is to create a **critical mass,** whereby the total number of customers attracted to several competing firms clustered in one location is greater than the total number who would shop at the same stores at scattered locations. Recognizing this effect, some firms use a follow-the-leader strategy when selecting new sites.

LOCATING A SINGLE FACILITY

Having examined trends and important factors for location, we now consider more specifically how a firm can make location decisions. This section considers the case of locating only one new facility. If it is part of a firm's larger network of facilities, we will assume there is no interdependence. This assumption holds in the situation described in Managerial Practice 9.3. That is, a decision to open a restaurant in Tampa, Florida, is independent of whether

Managerial Practice 9.3

Location Factors for a Fast-Food Restaurant Chain

In just a decade a fast-food restaurant chain grew from one to a thousand restaurants in North America and Japan. The exterior style and interior decor of all units are built to company specifications. Twenty percent of the stores are company owned, with the rest owned by franchisers. In either case, management considers six primary factors when making location decisions:

1. Area employment
2. Retail activity
3. Competitor locations
4. Traffic flow
5. Residential density
6. Accessibility and visibility

Area employment is crucial because the target market is 20- to 45-year-old workers on their lunch breaks. Areas with shopping centers, manufacturing plants, and large offices are ideal as long as firms allow employees to take lunch breaks off the premises. *Retail activity* in the area is important, as shoppers often decide on impulse to go to a restaurant. Being near *competitor locations* is seen as an advantage. Successful food outlets nearby indicate a good market. By observing competitors, management can assess the volume and direction of customer flows throughout the day and compare the volume with national averages. *Traffic flows* are impor-

tant because most business comes from people in cars, and 40 percent of sales are from the drive-by window. Management considers a traffic flow of 16,000 cars per 24-hour period good. *Residential density* is another important factor. A population of 20,000 residents within a two-mile radius is considered good and ensures nighttime and weekend business. An upper-middle-class population is preferred. *Accessibility and visibility* make up the last dominant factor. Management carefully considers possible backups of traffic into and out of the site during the noon rush hour. The volume and direction of traffic by time of day, traffic signals, intersections, and traffic medians are all part of accessibility. Visibility involves distance from the street and size of nearby buildings and signs.

Data are collected for each site for management's review, including information on all six dominant factors. For example, a manager must fill out an on-site evaluation form covering 16 characteristics. There are competitive analysis forms and a work map showing the location of current stores, competition, retail centers, plants, and the like. Management relies on judgment and past experience to make a decision about each site. The chain is also considering using more analytical methods to assist with more difficult decisions involving potential market saturation.

---

the chain has a restaurant in Austin, Texas. Let's begin by considering whether a new location is needed and then cover a systematic solution process aided by the load–distance method to deal with proximity issues.

On-Site Expansion, New Location, or Relocation

Management must first decide whether to expand on site, build another facility, or relocate to another site. A survey of *Fortune* 500 firms showed that 45 percent of expansions were on site, 43 percent were in new plants at new locations, and only 12 percent were relocations. On-site expansion has the advantage of keeping management together, reducing construction time and costs, and avoiding splitting up operations. Eventually, however, a plant may expand to the point that focus is lost and diseconomies of scale set in. Poor materials handling, employee "job bumping," increasingly complex production control, and simple lack of space all argue for building a new plant or relocating the existing one.

The advantages of building a new plant are that the firm does not have to rely on production from a single plant, escapes unproductive labor, can modernize with new production technology, and reduces transportation costs. Most firms that choose to relocate are small (less than 10 employees). They tend to be single-plant companies cramped for space and needing to redesign their production processes and layouts. More than 80 percent of all relocations are within 20 miles of the first location, which enables the firm to retain its current work force (Schmenner, 1982b).

A Systematic Selection Process

The process of selecting a new facility location involves a series of steps. First, the process is triggered by a perception that opening a facility—such as a new retail outlet or warehouse—in a new location will lead to increased profits. Those responsible for the selection decision can be a staff team in a large corporation or the individual owner of a small company.

Next, someone must identify the important location factors and categorize them as dominant or secondary. The analyst begins by considering alternative regions, then narrows the choices to alternative communities and finally to specific sites. The analyst may thoroughly evaluate between 5 and 15 sites. During the evaluation stage, the analyst collects data from various sources, including location consultants, state development agencies, city and county planning departments, chambers of commerce, land developers, electric power companies, banks, and on-site visits (see Managerial Practice 9.4).

The data collected are then analyzed, and the method used depends on whether a factor is *qualitative* or *quantitative*. A quantitative factor is more tangible and can be measured in dollars, such as annual transportation costs or taxes. It is not realistic to measure qualitative factors, such as community attitudes or quality of life, in the same way. For the quantitative factors, managers

Managerial Practice 9.4

Data Collection with the Tiger File

Many managers of small businesses can't wait to get access to the Census Bureau's new Tiger file, which is a minutely detailed computerized map of the entire United States. Tiger's formal name is the Topologically Integrated Geographic Encoding and Reference file. It lists in digital form every highway, street, bridge, and tunnel in the 50 states. When combined with a database such as the results of the 1990 census or a company's own customer files, Tiger gives desktop computer users the ability to ask various "what if" questions and print out the answers in map form. Retailers, bankers, franchisers, vehicle fleet operators, marketers, and even political consultants are excited about the combined Tiger–census file. For example, by combining population, age, and income figures with geography, retailers can pinpoint on a computer screen map the most attractive locations for a new store. And package delivery companies can use Tiger technology to figure out the most efficient routes for their truck fleets. Software companies are scrambling to take advantage of this statistical mother lode.

Source: "Businesses Map Plans for Use of Tiger Geographical Files," *Wall Street Journal*, June 8, 1990.

A technician uses a digitizing scanner to output topological information from the U.S. Census Bureau's Tiger file.

may request a projection of the dollar value of each one. These cash flows may be broken down into separate cost categories (such as inbound and outbound transportation, labor, construction, and utilities) and separate revenue sources (such as stock or bond issues, sales, and interest income). These financial factors can then be converted to a single measure of financial merit, such as present value or payback (see Supplement 1).

Management then evaluates qualitative factors pertaining to each site. Some managers are content with seeing only the expected performance on each factor. Others prefer to calculate a weighted score for each site, much the same way that a preference matrix is calculated for product or service planning (refer to Chapter 2).

The end result is a report containing site recommendations, as well as a summary of the data and analyses on which they are based. An audiovisual presentation of the key findings usually is presented to top management.

Application 9.1   *Calculating the Weighted Score*

A new medical facility, Health-Watch, is to be located in a fast-growing portion of a city. The accompanying table shows the location factors, weights, and scores (1 = poor, 5 = excellent) for one potential site. The weights in this case add up to 100 percent. What is the weighted score for this site?

Solution   The weighted scores for the last column are 100 (25 × 4), 60, 60, 60, 10, and 50. These weighted scores add up to 340, which can be compared with the total scores for other sites being evaluated. The site with the highest weighted score is best.

In this technique, management selects the factors and their weights. The factors and weights will differ from application to application. What is important in one situation can be unimportant or less important in another.

| | | | Weighted |
| | Weight | Score | Score |
Location Factor	(a)	(b)	(a × b)
Total patient miles per month	25	4	
Facility utilization	20	3	
Average time per emergency trip	20	3	
Expressway accessibility	15	4	
Land and construction costs	10	1	
Employee preferences	10	5	

Weighted Location Score for a Medical Facility's Site

Weighted Location Score = ____

Load–Distance Method

In the second step of the systematic selection process, the analyst must identify attractive candidate locations. The load–distance method can facilitate this step. Several of the location factors relate directly to distance: proximity to markets, average distance to target customers, proximity to suppliers and resources, and proximity to other company facilities. The **load–distance method** of evaluating locations deals with proximity factors and utilizes a mathematical model. The objective is to minimize the total weighted loads moving into and out of the facility. The loads are weighted by distance, so you can express the distance between two grid coordinates on a map. (You will also use this approach for layout planning in Chapter 10.)

Distance Measures. Look at Fig. 9.2 and imagine that point *A*, at coordinates (20, 10), represents a possible location for a new warehouse. Point *B*, at coordinates (80, 60), represents one of the plants supplying the new warehouse.

FIGURE 9.2

Distance Between
Two Points

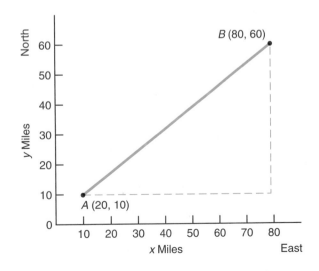

What is the distance between the two facilities? The best answer is the actual travel distance. For example, if shipments travel by truck, the distance depends on the highway system and the specific route taken. There is even computer software that gives the actual mileage between any two locations in the same country. For a rough calculation, which is the real purpose of the load–distance method, you can use either a euclidean or rectilinear distance measure.

Euclidean distance is the straight-line distance, or shortest possible path, between two points. In Fig. 9.2 the distance between points A and B is the length of the hypotenuse of a right triangle, or

$$d_{AB} = \sqrt{(x_A - x_B)^2 + (y_A - y_B)^2}$$

where

d_{AB} = distance between points A and B
x_A = x-coordinate of point A
y_A = y-coordinate of point A
x_B = x-coordinate of point B
y_B = y-coordinate of point B

Rectilinear distance assumes that the trip between two points is made with a series of 90° turns, as along city blocks. This distance is essentially the sum of the two dashed lines representing the base and side of the triangle in Fig. 9.2. The distance traveled in the x-direction is the absolute value of the difference in x-coordinates. Adding this result to the absolute value of the difference in the y-coordinates gives us

$$d_{AB} = |x_A - x_B| + |y_A - y_B|$$

Application 9.2 | *Calculating Distances*

What is the euclidean distance between points A and B in Fig. 9.2? The rectilinear distance?

Solution   Calculating the euclidean distance, we get

$$d_{AB} = \sqrt{(20 - 80)^2 + (10 - 60)^2} = 78.1$$

The rectilinear distance,

$$d_{AB} = |20 - 80| + |10 - 60| = 110$$

is longer. The two measures give quite different numbers: 78.1 versus 110. However, our interest is the *relative* performance of different locations, and we use only one of the distance measures throughout the calculations. When it comes to finding the best location, the distortion caused by using one measure when the other more closely approximates the actual distance is relatively small.

Calculating a Load–Distance Score. You can use either of the distance measures to calculate a load–distance score for any potential location. Simply multiply the loads flowing to and from a facility by the distances traveled. These flows may be shipments from suppliers, between plants, or to customers. They can also represent travel to or from the facility by employees or clients. Adjustments may be necessary, as when an inbound trip is twice as costly per mile as an outbound shipment. Expressed mathematically, the load–distance model is

$$ld = \sum_i l_i d_i$$

where

ld = total load–distance score, summed over all flows

l_i = load (such as tons or number of trips) traveling between the facility being located and location i

d_i = distance (actual, euclidean, or rectilinear) between the facility being located and location i

The higher the score, the worse the location.

Application 9.3 *Calculating Load–Distance Scores*

The Health-Watch facility is targeted to serve the seven census tracts shown in Fig. 9.3. The coordinates for the center of each census tract are shown, along with the projected populations. What is the total *ld* score if the facility is located at (7, 2), using rectilinear distance?

Solution The distance between census tract A at (2.5, 4.5) and the proposed location at (7, 2) is 4.5 miles in the east–west direction, plus 2.5 miles in the north–south direction, or 7 miles. This distance multiplied by the population equals 14, which is the *ld* score for census tract A. The sum of the *ld* scores for all tracts gives us the total *ld* score of 168 for location (7, 2). The results are shown in the following table.

Census Tract	Coordinates x	Coordinates y	Population (000) (l)	Rectilinear Distance (d)	l × d (000)
A	2.5	4.5	2	4.5 + 2.5 = 7	14
B	2.5	2.5	5	4.5 + 0.5 = 5	25
C	5.5	4.5	10	1.5 + 2.5 = 4	40
D	5	2	7	2 + 0 = 2	14
E	8	5	10	1 + 3 = 4	40
F	7	2	20	0 + 0 = 0	0
G	9	2.5	14	2 + 0.5 = 2.5	35
				Total *ld* =	168

It is possible to solve directly for the "optimal" location in Application 9.3.* However, practical considerations rarely allow managers to select this exact location. For example, land may not be available there at a reasonable price, or

---

*As long as rectilinear distance is assumed, the optimal site will have an *x*-coordinate at the median value of l_i ordered in the *x*-direction and a *y*-coordinate at the median value of l_i ordered in the *y*-direction. For more on this *cross-median* technique, see Fitzsimmons and Sullivan (1982) and Problem 19 at the end of this chapter.

FIGURE 9.3

Census Tracts in
a City

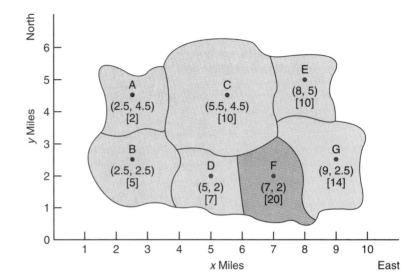

Note: Numbers in
parentheses are census
tract coordinates; the
number in brackets is
the population of the
census tract in
thousands.

other location factors may make the site undesirable. Further, the rectilinear distance measure may be unrealistic. For such reasons, the analyst should evaluate an array of location alternatives using the load–distance score method and either a full grid search or patterned search. Any distance measure can be used with these search procedures.

Full Grid Search. Intuitively, the location that minimizes ld is the one that generates big loads going short distances. Costing out different locations with this model is a relatively simple matter, following some systematic search process. Figure 9.4 shows the results of a full grid search. The total ld scores were calculated for several alternative locations (shown as dots). Of the points investigated, the (7, 2) location is best because its score of 168 is the lowest of the 15 points investigated. Should an acceptable medical facility site not be available in the immediate area of (7, 2), Fig. 9.4 shows the implications of selecting a location elsewhere. For example, a two-mile deviation directly north to (7, 4) increases the score to only 197, which is less of a penalty than the same deviation to the east or west.

Patterned Search. A patterned search is a quicker method. The analyst begins by locating the facility at the center of gravity of the target area. This location is usually not the optimum for the euclidean or rectilinear distance measures, but it still is an excellent starting point.* Its coordinates, denoted x^* and y^*, are

$$x^* = \frac{\sum_i l_i x_i}{\sum_i l_i} \quad \text{and} \quad y^* = \frac{\sum_i l_i y_i}{\sum_i l_i}$$

---

*If the distance measure is $[(x_i - x^*)^2 + (y_i - y^*)^2]$, that is, the *square* of the euclidean measure, the center of gravity location is optimal.

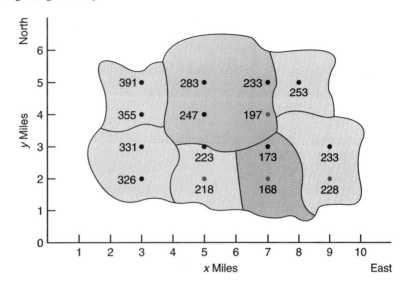

FIGURE 9.4

Load–Distance
Scores from Grid
Search

Using the center of gravity as the starting solution, the analyst next evaluates locations in the vicinity, say, one-half mile north, south, east, and west. If one or more of these locations have a load–distance score lower than the starting solution, the best one becomes the new starting solution. The analyst continues the process by searching in the near vicinity of this new starting solution. Eventually, none of the directional changes uncover a better solution. The current "starting solution" is then your final solution. Patterned search has the advantage of speed but does not yield the added information that a full grid search does.

Application 9.4   *Finding the Center of Gravity*

What is the target area's center of gravity for the Health-Watch medical facility in Application 9.3?

Solution   To calculate the center of gravity, we begin with the following information:

Census Tract	Coordinates x	Coordinates y	Population (000) l	lx	ly
A	2.5	4.5	2	5	9
B	2.5	2.5	5	12.5	12.5
C	5.5	4.5	10	55	45
D	5	2	7	35	14
E	8	5	10	80	50
F	7	2	20	140	40
G	9	2.5	14	126	35
			$\Sigma l_i = 68$	$\Sigma l_i x_i = 453.5$	$\Sigma l_i y_i = 205.5$

Next we solve for x^* and y^*.

$$x^* = \frac{\sum_i l_i x_i}{\sum_i l_i} = \frac{453.5}{68} = \underline{\underline{6.7}}$$

$$y^* = \frac{\sum_i l_i y_i}{\sum_i l_i} = \frac{205.5}{68} = \underline{\underline{3.0}}$$

The center of gravity is (6.7, 3.0), which is not necessarily optimal. It is in the general vicinity of location (7, 2), which was found to be best from the grid search in Figure 9.4. Using the center of gravity as a starting point, we can now begin a patterned search in its vicinity.

LOCATING WITHIN A NETWORK OF FACILITIES

Sometimes a new facility must be located within a network of existing facilities. There are two underlying situations. One concerns a firm whose facilities operate independently of one another, such as with many restaurants, health clinics, banks, and retail establishments in different cities. Locating these units can be treated as separate single-facility location problems, as described in the last section. The other situation concerns a firm whose facilities must interact with one another, such as with component manufacturing plants, assembly plants, and warehouses. This second situation introduces new issues, such as how to allocate work between the facilities and to determine the best capacity for each. We begin with plant charters, which are ways to organize work between multiple manufacturing plants owned by the same firm.

Plant Charters

When a company has several plants, management must figure how best to divide responsibilities among them. At least informally, each has a **plant charter,** which states its responsibilities and focuses its activities. Four types of plant charter are listed below, with the percentage in parentheses indicating frequencies found in actual practice (Schmenner, 1982b):

1. Product plant (58 percent)
2. Market-area plant (31 percent)
3. Process plant (9 percent)
4. General-purpose plant (3 percent)

Product Plant. A **product plant** is a facility that specializes in a certain product line or family of products. The most popular strategy is to have one plant or just a few to serve all market areas. Product specialization allows higher volume production than is possible otherwise. This strategy is particularly attractive when (1) production of certain products requires a favorable labor climate or proximity to suppliers and resources, and (2) outbound transportation costs are not excessive. Product plants tend to be nonunion, experience changing product mixes, and are more independent and self-sufficient, having their own staff and engineering capabilities.

Market-Area Plant. As its name implies, a **market-area plant** is a facility that produces all or most of the products for its assigned market area. Management chooses this strategy when the dominant location factor is proximity to markets. It is practical in situations where heavy or bulky products result in high outbound transportation costs, such as in the paper, plastics, pipe, glass, and oil refining industries. Because producing these commodity-like goods requires little customization, a product-focused strategy and high capital intensity can be used effectively.

Market-area plants also make sense when fast delivery times and customized products (rather than low transportation costs) are crucial. By establishing small beachhead plants for each market area early in the product life cycle, the firm maintains access to specific market areas. Initial costs can be high, but the payoff can be equally high as sales expand.

Process Plant. A **process plant** specializes in a certain segment of the firm's production. Each plant utilizes only a few technologies. This segregation provides higher volumes for each process, which is important when economies of scale are significant. Some process plants produce components that are sent on to a final assembly plant. However, process plants are utilized more frequently to produce complex products, such as computers. Even if a firm prefers less vertical integration, it may have developed a special technology that gives it a competitive advantage, which is ideal for a process plant. Process plants tend to have the highest capital intensity and are the most dependent on the rest of the corporation.

General-Purpose Plant. The **general-purpose plant** maximizes product and resource flexibility. Many Department of Defense and NASA suppliers have such plants. Also, thousands of workshops in towns and cities across the country are general-purpose plants. Multiplant firms rarely operate general-purpose plants. Normally, when a firm has grown to the point of having several plants, there is enough repeatability to focus on product, market, or process.

Manual Methods of Location Analysis

When a new facility (such as a branch bank, warehouse, or plant) is to be added to a network of other facilities, location selection becomes more complex. Management must decide not only where to locate the new facility, but also how to reallocate work among facilities to take best advantage of the new operation. Changing work allocations in turn affects the size (or capacity utilization) of the facilities. Thus the multiple-facility location problem has three dimensions—location, allocation, and capacity—that must be solved simultaneously. In many cases, the analyst can identify a workable solution merely by looking for patterns in the data and using trial-and-error calculations.

Manufacturing or Distribution Systems. In manufacturing or distribution systems, management can choose the sources of demand (plants, warehouses, distributors, retail outlets) that each new facility will serve. One approach is to divide the total market into regions, with a facility located (or to be located) in each region. Dividing the market into regions determines each facility's capacity and work allocation: Each facility serves its region and it must have enough capacity to do so. One goal of management may be to make all facilities similar in size to obtain economies of scale. The only remaining decision, then, concerns the specific location for each facility within its region. Single-facility location techniques, such as full grid search or patterned search, can be used for this purpose.

Service or Retail Systems. In service or retail systems the customers often choose the facility to serve them. This condition requires a different approach to location, allocation, and capacity decisions. Using a simple trial-and-error approach, the analyst would first select some tentative facility locations. Making an assumption about how customers select specific locations, the analyst obtains allocation and capacity estimates for each location. After evaluating the solutions obtained, the analyst can try other reasonable locations in the same manner. (Another approach to retail problems is a model developed by David Huff; see Fitzsimmons and Sullivan, 1982.)

The Transportation Method

The **transportation method** is an iterative procedure to determine the allocation pattern that minimizes the cost of shipping products from m plants, or "sources of supply," to n warehouses, or "destinations." It is a more nearly exact way to help solve multiple-facility location problems. It can also be used to determine an optimal production plan (see Chapter 14) or an optimal allocation of service accounts to service centers. Because of its importance to several areas in operations management, the transportation method is described more fully in Supplement 3. Here we apply it to multiple-facility location problems, where the sources are plants and the destinations are warehouses.

You should understand from the outset that the transportation method does not optimally solve all facets of the multiple-facility location problem. It only finds the best shipping pattern between plants and warehouses, *given* a particular set of plant locations and *given* the capacity assigned to each one. The manager must try a variety of location–capacity combinations and use the transportation method to find the optimal distribution for each one. The distribution costs (variable shipping and possibly variable production costs) are but one important input in evaluating this particular location–allocation combination. Investment costs and other fixed costs must also be considered, as well as the various qualitative factors. The manager must perform this full analysis for

FIGURE 9.5

Initial Tableau

Plant	Warehouse			Capacity
	1	2	3	
Phoenix	5.0	6.0	5.4	400
Atlanta	7.0	4.6	6.6	500
Requirements	200	400	300	900 / 900

each reasonable location–capacity combination. Given the importance of making a good decision, this extra effort is a small price to pay.

Setting Up the Initial Tableau. Whether a transportation problem is solved manually or by computer, it first must be formatted in a standard matrix, sometimes called a *tableau*, such as that shown in Fig. 9.5. The rows in the tableau (except the last one) represent plants, either existing ones or proposals for new locations. The columns (except the last one) represent warehouses. The last row is used to show each warehouse's demand, and the last column each plant's capacity. Each cell in the tableau represents the amount that the plant in the cell's row should ship to the warehouse in its column. The cost to ship one unit is shown in the upper right-hand corner of the cell. Costs are assumed to increase linearly with the size of the shipment. Sometimes it is impossible or undesirable for a particular plant to serve a particular warehouse. In such cases, simply assign a large positive number to the cell corresponding to such a shipment, such as 100 times the largest cost that otherwise appears in the matrix. This high cost should prevent the shipment from entering into the optimal solution.

In the transportation method, the sum of the shipments in a row must equal the corresponding plant's capacity. Similarly, the sum of shipments to a column must equal the corresponding warehouse's demand requirements. The transportation method also requires that the sum of capacities equals the sum of the demands.*

The basic steps in setting up an initial tableau follow:

1. Set up a matrix with a row for each plant (existing or new) being considered during this stage of the solution process. The matrix should also have a column for each warehouse.

---

*In many real problems, the sums may be unequal. If so, add either an extra row (a *dummy plant*) or column (a *dummy warehouse*) to the tableau. This case of unbalanced capacities and demands is discussed more fully in Supplement 3. Some software packages add the dummy row or column for you.

2. Add a column for plant capacities and a row for warehouse demands, and then insert their specific numerical values.
3. Fill in the body of the matrix by inserting the unit costs in the upper right-hand corner of each cell.

Application 9.5   *Setting Up the Initial Tableau*

The Sunbelt Pool Company has a plant in Phoenix that makes a line of swimming pool accessories sold throughout the South. Business is booming and exceeds the plant's 400-unit capacity. The estimated demand at its three major warehouses is 200, 400, and 300 units, respectively. Management is trying to decide whether to build a second 500-unit plant and is considering Atlanta as one possible location. Shipping costs per unit from Phoenix to its three warehouses are $5.00, $6.00, and $5.40, respectively. Shipping costs from Atlanta would be $7.00, $4.60, and $6.60, respectively. Management wants to determine the optimal allocation of shipments for an Atlanta location and two plant capacities of 400 and 500 units. (Note that the transportation method is not being used here to decide whether to build the Atlanta plant with these two capacities, only to determine the optimal shipment allocations given these choices.)

Set up the initial tableau for this location–capacity combination.

Solution   Figure 9.5 shows the initial tableau.

After the initial tableau is set up, the least-cost allocation pattern can be found either by solving manually using the transportation method (see Supplement 3) or, more likely, by using a computer package. In either case, the initial tableau is transformed through a series of iterations until the optimal tableau is reached. The optimal tableau shows how much to ship from each plant to each warehouse to minimize transportation costs. The number of nonzero shipments in the optimal solution will never exceed $m + n - 1$ cells. The shipments are such that each plant's capacity is exhausted and each warehouse demand is satisfied. The total transportation cost can be found by multiplying the quantities of the shipments by their respective unit costs and summing the products.

Application 9.6   *Interpreting the Optimal Solution*

The optimal solution for allocating shipments for an Atlanta location is shown in Fig. 9.6. Verify that each plant's capacity is exhausted and that each warehouse's demand is satisfied and then compute the total transportation cost of the solution.

Solution   Phoenix ships 200 units to warehouse 1 and 200 units to warehouse 3, exhausting its 400-unit capacity. Atlanta ships 400 units of its 500-unit capacity to warehouse 2 and the remaining 100 units to warehouse 3. All warehouse demand is satisfied: Warehouse 1 is fully supplied by Phoenix and warehouse 2 by Atlanta. Warehouse 3 receives 200 units from Phoenix and 100 units from Atlanta, satisfying its 300-unit demand. The total transportation cost is 200($5.00) + 200($5.40) + 400($4.60) + 100($6.60) = $4580.

FIGURE 9.6

Optimal Tableau

Plant	Warehouse			Capacity
	1	2	3	
Phoenix	5.0 200	6.0	5.4 200	400
Atlanta	7.0	4.6 400	6.6 100	500
Requirements	200	400	300	900 900

The Larger Solution Process. The optimal solution in Application 9.6 does not mean that the best choice is to open an Atlanta plant. It just means that the best allocation pattern, given the current choices on the other two dimensions of this multiple-facility location problem (i.e., a capacity of 400 units at Phoenix and the new plant's location at Atlanta), results in total *transportation* costs of $4580. Other costs and various qualitative factors must also be considered before this particular solution is fully evaluated. For example, the additional annual profits coming from the expansion must be balanced against the land and construction costs of a new plant in Atlanta. Thus management might use the preference matrix approach (see Application 9.1) to account for the full set of location factors.

The analyst should also evaluate other capacity and location combinations. For example, it is possible to expand at Phoenix and build a smaller plant at Atlanta. Alternatively, a new plant can be built at another location, or several new plants can be built. The analyst must repeat the analysis for each such likely location strategy.

Other Methods of Location Analysis

Many location analysis problems are even more complex than those discussed so far. Consider the complexity that a medium-sized manufacturer faces when distributing products through warehouses (often called *distribution centers*) to various demand centers. The problem is to determine the number, size, allocation pattern, and location of the warehouses. There could be thousands of demand centers, hundreds of potential warehouse locations, several plants, and multiple product lines. Transportation rates depend on the direction of shipment, product, quantity, rate breaks, and geographical area.

This kind of complexity requires use of a computer if the analyst is to make a comprehensive evaluation. Three basic types of computer models have been developed for this purpose: heuristic, simulation, and optimization.

Heuristics. Solution guidelines, or rules of thumb, that find feasible—but not necessarily the best—solutions to problems are called **heuristics.** Their advantages include efficiency and an ability to handle general views of a problem. The patterned search procedure described earlier for single-facility location problems is a typical heuristic procedure. One of the first heuristics to be computerized for location problems was proposed more than two decades ago to handle several hundred potential warehouse sites and several thousand demand centers (Kuehn and Hamburger, 1963). Many other heuristic models are available today for analyzing a variety of situations (see Khumawala and Whybark, 1971).

Simulation. A modeling technique that reproduces the behavior of a system is called **simulation.** It allows manipulation of certain variables and shows the effect on operating characteristics of interest (see Supplement 5). For location problems, simulation models allow the analyst to evaluate different location alternatives by trial and error. It is up to the analyst to seek out the most reasonable alternatives. Simulation handles more realistic views of a problem and involves the analyst in the solution process itself. For each run, the analyst inputs the facilities to be opened, and the simulator typically makes the allocation decisions based on some reasonable assumptions that have been written into the computer program. One of the more sophisticated simulations was used by the Ralston Purina Company to assist in locating warehouses (Markland, 1973). There were 137 demand centers, 5 field warehouses, and 4 plants with their associated warehouses. Random demand at each demand center by product type was simulated over a period of time. Demand was met by the closest warehouse having available inventory. Data were produced by simulating inventory levels, transportation costs, warehouse operating costs, and back orders. The simulation showed that the least-cost alternative would be to consolidate the five field warehouses into only three. Ralston Purina made this change and saved $132,000 per year.

Optimization. The transportation method was one of the first optimization procedures for solving one part (the allocation pattern) of multiple-facility location problems. In contrast to heuristics and simulation, **optimization** involves procedures to determine the "best" solution. Even though this approach might appear to be preferable, it has two limitations: (1) most optimization procedures utilize more simplified and less realistic views of a problem, and (2) they do not generate a variety of solutions, which is important to do because of the qualitative factors that are being ignored. Undoubtedly, the most sophisticated and realistic optimization techniques have been applied at Hunt-Wesson Foods (Geoffrion, 1976). As a result of the analysis, five changes were made in the company's network, reportedly saving millions of dollars.

SOLVED PROBLEMS

1. An electronics manufacturer must expand by building a second facility. The search has been narrowed to four locations, all acceptable to management in terms of dominant factors. Assessment of these sites in terms of seven

TABLE 9.1

Location Factor	Factor Weight	Factor Score for Each Location			
		A	B	C	D
1. Labor climate	20	5	4	4	5
2. Quality of life	16	2	3	4	1
3. Transportation system	16	3	4	3	2
4. Proximity to markets	14	5	3	4	4
5. Proximity to materials	12	2	3	3	4
6. Taxes	12	2	5	5	4
7. Utilities	10	5	4	3	3

Scoring key: 5 = excellent to 1 = poor.

location factors is shown in Table 9.1. For example, location A has a factor score of 5 (excellent) for labor climate; the weight for this factor (20) is the highest of any.

Calculate the weighted score for each location. Which location would you recommend?

Solution   Based on the weighted scores in Table 9.2, location C is the preferred site, although location B is a very close second.

2. The operations manager has narrowed the search for a new facility location to three communities. The annual fixed costs (for land, property taxes, insurance, equipment, and buildings) and the variable costs (for labor, materials, transportation and variable overhead) follow:

Community	Fixed Cost per Year ($000)	Variable Cost per Unit ($)
A	150	62
B	300	38
C	500	24
D	600	30

a. Plot the total cost curves for each community on a single graph. Identify on the graph the approximate range over which each community provides the lowest cost.

TABLE 9.2

Location Factor	Factor Weight	Weighted Score for Each Location			
		A	B	C	D
1. Labor climate	20	100	80	80	100
2. Quality of life	16	32	48	64	16
3. Transportation system	16	48	64	48	32
4. Proximity to markets	14	70	42	56	56
5. Proximity to materials	12	24	36	36	48
6. Taxes	12	24	60	60	48
7. Utilities	10	50	40	30	30
Total		348	370	374	330

FIGURE 9.7

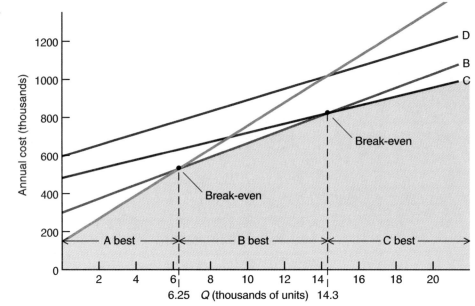

b. Using break-even analysis (see Chapters 2 and 5), calculate the break-even quantity between A and B and between B and C.

Solution   a. Figure 9.7 shows that Community A is best for low volumes, B for intermediate volumes, and C for high volumes. Community D is dominated by C, as both its fixed *and* variable costs are higher.

b. The break-even point between A and B is

$$\$150{,}000 + \$62Q = \$300{,}000 + \$38Q$$
$$Q = 6250 \text{ units}$$

The break-even point between B and C is

$$\$300{,}000 + \$38Q = \$500{,}000 + \$24Q$$
$$Q = 14{,}286 \text{ units}$$

3. A supplier to the electric utility industry has a strategy of market-area plants because its product is heavy and transportation costs are high. One market area includes the lower part of the Great Lakes region and the upper portion of the Southeastern region. Over 600,000 tons are to be shipped to eight major customer locations, as shown in Table 9.3.
   a. Calculate the center of gravity (rounding distance to the nearest tenth).
   b. Calculate the load–distance score for this location, using rectilinear distance.

Solution   a. The center of gravity is (12.4, 9.2).

$$\Sigma l_i = 5 + 92 + 70 + 35 + 9 + 227 + 16 + 153 = 607$$
$$\Sigma l_i x_i = 5(7) + 92(8) + 70(11) + 35(11) + 9(12) +$$
$$227(13) + 16(14) + 153(15) = 7504$$

TABLE 9.3

Customer Locations	Tons Shipped (000)	xy-Coordinates
Three Rivers, Mich.	5	(7, 13)
Fort Wayne, In.	92	(8, 12)
Columbus, Ohio	70	(11, 10)
Ashland, Ky.	35	(11, 7)
Kingsport, Tenn.	9	(12, 4)
Akron, Ohio	227	(13, 11)
Wheeling, W.V.	16	(14, 10)
Roanoke, Va.	153	(15, 5)

$$x^* = \frac{7504}{607} = 12.4$$

$$\Sigma l_i y_i = 5(13) + 92(12) + 70(10) + 35(7) + 9(4)$$
$$+ 227(11) + 16(10) + 153(5) = 5572$$

$$y^* = \frac{5572}{607} = 9.2$$

b. The load–distance score is

$$ld = 5(5.4 + 3.8) + 92(4.4 + 2.8) + 70(1.4 + 0.8)$$
$$+ 35(1.4 + 2.2) + 9(0.4 + 5.2) + 227(0.6 + 1.8)$$
$$+ 16(1.6 + 0.8) + 153(2.6 + 4.2) = 2662.4$$

FORMULA REVIEW

1. Euclidean distance:
$$d_{AB} = \sqrt{(x_A - x_B)^2 + (y_A - y_B)^2}$$

2. Rectilinear distance:
$$d_{AB} = |x_A - x_B| + |y_A - y_B|$$

3. Load–distance score:
$$ld = \sum_i l_i d_i$$

4. Center of gravity:
$$x^* = \frac{\sum_i l_i x_i}{\sum_i l_i} \quad \text{and} \quad y^* = \frac{\sum_i l_i y_i}{\sum_i l_i}$$

CHAPTER HIGHLIGHTS

• Three trends affecting U.S. business location patterns are geographic diversity, the growing Sunbelt, and the decline of urban areas.

• The globalization of operations affects both manufacturing and service industries. More facilities are being located in other countries (in both directions), and offshore sales (and imports) are increasing. Three factors that spur globalization are more open financial systems, improved transportation and communication technologies, and increased import penetration.

• Hot spots of global activity are the maquiladoras, the European Community, the East European and former Soviet Union market, the East Asian tigers, and services.

• Despite the advantages of global operations, differences in language, politics, and culture introduce new problems. Global, international, multinational, and transnational firms differ on how much their home offices retain centralized control.

• Location decisions depend on many factors. For a given situation some factors can be disregarded entirely; the remainder can be divided into dominant and secondary factors.

• Five groups of factors dominate most plant location decisions: favorable labor climate, proximity to markets, quality of life, proximity to suppliers and resources, and proximity to other company facilities. Which ones are "musts" depends on the type of business.

• Proximity to markets, clients, or customers is particularly dominant in service industries. A complicating factor in estimating the sales potential of a location is competition. Having competitor facilities nearby can be an asset or a liability, depending on the type of business.

• Most facility expansions occur on the same site; they are less disruptive and quicker. A point is reached, however, when focus is lost by not adding another facility or relocating the exist-

ing one. These alternatives have additional advantages, such as opportunities to modernize processes and reduce transportation costs. Relocation is chosen primarily by smaller firms, which typically move only short distances.

• One way of evaluating qualitative factors is to calculate a weighted score for each alternative location, using the preference matrix approach.

• The load–distance model brings together concerns of proximity (to markets, suppliers, resources, and other company facilities) during the early stages of location analysis. Either the euclidean or the rectilinear distance measure can be used to determine distances to reasonable locations. These alternatives can be assessed by making a full grid or patterned search. The center of gravity of an area is a good starting point for making a patterned search.

• Firms can choose among four multiplant strategies. Product plants are favored when labor climate or proximity to suppliers (or resources) is crucial. Market-area plants seek to minimize outbound transportation costs or to provide a quick, customized response to customers. With process plants, each plant performs a different segment of the production process. The plants tend to be more capital intensive, with larger economies of scale. General-purpose plants are rare in multiple-plant operations. They maximize flexibility without focusing on the product, market, or process.

• Multiple-facility problems have three dimensions: location, allocation, and capacity. Trial-and-error methods can begin with a proposed allocation and capacity plan, and then preferred locations can be determined using single-facility techniques. If customers pick the facility serving them, the process must be reversed.

• The transportation method is a basic tool for finding the best allocation pattern, given a particular combination of location–capacity choices. The analysis must be repeated for different location–capacity combinations and must be expanded to account for the full set of location factors.

● Location analysis for multiple facilities can be extremely complex. A variety of computerized heuristic, simulation, and optimization models have been developed over the last two decades to help analysts deal with this complexity.

KEY TERMS

critical mass **347**
euclidean distance **352**
facility location **344**
general-purpose plant **357**
globalization **339**
heuristics **361**

load–distance method **351**
maquiladoras **340**
market-area plant **357**
optimization **362**
plant charter **356**

process plant **357**
product plant **356**
rectilinear distance **352**
transportation method **358**
simulation **362**

STUDY QUESTIONS

1. What factors have expanded the range of possible locations?

2. What are the attractions of the Sunbelt for manufacturing plants? What can make foreign locations attractive?

3. Where is international activity particularly evident in the world today?

4. Why does an overseas location confront a manager with a different set of problems?

5. Some observers say that maquiladoras allow U.S. companies to have their unskilled jobs done across the border, while preserving in the United States the jobs of their skilled and knowledge workers. What ethical issues, if any, are involved with this use of maquiladoras?

6. Describe briefly the five dominant factors in plant location. For each one, identify a business for which it would be crucial.

7. Which location factor is particularly important to service industries? How is it related to competitor locations?

8. Under what conditions does a firm usually choose to relocate rather than expand on site?

9. What are the advantages of building another plant versus expanding on site?

10. What process can a firm use to pick a new facility location?

11. Financial analysis, such as net present value or payback, can assist in making a location decision. Explain why it normally is insufficient as the sole basis for making the decision.

12. "Euclidean and rectilinear distances differ. Furthermore, neither is correct in terms of actual distance. Therefore neither should be used for location analysis." Comment on this statement.

13. A full grid search is less efficient than a patterned search but may be preferable. Why?

14. Under what conditions would each of the four multiplant strategies likely be adopted?

15. At what point does a multiple-facility location problem break down into several single-facility location problems?

16. Why does the manual method for a multiple-facility problem depend on who decides how work is allocated?

17. What are the advantages and disadvantages of heuristic, simulation, and optimization computer models for multiple-facility location analysis?

18. "The transportation method is an optimization technique, but becomes part of a heuristic when applied to the multiple-facility location problem." Explain this statement.

PROBLEMS

Review Problems

1. Would your recommendation change in Solved Problem 1 if factors 1, 3, and 5 were ignored (that is, given weights of 0)?

2. An analyst collected the following information on where to locate an office complex (1 = poor, 10 = excellent).

Location Factors	Factor Weight	Factor Score A	Factor Score B
Construction	10	8	5
Utilities	10	3	4
Business services	20	4	7
Real estate cost	30	9	9
Quality of life	10	6	8
Transportation	20	7	6

a. Which location should be chosen on the basis of the total weighted score: A or B?
b. If the analyst weights the factors equally, does the choice change?

3. An operations manager narrowed her choice for a new plant to three locations. Fixed and variable costs follow.

Location	Fixed Cost per Year ($)	Variable Cost per Unit ($)
A	350,000	980
B	1,500,000	240
C	1,100,000	500

a. Plot the total cost curves for each community on a single graph (see Solved Problem 2). Identify on the graph the range in volume over which each location would be best.
b. What break-even quantities define each range?

4. Two location alternatives are under consideration for a new plant: Knoxville, Tennessee, and Dayton, Ohio. The Knoxville location is superior in terms of costs. However, the owners believe that sales volume would decline because this location is farther from the market and the firm's customers prefer local suppliers. The selling price of the product is $200 per unit in either case. Using the following information, determine which location yields the highest total profit contribution per year.

Location	Fixed Cost per Year	Variable Cost per Unit	Expected Annual Demand (Units)
Knoxville	$1,800,000	$60	25,000
Dayton	$2,400,000	$85	30,000

5. Excel Foods is planning a new warehouse to serve the Midwest, and St. Louis, Chicago, and Cincinnati are under consideration. For each location the annual fixed costs (rent, equipment, and insurance) and the variable costs (labor, transportation, and utilities) are listed. Sales projections indicate that the market will be between 250,000 and 450,000 units per year.

Cost	Chicago	Cincinnati	St. Louis
Fixed costs	$3,500,000	$3,350,000	$3,425,000
Variable cost/unit	$8.35	$8.25	$8.60

a. Plot the total cost curves for each location on a single graph.
b. Which city provides the lowest overall costs?

6. The following three points are the locations of important facilities in a transportation network: (10, 20), (20, 40), and (50, 0). The coordinates are in miles.
a. Calculate the euclidean distances (in miles) between each of the three pairs of facilities.
b. Calculate these distances using rectilinear distances.

7. The best location found so far in Fig. 9.4 was (7, 2), with a load–distance score of 168. Search in the neighborhood of this point for

a better solution, trying (6.5, 2), (7, 2.5), and (7, 1.5). Continue using rectilinear distances.

8. Davis, California, is considering the relocation of its main post office. The current facility has been outgrown and needs modernizing. Besides, a lot of money is unnecessarily spent transporting mail to and from the facility. Growing suburbs have shifted the population density from where it was 40 years ago, when the current facility was built.

Annette Werk, the current postmaster, asked her assistants to draw a grid map showing the seven aggregated mail source points. These aggregated mail source points are the result of grouping 40 substations in Davis into 7 larger ones. They represent points where mail is picked up and delivered. The coordinates and trips per day to and from the 7 aggregated mail source points and the current main post office (M) are shown in the following table. In effect, M acts as a mail source point even after relocation.

a. Calculate the center of gravity as a possible location for the new facility (round to the nearest whole number).

b. Compare the load–distance scores for the location in part (a) and the current location, using rectilinear distance.

Mail Source Point	Round Trips per Day (l)	xy-Coordinates (miles)
1	6	(2, 8)
2	3	(6, 1)
3	3	(8, 5)
4	3	(13, 3)
5	2	(15, 10)
6	7	(6, 14)
7	5	(18, 1)
M	3	(10, 3)

9. Reconsider Solved Problem 3 and evaluate the four points that are one unit of distance north, east, south, and west of the center of gravity. Use rectilinear distances. Does this

limited pattern search yield a better solution?

10. A manufacturer is investigating which location would best position its new plant relative to two suppliers (located in cities A and B) and one market area (represented by city C). Management has limited the search for this plant to those three locations. The following information has been collected.

Location	xy-Coordinates (miles)	Tons per Year (000)	Freight Rate ($/ ton-mile)
A	(100, 200)	4	3
B	(400, 100)	3	1
C	(100, 100)	4	3

a. Which of the three locations gives the lowest total cost, assuming euclidean distances? *Hint:* The cost of inbound shipments from supplier B is $3000 per mile (3000 × $1) between location B and the new plant.

b. Which location is best, assuming rectilinear distances?

c. What is the center of gravity (coordinates)?

11. The Acme Company has four factories that ship products to five warehouses. The shipping costs, requirements, and capacities are shown in the following tables.

From	Shipping Cost ($/case) to				
	W1	W2	W3	W4	W5
F1	1	3	4	5	6
F2	2	2	1	4	5
F3	1	5	1	3	1
F4	5	2	4	5	4

Requirement (000)	Capacity (000)
W1: 60	F1: 80
W2: 70	F2: 60
W3: 50	F3: 60
W4: 30	F4: 50
W5: 40	

a. Set up the initial tableau for this transportation problem.

TABLE 9.4

Port of Entry	Warehouse		
	Chicago	Atlanta	New York
A. Los Angeles			
Distance (miles)	1,800	2,600	3,200
Shipping cost ($/unit)	0.0017/mile	0.0017/mile	0.0017/mile
Number (units/year)	10,000	7,500	12,500
B. San Francisco			
Distance	1,700	2,800	3,000
Shipping cost ($/unit)	0.0020/mile	0.0020/mile	0.0020/mile
Number (units/year)	10,000	7,500	12,500

b. Using trial and error, determine a "good" solution, with no more than 8 nonzero shipments. Show that all capacities are exhausted and all demands met with your solution.

c. What is the total cost of your solution?

12. A personal computer manufacturer plans to locate its assembly plant in Taiwan and to ship its computers back to the United States through either Los Angeles or San Francisco. It has distribution centers in Atlanta, New York, and Chicago and will ship to them from whichever city is chosen as the port of entry on the West Coast. Overall transportation cost is the only criterion for choosing a port.

Using the load–distance model and the information in Table 9.4, select the more cost effective city.

13. The Pelican Company has four distribution centers (A, B, C, and D) that require 50,000, 40,000, 60,000, and 40,000 gallons of diesel fuel, respectively, per month for their long-haul trucks. Three fuel wholesalers (1, 2, and 3) have indicated their willingness to supply up to 60,000, 80,000, and 50,000 gallons of fuel, respectively. The total cost (shipping plus price) of delivering 1000 gallons of fuel from each wholesaler to each distribution center is shown in the following table.

Wholesaler	Distribution Center			
	A	B	C	D
1	1.70	1.60	1.60	1.60
2	1.50	1.80	1.60	1.70
3	1.80	1.50	1.80	1.60

a. Set up the initial tableau for this transportation problem.

b. Determine by trial and error a "good" solution, with no more than 6 nonzero shipments. Show that all capacities are exhausted and all demands met with your solution.

c. What is the total cost of your solution?

Advanced Problems

Supplement Connections: Problems 20–25 require prior reading of Supplement 3 (Transportation Method), and Problem 25 of Supplement 1 (Financial Analysis). A computer package is useful for solving Problems 20–25.

14. Suppose that two medical facilities, rather than one, are to serve the census tracts in Fig. 9.3. One option is to build them at locations C and G.

a. Assuming that the patients in each tract will go to the nearest facility, how much capacity does each facility need (in terms of total population served)? Are the capacities well balanced?

b. What is the total load-distance score for this solution, assuming rectilinear distance?

15. Reconsider Problem 14. Find, by trial and error, a better solution than opening medical facilities at locations C and G. Limit your search to locations B, C, D, and G, staying with rectilinear distance.
    a. What is the total load–distance score of your improved solution?
    b. How much capacity is needed at each medical facility in your solution?

16. A different option is being considered for building two medical facilities, rather than one, to serve the census tracts in Fig. 9.3. Facility 1 would serve the western region (census tracts A, B, C, and D), and facility 2 the eastern region (census tracts E, F, and G).
    a. Find the locations of the two facilities, using the center of gravity and rounding to the nearest tenth.
    b. How much capacity does each facility need (in terms of total population served)? Are the capacities well balanced?
    c. What is the total load–distance score for this solution, assuming rectilinear distance?

17. Management wants to locate two facilities to serve two groups of demand points. The following data were collected.

Demand Point	xy-Coordinates (Miles)	Trips per Day (*l*)
A	(0, 10)	10
B	(15, 30)	15
C	(20, 15)	20
D	(30, 30)	30
E	(40, 45)	15

a. Draw a grid map showing the locations of the demand points.
b. Divide the points into two groups on a north–south basis. The north facility will serve B, D, and E, while the south facility will serve A and C. Let the facility locations be the centers of gravity of the

two areas, rounding to the nearest whole numbers. What is the total load–distance score for the entire system, assuming euclidean distance?
c. Repeat part (b) for an east–west division. The west facility will serve A, B, and C, while the east facility will serve D and E. Is this solution better or worse than the one in part (b)?

18. PG Oil Company plans to open two new filling stations in a region encompassing population centers A through H. The objective is to maximize proximity to population centers. It is assumed that customers will go to the nearest available facility. A map of the area is shown in Fig. 9.8. The numbers are the actual distances between centers. Locations B and F are highway intersections, rather than population centers. Population densities and distances between each pair of points are given in Table 9.5. For example, the shortest distance from A to E (and vice versa) is 62.
    a. Management wants to limit the locations to these eight points and is giving particular attention to a plan for locating facilities at C and H. Calculate the total load–distance score for this plan.
    b. Try at least one other plan that you think might improve on this score.

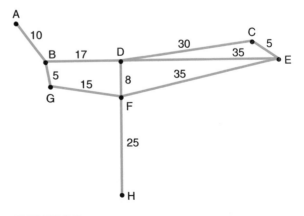

FIGURE 9.8

TABLE 9.5

From	A	B	C	D	E	F	G	H	Population Density
					To				
A	0	10	57	27	62	30	15	55	5
B	10	0	47	17	52	20	5	45	0
C	57	47	0	30	5	38	52	63	10
D	27	17	30	0	35	8	22	33	20
E	62	52	5	35	0	35	50	60	20
F	30	20	38	8	35	0	15	25	0
G	15	5	52	22	50	15	0	40	4
H	55	45	63	33	60	25	40	0	20

19. Continuing to assume rectilinear distance, use the cross-median technique (see the footnote on page 353) to find the optimal location for the problem in Application 9.3.
   a. First calculate the median value, which is one half the sum of the loads to all facilities.
   b. Order the facilities on the basis of their x-coordinates, starting with the facility having the smallest and ending with the one having the largest. Maintaining this order, add the facility loads until the total reaches or exceeds the median value calculated in part (a). Identify the facility that corresponds to the last load that entered the sum. Its x-coordinate is optimal for the new facility.
   c. Repeat part (b), except order the facilities on the basis of their y-coordinates, from smallest to largest. The y-coordinate of the facility corresponding to the last load entering the sum is optimal for the new facility.
   d. How does the optimal solution compare with the best location shown in Fig. 9.4 in terms of the load–distance score?

20. The Ajax International Company has four factories that ship products to five warehouses. The shipping costs, requirements, and capacities are shown in the following tables. Use the transportation method to find the shipping schedule that minimizes shipping cost.

Shipping Cost ($/case) to

From	W1	W2	W3	W4	W5
F1	1	3	3	5	6
F2	2	2	1	4	5
F3	1	5	1	3	1
F4	5	2	4	5	4

Requirement (000)	Capacity (000)
W1: 45	F1: 50
W2: 30	F2: 80
W3: 30	F3: 80
W4: 35	F4: 40
W5: 50	

21. Consider further the Ajax International Company situation described in Problem 20. Ajax has decided to close F3 because of high operating costs. In addition, the company has decided to add 80,000 units of capacity to F4. The logistics manager is worried about the effect of this move on transportation costs. Presently, F3 is shipping 30,000 units to W4 and 50,000 units to F5 at a cost of $140,000 [30,000(3) + 50,000(1)]. If these warehouses are now served by F4, the cost would increase to $350,000 [30,000(5) + 50,000(4)]. Thus the logistics manager has requested a budget increase of $210,000.
   a. Should the logistics manager get the budget increase?
   b. If not, how much would you budget for the increase in shipping costs?

22. Consider the facility location problem at the

Giant Farmer Company described in Application S3.1 in Supplement 3.

a. Find the minimum-cost shipping plan for a new plant location in Atlanta.

b. Find the minimum-cost plan for an alternative location in Memphis. The shipping costs per case from Memphis are $3 to Miami, $11 to Denver, $6 to Lincoln, and $5 to Jackson.

23. The Bright Paint Company has four factories (A, B, C, and D) that require 30,000, 20,000, 10,000, and 20,000 paint cans, respectively, per month. Three paint can suppliers (1, 2, and 3) have indicated their willingness to supply up to 40,000, 20,000, and 30,000 cans per month, respectively. The total cost (shipping plus price) of delivering 100 cans from each supplier to each Bright plant is shown in the following table.

	Bright Plant			
Supplier	A	B	C	D
1	$54	$48	$50	$46
2	52	50	54	48
3	46	48	50	52

Currently, supplier 1 is shipping 20,000 cans to plant B and 20,000 cans to D. Supplier 2 is shipping 30,000 cans to A, and supplier 3 is shipping 10,000 gallons to D. Does the present delivery arrangement minimize the cost to the Bright Paint Company? If not, find a plan that does minimize total costs.

24. The Chambers Corporation produces and markets a certain product, which it stocks in various warehouses throughout the country. Recently, its market research group compiled a forecast indicating that a significant increase in demand will occur in the near future, after which demand will level off for the foreseeable future. The company has decided to satisfy this demand by constructing new plant capacity. Chambers already has plants in Baltimore and Milwaukee and has no desire to relocate those facilities. Each plant is capable of producing 600,000 units per year.

After a thorough search, the company has developed two alternative sites and three capacity alternatives. Alternative 1 is to build a 600,000-unit plant in Portland. Alternative 2 is to build a 600,000-unit plant in San Antonio. Alternative 3 is to build a 300,000-unit plant in Portland and a 300,000-unit plant in San Antonio.

The company has four warehouses that distribute the product to retailers. The market research study provided the following data.

Warehouse	Expected Future Annual Demand (units)
Columbus (CO)	300,000
Los Angeles (LA)	600,000
Seattle (SE)	400,000
Atlanta (AT)	500,000

The logistics department compiled the following cost table that specified the cost per unit to ship the product from each plant to each warehouse in the most economical manner, subject to the reliability of the various carriers involved.

	Warehouse			
Plant	CO	LA	SE	AT
Baltimore	$0.20	$0.85	$0.75	$0.35
Milwaukee	0.15	0.70	0.65	0.55
Portland	0.60	0.30	0.10	0.85
San Antonio	0.45	0.40	0.65	0.55

As one part of the location–capacity decision, management would like to estimate the total distribution cost for each alternative. Use the transportation method to calculate these estimates.

25. Consider Problem 24 further. If the total cost of a plant with a 600,000-unit capacity is $6,250,000 and the cost of a plant with a 300,000-unit capacity is $3,000,000, would this change your recommendation? Assume an economic life of ten years, a hurdle rate of 12 percent, and equal product sales and production costs regardless of plant capacity or location.

Rhenish Breweries was founded in Milwaukee during the 1870s and remained a regional brewer until the early 1970s, when it expanded its market to the East Coast by building new production facilities at Troy, New York. At the present time, Rhenish wants to enter new markets in Arizona, California, Idaho, Nevada, Nevada, Oregon, Texas, and Washington. John Marlowe, president of Rhenish, has devised three alternative plans for expansion. Financing is required for all three plans, and Marlowe wants to earn an after-tax return of at least 8 percent on the investment. For internal planning purposes, assume straight-line depreciation.

The first plan locates one brewery in Oakland, California, to serve the new market in all seven western states. This plan would involve an initial expense of $10 million for equipment. This equipment would be depreciated over ten years on the straight-line method and would have an estimated salvage value of $300,000. For its brewery, Rhenish has agreed to lease for ten years a building owned by an Oakland bank. The yearly lease would be $240,000 for the first five years, then would increase to $300,000 a year for the last five years.

The second plan is to operate the Milwaukee brewery on two shifts daily to produce the additional beer required for the West Coast. This would require the plant to operate five days a week, 16 hours a day. Rhenish would be required to install additional tanks for $2.2 million, with a fully depreciated (straight-line) salvage value of $300,000 after ten years. Marlowe estimates that the total operating costs for Rhenish Breweries will be $400,000 higher for plan two than for plan one, due primarily to the inefficiencies of operating the Milwaukee plant for an extra shift. This amount was determined by estimating the total operating costs for each location. The cost estimates have allowed for all expected additional costs for both Oakland and Milwaukee, including inefficiency costs in both locations due to hiring new workers and new managers.

The third plan is to start a smaller facility in Oakland to serve part of the new region and to operate the Milwaukee brewery on the two-shift basis but with fewer people on the second shift than required under plan two. The yearly operating cost for plan three would be $220,000 more than that for plan one. The Oakland facility equipment could be furnished and installed at half the plan one cost and provide for 50 percent of total additional demand. The bank would lease a smaller building, starting at $150,000 rent a year for five years and increasing to $190,000 a year for the last five years. Additional tanks for the Milwaukee brewery would cost $1,100,000, and the salvage value after ten years would be $300,000.

Exhibit 1 gives the anticipated demand for each city in which Rhenish will have a distributor and the mileage from Milwaukee and from Oakland to each distribution city in the western region.

John Marlowe will not approve any expansion plan until all the financial implications have been fully analyzed. The current gross margin for each plan (revenues from sales minus ordinary operations costs) is $0.75 per case. All costs identified in each of the three plans are those in excess of the ordinary operations costs. These costs must be deducted from the gross margin to determine profit before taxes; the tax rate will be 40 percent, no matter which plan is selected. While Marlowe suspects that plan one is the optimal plan, he has no factual basis for that hunch. Finally, he asks an operations consultant to analyze the data and present him with (1) a plan that considers all costs in the proposed expansion and makes a recommendation for the optimal plan (with all calculations leading to that conclusion clearly identified), or (2) a recommendation not to expand, again with all supporting data and calculations to justify that recommendation.

Another factor that John Marlowe has to consider is the company's long-standing relationship with the local community, and especially with the local unions with which Rhenish has had amicable relations for years. Bill Fritz, the business agent for one of the major unions, visited John Marlowe to press for adding the additional capacity to the Milwaukee brewery. He stressed the good working relationship the union and

---

*Barry Kay, research assistant at Boston College, prepared this case for class discussion.

EXHIBIT 1

City	Yearly Demand (cases)	Distance Between Cities (miles)	
		Oakland	Milwaukee
Boise, Idaho	800,000	649	1944
Los Angeles	2,000,000	425	2102
Oakland	1,500,000	—	2194
Phoenix	900,000	818	1803
Portland	900,000	677	2233
Dallas	1,500,000	1850	1056
Oklahoma City	800,000	1647	886
Denver	700,000	1261	1036

Note: The minimum shipping cost is $0.25 per case, up to 500 miles. The cost increases by $0.01 per case for each 100 miles (or fraction thereof) over 500 miles. For plan one and plan three, shipment to a distributor in Oakland would not be necessary since distribution for Oakland will come directly from the Oakland Brewery facility.

Rhenish had sought to maintain over the years, and he indicated that he and his members would be very disappointed to see the additional brewery capacity located elsewhere. Soon after Fritz's visit, a group from the Chamber of Commerce visited Marlowe to urge him to "keep the jobs in Milwaukee" and not expand in a location other than Milwaukee. As with the unions, Marlowe doesn't want to create acrimony with the local business community. He is determined to try to factor the concerns of the unions and of the business community into his final decision.

QUESTIONS

1. As the consultant, you are to analyze all three plans to determine the overall cost implications related to each plan.
2. Present your recommendation whether to expand or not to expand. Indicate which of the three plans is best, including all of your analysis. In analyzing plan three, be prepared to justify your distribution mix between Oakland and Milwaukee.
3. Is there additional information you would like to have before you make your recommendation? If so, list it and explain why you need it.

SELECTED REFERENCES

Bartlett, Christopher, and Sumantra Ghoshal. *Managing Across Borders.* Boston: Harvard Business School Press, 1989.

"The Best Cities for Business." *Fortune,* November 4, 1991, pp. 52–84.

Fitzsimmons, James A. "A Methodology for Emergency Ambulance Development." *Management Science,* vol. 19, no. 6 (February 1973), pp. 627–636.

Fitzsimmons, James A., and Robert S. Sullivan. *Service Operations Management.* New York: McGraw-Hill, 1982.

Fulton, Maurice. "New Factors in Plant Location." *Harvard Business Review* (May–June 1971), pp. 4–17, 166–168.

Geoffrion, Arthur M. "Better Distribution Planning with Computer Models." *Harvard Business Review* (July–August 1976), pp. 92–99.

"A Global Fight in the Tire Industry." *New York Times,* March 10, 1988.

Hamel, Gary, and C.K. Prahalad. "Do You Really Have a Global Strategy?" *Harvard Business Review* (July–August 1985), pp. 139–148.

Harms, Craig S. "A Comparison of Facility Location Techniques." Unpublished doctoral dissertation, The Ohio State University, 1984.

Harris, Philip R., and Robert T. Moran. *Managing Cultural Differences.* Houston: Gulf Publishing Company, 1987.

Hayes, Robert H., and Steven C. Wheelwright. *Restoring Our Competitive Edge: Competing Through Manufacturing.* New York: John Wiley & Sons, 1984.

Kanter, Rosabeth Moss. "Transcending Business Boundaries: 12,000 World Managers View Change." *Harvard Business Review,* vol. 91, no. 3 (May–June 1991), pp. 151–164.

Khumawala, Basheer M., and D. Clay Whybark. "A Comparison of Some Recent Warehouse Location Techniques." *The Logistics Review,* vol. 7, no. 3 (Spring 1971).

Kolesar, P., and W.E. Walker. "An Algorithm for the Dynamic Relocation of Fire Companies." *Operations Research*, vol. 22, no. 2 (March–April 1974), pp. 249–274.

Kuehn, Alfred A., and Michael J. Hamburger. "A Heuristic Program for Locating Warehouses." *Management Science*, vol. 9, no. 4 (July 1963), pp. 643–666.

Love, Robert F., James G. Morris, and George O. Weslowsky. *Facilities Location: Models and Methods*. New York: North-Holland, 1988.

Magaziner, Ira C., and Mark Patinkin. *The Silent War*. New York: Random House, 1989.

Markland, Robert E. "Analyzing Geographical Discrete Warehousing Networks by Computer Simulation." *Decision Sciences*, vol. 4, no. 2 (April 1973), pp. 216–236.

Miller, Jeffrey G., and Aleda V. Roth. "Manufacturing Strategies: Executive Summary of the 1988 North American Manufacturing Futures Survey." Boston University, 1988.

Porter, Michael E. "The Competitive Advantage of Nations." *Harvard Business Review*, vol. 90, no. 2 (March–April 1990), pp. 73–93.

Schmenner, Roger W. *Making Business Location Decisions*. Englewood Cliffs, N.J.: Prentice-Hall, 1982(a).

Schmenner, Roger W. "Multiple Manufacturing Strategies Among the *Fortune* 500." *Journal of Operations Management*, vol. 2, no. 2 (February 1982b), pp. 77–86.

Skinner, Wickham. *Manufacturing in the Corporate Strategy*. New York: John Wiley & Sons, 1978.

"Spanning the Globe." *Wall Street Journal*, October 4, 1991.

Sugiura, Hideo. "How Honda Localizes Its Global Strategy." *Sloan Management Review* (Fall 1990), pp. 77–82.

Chapter 10

LAYOUT

What centers should
we work into the
layout?

Should we have a
process, product,
hybrid, or fixed
layout?

What performance
criteria do we need
to emphasize?

Can we create some
miniature product
layouts in our
facility?

What type of layout
pattern makes sense
for our warehouse?

What is the best
trade-off between
proximity and
privacy for our office
layout?

What is the desired
output rate for our
line?

Should we have a
paced or an
unpaced line?

Should we consider
a mixed-model line?

What should we do
to humanize product
layouts?

When International Paper Company sold its New York City headquarters, the chairman and his 125-person team moved to Purchase, New York, while 1000 other executives and employees in administration set up housekeeping in Memphis, Tennessee. A major reason for the move was to decentralize decision making, to move managers closer to their operations and customers. The separation created a psychological distance from headquarters, achieving the corporate strategy of pushing decision making down in the organization and streamlining headquarters. When someone is just a floor away, there is a tendency to walk up and discuss a decision. Meanwhile, in the service sector, Wendy's International Incorporated was pouring $40 million into refurbishing more than 500 restaurants. The goal was to achieve a very contemporary appeal, featuring stucco exteriors, earthtone colors, neon lighting, and backlighted awnings that are especially visible at night.

Such issues are part of facility layout. We've already considered what products and services to offer, what positioning strategy to use, what types of work to perform, what types of employees and technology to employ, how much plant and equipment capacity to provide, and where to locate facilities. Facility layout decisions also deal with questions concerning what, how much, and where, translating the broader decisions into actual physical arrangements of people, equipment, and space for the purpose of producing goods and services. In this chapter we examine layout in a variety of settings, along with techniques of layout analysis.

WHAT IS LAYOUT PLANNING?

Layout planning involves decisions about the physical arrangement of economic activity centers within a facility. An **economic activity center** can be anything that consumes space: a person or group of people, a machine, a workbench or work station, a department, a stairway or an aisle, a timecard rack, a cafeteria or storage room, and so on. The goal of layout planning is to allow workers and equipment to operate at peak effectiveness and efficiency. The term *physical arrangement* raises four questions for the manager:

1. **What centers should the layout include?** Centers should reflect the process design and maximize productivity. For example, a central storage area for tools is most efficient for certain processes, but keeping tools at individual work stations makes more sense for others. Centers also should reflect corporate strategy: International Paper's separation of its headquarters from the rest of the organization is an example.
2. **How much space and capacity does each center need?** Inadequate space can reduce productivity, deprive employees of privacy, and even

FIGURE 10.1

Identical Relative
Locations and
Different Absolute
Locations

Original layout

Revised layout

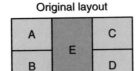
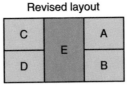

create health and safety hazards. However, excessive space is wasteful, can reduce productivity, and can isolate employees unnecessarily.

3. **How should each center's space be configured?** The amount of space, its shape, and the elements in a work center are all interrelated. For example, placement of a desk and chair relative to the other furniture is determined by the size and shape of the office, as well as the activities performed there. Providing a pleasing atmosphere is also part of the layout configuration, as with the refurbishing of Wendy's restaurants.

4. **Where should each center be located?** Location, whether in the middle of the facility or in a back room, can significantly affect productivity.

The fourth question has two dimensions: relative location and absolute location. Managers must consider both when modifying existing layouts to increase productivity. Look at the plan on the left in Fig. 10.1. It shows the location of five departments (A–E) on a floor, where department E has been allocated twice the space of the others. The location of A relative to B is the same as the relative location of C to D, so the distance between A and B is equal to the distance between C and D. Relative location is normally the crucial issue in both materials-handling cost and communication effectiveness.

Now look at the plan on the right. Although the relative locations are the same, absolute locations have changed. This modified layout might prove unworkable. For example, the cost of moving department C to the northwest corner could be excessive. Or C could be a dock that must abut a railroad spur, which currently comes in on the northeast side of the building; the cost of extending the spur also could be prohibitive.

STRATEGIC ISSUES

Operations managers must tie layout choices to higher-level managerial decisions, as Managerial Practice 10.1 illustrates. For example, if a retailer shifts its product plans and competitive priorities, it must communicate this shift through the "spatial language" of facility layout. If the retailer plans to sell higher-quality, higher-priced merchandise, the store layout should convey exclusiveness and luxury.

Layout has many practical and strategic implications. Proper layout facilitates the flow of materials and more efficient utilization of labor and equipment. Layout can also reduce hazards to workers, improve employee morale, and aid communication between workers or between supervisors and subordinates. Of course, the type of operation will determine layout requirements.

Among the several fundamental layout choices facing managers are whether to plan for current or future (and less predictable) needs, whether to select a

Managerial Practice 10.1

Retailers Match Layouts to Strategies

J.C. Penney

J.C. Penney is changing its strategy to avoid the second-tier status of some department stores. It is offering better-quality merchandise in more attractive stores. Although the stores still offer bottom-of-the-line price, the overall price mix is up. At the Penney's in Dallas' NorthPark Center, the average price of women's career dresses is $105, up 50 percent from two years earlier. Penney is also putting more emphasis on its specialties. Planners eliminated some departments, such as appliance, lawn and garden, paint, hardware, automotive, home electronics, and sporting goods, and expanded others, such as apparel, jewelry, and luggage. As the accompanying photographs illustrate, Penney has upgraded its image with parquet and carpeting, new mannequins, softer lighting, snazzy chrome-and-glass fixtures, wood paneling, and more attractive displays of merchandise. Over the past five years, annual revenue has grown 16 percent and net income has more than doubled, to $802 million.

The Limited

The Limited Inc., the trendy specialty retailer, is reformulating its recipe for success. Once a small outlet geared toward teenagers, the store has quadrupled in size and now woos older customers with the polished look of a European boutique. From the grainy wood floors to the black lacquered display cases, the store serves as a stage for up-to-the-moment sportswear for women and now men. The look of the stores is its latest weapon. While rivals have left their layouts basically unchanged, The Limited is tripling the size of its stores and spending millions on a fresh look. It gives its customers, who should spend more time in its stores and pay more for merchandise, an upscale ambience.

Wal-Mart Stores

Wal-Mart, a discounter newly anointed as the largest U.S. retailer, is experimenting with a prototype store in Rogers, Arkansas (population 24,000). The layout suggests that Wal-Mart believes its customers will be as concerned about service as about low prices. On entering the store, customers expecting the usual warehouse-like atmosphere of discount stores will be shocked. With wide aisles, less cramped displays, sitting areas for customers, and classy displays, it looks more like an upscale department store than a spartan discounter. Unlike department stores, however, the store has the same bargain-basement prices found in all its outlets. And the displays organize related products—such as shower curtains, towels, and ceramic bathroom accessories—into visual "vignettes" that encourage sales of "multiples," or related products. Many retailing executives consider Wal-Mart the leader in attention to the layout details that help shape shoppers' attitudes. The chain is particularly adept at striking the delicate balance needed to convince customers that its prices are low without making people feel that its stores are too cheap.

*T*hese photos show layouts of the men's clothing departments at J.C. Penny, before (top) and after (bottom) redesigning displays.

Sources: "Penney Moves Upscale in Merchandise But Still Has to Convince Public," *Wall Street Journal,* June 7, 1990; "Limited Inc., on New Tack, Pulls Ahead of Retail Gang," *Wall Street Journal,* February 24, 1989; "Wal-Mart's Store of the Future Blends Discount Prices, Department-Store Feel," *Wall Street Journal,* May 17, 1991.

single-story or multiple-story design, whether to open up the planning process to employee suggestions, what type of layout to choose, and what performance criteria to emphasize. Because of their strategic importance, we focus on the last two issues.

Choosing a Layout Type

The choice of layout type depends largely on the firm's positioning strategy. There are four basic types of layout: process, product, hybrid, and fixed.

Process Layout. When positioning strategy calls for low-volume, high-variety production, such as in a job shop, the operations manager must organize resources (employees and equipment) around the process. (See Fig. 2.5 in Chapter 2.) A **process layout,** which groups work stations or departments according to function, accomplishes this purpose. For example, all drilling equipment is located in one area of a machine shop, or all budget apparel is displayed in one area of a department store. The process layout is most common when the same operation must intermittently produce many different products or serve many different customers. Demand levels are too low or unpredictable for management to set aside human and capital resources exclusively for a particular product line or type of customer. Resources are relatively general purpose, flexible, and less capital intensive. Because the process layout is less vulnerable to changes in product mix or new marketing strategies, it is more flexible. Equipment utilization is high because the requirements for all products can be pooled. In addition, employee supervision can be more specialized, an important factor when job content requires a good deal of technical knowledge.

As you saw in Chapter 2, a process focus (and the accompanying process layout) also has its disadvantages. Processing rates tend to be slower, and productive time is lost in changing from one product or service to another. More space and capital are tied up in inventory, which helps work stations to work independently despite their variable output rates. The time lags between job starts and end points are relatively long, and materials handling tends to be costly. Diversity in routings and jumbled flows necessitate the use of variable path devices, such as carts rather than conveyors. A major challenge in designing a process layout is to locate centers so that they bring some order to the apparent chaos of the process-focused operation.

Product Layout. When a facility's positioning strategy calls for repetitive or continuous production, the operations manager dedicates resources to individual products or tasks. This strategy is achieved by a **product layout,** which arranges work stations or departments in a linear path. Output is balanced to move the product or customer along in a smooth, continuous flow. Operations arranges resources around the product's route, rather than share them across many products. (We demonstrate later that some product layouts, called *mixed-model lines*, can handle several products as long as their processing requirements are similar.) An automated car wash is a good example. Product layouts often follow a straight line, but this arrangement is not always best. In such cases, managers may opt for L, O, S, or U shapes. A product layout is often called a *production,* or *assembly, line.* The difference is that an assembly line is limited to assembly processes.

Product layouts often rely heavily on specialized, capital-intensive re- sources. These layouts are therefore riskier for products or services with short or uncertain lives. Their advantages—faster processing rates, lower invento- ries, and less unproductive time lost to changeovers and materials handling— are the mirror image of the disadvantages of process layouts.

One of the mysteries in process layouts—where to locate centers—is trivial for product layouts. Obviously, if a product's routing is A–B–C, A should be placed next to B and B next to C in the layout. This arrangement, which simply follows the product's routing, ensures that all interacting pairs of centers are as close together as possible (have a common boundary). The challenge of prod- uct layouts is to group activities into work stations and achieve the desired output rate with the least resources. The composition and number of work stations are crucial decisions.

Hybrid Layout. More often than not, a positioning strategy combines elements of both a product and process focus. This intermediate strategy calls for a **hy- brid layout,** which arranges some portions of the facility as a process layout and others as a product layout. Operations managers often create a hybrid layout when introducing flexible manufacturing systems (FMS). Group technology (GT) cells and one worker, multiple machines (OWMM) stations, which we cover later, are other hybrid layouts. Each of those technologies helps achieve repeatability, even when product volumes are too low to justify dedicating a single line to one product. They become "islands of automation," representing miniature product layouts, as all resources needed to make the family of parts are brought together as one center. The rest of the facility represents a process layout. Hybrid layouts also occur in facilities having both fabrication and as- sembly operations. Fabrication operations, where components are made from raw materials, tend to have a process focus. Assembly operations tend to have a product focus.

A retail store is an example of a hybrid layout in a nonmanufacturing setting. The manager may group similar merchandise, enabling customers to find de- sired items easily (a process layout). At the same time the layout often leads customers along predetermined paths, such as up and down aisles (a product layout). The intent is to maximize exposure to the full array of goods, thereby stimulating sales.

Fixed-Position Layout. The fourth basic type of layout is the **fixed-position layout.** In this arrangement, the product is fixed in place; workers, along with their tools and equipment, come to the product to work on it. This type of layout makes sense when the product is particularly massive or difficult to move, as in shipbuilding, assembling locomotives, making huge pressure ves- sels, building dams, or repairing home furnaces. A fixed-position layout mini- mizes the number of times that the product must be moved and often is the only feasible solution.

Performance Criteria

Other fundamental choices facing the layout planner concern *performance criteria*. As with decisions on product or service planning and location, the manager must decide early in the solution process which dimensions need emphasis in defining a good solution. Should the layout be developed to maximize sales or to minimize materials-handling costs? The answer depends on the situation, as Table 10.1 demonstrates. In most cases, multiple criteria are involved.

Capital Investment. Floor space, equipment needs, and inventory levels depend in part on whether management selects a process or a product layout. When volumes are low, higher resource utilization is possible with a process focus. This focus reduces equipment and space needs, although management must consider the possible disadvantage of added space and investment in inventory. Capital investment is an important criterion in all settings. If the objective is to increase privacy by adding partitions, the amount of investment required rises. If an existing layout is to be revised, renovation costs can be significant. Recent remodeling at Penney, Sears, and K mart stores had a total price tag of almost $5 billion.

Materials Handling. Relative locations of centers should allow large flows to go short distances. Frequent trips or interactions between work centers should be recognized by locating these centers close to one another. In a manufacturing plant, this approach minimizes materials-handling costs. In a warehouse, stock-picking costs are reduced by storing items typically needed for the same order next to one another. In a retail store, customer convenience improves if items are grouped predictably to minimize customer search and travel time. In an office, communication and cooperation often improve when people or departments that must interact frequently are located near one another. Telephone calls and memos can be poor substitutes for face-to-face communication.

TABLE 10.1 / *Performance Criteria for Four Different Settings*

Manufacturing Plant	Office	Warehouse	Retail Store
Capital investment	Capital investment	Capital investment	Capital investment
Materials handling	Communication	Stockpicking	Customer convenience
Flexibility	Flexibility	Flexibility	Flexibility
Work environment	Atmosphere	Work environment	Atmosphere
Maintenance	Organizational structure	Shelf life	Sales
Employee attitudes	Employee attitudes		
Labor productivity			

Flexibility. A flexible layout is best for many situations. (See Managerial Practice 10.2.) **Layout flexibility** means either that the facility remains desirable after significant changes occur or that it can be easily adapted in response to them. The changes can be in the mix of customers served by a store, goods made at a plant, space requirements in a warehouse, or organizational structure in an office. Layout flexibility in the first sense depends in part on management's ability to forecast well. Layout flexibility in the second sense means designing the layout to minimize the cost of revisions to it. Using modular furniture and partitions, rather than permanent load-bearing walls, is one way to minimize the cost of office layout changes. So can having wide bays (fewer columns), heavy-duty floors, and extra electrical connections in a plant.

Other Criteria. Table 10.1 shows other criteria that also can be important. Labor productivity can be affected if certain work stations can be operated by common personnel in some layouts but not in others. Downtime spent waiting for materials can be caused by materials-handling difficulties resulting from poor layout. Equipment maintenance can be made difficult by inadequate space or poor access. The work environment, including temperature, noise level, and safety, can be layout related; its counterpart in an office or store is the atmosphere created by the layout. Office layouts can reinforce the organizational structure by grouping all members of the same department in the same area. Encouraging sales is an important criterion for a store layout. Some warehouse layouts facilitate stock picking on a FIFO (first-in, first-out) basis, minimizing loss from spoilage or limited shelf life. Finally, employee attitudes may depend on whether the layout allows workers to socialize, reflects equitably the employee's level of responsibility, or puts the worker under the watchful eyes of the supervisor.

*M*odular furniture and movable partitions make it easy to rearrange this office when work requirements change.

Managerial Practice 10.2

Layout Flexibility at Work

Developers are finding ways to recycle vacant properties. A Los Angeles developer converted a men's clothing store into a restaurant, a movie palace into a performing arts center, and several historic office buildings into new offices. Elsewhere a Dallas office building is converted into condominiums, a Denver shopping center becomes a church, and an Ohio tire factory sees new life as an industrial mall. Recycling *new* office buildings, however, is proving to be a more intractable problem. Large floor areas leave too much space too far removed from windows to allow conversion to apartments, and the structures aren't designed to support the weight required for industrial or warehouse use.

Honda of America Manufacturing has just built its second auto plant in the United States at East Liberty, Ohio. Touted as a twenty-first-century manufacturing facility, the plant has the flexibility for adding more lines. As the plant manager said, "Maybe we can expand without expanding," by adding more production lines within the 1.4-million-square-foot building. The immediate purpose of the new plant is to build Civics, at a rate of 600 cars per day.

Sources: "Developers Recycle Vacant Properties," *Wall Street Journal,* September 23, 1991; "Honda Aims for Flexibility at New Auto Plant," *The Columbus Dispatch,* April 12, 1990.

CREATING HYBRID LAYOUTS

The higher volumes that characterize a product layout allow line flows, simplify materials handling, cut setups, and reduce labor costs. There's less need to decouple one operation from the next, allowing management to cut inventories. The Japanese refer to a product focus as *overlapped operations*, whereby materials move directly from one operation to the next without waiting in queues.

Unfortunately, volumes are not always high enough to justify dedicating a single line of multiple workers to a single product. In such situations, managers still may be able to derive the benefits of overlapped operations by creating miniature product layouts in some portions of the facility. Two techniques for creating these hybrid layouts are one worker, multiple machines (OWMM) stations and group technology (GT) cells. Flexible automation (see Chapter 6) is a third way to achieve the benefits of high-volume production when volumes for individual items are low.

One Worker, Multiple Machines

If volumes aren't sufficient to keep several workers busy on one production line, the manager might set up a line small enough to keep one worker busy. This is the theory behind the **one worker, multiple machines (OWMM)** concept, a process in which a worker operates several different machines simultaneously to achieve a line flow. It isn't unusual to have one worker operate several identical machines. For example, in the semiconductor industry one worker operates several saws that cut silicon bars into slices for computer chips. The difference with OWMM is that there are several different machines in the line.

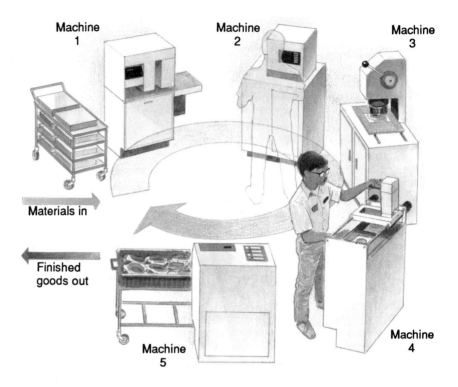

FIGURE 10.2   One Worker, Multiple Machines (OWMM) Concept

Figure 10.2 illustrates a five-machine OWMM, with the machines encircling one operator in the center. (A U shape is also common.) Each machine operates on its own for much of the cycle, and the worker steps in only when necessary. The operator moves around in the circle, performing those tasks (typically loading and unloading) that have not been automated. Different products or parts can be produced in an OWMM by changing the machine setups. If the setup on one machine is especially time consuming for one part, management can add a duplicate machine to the cell for use whenever that part is being produced.

An OWMM reduces inventory as well as labor requirements. Inventory is cut because materials do not pile up in queues but move directly into the next operation. The addition of several low-cost automated devices can maximize the number of machines included in an OWMM: automatic tool changers, loaders and unloaders, start and stop devices, and fail-safe devices that detect defective parts or products. The OWMM concept is being applied widely in Japan. For example, the Mitsubishi Electric Company converted more than 25 percent of its machine operations to OWMM.

Group Technology

A second option for achieving repeatability with low-volume processes is **group technology (GT).** This manufacturing technique groups parts or products with similar characteristics into *families* and sets aside groups of machines for their production. Families may be based on size, shape, manufacturing or routing requirements, or demand. The goal is to find a set of products with similar processing requirements and minimize machine changeover or setup. For example, all bolts might be assigned to the same family because they all require the same basic processing steps regardless of size or shape. Figure 10.3 shows 13 parts belonging to the same family.

Information for grouping parts into families comes from two possible sources. The simplest and least accurate is visual inspection of the different parts made. The second is examining the final product designs (see Chapter 2) and process design specifications (such as the process charts in Chapter 5). This second information source is more accurate but also more time consuming.

The next step is to organize the machine tools needed to perform the basic processes into separate areas called *cells*. Rather than group similar machines, the operations manager arranges the machines for line flows; that is, all of the machines needed to work on these parts are together in a cell, or group. Thus in each cell the machines require only minor adjustments to accommodate each batch from the same family of parts, greatly simplifying product changeovers. By also simplifying product routings, GT cells reduce the time a job is in the shop. Queues of materials waiting to be worked on are shortened or eliminated. Frequently, materials handling is automated so that, after loading raw materials into the cell, a worker doesn't handle machined parts until the job is completed. To summarize, GT cells provide the following benefits:

- Less setup time
- Lower work-in-process inventory
- Less materials handling
- Reduced cycle time
- Increased opportunities for automation

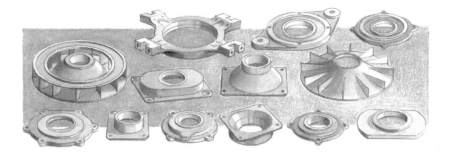

FIGURE 10.3 Thirteen Parts Belonging to the Same Family

Source: Mikell P. Groover, *Automation, Production Systems, and Computer-Aided Manufacturing* (Englewood Cliffs, N.J.: Prentice-Hall, 1980), p. 540. Reprinted by permission.

Figure 10.4 compares process flows before and after creating GT cells. Part (a) shows a shop floor where machines are grouped according to function: lathing, milling, drilling, grinding, and assembly. After lathing, a part moves to one of the milling machines, where it waits in line until it has a higher priority than any other job competing for the machine's capacity. When the milling operation on the part is finally done, the part is next moved over to a drilling machine, and so forth. The queues can be long, creating significant time delays. Flows of materials are very jumbled because the parts being processed in any one area of the shop have so many different routings.

FIGURE 10.4

Process Flows Before and After the Use of GT Cells

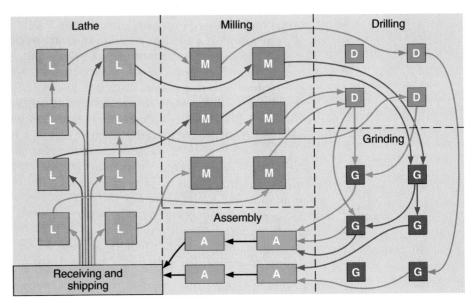

(a) Jumbled flows in a job shop without GT cells

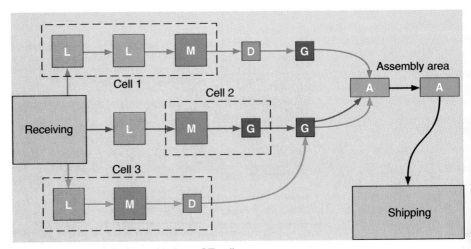

Source: Mikell P. Groover, *Automation, Production Systems, and Computer-Aided Manufacturing* (Englewood Cliffs, N.J.: Prentice-Hall, 1980), pp. 540–541. Reprinted by permission.

(b) Line flows in a job shop with three GT cells

Managerial Practice 10.3

Cummins Engine Uses Group Technology

Cummins Engine Company, a manufacturer of diesel engines and based in Columbus, Indiana, uses group technology to achieve higher-volume production at some of its operations, despite having more than 100,000 parts in its catalog. One engine family has 86 different flywheels, 49 flywheel housings, 17 starter motors, and 12 possible mountings. Cummins made the transition from a process layout to cellular production by reorganizing into product departments, each responsible for a family of related products. Components were classified based on volume, predictability of demand, stability of design, and changeover times. Management grouped machines into cells, U-shaped clusters that move a part from lathe, to grinder, to milling machine, with little interruption. Work-in-process inventory gets handed off from machine to machine without "resting" and thus goes from one operation to the next smoothly.

Management created 15 cells in the Columbus plant, each machining a comparatively small group of related parts: a water pump line, a flywheel line, a manifold line, and so forth. These hybrid layouts, dedicated to a narrower range of parts, required the purchase of some new machines. Cummins needed to invest only $60,000 for new machines, $105,000 for additional fixtures and tools, and about $40,000 to move things around, however. In the first year, floor space requirements were reduced by 25 percent, scrap by 30 percent, and work-in-process inventory by 90 percent. More than a million dollars was saved in labor cost. The hybrid layout allows high-volume and low-volume systems to coexist in the same facility.

Source: "Cummins Engine Flexes Its Factory," *Harvard Business Review* (March–April 1990), pp. 120–127.

By contrast, the manager of the shop in part (b) has identified three product families that account for a majority of the firm's production. One family always requires two lathing operations followed by one operation at the milling machines. The second family always requires a milling operation followed by a grinding operation. The third family requires the use of a lathe, milling machine, and drill press. For simplicity, Fig. 10.4 shows only the flows of parts assigned to these three families. The remaining parts are produced at machines outside the cells and still have jumbled routings. However, by creating three GT cells, the manager has definitely created more line flows and simplified routings. Managerial Practice 10.3 shows how Cummins Engine Company successfully uses group technology.

DESIGNING PROCESS LAYOUTS

The approach to designing a layout differs, depending on whether a process layout or product layout has been chosen. We do not consider fixed-position or hybrid layouts any further. When management decides on a fixed-position format, the layout problem is basically solved. As for the hybrid layout, part of it is designed using process-layout principles and part is designed using product-layout principles.

Let's begin with an approach to process layout. Three basic steps are involved, whether the design is for a new layout or for revising an existing one: (1) gather information, (2) develop a block plan, and (3) design a detailed layout.

Step 1: Gather Information

Figure 10.5 illustrates the type of information needed to begin designing a revised layout for Longhorn Machine, a machine shop with a process-focused positioning strategy. It produces a wide variety of small metal parts on general-purpose equipment. Its 32 machines are operated by a full shift of 26 workers and augmented by a second shift of only 6 workers.

Space Requirements by Center. As Fig. 10.5 shows, Longhorn has grouped its processes into six different departments, or centers. For example, department 1 is the burr and grind area and department 6 is the inspection area. The exact space requirements of each department, in square feet, are listed in Fig. 10.5(a). When calculating space requirements, the layout designer must tie them to capacity plans. First the designer itemizes the specific equipment and space needs for each center, then adds enough "circulation" space to provide for aisles and the like. Circulation space may consume at least 25 percent of the center's total space.

Available Space. Figure 10.5(b) shows the current block plan of Longhorn's plant. A **block plan** is a rough space allocation for each department and indicates its placement. When describing a new facility layout, rather than a modification of an existing one, the plan need only provide the facility's dimensions and space allocations. According to the Longhorn plan, the available space is 90 feet by 60 feet, or 5400 square feet. The designer could begin the design by dividing the total amount of space into six equal blocks (900 square feet each), one for each department. Actually, inspection needs only 700 square feet, and lathes and drills needs 1200 square feet. However, the equal space approximation is good enough until the designer reaches the last step—detailed layout.*

Closeness Ratings. The layout designer must also know which centers need to be located close to one another. Either a from–to matrix or a REL chart provides the needed information.

Figure 10.5(c) shows a **from–to matrix** for Longhorn. This matrix gives the number of trips (or some other measure of materials movement) between each pair of departments. The designer estimates the number of trips from routings and ordering frequencies for typical items made at the plant, statistical sampling, or polling supervisors and materials handlers. The right-hand portion of the matrix shows the number of trips in *both* directions.† The largest number of trips is between departments 3 and 6 (at 90 trips), with 1 and 6 close behind at 80 trips. Thus the designer should locate department 6 near both 1 and 3, which is not the arrangement in the current layout.

---

*If this approximation is too rough, a finer grid can be used, say, with four rows and six columns. A larger department (such as lathes and drills) could then be assigned more block spaces than are smaller departments.

†This approach assumes that materials-handling costs do not depend on the direction of flow. If this is not true, the numbers would have to be weighted differently.

FIGURE 10.5

Layout Information
for Longhorn
Machine

Department	Square feet
1. Burr and grind	1000
2. NC equipment	950
3. Shipping and receiving	750
4. Lathes and drills	1200
5. Tool crib	800
6. Inspection	700
Total	5400

(a) Space requirements by center

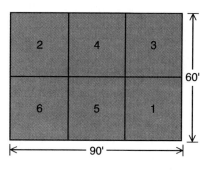

(b) Available space and current
block plan

From–to matrix (trips/day)

From \ To	1	2	3	4	5	6
1. Burr and grind		20		20		80
2. NC equipment			10		75	
3. Shipping and receiving				15		90
4. Lathes and drills					70	
5. Tool crib						
6. Inspection						

(c) Closeness ratings

1. Shipping and receiving
   (department 3) should
   remain where it is, since
   it is next to the dock.

2. Keep lathes and drills
   (department 4) at its
   current location because
   relocation costs are
   prohibitive.

(d) Other considerations

A **REL chart** (REL is short for *relationships*), which can be used in place of a from–to matrix, displays closeness ratings as letters, rather than numbers, and thus reflects the qualitative judgments of managers and employees. See Fig. 10.26(c) on page 423 for an example. An A rating could represent the judgment that it is absolutely necessary to locate two departments close to one another, E for especially important, I for important, O for ordinary closeness, U for unimportant, and X for undesirable. The A rating is higher than the E, but as the assessment is qualitative, the designer doesn't know by how much. One advantage of a REL chart is that the manager can account for multiple performance criteria (see Table 10.1) when selecting closeness ratings, whereas a from–to matrix focuses on materials-handling or stockpicking costs.

Other Considerations. Figure 10.5(d) shows the last information gathered for Longhorn. Some performance criteria depend on the absolute location of a department. For example, moving a department might be unwise because of relocation costs, noise, or management preference. A REL chart or from–to matrix cannot reflect these criteria. The layout designer must handle other considerations, such as those shown in Table 10.1, qualitatively and list them separately.

Step 2: Develop a Block Plan

The second step in layout design is to develop a block plan that satisfies performance criteria and area requirements insofar as possible. The most elementary way to do this is by trial and error, which depends on the designer's ability to spot patterns in the data. There is no guarantee that the designer will identify the best or even a nearly best solution. However, one study showed that such an approach, at least when supplemented by the use of a computer to evaluate solutions, often compares quite favorably with more sophisticated computerized techniques such as ALDEP or CRAFT (see pp. 394–395).

Application 10.1   *Developing a Block Plan*

Develop an acceptable block plan for Longhorn, using trial and error.

Solution   A good place to start is with the largest closeness ratings in Fig. 10.5(c) (say, 70 and above). A reasonable block plan would locate departments as follows:

1. Departments 3 and 6 close together
2. Departments 1 and 6 close together
3. Departments 2 and 5 close together
4. Departments 4 and 5 close together
5. Departments 3 and 4 at their current locations because of the other considerations

If after several attempts you cannot meet all five requirements, drop one or more and try again. If you can meet all five easily, add more (such as for interactions below 70).

The block plan in Fig. 10.6 was worked out by trial and error and satisfies all five requirements. Start by keeping departments 3 and 4 in their original locations. As the first requirement is to locate departments 3 and 6 close to one another, put 6 in the southeast corner of the layout. The second requirement is to have departments 1 and 6 close together, so place 1 in the space just to the left of 6, and so on.

Having a total desirability score is helpful in some respects for comparing alternative block plans. The designer could adapt the load–distance method for location problems (see Chapter 9) to this purpose when *relative* locations are a primary concern (such as for materials handling, stock-picking, and commu-

FIGURE 10.6

Proposed Block Plan

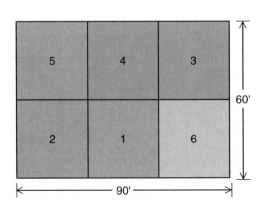

nication effectiveness). In terms of materials-handling costs,

$$ld = \sum_{j=i}^{n} \sum_{i=1}^{n} l_{ij}d_{ij}$$

where ld = total load–distance score measuring the materials-handling difficulties of the block plan*
   l_{ij} = load, measured as the number of trips between departments i and j in both directions†
   d_{ij} = units of distance (actual, euclidean, or rectilinear) between departments i and j, where $d_{ij} = 0$ (see Chapter 9 for distance computations)
   n = total number of departments

Of course, l_{ij} is not limited to a load measure but can be any closeness factor related to distance.

Application 10.2 | *Calculating the Total Desirability Score*

How much better, in terms of the *ld* score, is the proposed block plan? Use the rectilinear distance measure.

Solution   The accompanying table applies the formula to both plans. To fill in the first two columns, return to the from–to matrix in Fig. 10.5 and list each pair of departments that has a nonzero load. For the third column, calculate the rectilinear distances between the departments in the current layout. For example, in Fig. 10.5(b), departments 1 and 2 are in the southeast and northwest blocks of the plant. The distance between the centers of these blocks is three units of distance (two horizontally and one vertically), and each unit measures 30 feet. For the fourth column, multiply the loads by the distances and add the results for a total *ld* score of 785 for the current plan. Similar calculations for the proposed plan produce an *ld* score of only 400.

Load–Distance Scores: Current and Proposed

Department Pair (ij)	Closeness Rating (l_{ij})	Current Plan Distance (d_{ij})	$l_{ij}d_{ij}$	Proposed Plan Distance (d_{ij})	$l_{ij}d_{ij}$
1, 2	20	3	60	1	20
1, 4	20	2	40	1	20
1, 6	80	2	160	1	80
2, 3	10	2	20	3	30
2, 5	75	2	150	1	75
3, 4	15	1	15	1	15
3, 6	90	3	270	1	90
4, 5	70	1	70	1	70
			$ld = 785$		$ld = 400$

---

*A more elaborate treatment of l_{ij} is to multiply the number of trips by the cost to move one load for one unit of distance. The cost depends on the materials-handling methods used for transfers between departments, as well as the type of materials to be moved.

†Since l_{ij} represents the merged flow between department pairs in both directions, j needs to be summed only from i (rather than 1) to n.

Although the *ld* score for the proposed layout in Application 10.2 represents an almost 50 percent improvement, the designer may be able to do better. However, the designer must first determine whether the revised layout is worth the cost of relocating four of the six departments (all but 3 and 4). If relocation costs are too high, a less expensive proposal must be found. The calculations made for the current plan offer some clues: Much of the 785 score comes from trips between departments 3 and 6 (270) and between departments 1 and 6 (160). One option is to switch the locations of departments 5 and 6, putting department 6 closer to both 1 and 3. Additional calculations show that the *ld* score for this plan drops to 610 and that only two departments have to be relocated. Perhaps this compromise is best.

Step 3: Design a Detailed Layout

After finding a satisfactory block plan, the layout designer translates it into a detailed representation, showing the exact size and shape of each center, the arrangement of elements (such as desks, machines, or storage areas), and the location of aisles, stairways, and other service space. These visual representations can be two-dimensional drawings, three-dimensional models, or even computer-aided graphics. This last step in the layout design process is important because it helps decision makers grasp the essence of the proposal and even spot problems that might otherwise be overlooked. If others in the company are to be involved in layout decisions, the detailed layout becomes the focus of the discussion with them. The megafigure of King Soopers Bakery, on pages 186–187, is a good example of a detailed layout.

Aids for Process Layout Decisions

Finding an acceptable block plan is a complex process in real-life situations. A 20-department problem has 20! possible layouts, which means 2.43×10^{18} possibilities. If a computer evaluated one possibility each microsecond, eight hours a day, it would take the computer 250,000 years to arrive at the final solution. Fortunately, several computationally feasible aids are now available for helping managers make process layout decisions.

Automated Layout Design Program. **Automated layout design program (ALDEP)** is a computerized heuristic that uses REL chart information to construct a good layout. Being a heuristic method, it generally provides good—but not necessarily the best—solutions. The program constructs a layout from scratch, adding one department at a time. The program picks the first department randomly. The second department must have a strong REL rating with the first (say, A or E), the third must have a strong rating with the second, and so on. When no department has a strong rating with the department just added, the system again randomly selects the next department. The program computes a score for each solution generated and prints out those layouts with higher scores for the manager's consideration. The score is computed differently from the *ld* score used earlier. First, the letter ratings are converted into numerical equivalents, say, 6 for A, 5 for E, 4 for I, 3 for O, 2 for U, and 0 for

X. (These numerical equivalents are arbitrary, and others could be used. After numerical equivalents have been established, it is also possible to compute *ld* scores.) Second, these numerical equivalents are added to the total score whenever they belong to departments that touch somewhere along their borders.

Computerized Relative Allocation of Facilities Technique. Another powerful computer software package is **computerized relative allocation of facilities technique (CRAFT)**, a heuristic method that uses a from–to matrix and a series of paired exchanges of departments to find an acceptable solution. Working from an initial block plan (or starting solution), CRAFT evaluates all possible paired exchanges of departments. The exchange that helps the most (that is, causes the greatest reduction in the total *ld* score) is made, creating a new starting solution. This process continues until no other exchanges can be found to reduce the *ld* score. The starting solution at this point is also the final solution, which is printed out, along with the *ld* score.

Other models have been developed to handle multiple floors and relocation costs (see Cinar, 1975, and Hicks and Cowan, 1976). Goal programming, a special form of linear programming, has been used to optimize a solution with several criteria simultaneously (see Ritzman, Bradford, and Jacobs, 1979). One particularly intriguing development is a method that better integrates the last two steps of layout planning (the block plan and detailed layout). A detailed configuration (called a *design unit*) is preassigned to each center and must be maintained throughout the solution process. This constraint prevents unusual shapes from occurring and helps the manager better visualize the final layout (see Jacobs, 1987).

PROCESS LAYOUTS: WAREHOUSES AND OFFICES

We conclude the discussion of process layouts with two special cases: warehouses and offices, both of great importance. A typical manufacturer spends 6 to 8 percent of income from sales for warehousing, and there are 60 million Americans working in offices. Much of the preceding discussion still applies, but each of these two special cases has unique aspects.

Warehouse Layouts

Warehouses are similar to manufacturing plants in that materials are moved between activity centers. At the centers, transformation is one of storage, rather than a physical or chemical change. Figure 10.7(a) illustrates the simplest type of warehousing situation. The warehouse receives items at the dock and moves them to a storage area. At a later date, stockpickers withdraw inventory to fill individual customer orders. For example, according to the table in Fig. 10.7(b), 280 trips per week are made between the dock and the storage area for toasters.

A Layout Solution. We can find a layout solution by the method used in Applications 10.1 and 10.2. Or we can use an even simpler method, which is guar-

Storage area

Dock | Aisle

Storage area

(a) Dock and storage space

Department	Trips to and from dock	Area needed (blocks)
1. Toasters	280	1
2. Air conditioners	160	2
3. Microwaves	360	1
4. Stereos	375	3
5. TVs	800	4
6. Radios	150	1
7. Bulk storage	100	2

(b) Trips and space requirements

FIGURE 10.7   Layout Information for A-1 Distribution Systems

anteed to minimize the *ld* score. This shortcut is possible because all travel takes place between the dock and individual departments; there is no travel between departments. The decision rule is as follows:

Equal areas. If all departments require the same space, simply place the one generating the most trips closest to the dock, the one generating the next largest number of trips next closest to the dock, and so on.

Unequal areas. If some departments need more space than others, give the location closest to the dock to the department with the largest ratio of trip frequency to block space. The department with the second highest ratio gets the next closest location, and so on.

Application 10.3   *Determining a Warehouse Layout*

Determine a layout for the warehouse in Fig. 10.7 that minimizes the *ld* score.

Solution   Because the departments have different area requirements, we must first obtain the ratio of trips to block spaces. Department 3 (microwaves) has the highest ratio. Although only 360 trips per week are involved, the department occupies only one block of prime space. Ranking the remaining departments by their ratios (shown in parentheses), we get: 1 (280), 5 (200), 6 (150), 4 (125), 2 (80), and 7 (50). Figure 10.8 shows the layout derived from this ranking. Department 3 had first choice and could have been placed in either of the two locations nearest the dock. We chose the top one arbitrarily and assigned the bottom one to department 1.

Additional Layout Options. Although one advantage of the layout just proposed is simplicity, other options might be more effective. First, demand for different items is often seasonal. Thus an efficient layout might place radios close to

FIGURE 10.8

Best Block Plan for A-1 Distribution Systems

3	5	5	6	4	2	7

Dock | Aisle

1	5	5	4	4	2	7

*T*his high-rise forklift can store products in the space-saving warehouse.

the dock for Christmas but move air conditioners near the dock during the summer.

Second, various ways of utilizing space offer additional layout options. For example, an 82,000-square-foot, 32-foot-high, racked warehouse can handle the same volume as a 107,000-square-foot, low-ceiling warehouse. Productivity gains as high as 50 percent in order picking have been reported, which can help offset the added rack and equipment costs of such high-density designs. Another space-saving possibility is to assign all incoming materials to the nearest available space, rather than to a predetermined area where all like items are clustered. The location of each item is recorded in a computer. When it's time to retrieve an item, the system prints its location on the shipping bill. When more than one item is on the bill, the computer identifies the shortest route for the order picker. Canadiana Outdoor Products in Brampton, Ontario, introduced a computer system with terminals mounted on the lift trucks. This arrangement allowed drivers to track the exact location and contents of each storage bin in the warehouse. With this new system, Canadiana can handle quadrupled sales with less storage space.

Third, different *layout patterns* offer still more layout options. The warehouse in Fig. 10.7 has an out-and-back selection pattern, where items are picked one at a time, but there are other options. On a route collection trip, the order picker selects a variety of items to be shipped to a given customer. When batch picking, the order picker gathers the quantity of an item required to satisfy a group of customer orders to be shipped in the same truck or rail car. Finally, in the zone system, each picker is assigned to a zone. The picker gathers all needed items from the zone and places them on a powered conveyor line. Figure 10.9 illustrates the zone concept for a warehouse serving several toy supermarkets (such as Children's Palace). The conveyor line consists of five feeder lines and one trunk line. When the merchandise arrives at the control station, an operator directs it to the correct tractor trailer for outbound shipment. The advantage of the zone system is that pickers do not need to travel throughout the warehouse to fill orders; they are responsible only for their assigned zones.

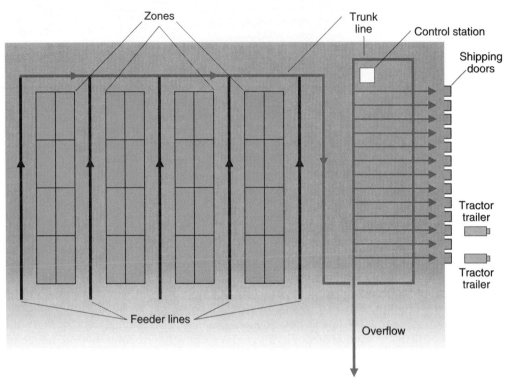

FIGURE 10.9   Zone System for a Warehouse

Office Layouts

More than 40 percent of the U.S. work force is employed in offices, and office layout can affect both productivity and the quality of work life. In a recent survey, three fourths of 1400 employees polled said productivity could be raised by improvements in their work environments.

Proximity. Accessibility to co-workers and supervisors can enhance communication and develop mutual interest. Conversations tend to become more formal as individuals are distanced from one another. The famous Hawthorne study in 1939 showed that the physical work setting influences group formation (Homans, 1950). In the study, management used spatial language to tell workers in the experimental group that they were important. Management changed both the absolute and relative locations of the workers by moving them to a separate room and away from the watchful eyes of a supervisor. The revised layout facilitated contact between workers and the setting of group norms. More recent studies confirm that proximity to others can be beneficial in clarifying what is expected of an employee on the job and in other ways.

Most formal procedures for designing office layouts try to maximize the proximity of workers whose jobs require frequent interaction. Data collected on the frequency and importance of interactions can be used in a REL chart or a from–to matrix. Certain procedures can be used to identify natural clusters of workers to be treated as a center in a block plan (see Jacobs, Bradford, and Ritzman, 1980). The goal of such approaches is to design layouts around work flows and communication patterns.

Privacy. Another key factor in office design—and one that is somewhat culturally dependent—is privacy. Outside disruptions, crowding, and feeling lost in the crowd can hurt a worker's performance. Employee reactions to open offices at Sperry Rand's and McDonald's world headquarters were favorable. However, when a newspaper company tried to increase worker proximity by going from private work spaces to an open-plan office, the results were disappointing (see Oldham and Brass, 1979). Employees felt like they were in a fishbowl and that they had little control over their environment. Studies at several state government departments (see Schuler, Ritzman, and Davis, 1981) revealed a strong link between privacy and satisfaction with the supervisor and the job.

Options in Office Layout. Providing both proximity and privacy for employees poses a dilemma for management. Proximity is gained by opening up the work area. Privacy is gained by more liberal space standards, baffled ceilings, doors, partitions, and thick carpeting that absorbs noise. However, these features can be expensive and reduce layout flexibility. Thus management must generally arrive at a compromise between proximity and privacy. Four different approaches are available: traditional layouts, office landscaping, activity settings, and electronic cottages. The choice requires an understanding of work requirements, the work force itself, and top management's philosophy of work.

Traditional layouts call for closed offices for some employees and open areas (or bullpens) for all others. The closed offices, with their solid doors and floor-to-ceiling walls, go to management and those employees whose work requires privacy. The resulting layout may be characterized by long hallways lined with closed doors, producing considerable isolation. Open areas are filled uniformly with rows of desks. In traditional layouts each person has a designated place. Its location, size, and furnishing signify the person's status in the organization.

An approach developed in Germany during the late 1950s puts everyone (including top management) in an open area. For example, the headquarters of Johnson Wax is designed with open offices. So is Hewlett-Packard's Waltham, Massachusetts, plant. A big bullpen with shoulder-high dividers partitions the space. The idea is to achieve closer cooperation among employees at *all* levels. However, the corporate nurse still keeps earplugs in inventory for employees bothered by noise. An extension to this concept is called *office landscaping*: Attractive plants, screens, and portable partitions increase privacy and cluster or separate groups. Movable work stations and accessories help maintain flexibility. Because the work stations (or cubicles) are only semiprivate, employees might have trouble concentrating or might feel uncomfortable trying to hold sensitive discussions. Construction costs are as much as 40 percent less than for traditional layouts, and rearrangement costs are less still.

*T*he headquarters of Johnson Wax has a grand spacious layout designed by Frank Lloyd Wright. However, some people would feel too exposed in such an open office setting.

Activity settings represent a relatively new concept for achieving both proximity and privacy (Stone and Luchetti, 1985). Multiple workplaces cover the full range of work needs, including a library, teleconferencing facility, reception area, conference room, special graphics area, and shared terminals. Employees move from one activity setting to the next as their work changes during the day. Each person also gets a small, personal office as a home base.

Some futurists expect more and more employees to work at home or in neighborhood offices, connected to the main office through the computer. Called *telecommuting* or *electronic cottages*, this approach represents a modern-day version of the cottage industries that existed prior to the Industrial Revolution. Besides saving on commuting time, it offers flexibility in work schedules. Many working men and women with children, for example, prefer such flexibility. More than nine million Americans already have a taste of this arrangement, working at least part of the week at home. There can be difficulties with telecommuting, however, such as lack of equipment and too many family disruptions. And opportunities for socialization and politicking can be too few. Some managers at Hartford Insurance complained that they couldn't supervise—much less get to know—employees they couldn't see. Unreliable telephone lines linking home terminals to the company's computer also caused difficulty. Managerial Practice 10.4 discusses the telecommuting policy of another company, Pacific Bell.

PRODUCT LAYOUTS

Product layouts raise management issues entirely different from those of process layouts. Often called a production or assembly line, a product layout arranges work stations in sequence. The product moves from one station to the next until its completion at the end of the line. Typically, one worker operates each station, performing repetitive tasks. There is little inventory to decouple

Managerial Practice 10.4

Telecommuting at Pacific Bell

Pacific Bell, a subsidiary of Pacific Telesis Group, has a formal telecommuting policy. More than 1000 of its managers work fairly regularly from sites other than their primary offices. The company opened two full-blown satellite offices four years ago, each able to accommodate 18 managers who communicate with the outside world via personal computers, modems, facsimile machines, copying equipment, and laser printers.

One of the managers in sales support, for example, works at a neighborhood satellite just 15 minutes from his home. He used to make a 26-mile commute to the downtown Los Angeles office, which took an hour when everything went well and up to 2½ hours when it rained. Free from home-office distractions, he feels that he is functioning more efficiently. He still prefers working at some kind of office to working at home, where there are distractions to do dishes, mow the lawn, or see what's in the refrigerator. Like other satellite workers, he visits the main office from time to time.

Source: "Close to You," *Wall Street Journal*, June 4, 1990.

stations, which would allow them to operate independently. Thus the line's output is only as fast as its slowest work station (that is, if the slowest station takes 45 seconds per unit, the line's output is one product every 45 seconds). The goal is to obtain work stations with well-balanced workloads (such as having every station take roughly 45 seconds per unit produced), which is achieved by line balancing.

Line Balancing

Line balancing is the process of assigning work to stations in a line so as to achieve the desired output rate with the smallest number of work stations. Normally one worker is assigned per station, which is what we assume in our subsequent examples. Thus the line that produces at the desired pace with the fewest number of workers is the most efficient one. Line balancing must be performed when a line is initially set up and when a line is rebalanced to change its hourly output rate. The analyst begins by separating the work into **work elements,** the smallest units of work that can be performed independently. The analyst then obtains the labor standard (see Chapter 7) for each element and identifies the work elements (called *immediate predecessors*) that must be done before the next can begin.

Precedence Diagram. Most lines must satisfy some technological precedence requirements but also allow for some latitude and more than one sequence of operations. To help you visualize immediate predecessors better, let's run through construction of a **precedence diagram.*** We denote the work elements by circles, with the time required to perform the work shown below each circle. Arrows lead from the immediate predecessor requirements to the next work element.

---

*Precedence relationships and precedence diagrams are important in the entirely different context of project scheduling, as discussed in Chapter 19.

Application 10.4 *Constructing a Precedence Diagram*

Green Grass, Inc., is expanding its product line to include a new fertilizer spreader called the Big Broadcaster. Operations plans to make the Big Broadcaster on a new assembly line, with most parts purchased from outside suppliers. Karen Annay, the plant manager, obtained the following information concerning work elements, labor standards, and immediate predecessors for the Big Broadcaster. Construct a precedence diagram for the Big Broadcaster.

Work Element	Description	Time (sec)	Immediate Predecessor(s)
Attach leg frame			
1	Bolt leg frame to hopper	51	None
2	Insert impeller shaft into hopper	7	1
3	Attach agitator to shaft	24	2
4	Secure with cotter pin	10	3
Attach axle			
5	Insert bearings into housings	25	1
6	Slip axle through first bearing and shaft	40	5
7	Slip axle through second bearing	20	4, 6
Attach drive wheel			
8	Slip on drive wheel	35	7
9	Place washer over axle	6	8
10	Secure with cotter pin	15	9
11	Push on hub cap	9	10
Attach free wheel			
12	Slip on free wheel	30	7
13	Place washer over axle	6	12
14	Secure with cotter pin	15	13
15	Push on hub cap	9	14
Mount lower post			
16	Bolt lower handle post to hopper	27	7
17	Seat post in square hole	13	16
18	Secure leg to support strap	60	17
Attach controls			
19	Insert control wire	28	11, 15, 18
20	Guide wire through slot	12	19
21	Slip T handle over lower post	21	20
22	Attach on–off control	26	21
23	Attach level	58	22
24	Mount nameplate	29	18
Total		576	

Solution Figure 10.10 shows the complete diagram. Begin with work element 1, which has no immediate predecessors. Next add elements 2 and 5, for which element 1 is the only immediate predecessor. After entering labor standards and arrows showing precedence, add elements 3 or 6, and so on. The diagram simplifies interpretation. Work element 24, for example, can be done anywhere on the line after element 18 is completed. Element 23, on the other hand, must await the completion of element 22.

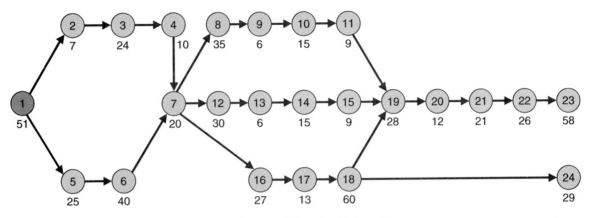

FIGURE 10.10   Precedence Diagram for Assembling the Big Broadcaster

Desired Output Rate. Closely related to demand forecasts, the output rate also depends on rebalancing frequency, capacity utilization, and job specialization. All else being equal, production rates should match demand rates as closely as possible. For example, if the demand rate is 4000 units per week and the line operates 80 hours per week, the production rate would ideally be 50 units (4000/80) per hour. Matching ensures on-time delivery and prevents the buildup of unwanted inventory. Its disadvantage is that it increases rebalancing frequency. Each time a line is rebalanced, many workers' jobs on the line must be redesigned. If the line is speeded up, a worker is given fewer work elements and more workers are required; if the line is slowed down, a worker is given more work elements and fewer workers are required. Time spent relearning jobs temporarily hurts productivity. The changeover may even require a new detailed layout for some stations. Some automobile plants are able to avoid frequent changes by eliminating a shift when demand falls and inventory becomes excessive, rather than gradually scaling back the output rate.

Management must also consider capacity utilization. Multiple shifts increase equipment utilization, which is crucial for capital-intensive facilities. However, higher pay rates or low demand may make multiple shifts undesirable or unnecessary. A third policy area related to the desired output rate is job specialization. As the desired output rate from a line increases, fewer work elements can be assigned to a station and jobs become more specialized. Recently, General Motors added a second shift to its Orion Township plant in Michigan. The line is designed to build 67 Cadillacs and Oldsmobiles an hour, an output rate that implies considerable job specialization and a fairly fast moving line.

Cycle Time. After determining the desired output rate for a line, the analyst can calculate the line's cycle time. A line's **cycle time** is the maximum time allowed for work on a unit at each station.* If the time required for work ele-

---

*Except in the context of line balancing, *cycle time* is the elapsed time between starting and completing a job. Some researchers and practitioners prefer the term *lead time*.

ments at a station exceeds the line's cycle time, the station will be a bottle-neck, preventing the line from reaching its desired output rate. The target cycle time is the reciprocal of the desired hourly output rate,

$$c = \left(\frac{1}{r}\right)(3600 \text{ seconds/hour})$$

where

$$c = \text{cycle time in seconds/unit}$$
$$r = \text{desired output rate in units/hour}$$

For example, if the line's desired output rate is 100 units per hour, the cycle time would be 36 seconds (3600/100).

Theoretical Minimum. To achieve the desired output rate, the line-balancing problem is to assign every work element to a station, satisfy all precedence requirements, and minimize the number of stations (n) formed. If each station is operated by a different worker, minimizing n also maximizes productivity. The ultimate in balance is when the sum of the work-element times at each station equals the cycle time (c). The workload at each station then is perfectly balanced, and no station has any idle time. For example, if the sum of each station's work-element times is exactly 36 seconds, which is also the cycle time, there is perfect balance. Of course, there is no slack (other than that built in the time standards) to allow for those units which take more time than expected. Normally, the goal of perfect balance is a practical impossibility, owing to the unevenness of work-element times and the loss of flexibility caused by precedence requirements. However, assuming perfect balance provides a benchmark: the smallest number of stations possible, called the **theoretical minimum (TM)** number of stations. Rounding up for fractional values, as fractional stations are impossible,

$$TM = \frac{t}{c}$$

where t is the total amount of productive time required to assemble each unit, or the sum of all work-element times. For example, if the sum of the work-element times is 442 seconds and the cycle time is 36 seconds, the smallest number of stations that *might* be possible is 13, because 12.28 (442/36) must be rounded up.

| *Application 10.5* | *Calculating the Cycle Time and Theoretical Minimum* |

Green Grass's plant manager has just received marketing's latest forecasts of Big Broadcaster sales for the next year. She wants its production line to be designed to make 2400 spreaders per week for at least the next three months. The plant will operate five days per week, one shift per day, and eight hours per shift. A few utility workers are used in the plant to relieve others for breaks, cover for absenteeism, and help at temporary bottlenecks. Because equipment failures will be negligible, the line should be operating 40 hours per week.

What should be the line's cycle time? What is the smallest number of work stations that the plant manager could hope for in designing the line for this cycle time?

Solution   The plant manager begins with the cycle time, first converting the desired output rate (2400 units per week) to an hourly rate. Dividing by 40 hours per week (one 8-hour shift, five days per week), she gets 60 units per hour, so

$$c = \left(\frac{1}{r}\right)(3600 \text{ sec/hr}) = \left(\frac{1}{60}\right)(3600) = 60 \text{ sec/unit}$$

The plant manager now calculates the theoretical minimum number of stations. The previously estimated total amount of productive work to be done is 576 seconds per spreader. (See table in Application 10.4 on page 402.) Dividing by the cycle time, assuming perfect balance, she gets

$$TM = \frac{t}{c} = \frac{576}{60} = 9.6 \quad \text{or} \quad 10 \text{ stations}$$

Idle Time, Efficiency, and Balance Delay. Minimizing n ensures automatically that we (1) minimize idle time, (2) maximize efficiency, and (3) minimize balance delay. These goals are used interchangeably in line balancing, so you need to be familiar with each one:

$$\text{Idle time} = nc - t$$

$$\text{Efficiency (\%)} = \left(\frac{t}{nc}\right)(100)$$

$$\text{Balance delay (\%)} = 100 - \text{Efficiency}$$

Idle time is the total unproductive time for all stations in the assembly of each unit. Each of the n stations spends c seconds per unit, which means that nc is the total time (productive time and idle time) spent per unit. Subtracting the total productive time t gives us the idle time. Efficiency is the ratio of productive time to total time, expressed as a percent. **Balance delay** is the amount by which efficiency falls short of 100 percent. As long as c is fixed, we can optimize all three goals by minimizing n.

Application 10.6   *Calculating a Solution's Efficiency*

Suppose that we can find a solution for Green Grass that requires only 10 stations, the theoretical minimum (or $n = TM = 10$). What would be the line's efficiency?

Solution

$$\text{Efficiency} = \left(\frac{t}{nc}\right)(100) = \frac{576}{(10)(60)}(100) = 96\%$$

Thus if we find a solution that achieves *TM*, the efficiency (sometimes called the *theoretical maximum efficiency*) will be only 96 percent.

Finding a Solution. An overwhelming number of assembly line solutions are possible, even for Green Grass's rather simple problem. The number of possibilities expands as quickly as for process layouts. Once again, computer assistance is available. One software package, for example, considers every feasible combination of work elements that does not violate precedence or cycle time requirements when forming a new station. The combination that minimizes the station's idle time is selected (see Hoffman, 1963). If any work elements remain unassigned, a second station is formed, and so on.

The approach that we use here is even simpler. At each iteration, a work element is selected from a list of candidates and assigned to a station. This process is repeated until all stations have been formed. Two decision rules are commonly used for selecting from the candidate list:

> **Rule 1.** Pick the candidate with the *longest work-element time.* This heuristic rule (see Chapter 9) tends to assign as quickly as possible those work elements most difficult to fit into a station. Work elements having shorter times should be saved for fine tuning the solution.
>
> **Rule 2.** Pick the candidate having the *largest number of followers.* Figure 10.10 shows, for example, that work element 18 has six followers and 21 has two followers. This rule helps keep options open for forming subsequent stations. Otherwise, precedence requirements may leave only a few possible sequences of work elements, all requiring an unnecessary amount of idle time as a result.

Let's now develop solutions, manually using these rules. Our overall solution procedure is much like the logic that would be used in computer programs:

> **Step 1.** Let $k = 1$, where k is a counter for the station being formed. It is incremented at step 5 if the current number of stations is insufficient to handle all work elements on the line.
>
> **Step 2.** Make a list of candidates. Each work element included in the list must satisfy three conditions:
>
> > **1.** It has not yet been assigned to this or any previous station.
> > **2.** All its predecessors have been assigned to this or a previous station.
> > **3.** Its time cannot exceed the station's idle time, which accounts for all work elements already assigned. If none has been assigned, the station's idle time equals the cycle time.
>
> If no such candidates can be found, go to step 5.

Step 3. Pick a candidate, using one of the two decision rules. If two or more candidates are tied, arbitrarily choose one of them. Assign it to station k.

Step 4. Calculate the cumulative time of all tasks assigned so far to station k. Subtract this total from the cycle time to find the station's idle time. Go to step 2.

Step 5. If some work elements are still unassigned, but none are candidates for station k, a new station must be started. Begin the new station by incrementing k by 1 and go to step 2. Otherwise, you have a complete solution. Stop.

Find a line-balancing solution using the manual solution procedure and largest work-element time rule to pick candidates (see step 3).

Solution   The worksheet below shows how to proceed, and the first few iterations reveal the pattern. Beginning with the first station, S1 ($k = 1$), the precedence diagram shows that only element 1 can be a candidate. It is the only one with all immediate predecessors (none, in this case) already assigned. With element 1 assigned, station S1 has an idle time of 9 seconds. For the second iteration, only element 2 is a candidate. Element 5 cannot be a candidate because its time exceeds 9 seconds. With station S1 now consisting of elements 1 and 2, its idle time drops to only 2 seconds. No candidates remain, as adding either 3 or 5 brings the work content of S1 over the cycle time. We therefore move on to the second station, S2 ($k = 2$). The candidates are 3 and 5, and 5 is picked because its time is longer (25 versus 24). This is the first instance of a real choice because each previous iteration had only one candidate. Continuing on, we find that the final solution calls for only 10 stations. The corresponding precedence diagram is shown in Fig. 10.11. The efficiency is 96 percent and the balance delay only 4 percent. Since $n = TM = 10$, we can do no better than this with a 60-second cycle time.

When implementing this solution, precedence requirements within each station must be observed. For example, the worker at station S6 can do element 11 at any time but cannot start element 14 until element 13 is finished.

Worksheet

Station (Steps 1 and 5)	Candidates (Step 2)	Choice (Step 3)	Cumulative Time (sec) (Step 4)	Idle Time ($c = 60$ sec) (Step 4)
S1	1	1	51	9
	2	2	58	2
S2	3, 5	5	25	35
	3	3	49	11
	4	4	59	1
S3	6	6	40	20
	7	7	20	0
S4	8, 12, 16	8	35	25
	9	9	41	19
	10	10	56	4
S5	11, 12, 16	12	30	30
	11, 13, 16	16	57	3
S6	11, 13, 17	17	13	47
	11, 13	11	22	38
	13	13	28	32
	14	14	43	17
	15	15	52	8
S7	18	18	60	0
S8	19, 24	24	29	31
	19	19	53	3
S9	20	20	12	48
	21	21	33	27
	22	22	59	1
S10	23	23	58	23

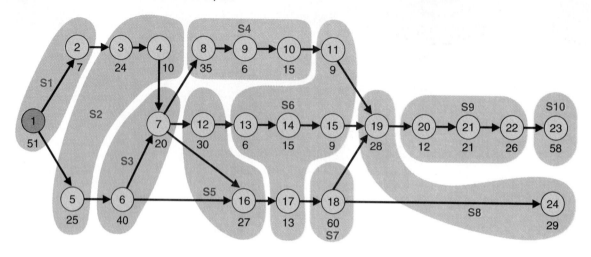

FIGURE 10.11   Big Broadcaster Precedence Diagram Solution Using Longest Work-Element Time Rule

Such a happy ending does not always occur, and sometimes another procedure would do better. Computer-based techniques tend to give acceptable, though not necessarily optimal, results. Human judgment and pattern recognition often allow us to improve on computer-generated solutions. In fact, manual methods are still the more prevalent in practice.

A Larger View

Management options go far beyond that of balancing a line for a given cycle time. Let's consider four of these options.

Pacing. Managers must decide whether to use inventory to decouple work stations. Paced lines have no buffer inventory, making them particularly susceptible to capacity losses and variability in work-element times. **Pacing** is the movement of product at each station to the subsequent one after a time interval equal to the cycle time has elapsed. Capacity losses, alignment problems, or missing components mean slowing down the entire line or pulling unfinished work off the line to be completed later. With unpaced lines, inventory storage areas are placed between stations. These storage areas make unexpected downtime at one station less likely to delay work downstream, but they do increase space and inventory costs.

Behavioral Options. The most controversial aspect of product layouts is behavioral response. Absenteeism, turnover, and grievance statistics point to production lines as likely generators of personnel problems. Paced production and high specialization (say, cycle times less than two minutes) are frequently identified as reasons for low job satisfaction. Workers generally favor inventory buffers as a means of avoiding mechanical pacing. One study even showed that productivity increased on unpaced lines.

Many companies are exploring job enlargement and rotation to increase job variety and reduce excessive specialization. For example, New York Life has redesigned the jobs of workers who process and evaluate claims applications. Instead of having a production line approach with several workers doing specialized tasks, each worker now is solely responsible for all processes on a given application. This approach increased worker responsibility and heightened morale. A manufacturing example is Deer & Company's plant in Ottumwa, Iowa, where its assembly line was redesigned to have two workers move the product and complete all the processes on what used to be a six-station line. This change allowed the line to better match actual demand and avoid frequent shutdowns because of inventory buildups. The two workers also had greater pride in their work (see Pesch, Jarvis, and Troyer, 1992). Such efforts are not always as successful, however, because some workers may react unfavorably to enlarged jobs.

Another option for humanizing assembly lines is to involve worker groups in decision making about who is assigned to each station, when jobs are rotated, which specific work elements are assigned to a station, and even how these tasks are performed. In Sweden, Volvo allows considerable group control. Management identifies for each group the type of work to be done, specifies the desired daily output rate, and provides the necessary resources. Each group decides the rest. The quality circles pioneered in Japanese industry, which are now becoming more widespread in the United States, are another example of employee involvement (see Chapter 7).

Other behavioral options include arranging station layouts to facilitate social interaction, creating stations where two or more people work together, and giving particular attention to personnel selection. Some workers are less likely to enjoy line work; others may actually prefer it. Even a factory's furnishings can make a difference. The Saab assembly plant in labor-starved Sweden is light and spacious, with walls and equipment in matching colors. On the top floor, a restaurant commands a view over the Oresund sound.

Mixed-Model Lines. A **mixed-model line** produces several items belonging to the same family, such as the Cadillac de Ville and Oldsmobile 98 models. Although it has important advantages, such as having both high-volume production *and* product variety, mixed-model production can seriously complicate scheduling. Information must be communicated for each unit about the specific parts to be produced at each station. Care must be taken to alternate from one model to another, so as not to overload some stations for too long. Despite these difficulties, the mixed-model line is often the only reasonable choice. When product plans call for many customer options, volumes may not be high enough to justify a separate line for each model.

Modified Cycle Times. A line's cycle time depends on the desired output rate (or sometimes on the maximum number of work stations allowed). In turn, the maximum line efficiency varies considerably with the cycle time selected. Thus exploring a range of cycle times makes sense. A manager might go with a particularly efficient solution even if it doesn't match the output rate. The manager can compensate for the mismatch by varying the number of hours the line operates, that is, by varying the amount of overtime, extending shifts, or adding extra shifts. Or multiple lines might be the answer instead.

Another possibility is to let finished-goods inventory build up for some time and then rebalance the line at a lower output rate to deplete the excess. Management's policy on the frequency of rebalancing applies here. Japanese automobile manufacturing strategy calls for rebalancing lines about twelve times a year. In the United States, the overall average is only about three times per year. The Japanese strategy minimizes inventories and balance delay. The major disadvantage of the Japanese approach is that it disrupts production during changeover from one line configuration to another. Greater worker flexibility, cross-training, and job rotation, which are additional elements of the Japanese approach (see Chapter 17), can minimize this disruption.

SOLVED PROBLEMS

1. A manager wants to know whether the plant's current process layout is adequate. Figure 10.12 shows the current layout and a from–to matrix for the facility. Safety and EPA regulations require departments E and F to remain at their current locations.
   a. Use trial and error to find a better layout.
   b. How much better is your layout over the current one, in terms of the *ld* score? Use rectilinear distance.

Solution

a. In addition to keeping departments E and F at their current locations, a good plan would locate the following department pairs close to one another: A and E, C and F, A and B, and C and E. Figure 10.13 was worked out by trial and error and satisfies all these requirements. Start by placing E and F at their current locations. Then because C must be as close as possible to both E and F, put C between them. The rest of the layout falls into place.

FIGURE 10.12

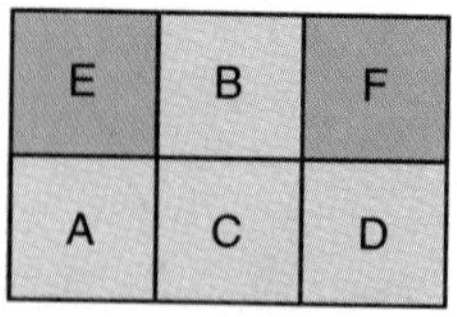

(a) Current block plan

From \ To	A	B	C	D	E	F
A		8	3		9	5
B				3		
C					8	9
D						3
E						3
F						

(b) From–to matrix

FIGURE 10.13

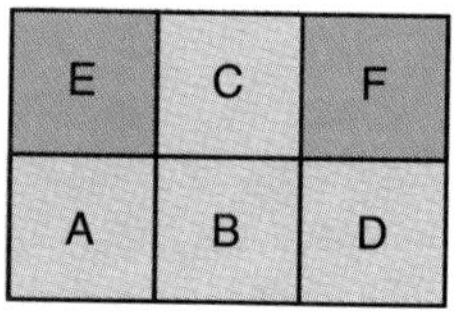

TABLE 10.2

Department Pair	Closeness Rating (I_{ij})	Current Plan		Proposed Plan	
		Distance (d_{ij})	$I_{ij}d_{ij}$	Distance (d_{ij})	$I_{ij}d_{ij}$
A, B	8	2	16	1	8
A, C	3	1	3	2	6
A, E	9	1	9	1	9
A, F	5	3	15	3	15
B, D	3	2	6	1	3
C, E	8	2	16	1	8
C, F	9	2	18	1	9
D, F	3	1	3	1	3
E, F	3	2	6	2	6
			$Id = 92$		$Id = 67$

b. Table 10.2 reveals that the *Id* score drops from 92 for the current plan to 67 for the revised plan, a 27 percent reduction.

2. Develop a layout for the warehouse docking area shown in Fig. 10.14, using rectilinear distances. Each of seven departments (A–G) requires one block space—except C, which needs two spaces. The daily trips to and from the dock are 390 for A, 180 for B, 220 for C, 250 for D, 160 for E, 120 for F, and 220 for G.

FIGURE 10.14

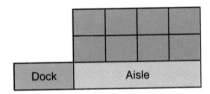

Solution

Sequencing departments by the ratio of trips per block space, we get A, D, G, B, E, F, and C. Giving preference to those higher in the sequence produces the layout shown in Fig. 10.15. There are other optimal solutions because some locations are equidistant from the dock.

FIGURE 10.15

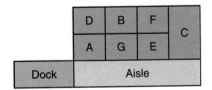

TABLE 10.3

Work Element	Time (sec)	Immediate Predecessor(s)
1	40	None
2	30	1
3	50	1
4	40	2
5	6	2
6	25	3
7	15	3
8	20	4, 5
9	18	6, 7
10	30	8, 9
	Total = 274	

  c. Work out a solution using the largest work-element time rule, showing your solution on a precedence diagram.
  d. What are the efficiency and balance delay of the solution found?

Solution
  a. Substituting in the cycle-time formula, we get

$$c = \left(\frac{1}{r}\right)(3600 \text{ sec/hr}) = \left(\frac{1}{60}\right)(3600 \text{ sec/hr}) = 60 \text{ sec/unit}$$

  b. The sum of the work-element times is 274 seconds, so

$$TM = \frac{t}{c} = \frac{274}{60} = 4.6 \quad \text{or} \quad 5 \text{ stations}$$

  which may not be achievable.
  c. The worksheet and precedence diagram for the solution are shown in Fig. 10.16.
  d. Calculating the efficiency, we get

$$\text{Efficiency} = \frac{t}{nc}(100) = \frac{274}{(6)(60)} = 76\%$$

  so the balance delay is 24 percent ($100\% - 76\%$).

FORMULA REVIEW

1. Load–distance score—process layouts:

$$ld = \sum_{j=i}^{n} \sum_{i=1}^{n} l_{ij}d_{ij}$$

2. Cycle time (in seconds):

$$c = \left(\frac{1}{r}\right)(3600 \text{ seconds/hour})$$

3. Theoretical minimum number of work stations:

$$TM = \frac{t}{c}$$

4. Idle time (in seconds) $= nc - t$

5. Efficiency $(\%) = \left(\dfrac{t}{nc}\right)(100)$

6. Balance delay $(\%) = 100 -$ Efficiency

FIGURE 10.16

Station	Candidate	Choice	Cumulative time (sec)	Idle time (c = 60 sec)
S1	1	1	40	20
S2	2, 3	3	50	10
S3	2, 6, 7	2	30	30
	5, 6, 7	6	55	5
S4	4, 5, 7	4	40	20
	5, 7	7	55	5
S5	5, 9	9	18	42
	5	5	24	36
	8	8	44	16
S6	10	10	30	30

(a) Worksheet

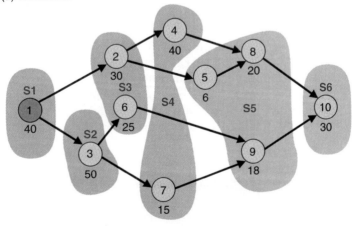

(b) Precedence diagram showing solution

CHAPTER HIGHLIGHTS

● Layout decisions go beyond placement of economic activity centers. Equally important are which centers to include, how much space they need, and how to configure their space.

● There are four layout types: process, product, hybrid, and fixed. Management's choice must be coupled with its positioning strategy. A process focus requires a process layout, whereas a product focus calls for a product layout. Hybrid layouts, such as OWMM, group technology cells, and FMS, reflect an intermediate positioning strategy.

● Capital investment, materials-handling cost, and flexibility are important criteria in judging most manufacturing and warehouse layouts. Entirely different criteria, such as sales or communication, might be emphasized for stores or offices.

● If product volumes are too low to justify dedicating a production line to a single product, it may still be possible to obtain overlapped operations. In such cases the one worker, multiple machines (OWMM) concept or group technology (GT) cells, where machines are arranged to produce families of parts, may be feasible.

● Designing a process layout involves gathering the necessary information, developing an acceptable block plan, and translating the block plan into a detailed layout. Information needed for process layouts includes space requirements by center, available space (including the block plan for an existing layout), closeness ratings, and other considerations. Closeness ratings can be tabulated on either a from–to matrix or a REL chart. A manual approach to finding a block plan begins with listing key requirements, based on large closeness ratings or other considerations. Trial and error is then used to find a block plan

that satisfies most of the requirements. A load–distance score helps evaluate the plan for relative location concerns.

● Several computer-based models, such as ALDEP and CRAFT, are now available to aid layout decision making.

● The simplest warehouse situation is the out-and-back selection pattern. Departmental proximity to the dock depends on the ratio of trip frequency to space needs. Other patterns are the route collection trip, batch picking, and the zone system.

● The effect of a layout on people is particularly apparent in offices. Layout affects productivity and the quality of work life. Four approaches to proximity–privacy trade-offs are traditional layouts, office landscaping, activity settings, and electronic cottages.

● The line-balancing problem is to assign tasks to stations so as to satisfy all precedence and cycle-time constraints, while minimizing the number of stations required. This in turn minimizes idle time, maximizes efficiency, and minimizes balance delay. The desired output rate from a line depends not only on demand forecasts but also on frequency of rebalancing, capacity utilization, and job specialization. One approach to line balancing is to create one station at a time. A work element selected from a list of candidates is added to a station at each iteration. Two commonly used decision rules for making this choice are the longest work-element time and largest number of followers rules.

● Management must look beyond the narrow view of line balancing. Line pacing, behavioral options, single or mixed-model lines, and cycle-time modification are options available to ensure the success of a product layout.

KEY TERMS

automated layout design
   program (ALDEP) **394**
balance delay **405**
block plan **390**

computerized relative
   allocation of facilities
   technique (CRAFT) **395**
cycle time **403**

economic activity center **378**
fixed-position layout **382**
from–to matrix **390**
group technology (GT) **387**

STUDY QUESTIONS

1. What are the types of choices that must be made in designing a layout? Which ones are the most strategic?

2. How does a process layout differ from a product layout? Illustrate each with an example that you have encountered at work or where you live.

3. With which other decision areas is layout strongly connected? Explain.

4. Identify the types of layout performance criteria that might be most important in the following settings.
   a. Bank   c. Law firm
   b. Parking lot   d. Small metal fabricator

5. What is the one worker, multiple machines (OWMM) concept? What is a group technology (GT) cell? What do they have in common? How do they differ?

6. An office of 120 employees must be revised to accommodate 30 new employees. While changing the layout, it makes sense to review it to be sure that it is as effective as possible. You want to improve communication, find space for everyone, create a good work environment, and minimize adverse reactions to space reductions and relocations.
   a. What information would you gather? How?
   b. How would you analyze this information?
   c. How much employee involvement would you recommend? Why?

7. Consider the layout of a retail store you recently visited as a customer. What criteria seemed most important to those who designed it? Why?

8. Think of a small- to medium-sized class that you have taken where there was no assigned seating. Did you tend to sit in the same seat each time? Which criterion discussed for office layouts were you implicitly satisfying?

9. Layouts are often designed to fit current work activities and interaction patterns. These, in turn, are partially shaped by the existing layout. Comment on this apparent circularity.

10. What information is needed before you can solve a line-balancing problem?

11. Suppose that a line's desired output rate is 20 units per hour. Why might management consider cycle times other than 180 seconds?

12. Why might employee dissatisfaction be higher on assembly lines? What steps might help to alleviate this problem? Will these steps always lead to higher satisfaction and productivity? Explain.

PROBLEMS

Review Problems

1. Baker Machine Company is a job shop specializing in precision parts for aerospace markets. Figure 10.17 shows the from–to matrix and the current block plan for the key manufacturing centers of the 75,000-square-foot facility. Using rectilinear distance (the current distance from inspection to shipping and receiving is 3 units of distance), calculate the change in the load–distance (*ld*) score if Baker exchanges the locations of the tool crib and inspection.

From \ To	1	2	3	4	5	6
1. Burr and grind		10		15		45
2. NC equipment					45	
3. Shipping and receiving				25		50
4. Lathes and drills					35	20
5. Tool crib						
6. Inspection						

(a) From–to matrix (trips/day)

3	4	2
1	5	6

(b) Current block plan

FIGURE 10.17

From \ To	A	B	C	D	E	F
Analyst A			6			
Analyst B				12		10
Analyst C				2	7	
Analyst D						4
Analyst E						
Analyst F						

(a) From–to matrix (contacts/day)

2	4	6
1	3	5

(b) Sketch of available
space

FIGURE 10.18

2. Use trial and error to find a particularly good block plan for Baker Machine (see Problem 1). Because of excessive relocation costs, shipping and receiving (department 3) must remain at its current location. How good is your new layout, once again assuming rectilinear distance?

3. The head of the information systems group at Conway Consulting must assign six new analysts to offices. The from–to matrix in Fig. 10.18(a) shows the expected frequency of contact between analysts. The block plan in Fig. 10.18(b) shows the available office locations (1–6) for the six analysts (A–F). Assume equal-sized offices and rectilinear distance. Owing to their tasks, analyst A must be assigned to location 1 and analyst D to location 6. What are the best locations for the other four analysts? What is the *ld* score for your layout?

4. A department within an insurance company is now designing its layout for newly built office space. From statistical samplings over the last three months, the from–to matrix in Fig. 10.19(a) was developed for daily trips between the department's offices.

From \ To	A	B	C	D	E	F
A		10	75			140
B					95	
C					130	130
D					10	
E						95
F						

(a) From–to matrix (trips/day)

C	F	A
B	E	D

(b) Alternative layout

FIGURE 10.19

a. If other factors are equal, which two offices should be located most closely?

b. Figure 10.19(b) shows one alternative layout for the department. What is the total load–distance score for this plan using rectilinear distance, assuming offices A and B are 3 units of distance apart?

c. Which switch of two departments will most improve the total load–distance score?

5. A firm with four departments has the from–to matrix and current block plan shown in Fig. 10.20.
   a. What is the load–distance score for the current layout? (Assume rectilinear distance.)
   b. Find a better layout. What is its total load–distance score?

From \ To	A	B	C	D
A		12	10	8
B			20	6
C				0
D				

(a) From–to matrix (trips/day)

A	B
C	D

(b) Current block plan

FIGURE 10.20

6. As director of the Office of Budget Management for Michigan's state government, Todd Paul manages a department of 120 employees assigned to eight different sections.

Workloads have expanded to the point that 30 new employees must be hired and placed somewhere within the existing layout. While changing the layout, Paul wishes to improve communication and create a good work environment. One special consideration is that the State Controlling Board (section 2) should occupy the upper-right location of the block plan. A from–to matrix was developed from questionnaires sent to each of the 120 current employees (Fig. 10.21). It contains section names and area requirements and represents the closeness ratings between each of the sections.
   a. Develop a square block plan (4 rows and 4 columns) for Paul. Calculate a score for your plan as you would do using ALDEP. In other words, add the closeness rating (6 for A, 5 for E, and so on) between two sections to the total score only if the sections share at least some of the same boundary (merely touching the corner doesn't count).
   b. What behavioral issues does Paul need to address when revising the layout?

7. The department of philosophy at a university in Ontario must assign six faculty members to their new offices. The from–to matrix in Fig. 10.22 indicates the expected number of contacts per day between professors. Also shown is a sketch of the available office spaces (1 through 6) for the six faculty members. Assume equally sized offices. The distance between office 1 and office 2 (as well

From \ To	1	2	3	4	5	6	7	8	Area needed (blocks)
1. Administration		3	2	10		2	2		1
2. State Controlling Board			3			2	2		5
3. Program clearinghouse						2	2	6	1
4. Social services						5	3	2	2
5. Institutions						8			3
6. Accounting									2
7. Education									1
8. Internal audit									1

FIGURE 10.21

From \ To	A	B	C	D	E	F
A		0	4	0	0	0
B			0	12	0	10
C				2	7	0
D					0	4
E						0
F						

(a) From–to matrix (contacts/day)

1	2
3	4
5	6

(b) Sketch of
available space

FIGURE 10.22

(a) Dock and storage space

Departments	Trips to and from dock	Area needed (blocks)
A	260	2
B	180	1
C	381	3
D	250	4
E	80	1
F	190	2
G	220	1

(b) Trips and space requirements

FIGURE 10.23

as the distance between offices 1 and 3) is one unit of distance.

  a. Because of their academic position professor A must be assigned to office 1, professor C must be assigned to office 2, and professor D must be assigned to office 6. What faculty members should be assigned to offices 3, 4, and 5, respectively, to minimize the total load–distance score? (Assume rectilinear distance.)

  b. What is the load–distance score of your solution?

8. Figure 10.23 shows the block layout configuration and required information for a warehouse docking area. What is the best layout, assuming an out-and-back selection pattern?

9. The layout configuration for a warehouse docking area is shown in Fig. 10.24, along with the travel frequencies and area requirements of the seven departments (A–G). An out-and-back selection pattern is used. What is the best layout?

10. Big Reaper plans to produce several new and larger truck models on an assembly line at its Seattle manufacturing facility. Four major warehousing areas in the plant, divided into

Departments	Trips to and from dock	Area needed (blocks)
A	320	3
B	240	1
C	178	2
D	460	4
E	300	1
F	60	1
G	280	2

(a) Required information

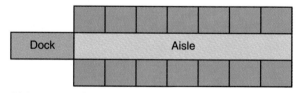

(b) Layout configuration

FIGURE 10.24

12 equal sections, will be used to store the parts and components needed for the new models. Based on current inventory and output plans, the average number of trips per day between storage and the assembly line

TABLE 10.4

Part Category	Trips per Day	Number of Sections Needed
A	80	1
B	140	2
C	60	1
D	240	4
E	320	2
F	150	1
G	60	1

TABLE 10.6

Work Element	Number of Followers	Work Element	Number of Followers
1	23	13	
2	20	14	
3	19	15	
4	18	16	
5	19	17	
6	18	18	
7	17	19	
8	8	20	
9	7	21	
10	6	22	
11	5	23	
12	8	24	

has been estimated for each of seven basic part categories. The number of storage sections needed for each one (Table 10.4) and the distance from each section to the assembly line (Table 10.5) have also been calculated. Assign each part category to one or more storage sections, so as to provide the right amount of space for each. Find the assignment that minimizes travel from storage to the assembly line. Owing to size restrictions, part category G cannot be assigned to section 1 or 2.

11. Table 10.6 has been partially completed from the information in Application 10.5 and Fig. 10.10 for the Big Broadcaster.
   a. Complete Table 10.6 by filling in the last column.
   b. Find a line-balancing solution using the largest number of followers rule. Break ties using the largest work-element time rule. If a tie remains, pick the work element with the highest numerical label.
   c. Calculate the efficiency and balance delay of your solution.

TABLE 10.5

Section	Distance to Assembly Line	Section	Distance to Assembly Line
1	60	7	190
2	80	8	230
3	90	9	300
4	110	10	305
5	140	11	320
6	160	12	360

12. A company wants to set up a line to produce 60 units per hour. The work elements and their precedence relationships follow.

Work Element	Time (sec)	Immediate Predecessor
1	40	—
2	30	1
3	50	1
4	40	2
5	6	2
6	25	3
7	15	3
8	20	4, 5
9	18	6, 7
10	30	8,9

   a. What is the theoretical minimum number of stations?
   b. How many stations are required, using the longest work-element time method?
   c. How many stations are required, using the largest number of followers method?
   d. Suppose that a solution requiring five stations has been found to this problem. What is its efficiency?

13. The Illinois Appliance Company is installing a line to produce a vacuum cleaner and you, as the operations manager, are responsible for designing the line. The line has to produce 480 units per day, and the company operates two 8-hour shifts each day. The work

elements, time requirements, and immediate predecessor(s) follow.

Work Element	Time (sec)	Immediate Predecessor
A	55	—
B	45	A
C	25	B
D	20	B
E	40	B
F	50	D
G	70	D
H	45	F, G
I	20	E
J	80	H, I

a. What is the theoretical number of stations?

b. If you balance the line using the longest work-element time rule, which elements are assigned to station 2?

14. Classic Communications has developed a new answering machine. Management wants to establish two assembly lines to make the machine. Each line includes 11 work elements and must produce 45 machines per hour. The following table gives the standard times and immediate predecessors for each work element to be performed.

Work Element	Work-Element Time (sec)	Immediate Predecessor
1	70	—
2	15	1
3	8	—
4	32	—
5	47	3, 4, 7
6	25	2, 5
7	61	—
8	52	—
9	29	7, 8
10	42	9
11	50	6, 10

a. Construct a precedence diagram.

b. What cycle time (in seconds) corresponds to 45 machines per hour?

c. What is the theoretical minimum number of stations for each line?

d. Use the longest work-element time rule to balance the line.

e. What is the efficiency of your line? How does it compare with theoretical maximum efficiency?

f. Can you find a way to improve the line's efficiency?

15. The *trim line* at PW is a small subassembly line that, along with other such lines, feeds into the final chasis line. The entire assembly line is to make PW's new E cars and will be composed of more than 900 work stations. The trim line itself involves only 13 work elements and must handle 20 cars per hour. In addition to the usual precedence constraints, there are two *zoning constraints*. First, work elements 11 and 12 should, preferably, be assigned to the same station; both use a common component and assigning them to the same station conserves storage space. Second, work elements 8 and 10 cannot be performed at the same station. Work-element data follow.

Work Element	Work-Element Time (min)	Immediate Predecessor
1	1.8	—
2	0.4	—
3	1.6	—
4	1.5	1
5	0.7	1
6	0.5	5
7	0.8	2
8	1.4	3
9	1.4	4
10	1.4	6, 7
11	0.5	8
12	1.0	10
13	0.8	9, 11, 12

a. Draw a precedence diagram.

b. What cycle time (in *minutes*) results in the desired output rate?

c. What is the theoretical minimum number of stations?

d. Using trial and error, balance the line as best you can.

e. What is the efficiency of your solution?

16. An assembly line must produce 40 wall air conditioners per hour. The following data give the necessary information.

Work Element	Work-Element Time (sec)	Immediate Predecessor
1	20	—
2	55	1
3	25	2
4	40	2
5	5	2
6	35	1
7	14	4, 5
8	40	3, 6, 7

a. Draw a precedence diagram.
b. What cycle time (in seconds) ensures the desired output rate?
c. What is the theoretical minimum number of stations? The theoretical maximum efficiency?
d. Design the line, using the longest work-element rule. What is its efficiency?
e. Can you find any way to improve the line's balance? If so, explain how.

Advanced Problems

A computer package is recommended for Problems 21(b), 22, and 23.

17. CCI Electronics makes various products for the communications industry. One of its manufacturing plants makes a device for sensing when telephone calls are placed. A from–to matrix and the current layout are shown in Fig. 10.25. Management is reasonably satisfied with the current layout, although it has heard some complaints about the placement of departments D, G, K, and L. Find a revised block plan for moving only these four departments, using trial and error. Show that the load–distance score is improved, assuming rectilinear distance.

18. A paced assembly line has been devised to make electric can openers, as the data on page 422 show.
a. What is the maximum hourly output rate from this line? (*Hint:* The line can go only as fast as its slowest work station.)
b. What cycle time corresponds to this maximum output rate?

From \ To	A	B	C	D	E	F	G	H	I	J	K	L
A. Network lead forming												80
B. Wire forming and subassembly									50	70		
C. Final assembly						120						
D. Coil and terminal eyeletting					40							
E. Presoldering				80							90	
F. Final testing							120					
G. Inventory storage		30						40	50			
H. Coil winding									80			
I. Coil assembly			70		40							60
J. Network preparation	90											
K. Soldering			80									
L. Network insertion			60									

(a) From–to matrix (trips/day)

L	H	B	K
F	I	J	A
C	D	E	G

(b) Current block plan

FIGURE 10.25

Station	Work-Element Assigned	Work-Element Time (min)
S1	1	1.8
S2	4, 5	0.5, 0.8
S3	3	2.0
S4	2, 6, 7	0.6, 0.6, 0.7
S5	8, 9, 10	0.5, 0.2, 0.9
S6	11	1.5

TABLE 10.7

Work Element	Time (min)	Immediate Predecessor
1	2	—
2	3	1
3	1	2
4	5	2
5	5	3, 4
6	4	5
7	1	4, 5
8	2	6
9	6	7
10	4	8
11	2	9, 10
12	6	11

c. If there is a worker at each station and the line operates at this maximum output rate, how much idle time is lost during each eight-hour shift?

d. What is the line's efficiency?

19. Sanders Manufacturing seeks a better layout for its plant. Figure 10.26(a) shows the departments to be located on the first floor of the plant. Figure 10.26(b) divides the available space into 9 rows and 12 columns. Each block represents 100 square feet, which means that 13 blocks should be allocated to materials storage, 5 blocks to forming, and so on. Productive space is lost to the elevator, stairs, office, and aisle. Their positions, plus those for departments 1 and 6, must remain fixed. Figure 10.26(c) gives a REL chart. The letters indicate the closeness score, whereas the numbers in parentheses explain the reason for the rating. For example, it's necessary (rating = A) for the forming department and the assembly department to be close to each other because personnel are shared and supervision is easier.

a. Develop an acceptable layout for Sanders, working the remaining departments around the prepositioned departments.

b. Calculate a score for your plan, as you would do using ALDEP (see Problem 6). Consider spaces separated only by the aisle to be adjacent.

20. The manager of the Tastegood Pizza Parlor wishes to organize the tasks involved in the preparation and delivery of pizzas. The manager plans to produce 100 pizzas per 10-hour workday. Table 10.7 presents work-element times and precedence relationships.

a. Construct a precedence diagram for this process.

b. What cycle time corresponds with the desired output rate?

c. Try to identify the best possible line balancing solution. What work elements are assigned to each station?

d. What is the impact on your solution if the time for work element 6 increases by 50 percent? Decreases by 50 percent?

21. Green Grass's plant manager (see Application 10.4) is willing to consider a line balance with an output rate of less than 60 units per hour, if the gain in efficiency is sufficient. Operating the line longer (either with a second shift or overtime) and setting up two lines are ways to compensate.

a. Calculate the theoretical maximum efficiency for output rates of 30, 35, 40, 45, 50, 55, and 60. Is there any possible gain in efficiency when the output rate is reduced to as low as 30?

b. Use the longest work-element time rule to explore solutions over the range of output rates where efficiency gains might be achieved.

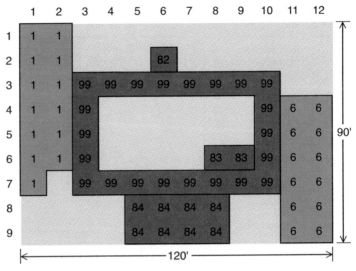

(a) Space requirements by center

Department	Square feet
1 Materials storage	1,300
2 Forming	500
3 Machining	1,000
4 Painting	600
5 Assembly	1,400
6 Stamping	1,200
7 Saw	800
8 Inspection	700
82 Elevator	100
83 Stairs	200
84 Office	800
99 Aisle	2,200
Total	10,800

(b) Available space (Productive space lost to elevator, stairs, office, and aisle is shown in purple, along with required locations for departments 1 and 6, shown in blue.)

Department	2	3	4	5	6	7	8
1 Materials storage	O (1)	O (1)	U	E (1)	U	O (1)	E (1)
2 Forming		E (1)	U	A (2,3)	U	I (1)	O (1)
3 Machining			I (1)	O (1)	U (1)	I (1)	U
4 Painting				E (2,3)	O	U (1)	E (4)
5 Assembly					X (5,6)	I (1)	I (1)
6 Stamping						I (1)	O (1)
7 Saw							I (1)
8 Inspection							

(c) Closeness ratings (REL chart)

Closeness ratings		Explanation codes	
Rating	Definition	Code	Meaning
A	Asolutely necessary	1	Materials handling
E	Especially important	2	Shared personnel
I	Important	3	Ease of supervision
O	Ordinary closeness	4	Space utilization
U	Unimportant	5	Noise
X	Undesirable	6	Employee attitudes

(d) Other Considerations

1. Owing to noise factors and the need for special foundations, the stamping department should be put in the southeast corner.

2. Materials storage should be on the northwest side, since this is where the shipping and receiving dock will be placed.

FIGURE 10.26

From \ To	1	2	3	4	5	6	7	8	9	10	11	12	13	14	15	16	99	Area needed (blocks)
1. Terminal storage		1		8	4		4											6
2. Shipping and receiving			1								2							6
3. Wire storage				8		5												6
4. Finished goods					11	16		1										6
5. Terminating						18	5			6			3	5	5			6
6. Cutting I							2											3
7. Cutting II								2		6			1	1	1			2
8. Painting										3								3
9. Processing																		3
10. Work-in-process													3	2	3			10
11. Rest rooms																		1
12. Supplies													2	2	1			4
13. Assembly I														2	2			4
14. Assembly II															1			4
15. Custom assembly																		3
16. Offices																		3
99. Dead space																		20

(a) From–to matrix

	1	2	3	4	5	6
1	4	4	2	2	99	99
2	4	4	2	2	3	3
3	4	4	2	2	3	3
4	5	1	1	1	3	3
5	5	1	1	1	10	10
6	5	6	6	6	10	10
7	5	7	7	11	10	10
8	5	9	9	9	10	10
9	5	8	8	8	10	10
10	12	12	12	99	99	99
11	13	14	12	99	99	99
12	13	14	15	99	99	99
13	13	14	15	99	99	99
14	13	14	15	99	99	99
15	16	16	16	99	99	99

(b) Current layout

FIGURE 10.27

22. Mohan Assemblies, Inc., manufactures customized wire harnesses for kitchen appliances, snowmobiles, farm machinery, and motorcycles. Figure 10.27(a) shows the from–to matrix, and Fig. 10.27(b) shows the current layout of the plant.

a. Find a better layout, but keep departments 2, 16, and 99 (dead space) at their current positions.

b. Calculate scores for both plants, as you would do using ALDEP (see Problem 6). How much better is your plan?

23. The associate administrator at Getwell Hospital wishes to evaluate the layout of the outpatient clinic. Figure 10.28 shows the interdepartmental flows (patients/day) between departments and the current layout.

a. Determine the effectiveness of the current layout, as measured by the total ld score, using rectilinear distances.

b. Try to find the best possible layout based on this same effectiveness measure.

c. What is the impact on your new solution if it must be revised to keep department 1 at its present location?

d. How should the layout found to part (c) be revised if the interdepartmental flow between the examining room and x-ray is increased by 50 percent? Decreased by 50 percent?

FIGURE 10.28

From \ To	1	2	3	4	5	6	7	8
1. Reception		25	35	5	10	15	0	20
2. Business office			5	10	15	0	0	15
3. Examining room				20	30	20	0	10
4. X-ray					25	15	0	20
5. Laboratory						20	0	25
6. Surgery							40	0
7. Post-surgery								15
8. Doctor's office								

(a) From–to matrix

4	6	5	7
2	8	3	1

(b) Current layout

CASE HIGHTEC, INC.

"It's hard to believe," thought Glenn Moore as he walked into the employee lunch area, "that it has been only six years since I founded Hightec." He was not interested in lunch, since it was only 9:30 A.M. His purpose was to inspect the new microcomputer, which was just purchased to better manage the company's inventory and accounting functions. The computer had to be housed at the rear of the employee lunch area, right next to the coffee, hot soup, and hot chocolate vending machines. There is absolutely no room for the computer elsewhere.

Hightec is a manufacturer of transducers. These devices convert gas or liquid pressure into an electrical signal. Another form of the device converts weight or force into an electrical signal. A typical customer order is for only three to ten units. The firm currently rents a 15,000-square-foot, L-shaped building housing four basic sections: the office area, an engineering area, a machine shop, and an assembly area. There are 80 employees, consisting of machinists, engineers, assemblers, secretaries, and salespersons.

Although Moore concentrated on finance and marketing during the first two years of Hightec's existence, his problems now lie more with production costs, inventory, and capacity. Sales have been increasing about 30 percent per year, and this growth is expected to continue. Specific symptoms of Hightec's problems include the following:

- Space limitations have delayed the purchase of a numerical control machine and a more efficient testing machine. Both promise greater capacity and higher productivity and are easily cost justified.
- The machine shop is so crowded that equipment not in constant use has been moved into the inventory storage area.
- More and more machines are being operated on a second- and third-shift basis than would otherwise be justified. Productivity is lower and quality is slipping.
- Approximately 10 percent of the work force's time is spent moving materials to and from the inventory storage area. Inventory at all stages of production is kept there. Since the supply room is so chaotic, it is difficult to find wanted parts. Considerable time is lost searching.

- Approximately 1000 square feet of storage space must be rented outside the plant.
- Moore has been forced to forgo bidding on several attractive jobs due to lack of capacity. One salesperson is particularly disgruntled with this decision, as she lost her commission.
- Several office workers have complained about the cramped quarters and lack of privacy. The quality of employee space also leaves an unfavorable impression on prospective customers visiting the plant.
- Additional help was just hired for the office. To make room for their desks, Moore had to discard his favorite tropical plant, which started as a cutting when Hightec was formed. It has sentimental value.

The Options

Moore has identified three options for increasing capacity at Hightec. The first is to renew the rental contract on the current facility for another five years and rent portable units to ease the cramped conditions. He

Department	2	3	4	5	6	7	8	9	10	11	12	13	14	15	Area needed (blocks)
1. Administrative office	I	A	E	U	A	E	O	O	O	O	I	E	O	U	3
2. Conference room		U	U	U	U	U	U	U	U	U	U	U	U	U	1
3. Engineering & mtls. mgt.			I	U	U	O	A	E	E	I	E	E	U	O	2
4. Production manager				U	A	A	A	A	A	I	I	E	O	A	1
5. Lunch room					U	U	U	U	U	U	U	U	U	U	2
6. Computer						A	X	U	U	U	O	I	U	U	1
7. Inventory storage							A	O	O	O	O	U	U	U	2
8. Machine shop								A	X	I	O	U	U	I	6
9. Assembly area									A	A	I	U	I	A	7
10. Cleaning										O	O	U	U	U	1
11. Welding											O	U	U	U	1
12. Electronic												E	U	U	1
13. Sales & accounting													O	U	2
14. Shipping and receiving														U	1
15. Load test															1
													Total		32

(a) Relationship Chart: Each block represents approximately 595 square feet.

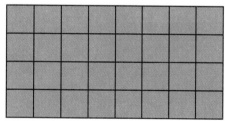

(b) Available space for new plan
  (Option 2)

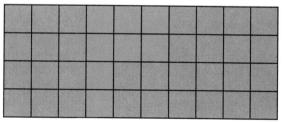

(c) Available space for renting two buildings
  (Option 3)

EXHIBIT 1

discarded this first alternative as being too piecemeal for a growing problem. The second alternative is to purchase land and build on it a new 19,000-square-foot facility. The most attractive site would cost $100,000 for land, and the construction cost is estimated at $40 per square foot. His cost of capital is around 15 percent.

The third alternative is to renew the rental contract on the current building for another five years and rent an adjacent 7000-square-foot building only 50 feet from the current one. The rental cost of both buildings would be $2800 per month. It would be necessary to build a $15,000 corridor connecting the buildings if this third option is chosen, although Moore estimates the relocation costs (such as for moving and installing the machines and the loss of regular-time capacity) to be $20,000 less than with the second alternative.

The Layout

Regardless of which option Moore chooses, he must improve on the existing layout. It suffers in terms of materials-handling costs and coordination between departments. When Moore initially designed it, he essentially placed the office first and then fit in the other departments as best as possible. The main consideration for the other departments was not to have the machine shop next to the clean room. Moore put together the information on the new layout, as shown in Exhibit 1. The projected area requirements should be sufficient for the next five years. Both layouts provide for 19,000 square feet. The REL chart gives particular emphasis to materials-handling and communication patterns.

Glenn Moore walked back to the office with a fresh cup of coffee in his hand. He hated hot chocolate and it was too early for soup. He wondered what should be done next. Whatever the choice, he wants a more attractive work environment for the engineering and materials management staffs, which are currently located in a cramped, open-office setting. It has been difficult attracting creative people in these areas. He made a mental note that the adjacent building currently is quite drab.

QUESTIONS

1. What expansion alternative do you recommend to Glenn Moore? Justify your position.
2. Design an effective block plan. Compute its "score," as would be done by ALDEP. Also cite any qualitative considerations that you believe make your design attractive.

SELECTED REFERENCES

Ackerman, K. B., and B. J. LaLonde. "Making Warehousing More Efficient." *Harvard Business Review* (March–April 1980), pp. 94–102.

Arcus, A. L. "COMSOAL: A Computer Method of Sequencing Operations for Assembly Lines." *International Journal of Production Research*, vol. 4, no. 4 (1966).

Chase, Richard B. "Survey of Paced Assembly Lines." *Industrial Engineering*, vol. 6, no. 2 (February 1974), pp. 14–18.

Cinar, U. "Facilities Planning: A Systems Analysis and Space Allocation Approach." In C. M. Eastman, ed., *Spatial Synthesis in Computer-Aided Building Design*. New York: John Wiley & Sons, 1975.

Eastman, C. M. *Spatial Synthesis in Computer-Aided Building Design*. New York: John Wiley & Sons, 1975.

El-Rayah, J. "The Efficiency of Balanced and Unbalanced Production Lines." *International Journal of Production Research*, vol. 17, no. 1 (1979), pp. 61–75.

Farnum, Gregory T. "Integrating Stamping Operations." *Manufacturing Engineering* (September 1986), pp. 36–38.

Flynn, Barbara B., and F. Robert Jacobs. "An Experimental Comparison of Cellular (Group Technology) Layout with Process Layout." *Decision Sciences*, vol. 18, no. 4 (Fall 1987), pp. 562–581.

Francis, Richard L., Leon F. McGinnis, Jr., and John A. White. *Facility Layout and Location: An Analytical Approach*, 2nd ed. Englewood Cliffs, N.J.: Prentice Hall, 1992.

Ghosh, Soumen, and Roger Gagnon. "A Comprehensive Literature Review and Hierarchical Taxonomy for the Design and Balancing of Assembly Lines." Working Paper Series, College of Administrative Science, Ohio State University (January 1986).

Hicks, P. E., and T. E. Cowan. "CRAFT-M for Layout Rearrangement." *Industrial Engineering*, May 1976.

Hoffman, T. R. "Assembly Line Balancing with a Precedence Matrix." *Management Science*, vol. 9, no. 4 (July 1963), pp. 551–562.

Homans, G. C. *The Human Group.* New York: Harcourt Brace, 1950.

Jacobs, F. Robert. "A Layout Planning System with Multiple Criteria and a Variable Domain Representation." *Management Science,* vol. 33, no. 8 (August 1987), pp. 1020–1034.

Jacobs, F. Robert, John W. Bradford, and Larry P. Ritzman. "Computerized Layout: An Integrated Approach to Spatial Planning and Communication Requirements." *Industrial Engineering,* vol. 12, no. 7 (July 1980), pp. 56–61.

Kilbridge, M. D., and L. Wester. "A Heuristic Method of Assembly Line Balancing." *Journal of Industrial Engineering,* vol. 12, no. 4 (July–August 1961), pp. 292–298.

Kottas, J. F., and H. Lau. "Some Problems with Transient Phenomena When Simulating Unpaced Lines." *Journal of Operations Management,* vol. 1, no. 3 (February 1981), pp. 155–164.

Liggett, R. S., and W. J. Mitchell. "Interactive Graphic Floor Plan Layout Method." *Computer Aided Design,* vol. 13, no. 5 (September 1981), pp. 289–298.

Muther, Richard. *Practical Plant Layout.* New York: McGraw-Hill, 1955.

Oldham, G. R., and D. J. Brass. "Employee Reactions to an Open-Plan Office: A Naturally Occurring Quasi-Experiment." *Administrative Science Quarterly,* vol. 24 (1979), pp. 267–294.

Pesch, Michael J., Larry Jarvis, and Loren Troyer. "Turning Around the Rust Belt Factory: The $1.98 Solution." *Production and Inventory Management Journal,* 1992.

Pinto, Peter D., David Dannenbring, and Basheer Khumawala. "Assembly Line Balancing with Processing Alternatives." *Management Science,* vol. 29, no. 7 (July 1983), pp. 817–830.

Ritzman, Larry P., John W. Bradford, and F. Robert Jacobs. "A Multiple Objective Approach to Space Planning for Academic Facilities." *Management Science,* vol. 25, no. 9 (September 1979), pp. 895–906.

Schuler, Randall S., Larry P. Ritzman, and Vicki L. Davis. "Merging Prescriptive and Behavioral Approaches for Office Layout." *Journal of Operations Management,* vol. 1, no. 3 (February 1981), pp. 131–142.

Scriabin, M., and R. C. Vergin. "Comparison of Computer Algorithms and Visual Based Methods for Plant Layout." *Management Science,* vol. 22, no. 2 (October 1975), pp. 172–181.

Seehof, J. M., and W. O. Evans. "Automated Layout Design Program." *Journal of Industrial Engineering,* vol. 18, no. 12 (December 1967), pp. 690–695.

Steel, F. I. *Physical Settings and Organization Development.* Reading, Mass.: Addison-Wesley, 1973.

Stone, Philip J., and Robert Luchetti. "Your Office Is Where You Are." *Harvard Business Review* (March–April 1985), pp. 102–117.

Chapter 11

FORECASTING

How can we design
the best forecasting
system for a given
situation?

What sort of controls
do we need to
impose on the
forecasting system?

Why is forecasting
important to us?

When can we best
use time series
models and when
can we best use
causal or qualitative
models?

Is it always true that
the most
sophisticated
forecasting system is
the best for our use?

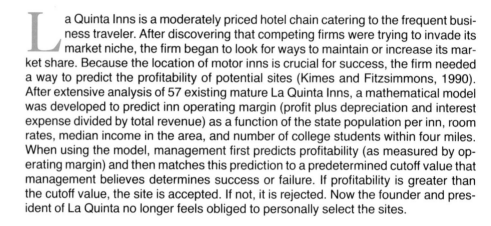

La Quinta Inns is a moderately priced hotel chain catering to the frequent business traveler. After discovering that competing firms were trying to invade its market niche, the firm began to look for ways to maintain or increase its market share. Because the location of motor inns is crucial for success, the firm needed a way to predict the profitability of potential sites (Kimes and Fitzsimmons, 1990). After extensive analysis of 57 existing mature La Quinta Inns, a mathematical model was developed to predict inn operating margin (profit plus depreciation and interest expense divided by total revenue) as a function of the state population per inn, room rates, median income in the area, and number of college students within four miles. When using the model, management first predicts profitability (as measured by operating margin) and then matches this prediction to a predetermined cutoff value that management believes determines success or failure. If profitability is greater than the cutoff value, the site is accepted. If not, it is rejected. Now the founder and president of La Quinta no longer feels obliged to personally select the sites.

The experience at La Quinta demonstrates the value of forecasting for location decisions. A **forecast** is a prediction of future events, in this case profitability. In operations management, planning often requires a variety of forecasts. For example, the manager of a McDonald's restaurant needs to forecast the number of customers at various times of the day and the products they will demand so that she can schedule the correct number of cooks and counter clerks. Or, how do you suppose the materials manager at a Black and Decker plant knows how many hand drills to stock in inventory without a forecast of customer orders? Forecasts may be needed for prices, costs, events (such as new laws or regulations, entry of competitors, or the shortage of critical resources), or the advent of new technologies. We shall discuss many uses of forecasts in operations management in the remainder of the text.

Forecasts are important sources of information for operations managers; they are no panacea, however. Forecasts are rarely perfect, regardless of the amount of historical data available or the amount of managerial experience imbedded within. Fortunately, forecasting methods have improved to the point where they provide useful estimates for planning purposes. In this chapter we will explore several forecasting methods commonly used today and the considerations managers should make in designing a forecasting system. Because of the pervasiveness of forecasting use, operations managers should take pains to learn about the advantages and limitations of the various methods available to them.

DEMAND CHARACTERISTICS

Why does forecasting customer demand pose a challenge? The answer is that demand for goods and services can vary greatly. Demand for letter sorting at a metropolitan post office peaks just before Christmas and again just before

Easter. But demand for haircuts at a local barbershop may be quite stable from week to week. The forecaster, either a professional statistician or a manager with years of experience and some intuition, often must act like a detective to uncover the underlying pattern of demand in a given situation, using whatever information is available. In this section, we first discuss the basic components of demand and then address the factors that affect demand in a particular situation.

Components of Demand

The pattern of demand for a product or service may be observed by its time series. A **time series** is a list of repeated observations of a phenomenon, such as demand, arranged in their order of occurrence. The five basic components of most demand time series are the average, trend, seasonal influence, cyclical movement, and random error. The *average* is simply the sum of the demand observations for each period divided by the number of data periods. A *trend* is a systematic increase or decrease in the average of the series over time. A *seasonal influence* is a predictable increase or decrease in demand, depending on the time of day, week, month, season, or year.

Cyclical movement arises from two influences. The first is the business cycle, which is a complex function of numerous economic factors that cause the economy to go from recession to expansion over a number of years. The other influence is the product or service life cycle, which reflects stages of demand growth and phaseout from the development stage through the decline stage (see Chapter 2 for the life-cycle audit). Cyclical movement is difficult to predict because forecasters often do not know the duration of the cycles. This uncertainty arises from an inability to predict the demand effects of national or international events, such as presidential elections, the Persian Gulf War, or political turmoil in Europe. It is also difficult to predict the rate of demand buildup or decline in the life cycle. Sometimes firms estimate the effects of a new product's life cycle by using the demand history for the product it is replacing as a starting point. For example, the demand rate for digital audio tapes might emulate the demand buildup for stereo cassette tapes in the early stage of their life cycle. The ability to make intelligent long-range forecasts depends on accurate estimates of cyclical movement.

Four of the components of demand—average, trend, seasonal influence, and cyclical movements—combine in varying degrees to define the underlying time pattern of demand for a product or service. The fifth component, *random error*, is the remaining element after all known components of demand have been identified. Random error results from chance variation, which, by definition, cannot be predicted.* Random error is the component of demand that makes every forecast wrong. Figure 11.1 shows the four components of a demand time series.

---

*If we make an error in estimating the trend, seasonal, or cyclical components, the error terms may be highly correlated and consequently not result from chance variation. In such cases we say that there is *autocorrelation* in the error terms.

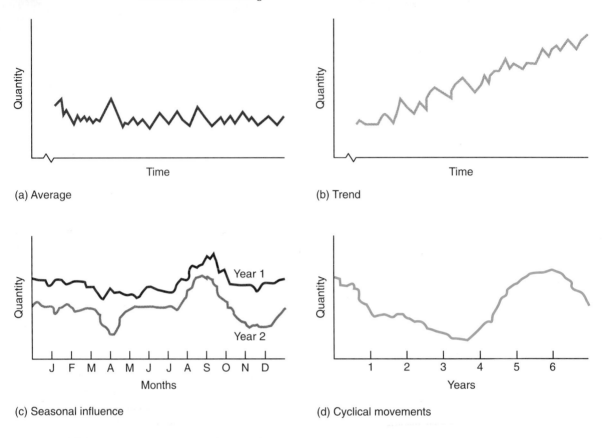

FIGURE 11.1   Components of Demand Time Series

Factors Affecting Demand

What causes the demand pattern for a particular product or service? If we knew the answer, forecasting would be much easier. Unfortunately, many factors affect demand at any given time. Table 11.1 shows two major categories of factors: external and internal.

External Factors. Management cannot control external factors directly, particularly the general state of the economy. Although a booming economy may positively influence demand, the effect may not be the same for all products and services. Furthermore, certain economic activities affect some products and services but not others. Local, state, and national governments affect demand by passing legislation regarding taxes, interest rates, or environmental regulations. For example, limiting the sulphur content of coal used in steam-powered electric generating plants reduces the demand for high-sulphur coal.

Certain external demand factors indicate the direction of change in demand for products or services. The three basic types of demand indicators are shown

TABLE 11.1 / Factors Affecting Demand for Goods and Services

External Factors	Internal Factors
General state of the economy	Product or service design
Government actions	Price and advertising promotions
Consumer tastes	Packaging design
Public image of product	Salesperson quotas or incentives
Competitor actions	Expansion or contraction of geographical
Availability and cost of complementary	market target areas
products	Product mix
	Backlog policy

in Table 11.2. **Leading indicators** are external factors with turning points that typically precede the peaks and troughs of the general business cycle. For example, an upswing in residential building contracts might precede an increase in the demand for plywood by several weeks and for homeowner's insurance by several months. This indicator gives advance warning to plywood manufacturers and insurance companies about possible demand increases in the near future. **Coincident indicators** are time series with turning points that generally match those of the general business cycle. **Lagging indicators** follow

TABLE 11.2 / Demand Indicators

Indicator	Data Source
Leading Indicators	
New corporations	Dun & Bradstreet
Business failures	Dun & Bradstreet
Residential building contracts	F. W. Dodge Corporation
Commercial/industrial building contracts	F. W. Dodge Corporation
Common-stock prices—industrial	Dow Jones
Wholesale commodity price index	Bureau of Labor Statistics
Average hours worked per week— manufacturing	Bureau of Labor Statistics
New orders for manufacturing durable goods	Department of Commerce
Coincident Indicators	
Gross national product (GNP)	Department of Commerce
Corporate profits	Department of Commerce
Unemployment	Bureau of Labor Statistics
Nonagricultural employment	Bureau of Labor Statistics
Nonfood wholesale prices	Bureau of Labor Statistics
Index of industrial production	Federal Reserve Board
Bank debits	Federal Reserve Board
Freight carloadings	Association of American Railroads
Lagging Indicators	
Personal income	Department of Commerce
Retail sales	Department of Commerce
Manufacturers' inventories	Department of Commerce
Consumer installment debt	Federal Reserve Board
Bank rates on business loans	Federal Reserve Board

those turning points, typically by several weeks or months. Knowing that a series is a lagging indicator can be useful. For example, a firm interested in expanding and needing a business loan should realize that interest rates will drop to a low point several weeks after the business cycle reaches its trough.

Returning to Table 11.1, let's look briefly at other external factors that affect demand. Consumer tastes can change quickly, as they often do in clothing fashions. The consumer's image of a product can be another big factor. For example, in the last decade foreign-car sales increased dramatically as a percentage of total car sales in the United States. Why? Because consumers believed that foreign cars were more fuel efficient and of superior quality.

In addition, competitors' actions regarding prices, advertising promotions, and new products also affect sales. For example, the Nike commercial in which NBA star Michael Jordan slam dunks a basketball while wearing Nike athletic shoes reduces consumer demand for the products of competitors, such as Reebok and L.A. Gear. Finally, the success of complementary products affects demand. The location of Honda's Marysville, Ohio, plant stimulated the sales of many automobile parts and components in that area. Future demand for products from their suppliers depends on the overall success of Honda in that location.

Internal Factors. Internal decisions can affect the demand for products or services. Recognizing that these decisions can be controlled encourages management to respond actively, rather than passively, to demand. The term **demand management** describes the process of influencing the timing and volume of demand or adapting to the undesirable effects of unchangeable demand patterns. The right side of Table 11.1 shows some of the ways in which management can affect demand.

Factors such as product or service design, price and advertising promotions, packaging design, salesperson quotas or incentives, and expansion or contraction of geographical market target areas can all contribute to changes in demand volume. For example, automobile manufacturers use rebates to boost car sales. However, the purpose of demand management goes beyond merely increasing customer demand. Management must also consider the timing of demand, an extremely important factor in efficiently utilizing resources and production capacity.

Trying to produce for peak customer demand during the peak demand period can be very costly. To avoid this situation, firms often use price incentives or advertising promotions to encourage customers to make purchases before or after traditional times of peak demand. For example, telephone companies encourage customers to make long distance calls after normal business hours by offering lower evening and weekend rates. This practice reduces the amount of resources needed to handle peak demand. Another tactic is to introduce a product that has a different heavy seasonal demand period. A producer of tractor lawn mowers, for instance, might also make snowmobiles to even out resource and production requirements over the year. In this way costly changes in work-force level and inventory can be minimized.

Finally, some companies use backlogs to stabilize resource requirements over time. When an inquiry or order is received, the producer specifies a delivery date, which depends on the current workload and capacity. Doctors, dentists, and other professionals use this approach by asking patients to make appointments for their services. Manufacturers of custom-built products also work to backlogs of demand.

DESIGNING THE FORECASTING SYSTEM

Even though we devote most of this chapter to discussing a number of forecasting techniques, it would be incorrect to assume that all a manager must do is choose a technique, make the forecasts, and proceed to the next stage—analyzing operations management problems. Unfortunately, the process isn't that simple. While the choice of method is certainly an important aspect of designing a forecasting system, other considerations are also important. When designing a demand forecasting system the manager must determine (1) what to forecast, (2) what type of forecasting technique to use, and (3) what kind of computer hardware or software (or both) is appropriate.

Deciding What to Forecast

It is not uncommon to hear operations managers say that forecasts of demand should be made for all goods or services produced by their companies. Although some sort of demand estimate is needed for all items, it may be easier to forecast the total demand for groups of products and then derive individual product forecasts. Also, selecting the correct unit of measurement (such as product units or machine hours) for the forecasts can be as important as choosing the best method.

Level of Aggregation. Very few companies err by more than 5 percent when forecasting total demand for all their products. However, errors in forecasts for individual items range from -100 percent to $+300$ percent, or more (Plossl, 1979). The greater the aggregation is, the more accurate are the forecasts. Many companies employ a two-tier forecasting system whereby forecasts are made first for **product families,** a group of goods or services that have similar demand requirements and common processing, labor, and materials requirements. Forecasts for individual items then are derived in such a way that their sum equals the total forecast for the family. This approach maintains consistency between planning for the final stages of manufacturing (which requires the unit forecasts) and longer-term planning for sales, profit, and capacity (which requires the product family forecasts).

Units of Measurement. Forecasts that serve as input to planning and the analysis of operations problems are most useful if they are based on product units, rather than dollars. Forecasts of sales revenue are not very helpful because prices can and often do fluctuate. Thus even though total sales in dollars might be the same from month to month, the actual number of units of demand could vary widely. Forecasting the number of units of demand and then translating them to sales revenue estimates by multiplying them by the price is often the better method.

Forecasting the number of units of demand for a product might not be possible. Companies producing goods or services to customer order face this problem. In such situations it is better to forecast the standard labor or machine *hours* required of each of the critical resources, based on historical patterns. For such companies, estimates of labor or machine hours are important to scheduling and capacity planning.

Choosing the Type of Forecasting Technique

Because demand exhibits many different characteristics, several different forecasting methods are needed. The forecaster's objective is to develop a useful forecast from the information at hand. To achieve this objective, the forecaster must select the appropriate technique. This choice sometimes involves a trade-off between forecast accuracy and costs, such as software purchases, the time to develop a forecast, and personnel training. Three general types of forecasting techniques are used for demand forecasting: time series analysis, causal methods, and qualitative techniques. **Time series analysis** is a statistical approach that relies heavily on historical demand data to project the future size of demand but recognizes trends and seasonal patterns. **Causal methods** use historical data on independent variables, such as promotional campaigns, economic conditions, and competitors' actions, to predict demand. **Qualitative techniques** translate managerial judgment, expert opinion, survey results, or all three, into quantitative estimates. We describe each technique in more detail later in this chapter. First, however, let's consider the conditions under which these techniques are likely to be applied. Table 11.3 contains examples of demand forecasting applications and the typical planning horizon for each.

Short Term. In the short term (here, 0–3 months in the future) managers are typically interested in forecasts of demand for individual products or services. There is little time to satisfy demand, so forecasts need to be as accurate as possible for planning purposes. Time series analysis is the method most often used for short-term forecasting. It is a relatively inexpensive way to generate the large number of forecasts required. In the short term the quality of these forecasts can be very good.

While causal models can be used for short-term forecasts, they are not used extensively for this purpose because they are much more costly than time series analysis and require more time to develop. In the short term, operations managers rarely can wait for development of causal models, even though they may be more accurate than time series models. Finally, managers use qualitative techniques for short-term forecasts when historical data are not available for a specific item, such as the introduction of a new product. However, these forecast methods are also more expensive than forecasts generated from time series analysis.

TABLE 11.3 / Demand Forecast Applications

Application	Time Horizon		
	Short Term (0–3 months)	Medium Term (3 months–2 years)	Long Term (more than 2 years)
Forecast quantity	Individual products or services	Total sales Groups or families of products or services	Total sales
Decision area	Inventory management Final assembly scheduling Work-force scheduling Master production scheduling	Staff planning Production planning Master production scheduling Purchasing Distribution	Facility location Capacity planning Process design
Forecasting technique	Time series Causal Qualitative	Causal Qualitative	Causal Qualitative

Medium Term. The time horizon for the medium term is between three months and two years. For planning purposes the level of forecast detail required is not as great as for the short term. Managers typically forecast total sales demand in dollars or in the number of units of a group (or family) of similar products or services. The need for medium-term forecasts arises from planning problems related to issues of capacity, such as those shown in Table 11.3. Causal models are commonly used for medium-term forecasts. These models typically do a good job of identifying periods when the growth rate of demand will change, as when slow sales growth will turn into rapid decline. Determination of these *turning points* is very important for the operations manager, particularly in the medium and long term.

Some qualitative methods of forecasting are also helpful in identifying turning points. As we mentioned earlier, however, they are most often used when no historical data exist. Time series analysis typically does not yield accurate results in the medium or long term primarily because it assumes that existing patterns will continue in the future. Although this assumption may be valid for the short term, it is less accurate over longer time horizons.

Long Term. For time horizons exceeding two years, forecasts are usually developed for total sales demand in dollars or some other common unit of measurement, such as barrels, pounds, or kilowatts. Accurate long-term forecasts of demand for individual products or services not only are very difficult to make but also are too detailed for long-range planning purposes. Table 11.3 shows that three decision areas—facility location, capacity planning, and process design—require market demand estimates for an extended period into the future.

Causal models and qualitative methods are the primary techniques used for long-term forecasting. However, even mathematically derived causal model forecasts have to be tempered by managerial experience and judgment because of the time horizon involved and the potential consequences of decisions based on them.

Forecasting with Computers

In most short-term forecasting applications, computers are a necessity, not a luxury. Typically, manufacturing companies have hundreds or thousands of products to forecast on a repetitive basis. Service firms have similar problems. For example, an express delivery company such as Federal Express or UPS must calculate demand forecasts for each of its services for every collection station. This undertaking involves voluminous data that must be manipulated frequently. Analysts must examine the time series for each product or service and arrive at a forecast. To do this manually is unthinkable. Computerizing the forecasting system can have strategic benefits, as Managerial Practice 11.1 demonstrates.

The decision to invest in a computerized forecasting system is an important one as demonstrated by the Rocky Mountain experience. Many forecasting software packages are available for all sizes of computers. These packages offer a wide variety of forecasting capabilities and report formats. General-purpose statistical packages include SAS, SPSS, and Minitab. Applications-oriented packages—such as General Electric's *Time Series Forecasting System* and IBM's *Consumer Goods System* (COGS), *Inventory Management Program and Control Technique* (IMPACT), and *Manufacturing Accounting Production Information Control System* (MAPICS)—contain forecasting modules used by many firms. Since the introduction of microcomputers, scores of software packages have been developed for virtually all the popular personal computers. The applications range from simple to very sophisticated programs. These microcomputer packages are priced to make them attractive alternatives to traditional mainframe packages.

Some techniques are more cost effective for short time horizons; others are more appropriate for long time horizons. Thus a forecasting software package usually is selected jointly by marketing and operations. Typically, an implementation team consisting of marketing and operations staff is charged with selecting a package from the wide variety available. The team may ask their departments for a "wish list" and then categorize the wishes as "musts" and "wants." Final selection is based on (1) how well the package satisfies the musts and wants, (2) the cost of buying or leasing the package, (3) the level of clerical support required, and (4) the amount of programmer maintenance required.

TIME SERIES ANALYSIS

In the simplest form of time series analysis, the only information used is the historical record of demand. The analyst isn't concerned with changes in the external and internal factors, listed in Table 11.1, and assumes that what has

Rocky Mountain Bank Note is a leading manufacturer of personalized bank checks. The firm manufactures more than 1000 checking products at 20 imprinting plants using complex manufacturing processes, including both make-to-stock and assemble-to-order strategies. The base material of preprinted assemblies and components is supplied by the central base stock facility as well as assorted suppliers. The plants then take the base material and produce the products to their customers' orders. Competition is keen, and Rocky Mountain competes on the basis of superior quality, customer service, and price. Consequently, the firm places a high premium on accurate forecasts to achieve high levels of customer service at low cost.

In 1987 the materials group was using simple, manual forecasting methods for each plant, taking a three-month average and modifying it using their experience and judgment. This process was time consuming and resulted in only marginal accuracy. Because of the poor forecasts, the plants often ran out of base material. Dissatisfied with deteriorating inventory and scheduling performance, management decided to purchase computer software that incorporates advanced statistical capabilities. The software can simultaneously produce forecasts for thousands of items and features an "auto-

Computerized Forecasting at Rocky Mountain Bank Note

matic forecasting expert system" that performs all the mathematical computations but allows for manual adjustments to the forecasts based on managerial judgment. With the new system the company's plants, located in 16 states, transmit inventory data via modem on the firm's IBM PS/2 computer network. The data then go to a mainframe computer for consolidation. Forecasts are generated for each time series so that the firm's production schedule for the next quarter can be developed.

The computerized forecasting system was very successful. Management credited the system with the following benefits:

- A 15 percent reduction in inventory costs
- A reduction in schedule changes, from 20 percent to less than 10 percent
- A reduction in the time required to make a forecast, from two weeks to two days
- A 50 percent reduction in the staff assigned to forecasting

Source: "Forecasting Pays Dividends for Check Manufacturer," *P&IM Review with APICS News*, May 1990, pp. 38–39.

(a)

(b)

*A*t a Rocky Mountain Bank Note facility (a) rolls of preprinted checks await further processing, and (b) an artist renders check designs to customer specifications.

occurred in the past will continue to occur in the future. Methods of time series analysis focus on the average, trend, and seasonal influence characteristics of a time series. The analyst's task is to try to replicate these characteristics when projecting future demand.

Estimating the Average

Consider Fig. 11.2, which shows patient arrivals at a medical clinic over the past 28 weeks. This graph is useful because it enables the analyst to hypothesize which of the five components of demand are represented in the time series. For purposes of discussion let's assume that you are the analyst. Let's further assume that this series has only an average component and random errors. The simple moving average and exponential smoothing models are useful for forecasting the average of a time series such as this.

Simple Moving Average. You can use the simple **moving average method** to estimate the average of a demand time series and remove the effects of random fluctuation. This method is most useful when demand does not have a pronounced trend or any seasonal influences. To use a moving average model you simply calculate the average demand for the N most recent time periods and use it as the forecast for the next time period.* Next period, after the demand is known, the oldest demand from the previous average is replaced by the most recent demand and the average is recomputed. In this way you always use the N most recent demands, and the average "moves" from period to period.

---

*In this section our calculations for the series are carried to one decimal place. If the time series is expressed in discrete units, such as patient arrivals, the *forecast* should be rounded to the nearest integer in practice.

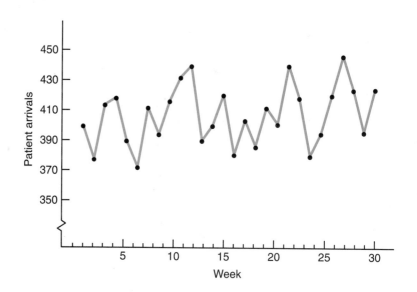

FIGURE 11.2

Weekly Patient Arrivals at a Medical Clinic

Specifically, the calculation involves

$$\text{Average:} \quad A_t = \frac{D_t + D_{t-1} + D_{t-2} + \cdots + D_{t-N+1}}{N}$$

$$\text{Forecast:} \quad F_{t+1} = A_t$$

where

$$D_t = \text{actual demand in period } t$$

$$N = \text{total number of periods in the average}$$

$$A_t = \text{average computed for period } t$$

$$F_{t+1} = \text{forecast for period } t + 1$$

With the moving average method, the forecast of next period's demand is equal to the average computed this period. In fact, the forecast of demand for any period in the future is the average computed in the current period. This is true for all the methods for estimating the average we discuss in this chapter.

Application 11.1   *Using the Moving Average Method to Estimate the Average Demand*

Compute a three-week moving average forecast for the arrival of medical clinic patients in week 4, using the actual number of patient arrivals in weeks 1 through 3.

Week	Patient Arrivals
1	400
2	380
3	411

If the actual number of patient arrivals is 415 in week 4, what is the forecast for week 5?

Solution   The moving average at the end of week 3 is

$$A_3 = \frac{411 + 380 + 400}{3} = 397.0$$

Thus the forecast for week 4 is 397 patients.

The forecast for week 5 requires the actual arrivals from weeks 2–4, the three most recent weeks of data.

$$A_4 = \frac{415 + 411 + 380}{3} = 402.0$$

The forecast for week 5 is 402 patients. In addition, as we are now in week 4, the forecast for week 6 and beyond is also 402 patients.

The stability of the demand series generally determines how many periods to include (that is, the value of N): Use large values of N for demand series that are stable and small values of N for those that are susceptible to changes in the underlying average.

FIGURE 11.3

Comparison of Three-
Week and Six-Week
Moving Average
Forecasts

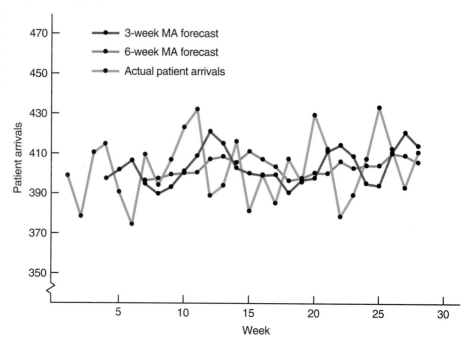

For purpose of comparison we calculated a three-week and a six-week moving average forecast for the medical clinic data. Figure 11.3 shows this comparison, along with actual patient arrivals. Note that the three-week moving average forecast varies more and reacts more quickly to large swings in demand. This sensitivity can be advantageous if, for example, the underlying average of the series is changing over time because of an unsuspected trend in the data. Conversely, the six-week moving average forecast is more stable because large swings in demand tend to cancel each other.

Including more historical data in the average results in a forecast that is less susceptible to random variations. If the underlying average in the series is changing, however, the forecasts will tend to lag behind the changes for a longer time interval because of the longer time necessary to remove the old data from the forecast. We address other considerations for the choice of N when we discuss choosing a time series method.

Weighted Moving Average. In the simple moving average method each demand has the same weight in the average, namely, $1/N$. In the **weighted moving average method,** each historical demand in the average can have its own weight, W_i, such that the sum of the weights equals 1.0. Specifically, the calculation becomes:

Average: $\quad A_t = W_1D_t + W_2D_{t-1} + \cdots + W_ND_{t-N+1}$

Forecast: $\quad F_{t+1} = A_t$

where $\qquad\qquad\qquad\qquad\qquad \displaystyle\sum_{i=1}^{N} W_i = 1$

The weighted moving average method allows you to emphasize recent demand over earlier demand. The forecast will be more responsive to changes in the underlying average of the demand series than the simple moving average forecast. Nonetheless, the weighted moving average forecast will still lag behind demand because it merely averages *past* demands. This is especially true when a trend is present because the average of the time series is systematically increasing or decreasing. We will discuss another method for dealing with trends later.

Application 11.2	*Using the Weighted Moving Average Method to Estimate the Average Demand*

The analyst for the medical clinic has assigned weights of 70 percent to the most recent demand, 20 percent to the demand one week ago, and 10 percent to the demand two weeks ago. Using the data for the first three weeks from Application 11.1, calculate the weighted moving average forecast for week 4.

Solution   The average demand in week 3 is

$$A_3 = 0.70(411) + 0.20(380) + 0.10(400) = 403.7$$

The forecast for week 4 therefore is 404 patients.

Now suppose that the actual demand for week 4 is 415 patients. The new average and the forecast for week 5 would be

$$A_4 = 0.70(415) + 0.20(411) + 0.10(380) = 410.7$$

$$F_5 = 411 \text{ patients}$$

The weighted moving average method has the same shortcomings as the simple moving average method: You must retain data for N periods of demand to calculate the average for each period. Keeping this amount of data isn't a great burden in simple situations, such as our three-week and six-week examples. Some time series are quite stable, however, and moving average calculations for 200 or more periods are not uncommon. For a company that has to forecast many different demands, data storage and update costs should be balanced against the adequacy of the method to provide useful forecasts.

Exponential Smoothing. The **exponential smoothing method** calculates the average of a time series by giving recent demands more weight than earlier demands. It is the most frequently used formal forecasting method because of its simplicity and the small amount of data needed to support it. Unlike the weighted moving average method, which requires N periods of past demand and N weights, exponential smoothing requires only three items of data: the average of the series as of the last period; the demand for this period; and a smoothing parameter, alpha (α). As before, you calculate an average of past demands at the end of the current period and use it as a forecast for the next period. You can adjust the amount of emphasis given to the most recent demand levels simply by adjusting the smoothing parameter. Larger α values emphasize recent demands and result in forecasts more responsive to changes in the underlying average. Smaller α values treat past demand more uniformly and result in more stable forecasts. In practice, various values of α are tried and the one producing the best forecasts is chosen. We will discuss the choice of α further when we discuss the criteria for selecting time series methods.

The equations for the average of a demand series and the forecast using exponential smoothing are

$$\text{Average:} \qquad A_t = \alpha D_t + (1 - \alpha)A_{t-1}$$

$$\text{Forecast:} \qquad F_{t+1} = A_t$$

where

$$\alpha = \text{smoothing parameter with} \\ \text{a value between 0 and 1}$$

Exponential smoothing requires an initial estimate of the average to get started. This approach uses one of two methods: Either you use last period's demand as your estimate, or if you have some historical data, you can compute the average of several recent periods of demand. The effect of your estimate on successive estimates of the average diminishes over time because, with exponential smoothing, the weights placed on each successive historical demand used to calculate the average decay at an exponential rate. This can be seen by working with the estimate for the average in period t:

$$A_t = \alpha D_t + (1 - \alpha)A_{t-1}$$

and expanding it:

$$A_t = \alpha D_t + (1 - \alpha)[\alpha D_{t-1} + (1 - \alpha)A_{t-2}]$$
$$= \alpha D_t + \alpha(1 - \alpha)D_{t-1} + (1 - \alpha)^2 A_{t-2}$$

and continuing to expand it to get a general form of the equation for A_t:

$$A_t = \alpha D_t + \alpha(1 - \alpha)D_{t-1} + \alpha(1 - \alpha)^2 D_{t-2} + \alpha(1 - \alpha)^3 D_{t-3} + \cdots$$

Table 11.4 shows the general expressions for the weights to be placed on the ten most recent demands in a series and the corresponding numerical

TABLE 11.4 / Exponential Smoothing Weights

Demand	Weight	Numerical Weights for		
		$\alpha = 0.1$	$\alpha = 0.2$	$\alpha = 0.8$
D_t	α	0.1000	0.2000	0.8000
D_{t-1}	$\alpha(1 - \alpha)^1$	0.0900	0.1600	0.1600
D_{t-2}	$\alpha(1 - \alpha)^2$	0.0810	0.1280	0.0320
D_{t-3}	$\alpha(1 - \alpha)^3$	0.0729	0.1024	0.0064
D_{t-4}	$\alpha(1 - \alpha)^4$	0.0656	0.0819	0.0013
D_{t-5}	$\alpha(1 - \alpha)^5$	0.0590	0.0655	0.0003
D_{t-6}	$\alpha(1 - \alpha)^6$	0.0531	0.0524	0.0001
D_{t-7}	$\alpha(1 - \alpha)^7$	0.0478	0.0419	0.0000
D_{t-8}	$\alpha(1 - \alpha)^8$	0.0430	0.0336	0.0000
D_{t-9}	$\alpha(1 - \alpha)^9$	0.0387	0.0268	0.0000

weights for three assumed values of α. As with the weighted moving average method, the sum of the weights must equal 1.0, which is implicit in the exponential smoothing equation.

Application 11.3 *Using Exponential Smoothing to Estimate the Average Demand*

Again consider the patient arrival data in Application 11.1. It is now the end of week 3. Calculate the exponential smoothing forecast for week 4 using $\alpha = 0.10$.

Solution   The exponential smoothing method requires estimating an initial value for the average. Suppose that you take the demand data for the past two weeks and average them, arriving at a value of 390 [(400 + 380)/2] as an estimate of the past average. To obtain the forecast for week 4, using exponential smoothing with an assumed $\alpha = 0.10$, you can calculate the average at the end of week 3 as follows:

$$A_3 = 0.10(411) + 0.90(390) = 392.1$$

Thus the forecast for week 4 would be 392 patients. If the actual demand for week 4 proved to be 415, the new average would be

$$A_4 = 0.10(415) + 0.90(392.1) = 394.4$$

and the forecast for week 5 would be $F_5 = 394$ patients.

Exponential smoothing has the advantages of simplicity and minimal data requirements. It is inexpensive to use and therefore very attractive to firms that make thousands of forecasts for each time period. However, its simplicity is also a disadvantage when the underlying average is changing, as in the case of a demand series with a trend. Like any method geared solely to the assumption of a stable average, exponential smoothing results will lag behind changes in the underlying average of demand. Higher α values may help to reduce forecast errors; however, the lags will still be there to some degree. Typically, if large α values (greater than 0.50, for example) are required for an exponential smoothing application, chances are good that a more sophisticated model is needed because of a significant trend and/or seasonal influence in the demand series. We address the issue of choosing the best α value later in the chapter.

Including a Trend

Let's now consider a demand time series that has a trend. Although a number of forecasting methods that recognize a trend are available, we focus on exponential smoothing because it is so widely used in practice. When a trend is present, the average of the series is systematically increasing or decreasing over time. This means that exponential smoothing approaches must be modified; otherwise, the forecasts will always be below or above the actual demand. An estimate of the current trend in a time series is the difference between the simple average of the series computed in the current period and the average computed last period. To obtain a better estimate of a long-term trend, you can reduce the effects of random causes by averaging the current estimates. The method for estimating a trend is similar to that used for estimating the demand average with exponential smoothing.

The method for incorporating a trend in an exponentially smoothed forecast is called the **trend-adjusted exponential smoothing method** because the estimate for the average, as well as for the trend, is smoothed. For each period you calculate the

Average: $A_t = \alpha D_t + (1 - \alpha)(A_{t-1} + T_{t-1})$

Current estimate of trend: $CT_t = A_t - A_{t-1}$

Average trend: $T_t = \beta CT_t + (1 - \beta)T_{t-1}$

Forecast: $F_{t+1} = A_t + T_t$

where

A_t = exponentially smoothed average of the series in period t

CT_t = current estimate of the trend in period t

T_t = exponentially smoothed average of the trend in period t

F_{t+1} = forecast for next period

α = smoothing parameter for the average with a value between 0 and 1

β = smoothing parameter for the trend with a value between 0 and 1

You need an initial estimate for the average and the trend to get started. You can derive these estimates from past data, as we discussed for the exponential smoothing method, or simply make an educated guess based on past experience if no historical data exist. Various values of α and β are tried, and the combination producing the best forecasts is chosen.

Application 11.4 *Using Trend-Adjusted Exponential Smoothing to Forecast a Demand Series with a Trend*

Medanalysis, Inc., provides medical laboratory service to patients of Health Providers, a group of ten family-practice doctors associated with a new health maintenance program. We are interested in forecasting the number of patients requesting blood analysis per week. Publicity about the damaging effects of cholesterol on the heart has caused a national increase in the requests for standard blood tests. An average of 28 patients per week required blood tests over the past four weeks. The trend over that period was 3 additional patients per week. This week's demand was 27 blood tests—below the historical average but reasonably in line with past performance. Use alpha (α) = 0.2 and beta (β) = 0.2 to calculate the forecast for next week.

Solution Our calculations for the forecast for week 2 (next week) are as follows:

$A_1 = 0.2(27) + 0.8(28 + 3) = 30.2$ $T_1 = 0.2(2.2) + 0.8(3) = 2.8$

$CT_1 = 30.2 - 28 = 2.2$ $F_2 = 30.2 + 2.8 = 33.0$ tests

If the actual number of blood tests requested in week 2 proved to be 44, the updated forecast for week 3 would be

$A_2 = 0.2(44) + 0.8(30.2 + 2.8) = 35.2$ $T_2 = 0.2(5.0) + 0.8(2.8) = 3.2$

$CT_2 = 35.2 - 30.2 = 5.0$ $F_3 = 35.2 + 3.2 = 38.4$ or 38 tests

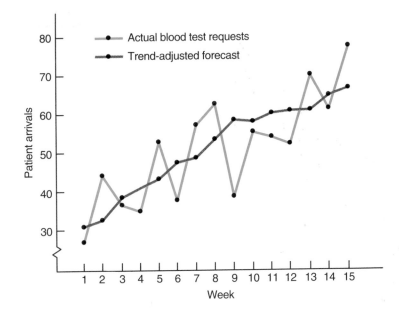

FIGURE 11.4

Trend-Adjustment
Forecast for
Medanalysis

For illustrative purposes, we plotted the trend-adjusted forecast for Med-analysis for a period of 15 weeks in Fig. 11.4. At the end of each week we calculated a forecast for the next week, using the number of blood tests for the current week.

Several comments are in order at this point. First, we did not look very closely at other α and β values, so we may be able to come up with a better forecast by using different values. (We discuss how to choose the best values after covering forecast errors and their measurement.) Second, we can make forecasts for periods beyond the next period simply by multiplying the trend estimate by the number of additional periods that we want in the forecast and adding the result to the current average. For example, if we are at the end of week 2 and want to estimate the demand for blood tests in week 6, the forecast would be

$$F_6 = 35.2 + 4(3.2) = 48 \text{ tests}$$

However, the further we project our trend estimate the more tenuous our forecast becomes. In general, the use of time series methods should be restricted to the short term (see Table 11.3).

Seasonal Influences

Many organizations experience seasonal demand for their goods or services. The volume of letters processed by the U.S. Postal Service increases dramatically during the Christmas holiday period. Demands for products such as lawn and garden supplies, snow shovels, automobile tires, clothing, and construction supplies are subject to seasonal influences. Even the demand for telephone service is seasonal, as anyone trying to call relatives during holiday periods is well aware. A number of methods are available for forecasting time series with seasonal influences. We present only the **multiplicative seasonal method,** whereby seasonal factors are multiplied by an estimate of average demand to arrive at a seasonal forecast.

The procedure we present makes use of simple averages of past demands even though more sophisticated methods for calculating averages, such as moving averages or exponential smoothing, could also be used. First, we need to define the variables encountered in using the procedure:

$$D_{y,t} = \text{demand in period } t \text{ in year } y$$
$$\bar{D}_y = \text{average demand per period in year } y$$
$$\hat{D}_y = \text{projected average demand per period for some future year } y$$
$$f_{y,t} = \text{seasonal factor for period } t \text{ in year } y$$
$$\bar{f}_t = \text{average seasonal factor for period } t$$
$$F_{y,t} = \text{forecast for period } t \text{ in some future year } y$$
$$m = \text{number of years of past data}$$
$$n = \text{number of demand periods each year}$$

The procedure for calculating seasonal factors consists of three steps:

1. Calculate the average demand per period for each year of past data.

$$\bar{D}_y = \frac{\sum_{t=1}^{n} D_{y,t}}{n}$$

2. Divide the actual demand for each period by the average demand per period to get a seasonal factor for each period. Repeat for each year of data.

$$f_{y,t} = \frac{D_{y,t}}{\bar{D}_y}$$

3. Calculate the average seasonal factor for each period.

$$\bar{f}_t = \frac{\sum_{y=1}^{m} f_{y,t}}{m}$$

To forecast a given period t in a future year y, simply estimate the average demand per period for that year, $\hat{D}_y$, and multiply it by the appropriate seasonal factor:

$$F_{y,t} = \hat{D}_y \bar{f}_t$$

Application 11.5   *Using the Multiplicative Seasonal Method to Forecast the Number of Customers*

The manager of the Stanley Steamer carpet cleaning company in Westerville needs a quarterly forecast of the number of customers she will have in 1994. Her carpet cleaning business is seasonal, with a peak in the third quarter and a trough in the first quarter. The following are the quarterly demand data from 1990 through 1993.

Quarter	1990	1991	1992	1993
1	45	70	100	100
2	335	370	585	725
3	520	590	830	1160
4	100	170	285	215
Total	1000	1200	1800	2200

Forecast customer demand for each quarter of 1994 based on the manager's estimate of total 1994 demand of 2600 customers in 1994.

Solution We begin with 1990 to demonstrate the computation of the seasonal factors for a given year. Note that

$$\sum_{t=1}^{4} D_{1990,t} = 1000$$

Consequently, the average demand per quarter, $\bar{D}_{1990}$, is 250 (1000/4) customers. The seasonal factors for 1990 are

$$f_{1990,1} = \frac{45}{250} = 0.18 \qquad f_{1990,3} = \frac{520}{250} = 2.08$$

$$f_{1990,2} = \frac{335}{250} = 1.34 \qquad f_{1990,4} = \frac{100}{250} = 0.40$$

The following table shows the seasonal factors for the remaining years and, in the last column, the average seasonal factor for each quarter. For example, $\bar{f}_1 = (0.18 + 0.23 + 0.22 + 0.18)/4 = 0.20$. Note that the total of the average seasonal factors equals the number of periods in the year.

Calculation of Seasonal Factors

Quarter (t)	1990 Demand ($D_{1990,t}$)	1990 Seasonal Factor* ($f_{1990,t}$)	1991 Demand ($D_{1991,t}$)	1991 Seasonal Factor* ($f_{1991,t}$)	1992 Demand ($D_{1992,t}$)	1992 Seasonal Factor* ($f_{1992,t}$)	1993 Demand ($D_{1993,t}$)	1993 Seasonal Factor* ($f_{1993,t}$)	Average Seasonal Factor† ($\bar{f}_t$)
1	45	0.18	70	0.23	100	0.22	100	0.18	0.20
2	335	1.34	370	1.23	585	1.30	725	1.32	1.30
3	520	2.08	590	1.97	830	1.84	1160	2.11	2.00
4	100	0.40	170	0.57	285	0.63	215	0.39	0.50
Total	1000		1200		1800		2200		4.00
Quarterly average demand ($\bar{D}_y$)	250		300		450		550		

*Actual demand in a quarter divided by the average demand per quarter; subject to minor roundoff error.
†Average of the quarterly seasonal factors.

The projected demand for 1994 is 2600 units. Therefore the average projected demand per quarter, $\bar{D}_{1994}$, is 650 (2600/4) customers. We make the quarterly forecasts simply by multiplying the seasonal factor for each quarter by $\bar{D}_{1994}$:

$$F_{1994,1} = 650(0.20) = \ \ 130$$

$$F_{1994,2} = 650(1.30) = \ \ 845$$

$$F_{1994,3} = 650(2.00) = 1300$$

$$F_{1994,4} = 650(0.50) = \ \ 325$$

[handwritten annotation: moving average / single exponentially smoothed average]

At the end of each year, you can update the average seasonal factor for each quarter by calculating the average of all historical seasonal factors for that quarter, or by calculating a moving average or single exponentially smoothed average if you want some control over the relevance of past demand patterns.

The multiplicative seasonal method gets its name from the way seasonal factors are calculated and used. Multiplying the seasonal factor by an estimate of the average period demand implies that the seasonal influence depends on the level of demand. The peaks and valleys are more extreme when the average demand level is high, a situation faced most often by firms that produce goods and services having a seasonal demand. An alternative to the multiplicative seasonal method is the *additive seasonal method*, which implies a constant seasonal influence, regardless of the average level of demand. For purposes of comparison, Fig. 11.5(a) shows the pattern of additive seasonal influences and Fig. 11.5(b) shows that of multiplicative seasonal influences.

Focus Forecasting

Does a more sophisticated forecasting model always produce a better forecast? Is there one best forecasting technique for all products or services? The answer to both questions is *no*. In 1978 Bernard Smith, an inventory manager at American Hardware Supply, recognized these realities of forecasting and developed what he called **focus forecasting,** which selects the best forecast from a group of forecasts generated by simple techniques.

Smith was responsible for an inventory of 100,000 different items purchased by the company's 21 buyers. Originally, the company used a basic exponential smoothing system with a sophisticated method for projecting seasonal influences. It used these forecasts to determine purchase quantities. However, the buyers were changing 53 percent of the forecasted purchase quantities, mainly because they did not understand exponential smoothing and consequently did not trust the system. Their constant changes resulted in excessive purchases and levels of inventory.

Smith decided to survey the buyers to find out how they arrived at their own forecasts. One buyer computed the percentage increase in demand experienced during the last period and used it to project the increase in demand for

FIGURE 11.5

Comparison of
Influences

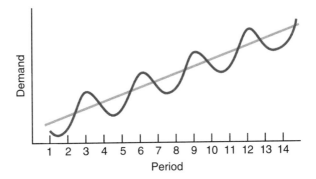

(a) Comparison of additive influences

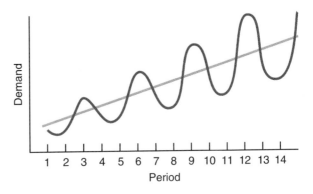

(b) Comparison of multiplicative influences

the next period. Another buyer simply used the demand from the last period as the forecast for the next period. Other buyers used similar, simple methods for forecasting demand. Each buyer was responsible for a different group of items, and Smith had no reason to believe that any one of the methods would work for all items.

Using the suggested methods from the buyers and adding some statistical methods, including exponential smoothing, Smith selected seven forecast methods as the basis for his focus forecasting technique. Every month the computer uses all seven methods to make forecasts for each item. Historical data are used as the starting point for each method, and forecasts are made for recent demand. The method that produces the best forecast for recent data is used to make the current demand forecast for an item. The following month, the "best" forecasting method for an item may be different from the one chosen for the current month.

Each month the computer prints the forecast for each of the 100,000 items. Buyers can still override the computer forecast, although Smith claims that his system provides excellent short-term forecasts for American Hardware Supply. The system is used for expensive as well as inexpensive items and has much more credibility with the buyers than the previous system.

CHOOSING A TIME SERIES METHOD

Now that we have discussed some of the various techniques for time series forecasting, we will address the considerations managers must make in selecting the best one. One important consideration is forecast performance, as measured by forecast errors. How are forecast errors measured, and how can managers detect when something is going wrong with the forecasting system? We will address those questions first. Then, given the forecast performance of several alternative approaches, we will discuss criteria managers use to choose the appropriate time series forecasting technique.

Forecast Error

A Chinese proverb says, "To prophesy is extremely difficult, especially with respect to the future." And so it is with forecasting—forecasts almost always contain errors. Forecast errors sometimes result from an inability to assess accurately the underlying components of demand and sometimes from random causes outside a firm's control.

Measures of Forecast Error. Before they can think about minimizing forecast error, managers must first have some means of measuring it. **Forecast error** is simply the difference between the forecast and actual demand for a given period. Specifically,

$$E_t = D_t - F_t$$

where

$$E_t = \text{forecast error for period } t$$
$$D_t = \text{actual demand for period } t$$
$$F_t = \text{forecast for period } t$$

Managers are usually more interested in measuring forecast error over a relatively long period of time, however. The following are some of the more commonly used methods:

Cumulative sum of forecast errors: $\quad CFE = \sum_{t=1}^{n} E_t$

Mean squared error: $\quad MSE = \dfrac{\sum\limits_{t=1}^{n} E_t^2}{n}$

Standard deviation of forecast errors: $\quad \sigma = \sqrt{\dfrac{\sum\limits_{t=1}^{n} E_t^2}{n}}$

$$\text{Mean absolute deviation of forecast errors:} \qquad MAD = \frac{\sum_{t=1}^{n} |E_t|}{n}$$

$$\text{Mean absolute percent error:} \qquad MAPE = \frac{\sum_{t=1}^{n} \frac{|E_t|}{D_t} (100)}{n} \qquad \text{(expressed as a percentage)}$$

Note that n is the total number of periods, and recall that the mathematical symbol $|\ \ |$ is used to indicate absolute value, or to disregard positive and negative signs.

The **cumulative sum of forecast errors (CFE)** is useful in measuring the *bias* in a forecast. Bias refers to the tendency of a forecast to always be too high or too low. For example, if a forecast is always lower than actual demand, the value of CFE will gradually get larger and larger. This increasingly large error indicates some systematic deficiency in the forecasting approach. Perhaps the analyst omitted a trend element or a cyclical influence, or perhaps the seasonality of the demand changed from its historical pattern. We explain later how to use CFE to develop a tracking signal to indicate when you should be concerned about forecast performance.

The **mean squared error (MSE), standard deviation (σ),** and the **mean absolute deviation (MAD)** measure the dispersion of forecast errors. If MSE, σ, or MAD is small, the forecast is typically close to actual demand, whereas if any are large, there is the possibility of large forecast errors.* The measures differ in the way they emphasize errors. Large errors get far more weight in MSE and σ, which is the square root of MSE, because the errors are squared. In practice, MAD is a popular measure of forecast error because managers can easily understand it; it is merely the mean of the forecast errors over a series of time periods, without regard to whether the error was an overestimate or underestimate. This measurement is also used in tracking signals and inventory control. You will see in Chapter 13 that MAD or σ can be used to determine safety stocks for inventory items. The greater that MAD or σ is, the larger the safety stock required, placing a premium on forecasting methods that result in small forecast errors.

If forecast errors are normally distributed with a mean of zero, there is a simple relationship between σ and MAD:

$$\sigma = \sqrt{\frac{\pi}{2}} MAD \approx 1.25 MAD$$

or

$$MAD = 0.7978\sigma \approx 0.8\sigma$$

where $\pi = 3.1416$. This relationship enables us to use the normal probability tables with MAD, which we discuss later in the chapter.

---

*The standard deviation (σ) is a poor measure of forecast error variability if the forecasts are biased. For example, if all the forecast errors were $+10$, the standard deviation of forecast errors *should* be 0 (no variation), but the formula for σ would yield a value of greater than zero.

The **mean absolute percent error (*MAPE*)** relates the forecast error to the level of demand and is useful for putting forecast performance in the proper perspective. For example, an absolute forecast error of 100 results in a larger percentage error when the demand is 200 units than when the demand is 10,000 units. Application 11.6 shows how these measures of forecast error are calculated.

Application 11.6 *Calculating Forecast Error Measures*

The following table shows the actual sales of a product and the forecasts made for each of the last eight months. Calculate the common measures of forecast error for this product.

Calculations for Forecast Error Measures

Month (t)	Demand (D_t)	Forecast (F_t)	Error (E_t)	Error Squared (E_t^2)	Absolute Error ($|E_t|$)	Absolute Percent Error ($|E_t|/D_t$)100
1	200	225	−25	625	25	12.5%
2	240	220	20	400	20	8.3
3	300	285	15	225	15	5.0
4	270	290	−20	400	20	7.4
5	230	250	−20	400	20	8.7
6	260	240	20	400	20	7.7
7	210	250	−40	1600	40	19.0
8	275	240	35	1225	35	12.7
Total			−15	5275	195	81.3%

Solution The table also shows the first set of calculations required to obtain the common measures of forecast error. Using those results and the formulas for the measures, we get

$$\text{Cumulative forecast error } (CFE) = -15$$

$$\text{Mean squared error } (MSE) = \frac{5275}{8} = 659.4$$

$$\text{Standard deviation } (\sigma) = \sqrt{\frac{5275}{8}} = 25.7$$

$$\text{Mean absolute deviation } (MAD) = \frac{195}{8} = 24.4$$

$$\text{Mean absolute percent error } (MAPE) = \frac{81.3\%}{8} = 10.2\%$$

For a *CFE* of −15, we can say that the forecast has a tendency to overestimate demand. The *MSE*, σ, and *MAD* statistics give us measures of forecast error variability. A *MAD* of 24.4 tells us that the average forecast error was 24.4 units. The value of σ tells us that the sample distribution of forecast errors has a standard deviation of 25.7 units. This information can be useful in designing inventory systems, for example. Note that the relationship between σ and *MAD* (that is, σ ≈ 1.25 *MAD*) does not hold here because the number of periods is small and the errors are not normally distributed. A *MAPE* of 10.2 percent implies that, on average, the error was about 10 percent of the actual demand. Of course, these measures become more reliable as the number of periods of data increases.

Tracking Signals. A **tracking signal** is a measure that indicates whether a method of forecasting has any built-in biases over a period of time. If a correct forecasting system is being used, *CFE* tends to be zero. At any time, however, random errors can cause *CFE* to be nonzero. The tracking signal formula is

$$\text{Tracking signal} = \frac{CFE}{MAD}$$

Each period, *CFE* is updated to reflect current error. The mean absolute deviation can be calculated in one of two ways: the simple average of all absolute errors (as we demonstrated in Application 11.6) or as a weighted average using the exponential smoothing method; that is

$$MAD_t = \alpha|E_t| + (1 - \alpha)MAD_{t-1}$$

The latter approach has certain advantages: Less historical data have to be retained for each estimate, and recent forecast performance can be emphasized more than past performance.

The tracking signal measures the number of *MAD*s represented by the cumulative sum of forecast errors. You can specify limits based on the normal probability tables by using the relationship between *MAD* and σ: *MAD* = 0.8σ. If the tracking signal falls outside those limits, you should check your forecast model because it no longer is tracking demand adequately. This approach is useful in computerized forecasting systems because it alerts analysts to forecasts that need attention. Table 11.5 shows the area of the normal probability distribution within the control limits of 1 to 4 *MAD*s. Figure 11.6 shows a tracking signal in operation.

TABLE 11.5 / *Percentage of the Area of the Normal Probability Distribution Within the Control Limits of the Tracking Signal*

Number of *MAD*s	Number of σ's*	Percentage of Area Within Control Limits[†]
±1.0	±0.80	57.62
±1.5	±1.20	76.98
±2.0	±1.60	89.04
±2.5	±2.00	95.44
±3.0	±2.40	98.36
±3.5	±2.80	99.48
±4.0	±3.20	99.86

*The equivalent number of standard deviations is found by using the approximation of *MAD* ≈ 0.8.

[†]The area of the normal curve included within the control limits is found in Appendix 5. For example, the cumulative area from −∝ to 0.80 is 0.7881. The area between 0 and +0.80σ is 0.7881 − 0.5000 = 0.2881. Since the normal curve is symmetric, the area between −0.80σ and 0 is also 0.2881. Therefore the area between ±0.80σ is 0.2881 + 0.2881 = 0.5762.

FIGURE 11.6

Tracking Signal

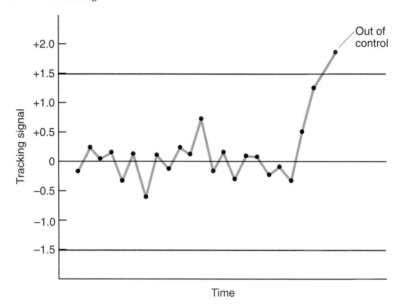

Choosing the limits for the tracking signal involves a trade-off between the cost of poor forecasts and the cost of checking for a problem when none exist. For example, suppose that $CFE = 180$ and $MAD = 100$; the tracking signal would be $+1.8$. If we had set the control limits of the tracking signal at ± 1.5, as in Fig. 11.6, we would check our forecasting method to see whether changes in the demand pattern indicate a needed change (1) in the model form (such as adding a trend estimate) or (2) in the values of the smoothing parameters. However, there is a chance that the value of $+1.8$ results from random variation only. In fact, with a limit of ± 1.5, there is a probability of 0.115 (one half the area outside the control limits) that we could get a value of the tracking signal greater than $+1.5$ as a result of random variation.

Forecast Error Ranges. MAD can also be used to provide additional information to managers. Single-number forecasts are rarely useful because forecasts are almost always wrong. Consequently, managers know that if they get a single number for forecasted product demand, actual demand will likely be anything but that figure. A far more useful approach is to provide the manager with a forecasted value and an error range, which can be done by using MAD. For example, suppose that the forecasted value for a product is 1000 units, with a MAD of 20 units. Using Table 11.5, an analyst could say that there is about a 95 percent chance that actual demand will fall within ± 2.5 MADs of the forecast. The analyst could tell the manager that the forecast is for 1000 units, with a 95 percent confidence level that actual demand will fall in the range of 950 to 1050 units. This information gives the manager a better feel for the uncertainty in the forecast and allows the manager to better plan inventories, staffing levels, and the like.

Criteria for Selecting Time Series Methods

A major use of forecast error measures is to provide input to choosing the best forecasting method for a given product or service. To illustrate, let's return to the medical clinic example in Applications 11.1–11.3 and the methods we used to forecast weekly patient arrivals. For purposes of the following discussion, we add another single exponential smoothing method with $\alpha = 0.2$. We also focus on *MAD* as a measure of forecast error dispersion, but we could just as well have used the mean squared error or standard deviation.

Table 11.6 shows the forecast error performance of the methods used for the medical clinic if all 28 periods of data are utilized. The criteria to use in making choices of this sort include (1) minimizing bias, (2) minimizing *MAD*, and (3) meeting managerial expectations of changes in the components of demand. The first two criteria are statistical measures based on historical performance; the third reflects expectations of the future that may not be rooted in the past. The tracking signal is useful *after* you have selected a method—to identify when you should closely examine the method to determine whether it should be changed.

Using Statistical Criteria. Let's begin by selecting the best value of N for moving average methods based on *MAD* and bias considerations.* Regardless of the method, we would like to have forecasts with zero bias and zero *MAD*. As this result is impossible, we face a trade-off between bias and *MAD*, as demonstrated in Table 11.6. A value of $N = 3$ weeks gives us a lower bias but a greater *MAD* than does a value of $N = 6$ weeks. Normally, preference is given to lower values of *MAD*. However, in this example, the two values of *MAD* are not that much different, whereas the measures of bias are very different. A positive value for *CFE* indicates that, on balance, the forecasts have been too

---

*No attempt was made to find the "best" methods in Table 11.6. The results and our discussion should be viewed as illustrative of the uses of forecast measures in the selection of a method.

TABLE 11.6 / Forecast Error Performance of Various Forecasting Methods for a Medical Clinic

Method	Cumulative Sum of Forecast Errors (CFE—bias)	Mean Absolute Deviation (MAD)	Tracking Signal* (CFE/MAD)
Simple moving average			
Three-week	23.1	17.1	1.35
Six-week	69.8	15.5	4.50
Weighted moving average			
0.70, 0.20, 0.10	14.0	18.4	0.76
Exponential smoothing			
$\alpha = 0.1$	65.6	14.8	4.43
$\alpha = 0.2$	41.0	15.3	2.68

*The tracking signal was calculated at the end of week 28, using *MAD* as a simple average of absolute deviations. An exponentially smoothed *MAD* could also have been used.

low. This result can be detrimental to clinic operations, particularly if purchasing procedures and staffing schedules are based on the raw forecasts. If the difference in *MAD* is not of concern to management, $N = 3$ seems like a good choice for the simple moving average.

Similar considerations are involved in choosing α for exponential smoothing. Again, the differences in *MAD* are slight, but the differences in bias are considerable. Larger α values seem to result in less bias than do smaller values in this example. Consequently, if we were to use exponential smoothing, $\alpha = 0.2$ would be best.

Which method should we choose, based on the statistical measures of forecast error in Table 11.6? The differences between *MAD*s in our example are managerially insignificant. Consequently, we focus on the bias measure and make our choice from the moving average method with $N = 3$, the weighted moving average method, or the exponential smoothing method with $\alpha = 0.2$. Note that these three methods all give greater weight to the most recent levels of demand and less weight to earlier levels. This weighting is evidence of a trend or seasonal component of demand in the time series. We assumed that the only components of demand were its historical average and random error. If another component were present, we typically would see low N values or high α values. The weighted moving average method provided an acceptable forecast. The weights were nearly equivalent to $\alpha = 0.70$ in the exponential smoothing method.

The tracking signal in Table 11.6 also tells us that something might be wrong. Suppose that we had set the limit at ± 2.5, which means that there is approximately a 2.28 percent probability that a tracking signal value will exceed $+2.5$ when nothing is wrong. Then if we had chosen a six-week moving average or any of the exponential smoothing methods, the tracking signal would have indicated a problem with our assumptions. Consequently, of the methods from which to choose, the three-week moving average or the weighted moving average looks best. However, we would be well advised to explore other methods—particularly one including trends—before making a final selection.

Using Managerial Expectations. In Table 11.1 we identified several external and internal factors that can affect demand. These factors can lead to changes in the nature of the components of demand, such as a change in the average level, the rate of a trend, or the timing and size of peaks in a seasonal demand series. Such changes can cause historical customer demand data to lose their relevance for projecting future demand. In some cases, managers might use the parameters of a time series model as policy variables, depicting expectations of changes in the underlying components of demand. Managers can use two general guidelines in this regard:

1. For projections of stable demand patterns, low α and β values or large N values give the best results and emphasize historical experience.
2. For projections of changing demand patterns, high α and β values or small N values give the best results. When the historical components of demand are changing, recent history should be emphasized.

Regardless of the basis for choosing these parameters originally, managers should monitor forecast error and modify the parameters as needed. In this way, managers can detect a poor choice and correct it.

CAUSAL METHODS: LINEAR REGRESSION

Causal methods are used when historical data are available and the relationship between the factor to be forecasted and other external or internal factors (such as those in Table 11.1) can be identified. These relationships are expressed in mathematical terms and can be very complex. Causal methods provide the most sophisticated forecasting tools and are by far better than time-series methods for predicting turning points in demand and preparing long-range forecasts. From the number of sophisticated causal methods used, we focus on linear regression because it is one of the best-known and most commonly used.

In **linear regression,** one variable, called a **dependent variable,** is related to one or more **independent variables** by a linear equation. The dependent variable, such as demand for doorknobs, is the one the manager wants to forecast. The independent variables, such as advertising expenditures and new housing starts, are assumed to have affected the dependent variable and thereby "caused" the results observed in the past. Also, time could be used as an independent variable, as a surrogate representing an unspecified group of variables contributing to trends or seasonal patterns in the data.

To illustrate the use of linear regression we use the simplest of models, in which the dependent variable is a function of only one independent variable. The linear regression method requires that we first hypothesize a relationship between the dependent variable and the independent variable. In the simplest case, we hypothesize that the relationship would be a straight line:

$$Y = \alpha + \beta X + u$$

where

$$Y = \text{dependent variable}$$
$$X = \text{independent variable}$$
$$\alpha = Y \text{ intercept of the line}$$
$$\beta = \text{slope of the line}$$
$$u = \text{random error}$$

We do not know the α and β values, so we must estimate them from a sample of data. These data are used to calculate a, the estimate of α, and b, the estimate of β, using a technique called *least squares*. The objective is to find values of a and b that minimize the sum of the squared deviations of the *actual* Y_i values from the *estimated* values:

$$\text{Minimize} \sum_{i=1}^{n} [Y_i - (a + bX_i)]^2$$

where n is the number of data points in the sample.

The process of finding the values of a and b that minimize the sum of squared deviations is complex, so we'll merely state the equations here:

$$a = \bar{Y} - b\bar{X} \quad \text{and} \quad b = \frac{\Sigma XY - n\bar{X}\bar{Y}}{\Sigma X^2 - n\bar{X}^2}$$

where a = estimate of the Y intercept
         b = estimate of the slope of the line
         $\bar{Y}$ = average of the Y values
         $\bar{X}$ = average of the X values

We use the values of a and b to forecast the dependent variable with the equation:

$$Y_R = a + bX$$

Regression analysis also provides measures of forecast accuracy. The three measures most often used are the correlation coefficient, the coefficient of determination, and the standard error of the estimate. All three can be used to judge whether the independent variable chosen for the model is a good choice.

The **correlation coefficient** measures the direction and strength of the linear relationship between the independent variable and the dependent variable. The correlation coefficient can be calculated using the following equation:

$$r = \frac{n\Sigma XY - \Sigma X\,\Sigma Y}{\sqrt{[n\Sigma X^2 - (\Sigma X)^2][n\Sigma Y^2 - (\Sigma Y)^2]}}$$

Values of r can range from -1.00 to $+1.00$. A correlation coefficient of $+1.00$ implies that period-by-period changes in direction (increases or decreases) of the independent variable are always accompanied by changes in the same direction by the dependent variable. An r value of -1.00 means that decreases in the independent variable are always accompanied by increases in the dependent variable and vice versa. A zero value of r means that there is no relationship between the variables. The closer the *absolute value* of r is to 1.00, the better the regression line fits the points.

The **coefficient of determination** measures the amount of variation in the dependent variable that is explained by the regression line. It can be calculated with the following equation:

$$r^2 = \frac{a\Sigma Y + b\Sigma XY - n\bar{Y}^2}{\Sigma Y^2 - n\bar{Y}^2}$$

The value of r^2 ranges from 0.00 to 1.00. Regression equations with a value of r^2 close to 1.00 are desirable because the variations in the dependent variable and the forecast generated by the regression equation are closely synchronized.

Finally, the **standard error of the estimate** measures how closely the data on the dependent variable cluster around the regression line. The equation for the standard error of the estimate is as follows:

$$S_{yx} = \sqrt{\frac{\Sigma Y^2 - a\Sigma Y - b\Sigma XY}{n - 2}}$$

Although there is some similarity to the sample standard deviation, s_{yx} measures the error from the dependent variable (Y) to the regression line, rather than the mean. When judging which independent variable to include in the regression equation, the smallest value of s_{yx} is best.

Application 11.7   *Using Linear Regression to Forecast Product Demand*

You are in charge of inventory for your company. As part of your job, you must obtain forecasts of demand for the products stocked in inventory. During a luncheon meeting, the marketing manager gives you information about the advertising budget for a particular product. The following are sales and advertising data for the past five months.

Month	Sales (000 units)	Advertising ($000)
1	264	2.5
2	116	1.3
3	165	1.4
4	101	1.0
5	209	2.0

The marketing manager said that next month the company will spend $1750 on advertising for the product. Use linear regression to develop an equation and a forecast for this product.

Solution

Month	Sales (Y)	Advertising (X)	(XY)	X^2	Y^2
1	264	2.5	660.0	6.25	69,696
2	116	1.3	150.8	1.69	13,456
3	165	1.4	231.0	1.96	27,225
4	101	1.0	101.0	1.00	10,201
5	209	2.0	418.0	4.00	43,681
Total	855	8.2	1560.8	14.90	164,259

$$\bar{X} = \frac{8.2}{5} = 1.64 \quad \text{and} \quad \bar{Y} = \frac{855}{5} = 171.00$$

$$b = \frac{\Sigma XY - n\bar{X}\bar{Y}}{\Sigma X^2 - n\bar{X}^2} = \frac{1560.8 - 5(1.64)(171)}{14.9 - 5(1.64)^2}$$

$$= \frac{158.60}{1.452} = 109.229$$

$$a = \bar{Y} - b\bar{X} = 171.00 - 109.229(1.64) = -8.136$$

The regression equation is

$$Y_R = -8.136 + 109.229X$$

The choice of advertising seems to be a good one for this forecasting equation. As shown below, the correlation coefficient and the coefficient of determination are both high.

$$r = \frac{n\Sigma XY - \Sigma X \Sigma Y}{\sqrt{[n\Sigma X^2 - (\Sigma X)^2][n\Sigma Y^2 - (\Sigma Y)^2]}} = \frac{5(1560.8) - (8.2)(855)}{\sqrt{[5(14.90) - (8.2)^2][5(164,259) - (855)^2]}}$$

$$= \frac{7804 - 7011}{\sqrt{[74.5 - 67.24][821,295 - 731,025]}} = 0.98$$

$$r^2 = \frac{a\Sigma Y + b\Sigma XY - n\bar{Y}^2}{\Sigma Y^2 - n\bar{Y}^2} = \frac{-8.136(855) + 109.229(1560.8) - 5(171)^2}{164,259 - 5(171)^2}$$

$$= \frac{17,323.34}{18,054.00} = 0.96$$

The standard error of the estimate for this regression equation is

$$s_{yx} = \sqrt{\frac{\Sigma Y^2 - a\Sigma Y - b\Sigma XY}{n-2}} = \sqrt{\frac{164,259 - (-8.136)(855) - 109.229(1560.8)}{5-2}}$$

$$s_{yx} = \sqrt{\frac{730.66}{3}} = 15.61$$

The forecast for month 6 is

$$Y_R = -8.136 + 109.229(1.75)$$
$$= 183.015 \quad \text{or} \quad 183,015 \text{ units}$$

Regression analysis can provide useful guidance for important operations management decisions, such as inventory management, capacity planning, and process design. However, this approach is relatively costly because of the large amounts of data needed to obtain useful linear regression relationships. In Application 11.7 we started with the assumption that sales were linearly related to advertising expenditures. However, we could have assumed that sales were related to the square root of advertising expenditures, for example. It may have resulted in better forecasts. In addition, independent variables other than advertising expenditures may also be important, such as new corporation startups or residential building contracts. Considerable analysis may be required before an acceptable model is developed. Nonetheless, linear regression models are useful for predicting turning points and can be useful tools for solving many planning problems.

QUALITATIVE METHODS

The time series and causal methods of forecasting require a considerable amount of historical data. As we have shown, these techniques can produce reasonably accurate forecasts. Sometimes, however, adequate historical data are lacking, such as when a new product is introduced or there is a need to forecast long-term technological change. Qualitative techniques, which are designed for these situations, rely on managerial judgment and experience and other forms of qualitative information to generate forecasts. In this section we discuss four of the more successful qualitative techniques currently in use: sales force estimates, executive judgment, market research, and the Delphi method.

Sales Force Estimates

Sometimes the best information about future demand comes from the persons closest to the customer. **Sales force estimates** is a method of compiling a forecast based on periodic personal estimates of future demands made by members of the sales force. There are several advantages to this approach. First, the sales force is the group most likely to know which products or services, and in what quantities, customers will be buying in the near future. Second, if the firm's market covers a large area, the forecasts will already be divided by district or region. This information can be useful for inventory management, distribution, and sales force staffing purposes. Finally, the forecasts can be easily aggregated to any level of detail desired: District sales can be summed to get regional sales; regional sales can be summed to get national sales.

This approach has several disadvantages. First, individual biases of the salespersons may taint the forecast; moreover, some people are naturally optimistic, others more cautious. Second, salespersons may not always be able to detect the difference between what a customer "wants" (a wish list) and what a customer "needs" (a necessary purchase). Finally, if the firm uses individual sales as a performance measure, the salespersons may underestimate their forecasts so that their performance will "look good" when they exceed their projections. If managers are not careful with this approach, the sales estimates may become a "self-fulfilling prophecy."

Executive Judgment

When a new product or service is contemplated, sales force estimates may not be accurate enough. **Executive judgment** is a forecasting method that summarizes the opinions of a group of executives to arrive at a single forecast. The opinions are based on the executives' experience with similar products or services. Sometimes executive judgment is used to modify an existing sales forecast to account for unusual circumstances, such as a new sales promotion or unexpected international events.

There are several disadvantages to this method of forecasting. Executive judgment can be costly because it takes executive time, although that may be warranted under certain circumstances. The risk in this approach is that it sometimes goes out of control. If executives are allowed to modify a forecast without collectively agreeing to the changes, the resulting forecast will not be useful. For example, suppose the marketing manager sees the sales force estimates and, feeling a bit more optimistic than the sales force, increases the forecast to ensure enough product is available. After receiving the market forecasts, the manufacturing manager begins to plan the production of the product. However, the marketing manager has been upset with the manufacturing manager in the past because not enough product was available when customers demanded it. Consequently, the manufacturing manager further increases the forecast. This house of cards collapses when actual sales are much lower than the forecasts, and everyone blames someone else for the extra inventory that was created. The key to effective use of executive judgment is not a series of independent modifications but consensus among the executives for a single forecast.

Market Research

Suppose that you are planning a new business that would allow consumers to shop for groceries by using a personal computer in their homes. One way to determine consumer interest is to do market research. **Market research** is a systematic approach to creating and testing hypotheses about the market. Data usually are gathered by survey methods.

Designing and conducting a market research study includes the following activities. First, you need to design a questionnaire that requests the needed economic and demographic information from each person interviewed. As part of the questionnaire, you need to ask whether the interviewee would be interested in using your service. Second, in conjunction with the design of the questionnaire, you need to decide how to administer it. You have three choices: telephone polling, mailings, or personal interviews.

Third, you need to select a representative sample of households to survey. The sample should include a random selection within the market area of your proposed service. Finally, after collecting the information, you must analyze it. Analysis requires that you must exercise a considerable amount of judgment in interpreting the responses, determining their adequacy, and making allowance

A specially trained moderator conducts a focus group and in-depth interview session at a Market Segment Research facility. This information-gathering method yields valuable, qualitative data for market research.

for economic or competition factors not included in the questionnaire. Moreover, the response rate on mailed questionnaires is typically poor (30 percent is often considered high), and you must weigh the possibility that the respondents are an atypical group that no longer represents a random sample of your potential market.

Market research can be used to forecast demand for the short, medium, and long terms. Accuracy is excellent for the short term, good for the medium term, and only fair for the long term. Although market research yields many benefits, it has some shortcomings. One shortcoming is the numerous qualifications and hedges typically included in the findings. For example, a finding might be, "The new diet burger product received good customer acceptance in our survey; however, we were unable to assess its longer-term acceptance once other competitor products make their appearance." Another shortcoming is the length of time needed to prepare a good survey, collect the data, and then make the analysis. Even though market surveys are excellent for the short term, don't expect to get an answer quickly if the survey instrument has not been developed. Finally, there is the risk that the survey will produce imitative, rather than innovative, ideas because the customer's reference point is often limited.

Delphi Method

The **Delphi method** is a process of gaining consensus from a group of experts while maintaining their anonymity. This form of forecasting is useful when there are no historical data from which to develop statistical models—when judgment or opinion, based on experience and study of the market, industry, or scientific developments, are the only bases for making informed projections. The process involves a coordinator who sends questions to each member of the group, who may not even know who else is participating. The experts respond to the questions and argue in support of their responses. The coordinator pools the responses and prepares a report consisting of a statistical summary of the responses as well as a summary of arguments for particular responses. The coordinator then sends the report to the same group for another round. The participants can repeat or modify their previous responses. Some form of consensus is usually obtained in two to four rounds. The Delphi method can be used to develop long-range forecasts of product demand and new product sales projections.

One of the more useful applications for the Delphi method is that of **technological forecasting.** The rate of technological change is increasing much more rapidly than ever before. Computer science is just one field experiencing explosive technological change; computers become obsolete soon after they are produced. Today, an almost completely automated factory is possible. What's next? Trying to answer that question is the focus of technological forecasting. The Delphi method can be used to obtain a consensus answer from a panel of experts. The panel members may be asked to specify the scientific advances they envision, as well as changes in environmental and social forces such as quality of life, governmental regulations, and competitor actions. The questions are typically directed toward specific organizations or industries. The results of such a process can provide direction for a firm's research and development staff.

The Delphi method has a number of shortcomings, including the following major ones:

- The process can take a long time (sometimes a year or more). During that time the constituency of the expert group may change, thereby confounding the results or at least further lengthening the process.
- Because the process preserves the anonymity of the experts, there is risk that their responses will be less meaningful than if they were accountable for them.
- There is little evidence to show that Delphi forecasts achieve high degrees of accuracy. However, they are known to be fair to good in identifying turning points in new product demand.
- Poorly designed questionnaires will result in ambiguous or false conclusions.

The potential for these shortcomings should be carefully considered before undertaking the Delphi method.

COMPUTER SOLVED PROBLEM
Forecasting the Weight of a Box of Cereal

The product manager at Johnson Cereals is concerned about the actual weight of the company's 10-ounce box of oats cereal. The manager has obtained the following data from a random sample of cereal boxes over an eight-hour period. Specifically, the manager would like to know if a general trend is occurring over time.

Hour	Weight (oz)	Hour	Weight (oz)
08:00	9.8	12:00	10.4
08:30	10.1	12:30	10.0
09:00	10.0	1:00	10.2
09:30	9.6	1:30	10.3
10:00	9.9	2:00	10.4
10:30	10.3	2:30	10.5
11:00	10.7	3:00	10.7
11:30	10.5	3:30	10.8

a. Develop a three-period moving average forecast and an optimized (based on minimizing *MAD*) moving average forecast.
b. Develop two exponential smoothing forecasts, one with alpha = 0.3 and one that is optimized (based on minimizing *MAD*).
c. Contrast the results obtained in parts (a) and (b).
d. Analyze the data using the trend-adjusted exponential smoothing model based on minimizing *MAD*. Does a trend exist?

Solution
This problem is solved using CMOM (Forecasting module). Your output may look different if you are using another software package.

a. Printout 1 presents the moving average model analysis. Notice that the number of periods for the optimized mode has increased from three to eight. However, the resultant forecast value has changed only slightly, from 10.67 to 10.41. The corresponding *MAD* values are also close in magnitude.

PRINTOUT 1

CMOM–FORECASTING

MOVING AVERAGES

SOLUTION

AVERAGE WEIGHT	:	10.2625
MEAN SQUARE ERROR	:	0.1192
MEAN ABSOLUTE DEVIATION	:	0.2795
FORECAST VALUE	:	10.6667

OPTIMIZED COEFFICIENTS

NUMBER OF TIME PERIODS	:	8
MEAN ABSOLUTE DEVIATION	:	0.2016
FORECAST VALUE	:	10.4100

---

b. Printout 2 presents the exponential smoothing model analysis. The optimized smoothing coefficient is more than twice as large as the original coefficient (0.3 versus 0.65). However, the forecasted values are nearly identical (10.56 versus 10.73).

PRINTOUT 2

CMOM–FORECASTING

SIMPLE EXPONENTIAL SMOOTHING

SOLUTION

AVERAGE WEIGHT	:	10.2353
MEAN SQUARE ERROR	:	0.0907
MEAN ABSOLUTE DEVIATION	:	0.2422
FORECAST VALUE	:	10.5599

OPTIMIZED COEFFICIENTS

SMOOTHING COEFFICIENT	:	0.6500
MEAN ABSOLUTE DEVIATION	:	0.2072
FORECAST VALUE	:	10.7300

---

c. The forecasts range from 10.41 ounces to 10.73 ounces, with an average value of 10.58 ounces. The best forecast, based on *MAD*, is the eight-period moving average forecast; however, you need to retain eight periods of past demand for each forecast. The optimized exponential smoothing forecast is almost as good with respect to *MAD* and requires only three pieces of data to compute: smoothing coefficient, past average, and current weight.

d. The results of the trend model are given in Printout 3. These results reveal higher forecasted values, 10.6974 and 10.89, compared to those reported in parts (a) and (b). The *MAD* value for the optimized case is the lowest value reported for all options. This would suggest the presence of a linear trend in the data.

PRINTOUT 3

CMOM–FORECASTING

SMOOTHING WITH TREND FACTORING

SOLUTION

AVERAGE WEIGHT	:	10.2353
MEAN SQUARE ERROR	:	0.0847
MEAN ABSOLUTE DEVIATION	:	0.2302
FORECAST VALUE	:	10.6974

OPTIMIZED COEFFICIENTS

SMOOTHING COEFFICIENT (AVERAGE)	:	0.8050
SMOOTHING COEFFICIENT (TREND)	:	0.0100
MEAN ABSOLUTE DEVIATION	:	0.1842
FORECAST VALUE	:	10.8900

SOLVED PROBLEMS

In Problems 1, 2, and 3 we have calculated the average to one decimal place and rounded the forecast to the closest integer.

1. The Polish General's Pizza Parlor is a small restaurant catering to patrons with a taste for European pizza. One of its specialties is Polish Prize pizza. The manager must forecast weekly demand for these special pizzas so that he can order pizza shells weekly. Recently, demand has been as follows.

Week of	Number of Polish Prize Pizzas	Week of	Number of Polish Prize Pizzas
June 2	50	June 23	56
June 9	65	July 7	60
June 16	52	July 7	60

a. Forecast the demand for Polish Prize pizza for June 23–July 7, using the three-period moving average method.
b. Repeat part (a), using the weighted moving average method. The weights are 0.50, 0.30, and 0.20, with 0.50 referring to the most recent demand.
c. Calculate the *MAD* for each method.

Solution

a. $$A_t = \frac{D_t + D_{t-1} + D_{t-2}}{3} \quad \text{and} \quad F_{t+1} = A_t$$

Week Forecast Calculated	A_t	Forecast for Following Week (F_{t+1})
June 16	(52 + 65 + 50)/3 =	55.7, or 56
June 23	(56 + 52 + 65)/3 =	57.7, or 58
June 30	(55 + 56 + 52)/3 =	54.3, or 54

b. $A_t = 0.50D_t + 0.30D_{t-1} + 0.20D_{t-2}$

Week Forecast Calculated	A_t	Forecast for Following Week (F_{t+1})
June 16	0.50(52) + 0.30(65) + 0.20(50) =	55.5, or 56
June 23	0.50(56) + 0.30(52) + 0.20(65) =	56.6, or 57
June 30	0.50(55) + 0.30(56) + 0.20(52) =	54.7, or 55

c.

Week (t)	Actual Demand (D_t)	3-Week Moving Average Forecast (F_t)	Absolute Error $(\lvert E_t \rvert)$	Weighted Moving Average Forecast (F_t)	Absolute Error $(\lvert E_t \rvert)$
June 23	56	56	0	56	0
June 30	55	58	3	57	2
July 7	60	54	6	55	5
Total			9		7
MAD			9/3 = 3.0		7/3 = 2.3

For this limited set of data, the weighted moving average method resulted in a slightly lower mean absolute deviation. However, final conclusions can be made only after analyzing much more data.

2. The monthly demand for units manufactured by the Acme Rocket company has been as follows:

Month	Units	Month	Units
May	100	September	105
June	80	October	110
July	110	November	125
August	115	December	120

a. Use the exponential smoothing method to forecast the number of units for June through December. The initial forecast for May was 105 units; $\alpha = 0.2$.

b. Calculate the absolute percentage error for each month from June through December and the *MAD* and *MAPE* of forecast error as of the end of December.

c. Calculate the tracking signal as of the end of December. What can you say about the performance of your forecasting method?

Solution   a. $A_t = 0.2D_t + 0.8A_{t-1}$ and $F_{t+1} = A_t$

Month Forecast Calculated	A_t		Forecast for Following Month (F_{t+1})
May	$0.2(100) + 0.8(105)$	$=$	104.0, or 104
June	$0.2(80)\ \ + 0.8(104)$	$=$	99.2, or 99
July	$0.2(110) + 0.8(99.2)$	$=$	101.4, or 101
August	$0.2(115) + 0.8(101.4)$	$=$	104.1, or 104
September	$0.2(105) + 0.8(104.1)$	$=$	104.3, or 104
October	$0.2(110) + 0.8(104.3)$	$=$	105.4, or 105
November	$0.2(125) + 0.8(105.4)$	$=$	109.3, or 109

b.

Month (t)	Actual Demand (D_t)	Forecast (F_t)	Error (E_t)	Absolute Error ($|E_t|$)	Absolute Percentage Error
June	80	104	-24	24	30.0%
July	110	99	11	11	10.0
August	115	101	14	14	12.2
September	105	104	1	1	0.9
October	110	104	6	6	5.4
November	125	105	20	20	16.0
December	120	109	11	11	9.2
Total			39	87	83.7%

$$MAD = \frac{87}{7} = 12.4$$

$$MAPE = \frac{83.7\%}{7} = 11.9\%$$

c. As of the end of December, the cumulative sum of forecast errors (CFE) is 39. Using the mean absolute deviation calculated in part (b), we calculate the tracking signal as follows:

$$\text{Tracking signal} = \frac{CFE}{MAD} = \frac{39}{12.4} = 3.14$$

The value of the tracking signal indicates a very small probability that a value of 3.14 could be generated completely by chance. Consequently, we should revise our approach. The long string of forecasts lower than actual demand suggests use of a trends method.

3. The demand for Krispee Crunchies, a favorite breakfast cereal for people born in the 1940s, is experiencing a decline in demand. The company wants to monitor demand for this product closely as it nears the end of its life cycle. The trend-adjusted exponential smoothing method is used with $\alpha = 0.1$ and $\beta = 0.2$. At the end of December, the January estimate for the average number of cases sold per month was 900,000 and the trend was $-50,000$ per month. The following is the actual sales history for January, February, and March. Generate forecasts for February, March, and April.

Month	Sales
January	890,000
February	800,000
March	825,000

Solution   We are given the initial condition as of the end of December and actual demand for January, February, and March. The forecast method must now be updated and a forecast prepared for April. All data are expressed in thousands of cases. Our equations for use with trend-adjusted exponential smoothing are

$$A_t = 0.1D_t + 0.9(A_{t-1} + T_{t-1})$$
$$CT_t = A_t - A_{t-1}$$
$$T_t = 0.2CT_t + 0.8T_{t-1}$$
$$F_{t+1} = A_t + T_t$$

January:

$$A_{Jan} = 0.1(890) + 0.9(900 - 50) = 854.0$$
$$CT_{Jan} = 854.0 - 900.0 = -46.0$$
$$T_{Jan} = 0.2(-46.0) + 0.8(-50.0) = -49.2$$

Forecast for February $= 854.0 - 49.2 = 804.8$, or 804,800 cases.

February:

$$A_{Feb} = 0.1(800) + 0.9(854.0 - 49.2) = 804.3$$
$$CT_{Feb} = 804.3 - 854.0 = -49.7$$
$$T_{Feb} = 0.2(-49.7) + 0.8(-49.2) = -49.3$$

Forecast for March $= 804.3 - 49.3 = 755.0$, or 755,000 cases.

March:

$$A_{Mar} = 0.1(825) + 0.9(804.3 - 49.3) = 762.0$$
$$CT_{Mar} = 762.0 - 804.3 = -42.3$$
$$T_{Mar} = 0.2(-42.3) + 0.8(-49.3) = -47.9$$

Forecast for April $= 762.0 - 47.9 = 714.1$, or 714,100 cases.

4. The Northville Post Office experiences a "seasonal" pattern of daily mail volume every week. The following data for two representative weeks are

expressed in thousands of pieces of mail.

Day	Week 1	Week 2
Monday	20	15
Tuesday	30	32
Wednesday	35	30
Thursday	50	48
Friday	70	72
Saturday	15	10
Sunday	5	8
Total	225	215

a. Calculate seasonal factors for each day of the week.
b. If the postmaster estimates that there will be 230,000 pieces of mail to sort next week, forecast the volume for each day of the week.

Solution

a. We calculate the average daily mail volume and divide the actual mail volume for each day by this value to get the seasonal factor. We then average the seasonal factors to get the final factor to use in the forecast.

Day	Week 1 Mail Volume	Seasonal Factor	Week 2 Mail Volume	Seasonal Factor	Average Seasonal Factor
Monday	20	0.622	15	0.488	0.555
Tuesday	30	0.933	32	1.042	0.9875
Wednesday	35	1.089	30	0.977	1.033
Thursday	50	1.555	48	1.563	1.559
Friday	70	2.178	72	2.344	2.261
Saturday	15	0.467	10	0.326	0.3965
Sunday	5	0.156	8	0.260	0.208
Total	225		215		
Average	32.143		30.714		

b. The average daily mail volume is expected to be 32,857 (230,000/7) pieces of mail. Using the average seasonal factors calculated in part (a), we obtain the following forecasts.

Day	Calculation		Forecast
Monday	0.555(32,857)	=	18,236
Tuesday	0.9875(32,857)	=	32,446
Wednesday	1.033(32,857)	=	33,941
Thursday	1.559(32,857)	=	51,224
Friday	2.261(32,857)	=	74,290
Saturday	0.3965(32,857)	=	13,028
Sunday	0.208(32,857)	=	6,834

5. Periodically the manager of Chicken Palace offers carry-out five-piece chicken dinners at special prices on certain days. Having done this a number of times, he noticed that price affected total sales. Given the following

data, how many dinners can he expect to sell at $3.00 each?

Day	Price	Dinners Sold
1	$2.70	760
2	$3.50	510
3	$2.00	980
4	$4.20	250
5	$3.10	320
6	$4.05	480

Solution

Let Y be the number of dinners sold and X be the price. Given the computations in the following table, we first determine (i) the regression equation where the number of dinners sold is a function of price; (ii) the correlation coefficient, the coefficient of determination, and the standard error of the estimate to see how well the regression equation fits the data; and finally, (iii) the sales forecast at a price of $3.00.

Day	X	Y	XY	X^2	Y^2
1	$ 2.70	760	2052	7.2900	577,600
2	$ 3.50	510	1785	12.2500	260,100
3	$ 2.00	980	1960	4.0000	960,400
4	$ 4.20	250	1050	17.6400	62,500
5	$ 3.10	320	992	9.6100	102,400
6	$ 4.05	480	1944	16.4025	230,400
	$19.55	3300	9783	67.1925	2,193,400
Average	$ 3.258	550			

i) Regression Equation:

$$b = \frac{\Sigma XY - n\,\bar{X}\bar{Y}}{\Sigma X^2 - n\bar{X}^2} = \frac{9783 - 6(3.258)(550)}{67.1925 - 6(3.258)^2}$$

$$= \frac{-968.4}{3.5051} = -276.28$$

$$a = \bar{Y} - b\bar{X} = 550 - (-276.28)(3.258) = 1450.12$$

Therefore, the regression line is

$$Y_R = 1450.12 - 276.28X$$

ii) Measures of Forecast Accuracy:

$$r = \frac{n\Sigma XY - \Sigma X\,\Sigma Y}{\sqrt{[n\Sigma X^2 - (\Sigma X)^2][n\Sigma Y^2 - (\Sigma Y)^2]}}$$

$$= \frac{6(9783) - (19.55)(3300)}{\sqrt{[6(67.1925) - (19.55)^2][6(2,193,400) - (3300)^2]}}$$

$$= \frac{58,698 - 64,515}{\sqrt{[20.9525][2,270,400]}} = \frac{-5817}{6897.14} = 0.84$$

$$r^2 = \frac{a\Sigma Y + b\Sigma XY - n\bar{Y}^2}{\Sigma Y^2 - n\bar{Y}^2}$$

$$= \frac{1450.12(3300) + (-276.28)(9783) - 6(550)^2}{2,193,400 - 6(550)^2}$$

$$= \frac{4,785,396 - 2,702,847.2 - 1,815,000}{378,400}$$

$$= \frac{267,548.8}{378,400} = 0.71$$

$$s_{yx} = \sqrt{\frac{\Sigma Y^2 - a\Sigma Y - b\Sigma XY}{n - 2}}$$

$$= \sqrt{\frac{2,193,400 - 1450.12(3300) - (-276.28)(9783)}{6 - 2}}$$

$$= \sqrt{\frac{110851.2}{4}} = 166.47$$

The coefficient of determination (r^2) of only 71 percent indicates that other variables (in addition to price) have an appreciable effect on sales. The correlation coefficient (r) shows reasonable correlation between the variables. The standard error of the estimate (s_{yx}) is large relative to average sales and reflects the possibility for sizable forecast errors.

iii) Forecast: Presuming the regression equation is satisfactory to the manager, the estimated sales at a price of $3.00 per dinner is:

$$Y_R = 1450.12 - 276.28(3.00) = 621.28 \quad \text{or} \quad 621 \text{ dinners}$$

FORMULA REVIEW

1. Simple moving average:

$$A_t = \frac{D_t + D_{t-1} + D_{t-2} + \cdots + D_{t-N+1}}{N}$$

2. Weighted moving average:

$$A_t = W_1 D_t + W_2 D_{t-1} + \cdots + W_N D_{t-N+1}$$

3. Exponential smoothing:

$$A_t = \alpha D_t + (1 - \alpha)A_{t-1}$$

4. Trend-adjusted exponential smoothing:

$$A_t = \alpha D_t + (1 - \alpha)(A_{t-1} + T_{t-1}) \qquad\qquad T_t = \beta CT_t + (1 - \beta)T_{t-1}$$

$$CT_t = A_t - A_{t-1} \qquad\qquad F_{t+1} = A_t + T_t$$

5. Seasonal factors:

$$\bar{D}_y = \frac{\sum_{t=1}^{n} D_{y,t}}{n} \qquad\qquad \bar{f}_t = \frac{\sum_{y=1}^{m} f_{y,t}}{m}$$

$$f_{y,t} = \frac{D_{y,t}}{\bar{D}_y} \qquad\qquad F_{y,t} = \tilde{D}_y \bar{f}_t$$

6. Forecast error:

$$E_t = D_t - F_t$$

7. Forecast error measures:

$$CFE = \sum_{t=1}^{n} E_t$$

$$\sigma = \sqrt{\frac{\sum_{t=1}^{n} E_t^2}{n}}$$

$$MSE = \frac{\sum_{t=1}^{n} E_t^2}{n}$$

$$MAD = \frac{\sum_{t=1}^{n} |E_t|}{n} \qquad\qquad \text{Tracking Signal} = \frac{CFE}{MAD}$$

$$MAPE = \frac{\sum_{t=1}^{n} \frac{|E_t|}{D_t} (100)}{n} \quad \text{(expressed as a percentage)}$$

8. Linear regression:

$$a = \bar{Y} - b\bar{X}$$

$$b = \frac{\Sigma XY - n\bar{X}\bar{Y}}{\Sigma X^2 - n\bar{X}^2}$$

$$r = \frac{n\Sigma XY - \Sigma X \,\Sigma Y}{\sqrt{[n\Sigma X^2 - (\Sigma X)^2][n\Sigma Y^2 - (\Sigma Y)^2]}}$$

$$r^2 = \frac{a\Sigma Y + b\Sigma XY - n\bar{Y}^2}{\Sigma Y^2 - n\bar{Y}^2}$$

$$s_{yx} = \sqrt{\frac{\Sigma Y^2 - a\Sigma Y - b\Sigma XY}{n - 2}}$$

CHAPTER HIGHLIGHTS

• Three general types of demand forecasting are used: time series analysis, causal methods, and qualitative techniques. All three are useful for short-term forecasting, whereas causal methods and qualitative techniques are more appropriate for medium- and long-term forecasting.

• The five basic components of demand are the average, trend, seasonal influence, cyclical movement, and random error. An understanding of the external factors (beyond management's control) and the internal factors (within management's control) that affect the components of demand is essential for making accurate forecasts.

• Designing a forecasting system involves determining what to forecast, what forecasting method and software package (in computerized systems) to use, and how the system can assist managerial decision making. Deciding what to forecast requires consideration of the level of aggregation required and the units of measure.

• Simple moving averages, weighted moving averages, and exponential smoothing are techniques used to estimate the average of a time series. The exponential smoothing technique has the advantage of requiring a minimal amount of data to be kept for use in updating the forecast.

• Trend-adjusted exponential smoothing is a method for including a trend estimate in exponentially smoothed forecasts. Estimates for the series average and the trend are smoothed to provide the forecast.

• Although many techniques allow for seasonal influences, a simple approach is the multiplicative method, which is based on the assumption that the seasonal influence is proportional to the level of average demand.

• The cumulative sum of forecast errors (CFE), the mean squared error (MSE), the standard deviation of forecast errors (σ), the mean absolute deviation (MAD), and the mean absolute percent error ($MAPE$) are all measures of forecast error used in practice. CFE and MAD are used to develop a tracking signal that determines when a forecasting method no longer is yielding acceptable forecasts. Forecast error measures can also be used to select the best forecast methods from available alternatives.

• Causal forecasting methods are more sophisticated than time series methods and hypothesize a functional relationship between the factor to be forecasted and other internal or external factors. Linear regression is one of the more popular causal methods used in forecasting.

• Qualitative techniques of forecasting are useful in situations where relevant historical data are lacking. These techniques are based on the judgment, experience, and expertise of those who do the forecasting. Sales force estimates, executive judgment, market research, and the Delphi method are four examples of qualitative techniques. The Delphi method has been used to make forecasts of technological change.

KEY TERMS

causal methods **436**
coefficient of
    determination **460**
coincident indicators **433**
correlation coefficient **460**
cumulative sum of forecast
    errors (*CFE*) **453**
Delphi method **465**
demand management **434**
dependent variable **459**

executive judgment **463**
exponential smoothing
    method **443**
focus forecasting **450**
forecast **430**
forecast error **452**
independent variables **459**
lagging indicators **433**
leading indicators **433**
linear regression **459**
market research **464**

mean absolute deviation
    (*MAD*) **453**
mean absolute percent error
    (*MAPE*) **454**
mean squared error
    (*MSE*) **453**
moving average method **440**
multiplicative seasonal
    method **448**
product families **435**
qualitative techniques **436**

STUDY QUESTIONS

1. You have thousands of items in your product line and must forecast demand for each one on a weekly basis. Which of the three approaches (time series analysis, causal, or qualitative) would you use? Why?

2. You are the owner–manager of a new movie theater in town. The problem you face is that you get an overflow crowd of teenagers for your Friday and Saturday night showings of the horror movie "Bad Dreams on Mohican Way—Part 16" and very little attendance for other movies shown during the rest of the week. Discuss several ways in which you could use demand management to smooth the load on your facilities over the week and during the day on Saturday.

3. If you had to choose among simple moving averages, weighted moving averages, and exponential smoothing to forecast demand for a product having no trend or seasonal components, which method would you choose? Why?

4. For what type of demand pattern is the exponential smoothing method with a low α value most appropriate? Explain.

5. You had just spent eight months developing a method to forecast hourly check volumes to be processed by the encoding department of a large bank. Based on historical data, your method's forecasts resulted in a *MAD* of 500 checks. The first week you used the new method, the actual *MAD* was 1000 checks. Should you be concerned? Explain.

6. How can you use simple linear regression in conjunction with the seasonal factors approach to seasonal forecasting?

7. As a consultant, you have been asked to look into the forecasting problems of a certain company. The company has been plotting the cumulative forecast error for each of its forecasts and using the results to judge the adequacy of its forecasting system. What are your reactions to this approach? What would you recommend?

8. As part of its product planning program, your company is interested in determining when the gasoline engine will be replaced by some other source of power for the automobile. How would you go about preparing such a forecast?

9. What are the trade-offs you must make in selecting a forecast method on the basis of forecast error?

10. You have received two forecasts for a certain product. The first says that demand next month will be 500 units. The other says that demand next month will be between 400 and 600 units. Which of the two forecasts would you prefer? Why?

PROBLEMS

Review Problems

1. The owner of a computer store rents printers to some of her preferred customers. She is interested in arriving at a forecast of rentals so she can order the correct amount of supplies, such as ribbons and paper, that go with the printers. Data for the last ten weeks are:

Week	Rentals	Week	Rentals
1	12	6	15
2	16	7	18
3	14	8	20
4	10	9	16
5	13	10	17

a. Prepare a forecast for weeks 6–10 using a five-week moving average. What is the forecast for week 11?

b. Compute the mean absolute deviation as of the end of week 10.

2. The Midwest Telephone Company provides phone installation services. The manager of the installers is interested in forecasting the demand for phone installation so he can plan for the number of installers required. The number of weekly phone installation requests for the last ten weeks were:

Week	Installation Requests	Week	Installation Requests
1	25	6	29
2	28	7	30
3	22	8	36
4	37	9	39
5	33	10	42

a. Using a four-week moving average, forecast the number of requests for weeks 8, 9, and 10.

b. Using a six-week moving average, forecast the number of requests for weeks 8, 9, and 10.

c. Compare the performance of the two methods with a simple calculation of forecast error. Explain the relative performances of the two methods.

3. Karl's Copiers sells and repairs photocopy machines. The manager needs weekly forecasts of repair-service calls so he can schedule service personnel. The forecast for the week of July 3 was 23 calls. The manager uses exponential smoothing with an $\alpha = 0.3$. Forecast the number of calls for the week of August 7, which is next week.

Week of	Actual Service Calls
July 3	28
July 10	33
July 17	36
July 24	35
July 31	41

4. The K & R Camera Shop sells all of the latest cameras and accessories. To maintain good customer service, the manager must forecast demand for the items she sells. Lately the XR-42S zoom lens has been very popular. Recent monthly demand for this item has been:

Month	Number of Lenses Sold
1	12
2	16
3	15
4	21
5	19
6	23

a. Forecast XR-42S demand for months 4–6, using a weighted moving average. The weights are 0.5, 0.3, and 0.2, where 0.5 refers to the most recent demand.

b. Repeat part (a), using exponential smoothing with $\alpha = 0.2$. Assume that the average at the end of month 2 was 15 lenses.

c. What is the forecast for week 7, using each method? Based on these limited data, which method do you have more confidence in? Discuss.

5. The management of a vending machine company has recently decided to carry a new brand of soda in the numerous vending machines across its territory. Management is interested in the future volume of sales to see whether it should continue to carry the new brand. If enough sales growth is projected, it will continue to carry the new soda; otherwise, another brand will replace it. At the end of April the average monthly volume of the new soda was 700 cans and the trend was +50 per month. The actual volume figures for May, June, and July are 760, 800, and 820, respectively. Use trend-adjusted exponential smoothing with $\alpha = 0.2$ and $\beta = 0.1$ to forecast usage for June, July, and August.

6. Sunnyvale Bank in Yuma, Arizona, recently installed a new automatic teller machine in its downtown branch. The new machine not

only performs the standard banking services but also handles loan applications and certain limited investment transactions. The new machine is slightly more complicated to use than the standard one, so management is interested in tracking its past use and projecting its future use. Additional machines may be needed if the projected use is high enough.

At the end of March the average monthly use was 600 customers and the trend was +60 per month. The actual use figures for April, May, and June are 680, 710, and 790, respectively. Use trend-adjusted exponential smoothing with $\alpha = 0.3$ and $\beta = 0.1$ to forecast usage for May, June, and July.

7. Consider the following data for the sales of a particular product over the past four weeks.

Week	Sales (units)	Week	Sales (units)
1	19	3	22
2	25	4	30

a. Use exponential smoothing with $\alpha = 0.7$ to forecast sales for weeks 2–5. Assume that the average of the time series was 20 units just before week 1.

b. Use trend-adjusted exponential smoothing with $\alpha = 0.1$ and $\beta = 0.1$ to forecast sales for weeks 2–5. Assume that the average of the series was 20 units and that the average trend was 3 units per week just before week 1.

c. Compare the performance of these two methods using appropriate measures of forecast error. Which method seems to fit the data better?

8. The following data are for calculator sales of an electronics store over the past five weeks.

Week	Sales (units)	Week	Sales (units)
1	26	4	30
2	29	5	33
3	23		

Use trend-adjusted exponential smoothing with $\alpha = 0.2$ and $\beta = 0.2$ to forecast sales for weeks 3–6. Assume that the average of the time series was 25 units and that the av-erage trend was +2 units per week just before week 1.

9. The manager of Snyder's Garden Center must make her annual purchasing plans for rakes, gloves, and other gardening items. One of the items she stocks is Fast-Grow, a liquid fertilizer. The sales of this item are seasonal, with peaks in the spring, summer, and fall months. Quarterly data for the last two years, expressed in cases, follow:

Quarter	1991	1992
1	30	50
2	370	420
3	290	330
4	180	210
Total	870	1010

If the expected sales for Fast-Grow are 1150 cases for 1993, prepare a forecast for each quarter of the year.

10. North American Auto rents cars to traveling salespersons and tourists at all major airports in the United States and Canada. A key to good customer service and continued customer loyalty is to have enough cars available when they are demanded. The summer months have the highest demand due to large numbers of vacationers. The numbers of cars demanded over the past two years follow.

Forecast the number of cars needed for each month of 1993, if the total number of cars demanded is estimated to be 915.

Month	1991	1992
January	25	28
February	29	33
March	35	41
April	47	55
May	75	79
June	98	104
July	120	142
August	144	153
September	60	62
October	49	54
November	41	47
December	30	36
Total	753	834

11. Demand for oil changes at Tony's Garage has been as follows.

Month	Number of Oil Changes
May	21
June	26
July	37
August	32
September	39
October	31
November	40
December	42

a. Use simple linear regression analysis to develop a forecasting model for monthly demand. In this application the dependent variable (Y) is monthly demand and the independent variable (X) is the month. For May let $X = 1$, for June let $X = 2$, and so on.

b. Use the model to forecast demand for January, February, and March. Here $X = 9$, 10, and 11, respectively.

12. The elemental standard data approach (see Chapter 7) uses linear regression to derive relationships between the normal time to perform an activity and some characteristics of the job. For example, the normal time for producing and cutting a gear is a function of the number of gear teeth. The normal times to cut an eight-inch-diameter gear for the last five jobs were:

Job Number	Cutting Time (min)	Teeth
2542	115	23
2557	84	17
2571	52	10
2593	138	28
2611	67	14

The next eight-inch gear is to have 20 teeth. How long will it take to cut the gear?

13. Ohio Swiss Milk Products manufactures and distributes ice cream in ten communities located in Ohio, Kentucky, and West Virginia. The company wants to expand operations by locating another plant in northern Ohio. An issue of current concern is the size of the new plant because it will be a function of

the expected demand for ice cream within the typical 900-square-mile area normally served by a plant. A market survey is currently underway, attempting to determine the demand for Ohio Swiss ice cream in the 900-square-mile area surrounding each of four potential sites. However, one of the major inputs to the final location decision is the manufacturing cost per gallon of ice cream (exclusive of raw materials costs), which depends on the size of the plant.

Ohio Swiss has experienced economies of scale in the production of ice cream, but the staff has never estimated the relationship between the manufacturing cost per gallon and the number of gallons produced in a year. The board of directors asked the staff to estimate this relationship so that the manufacturing cost per gallon for the new plant can be estimated when the demand has been estimated for each potential site. The following data have been collected.

Plant (i)	Cost per 1000 Gal (Y_i)	Gallons Produced (000) (X_i)
1	$ 1015	416.9
2	973	472.5
3	1046	250.0
4	1006	372.1
5	1058	238.1
6	1068	258.6
7	967	597.0
8	997	414.0
9	1044	263.2
10	1008	372.0
	$10,182	3,654.4

a. Develop a regression equation to forecast the cost per gallon as a function of the number of gallons produced.

b. Compute the correlation coefficient, the coefficient of determination, and the standard error of the estimate. Comment on your regression equation in light of these measures.

c. Suppose the market survey indicates a demand of 325,000 gallons in the Bucy-

rus, Ohio, area. Estimate the manufacturing cost per gallon for a plant
producing 325,000 gallons per year.

Advanced Problems

These problems involve considerable computations. We recommend that you use a computer to
solve them.

14. The manager of a large public library must
    schedule employees to reshelve books and
    periodicals checked out of the library. The
    number of items checked out will determine
    the labor requirements and whether addi-
    tional shelf and storage space is needed.
    Data follow for the number of items checked
    out of the library for the past three years.

Month	1990	1991	1992
January	2045	1986	1847
February	2321	2564	2669
March	2419	2635	2467
April	2088	2150	2432
May	2667	2201	2464
June	2122	2663	1378
July	2206	2055	2217
August	1869	1678	2445
September	2441	1845	1894
October	2291	2065	1922
November	2364	2147	2431
December	2189	2451	2274

    The manager needs a time series method
    for forecasting the number of items checked
    out. Find the best simple moving average
    solution you can. You must decide what is
    meant by "best" and justify your decision.

15. Using the data in Problem 14, find the best
    exponential smoothing solution you can.
    Justify your choice.

16. Using the data in Problem 14, find the best
    trend-adjusted exponential smoothing solu-
    tion you can. Compare the performance of
    this method with that of the best moving av-
    erage and the exponential smoothing meth-
    ods. Which of the three would you choose?

17. The manager of a public warehouse must
    schedule employees and plan for additional

capacity as needed to ensure proper customer service. One of the important inputs
to her plans is the forecast of inbound shipments per month. These shipments determine labor requirements and affect the need
for warehouse space. Data on the inbound
shipments for the past three years follow.

Inbound Shipments

Month	1990	1991	1992
January	2664	1882	1983
February	2365	1922	2291
March	1891	1928	2162
April	1731	1594	1969
May	2441	2020	1845
June	1478	2445	1868
July	2215	2054	2205
August	1373	2662	2122
September	2460	2200	2667
October	2088	2150	2432
November	2467	2635	2419
December	2321	2564	2669

Use time series analysis to arrive at the
best forecasting method for the data. You
must decide what is meant by "best" and
justify your decision.

18. The Midwest Typewriter Company serves a
    large number of businesses in the Great
    Lakes region. The company sells supplies
    and replacements and performs service on
    all typewriters and word processors sold
    through seven sales offices. Many items are
    stocked, and so close inventory control is
    necessary to assure customers of efficient
    service. Recently, business has been increas-
    ing and management is concerned about
    stockouts. A forecasting method to estimate
    requirements several months in advance
    is needed so that adequate replenishment
    quantities can be purchased. An example of
    the sales growth experienced over the last 50
    months is the demand for item HD-37, a
    high-density typewriter ribbon, shown in
    Table 11.7.

    a. Develop an exponential smoothing solu-
       tion for forecasting demand for this item.

TABLE 11.7

Month	HD-37 Sales	Month	HD-37 Sales
1	80	26	1296
2	132	27	1199
3	143	28	1267
4	180	29	1300
5	200	30	1370
6	168	31	1489
7	212	32	1499
8	254	33	1669
9	397	34	1716
10	385	35	1603
11	472	36	1812
12	397	37	1817
13	476	38	1798
14	699	39	1873
15	545	40	1923
16	837	41	2028
17	743	42	2049
18	722	43	2084
19	735	44	2083
20	838	45	2121
21	1057	46	2072
22	930	47	2262
23	1085	48	2371
24	1090	49	2309
25	1218	50	2422

Select the method, find the "best" parameter(s) for it, and justify your choices. Forecast demand for months 51–53.

b. A consultant to Midwest's management suggested that new office building leases would be a good leading indicator for company sales. He quoted a recent university study finding that new office building leases preceded office equipment and supply sales by three months. He supplied the data in Table 11.8.

  Based on the study findings, leases in month 1 affected sales in month 4; leases in month 2 affected sales in month 5; and so on. Use linear regression to develop a forecasting model for sales, with leases as the independent variable. Forecast sales for months 51–53.

c. Which of the two models do you feel will provide the best forecasts? Explain. Your instructor has the actual data for months 51–53 and will compare them to the forecast you supply.

19. A certain food item at Wise Owl Supermarkets has the following demand pattern.

Month	Demand	Month	Demand
1	13	13	17
2	17	14	23
3	21	15	36
4	19	16	21
5	34	17	16
6	18	18	19
7	22	19	21
8	20	20	38
9	21	21	22
10	34	22	25
11	23	23	21
12	19	24	18

  Find the "best" forecast you can for month 25, justifying the methodology you used. You may use some of the data to find the best parameter value(s) for your method, and the rest to test the forecast model. Your justification should include both quantitative and qualitative considerations.

TABLE 11.8

Month	Leases	Month	Leases
1	32	26	281
2	29	27	298
3	32	28	314
4	54	29	323
5	53	30	309
6	89	31	343
7	74	32	357
8	93	33	353
9	120	34	360
10	113	35	370
11	147	36	386
12	126	37	389
13	138	38	399
14	145	39	409
15	160	40	410
16	196	41	413
17	180	42	439
18	197	43	454
19	203	44	441
20	223	45	470
21	247	46	469
22	242	47	490
23	234	48	496
24	254	49	509
25	271	50	522

CASE   YANKEE FORK AND HOE COMPANY

The Yankee Fork and Hoe Company is a leading producer of garden tools ranging from wheelbarrows, mortar pans, and hand trucks, to shovels, rakes, and trowels. The tools are sold in four different product lines ranging from the top-of-the-line Hercules products, which are rugged tools for the toughest jobs, to the Garden Helper products, which are economy tools for the occasional user. The market for garden tools is extremely competitive because of the simple makeup of the products and the large number of competing producers. In addition, more people are using power tools, such as lawn edgers, hedge trimmers, and thatchers, reducing demand for their manual counterparts. These factors compel Yankee to maintain low prices while retaining high quality and dependable delivery.

Garden tools represent a mature industry. Unless new manual products can be developed, or there is a sudden resurgence in home gardening, the prospects for large increases in sales are not bright. It is a constant battle to keep ahead of the competition. No one knew this better than Alan Roberts, president of Yankee. He started with the company in the final assembly area 30 years ago and lived through the early years of rapid growth, which has now leveled off. The tools sold today are, by and large, the same ones sold 30 years ago, give or take a few enhancements in design. The only way to generate new sales and retain old customers is to provide superior customer service and produce a product with high customer value. This puts pressure on the manufacturing system, which Roberts thought was having difficulties lately. Recently he has been receiving calls from long-time customers, such as Sears and Tru-Value Hardware Stores, complaining about late shipments. These customers advertise promotions for garden tools and so require on-time delivery.

Roberts knew that performance had to improve quickly—losing customers like Sears and Tru-Value would be disastrous. He decided to ask consultant Sharon Place to look into the matter and report to him in one week. Roberts suggested that she focus on the bow rake as a case-in-point since it is a high-volume product and has been a major source of customer complaints of late.

Planning Bow Rake Production

A bow rake consists of a head with 12 teeth spaced one inch apart, a hardwood handle, a bow that attaches the head to the handle, and a metal ferrule that reinforces the area where the bow inserts into the handle. The bow is a metal strip that is welded to the ends of the rake head and bent in the middle to form a flat tab for insertion into the handle. The rake is about 64 inches long.

Place decided to find out how Yankee planned bow rake production. She went straight to Phil Stanton, production planner. Stanton gave this account:

Because we are in a mature business, planning is a little informal around here. To begin, marketing determines the forecast for bow rakes by month for the next year. Then they pass it along to me. Quite frankly, the forecasts are usually inflated—must be their big egos over there. I have to be careful because we enter into long-term purchasing agreements for

steel, and it is expensive to have it just sit around. So, I usually reduce the forecast by about 10 percent or so. I use the modified forecast to generate a monthly final assembly schedule, which determines what I need to have from the forging and woodworking areas. The system works well if the forecasts are good. But when marketing comes to me and says they are behind on customer orders, as they often do near the end of the year, it wreaks havoc on the schedules. Forging gets hit the hardest. For example, the presses that stamp the rake heads from blanks of steel can handle only 7000 heads per day, and the bow rolling machine can do only 5000 per day. Both of these operations are required for many other products as well. This area must be planned carefully.

Because the marketing department seemed to be providing crucial information to Stanton, Place decided to see the marketing manager, Ron Adams. Adams explained how he arrived at the bow rake forecasts:

As Phil explained, we are in a mature business. Things don't change much from year to year. Sure, sometimes we put on a sales promotion of some kind, but we try to give Phil enough warning before the demand kicks in—usually a month or so. Basically, we use the time series of bow rake shipments as a starting point for the forecast. We use "shipment" data because they are hard numbers—what we actually shipped in a given month. [See Exhibit 1.] They reflect our physical capacity to produce. I meet with several managers from the various sales regions to arrive at a forecast to give to Phil. It is essentially the

EXHIBIT 1 / Four-Year History of Bow Rake Shipments

Month	Actual Shipments			
	Year 1	Year 2	Year 3	Year 4
1	34,001	40,693	39,508	39,436
2	46,738	39,952	36,515	38,874
3	37,219	35,560	40,739	42,327
4	38,038	38,040	38,561	41,315
5	19,480	24,670	28,768	27,719
6	15,229	8,899	18,669	11,779
7	15,308	22,473	11,068	21,451
8	9,648	12,849	23,919	20,125
9	21,792	20,005	20,215	15,802
10	37,717	55,405	56,130	39,223
11	101,630	86,434	81,202	108,154
12	72,611	75,244	77,409	77,430

EXHIBIT 2 / Four-Year Demand History of the Bow Rake

Month	Actual Demands*			
	Year 1	Year 2	Year 3	Year 4
1	54,525	52,978	52,066	51,141
2	58,142	58,145	61,921	62,647
3	18,362	19,756	23,249	23,278
4	25,429	25,975	27,083	26,150
5	22,322	23,720	25,072	27,445
6	14,617	13,376	15,598	16,579
7	15,534	16,609	14,807	18,261
8	15,108	18,359	18,969	18,627
9	15,408	18,124	20,202	22,084
10	53,918	56,279	56,149	56,868
11	83,188	83,298	82,176	84,064
12	72,913	74,194	75,539	76,531

*These are the number of units promised for delivery each month.

shipping data from last year, modified for anticipated promotions, changes in the economy, and shortages we experienced last year. Even though we take a lot of time getting the forecast, it never seems to help us avoid customer problems.

The Problem

Place pondered the comments from Stanton and Adams. She understood Stanton's concern for costs and keeping inventory low and Adams's concern for having enough rakes on hand to make timely shipments. Both are also reasonably concerned about capacity.

Yet, she decided to check actual customer demands for the bow rake over the past four years before making her final report to Roberts. (See Exhibit 2.)

QUESTIONS

1. Comment on the forecasting system being used by Yankee. Suggest any changes or improvements you feel are justified.
2. Develop your own forecast for bow rakes for each month of next year (year 5). Justify your forecast and the method you used.

SELECTED REFERENCES

Adam, Everett E. "Individual Item Forecasting Model Evaluation." *Decision Sciences*, vol. 4, no. 4 (1973).

Box, George E.P., and Gwilym M. Jenkins. *Time Series Analysis: Forecasting and Control.* San Francisco: Holden-Day, 1970.

Brown R.G. *Statistical Forecasting for Inventory Control.* New York: McGraw-Hill, 1959.

Chambers, John C., Satinder K. Mullick, and Donald D. Smith. "How to Choose the Right Forecasting Technique." *Harvard Business Review* (July–August 1971), pp. 45–74.

Eilon, Samuel, and Joseph Elmaleh. "Adaptive Limits in Inventory Control." *Management Science*, vol. 16, no. 8 (April 1970), pp. B533–B548.

Flowers, A.D. "A Simulation Study of Smoothing Constant Limits for an Adaptive Forecasting System." *Journal of Operations Management*, vol. 2 (1980), pp. 84–94.

Gardner, Everette S. "The Strange Case of the Lagging Forecasts." *Interfaces*, vol. 14, no. 3 (May–June 1984), pp. 47–50.

Gardner, Everette S., and David G. Dannenbring. "Forecasting with Exponential Smoothing: Some Guidelines for Model Selection." *Decision Sciences*, vol. 11, no. 2 (April 1980), pp. 370–383.

Huang, D.S. *Regression and Econometric Methods*. New York: John Wiley & Sons, 1970.

Kimes, Sheryl E., and James A. Fitzsimmons. "Selecting Profitable Hotel Sites at La Quinta Motor Inns." *Interfaces*, vol. 20, no. 2 (March–April 1990), pp. 12–20.

Mabert, Vincent A. "Forecast Modification Based on Residual Analysis: A Case Study of Check Volume Estimation." *Decision Sciences*, vol. 9, no. 2 (April 1978), pp. 285–296.

Makridakis, Spyros, Steven C. Wheelwright, and Victor E. McGee. *Forecasting: Methods and Applications*, 2nd ed. New York: John Wiley & Sons, 1983.

Plossl, George W. "Getting the Most from Forecasts." Paper presented at the APICS 1972 International Conference and reprinted in *Forecasting*. Falls Church, Va.: American Production and Inventory Control Society, 2nd ed., 1979.

Sanders, Nada R., and Larry P. Ritzman. "The Need for Contextual and Technical Knowledge in Judgmental Forecasting." *Journal of Behavioral Decision Making*, vol. 5, no. 1 (January–March 1992), pp. 39–52.

Shiskin, Julius, Allan H. Young, and John Musgrave. "The X-11 Variant of the Census II Seasonal Adjustment Program." U.S. Bureau of the Census, Technical Paper no. 15, February 1967.

Smith, Bernard. *Focus Forecasting: Computer Techniques for Inventory Control*. Boston: CBI Publishing, 1978.

Stratton, William B. "How to Design a Viable Forecasting System." *Production and Inventory Management*, vol. 20, no. 1 (First Quarter 1979), pp. 17–27.

Trigg, D.W., and A.G. Leach. "Exponential Smoothing with an Adaptive Response Rate." *Operational Research Quarterly*, vol. 18, no. 1 (March 1967), pp. 53–59.

Whybark, D. Clay. "A Comparison of Adaptive Forecasting Techniques." *The Logistics and Transportation Review*, vol. 8, no. 3 (1972), pp. 13–26.

Wood, Steve D. "Forecasting Patient Census: Commonalities in Time Series Models." *Health Services Research*, vol. 11, no. 2 (1976), p. 158.

Chapter 12

MATERIALS MANAGEMENT

*Key Questions
from Managers*

Should we move to
a more integrated
organizational
structure?

How should we
select, evaluate, and
support suppliers?

Should we do more
centralized buying?
Should we use long-
term contracts?

Should we add
distribution centers
and position
inventory closer to
customers?

Should we place
inventory toward
end items,
purchased items, or
somewhere
between?

What are our best
options for reducing
inventory wisely?

Which items
demand our closest
attention and
control?

How can we link
materials
management to
competitive
priorities?

un Microsystems Incorporated, a computer work-station maker in Mountain View, California, enjoyed seven years of sizzling growth until 1989 when its president announced a $27 million loss for the fiscal fourth quarter. What went wrong to alter the company's outlook? Although several major problems in forecasting, production planning, and inventory control affected Sun at once, an especially troubling one was its new computerized record-keeping system for customer orders and inventory control. After considering such a move for years, Sun found soon enough that its new system didn't work. For several weeks the company lost track of orders, didn't track inventory well, and didn't get key reports. To close the books on its June quarter, Sun had to finish some of the accounting work by hand. Painful shortages occurred for some key components such as color monitors. These component shortages made it impossible for Sun to fill many orders for a new Sun-designed microprocessor called Sparc. Finally the company failed to stop hiring soon after production, order, and inventory problems caused sales to slow down. ("Internal Operations Problems," 1989)

Short-range decisions about supplies, inventories, production levels, staffing patterns, schedules, and distribution are the concern of **materials management.** Decisions in these areas affect the management of materials either directly or indirectly. We begin by examining the role of materials and inventory in the U.S. economy. We then describe materials management tasks, focusing on purchasing and distribution. We conclude by presenting several important inventory concepts and management decisions, some of which you'll need to know for subsequent chapters.

IMPORTANCE OF MATERIALS MANAGEMENT

As materials management decisions have short time horizons, they are by definition more tactical than strategic. (See Chapter 1.) However, they have a major cumulative effect and therefore attract considerable managerial attention. There are two reasons why tactical decisions about materials are considered so important: (1) the central role of materials in production and (2) the impact of inventories on company profitability.

Central Role of Materials

Managing materials is common to organizations in every segment of the economy. Materials are necessary inputs to churches, governments, manufacturers, wholesalers, retailers, and universities. Manufacturers make products from materials purchased from outside suppliers. Service industries use materials in the form of physical items (facilitating goods) purchased from suppliers—one of the three components of a service bundle (see Chapter 2). The cost of purchased materials is substantial and growing. The typical U.S. manufacturer spent 40 percent of its total income from sales on purchased materials and services in 1945. The proportion rose to 50 percent in 1960 and stands at more than 60 percent today.

Only about 15–20 percent of income from sales is now spent on labor (wages, salaries, and benefits), with the remainder contributed to net income, depreciation, taxes, and retained earnings. The proportion spent on purchased materials varies from industry to industry. At one extreme, the petroleum refining industry spends more than 80 percent of its income from sales on materials; the pharmaceutical industry is at the other extreme, at only 25 percent. There is also some variation by country. Owing to the lack of natural resources, Japanese firms must spend, on average, 7 percent more of their income from sales on materials than firms in North America and Europe. Despite such variations, one conclusion is clear: Most firms fall within the 45–65 percent range, giving materials great profit-making potential. A small percentage reduction in such a large component of the sales dollar translates into large profit gains, as Application 12.1 shows.

Application 12.1   *Profit-Making Potential of Materials*

A company's sales this year will be $100 million. Cost of materials represents 60 percent of income from sales, and 15 percent goes for salaries, wages, and benefits. A 10 percent gross profit (before taxes) is expected. Management wants to increase gross profits by $1 million next year, from $10 million to $11 million. Management is considering three options: increase sales, reduce labor costs (through increased productivity), or reduce materials costs. Which option requires the least percentage change?

Solution   The following calculations show that the company could increase sales by *10 percent* or reduce labor costs by almost *7 percent*. Reducing materials costs requires less than a *2 percent* change to achieve the same increase in profits. Since smaller percentage changes normally are easier (cost less) to achieve, materials have a high profit-making potential.

Alternative	Percent Change
1. Increase sales by $10 million (10% of which yields $1 million in gross profits).	$\left(\dfrac{\$10\text{ million}}{\$100\text{ million}}\right)(100) = \underline{\underline{10\%}}$
2. Reduce labor costs by $1 million.	$\left(\dfrac{\$1\text{ million}}{\$15\text{ million}}\right)(100) = \underline{\underline{7\%}}$
3. Reduce materials costs by $1 million.	$\left(\dfrac{\$1\text{ million}}{\$60\text{ million}}\right)(100) = \underline{\underline{2\%}}$

Impact of Inventory

Materials also are important because of the investment tied up in them. In 1990 more than $1 trillion in inventory were held in the U.S. economy. This inventory total is 2.7 times larger than the economy's monthly sales to final consumers. In effect, the economy holds 2.7 months' sales volume in inventory.

FIGURE 12.1

Where Inventories
Are Held

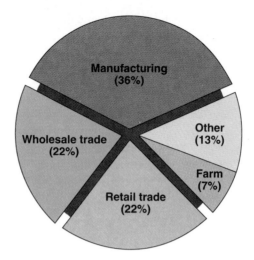

*Source: Economic Report
of the President, 1991.*

That business organizations have found ways to reduce this ratio is a tribute to the importance attached to cutting inventories. The ratio is the lowest in 50 years, with the average being 3.1 months in the 1980s and an even higher 3.6 months in the 1970s.

Consider a second ratio: Inventory investment in the U.S. economy is almost double all business investment (by both the manufacturing and service sectors) in new plants and equipment each year. Each dollar tied up in inventory is a dollar unavailable for investment in new products or services, technological improvements, or capacity increases.

Figure 12.1 shows that most inventory is held by manufacturers, wholesalers, and retailers. Because only 36 percent is held by manufacturers, materials management is of concern throughout the entire economy.

FUNCTION OF MATERIALS MANAGEMENT

Some argue that, ideally, one person in a firm should make all materials management decisions because they are so interrelated. However, the sheer magnitude of this task in most firms makes that impossible. It isn't unusual for a business unit to be responsible for thousands of employees and product items, hundreds of work centers, and several plants and to have hundreds of suppliers. Trying to develop weekly plans even three months into the future for purchasing, inventory, output rates, work-force levels, and shipping schedules would be a mind boggling job for just one person.

In practice, several departments in an organization typically specialize in certain aspects of materials management. Table 12.1 shows where manufacturing firms usually assign tasks in materials management. Many of these same tasks are performed in service industries, but "manufacturing" might be called "operations," and "production control" wouldn't even exist. Tasks such as staff planning, work-force scheduling, and operations scheduling (the equivalent of production control in service industries) are usually decentralized. For

TABLE 12.1 / *Materials Management Task Assignments*

Department	Task Assignment
Purchasing	Supplier selection Issuing purchase releases Inbound transportation
Manufacturing	Manufacturing/distribution systems development Receiving Factory stockroom operation Finished goods warehousing at the plant
Production control	Assigning delivery due dates to orders Finished goods inventory control (plant) Master production scheduling WIP inventory control Raw materials inventory control Detailed production scheduling
Distribution	Finished goods inventory control at distribution centers (DCs) Outbound transportation: DCs to customer Shipping Outbound transportation: plant to DCs
Marketing	Forecasting Processing incoming customer orders

Source: Jeffrey G. Miller, Peter Gilmour, and Roland Van Dierdonck, "Organizing for Materials Management," Working Paper HBS 80–23, Graduate School of Business Administration, Harvard University, 1980.

example, branch managers at retail stores or banks develop schedules for the activities and employees in their own units. Each task in Table 12.1 is assigned to one of five departments. For example, managers assign supplier selection most often to the purchasing department.

Since the early 1960s, there has been growing sentiment for (1) grouping most materials management tasks under one roof and (2) elevating the manager of this new group to a higher position in the company. This new department is typically called materials management, although the name *logistics management* is used sometimes. At one organizational extreme is the *segmented structure*, which is the arrangement traditionally used. Of particular concern is the placement of three departments: purchasing, production control, and distribution. In a segmented organization the manager of each of these departments reports to a different person. At the other organizational extreme is the *integrated structure*, which creates a materials management department headed by a key executive. This structure not only elevates the function but also recognizes that the various materials management tasks are all part of the same broad activity. This structure brings together all tasks related to flows of materials, beginning with the purchase of raw materials and ending with the distribution of the finished product or service.

In one survey, only 10 percent of the firms responding still used the traditional segmented structure. Another 40 percent grouped the three key departments into an integrated structure. The remaining 50 percent used hybrid structures, with only two of the three departments reporting to the same executive. The department most likely to be left out was distribution, which usually continued reporting to marketing.

PURCHASING AND DISTRIBUTION

Although subsequent chapters deal with most of the materials management tasks, they do not include a discussion of certain aspects of purchasing and distribution. Entire books have been written about each of these functions, so we provide only a brief introduction to them.

Purchasing

Purchasing is the management of the acquisition process, which includes deciding which suppliers to use, negotiating contracts, and deciding whether to buy locally or centrally. As the starting point of the materials management cycle—acquisition, storage, conversion, storage, and distribution—purchasing is of strategic importance: It must satisfy the firm's long-term supply needs and support the firm's production capabilities. This task is crucial for any organization, whether retailer, service provider, or manufacturer. After introducing the basic steps in the acquisition process, this section looks at certain decision areas that are particularly important, including supplier selection and relations, contracting, and centralized buying. In addition, purchasing managers can have valuable input into value analysis (which is technically not just a purchasing responsibility), so we conclude this section with a brief discussion of that topic.

The Acquisition Process. The usual steps in the acquisition process follow:

1. **Receive a request to place an order.** The request (called a *purchase requisition*) includes the item description, quantity and quality desired, and desired delivery date. At a manufacturing firm the purchasing department normally receives authority to buy from the production control department. Production control, in turn, is guided by the make-or-buy decisions that have been made in setting the process design (see Chapter 5). The purchasing department typically makes important inputs into these make-or-buy decisions because it is most aware of supplier capabilities and performance. At a retailing firm, on the other hand, deciding what to buy is the same as deciding what merchandise to sell; marketing and purchasing decisions are intermixed.

2. **Select a supplier.** This step involves identifying suppliers capable of providing the items, grouping items that can be supplied from the same supplier, asking for bids on the needed items, evaluating the bids in terms of multiple criteria, and selecting a supplier. In other cases, a long-term contract has already been set up for this item, so this step is not necessary.

3. **Place the order.** The ordering procedure can be complex and time consuming, as with expensive one-time purchases, or as simple as a phone call for a standard item routinely ordered from the same supplier. In some high-usage situations the supplier makes shipments daily or even on a shift-by-shift basis without being prompted by purchase orders. Some firms are linked by computer to their supplier, simplifying the ordering process even more.

4. **Track the order.** Tracking includes routine follow-up of orders, so as to anticipate late deliveries or probable deviations from requested order quantities. Suppliers are contacted by letter, telex, fax, or telephone. Follow-up is particularly important for large purchases, when a delay is disruptive to production plans or when a delay could mean loss of customer goodwill and future sales.

5. **Receive the order.** Incoming shipments must usually be checked for quantity and quality, with notices going to purchasing, the unit placing the purchase requisition, inventory control, and accounting. If the shipment is not satisfactory, purchasing must decide whether to return it to the supplier. Records on punctuality, quality, quantity deviations, and price must be updated as part of supplier evaluation. Purchasing must coordinate closely with accounting so that suppliers are paid accurately and on time.

Supplier Selection. Purchasing is the eyes and ears of the organization in the supplier marketplace, continuously seeking better buys. This process begins with the supplier selection decision. Purchasing agents for some companies establish formal rating procedures to help them select new suppliers or periodically review the performance of current suppliers. The various competitive priorities (see Chapter 2) are a starting point in developing the list of performance criteria to be used. A recent study of food service firms, for example, found on-time delivery and quality to be the top two criteria (Reid and Riegel, 1989). Three criteria considered in a selection decision almost always are price, quality, and delivery. Beginning with *price*, recall that a typical firm is now spending more than 60 percent of its total income from sales on purchased items. Thus finding suppliers who charge lower prices is a key to healthy profit margins.

As important as it is, price is not the only consideration. The *quality* of a supplier's materials can be very important. The hidden costs of poor quality can be high (see Chapter 3), particularly if defects are not detected until after considerable value has been added by subsequent manufacturing operations. The hidden costs of poor quality are not limited to manufacturers. For a retailer, poor quality can mean loss of goodwill and future sales.

The third criterion is *delivery*. Shorter lead times and on-time delivery help the buying firm maintain acceptable customer service with less inventory. For example, Maimonides Medical Center, a 700-bed hospital in Brooklyn, buys much of its materials from one supplier. The supplier offers very short lead times from a nearby warehouse, which allowed Maimonides to pare its inventory from about $1200 to only $150 per bed. The benefits of fast, on-time deliveries also apply to the manufacturing sector. Many manufacturing firms seek just-in-time (JIT) delivery from their suppliers to minimize inventory levels. (JIT systems are intended to minimize inventory buildups by coordinating the flow of materials between production processes; see Chapter 17.) This constraint means that suppliers must have nearby plants or warehouses. For example, Kasle Steel Corporation built a steel-processing plant adjacent to GM's Buick facility in Flint, Michigan, even though it already had two plants only 70 miles away. This new plant is part of a complex (called "Buick City") in which all parts are supplied to the GM facility by nearby plants. These clustered suppliers ship very small quantities frequently, to minimize the assembly plant's inventory. There is a 20-minute window during which a quantity of a particular part must be delivered; otherwise, the production line may be shut down.

Supplier Relations. A second purchasing issue of strategic importance is the type of relations maintained with suppliers. A firm can relate to a supplier either competitively or cooperatively, as we see in Managerial Practice 12.1. The competitive orientation is particularly prevalent in North America. Negotiations between buyer and seller are viewed as a zero-sum game: Whatever is lost by one side is gained by the other. Short-term advantages are prized over long-term commitments. The buyer may try to beat the supplier's price down to the lowest survival level or to push demand to high levels during boom times and order almost nothing during recessions. The supplier, on the other hand, presses for higher prices for specific levels of quality, customer service, and volume flexibility. Which party wins depends largely on who has the most *clout*. The buyer has more clout, and thus the upper hand, when

1. the buyer represents a significant share of the supplier's sales.
2. the purchased item is standardized, with substitutes offered by other suppliers.
3. the buyer could integrate backward into the supplier's business.
4. the supplier could not integrate forward into the buyer's business.
5. switching to a new supplier is not costly.

Conversely, the supplier is more powerful if these situations are reversed.

A good example of using clout to advantage when buying services is the ability of large U.S. companies to negotiate sizable travel discounts with the airlines. In 1990 they got special rates on 36 percent of their airline tickets, compared with 10 percent just the year before. The corporate-negotiated discount fares are only about 25 percent of coach fare for the average trip. Leisure travelers and small businesses don't have the clout to negotiate such deals. Another example is *managed care* in the health industry, under which large companies—usually through an insurance carrier—set up networks of doctors and hospitals. In return for the flow of patients, the companies negotiate discounts in the fees charged for their employees' health care. Southwestern Bell held the increase in its costs to only 7 percent in 1989, which was less than half the national average increase, due to the clout it gained from managed care.

Competitive Versus Cooperative Orientations

Competitive

Phar-Mor is the largest and fastest-growing deep-discount chain in the United States. Its sales surpassed $3 billion in 1991. You never know what you might find there. One day it has Crest toothpaste; another day, it doesn't. What Phar-Mor almost always has is very low prices, from 99-cent movie rentals to greeting cards marked off 50 percent. Like the no-frill warehouse clubs that emerged in the 1980s, Phar-Mor appeals to penny-pinching consumers, who may drive 30 minutes for a discounted bar of Camay soap. The privately owned company, founded nine years ago in Youngstown, Ohio, makes such bargains possible through bare-knuckle negotiating with its suppliers. "We're very aggressive in all our purchases," says David Shapira, the chief executive officer. "We push people to where they squeak." Phar-Mor's lifeline is high volumes and clout, allowing it to drive down costs by buying in bulk and clearing out discontinued products.

Cooperative

Bumper Works, a small 100-employee firm in Danville, Illinois, recently became the sole supplier of bumpers to U.S. facilities in which Toyota attaches rear bumpers and other accessories to trucks made in Japan. Toyota has helped its supplier make the bumpers better, cheaper, and faster. It flew a task force from Bumper Works to Japan for a round of meetings and tours, to better understand the Toyota manufacturing system. Then a manufacturing expert from Japan came to Danville and helped devise ways to cut the time to change dies in the metal stamping presses from more than 90 minutes to 22 minutes. Later Toyota dispatched two more consultants from Japan who helped improve the plant's layout, train employees in new jobs, monitor production rates, label bins of parts for easier identification, improve quality, and cut inventory. Slowly, the approach is paying off. Productivity is up 60 percent from a year ago; the number of defects has been reduced by 80 percent. Wasted metal cost Bumper Works $1.28 per bumper last November. Now that's down to 73 cents. Toyota, meanwhile, plans to start such cooperative efforts with its other suppliers.

Sources: "Brash Phar-Mor Chain Has Uneven Selection, But It's Always Cheap," *Wall Street Journal*, June 24, 1991; "Japanese Auto Makers Help U.S. Suppliers Become More Efficient," *Wall Street Journal*, September 9, 1991.

A Phar-Mor store interior.

The cooperative orientation to supplier relations is attracting more attention, particularly because of its success with certain Japanese firms. The buyer and seller are seen as partners, each helping the other as much as possible. A cooperative orientation means long-term commitment, joint work on quality, and support by the buyer of the managerial, technological, and capacity development of the supplier. One important variable is the number of suppliers. A cooperative orientation favors few suppliers of a particular item, with just one or two suppliers being the ideal number. One big advantage is increased volumes. The supplier gains repeatability, which helps movement toward the product-focused strategy of a high-volume, low-cost producer (see Chapter 2).

When contracts are large, the supplier might even have to build a new facility and hire a new work force. Being assured of a long-term relationship can make the difference in whether the supplier builds a new facility, particularly if it is to be located close to the buyer's plant. Fewer suppliers also can help the buyer; they become almost an extension of the buyer. (See Chapter 17.)

A cooperative orientation means more than reducing the number of suppliers: It means sharing more information on future buying intentions. This forward visibility allows suppliers to make better forecasts of future demand, making them more efficient and reliable. The buyer visits suppliers' plants, cultivates cooperative attitudes, and jealously guards the relationships. The buyer can even suggest ways to improve the supplier's operations. Trust in the supplier might mean that the buyer does not inspect incoming materials. It can also mean looser specifications on purchase orders, involving the supplier more in designing parts, implementing cost-reduction ideas, and sharing in cost savings. Reducing the number of suppliers can have its disadvantages, however, such as increased risk of an interruption in supply or reduced competitive pressures for a sole-source supplier to continue improving its performance.

Thus neither orientation is always best. What works for one organization might not work for another. The Air Force recently used a *competitive* orientation by dividing a huge jet-engine contract between General Electric and the former exclusive contract holder, Pratt & Whitney. The Air Force expects competition to save cost. In the mid-1980s GM began pursuing a *cooperative* orientation by paring the number of major suppliers (4000 in 1984, versus only 300 at Toyota), leaving only the most efficient ones. Suppliers who meet GM's tougher requirements will get long-term contracts. This benefit gives suppliers enough volume to recoup investments in cost-saving equipment and new capacity. GM's purchasing strategy also has a competitive element. It is demanding 7 percent price reductions from its suppliers over the next three years and hinting that it could build the parts in-house rather than buy from the suppliers if the rollbacks aren't granted.

Contracting. Purchasing must decide how to contract for each of the thousands of items that most firms buy. The procedure selected depends a great deal on volume and usage rates. When demand is low, as with customized items not held in inventory, a buyer has three options: competitive bidding, sole-source contracting, and supplier catalogues.

Competitive bidding means that several suppliers are asked to submit formal quotations. The lowest *and* best (most capable) bidder receives the contract. This method is not mandatory in the private sector but is prudent when the expenditure to be made is great, as with heavy equipment or a computer system. If the dollar value of the purchase is low or time is of the essence, sole-source contracting or supplier catalogues may be best. With sole-source contracting, a company negotiates a contract with a single supplier. This approach reduces purchasing lead time but doesn't guarantee the best buy, particularly if the buyer is unaware of comparative prices. Using supplier catalogues, the buyer simply looks through several and makes a selection. The cost of any further search outweighs the benefits.

Contracting procedures can be quite different with high demand, as with standardized items for which demand is continuous. There are two options: preselected suppliers and long-term contracts. With the first option, competitive bidding is not used for each order placed. When requisitions are received from production control, purchasing immediately sends to the preselected supplier a purchase order specifying the product, quantity, and delivery due date. In this way, delays caused by supplier selection procedures are avoided.

If demands are high enough, the second option may be used. Actually, a long-term contract is a special case of using preselected suppliers. Long-term contracts covering one or more years are negotiated, with delivery dates, quantities, and often prices left open. The buying firm commits to a supplier for the agreed-on period of time and sends it periodic estimates of future needs. When a new order is placed, purchasing does not need to write a purchase order. Most long-term contracts are either *blanket* or *open-ended* contracts. A blanket contract covers a variety of items, whereas an open-ended contract allows items to be added or the contract period extended. Long-term contracts save paperwork and reserve supplier capacity. As annual volumes are large, price concessions are possible. Suppliers prefer long-term contracts because they make future demand more certain. Long-term contracts are consistent with the cooperative orientation to supplier relations.

Centralized Buying. When an organization has several facilities (such as stores, hospitals, or plants), management must decide whether to buy locally or centrally. In deciding the best strategy for a particular item, management must weigh the advantages and disadvantages of each.

Centralized buying can increase purchasing clout. Savings can be significant, often on the order of 10 percent or more. Increased buying power can mean getting better service, ensuring long-term supply availability, or developing new supplier capability. The globalization of production and purchasing favors more centralization, making specialized knowledge and skills desirable when buying from foreign sources. A firm's product often is made of parts from all over the globe. Many future buyers will need to be conversant in at least two languages, possibly more. They also will need to understand international commercial and contract law regarding the transfer of goods and services. Working with customs and other government agencies will become a way of life for many. Another trend that favors centralization is the growth of computer-based information systems, which gives specialists at headquarters access to data previously available only at the local level.

Despite these advantages, centralized buying for all items would be a mistake. Items unique to a particular facility should be purchased locally whenever possible. The same holds for purchases that must be closely meshed with production schedules, as with just-in-time systems (see Chapter 17). Centralized purchasing often means longer lead times, involving another level in the firm's hierarchy. Probably the biggest disadvantage of centralized buying is loss of control at the local level. Plants or divisions may be evaluated as profit or cost centers, even though they may not control a major cost item. Such divisions of authority can dampen the essential entrepreneurial spirit at the local level. Perhaps the best solution is a compromise strategy, whereby local autonomy and centralized buying are both possible. For example, the corporate purchasing group at IBM negotiates contracts on a centralized basis only at the request of local plants. Then management at one of the facilities monitors the contract for all the participants.

Value Analysis. **Value analysis** is a systematic effort to reduce the cost or improve the performance of items either purchased or produced. It concentrates on the *function* of the item and asks questions such as, What is the function of the item? Is the function necessary? Can a lower-cost standard part that serves the purpose be identified? Can the item be simplified, or its specifications relaxed, to achieve a lower price? Value analysis should be performed periodically on the large dollar-volume items, for which potential savings are greatest. It is usually done on a team basis, involving purchasing, production, and engineering. Each type of specialist brings different perspectives to the analysis.

Distribution

While purchasing deals with inbound materials, distribution deals with outbound flows. **Distribution** is the management of the flow of materials from manufacturers to customers, involving the storage and transportation of products. Distribution broadens the marketplace for a firm, adding time and place value to its products. Here we briefly consider three issues distribution managers face: where to stock finished goods; what transportation mode to use; and scheduling, routing, and carrier selection.

Placement of Finished Goods Inventory. A fundamental choice is where to stock inventory of finished goods. Forward placement means locating stock closer to customers at a warehouse (now usually called a *distribution center*, or DC) or with a wholesaler or retailer. Backward placement means holding the inventory at the manufacturing plant or maintaining no inventory. Forward placement can have two advantages: fast delivery times and reduced transportation costs. Dubbed the "warm puppy effect," proximity to a stocking point can give customers a comfortable feeling which, in turn, can stimulate sales. Finding the best way to position inventory is particularly important for international operations, as Managerial Practice 12.2 shows. Firms from around the world are trying to position themselves to capitalize on the new trading structures made possible by the European Community (EC) accords as well as the newly opened East European markets. Firms are working hard to open up DCs in strategic cities to support their sales activities.

Forward placement might also help avoid the premium rates of less-than-carload (LCL) shipments. Shipments out of the plant can be concentrated on a few routes (to the DCs), rather than fragmented for scattered customer locations. Even outbound shipments from DCs to customer destinations can frequently be large enough to achieve full carload (CL) rates, particularly if several plants are providing a variety of products to the DCs. For example,

Managerial Practice 12.2

International Distribution Systems

IKEA is a Scandinavian retailer that claims to be the world's largest-volume furniture chain, selling $3.8 billion per year of ready-to-assemble furniture and housewares in 100 stores worldwide. Its sales per square foot are about $350—three times the average for traditional furniture stores. But the company has not exactly taken America by storm. In the first seven years since IKEA—pronounced "eye-key-ah"—opened its first mammoth U.S. store, near Philadelphia, it has followed suit in just six other cities: Elizabeth, New Jersey; Burbank, California; Hicksville, New York; Washington; Baltimore; and Pittsburgh. But its U.S. sales increased by 68 percent in 1991, from $169 million to $284 million. The slow pace has nothing to do with its concept, merchandise, or innovative store layouts, which are praised even by rivals.

"Our problem," says Anders Moberg, president of the Humlebaek (Denmark)-based retailer, "is with distribution—finding warehouses and setting up a network."

IKEA has tackled the issue by building huge distribution centers in Philadelphia and Montreal, to serve eastern stores, and, more recently, near Los Angeles to prepare for West Coast expansion. It opened two new stores in Los Angeles, in 1992, and acquired three new store locations through merger. From then on, IKEA expects to add two or three stores a year. "Forty percent of our investment in the next three to five years will be in the U.S.," says Moberg.

Source: "Why Competitors Shop for Ideas at IKEA," *Business Week*, October 9, 1989.

General Foods mixes products received from various plants at its distribution centers and reships them to customers at full CL rates.

Forward placement is not always possible or advisable. If competitive priorities call for customized products, it doesn't make sense to have finished goods inventory. The risk of creating unwanted products is too great. A second argument against forward placement is the *pooling effect*. The demand in a region may be unpredictably high one month and low the next. If demand in several such regions were pooled, as would be the case if inventories were placed in a central warehouse, the highs in some regions would tend to cancel the lows in others. Demand is less erratic and more predictable when inventory is centralized rather than regionalized. Inventories for the whole system can be lower, and costly reshipments from one DC to another can be minimized.

Ethan Allan provides a good example of the pooling effect. Originally, each of the 40 retailers of Ethan Allen products in the New York metropolitan area maintained its own inventory. The aggregate inventory value averaged $3 million, and customer service was poor. The probability that all items in a customer's order were on hand was only 0.25. Ethan Allen solved this dilemma by creating one large field warehouse to serve all 40 retailers. The retailers no longer need to carry separate inventories, except for display purposes. Inventory dropped to $700,000, and the probability of filling a customer's order from DC inventory increased to 0.80.

Selection of Transportation Mode. The five basic modes of transportation are highway, rail, water, pipeline, and air. Each has its own advantages and limitations.

Highway transportation provides the flexibility of shipping to almost any location in the United States. No rehandling is needed for pickup and delivery.

Transit times are good, and rates are usually less than rail rates for small quantities and short hauls. Truckers haul 40 percent of U.S. freight, whereas railroads move 30 percent (down from 50 percent in 1947). Rail transportation can move large quantities very cheaply, but transit times are long and variable. This mode is usually best for shipping raw materials, rather than finished goods. Rail shipments often require pickup and delivery rehandling. Water transportation provides high capacity at low unit cost, but transit times are slow and large areas are inaccessible to waterborne carriers. Pipeline transportation is highly specialized, with limited geographical flexibility. It is limited to liquids, gases, or solids in slurry form. No packaging is needed, and operating costs per mile are low. While most pipelines move petroleum, some companies use them to transport fish and coal. Air transportation is the fastest and most expensive mode. Although volumes are increasing geometrically, they still represent only 1 percent of all freight moved. Air transportation is limited by the availability of airport facilities and requires pickup and delivery rehandling.

In addition to these primary modes, special service modes and hybrids, such as parcel post, air express, bus service, freight forwarder, and piggyback, are available. Different forms of ownership and management are possible. A firm can integrate forward and become a *private carrier*, owning and operating its own fleet. It can instead leave the transportation to a *contract carrier*, negotiating with the carrier for a specified amount, type, and frequency of shipment. A contract carrier does not provide service to the general public, instead serving specific customers. Or the firm can select a *common carrier*, which by law must serve all customers without discrimination. This option gives the firm the least control over carrier availability but makes sense for low-volume producers with geographically dispersed markets.

Scheduling, Routing, and Carrier Selection. Several activities are involved in the day-to-day control of freight movement. The shipping schedule must mesh with purchasing and production control schedules. It also reflects the trade-off between transportation costs and customer response times. By delaying a shipment for another two days, it may be possible to achieve full carload (CL) rates for a rail shipment or full truckload (TL) rates for truck shipments. Routing choices must also be made. A central post office, operating its own fleet to collect mail from outlying areas, must determine the route to each pickup point. A manufacturer can select a routing that combines shipments to multiple customers and gains lower freight rates. The firm may even negotiate lower rates if it develops routings where large volumes can be shipped on a regular basis. These choices are complex. Even before deregulation, the U.S. freight rate structure seemed chaotic to the uninitiated. Now rates and services vary markedly, depending on the specific mode and carrier chosen.

INVENTORY CONCEPTS

Clearly, materials management exerts great influence on company success, requiring coordination among several decision areas and departments. An essential part of materials management is inventory control. **Inventory** is a stock of materials held to satisfy some eventual demand. Inventory is created when the rate of receipts exceeds the rate of disbursements. It is depleted when disbursements exceed receipts.

In this section we focus on basic terminology and fundamentals needed to understand inventory: accounting categories, bills of materials, types of demand, inventory costs, and types of inventory. These concepts are basic to the management of inventory.

Accounting Categories

Inventory for a manufacturing plant exists in three forms, or accounting categories: raw materials, work-in-process, and finished goods. As shown in Fig. 12.2, inventory can be held in various forms and locations, or stocking points. In the system shown in Fig. 12.2, raw materials are kept at two stocking points: the supplier's facility and the plant. The raw materials at the plant pass through one or more processes, which transform them into various levels of work-in-process (WIP) inventory. When this inventory is processed at the final operation, it becomes finished goods inventory. Finished goods can be held at the plant, a DC, and retail locations. Material flow systems can be more or less complex than that shown. A small retailer must manage only store inventories, a relatively simple system. A large retailer, such as Kroger, often integrates backward to include distribution centers and even manufacturing plants, which creates a more complex system. A process-focused manufacturer usually ships directly to the customer, creating a simple system with no intervening DCs or retail stocking points. A product-focused manufacturer may integrate backward to the point where it has its own feeder plants, which in turn supply its assembly plants. A multiplant operation is particularly challenging because inventories must be coordinated at more stocking points.

Bill of Materials

Manufacturing operations abound with inventory terms: parent, component, bill of materials, usage quantity, end item, intermediate item, subassembly,

FIGURE 12.2

Inventory at
Successive Stocking
Points

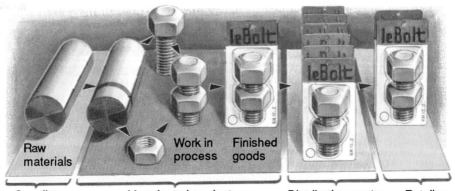

(a)

(b)

Raw materials and work-in-process inventory at Anheuser-Busch: Workers add a container of blended hops—the raw materials—to the wort. The WIP inventory is the mixture being brewed in the huge kettles, which have a capacity of approximately 650 barrels of beer (a). Finished goods inventory comes off Anheuser-Busch's bottling line, which operates 24 hours a day, 365 days a week (b).

purchased item, routing, and part commonality. One frequent distinction made in manufacturing is whether an item is a parent or a component. A **parent** is an item manufactured from one or more component items. The chair in which you are sitting is a parent, made from legs, arms, a seat, and fasteners. A **component** is an item, possibly one of several, that goes through one or more operations to be transformed into a parent.

A **bill of materials (BOM)** is a diagram or record of all the components of an item, the parent–component relationships, and usage quantities. The BOM in Fig. 12.3 shows that item A is made from items B and C. Item B, in turn, is made from D and E, and E is made from F. Items A, B, and E are parents because they are made from other items by passing them through one or more operations. All items except A are also components because they are needed to make a parent. The BOM also provides another type of information. A **usage quantity** is the number of units of a component needed to make one unit of its immediate parent. Figure 12.3 shows usage quantities in parentheses, one for each parent–component relationship. Note that one unit of A is made from two units of B and one unit of C. All other usage quantities are one unit, except for the three units of F needed to make one unit of E.

A BOM introduces another useful set of terms: end items, intermediate items, subassemblies, and purchased items. An **end item** is typically the final product sold to the customer; it is a parent but not a component. Item A in Fig.

FIGURE 12.3

A Bill of Materials
for Item A

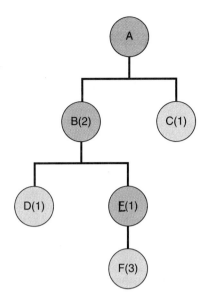

12.3 qualifies as an end item. Inventory for end items is classified in accounting statements as either work-in-process (WIP) or finished goods. If work remains to be done on the end item, it is WIP. An **intermediate item** is one that has at least one parent and at least one component. Both items B and E in Fig. 12.3 qualify as intermediate items. Some products have several levels of intermediate items, where the parent of one intermediate item is also an intermediate item. Inventory of intermediate items—whether completed or still on the shop floor—is classified as WIP. A **subassembly** is a special case of an intermediate item: It is *assembled* (as opposed to other types of transformation) from *more* than one component. A **purchased item** is one that has no components because it comes from a supplier, but it has one or more parents. Examples are items C, D, and F in Fig. 12.3. Inventory of purchased items is treated as raw materials in accounting statements.

Another concept related to the notion of parents and components is part commonality, sometimes called *standardization of parts*. **Part commonality** is the degree to which a part (component) has more than one parent. A giant step toward part commonality took place in the early 1800s, when Eli Whitney introduced interchangeable parts for manufacturing firearms. Working toward more standardized parts continues to this day, as Managerial Practice 12.3 shows. Part commonality increases repeatability—which has several advantages for process design (see Chapters 5 and 6)—and helps minimize inventory. Today, almost 90 percent of manufacturing firms have at least some part commonality, with 44 percent reporting that it is extensive (Sharma, 1987).

A companion document to the BOM is a routing. Taken together, they communicate the process design choices that have been made, telling how a particular item is to be manufactured. A **routing** lists the sequence of operations to be performed on an item, the standard times, and the operations at which each

Managerial Practice 12.3

Part Commonality in the Automobile Industry

At Ford

Ford Motor Company geared up a manufacturing plant in Romeo, Michigan, to build a family of new, innovative modular engines. The company's billion-dollar gamble bucks the tradition of outfitting individual factories to build a single engine type. Ford is designing V-8 and V-6 engines around a basic building block—in this case, a combustion chamber designed for maximum fuel economy. The factory is equipped with enough flexible automation (see Chapter 6) to build several different models—everything from cast-iron workhorses to high-performance aluminum thoroughbreds. Just as important, part commonality has increased. Although manufacturing engineers traditionally have little say over engine design itself, Ford made them an integral part of the process this time. They helped reduce the number of different parts by 25 percent overall. Most parts, such as pistons, will be used in more than one engine design.

The modular engine family will have about 350 parts in common.

At GM

GM has a campaign to cut costs through simplification. Its plans include reducing the number of different car batteries from 12 to 5, cutting the number of ignitions from 17 to 3, and using three air-conditioner compressors instead of five. Some of the results are striking. Designers cut the number of parts in a pickup by 46 percent. Engineers reduced the number of parts in the bumper of the restyled 1991 Buick Park Avenue to 44, from 108 in the 1990 model. That cut the time needed to assemble the bumper from ten minutes to five. The higher production volumes for the typical part also reduce per-unit fabrication costs.

Sources: "A Dozen Motor Factories—Under One Roof," *Business Week,* November 20, 1989; "Crisis Is Galvanizing Detroit's Big Three," *Wall Street Journal,* May 2, 1991.

component is needed. Each manufactured item has a routing. Figure 12.4 shows the BOM and routing for an item made from three purchased items. Ten operations are performed in making item G from three components (C, D, and K).

Types of Demand

Another important inventory concept is the type of demand, which can be either independent or dependent. **Independent demand** for an item is influenced by market conditions and is not related to production decisions for any other item held in stock. In manufacturing only end items have exclusively independent demand. Components at the WIP level can experience independent demand only when customers ask for spare-part replacements. In the service industry, such as selling merchandise at a single site, parent–component relationships do not exist. There are no parents, and the merchandise experiences only independent demand. Independent-demand systems are covered in detail in Chapter 13.

Dependent demand for an item derives from the production decisions for its parents. Suppose that the arm for a stereo turntable, component B, has only one parent, turntable model A, and that the usage quantity is one. If operations plans to release a production order of 100 model A turntables three weeks from now, the operations manager can expect the demand for B to be zero during the next two weeks but 100 units by the end of the third week. By contrast,

FIGURE 12.4

Item G: (a) Routing;
(b) Bill of Materials

Operation		Standard times (hours)		
Sequence no.	Description	Processing	Setup	Component
1	Shear	0.10	0.40	Raw material C
2	Blank	0.08	0.50	
3	First inspection	0.06	–	
4	Saw	0.33	1.40	Raw material D
5	Heat treat	–	10.00	
6	Subassemble C and D	1.30	–	
7	Sand blast	0.28	0.25	
8	Clean	0.16	–	
9	Impregnate with K	0.45	0.10	Raw material K
10	Final inspection	0.10	–	

(a)

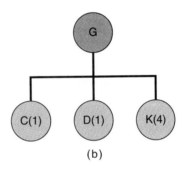

(b)

the operations manager can only *forecast* independent demand. Entirely different production and inventory control systems will be utilized, depending on whether demand is dependent (being derived) or independent (being forecast). Chapters 16 and 17 cover dependent-demand systems.

Inventory Costs

Table 12.2 lists the conflicting costs and pressures that argue for both low and high inventories. A manager must assess each one before reaching any conclusions about appropriate inventory levels. Let's examine each of these costs, beginning with holding costs.

TABLE 12.2 / Conflicting Pressures on Inventory Levels

Pressures for Small Inventories	Pressures for Large Inventories
Interest or opportunity cost	Customer service
Storage and handling cost	Ordering or setup cost
Property taxes	Labor and facility utilization
Insurance premiums	Transportation cost
Shrinkage costs: pilferage, obsolescence, and deterioration	Cost of purchased items

Holding (Carrying) Cost. The primary reason for keeping inventories low is that inventory represents money invested temporarily in goods for which a firm must pay (rather than receive) interest on the investment. **Inventory holding (or carrying) cost** is the cost of keeping items on hand, including interest, storage and handling, taxes, insurance, and shrinkage. Companies usually state an item's holding cost per period of time as a percentage of its value. The annual cost to maintain one unit in inventory during the year typically ranges from 20 to 40 percent of its value. Suppose that a firm's holding costs are 30 percent. If the inventory level averages 20 percent of sales, the cost to hold inventory is 6 percent [0.30(0.20)] of total sales. This cost is sizable in terms of gross profit margins, which often are less than 10 percent.

The left-hand column of Table 12.2 shows the components of holding cost. Interest or opportunity cost, whichever is greater, usually is the largest component. To finance inventory, a company may obtain a loan or forgo the opportunity of an investment promising an attractive return. These factors alone can peg holding cost as high as 15 percent.

Then there are storage and handling costs. Inventory takes up space and must be moved into and out of storage. Several years ago, managers at Ford Motor Company were amazed at the small size of certain Japanese plants. Toyota's Kamego engine plant occupies only 300,000 square feet but achieves the same output rate as the 900,000-square-foot plant Ford built in Europe. The essential difference is that Toyota found ways to get by with much less inventory (see JIT in Chapter 17).

Determining how much to increase holding costs to account for storage and materials handling is not a clear-cut procedure. Managers are tempted to calculate an *allocated cost* for space and materials handling, but that would overstate their costs. In the short run, in fact, a manager might be able to increase inventory well beyond its current level without incurring any new *out-of-pocket* costs for either storage space or materials handling. To arrive at a true cost, the manager should follow one guiding principle: *Include only those costs that actually change because of the decision being made.* If the decision is to store short-term inventories in public warehouses, where the charge is based on the amount of space used, the storage cost is relevant. If the decision is to store short-term inventories in the firm's facilities, however, there is no real storage cost when space is abundant and has no other short-term value.

The final components of holding cost are taxes, insurance, and shrinkage (pilferage, obsolescence, and deterioration). Taxes and insurance are self-explanatory, but the three forms of shrinkage need further explanation. Pilferage is theft of inventory by customers or employees. Managerial Practice 12.4 shows that it is a significant percentage of sales for some businesses. Obsolescence occurs when inventory cannot be used or sold at full value, owing to model changes, engineering modifications, or unexpectedly low demand. Deterioration through physical spoilage or damage results in lost value. Food and beverages, for example, lose value and might even have to be discarded when their shelf life is reached. When the rate of deterioration is high, building up large inventories may be unwise.

If these components of holding cost were the only measures affecting inven-

Managerial Practice 12.4

Inventory and Ethics

U.S. retailers continue to lose the war against shoplifting, which is the fastest-growing larceny and now amounts to a $9 billion-a-year problem. Professional thieves these days thwart antitheft tags by stuffing merchandise into bags lined with aluminum foil. Or they smuggle untagged goods out in oversized girdles. Closed-circuit TV cameras don't stop them either. Even hiding store security guards in portable pillars with two-way mirrors, called Trojan horses, hasn't prevented shoplifting from escalating.

To turn the tide, several of Chicago's biggest retailers went to unusual lengths to corral shoplifting pros. For two years they bankrolled a suburban thrift shop as a front. Five sheriff's deputies played store clerks to legitimate customers in the front of the J&O Clothing store while acting as "fences" for stolen apparel in the back office. The undercover cops paid top dollar for Perry Ellis suits, Liz Claiborne dresses, and other designer clothes snitched from the stores by professional shoplifters. And they videotaped the illicit deals with a hidden camera. The sting brought indictments against 36 people and is expected to be tried elsewhere in the country.

Source: "Chicago Retailers' 'Sting' Aims to Put Shopping Professionals Out of Business," *Wall Street Journal*, June 5, 1990.

tory choices, holding inventory would not be rational. The fact that inventory held in the U.S. economy exceeds the $1 trillion mark suggests that other performance measures are also important. The pressures for large inventories listed in the right-hand side of Table 12.2 indicate why inventory exists despite its expense. Let's look briefly at each, beginning with customer service.

Customer Service. Creating inventory can speed up delivery and improve on-time delivery. Inventory reduces the cost of stockouts or back orders, which are key concerns for wholesalers and retailers. A **stockout** is not having a standard item on hand to satisfy demand for the item the moment it occurs, resulting in loss of the sale. A **back order** is not having a customer order ready when promised or demanded but filling the order later. Customers are willing to wait but are not happy about it. Inventory also increases the percentage of on-time deliveries, a key measure for manufacturers. Translating such measures into a dollar cost, as for stockout or back-order costs, can be difficult if not impossible. However, this inability does not diminish the importance of customer service, and managers must carefully watch all aspects of it.

Ordering Cost. Placing a new order involves a cost. **Ordering cost** is the cost of preparing a purchase order for a supplier or a production order for the shop. For the same item, the cost is the same, regardless of the order size. For a purchased item, someone has to take the time to decide how much to order, select a supplier, and negotiate terms. Time is also spent on paperwork, follow-up, and receiving. Most of the same activities are involved in placing a production order for a manufactured item, but the type of paperwork changes. In this case, a blueprint and routing must often accompany the shop order.

Independent of order size

Setup Cost. **Setup** (or changeover) **cost** is the cost involved in changing over a machine to produce a different component or item. This cost also is independent of order size. Labor and equipment time is lost. Different tooling or fixtures might be needed, and the machine might have to be cleaned. Scrap or rework can be substantially higher at the start of the run, making scrap a function of setup frequency.

Labor and Equipment Utilization. Management can increase work-force productivity and facility utilization in three ways by creating more inventory. First, setup time, which is unproductive because it does not add value to a product, can be reduced by placing larger, less frequent production orders. Although inventories increase, downtime for setups decreases. Second, component stockouts, which decrease productivity because parent orders must be rescheduled, can be coped with in many ways, but each action has a cost. The third way that inventories can improve resource utilization is in helping stabilize a manufacturer's output rate, even when demand is cyclical or seasonal. Inventory built during slack periods can handle extra demand in peak seasons. Varying the work force through extra shifts, hiring, layoffs, and overtime can be minimized. Equipment capacities can also be less, since capacity does not need to match peak demand.

Transportation Cost. Sometimes, outbound transportation cost can be reduced by increasing inventory levels. Large inventory allows more time to help ensure carload shipments and minimizes the need for expedited shipments by more expensive modes of transportation. As we have already noted, forward placement of inventory can reduce outbound transportation cost, even though the pooling effect is lessened and more inventory is necessary. Inbound transportation cost may also be reduced by creating more inventory. Sometimes, several items are ordered from the same supplier. Combining these orders and placing them at the same time may lead to CL rather than LCL rates.

Cost of Purchased Items. A firm can often reduce total payments to suppliers if it can tolerate higher inventory levels. Suppose that a firm learns that a key supplier is about to increase prices. It might be cheaper for the firm to order a larger quantity than usual—in effect delaying the price increase—even though inventory will increase temporarily. Similarly, a firm can take advantage of quantity discounts. A **quantity discount**, whereby the price per unit drops when the order is sufficiently large, is an incentive to order larger quantities.

Types of Inventory

Inventory can be viewed as a necessary evil. Although it costs money to hold, inventory helps maintain customer service, improves resource utilization, and reduces ordering, setup, transportation, and purchased materials costs. Another perspective on inventory is to classify it by purpose. In this context, there are four types of inventory: cycle, safety, anticipation, and pipeline.

Cycle Inventory. One purpose of inventory is a longer ordering cycle, saving in several cost categories on the right-hand side of Table 12.2. Determining how frequently to order, and in what quantity, is called **lot sizing.** Two principles apply:

1. The lot size (Q) varies in direct proportion to the elapsed time (or cycle) between orders. If a lot is ordered every five weeks, the average lot size must equal five weeks' demand. Large lot cycles go with infrequent orders.
2. The longer the time between orders, the greater the cycle inventory. **Cycle inventory** is the portion of total inventory that varies directly with lot size. More specifically,

$$\text{Cycle inventory} = \frac{Q^*}{2}$$

We divide Q by 2 to get the average cycle inventory. At the beginning of the interval the cycle inventory is at its maximum, or Q. At the end of the interval, just before a new lot arrives, cycle inventory drops to its minimum, or 0. Assuming that the demand is constant, the average cycle inventory is the average of these two extremes, found by dividing Q by 2 [$(Q + 0)/2 = Q/2$].

Application 12.2	*Calculating Cycle Inventory*
	The lot size of an item is 100 units, and the ordering frequency averages two months. What is the item's annual demand and cycle inventory?
Solution	The first principle tells us that 100 units is a 2-month supply, so a 12-month supply must be six times as large, or 600 units. The second principle and formula tell us that the average cycle inventory is 50 (100/2).

Now consider the advantages of large cycle inventory: better customer service, less frequent orders and setups, and reduced transportation and purchasing costs. Increasing Q (and therefore cycle inventory) normally improves customer service because (1) the possibility of a stockout exists only at the end of a cycle, and (2) there are fewer cycles per year when Q is larger.† Thus a higher Q means fewer risks of stockout. Following similar reasoning, increasing Q also reduces the annual cost of orders and setups, since fewer are made per year. Larger lot sizes also might make CL rates or quantity discount prices possible, thereby decreasing the costs of transportation and raw materials.

Safety Stock Inventory. Another purpose of inventory is to avoid customer service problems and the hidden costs of unavailable components. **Safety stock**

---

*This formula is exact only when the demand rate is constant and uniform. Our research shows that the formula provides a reasonably good estimate for dependent demand, where demand rates are not constant. Factors other than the demand rate, such as scrap losses, can also cause estimating errors when this simple formula is used.

†We found exceptions to this relationship between Q and customer service in manufacturing. Larger lot sizes can create more feast-or-famine capacity requirements, which hurt a manufacturer's ability to ship on time. In such cases, larger lot sizes hurt on-time delivery performance.

inventory is inventory used to protect against uncertainties in demand, lead time, and supply. An unreliable supplier who deviates frequently from the requested lot size or promised delivery time makes maintaining safety stock desirable. Moreover, if a manufactured item is subject to significant and frequent amounts of scrap or rework, safety stock is needed.

There is a simple way to create safety stock: Place an order for delivery earlier than when the item is typically needed.* The replenishment order therefore arrives ahead of time, giving a cushion against uncertainty. For example, suppose that the average lead time from a supplier is three weeks, but a firm orders five weeks in advance just to be safe. This policy creates a safety stock equal to two (5 − 3) weeks of supply.

Anticipation Inventory. **Anticipation inventory** is inventory used to absorb uneven rates of demand or supply, which business often faces. Manufacturers of air conditioners, for example, can experience 90 percent of their annual demand during just three months of a year. Such uneven demand may lead a manufacturer to stockpile inventory during periods of low demand, so that output levels do not have to be increased much when demand rates peak. Smoothing output rates with inventory can increase productivity because varying output rates and work-force size can be costly. Anticipation inventory also can help when supply, rather than demand, is uneven. A company may stock up on a certain purchased item if its suppliers are threatened with a strike or severe capacity limitations.

Pipeline (Transit) Inventory. **Pipeline inventory** is inventory in transit, that is, moving from point to point in the materials flow system. Materials move from suppliers to the plant, from one operation to the next in the plant, from a plant to a DC or customer, and from a DC to a retailer. Because this movement takes time, pipeline inventory is necessary. Pipeline inventory is the sum of all **scheduled receipts** (sometimes called **open orders**), or orders that have been placed but not yet received. Pipeline inventory exists in three stages: inbound, within the plant, and outbound. The inbound stage includes scheduled receipts of raw materials that have been paid for (a firm does not incur holding costs until it owns the inventory) but are not yet available for use. Within the plant the pipeline includes all scheduled receipts for production orders sent to the shop. Thus pipeline inventory in the plant represents WIP inventory. In a system of plants, much of the pipeline inventory may be traveling between plants. Inventory in the outbound stage consists of finished goods that have been shipped but not yet paid for by the customer.

Pipeline inventory between two points can be measured as the average *demand during lead time*:

$$\text{Pipeline inventory} = \bar{D}_L = dL$$

---

*When orders are placed at fixed intervals, there is a second way: Place an order for more than is typically needed through the next delivery date. (See Chapter 13.)

where d = average demand for the item per period
     L = the number of periods in the item's lead time to move
        between two points; either for transportation or production
     $\bar{D}_L$ = average demand during the lead time

Note that the lot size does not directly affect the average level of the pipeline inventory.* Increasing Q does inflate the size of a scheduled receipt, but this increase is canceled by a proportionate decrease in the number of orders placed per year.

Application 12.3	*Estimating Inventory Levels*

A plant makes monthly shipments to a wholesaler of a particular item in average lot sizes of 280 units. The average demand experienced by the wholesaler is 70 units per week, and the lead time from the plant is 3 weeks. On average, how much cycle inventory and pipeline inventory does the wholesaler carry?

Solution

$$\text{Cycle inventory} = \frac{Q}{2} = \frac{280}{2} = 140 \text{ units}$$

$$\text{Pipeline inventory} = \bar{D}_L = dL = (70 \text{ units/week})(3 \text{ weeks}) = 210 \text{ units}$$

The wholesaler's cycle inventory is 140 units, whereas the pipeline inventory, or inventory in transit, is 210 units.

INVENTORY MANAGEMENT

We conclude with some decisions that managers make to control inventories: inventory measures, inventory placement, inventory reduction, ABC analysis, and links to operations strategy. These management issues are relevant for each of the next five chapters that deal with some phase of inventory management, either directly or indirectly.

Inventory Measures

Management begins with measurement. For this reason, managers closely monitor measures of inventories to keep them at acceptable levels. Inventories are reported to them in three basic ways: average aggregate inventory value, weeks of supply, and inventory turnover.

All methods of measuring inventory begin with a physical count of units, volume, or weight. However, one unit of item A may be worth only pennies, whereas one unit of item B may be valued in the thousands of dollars. The **average aggregate inventory value** is the total value of all items held in inventory. It is an "average" because it usually represents the inventory investment over some time interval longer than just a moment in time. This measure is found by multiplying the number of units of each item typically on hand by

---

*There can be an indirect effect, however. If the lead time gets longer with larger lot sizes, then $\bar{D}_L$ (and therefore pipeline inventory) will increase.

its per unit value to obtain the inventory value of each item and then adding the values of all the items. This total value tells managers how much of a firm's assets are tied up in inventory. Manufacturing firms typically have about 25 percent of their total assets in inventory, whereas wholesalers and retailers average about 75 percent.

To some extent, managers can decide whether the aggregate inventory value is too low or too high by historical or industry comparison or by managerial judgment. However, they cannot do so realistically without taking demand into account. Managers can include demand rates by using the measures weeks of supply and inventory turnover. **Weeks of supply** is an inventory measure found by dividing the average aggregate inventory value by the sales per week at cost. (In some low-inventory operations, days or even hours are a better unit of time for measuring inventory.) Although the numerator includes the value of all items (raw materials, WIP, and finished goods), the denominator represents only the finished goods sold—and at the cost to make them rather than the sale price after markups. This cost is referred to as the "cost of goods sold." One reason for expressing value at cost is that inventory measures can also be expressed for individual items, and final sales dollars have meaning only for end items—not intermediate or purchased items when there is part commonality. **Inventory turnover** (or *turns*) is an inventory measure found by dividing annual sales at cost by the average aggregate inventory value maintained during the year.

To summarize:

(handwritten annotation: raw material, WIP, finished goods)

$$\text{Weeks of supply} = \frac{\text{Average aggregate inventory value}}{\text{Weekly sales (at cost)}}$$

(handwritten annotation: not sale price, finished goods)

$$\text{Inventory turnover} = \frac{\text{Annual sales (at cost)}}{\text{Average aggregate inventory value}}$$

The "best" inventory level, even when expressed as turnover, cannot be determined easily. Although 6 or 7 turns per year is typical, the average high-tech firm settles for only about 3 turns. At the other extreme, some Japanese automobile firms report 40 turns per year.

Application 12.4   *Calculating Inventory Measures*

A company averaged $2 million in inventory last year and the cost of goods sold was $10 million. If the company has 52 business weeks per year, how many weeks of supply were held in inventory? What was the inventory turnover?

Solution   The average aggregate inventory value of $2 million translates into 10.4 weeks of supply and 5 turns per year:

$$\text{Weeks of supply} = \frac{\$2 \text{ million}}{\$10 \text{ million}/52 \text{ weeks}} = 10.4 \text{ weeks}$$

and

$$\text{Inventory turnover} = \frac{\$10 \text{ million}}{\$2 \text{ million}} = 5 \text{ turns/year}$$

Inventory Placement

Just as distribution managers decide where to place finished goods inventory, manufacturing managers make similar decisions for raw materials and WIP within the plant. Inventory held toward the end-item level means short delivery times—but a higher dollar investment in inventory. Inventory placement at Shamrock Chemicals, a Newark, New Jersey, manufacturer of materials used in printing inks, illustrates this trade-off. It enjoys sales of more than $15 million because it can ship any of its products the same day a customer orders it. But because end items are treated as standards rather than specials, Shamrock is forced to maintain a hefty inventory. Holding inventory lower in the BOM would reduce the cost of carrying inventory, and part commonality might allow more repeatability—but at the expense of the quick customer response times that give Shamrock its competitive advantage.

Managers make inventory placement decisions, in general, by designating an item as either a special or a standard. A **special** is an item made to order. If it is purchased, it is bought to order. Just enough are ordered to cover the latest customer request. Production of a special's parent must be delayed by the special's lead time. A **standard** is an item made to stock and normally is available when needed. Overlaying lead times on the BOM allows the manager to calculate customer response times for different placement strategies. Making an item a standard in effect cuts its lead time to zero, except for shipping time. The customer response time is the total lead time along the longest path down to a standard or the bottom of the BOM, whichever comes first.

Application 12.5	*Estimating Customer Response Times*

A manager is evaluating six strategies of inventory placement for item A in Fig. 12.5. Strategy 1 has no standards, 2 makes D a standard, 3 makes C and D standards, 4 makes B a standard, 5 makes B and E standards, and 6 makes A a standard. What are the customer response times for each strategy?

Solution   Strategy 1 means that the customer waits 17 weeks after placing the order before it is shipped. The longest path is D–B–A. Once an order is received, it takes 5 weeks to get D, another 11 weeks to make B, and still another week to assemble B and E to make A. Item E is not on the longest path; it can be bought in just one week, whereas B won't be ready for 16 weeks. Similar computations for the other strategies are shown in the following table.

Strategy	Standard Items	Longest Path	Customer Response Time (weeks)
1	None	D–B–A	17 (5 + 11 + 1)
2	D	C–B–A	13 (1 + 11 + 1)
3	C and D	B–A	12 (11 + 1)
4	B	E–A	2 (1 + 1)
5	B and E	A	1
6	A	—	0

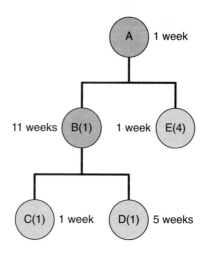

Inventory Reduction

Managers are always eager to find cost-effective ways to reduce inventory. (We examine various ways for finding optimal lot sizes in Chapter 13.) Several basic tactics—which we call *levers*—can be used to reduce inventory. Table 12.3 shows levers for each type of inventory. A primary lever is one that must be activated if inventory is to be reduced. A secondary lever decreases the penalty cost of applying the primary lever and reduces the need for having inventory in the first place.

Cycle Inventory. Because the cycle inventory level equals $Q/2$, the primary lever is simply to reduce the lot size Q. Several Japanese firms have reduced Q to the point where it is only a fraction of a shift's supply (see JIT in Chapter 17). These lots are extremely small, when compared to traditional lot sizes equaling several weeks' (or even months') supply. However, making such reductions in Q without making any other changes can be devastating. For example, setup costs can skyrocket, which leads to use of the two secondary levers.

Managers and the work force should not accept current costs at face value but should seek ways to reduce them. They should find ways to streamline methods for placing orders and making setups. Such improvements can reduce ordering and setup costs, which then allows Q to be reduced. Increased repeatability can also help reduce cycle inventory. Devoting resources exclusively to a single product eliminates the need for changeovers. Or, at least, the increased volumes may justify new setup methods. Other possibilities are the one worker, multiple machines concept; group technology; or flexible automation. (See Chapters 6 and 10.) Part commonality might increase volumes to the point where transportation costs and quantity discounts no longer stand in the way of small lot sizes. Another way to increase repeatability and volume is to centralize buying.

TABLE 12.3 / *Levers for Reducing Inventory*

Type of Inventory	Primary Lever	Secondary Lever
Cycle	Reduce Q	Reduce ordering and setup cost Increase repeatability
Safety stock	Place orders closer to the time when they must be received	Improve forecasting Reduce lead time Reduce supply uncertainties Increase equipment and labor buffers
Anticipation	Vary the production rate to follow the demand rate	Level out demand rates
Pipeline	Cut production–distribution lead time	Forward placement Selection of suppliers and carriers Reduce Q

Safety Stock Inventory. Recall that safety stock inventory can be created by releasing orders well before materials or parts are needed. Table 12.3 shows that the primary lever for reducing this type of inventory is to place orders closer to the time when they must be received. However, this approach can lead to unacceptable customer service—unless demand, supply, and delivery uncertainties can be minimized.

Four secondary levers can be used. First, improve demand forecasts, so that there are fewer surprises from customers. Perhaps customers can even be encouraged to order items before they need them. A second possibility is to find ways to cut lead times of purchased or produced items. Cutting lead times reduces demand uncertainty during lead time. For example, local suppliers could be selected whenever possible. A third option is to reduce supply uncertainties. Suppliers may be more reliable if production plans are shared with them, permitting them to make more realistic forecasts. Surprises from unexpected scrap or rework can be reduced by improving manufacturing processes. Preventive maintenance can minimize unexpected downtime caused by equipment failure. A fourth secondary lever for reducing safety stock is to rely more on equipment and labor buffers, such as capacity cushions and cross-trained workers. In fact, these are the only buffers available to businesses in the service sector because they cannot inventory their services.

Anticipation Inventory. Table 12.3 shows that the primary lever to reduce anticipation inventory is simply to match demand rate with production rate. This strategy can be more successful if customer demand can be leveled out by adding new products with different demand cycles so that peaks in the demand for one product compensate for the seasonal low for another. Off-season promotional campaigns or seasonal pricing plans are other options (Chapter 14).

Pipeline Inventory. An operations manager has direct control over lead time but not demand rate. Because pipeline inventory is a function of the demand during lead time, it can be cut only by reducing lead time. Various secondary levers can help managers cut lead times. First, we have already established that forward placement of inventory cuts lead time. Second, a firm might find more responsive suppliers, select new carriers for shipments between stocking locations, or improve materials handling within the plant. Introducing a computer system could overcome information delays between a DC and retailer. Third, decreasing Q may help, at least in those cases where lead time depends on lot size. Smaller jobs generally require less time to complete.

ABC Analysis

Thousands of items are held in inventory by a typical organization, but only a small percentage of them deserve management's closest attention and tightest control. The management-by-exception principle, when applied to inventory, is called **ABC analysis,** which is the process of dividing items into three classes according to their dollar usage. Class A items represent only about 20 percent of the items but account for 80 percent of the dollar usage. Class B accounts for another 30 percent of the items, which represent only 15 percent of the dollar usage. Finally, 50 percent of the items fall in Class C and represent a mere 5 percent of the dollar usage.

An ABC analysis is a two-step process. The first step is to assign each item to a class. The analyst begins by calculating the dollar usage for each item. An item's dollar usage is simply its annual demand rate multiplied by the dollar value (cost) of one unit. After ranking the items on the basis of dollar usage, the analyst assigns approximately the top 20 percent of the items to class A, the next 30 percent to class B, and the bottom 50 percent to class C. These dividing lines between classes are inexact, but class A items normally account for the bulk of the dollar usage.

The second step is for management to tightly control the inventory levels of class A items, using the levers just discussed. A manager can direct that class A items be reviewed frequently to reduce the average lot size. A manager can also demand precise inventory records. If the records show an on-hand balance of 100 units, but the actual balance is 200 units, costly inventory is being carried needlessly. If a class A item is bought outside the firm, purchasing may be able to reduce its cost through centralized buying, switching suppliers, or more effective contract negotiation.

For class C items, much looser control is appropriate. A stockout of a class C item can be as critical as for a class A item, but the inventory holding cost of class C items tends to be low. These features suggest that higher inventory levels should be tolerated and that more safety stock, larger lot sizes, and perhaps even a visual system (see Chapter 13) may suffice for class C items.

Links to Operations Strategy

Managers must link their inventory and scheduling policies with operations strategy. Much depends on the positioning strategy chosen. Inventory choices for a process-focused firm (such as Lower Florida Keys Health System in Chapter 2) should be quite different from those for a product-focused firm (such as Chaparral Steel in Chapter 2). A product-focused firm tends to have

1. less tolerance for "cushions."
2. less pressure for an integrated organizational structure.
3. longer planning horizons.
4. more formalized supplier and customer relationships.
5. information systems oriented to forecasts and inventory records.

Cushions. One strategy for capacity planning (see Chapter 8) favors large capacity cushions that require extra equipment and result in lower utilization rates. Two other cushions are extra workers and high inventories. All firms use these cushions, but in varying degrees. A firm with a product focus has less tolerance for cushions for three basic reasons. First, there is less need for a buffer because operations are less complex. For example, an operation with a product focus is characterized by high repeatability, standard products or services, low volume flexibility, and streamlined routings.

Second, there is less need to buffer against uncertainty. On the demand side, the higher volumes of a product focus make it easier to forecast customer demand. Standard products or services mean fewer last-minute design changes from customers or engineers. On the supply side, higher volumes give a company more clout in finding reliable suppliers. The high volumes within the firm's own plant reduce the uncertainty in both lead times and production quantities caused by capacity bottlenecks, rework, and scrap. Short lead times mean small WIP inventories. Figure 12.6, based on a survey of 110 companies, clearly shows that product-focused firms carry less WIP inventory.

Source: Deven Sharma, "Manufacturing Strategy: An Empirical Analysis," Unpublished dissertation, Ohio State University, 1987.

FIGURE 12.6

Positioning Strategy and WIP Inventory

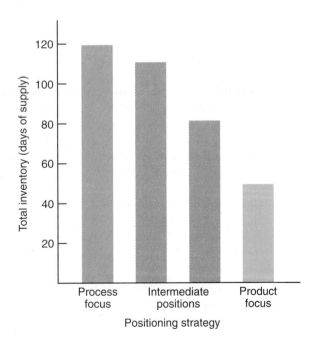

Third, a firm with a product focus is likely to emphasize low price as a competitive priority. Minimal cushions are critical to higher productivity and lower costs. Large safety stock inventories and extra workers are too costly a luxury.

Integrated Organizational Structure. We have previously mentioned the trend toward an integrated organizational structure, in which three key departments (purchasing, production control, and distribution) report to the same executive. Integration requires a high degree of coordination and cooperation among these departments, as well as with manufacturing and marketing. Although integration seems a good idea, the number of firms that have an integrated structure and the number that don't are fairly even.

Integration comes at a cost and should be pursued only when benefits exceed costs. Benefits are greatest in the uncertain environment of a process focus. Demand and supply uncertainties mean unexpected changes and updates, which in turn call for more coordination. When uncertainty is low, an organization can afford to be more compartmentalized and fragmented. Turning from benefits to costs, some aspects of the distribution function are simplified with a process focus, as there is little finished goods inventory and few, if any, DCs to manage. Making the distribution department part of an integrated structure therefore doesn't add much complexity in a process-focused firm. Finally, the greater ability to create finished goods inventory with a product focus uncouples operations from distribution. Distribution is more likely to be housed with marketing and separated from purchasing and production planning.

Planning Horizons. Production plans and schedules project further into the future for a product focus for two reasons. First, forward scheduling is feasible. Increased demand and supply certainty means that schedules can be developed with greater assurance. A product-focused firm allows few of the last-minute disruptions that are commonplace at process-focused firms. Second, a product focus creates a strong incentive to plan ahead. Maximizing facility and equipment utilization has top priority because the facility is so capital intensive. High utilization rates depend on forward scheduling.

Supplier and Customer Relationships. Both supplier and customer relationships are more formal and extensive with a product focus. Firms negotiate annual supply contracts with key suppliers rather than use the full purchasing cycle for each new purchase. Contract terms tend to be more attractive than terms for individual purchases. With high volumes, a firm can exert more control over suppliers, and, conversely, suppliers naturally cater to larger customers. Distribution channels are also more formal because markets are more scattered, requiring a network of regional DCs. With a process focus and its customized products, positioning inventory at DCs close to the customer is impossible. Typically, shipments are made directly from the plant to the customer.

Information Systems. Information requirements for a product focus are oriented to demand forecasts and current inventory levels. Items tend to be standards rather than specials. This situation differs from that of process-focused firms, where information is oriented to the bidding process and specific customer orders. Here, output plans are communicated by releasing jobs with detailed routing information.

SOLVED PROBLEMS

1. Item A has 6 components: B, C, D, E, F, and G. You have the following information about them.

   - Items D and E are purchased items. They both have a single parent: item B.
   - Items F and G are also purchased items. They both have a single parent: item C.
   - Items B and C are intermediate items. They both have a single parent: item A.

   a. Draw the bill of materials for item A. Assume that all usage quantities are one-for-one.
   b. Specify the customer response time in each of the situations (i)–(iii) for the following lead times.

A: 1 week	C: 3 weeks	E: 6 weeks	G: 3 weeks
B: 2 weeks	D: 3 weeks	F: 4 weeks	

   i. All items are specials.　　iii. Only items E and F are standard.
   ii. Only item E is a standard.

Solution　　a.

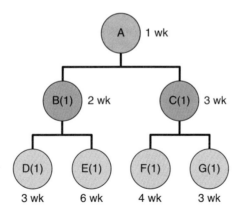

   b. The response time is determined by finding the longest time path from the end item to the bottom of the bill of materials or a standard item, assuming that standard items are immediately available.
   i. All items are specials: The longest path is E–B–A at 9 weeks.
   ii. Only item E is a standard: The longest path now is F–C–A at 8 weeks.
   iii. Only items E and F are standard: The longest path now is G–C–A at 7 weeks.

2. A DC experiences an average weekly demand of 50 units for one of its items. The product is valued at $650 per unit. Average inbound shipments from the factory warehouse average 350 units. Average lead time (including ordering delays and transit time) is two weeks. The DC operates 52 weeks per year and carries a one-week supply of inventory as safety stock and no anticipation inventory.

a. What is the average aggregate inventory value being held by the DC?

b. How many weeks of supply are held? What are annual sales? What is the inventory turnover?

c. What type of inventory (cycle, safety stock, or pipeline) is the biggest target for inventory reduction? What is the primary lever?

Solution   a.

Type of Inventory	Calculation		Inventory Value
Cycle	(350 units/2)($650/unit)	=	$113,750
Safety	(1 wk)(50 units/wk)($650/unit)	=	32,500
Anticipation	0		0
Pipeline	(50 units/wk)(2 wk)($650/unit)	=	65,000
	Average aggregate inventory value	=	$211,250

b. Weeks of supply $= \dfrac{\$211,250}{(50)(\$650)} = 6.5$ wk

   Annual sales $=$ (50 units/wk)(52 wk/yr)($650/unit) $=$ $1,690,000

   Turnover $= \dfrac{\$1,690,000/\text{yr}}{\$211,250} = 8$ turns/yr

c. Cycle inventory, valued at $113,750, is the largest component of the average aggregate inventory value. The primary lever is to reduce the lot size ($Q = 350$).

FORMULA REVIEW

1. Cycle inventory: $\dfrac{Q}{2}$

2. Pipeline inventory: $\bar{D}_L = dL$

3. Weeks of supply: $\dfrac{\text{Average aggregate inventory value}}{\text{Weekly sales (at cost)}}$

4. Inventory turnover: $\dfrac{\text{Annual sales (at cost)}}{\text{Average aggregate inventory value}}$

CHAPTER HIGHLIGHTS

● Materials management deals with purchasing, inventories, production plans, staffing plans, schedules, and distribution. Managing materials is a common organizational function in every segment of the economy.

● Purchased materials now represent more than 60 percent of the total income from sales for a typical manufacturer. The ratio of inventory to final sales per month averages 2.7:1 for the U.S. economy. Inventory investment is almost double the annual investment in new equipment and facilities. These three statistics are strong motivators for managing materials better.

● Decisions in materials management by necessity involve several departments specializing in certain aspects of materials management. There is growing sentiment for more integrated organizational structures, bringing purchasing, production control, and distribution into a single department headed by a key executive.

● Usually there are five steps in the acquisition cycle: receive a request to place an order, select a supplier, place the order, track the order, and receive the order.

● Purchasing activities of strategic importance include supplier selection, value analysis, supplier relations, and contracting.

● Distribution is responsible for finished goods inventory placement, transportation mode selection, and shipping schedule, route, and carrier selection.

● Forward placement of inventory at DCs can cut delivery times and transportation costs, although the pooling effect is less and can result in higher inventory levels. Forward placement is not advisable if the product is customized.

● Inventory falls into three accounting categories: raw materials, work-in-process, finished goods.

● A bill of materials introduces the concepts of parents, components, usage quantities, end items, intermediate items, purchased items, and subassemblies. Taken together, the BOM and routing (sequence of operations) tell how an item is to be manufactured.

● Whether an item is subject to independent or dependent demand is a key to how its inventory is managed. Dependent demand can be derived from production plans of parent items, but independent demand must be forecast.

● Pressures working against minimal inventory are customer service, ordering cost, setup cost, labor and equipment utilization, transportation cost, and purchased materials cost.

● The four types of inventory are cycle, safety stock, anticipation, and pipeline. Levers can be used to reduce each type of inventory. Secondary levers have to be used in conjunction with the primary levers.

● Inventory can be measured by average aggregate inventory value, weeks of supply, or inventory turnover. Inventory holding costs have several components: interest (or opportunity cost), storage and handling, taxes, insurance, and shrinkage.

● Inventory placement decisions at the plant level are made according to whether an item is a standard or a special. Managers must balance customer response time and inventory costs.

● ABC analysis helps managers focus on the few significant items that account for the bulk of inventory dollar usage. Class A items deserve the most attention, with less attention justified for class B and class C items.

● Materials management must fit operations strategy. When competitive priorities favor a product focus, the tendencies are for (1) less tolerance for cushions, (2) less pressure for an integrated organizational structure, (3) longer planning horizons, (4) more formalized supplier and customer relationships, and (5) information systems oriented to forecasts and inventory records.

KEY TERMS

ABC analysis **516**
anticipation inventory **510**
average aggregate inventory
    value **511**
back order **507**
bill of materials (BOM) **502**
component **502**
cycle inventory **509**
dependent demand **504**
distribution **498**
end item **502**
independent demand **504**
intermediate item **503**

inventory **500**
inventory holding cost **506**
inventory turnover **512**
lot sizing **509**
materials management **488**
open orders **510**
ordering cost **507**
parent **502**
part commonality **503**
pipeline inventory **510**
purchased item **503**
purchasing **492**
quantity discount **508**

routing **503**
safety stock inventory **509**
scheduled receipts **510**
setup cost **507**
special **513**
standard **513**
stockout **507**
subassembly **503**
usage quantity **502**
value analysis **498**
weeks of supply **512**

STUDY QUESTIONS

1. Some people call inventory the "root of all evil." Tying money up in inventory lessens opportunities to improve productivity. The reasons that make inventory attractive are the same ones that stand in the way of substantial improvements in efficiency. Do you agree or disagree with this position? Why?

2. Since organizations in the service sector do not manufacture products from raw materials, materials management concepts do not apply to them. Do you agree or disagree? Why?

3. It has been said that "if not controlled, work will flow to the competent people until they are submerged." What does this imply for centralizing all materials management functions under one key executive?

4. Suppose that you are a buyer charged with selecting one or more suppliers of an expensive, high-volume part going into a new product line. How would you proceed?

5. What steps would you take to make supplier relations more cooperative? Is a cooperative orientation always best?

6. When would you favor
   a. long-term purchase contracts?
   b. centralized buying?

7. The Defense Industry Initiative on Business Ethics and Conduct is just a few years old. Under the project, 46 contractors agreed to establish internal codes of ethics, to conduct training sessions, and to report suspected abuses. Suppose that you are a defense contracts manager. You have a friend in the military whom you have known for 20 years, and she gave you inside information about another contractor's bid. What would you do if your company was part of the industry's ethics project? If your company were not in it?

8. Ethan Allen *reduced* inventory by creating more DCs. Wouldn't forward placement of inventory at DCs *increase* inventory, since there is less of a pooling effect? Explain.

9. With the help of Fig. 12.5 you found that making the end item a standard item provides the best customer response time. What are the cost implications of such a move?

10. You have been asked to review the policies of a company for which the dollar value of inventory now exceeds 40 percent of total sales. How would you go about identifying opportunities for inventory reduction? To what extent can some of your ideas help im-

prove delivery times and reduce transportation costs?

11. The purpose of safety stock inventory is to protect against uncertainty in demand, lead time, and supply. What is the purpose of cycle inventory?

12. What can be done to reduce the cost of buying and holding materials purchased from suppliers?

13. USX Corporation recently fed caviar and filet mignon to executives from 300 of its biggest suppliers. The dinner was part of a two-day, $250,000 courtship to sell them on the virtues of relocating to Gary, Indiana. USX buys nearly $1 billion in products annually for its flagship plant in Gary and believes that greater supplier proximity would increase its inventory turnover.

a. Explain how cycle inventory, safety stock, and pipeline inventory could be reduced by having suppliers nearby.

b. Is USX's approach to its suppliers ethically correct? How much does it differ from a salesperson giving expensive presents to buyers of important customers?

14. What is the meaning and purpose of ABC analysis?

15. Give three examples of how competitive priorities can affect choices made in materials management.

PROBLEMS

Review Problems

1. A company enjoys $500 million in sales and a 15 percent gross profit margin (before taxes). Cost of materials is 60 percent of income from sales. The materials manager believes that $20 million can be saved through improved purchasing policies.
   a. What would be the percentage change in cost of materials?
   b. What percentage change in sales would be necessary to achieve the same result in gross profits?

2. Joan Pontius, the materials manager at Money Enterprises, is beginning to look for ways to reduce inventories. A recent accounting statement shows inventories at the following levels.

Raw materials	$2,845,000
Work-in-process	5,670,000
Finished goods	2,985,000

This year's cost of goods sold should be about $29.9 million. Assuming 52 business weeks per year, express total inventory as
   a. weeks of supply.
   b. inventory turns.

3. One product line is experiencing 8 turns per year, and its annual sales volume (at cost) is $775,000. How much inventory is being held, on the average?

4. Henderson Corporation is a supplier of alloy ball bearings to auto manufacturers in Detroit. Because of its specialized manufacturing process, considerable work-in-process and raw materials are needed. The current inventory levels are $1,152,000 and $2,725,000, respectively. In addition, finished goods inventory is $3,225,000 and sales (at cost) for the current year are expected to be about $24 million. Express total inventory as
   a. weeks of supply.
   b. inventory turns.

5. The following data have been collected for a firm.

Cost of goods sold	$3,500,000
Gross profit	700,000
Operating costs	500,000
Operating profit	200,000
Total inventory	1,200,000
Fixed assets	750,000
Long-term debt	300,000

Assuming 52 business weeks per year, express total inventory as being held in terms of

a. weeks of supply.
b. inventory turns.

6. Consider the bill of materials in Fig. 12.7.

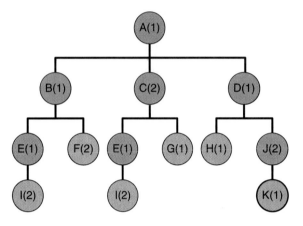

FIGURE 12.7

a. How many immediate parents (one level above) does item I have? How many immediate parents does item E have?
b. How many unique components does item A have at all levels?
c. How many purchased items does item A have at all levels?
d. How many intermediate items does item A have at all levels?
e. The items have the following lead times.

A: 2 weeks	G: 5 weeks
B: 1 week	H: 3 weeks
C: 3 weeks	I: 2 weeks
D: 2 weeks	J: 2 weeks
E: 4 weeks	K: 1 week
F: 3 weeks	

What is the customer response time if
i. all items are specials?
ii. only items E and I are standard?
iii. only items E, F, G, H, and I are standard?

7. Item A is made from components B, C, and D. Item B, in turn, is made from C. Item D is also an intermediate item, made from B. Usage quantities are all two, except that only one unit of item C is needed to make one unit of B. Draw the bill of materials for item A.

8. Item A is made from components B, C, D, and E. Item B is made from items D and F. Item C is made from items B and F. Item D is made from G. Usage quantities are all one except that two units of D are needed to make one unit of A, three units of B are needed to make one unit of E, and two units of G are needed to make one unit of D. Draw the bill of materials for item A.

9. What is the customer response time (in weeks) for item A, based on the following information and the BOM shown in Fig. 12.8?

Item	Lead Time (weeks)	Type of Item
A	2	Special
B	3	Special
C	8	Standard
D	4	Special
E	2	Special
F	15	Standard

10. Item A is made from components B and C. Item B, in turn, is made from D and E. Item C is also an intermediate item, made from F and H. Finally, intermediate item E is made from H and G. Note that item H has two parents. The item lead times are:

A: 1 week	D: 6 weeks	G: 1 week
B: 2 weeks	E: 3 weeks	H: 3 weeks
C: 5 weeks	F: 4 weeks	

a. What is the customer response time if only items F and H are standard?
b. What is the customer response time if only item A is standard?

11. Item A is made from components B and C. Item B, in turn, is made from D and E. Items C and D are also intermediate items. C is made from F and G. D is made from

Item	Lead time (weeks)	Type of item
A	2	Special
B	3	Special
C	8	Standard
D	4	Special
E	2	Special
F	15	Standard

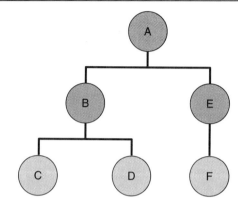

FIGURE 12.8

only G. Note that G has two parents.

A: 2 weeks D: 2 weeks G: 1 week
B: 3 weeks E: 4 weeks
C: 3 weeks F: 2 weeks

a. What is the customer response time if all items are specials?
b. What is the customer response time if only G is standard?
c. What is the customer response time if only B is standard?

12. Consider the BOM in Fig.. 12.9, on which lead times are overlaid.
   a. What would be the customer response time if every item is a special?
   b. What would be the customer response time if items D, E, and F are made standards?

13. A subassembly is produced in lots of 500 units. It is assembled from two components worth $50. The value added (for labor and variable overhead) in manufacturing one unit from its two components is $45, bringing the total cost per completed unit to $95.

The typical lead time for the item is 5 weeks and its annual demand is 1976 units. There are 52 business weeks per year.

a. How many units of cycle inventory are held, on average, for the subassembly? What is the dollar value of this cycle inventory?
b. How many units of pipeline inventory are held, on average, for the subassembly? What is the dollar value of this inventory? *Hint:* Assume that the typical job in pipeline inventory is 50 percent completed. Thus one-half the labor and variable overhead costs has been added, bringing the unit cost to $72.50 ($50 + $45/2).

14. Sterling Incorporated is a manufacturer of consumer electric goods and has five DCs in different regions of the country. For one of its products, a high-performance VCR priced at $500 per unit, the average weekly demand at *each* DC is 75 units. Average shipment size to each DC is 400 units, and the average lead time for delivery is two weeks. Each DC carries two weeks of supply as safety stock, but no anticipation inventory is held.

a. On the average, how many dollars of pipeline inventory will be in transit to each DC?

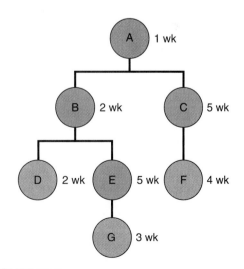

FIGURE 12.9

b. How much total inventory (cycle, safety stock, and pipeline) inventory does Sterling hold, summed across all five DCs?

15. Ben Incorporated is a manufacturer of motorcycle subassemblies that are produced in lots of 150 units. The raw material cost for the subassembly is $300, while the value added in manufacturing one unit from its components is $200, bringing the total cost per completed unit to $500. The lead time to make the subassembly is four weeks, and the annual demand is 2000 units. The company operates 50 weeks per year.
   a. How many units of the subassembly are being held, on the average, as cycle inventory?
   b. How much pipeline inventory is being held, on the average?

16. The Foresite Company periodically evaluates its suppliers to spot problem areas. One of its essential raw materials is provided by three suppliers. Purchases currently are equally distributed among the suppliers. Ratings (high values mean good performance) of the suppliers based on six weighted performance criteria are shown in Table 12.4.
   a. Calculate a total weighted score for each supplier using a preference matrix. (See Chapter 2.)
   b. What changes, if any, do you recommend in the company's purchasing policy?

17. McKenzie Industries is considering using ABC analysis to focus attention on its most critical inventory items. A random sample

of 20 items has been taken, and the dollar usages have already been calculated, as shown in the following table.

Item	Dollar Usage	Item	Dollar Usage
1	$ 9,200	11	$ 300
2	400	12	10,400
3	33,400	13	70,800
4	8,100	14	6,800
5	1,100	15	57,900
6	600	16	3,900
7	44,000	17	700
8	900	18	4,800
9	100	19	19,000
10	700	20	15,500

Rank the items and assign them to an A, B, or C class. On the basis of this sample, does it appear that ABC analysis will help management identify the significant few items?

Advanced Problems

18. Suppose that a product has an annual demand of 390 units. The lot size is 130 units, and the lead time is four weeks. The firm has 52 business weeks per year.
   a. If over the course of a year 390 units must be ordered at a rate of 130 units per order, how many orders will be placed?
   b. Multiply your answer in part (a) by both the lot size and lead time. This number is the *unit-weeks* of pipeline inventory held at one time or another during the year.

TABLE 12.4

Performance Criterion		Rating		
		Supplier A	Supplier B	Supplier C
1. Price	0.2	0.4	0.7	0.5
2. Quality	0.2	0.3	0.4	0.8
3. Delivery	0.2	0.4	0.5	0.6
4. Production facilities and capacity	0.1	0.6	0.8	0.7
5. Warranties and claims policies	0.2	0.7	0.8	0.7
6. Financial position	0.1	0.8	0.9	0.9

TABLE 12.5

	Lead	Inventory Policies (Weeks of Supply)		
Item	Time (wk)	Lot Size	Safety Stock	Anticipation
A	1	1	1	0
B	11	4	0	1
C	1	4	1	0
D	5	8	0	0
E	2	4	2	0

c. Divide your answer in part (b) by 52 to get the average pipeline inventory (in units) per week.

d. Now set up a mathematical expression for pipeline inventory, using D for annual demand, Q for lot size, and L for lead time. How does your final expression, simplified, relate to the notion that pipeline inventory is approximated by $\bar{D}_L$?

19. End item A is assembled from 1 unit of B and 4 units of purchased item E. Item B is manufactured from 1 unit of purchased item C and 1 unit of purchased item D. The weekly demand for item A averages 10 units. Because there is no part commonality, the demand for items B, C, D, and E can be derived from demand for A. The per unit purchase price is $30 for C, $40 for D, and $25 for E. The added cost to manufacture B from C and D is $70 per unit, bringing the value of one finished unit of B to $140 ($30 + $40 + $70). The value of one unit of B is only $105 ($30 + $40 + $70/2) if it is in the pipeline as WIP, assuming that it is half finished on the shop floor. Similar reasoning applies to item A, which costs $20 (value added only) to manufacture from B and E. Table 12.5 gives lead times and management's current policies on lot sizes, safety stock, and anticipation inventory. For example, the lot size of item D is 80 units [(8 weeks)(10 units/week)]. No anticipation inventory is held, except an average of 10 units per week for item B.

a. Draw the bill of materials for item A.
b. What is the value of one unit of A upon completion? While it is being manufactured from B and E (i.e., still WIP)?
c. Calculate the average number of units held in inventory for each item, broken down as cycle, safety stock, anticipation, and pipeline inventory. Then convert your answer to dollar equivalents.
d. How much inventory is being held in total, summed across all five items. How many weeks of supply is being held, as only item A is sold to the customer? What is the inventory turnover?
e. Which item and type of inventory is the best target for improvement? Which primary lever should be applied?

CASE   COMMONWEALTH WOODWORKS*

Commonwealth Woodworks is a Massachusetts company that manufactures a wide range of architectural woodworking products. The custom cabinet shop manufactures cabinets, shelving, and wood trim for a variety of residential, commercial, and educational customers. These products usually are sold directly to building contractors and are built in accordance with plans and specifications from architects, interior designers, and owners. Raw materials are not ordered and work is not begun until Commonwealth has a firm

---

*Barry Kay, research assistant at Boston College, prepared this case for class discussion.

order from the customer; therefore, inventory control has never been a major problem for this division of the business.

Several years ago, Tim O'Donnell, the founder and president of Commonwealth, wanted to capitalize on the building boom then in progress. He decided to expand his product line from custom cabinets and architectural woodwork by offering architectural "prehung" door units for use in the residential construction industry. Unlike his custom cabinet business, these door units are manufactured in quantity and sold through lumber dealers and "home improvement centers," dealers that cater to both contractors and to "do-it-yourselfers."

The traditional doorway consists of a wood or metal frame that is installed in a wall as the wall is constructed. If the door is to be wood, it usually is delivered to the building site shortly before installation is required. Carpenters would "fit" the door to the frame by planing small quantities of wood off each edge of the door (often 1/8 inch or less) and installing the door hinges and lock. The prehung door unit, on the other hand, is a factory-built unit that is delivered to the customer with the wood door already installed in a wooden frame. The hinges hold the door in place during transportation and installation, and the wood door has been drilled to receive the lock. This unit allows the customer to set the door unit into place and build it into the wall without any further work required for fitting and installation. Using prehung door units means a considerable savings of time and money for the contractor. For the do-it-yourselfer, prehung units require fewer carpentry skills for installation.

The door units made by Commonwealth contain some components that are bought ready to use and others that require fabrication by the company from raw materials before they can be assembled into the door unit. Commonwealth buys the doors from a manufacturer. They arrive as blank "slabs" cut to the nominal size of the opening. For prehung units, most doors are 6'8" (80 inches) high and the widths vary from 2'4" (28 inches) to 3' (36 inches). Once the doors go into fabrication, they are machined to receive the hinges and drilled to receive the lock. They are then planed to remove just enough edge material so that they fit snugly into the frame without sticking or binding. Purchased items that do not require any additional fabrication are the lock and the hinges (one pair per door). The frames are made from lumber purchased from a wholesale lumber distributor. The frame consists of six pieces of casing trim, which forms the visible frame surrounding the door. Each frame has two top casings, two left casings, and two right casings, all cut to exact lengths by Commonwealth with special stationary saws. In addition, the part of the frame that fits inside the wall consists of a top piece (the door header), a hinge side, and a strike side (the side that engages the lock bolt to keep the door shut). These side pieces are called door jambs; the hinge side and the strike side are not interchangeable. The door headers are all the same length when they are delivered to Commonwealth, which cuts them to fit the actual width of the door units being manufactured. Other pieces of wood used to strengthen the frame unit are fabricated from scrap lumber that the shop produces in abundance from all of its operations.

Standard delivery time for each component (Exhibit 1) is four weeks from order date, while special delivery takes only two weeks. Commonwealth's policy is to order all purchased components at the end of each month. The costs of the components are shown in Exhibit 1.

The current selling prices for the units vary with the width of the door. Commonwealth sells the 28-inch unit for $145, the 32-inch unit for $152, and the 36-inch unit for $158. The cost of variable labor and overhead for assembly of each complete unit is $40 for regular time and $60 for overtime. Setup time for a

EXHIBIT 1

Item	Standard Delivery Price	Special Delivery Price
Door slab, 28" × 80"	$30	$35
Door slab, 32" × 80"	$35	$40
Door slab, 36" × 80"	$40	$45
Lock	$10	$12
Hinges (per pair)	$ 5	$ 8
Frame casing (top and sides)	$ 2 per piece	$ 4 per piece
Frame head and jambs	$ 2 per piece	$ 3 per piece

EXHIBIT 2 / Anticipated Demand per Week for 1993

Unit	1st Quarter	2nd Quarter	3rd Quarter	4th Quarter
28″	30	35	35	20
32″	35	42	45	30
36″	25	30	30	20
Total	90	107	110	70

specific door unit width requires one hour, at a cost of $100. Production is scheduled on a weekly basis. On Friday afternoons, a work order detailing production requirements for the following week is sent to the shop supervisor. Finished door units are shipped to customers every Friday afternoon. O'Donnell uses a week-to-month conversion factor of 4.333 weeks per month [52 weeks per year/12 months per year]. Although production lot sizes can vary from week to week, based on actual demand, the average lot size is 34 units of a given door width. Lead time averages 2 days. Based on the size of the current work force, maximum production capacity is 100 units per week during a 40-hour week (if no overtime is worked). O'Donnell does not want to either hire or fire workers to adjust production schedules. Commonwealth can work overtime up to 10 hours a week (2 hours a day), if necessary, to increase weekly output without a decrease in productivity per hour. O'Donnell's cost records indicate that overtime above 2 hours a day will bring a decline in productivity of 30 percent. O'Donnell can reduce production from 40 hours to 35 hours a week, reducing production quantities and variable labor and overhead costs proportionally. He cannot drop production time below 35 hours a week, due to the union agreement.

In mid-December of this year (1992), O'Donnell made his initial forecast for next year (1993), as shown in Exhibit 2. Commonwealth's finished inventory at the end of this year will be exactly the anticipated demand for the first week of next year, 90 units. O'Donnell's inventory plan calls for Commonwealth to have minimum finished inventory at the end of each week equal to the anticipated demand for the following week. Any inventory not sold within a month after it is finished will incur a monthly holding cost equal to 3 percent of its value. The inventory at the end of this year is shown in Exhibit 3. Any raw materials that have been received but not yet entered into production during the month following their delivery to Commonwealth will, likewise, incur monthly costs equal to 3 percent of their value.

For the purpose of developing his plan, O'Donnell assumes that demand for January 1994 will be the same as for January 1993.

QUESTIONS

1. Draw the bill of materials for each of the different prehung door units manufactured by Commonwealth.

2. Prepare a monthly production plan for 1993. Each type of door unit should have a separate plan, but you must consider the various limitations already described, including minimum and maximum production capacity, that Commonwealth must follow. A tabular format (page 530) is suggested, but other formats may be used.

EXHIBIT 3

Item	End-of-Year Inventory (1992)	Scheduled Receipts January 2, 1993
Door slab, 28″ × 80″	90 units	30 units
Door slab, 32″ × 80″	70 units	70 units
Door slab, 36″ × 80″	70 units	30 units
Lock	200 units	0
Hinges	200 pairs	0
Frame casing (1 top and 2 side)	400 sets	0
Frame head (1) and jambs (2)	400 sets	0
Finished unit, 36″	30 units	0
Finished unit, 32″	35 units	0
Finished unit, 28″	25 units	0

A Hypothetical Door Unit

	January	February	March	. . .	December
Beginning finished inventory	20	10	10	. . .	20
Demand for the month	− 80	− 50	− 45	. . .	− 55
Production for the month	70	50	50	. . .	40
Ending finished inventory	10	10	15	. . .	5

3. How much cycle, safety stock, anticipation, and pipeline inventory will be held on average during the year with your production plan? In what categories is inventory the highest? What could be done to reduce these inventories?

4. Based on the inventory given in Exhibit 3 and the production schedules for January and February 1993, prepare the purchase orders that Commonwealth must place at the end of December 1992 to maintain its production schedule without interruption.

5. Suppose that 6 months have passed and now, in late June 1993, O'Donnell is told by his various customers that, due to the slump in the building industry, they will be reducing their orders for the third and fourth quarters. O'Donnell finds that the overall reductions in orders amount to a 20 percent across-the-board decline from his earlier estimates for the third and fourth quarters. Given that the actual demand during the first and second quarters was exactly as O'Donnell had forecasted, update the plan for the third and fourth quarters of 1993 to adjust for the decrease in demand from what was forecasted in December 1992. The demand for January 1994 is still forecasted to be the same as for January 1993. What are the changes you must make to the weekly production schedules to adjust for this downturn in demand? What are the additional costs Commonwealth will incur due to these changes?

SELECTED REFERENCES

Ammer, Dean S. *Materials Management*. Homewood, Ill.: Richard D. Irwin, 1962.

Banerjee, Avijit. "An Integrated Inventory Model for a Purchaser and a Vendor." *Proceedings of the 1985 Annual Meeting*, American Institute for Decision Sciences (November 1985), pp. 746–748.

Burt, D. *Proactive Purchasing*. Englewood Cliffs, N.J.: Prentice-Hall, 1984.

Corey, E. Raymond. "Should Companies Centralize Procurement?" *Harvard Business Review* (November–December 1978), pp. 102–110.

Dobler, Donald W., Lamar Lee, Jr., and David N. Burt. *Purchasing and Materials Management*. New York: McGraw-Hill, 1984.

"Internal Operations Problems Leave Firm Reeling." *Wall Street Journal*, August 11, 1989.

Kelly, Scott W., and Michael J. Dorsch. "Ethical Climate, Organizational Commitment, and Indebtedness Among Purchasing Executives." *Journal of Personal Selling & Sales Management*, vol. 11, no. 4 (Fall 1991), pp. 55–66.

McLeavey, Dennis W., and S.L. Narasimhan. *Production Planning and Inventory Control*. Newton, Mass.: Allyn and Bacon, 1985.

Miller, Jeffrey G., and P. Gilmour. "Materials Managers: Who Needs Them?" *Harvard Business Review* (July–August 1979), pp. 143–153.

Miller, Jeffrey G., and Aleda V. Roth. "Manufacturing Strategies: Executive Summary of the 1988 North American Manufacturing Futures Survey." Research Report, Boston University, 1988.

Narasimhan, Ram. "An Analytical Approach to Supplier Selection." *Journal of Purchasing and Materials Management* (Winter 1983), pp. 27–32.

Pittiglio, Rabin, Todd, and McGrath, "Assessing High Tech Inventory Management." *P&IM Review and APICS News* (July 1984), pp. 52–55.

Reid, R. Dan, and Carl D. Riegel. "Purchasing Practices of Large Food Service Firms." Center for Advanced Purchasing Studies, Tempe, Arizona, 1989, pp. 20–21.

Schonberger, R., and J. Gilbert. "Just-In-Time Purchasing: A Challenge for U.S. Industry." *California Management Review*, vol. 26, no. 1 (Fall 1983), pp. 54–68.

Sharma, Deven. "Manufacturing Strategy: An Empirical Analysis." Unpublished dissertation, Ohio State University, 1987.

Van Dierdonck, Roland, and Jeffrey G. Miller. "Designing Production Planning and Control Systems." *Journal of Operations Management*, vol. 1, no. 1 (August 1980), pp. 37–46.

Vollmann, Thomas E., William L. Berry, and D. Clay Whybark. *Manufacturing Planning and Control Systems*. Homewood, Ill.: Richard D. Irwin, 1988.

Chapter 13

INDEPENDENT-DEMAND INVENTORY SYSTEMS

How large should our cycle inventories be?

How often should we update our lot sizes, safety stocks, and lead times?

What type of system—a Q system, a P system, or some hybrid—should we use to control inventories?

How do we handle quantity discounts? Should we hedge against price increases?

How much effort must we spend to maintain accurate inventory records?

Should we use a manual or computerized system?

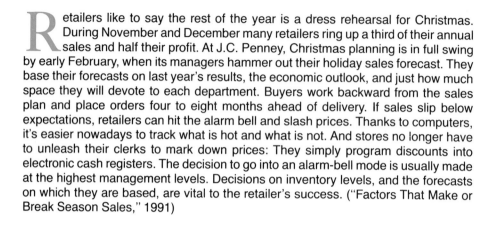

Retailers like to say the rest of the year is a dress rehearsal for Christmas. During November and December many retailers ring up a third of their annual sales and half their profit. At J.C. Penney, Christmas planning is in full swing by early February, when its managers hammer out their holiday sales forecast. They base their forecasts on last year's results, the economic outlook, and just how much space they will devote to each department. Buyers work backward from the sales plan and place orders four to eight months ahead of delivery. If sales slip below expectations, retailers can hit the alarm bell and slash prices. Thanks to computers, it's easier nowadays to track what is hot and what is not. And stores no longer have to unleash their clerks to mark down prices: They simply program discounts into electronic cash registers. The decision to go into an alarm-bell mode is usually made at the highest management levels. Decisions on inventory levels, and the forecasts on which they are based, are vital to the retailer's success. ("Factors That Make or Break Season Sales," 1991)

Chapter 12 explained that an important key to managing inventory is whether an item is subject to dependent or independent demand. J.C. Penney manages independent-demand items and uses a very different inventory control system than does a firm that manages dependent-demand items. For example, if a guitar manufacturer knows he will produce 500 guitars next month, there is a way (see Chapter 16) to calculate the number of component items—such as strings and sound boxes—that must be in stock at a given time. However, the owner of a bookstore may not be sure how many copies of the latest best-seller customers will purchase during the coming month. As a result, she may decide to stock extra copies as a safeguard.

This chapter focuses on independent demand, which is the type of demand the bookstore owner and J.C. Penney face. Independent-demand inventory includes four categories:

1. Wholesale and retail merchandise, amounting to 44 percent of the U.S. economy's inventory
2. Service-industry inventory, such as medical supplies for hospitals, stamps and mailing labels for post offices, and office supplies for law firms
3. End-item and replacement-part inventories at manufacturing firms
4. Maintenance, repair, and operating supplies (MRO) at manufacturing companies, that is, items that do not become part of the final product, such as employee uniforms, fuel, paint, and machine repair parts

We begin with key features of independent-demand items, including typical problems that a manager faces. We then discuss a fundamental concern: determining the appropriate size and frequency of new orders. Given this foundation on economic lot sizes, we consider three common inventory control systems: continuous review, periodic review, and hybrid systems. We conclude with two special cases of lot-sizing problems and with practical issues.

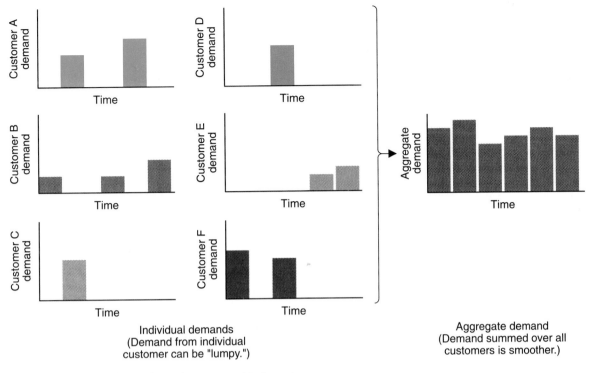

FIGURE 13.1   Independent Demand Is Smoother

KEY FEATURES OF INDEPENDENT DEMAND

Figure 13.1 shows how market conditions influence independent demand. Demand from any one customer is usually "lumpy." Because low demand from some customers is often offset by high demand from others, however, total demand can be fairly constant. Thus total demand may follow a relatively smooth pattern, with some random fluctuations. Good demand forecasts are important, as Managerial Practice 13.1 shows. Dependent-demand items exhibit a very different pattern. Demand for those items occurs only when operations releases an order for one of the parents. Such orders can be relatively infrequent, unless the item has many parents that are ordered frequently. The result is a lumpy, on-again, off-again pattern.

ECONOMIC ORDER QUANTITY

Even though independent demand is fairly smooth, choosing the best lot sizes is not that straightforward. For example, a policy of replenishing inventory only every five months keeps ordering costs low but raises the level of inventories and holding costs. A good starting point for finding reasonable lot sizes is the **economic order quantity (*EOQ*),** which is the lot size that minimizes total annual inventory holding and ordering costs. It is based on the following assumptions.

Managerial Practice 13.1

Demand Uncertainties and Judgment at Gap Incorporated

Gap Incorporated is a 21-year-old apparel chain that stocks its shelves with simple, no-frills clothing that is attracting a wide spectrum of consumers—from teenagers to celebrities. When estimating future demand for different types of merchandise, Gap's managers consider past demand patterns and sometimes even field test new styles. For example, Gap introduced a woman's sleeveless T-shirt that sold well at 35 stores in the South. However, its managers also use considerable judgment in making their demand forecasts.

Millard Drexler, Gap's 46-year-old president, largely relies on gut instinct. The four-year-old GapKids line was conceived at a meeting as he and other Gap executives shared frustrations about the difficulty of finding all-cotton clothes for their children. Despite inconclusive results from testing the idea at a Gap store in San Francisco, Drexler went ahead because "we loved what the clothes looked like." The new line proved highly successful. More recently Drexler dropped in on a GapKids manager who was sitting on the floor and peering at socks with striped patterns. "I think you'll do business on stripes," Drexler announced, "but not on those stripes." He had trouble explaining why, saying finally that the colors were too dull.

Source: "Gap Inc. Is Prospering Even as It Disdains Usual Holiday Hype," *Wall Street Journal,* December 19, 1991.

1. The demand rate for the item is constant (for example, always ten units per day).

2. The item is produced or purchased in lots, and a complete order for the item is received once, rather than piecemeal. There are no constraints on the size of each lot, such as truck capacity or materials-handling limitations.

3. There are only two relevant costs. The first is inventory holding cost, which is found by multiplying the average inventory level (in units) by the cost to hold one unit for a specific period of time. The second is the fixed cost per lot for ordering or setup. Ordering costs include the time needed to prepare a purchase or shop order; setup costs include the time to change the tooling at one or more machines to handle the new order (see Chapter 12). The cost of materials, for example, is assumed to be unaffected by the lot-sizing decision, ruling out situations involving quantity discounts or price increases expected in the near future.

4. Decisions for one item can be made independently of decisions made for other items. For example, there is no advantage in combining several orders going to the same supplier, or in coordinating the orders for a group of items to level out capacity requirements in the shop.

5. There is no uncertainty in demand, lead time, or supply. The demand rate is not only constant (see first assumption) but also is known. The lead time is also constant and known (for example, always 14 days). Finally, there is no uncertainty in supply. The amount received is exactly what was ordered. This assumption rules out short shipments from a supplier or scrap losses in the shop. Given complete certainty, no stockouts arise because the planner can determine exactly when to order to avoid them.

Total Inventory Cost

Based on the *EOQ* assumptions, on-hand inventory behaves as shown in Fig. 13.2. The straight-line depletion of inventory during the period results in an average cycle inventory (see Chapter 12) equal to one-half the lot size Q. Consequently, the total cost* of ordering Q units each time a planner or buyer places an order is

Total cost = Annual holding cost + Annual ordering or setup cost

or
$$C = \frac{Q}{2}\,(H) + \frac{D}{Q}\,(S)$$

where

C = total cost per year

D = annual demand, in units per year

H = cost of holding one unit in inventory for a year, often calculated as a percentage of the item's value (see Chapter 12)

S = cost of ordering or setting up one lot, in dollars per lot

Q = lot size, in units

The annual holding cost is the average cycle inventory over the course of a year multiplied by the cost of holding one unit for a year. This cost increases linearly as Q increases. The second term on the right-hand side of the equation is the number of lots ordered per year multiplied by the cost to place each order. The average number of orders per year is annual demand divided by Q. For example, if 1200 units must be ordered each year and the average lot size is 100 units, then 12 orders would be placed during the year. The annual ordering or setup cost decreases as Q increases because fewer orders are placed. The number of orders actually placed for a *given* year is always a whole number although the formula allows the use of fractional values. There is no need to round a number, however, because what is being calculated is an average across multiple years. It is realistic for such averages to be noninteger.

---

*It usually is convenient (though not necessary) to express the total cost on an annual basis. Any time horizon can be selected, as long as D and H cover the same period of time. If the total cost is calculated on a monthly basis, D must be monthly demand and H must be the cost of holding a unit for one month.

FIGURE 13.2

Cycle-Inventory Levels

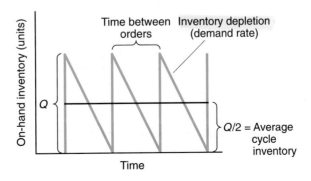

Application 13.1	*Costing Out a Lot-Sizing Policy*

A museum of natural history opened a gift shop two years ago. The shop's product plan calls for ten general groups of merchandise: containers, artworks, Eskimo crafts, Indian goods, geological items, paper goods, books, jewelry, scientific instruments (such as binoculars and barometers), and seasonal goods. Each group in turn breaks down into more specific categories. Annual sales now exceed $230,000 and are still climbing. However, managing inventories has become a problem. Inventory turnover is much too low, which squeezes profit margins and causes cash-flow problems.

One of the top-selling items in the container group at the museum's gift shop is a birdfeeder. Sales are 18 units per week, and the supplier charges $60 per unit. The cost of placing an order with the supplier is $45. Annual holding costs are 25 percent of a feeder's value, and the museum operates 52 weeks per year. Management chose a 390-unit lot size so that new orders can be placed less frequently. What is the annual cost of the current policy of using a 390-unit lot size?

Solution We begin by computing the annual demand and holding cost as

$$D = (18 \text{ units/week})(52 \text{ weeks/year}) = 936 \text{ units}$$
$$H = 0.25(\$60/\text{unit}) = \$15$$

Thus the annual cost is

$$C = \frac{Q}{2}(H) + \frac{D}{Q}(S)$$

$$= \frac{390}{2}(\$15) + \frac{936}{390}(\$45)$$

$$= \$2925 + \$108 = \$3033$$

Calculating the Economic Order Quantity

Figure 13.3 shows the results of trying several Q values for the birdfeeder in Application 13.1. Eight different lot sizes were evaluated in addition to the current one. Both holding and ordering costs were plotted, but their sum—the total cost curve—is the important feature. The graph shows that the best lot size, or *EOQ*, is the lowest point on the total cost curve, or between 50 and 100 units. Obviously, reducing the current lot size policy ($Q = 390$) can result in significant savings.

A more efficient approach is to use the *EOQ* formula:

$$EOQ = \sqrt{\frac{2DS}{H}}$$

For those of you who have had calculus, this formula is obtained by taking the first derivative of the total cost function with respect to Q, setting it equal to zero, and solving for Q. Coincidentally, as you can see in Fig. 13.3, the *EOQ* is the order quantity where annual holding costs equal annual ordering costs. The *EOQ* formula has been around a long time, being developed by F.W. Harris more than 75 years ago.

FIGURE 13.3

Total Inventory Cost
Function for
Birdfeeder

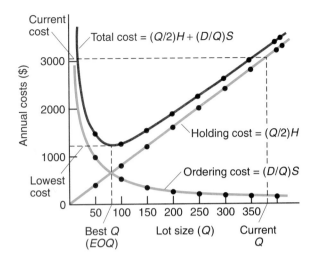

It is sometimes important to express a lot size as the time between replenishment orders, rather than as the number of units. The **time between orders** **(TBO)** for a particular lot size is the average time that elapses between placing replenishment orders of Q units. Expressed as a fraction of a year, TBO is simply Q divided by the annual demand. When using the EOQ and expressing time in terms of months, the TBO is

$$\frac{12}{\frac{D}{Q}} : \frac{12 \cdot 30Q}{D} \qquad\qquad TBO = \frac{EOQ}{D} \text{ (12 months/year)}$$

Application 13.2

Finding the EOQ, Total Cost, and TBO

For the birdfeeders in Application 13.1, calculate the EOQ and its total annual cost. How frequently should orders be placed?

Solution The EOQ is 75 units and the cost $1124. This cost is much less than the $3033 cost of the current policy of placing 390-unit orders.

$$EOQ = \sqrt{\frac{2DS}{H}} = \sqrt{\frac{2(936)(45)}{15}} = 74.94 \qquad \text{or} \qquad 75$$

$$C = \left(\frac{75}{2}\right)(\$15) + \left(\frac{936}{75}\right)(\$45) = \$562 + \$562 = \$1124$$

The time between orders (TBO) when using the EOQ, expressed both in months and in weeks (assuming 52 business weeks per year), is

$$TBO = \frac{EOQ}{D} \text{ (12 months/year)} = \frac{75}{936}(12) = 0.96 \text{ month}$$

$$TBO = \frac{EOQ}{D} \text{ (52 weeks/year)} = \frac{75}{936}(52) = 4.17 \text{ weeks}$$

Sensitivity Analysis

Subjecting the *EOQ* formula to sensitivity analysis can yield valuable insights into the management of inventories. (Remember that sensitivity analysis is a technique for systematically changing critical parameters to determine their effects.) Different values are substituted into the numerator or denominator of the formula and the results are noted. Sensitivity analysis can be used to help answer questions such as:

- *What happens to cycle inventory if the demand rate increases?* Because *D* is in the numerator, the *EOQ* (and therefore the best cycle inventory level) increases in proportion to the square root of the annual demand. Lot size should be increased therefore when demand rises but at a slower rate than actual demand. This is one reason why higher repeatability, such as that gained from more part commonality or less product customization, helps reduce costs (see the levers to reduce inventory in Chapter 12). Stated differently, if the demands for two parts (D_1 and D_2) are combined into *D* through part commonality, then the *EOQ* of *D* will be smaller than the sum of EOQ_1 and EOQ_2.

- *What happens to lot sizes if setup costs decrease?* Reducing *S* reduces the *EOQ* and, consequently, reduces the average cycle inventory. Smaller lot sizes can now be economically produced, which is why manufacturers are so concerned about cutting setup time and costs. When setups become trivial, a major impediment to small-lot production is removed.

- *What happens if interest rates drop?* Interest, or the cost of capital, is one component of the holding cost (see Chapter 12). Because *H* is in the denominator, the *EOQ* increases when *H* decreases. Larger lot sizes are justified by lower holding costs. The cycle inventory varies inversely with the square root of *H*.

- *How critical are errors in estimating D, H, and S?* As the *EOQ* is a function of the square root of these variables, it is rather insensitive to estimating errors. Furthermore, an error in one variable tends to cancel out an error in another, leading to the model's robustness.

Limitations

The economic order quantity is optimal only when the five assumptions presented earlier are satisfied. This constraint would seem to invalidate use of the *EOQ* because very few situations are so simple and well-behaved. In fact, different lot-sizing approaches *are* needed to reflect quantity discounts, uneven demand rates, or interactions between items, some of which we introduce briefly later in this chapter. However, the *EOQ* is often a reasonable first approximation of average lot sizes, even when several of the assumptions do not quite apply. The following two sections (continuous and periodic review systems) present ways to relax the fifth assumption, that demand is known with certainty.

CONTINUOUS REVIEW SYSTEM (Q SYSTEM)

Now that we know how much to order, we must determine when to reorder. An inventory control system brings together both dimensions—the sizing and timing—as it replenishes inventory over time. One of the best-known inventory control systems is the **continuous review system,** in which the remaining quantity of an item is reviewed each time a withdrawal is made from inventory, to determine whether it is time to reorder. In practice, these reviews are done frequently, such as on a daily basis, rather than continuously, on each withdrawal. Continuous reviews are easier to do with the advent of computers and electronic cash registers linked to inventory records. At each review a decision is made about an item's inventory position, which, if judged too low, triggers a new order. The **inventory position (*IP*)** measures the item's ability to satisfy future demand, relying only on scheduled receipts (see Chapter 12) and on-hand inventory. More specifically, it is

$$IP = OH + SR - BO$$

where

$$
\begin{aligned}
IP &= \text{inventory position of the item (in units)} \\
OH &= \text{number of units in on-hand inventory} \\
SR &= \text{scheduled receipts (open orders)} \\
BO &= \text{number of units either back ordered or allocated}
\end{aligned}
$$

Recall that a back order is an unfilled customer order or commitment. It is an immediate (or past due) demand for an item that is out of stock. Back orders should occur only when customers will allow shortages to be filled later and won't take their business elsewhere. Allocated inventory is on-hand inventory set aside or earmarked to meet past demand. For example, some of a component's on-hand inventory may be allocated for a parent's order even though inventory has yet to be physically removed from the storeroom.

The continuous review system, sometimes called a **reorder point system (ROP),** *Q* system, or fixed order quantity system, can be described as follows:

> Place an order for *Q* units whenever a withdrawal brings the inventory position to the reorder point *R* (described in the following section), that is, the minimum level allowed.

The *Q* system has just two parameters: *Q* and *R*. Each new order is of the same size: *Q* units. But *Q* can be based on the *EOQ*, a price-break quantity (the minimum lot size that qualifies for a quantity discount), a container size (such as a truckload), or some other quantity selected by management.

Figure 13.4 shows how the system operates. The downward sloping line represents the on-hand inventory, which is being depleted at a fairly steady rate. When it reaches the reorder point *R*, the horizontal line, a new order for *Q* units is placed. The on-hand inventory continues to drop throughout lead time *L*, until the order is received. At that time, which marks the end of the lead time, on-hand inventory jumps vertically by *Q* units.

FIGURE 13.4

Illustration of a
Q System

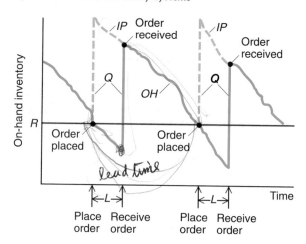

The inventory position IP is also shown in Fig. 13.4. It corresponds to the on-hand inventory, except during the lead time. Just after a new order is placed, marking the start of the lead time, IP increases by Q, the size of the new scheduled receipt (dashed line). IP exceeds OH by this same margin throughout the lead time.* At the end of the lead time, when the scheduled receipts convert to on-hand inventory, $IP = OH$ once again. The key point here is simple: Compare IP, not OH, with R in deciding whether to reorder. A common error is to ignore scheduled receipts or back orders, which causes erratic inventory behavior.

Application 13.3	Determining When to Reorder

On-hand inventory of an item is only 10 units and the reorder point R is 100. There are no back orders, but there is one open order for 200 units. Should a new order be placed?

Solution

$$IP = OH + SR - BO$$

$$= 10 + 200 - 0 = 210$$

As IP exceeds R (210 versus 100), don't reorder.

Selecting the Reorder Point

Recall one of the assumptions made for calculating the EOQ: There is no uncertainty in demand, lead time, or supply. For the museum gift shop application, suppose that the demand for feeders is always 18 per week, the lead time is always two weeks, and the supplier always ships the exact amount ordered on time. In this ideal world, the museum's buyer could wait until the inventory

---

*A possible exception is the unlikely situation of long lead times and small lot sizes, when more than one scheduled receipt is open at the same time.

position drops to 36 units [(18 units/week)(2 weeks)] to place a new order. Thus the reorder point R equals the *demand during lead time,* with no allowance for safety stock; a new order arrives at the moment that inventory drops to zero.

In reality, behavior isn't nearly so predictable. Demand is a random variable. At best, the museum's buyer knows that *average* demand is 18 feeders per week, which means that a variable number of feeders may be purchased during the two-week lead time. Suppose that she set R at 46 units, thereby placing orders in advance of when they are typically needed. This approach would create a safety stock (see Chapter 12) of 10 units (46 − 36) to buffer against uncertain demand.*

More formally, the reorder point is

$$R = \bar{D}_L + B$$

where R = reorder point

$\bar{D}_L$ = average demand during lead time L

B = safety stock or buffer

Because $\bar{D}_L$ is determined to a large degree by customers, the real decision to be made when selecting R concerns the safety stock level B. Deciding on a small or large B is a trade-off between customer service and inventory holding costs. Cost minimization models can be used to find the best B, but they require an estimate of stockout or back-order costs. This task is difficult and is not usually done. The usual approach is for management—based on judgment—to set a reasonable service level policy and then determine the safety stock level that satisfies this policy.

Choosing an Appropriate Service Level Policy

Managers express service levels in various ways, such as:

- The desired probability of not running out of stock in any one inventory cycle, often called the **cycle-service level**
- The preferred proportion of annual demand (in units, customer orders, or dollars) instantaneously filled from stock, commonly called the **fill rate**
- The number of stockouts tolerated per year
- The preferred proportion of days in the year when an item is not out of stock

For brevity, we will consider only the first measure. Establishing a policy based on the cycle-service level is natural because a stockout can occur only at the end of an inventory cycle (sometime during the lead time).

---

*In this discussion we assume that demand is the only source of uncertainty. If lead time were also a random variable, the variability in demand during lead time would be even higher. If there were supply uncertainty, *IP* would also become a random variable because the number of units actually received from scheduled receipts would be uncertain. These additional uncertainties would mandate higher safety stock levels. Simulation analysis (see Supplement 5) can help determine how much.

Working with a Normal Probability Distribution

A typical assumption when selecting the reorder point is that D_L the actual demand during lead time L, is normally distributed, as shown in Fig. 13.5. The manager must estimate the mean and standard deviation of this distribution either from past history or based on judgment.

The second step is to compute the safety stock:

$$B = z\sigma_L$$

where z = number of standard deviations from the mean needed to implement the cycle-service level

   σ_L = standard deviation of D_L probability distribution*

The higher the value of z, the higher will be B and the cycle-service level. If z is 0, there is no safety stock and stockouts will occur during 50 percent of the cycles. Note also the implications for forecasting (see Chapter 11). The better the job of forecasting demand and lead times, the smaller will be the values of σ_L and B. Lower safety stocks are one reward for accurate forecasts.

Application 13.4	*Finding B and R for a Normal Probability Distribution*

Returning to the birdfeeders, suppose that demand during lead time is normally distributed with $\bar{D}_L$ at 36 units and $\sigma_L = 15$. What safety stock should be carried for a 90 percent cycle-service level? What is R?

Solution   The first step is to find z, the number of standard deviations to the right of $\bar{D}_L$ in Fig. 13.5 that places 90 percent of the area under the curve to the left of that point. Consult the normal table in Appendix 3 at the back of the book and look for 0.90 in the body of the table. The closest number is 0.8997, which corresponds to 1.2 in the row heading and 0.08 in the column heading. Adding these values gives us a z of 1.28. With this information, we can now calculate B as 19 and R as 55.

$$B = z\sigma_L = 1.28(15) = 19.2 \quad \text{or} \quad 19$$
$$R = \bar{D}_L + B = 36 + 19 = 55$$

Selecting R requires knowledge of the standard deviation of demand during the lead time (σ_L), but it is unlikely that this parameter can be obtained *directly* from past records. Demand data may be collected on a daily, weekly, or monthly basis—but not for a time interval exactly equal to the lead time. For example, assume that records report only daily demand. The standard deviation of daily demand can be readily calculated, but the lead time may be several days. If the daily demand probability distributions are independent (i.e., the demand one day does not affect demand the next day) and they are iden-

---

*Some inventory planners prefer to work with the mean absolute deviation (*MAD*), rather than the standard deviation, because it's easier to calculate. Recall from Chapter 11 that to convert *MAD* to the standard deviation, you simply multiply the *MAD* value by 1.25. Then proceed as usual to calculate B.

FIGURE 13.5

Normal D_L
Probability
Distribution

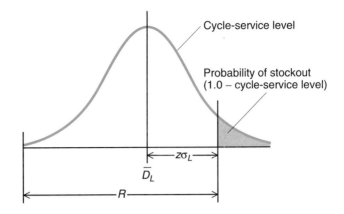

tical, the following conversion is possible:

$$\sigma_L = \sigma_t \sqrt{L_t}$$

where

σ_t = known standard deviation of demand over some time interval t
σ_L = standard deviation of demand during
      lead time (which must be calculated to find the safety stock)
L_t = lead time L, expressed as a multiple (or fraction) of time interval t

After applying the conversion formula, you use the resulting σ_L as before to find the safety stock B.

Application 13.5	*Converting from σ_t to σ_L*

The standard deviation in demand per week is estimated from past records to be 50 units, but the lead time is four weeks. What is the standard deviation of demand during the four-week lead time?

Solution   In this case, $t = 1$ and $L_t = 4$, so σ_L is 100 units.*

$$\sigma_L = 50 \sqrt{4} = 50(2) = 100$$

Working with a Discrete Probability Distribution

We can use the same general approach with other probability distributions. A manager is more likely to use a discrete probability distribution when data are unavailable and judgment is the main source of the estimates. A discrete prob-

---

*This formula comes from basic statistics. The standard deviation of the sum of two or more identically distributed independent random variables is the square root of the sum of their variances. Here, the demand for each week in the lead time is an independent random variable. Therefore

$$\sigma_L = \sqrt{50^2 + 50^2 + 50^2 + 50^2}$$

which simplifies to $50\sqrt{4} = 100$.

ability distribution lists each possible demand during the lead time, along with its probability. For simplicity, assume that the demands listed are the only ones that can occur (nothing in between). Set R so that the probabilities of demand at or below its level total the desired cycle-service level. To identify the amount of safety stock B that will be carried with the reorder point selected, subtract $\bar{D}_L$ from R.

Application 13.6 | *Calculating R and B for a Discrete Probability Distribution*

Based on past records and judgment, the following probability distribution has been estimated for D_L, the demand during lead time of birdfeeders.

D_L(units)	Probability
10	0.10
20	0.15
30	0.20
40	0.25
50	0.20
60	0.10
	1.00

The lead time is two weeks and the average weekly demand is 18 feeders. Museum management selected a 90 percent cycle-service level (9 out of 10 cycles). In other words, the only time that the birdfeeders ordered would *not* be enough is when $D_L =$ 60, which happens only 10 percent of the time. What reorder point should be used? What is the safety stock?

Solution The reorder point R should be 50. The probability that this quantity is enough to avoid a stockout during the lead time is 0.90 (0.10 + 0.15 + 0.20 + 0.25 + 0.20).

The expected value of the demand-during-lead-time distribution, $\bar{D}_L$, is calculated as

$$\bar{D}_L = 10(0.10) + 20(0.15) + \cdots + 60(0.10) = 36 \text{ units}$$

We can now calculate the value of B for $R = 50$ units:

$$R = \bar{D}_L + B$$

$$50 = 36 + B$$

$$B = 14 \text{ units}$$

The B and R calculated in Application 13.6 differ from those found in Application 13.4 because two different probability distributions were used. Setting R at 55, as done with the normal distribution, would not make sense for the discrete distribution because D_L is assumed never to take on such a value. Regardless of the method chosen, R must be known before a reorder point system can be implemented. And knowing B is important information so that managers know which safety stocks are particularly costly. With the normal distribution, B is calculated first and then R is derived. The sequence is reversed with a discrete distribution.

PERIODIC REVIEW SYSTEM (P SYSTEM)

Another popular inventory control system is the **periodic review system,** in which an item's inventory position is reviewed periodically rather than continuously. A new order is placed at the end of each review, and the number of periods (P) between orders is fixed. Demand is a random variable, so the total demand between reviews varies, and the lot size Q changes from one order to the next. Note the differences between this system and the Q system, in which Q is fixed and the time between orders varies. An example of the periodic review system is a soft-drink supplier who makes weekly rounds of grocery stores. Each week, store inventory positions are reviewed and restocked, supposedly with enough items to meet demand until the next week.

As in the previous section we carry forward unchanged the first four assumptions for deriving the EOQ, but we relax the fifth one to allow for demand uncertainty. The periodic review system, also called the P system, periodic order system, fixed interval reorder system, or periodic reorder system, works as follows:

> Review the item's inventory position IP every P time periods. Place an order equal to $(T - IP)$ where T is the target inventory, that is, the desired inventory position just after a new order has been placed.

Figure 13.6 illustrates how a P system operates. The downward sloping line again represents on-hand inventory. When the predetermined time P has elapsed since the last review, an order is placed to bring the inventory position (dashed line) up to the horizontal line that represents T. The lot size for the first review is Q_1, the difference between IP_1 and T. As with the continuous review system, IP and OH differ only during the lead time. When the open order arrives, at the end of the lead time, OH and IP are once again identical. Figure 13.6 shows that lot sizes vary from one cycle to the next. Note that Q_2 is larger than Q_1. The reason is that the inventory position is lower at the second review, meaning that a greater quantity is needed to "order up to" T.

FIGURE 13.6

Illustration of the
P System

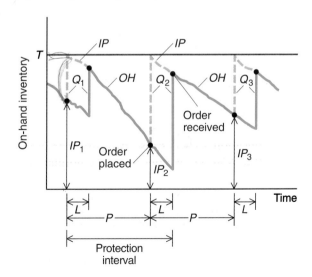

Application 13.7	Determining How Much to Reorder

There is a back order of 5 units of an item having no on-hand inventory. Now is the time to review. How much should be reordered if *T* is 400 and there are no scheduled receipts?

Solution

$$IP = OH + SR - BO$$
$$= 0 + 0 - 5 = -5 \text{ units}$$
$$T - IP = 400 - (-5) = 405 \text{ units}$$

That is, 405 units must be ordered to bring the inventory position up to *T* units.

Selecting the Reorder Interval

The *P* system also has just two parameters: *P* and *T*. Let's first consider *P*. It can be any convenient interval, such as each Friday or every other Friday. Another option is to base *P* on the cost trade-offs of the *EOQ*. For example, if *P* is expressed in weeks and there are 52 work weeks in a year,

$$P = \frac{EOQ}{D} (52)$$

Dividing the *EOQ* by the annual demand *D* gives us the fraction of a year between orders. Multiplying by 52 converts this fraction into weeks. This conversion is identical to how *TBO* was calculated earlier for the *EOQ*.

Selecting the Target Inventory Level

Now let's consider how to calculate the target inventory *T*. If you look closely at Fig. 13.6, you will discover that an order must be large enough to make the inventory position *IP* last beyond the next review, or *P* periods away. The decision maker must wait one full period *P* to revise, correct, and reestablish the inventory position. Then a new order is placed, which will take *L* periods to arrive. Therefore, the decision maker needs a protection interval of *P* + *L*, as Fig. 13.6 shows. This observation identifies a fundamental difference between the *Q* and the *P* systems: A *Q* system needs stockout protection only during the lead time, as orders can be placed at any time and will be received shortly (*L* periods) thereafter. A *P* system, however, needs stockout protection for the longer *P* + *L* protection interval.

Therefore *T* must at least equal the expected demand during the protection interval *P* + *L*. This level does not allow for any safety stock. When *B* is added, it should be enough to protect against demand uncertainty over the entire protection interval. Thus

$$T = \bar{D}_{P+L} + B = \bar{D}_{P+L} + z\sigma_{P+L}$$

where $\bar{D}_{P+L}$ = average demand until the next review in *P* periods plus the average demand during one lead time of *L* periods

       σ_{P+L} = standard deviation of demand during *P* + *L* time periods

z = number of desired standard deviations to implement the cycle-service level (same as for a Q system)

Because a P system requires safety stock to cover demand uncertainty over a longer time period than for a Q system, a P system requires more safety stock (σ_{P+L} exceeds σ_L). Thus overall inventory levels are somewhat higher with a P system.

Application 13.8	*Calculating P and T*

An item's demand is normally distributed with a mean of 40 units per week and a standard deviation in *weekly* demand of 15 units. Lead time is 3 weeks, and the business operates 52 weeks per year. A P system is used. What P approximates the cost trade-offs of a 400-unit *EOQ*? What T is needed for an 80 percent cycle-service level?

Solution First, we find D and then P:

$$D = (40 \text{ units/week})(52 \text{ weeks/year}) = 2080 \text{ units}$$

$$P = \frac{EOQ}{D}(52) = \frac{400}{2080}(52) = 10 \text{ weeks}$$

We therefore would review the item every 10 weeks. We now find the standard deviation of demand over the protection interval ($P_t + L_t = 13$), and P_t is the time between reviews expressed as a multiple (or fraction) of time interval t, where $t = 1$ week:

$$\sigma_{P+L} = \sigma_t \sqrt{P_t + L_t} = 15\sqrt{13} = 54 \text{ units}$$

Before calculating T, we also need a z value. We find it for an 80 percent cycle-service level in Appendix 3 at the back of the book ($z = 0.84$). Now solve for T:

$$T = \bar{D}_{P+L} + z\sigma_{P+L}$$

$$= (40 \text{ units/week})(13 \text{ weeks}) + (0.84)(54 \text{ units}) = 565 \text{ units}$$

Each time we would order as many units as needed to make the inventory position *IP* (counting the new order) equal to the target inventory of 565 units.

Comparative Advantages of the Q and P Systems

Neither the Q nor P system is best in all situations, as shown in Table 13.1. It lists three P-system advantages, which must be balanced against three Q-system advantages. The advantages of one system are implicitly disadvantages of the other one.

***P*-System Advantages.** The first advantage of P systems is that replenishments can be made at fixed time intervals. This procedure can be administratively convenient, particularly if inventory control is but one of several duties of an employee. Some employees prefer to set aside a day or part of a day on a regular basis to concentrate on this particular task. Fixed replenishment intervals are also better for transportation systems that fix the time of pickups (or deliveries) on a daily, weekly, or even monthly basis. For example, bread is usually delivered to particular grocery stores on a fixed schedule, which allows the route between stores to be standardized.

TABLE 13.1 / *Comparison of Q and P Systems*

Advantages of P System	Advantages of Q System
Fixed replenishment intervals	Can individualize the replenishment intervals
Can combine orders to same supplier	More suited for quantity discounts or capacity limitations *Fixed lot size .*
Perpetual inventory system not mandatory	Less safety stock

The second advantage of *P* systems is that orders for multiple items can be combined.* Similar items being ordered at the same time from the same supplier can be combined into a single purchase order. This approach may result in a "family contract" that can lead to a price break. But even without a price break, combining orders can save the buyer some paperwork and reduce ordering cost. This procedure also makes follow-up of open orders easier. When buyers call suppliers to check on the status of one item, they can also ask about the others listed on the family contracts. Suppliers may also prefer combined orders. For example, all items in the order might be shipped at the same time, reducing transportation costs and increasing vehicle utilization.

The third advantage of *P* systems is that the inventory position *IP* needs to be known only when a review is made. This differs from a *Q* system, where some means must be available on a continuous basis to determine when to reorder. When inventory records are always up-to-date, the system is called a **perpetual inventory system.**

As the next replenishment decision can be required at any time in a *Q* system, management cannot afford the luxury of infrequently updated records. Not needing a perpetual inventory system can be an advantage for small, manual applications. When a decision is made to computerize record keeping, with a transaction report for each receipt or withdrawal, this *P* system advantage disappears.

Q-System Advantages. The first advantage of *Q* systems is that the review frequency of each item can be individualized. In a typical *P* system, administrative convenience or ease in combining orders means the periods between orders are the same for a large number of (if not all) items. Instead, by tailoring the review frequency to each item, the total ordering and holding cost can be reduced.

A second advantage of *Q* systems is that fixed lot sizes are sometimes desirable or even mandatory, as in the case of quantity discounts for purchases that exceed a certain size. Physical limitations may also require a fixed lot size. Truckload capacities, materials-handling methods, and furnace capacities are three examples.

The final advantage of *Q* systems, lower safety stocks, was addressed earlier. They must guard against demand uncertainty for just the lead time *L*. For a *P*

---

*Combining orders is also possible with a modified *Q* system. Each item is assigned a reorder point *R* as well as a higher *can-order* point. Whenever the first item in the group reaches *R*, it is ordered along with all other items that have reached their can-order points.

system, demand uncertainty must be covered for a $P + L$ elapsed time. This extended coverage forces safety stock to be increased.

In conclusion, the choice between Q and P systems is not clear-cut. Which one is best depends on the relative importance of its advantages (Table 13.1) in various situations. Management must weigh each alternative carefully in selecting the best system.

HYBRID SYSTEMS

Various hybrid inventory control systems are also used. They include some but not all the features of the P and Q systems. We briefly examine three such systems: optional replenishment, base-stock, and visual.

The optional replenishment system, sometimes called the optional review, min–max, or s,S system, is much like the P system. The **optional replenishment system** reviews the inventory position at fixed time intervals and, if the position has dropped to (or below) a predetermined level, places a variable-sized order to cover expected needs. The new order is large enough to bring the inventory position up to a target inventory, similar to T for the P system. However, orders are not placed after a review unless the inventory position has dropped to a minimum level. The minimum level acts as the reorder point R does in a Q system. Its effect is to ensure that a reasonable order quantity is placed. If the target is 100 and the minimum level is 60, the minimum order size is 40 (100 − 60). As the optional review system also avoids continuous reviews, it is particularly attractive when review and ordering costs are both significant.

A **base-stock system** (in its simplest form) issues a replenishment order each time a withdrawal is made. The order quantity Q equals the amount of the withdrawal. That is, if ten units are removed from inventory to fill an order, a ten-unit replenishment order is placed. This one-for-one replacement policy maintains the inventory position at a base-stock level equal to the expected demand during the lead time plus safety stock. The base-stock level therefore is equivalent to the reorder point in a Q system. However, order quantities now vary to keep the inventory position at R at all times. Because this is the lowest IP possible to maintain a specified service level, the base-stock system can be seen as a way to minimize cycle inventory. More orders are placed but each is smaller, which is appropriate for very expensive items, such as replacement engines for jet airplanes. No more inventory is held than the maximum demand expected until a replacement order can be received.

In actual practice, the base-stock system is often modified in one of two ways. First, replenishment orders can be accumulated so that orders can be made at fixed time intervals, as with the P system. For example, a distribution center may receive weekly shipments from a manufacturing plant, with the quantity shipped equaling the total withdrawals at the DC since the prior week's shipment. Second, replenishment orders can be accumulated to achieve a fixed order quantity, as with a Q system. (This second modification to the base-stock system came about with the introduction of the Kanban system by Toyota in Japan, as discussed in Chapter 17.) Small-lot production in standard lot sizes is achieved, leading to minimal inventory levels.

Visual systems are a third hybrid. They are easy to administer because records on the current inventory position are not kept. The historical usage rate can simply be reconstructed from past purchase orders. Visual systems are intended for use with low-valued items that have a steady demand, such as nuts and bolts. Overstocking is common, but the extra inventory holding cost is minimal because the items have such little value. The two basic approaches used are the single-bin system and the two-bin system.

In the **single-bin system,** a maximum level is marked on the storage shelf or bin or on a measuring rod. The inventory level is brought up to the mark periodically, say, once a week. Examples include gasoline storage tanks at service stations and storage bins for small parts at manufacturing plants. This method is essentially a *P* system, with the target inventory *T* and current *IP* established visually.

In the **two-bin system,** an item's inventory is stored at two different locations. The first bin is the place where inventory is first withdrawn. If it is empty, the second bin provides backup to cover demand until a replenishment order arrives. An empty first bin signals the need to place a new order. Premade order forms may be placed near the bins so that workers can send one to purchasing or even directly to the supplier. When the new order arrives, the second bin is restored to its normal level and the rest is put in the first bin. The two-bin system is really a *Q* system, with the normal level in the second bin being the reorder point *R*. The system can also be implemented with just one bin by marking the bin at the reorder point level. Sometimes the reorder point is even built into the product by the supplier. A calendar is a good example, with a notice inserted toward the end to remind us to reorder for the new year.

QUANTITY DISCOUNTS

In Chapter 12, you learned that quantity discounts, which are price incentives to purchase large quantities, are one of the pressures for higher inventory. Table 13.2 shows one discount schedule from a supplier. The item's price is no longer fixed, as assumed in the *EOQ* derivation. A new approach is needed to find the best lot size.

We begin by recognizing that the total cost now must include the cost of materials. For a given per-unit price level P_j, the total cost is

$$C = \frac{Q}{2}(iP_j) + \frac{D}{Q}(S) + P_j D$$

TABLE 13.2 / *A Quantity Discount Schedule*

Order Quantity	Price per Unit
0–99	$4.00
100–199	3.50
200 and over	3.00

where *i* is the inventory holding cost expressed as a proportion of the unit price. All other parameters are the same as before.

The total cost equation yields U-shaped total cost curves—one for each price level—as shown in Fig. 13.7. No single curve is relevant to all purchase quantities. The relevant or *feasible* total cost begins with the top curve, then drops down, curve by curve, at the price breaks. **A price break** is the minimum quantity needed to get a discount. In Fig. 13.7, there are two price breaks: at $Q = 100$ and $Q = 200$. The result is a single total cost curve, with discontinuities at the price breaks.

Figure 13.7 also reveals something else. The minimum points on the curves, found with the *EOQ* formula at each price level, are not always feasible. For example, the minimum point for the $3.00 curve appears to be about 175 units. However, the quantity discount schedule in Table 13.2 shows that the supplier would not sell you that quantity at the $3.00 unit price. You must therefore pay attention only to price–quantity combinations, shown as solid lines in Fig. 13.7, as you search for the best lot size.

The three-step procedure for finding the best lot size is:

> **Step 1.** Beginning with the *lowest* price, calculate the *EOQ*s for each price level. Each subsequent *EOQ* is smaller than the previous one, because iP_j gets larger. Continue until you find the first *feasible EOQ* that lies in the range corresponding to its price.
>
> **Step 2.** If the *EOQ* for the *lowest* price is feasible, this is the best lot size. Otherwise, go to step 3.
>
> **Step 3.** Calculate the total cost for each price level. Use the *EOQ* quantity when feasible. Otherwise, use the price break quantity for that price. The quantity with the lowest total cost is the best lot size.

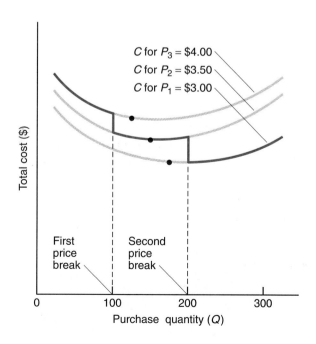

FIGURE 13.7

Total Cost Curves
with Quantity
Discounts

Application 13.9   *Finding Q with Quantity Discounts*

The birdfeeder supplier has introduced quantity discounts to encourage larger order quantities. The price schedule is

Order Quantity	Price per Unit	
0–299	$60.00	7 5
300–499	58.80	3 00
500 or more	57.00	500 .

The museum's annual demand remains at 936 units, ordering cost at $45 per order, and annual holding cost at 25 percent of the birdfeeder's per unit price. What quantity of birdfeeders should the museum order to minimize all costs?

Solution   **Step 1.** Find the first feasible *EOQ*, starting with the lowest price level:

$$EOQ_{57.00} = \sqrt{\frac{2DS}{iP_1}} = \sqrt{\frac{2(936)(45)}{(0.25)(57.00)}} = 77 \text{ units}$$

As a 77-unit order actually costs $60 per unit, instead of $57 per unit, this *EOQ* is infeasible. We now try the $58.80 level:

$$EOQ_{58.80} = \sqrt{\frac{2(936)(45)}{(0.25)(58.80)}} = 76 \text{ units}$$

This quantity is also infeasible, so we move to the highest price level:

$$EOQ_{60.00} = \sqrt{\frac{2(936)(45)}{(0.25)(60.00)}} = 75 \text{ units}$$

This quantity is feasible.

Step 2. The *EOQ* for the *lowest* price ($P_1 = \$57.00$) is not feasible, so we go to step 3.

Step 3. Calculate the total cost of the first feasible *EOQ* (75 units) and each price-break quantity greater than 75 units (300 units and 500 units).

$$C = \frac{Q}{2}(iP_i) + \frac{D}{Q}(S) + P_iD$$

$$C_{75} = \frac{75}{2}(0.25 \times 60.00) + \frac{936}{75}(45) + (60.00)(936) = \$57,284$$

$$C_{300} = \frac{300}{2}(0.25 \times 58.80) + \frac{936}{300}(45) + (58.80)(936) = \$57,382$$

$$C_{500} = \frac{500}{2}(0.25 \times 57.00) + \frac{936}{500}(45) + (57.00)(936) = \$56,999$$

The best purchase quantity is 500 units, which qualifies for the deepest discount. It doesn't always work out this way, such as when discounts are small, *i* is large, and *D* is small.

Managerial Practice·13.2

One-Period Decisions and
Inventory Gluts

Linda Koslow is the general manager of a Marshall Field's department store in an affluent suburb
of Chicago. Her biggest responsibility is to keep expenses and inventories in line with sales trends. In essence, much of her success depends on her ability to
predict shoppers' whims.

The year 1987 was particularly difficult for Marshall
Field's. First the October 19 stock-market crash made
forecasts for Christmas sales highly uncertain. In addition, an election day coat sale on November 3 flopped,
partly because of warm weather, which generally de-

pressed sales of winter goods.
Koslow knew the five-week
Christmas season would be cru-
cial, since that period accounts for a quarter of the store's
$90 million in sales and an even larger share of profits.
Because of the tough sales climate, she decided to discount many items more aggressively and earlier than
originally intended.

Source: "Christmas Sales' Lack of Momentum Test Store
Manager's Mettle," *Wall Street Journal*," December 16,
1987.

ONE-PERIOD DECISIONS

One of the dilemmas facing many retailers, as Managerial Practice 13.2 shows, is how to handle seasonal goods. These items are in demand during only one season of the year. To make matters worse, some of these items are stylish or high-fashion goods and probably cannot be sold at full markup next year. Furthermore, the lead time can be longer than the selling season, allowing no second chance to rush through another order to cover unexpectedly high demand. This type of situation is often called the "newsboy problem." If the newspaper seller does not buy enough papers to resell on the street corner, sales opportunities are lost. If the seller buys too many, the overage cannot be sold because nobody wants yesterday's newspaper.

A straightforward way to analyze such problems and decide on the best order quantity is with a payoff matrix. A **payoff matrix** is a table showing the profits for each purchase quantity at each assumed demand level. Each row in the matrix represents a different order quantity and each column represents a different demand level. For each cell in the matrix,

$$\text{Payoff} = \begin{cases} pQ, & \text{if } Q \leqslant D \\ pD - l(Q - D), & \text{if } Q > D \end{cases}$$

where

p = profit per unit sold during the season
l = loss per unit disposed of after the season
Q = purchase quantity
D = demand level

After calculating the payoff matrix, we can obtain the best order quantity Q. A reasonable approach is to pick the Q with the highest *expected* payoff, which takes demand probabilities into account. Using this strategy for all such items over many selling seasons would maximize profits. The expected value is simply an arithmetic mean. We calculate it for a specific Q by (1) multiplying each payoff in the row by the demand probability associated with the payoff and (2) adding these products.

Application 13.10   *Finding Q for One-Time Inventory Decisions*

One item sold at a museum of natural history is Christmas ornaments carved from wood. The gift shop makes a $10 profit per unit sold during the season, but it takes a $5 loss per unit after the season is over. Selling at a loss is equivalent in cost to carrying inventory for another full year. The following discrete probability distribution for the season's demand has been identified. The levels, along with probability estimates, are

Demand (D)	Demand Probability
10	0.2
20	0.3
30	0.3
40	0.1
50	0.1

How many ornaments should the museum's buyer order?

Solution   Each demand level is a candidate for best order quantity, so the payoff matrix should have five rows. The resulting matrix follows.

Q \ D	10	20	30	40	50
10	$100	$100	$100	$100	$100
20	50	200	200	200	200
30	0	150	300	300	300
40	−50	100	250	400	400
50	−100	50	200	350	500

For example, the payoff when $Q = 40$ and $D = 50$ is

$$pQ = (\$10)(40) = \$400$$

whereas when $Q = 40$ and $D = 30$ the payoff is only

$$pD - l(Q - D) = (\$10)(30) - (\$5)(40 - 30) = \$250$$

Now we calculate the expected payoff for each Q. For example, the expected payoff for $Q = 30$ is

$$0.2(\$0) + 0.3(\$150) + 0.3(\$300) + 0.1(\$300) + 0.1(\$300) = \$195$$

Making these calculations for each row in the payoff matrix, we get

Order Quantity (Q)	Expected Payoff
10	$100
20	170
30	195
40	175
50	140

Since $Q = 30$ has the highest payoff at $195, it is the best order quantity.

The need for one-time inventory decisions also can arise in manufacturing plants when (1) customized items (specials) are made (or purchased) to order *and* (2) scrap quantities are high. A special item is never intentionally held in stock because the demand for it is too unpredictable. In fact, it may never be ordered again. This means that a manufacturer would like to make just the amount requested by the customer—no more, no less. The manufacturer also would like to satisfy an order in just one run to avoid an extra setup and to prevent a delay in delivering goods ordered. These two goals may conflict. Suppose that a customer places an order for 20 units. If the manager orders 20 units from the shop (supplier, if it is a purchased item), one or two units may have to be scrapped. This shortage forces the manager to place a second (or even third) order to replace the defective units. Replacement can be costly if setup time is high and can also delay shipment to the customer. To avoid such problems, the manager could order more than 20 units the first time. If some units are left over, the customer might be willing to buy the extras or the manager might find an internal use for them. For example, some manufacturing companies set up a special account for obsolete materials. These materials can be "bought" by departments within the company at less than their normal cost, as an incentive to use them.

PRACTICAL ISSUES

Operating an actual inventory system involves additional issues, such as (1) how to maintain accurate records and (2) what types of computer support might be advisable. Let's consider both of these issues.

Inventory Records

Information on the amount of on-hand inventory and scheduled receipts is needed for both inventory management and accounting purposes. Sometimes, only periodic checks are made, as when a facility is shut down once a year for several days to count all inventory. At the other extreme are perpetual inventory records, in which a transaction report is made for each withdrawal and receipt. In manual systems, this information is posted to some type of written record. (Forms of manual record keeping include Kardex, visirecord, rotary wheel files, books, and logs.) In computerized systems, which often are coupled with automated identification procedures (see Chapter 6), this information is maintained on disk or tape. In either case, on-hand and scheduled receipt balances are updated the same way. Suppose that a scheduled receipt of 300 units is received, but the supplier actually shipped only 295 units, owing to scrap losses. The buyer decides to accept the order as is rather than request a second shipment of 5 units. The buyer will simply release the next order a few days earlier than usual. For this transaction, the correct adjustments would be to (1) increase on-hand inventory by 295 units and (2) delete the 300-unit scheduled receipt from the records.

Managers must insist on accurate inventory records. One method of tracking inventory is to assign responsibility to specific employees for issuing and receiving materials and faithfully reporting each transaction. Inventory accuracy becomes their responsibility, and they are held accountable for it. A second method is to have closed stores, whereby the inventory is actually secured behind locked doors or gates to prevent unauthorized or unreported withdrawals. This method also guards against storing new receipts in the wrong locations, where they can be lost for months. **Cycle counting** is a third method, whereby storeroom personnel physically count a small percentage of the total number of items each day, correcting errors they find. Class A items are counted most frequently. A final method, for computer systems, is to make logic error checks on each transaction reported and fully investigate discrepancies. Examples of discrepancies are (1) actual receipts when there is no record of scheduled receipts, (2) disbursements that exceed the current on-hand balance, and (3) receipts with a nonexistent part number.

These four methods can keep inventory record accuracy within acceptable bounds. Accuracy pays off mainly through better customer service, although some inventory reductions can be achieved by improving accuracy. A side benefit is that auditors may not require end-of-year counts if records prove to be sufficiently accurate.

Computer Support

As you have discovered by now, managing inventories requires many calculations. Because computers excel at massive data manipulation, it isn't surprising that many companies are computerizing at least parts of their inventory systems. For example, Walgreens, one of the largest and most sophisticated U.S. retailers, implemented computer processing and automatic identification of its inventory at all five of its DCs. All Walgreen stores are then linked into the DC network, so store personnel can place replenishment orders directly from the actual shelf locations.

*O*ne important use of the computer is for inventory control. This Walgreens employee is monitoring shelf stock so that replenishment orders can be placed, on the spot, when necessary.

Managerial Practice 13.3

Computerized Inventory Control for a Competitive Advantage

- At Nissenbaum's auto junkyard in Somerville, Massachusetts, someone on the phone wants an engine for a 1979 Buick. Nissenbaum's, which seems to have everything, doesn't have one of those. So salesman David Butland turns to a nearby personal computer, types a brief message, and patches his request by satellite to 600 junkyards across the country. Within minutes, he is offered engines from Texas, California, and Maine. He buys the one from Maine for $550, and sells it to the customer for $700. "We probably boosted our looking-for-parts business by 75 percent since we got this," says Butland, patting the keyboard.
- Philip Cavavetta buys merchandise for his Boston-area drugstore from two wholesalers. One of them, McKesson, is getting more of his business these days because "their computer system is so good," he explains. A clerk in his store walks down the aisles once a week with a McKesson-supplied computer in his palm. If the store is low on an item, the clerk waves his scanner over a label affixed to the shelf. The computer takes note, and when the clerk is finished, transmits the order to McKesson.
- Levi Strauss & Company now offers a "LeviLink" computer system that automatically replenishes retailers' inventories, without receiving an order. Similarly, Wooster, Ohio's Rubbermaid Incorporated tracks its retail customers' inventories with a computer hookup to the retailers' point-of-sale data. This, says Rubbermaid President Wolf Schmidt, "avoids dead periods" between customer orders and shipments, thus helping retailers lower their inventory.

Sources: "Computer Finds a Role in Buying and Selling, Reshaping Businesses," *Wall Street Journal*, March 18, 1987; "As Stores Scrimp More and Order Less, Suppliers Take on Greater Risks, Costs," *Wall Street Journal*, December 10, 1991.

Several inventory system software packages are generally available, in addition to the in-house systems developed by individual companies. Five of the most common uses of such packages are for updating records, providing management reports, automating the reordering process, generating exception reports, and recomputing decision parameters. Managerial Practice 13.3 illustrates even more uses.

Updating Records. At the time of each transaction, the computer updates on-hand inventory and scheduled receipt balances. Other information, such as recent demand rates, yield losses, price changes, lead times, and supplier performance, also can be updated and displayed on request.

Providing Management Reports. Management can get reports on inventory investment that show measures such as dollar value of inventory, weeks of supply, and turns. These data are often compared to measures from prior periods and can be broken down into various categories. For example, individual departments in a department store usually act as autonomous profit centers, and periodic inventory reports for each one help top management assess performance. Other information important to management includes customer service measures (such as the number of stockouts) and the costs of operating the inventory system itself. Sometimes management compensation plans are geared to such performance measures. Eaton Corporation, a Cleveland-based manufacturer, bases incentive bonuses mainly on each unit's operating profit as a percentage of assets (including inventory) employed, instead of simply rewarding sales or profit gains.

Automatic Reordering. The decision rules already described for the Q and P systems can be programmed easily to generate purchase orders, shop orders, or action notices automatically. In some cases, as with class A items, an inventory analyst reviews computer-generated action notices before authorizing a new order or following up on an order when scheduled receipts are late. The computer saves considerable time because it brings only certain types of items and actions to the analyst's attention. After the analyst makes a decision, the computer can also be programmed to generate the paperwork for a purchase order or shop order.

Generating Exception Reports. An **exception report** is a computer-generated report pointing out some unusual situation needing management's attention. For example, actual lead times or demand rates might be deviating considerably from those forecast. Or a transaction report might show an impossibly large withdrawal, based on the current on-hand record. Such exceptions to normal conditions can be displayed on a computer screen or printed out as hard copy for the analyst to assess.

Recomputing Decision Parameters. A computer can be programmed to periodically recompute parameters such as Q and R for a Q system or P and T for a P system. Costs, lead times, or demands may have changed. Demand forecasts can be revised to recognize new trends. Lead times can be updated, based on recent experience. Current and proposed parameters (such as Q and R) can be simulated, with projections of summary statistics on inventory and customer service levels displayed on a customer screen or printed out.

SOLVED PROBLEMS

1. Suppose that we incorrectly estimate inventory holding cost to be double its true value when computing the *EOQ*.
   a. What is the percentage change in lot size?
   b. What is the new lot size if $D = 936$ units, $S = \$45$, and $H = \$15$? (As in Application 13.1.)
   c. What is the change in total cost?

Solution   a. Using double the true value of H gives us

$$Q = \sqrt{\frac{2DS}{2H}} = \frac{1}{\sqrt{2}}\sqrt{\frac{2DS}{H}}$$

where the real *EOQ* is $$EOQ = \sqrt{\frac{2DS}{H}}$$

Dividing the first equation by the second and simplifying, we get the square root of ½, or 0.707. Thus the 100 percent error deflates the EOQ to 70.7 percent of its true value, a 29.3 percent change.

b. The correct EOQ is

$$EOQ = \sqrt{\frac{2DS}{H}} = \sqrt{\frac{2(936)(45)}{15}} = 75 \text{ units}$$

Multiplying by 0.707 reduces the EOQ to 53 units, which we can verify by using $H = \$30$ in the EOQ formula:

c.

$$EOQ = \sqrt{\frac{2(936)(45)}{30}} = 53 \text{ units}$$

$$C = \frac{Q}{2}(H) + \frac{D}{Q}(S)$$

$$C_{75} = \frac{75}{2}(15) + \frac{936}{75}(45) = \$1124$$

$$C_{53} = \frac{53}{2}(15) + \frac{936}{53}(45) = \$1192$$

The estimation error increases total cost from $1124 to $1192, a 6 percent change. This is a relatively small penalty for a 100 percent error in estimating holding cost.

2. A regional warehouse purchases hand tools from various suppliers and then distributes them on demand to retailers in the region. The warehouse operates 5 days per week, 52 weeks per year. Only when it is open can demand be experienced or orders received. The following data are estimated for ⅜-inch hand drills with double insulation and variable speeds.

Average daily demand = 100 drills
Standard deviation of daily demand (σ_l) = 30 drills
Lead time (L) = 3 days
Holding cost (H) = $9.30 per unit per year
Ordering cost (S) = $35 per order
Cycle-service level = 92 percent

The warehouse uses a continuous review system.
a. What Q and R should be used?
b. If on-hand inventory is 40 units and there is one open order for 442 drills and no back orders, should a new order be placed?

a. $D = $ (100 drills/day)(5 days/week)(52 weeks/year) $= 26,000$ drills

$$EOQ = \sqrt{\frac{2DS}{H}} = \sqrt{\frac{2(26000)(35)}{9.30}} = 442 \text{ drills}$$

Appendix 3 at the back of the book shows that a 92 percent cycle-service level corresponds to $z = 1.40$. Therefore

$$B = z\sigma_L = z\sigma_t\sqrt{L_t} = 1.40(30)\sqrt{3} = 72.75 \quad \text{or} \quad 73 \text{ drills}$$

We add this value of B to the average demand during lead time to obtain

$$R = \bar{D}_L + B = 100(3) + 73 = 373 \text{ drills}$$

With a continuous review system, $Q = 442$ and $R = 373$.

b. $IP = OH + SR - BO = 40 + 442 - 0 = 482 \text{ drills}$

Since IP (482) exceeds R (373), do not place a new order.

3. Suppose that the warehouse uses a periodic review system (P system), but otherwise the data are the same as in Solved Problem 2.
    a. Calculate the P in workdays that gives approximately the same number of orders per year as the EOQ. Round your answer to the nearest day.
    b. What is the value of T?
    c. It is time to review the item. On-hand inventory is 412 units; there are no scheduled receipts and no back orders. How much should be reordered?

Solution

a. $P = \dfrac{EOQ}{D}(260 \text{ days/year}) = \dfrac{442}{26000}(260) = 4.42 \quad \text{or} \quad 4 \text{ days}$

b. $B = z\sigma_{P+L} = 1.40(30)\sqrt{(4 + 3)} = 111.12 \quad \text{or} \quad 111 \text{ drills}$

$$T = \bar{D}_{P+L} + B = 100(4 + 3) + 111 = 811 \text{ drills}$$

c. $IP = OH + SR - BO = 412 + 0 - 0 = 412 \text{ drills}$

$$Q = T - IP = 811 - 412 = 399 \text{ drills}$$

4. The following discrete probability distribution has been estimated for demand during lead time.

D_L (units)	Probability
0	0.15
50	0.30
100	0.20
150	0.10
200	0.10
250	0.10
300	0.05
	1.00

a. With a continuous review system and a 75 percent cycle-service level, what should be the reorder point?
b. What is the safety stock with this R?

Solution a. *R* should be 150 because the probabilities of demand being less than or equal to it sum to 0.75 (0.15 + 0.30 + 0.20 + 0.10).

b. $\bar{D}_L$ = 0(0.15) + 50(0.30) + 100(0.20) + 150(0.10)
    + 200(0.10) + 250(0.10) + 300(0.05) = 110

$$R = \bar{D}_L + B$$

$$150 = 110 + B$$

$$B = 40 \text{ units}$$

5. A hospital uses disposable surgical packages. The supplier's price schedule is

Order Quantity	Price per Unit
0–99	$50
100 or more	45

Ordering cost is $16 per order and annual holding cost is 20 percent of the per unit purchase price. Annual demand is 1800 packages. What is the best purchase quantity?

Solution **Step 1.** We first calculate

$$EOQ_{45.00} = \sqrt{\frac{2DS}{iP_j}} = \sqrt{\frac{2(1800)(16)}{(0.2)(45)}} = 80 \text{ units}$$

Since it is infeasible, we calculate

$$EOQ_{50.00} = \sqrt{\frac{2(1800)(16)}{(0.2)(50)}} = 76 \text{ units, a feasible lot}$$

Step 2. The *EOQ* for the lowest price is infeasible, so we go to step 3.

Step 3. $TC = \dfrac{Q}{2}(iP_j) + \dfrac{D}{Q}(S) + P_jD$

$$TC_{76} = \frac{76}{2}(0.20 \times 50) + \frac{1800}{76}(16) + 50(1800) = \$90{,}759$$

$$TC_{100} = \frac{100}{2}(0.20 \times 45) + \frac{1800}{100}(16) + 45(1800) = \$81{,}738$$

The best purchase quantity is the price-break quantity, or 100 units.

FORMULA REVIEW

1. Total relevant cost: $C = \dfrac{Q}{2}(H) + \dfrac{D}{Q}(S)$ (No quantity discounts)

$C = \dfrac{Q}{2}(iP_j) + \dfrac{D}{Q}(S) + P_jD$ (With quantity discounts)

2. Economic order quantity:

$$EOQ = \sqrt{\frac{2DS}{H}}$$

3. Inventory position:

$$IP = OH + SR - BO$$

4. Reorder point:

$$R = \bar{D}_L + B$$

5. Safety stock:

$$B = z\sigma_L \qquad \text{(Continuous review system)}$$

$$B = z\sigma_{P+L} \qquad \text{(Periodic review system)}$$

6. Standard deviation of demand:

$$\sigma_L = \sigma_t\sqrt{L_t} \qquad \text{(Continuous review system)}$$

$$\sigma_{P+L} = \sigma_t\sqrt{P_t + L_t} \qquad \text{(Periodic review system)}$$

7. Reorder interval and time between orders (with 52 weeks/year):

$$P = \frac{EOQ}{D}(52)$$

8. Inventory target:

$$T = \bar{D}_{P+L} + z\sigma_{P+L}$$

9. Payoff matrix:

$$\text{Payoff} = \begin{cases} pQ, & \text{if } Q \leq D \\ pD - l(Q - D), & \text{if } Q > D \end{cases}$$

CHAPTER HIGHLIGHTS

● Inventory management methods depend on the nature of demand. The two broad categories of demand are: independent and dependent. Independent demand is generated directly by the customer, and total demand for independent-demand items is often more uniform than for dependent-demand items. All types of organizations maintain independent-demand inventories. In the service sector, wholesale and retail merchandise alone accounts for 44 percent of the inventory in the U.S. economy.

● A basic question in inventory management is whether to order infrequently in large quantities or frequently in small quantities. Calculation of the EOQ facilitates this choice by providing the lot size Q that minimizes the sum of holding and ordering (or setup) costs. Basic EOQ assumptions include constant demand, receipts in full lots, only two relevant costs, single-item decisions, and no uncertainty.

● In the continuous review system (or Q system), the buyer places orders of a fixed lot size Q

whenever the inventory position IP drops to the reorder point R. The reorder point answers the second basic question in inventory management: when to place the next order. The reorder point equals the expected average demand during the lead time D_L and safety stock B to handle demand uncertainties. The size of the safety stock depends on the desired customer service level. The inventory position IP is equal to on-hand inventory plus scheduled receipts minus any back ordered or allocated demand.

● In the periodic review system (or P system), the buyer places orders every P fixed time intervals. The order quantity is the difference between the target inventory T and the current inventory position and can vary from order to order. T is established to cover expected demand and safety stock B over $P + L$ time periods.

● The choice between P and Q systems is not clear-cut. Fixed replenishment intervals, combined orders, type of record keeping, individual replenishment intervals, quantity discounts, and safety stocks all have to be considered.

● Various hybrid inventory systems, including optional replenishment, base-stock, and visual systems, are used in practice. The base-stock system minimizes cycle inventory by maintaining the inventory position at the base-stock level. Visual systems, such as single-bin and two-bin systems, are adaptations of the P and Q systems that eliminate the need for records.

● When quantity discounts are available, the total relevant cost includes annual holding, ordering, and materials costs. Purchasing larger quantities to achieve price discounts is not always the best strategy.

● Retailers, as well as manufacturers of specials, often face one-time inventory decisions. Demand uncertainty can lead to ordering too much or too little, which can result in cost or customer service penalties. The most straightforward approach to one-time inventory decisions is to calculate the expected payoff over a range of reasonable alternatives and choose the one with the best expected payoff.

● At a minimum, inventory levels must be measured annually. Records are likely to be maintained for on-hand inventory and scheduled receipts balances. Clearly assigned responsibility, closed stores, cycle counting, and logic error checks are methods used to maintain accurate records.

● Computer software packages are available to assist in updating records, providing management reports, automatic reordering, generating exception reports, and recomputing decision parameters.

KEY TERMS

base-stock system **549**
continuous review system **539**
cycle counting **556**
cycle-service level **541**
economic order quantity
　(EOQ) **533**
exception report **558**
fill rate **541**

inventory position (IP) **539**
optional replenishment
　system **549**
payoff matrix **553**
periodic review system **545**
perpetual inventory
　system **548**
price break **551**

reorder point system
　(ROP) **539**
single-bin system **550**
time between orders
　(TBO) **537**
two-bin system **550**
visual systems **550**

STUDY QUESTIONS

1. When can the cost of materials paid to the supplier no longer be ignored in finding a reasonable lot size?

2. What is the relationship between an item's lot size and the frequency of placing orders for it?

3. How are the best lot size Q and reorder point R affected by
   a. increases in demand?
   b. decreases in setup costs?
   c. increases in interest rates?
   d. forecast errors in D, H, or S?

4. "Its assumptions are so unrealistic that the *EOQ* provides little guidance in managing inventories." Comment.

5. What should be considered in setting a service level policy?

6. Blood is collected for medical purposes at various sites (such as at mobile units), tested, separated into components, and shipped to a hospital blood bank. Each bank holds the components in inventory and issues them as needed to satisfy transfusion requests. There are eight major types of blood, and each type has many components (such as red cells, white cells, and plasma). Each component has a different medical purpose and a different lifetime. For example, the lifetime for white cells is only 6 hours, but the lifetime for red cells is now 35 days. What type of management issues are involved in this particular type of inventory control? Does perishability require different records than for other situations? How?

7. What two basic questions are answered by Q and R of the Q system? By P and T of the P system?

8. Under what conditions would you prefer to use a Q system? A P system? A base-stock system? A visual system?

9. When do one-time inventory decisions arise? What information should be gathered in making a final choice?

10. Suppose that you are a buyer of an important raw material. Rumor has it that a sizable price increase will take place in the near future. How might you decide whether to hedge against the price increase by buying more than usual with the next order?

11. What are the rewards and costs of having accurate inventory records? How can accuracy be increased?

PROBLEMS

Review Problems

1. An ophthalmologist's office sells gas-permeable contact lenses for only $50 per pair. The following information is available for these lenses.

   - Demand = 60 pairs/week
   - Order cost = $60/order
   - Annual holding cost = 20 percent of selling price
   - Desired cycle-service level = 80 percent
   - Lead time = 2 weeks (12 working days)
   - Standard deviation of weekly demand = 10 pairs
   - Current on-hand inventory is 160 units, with no open orders or back orders

   The store operates 52 weeks per year, 6 days per week. It has a continuous inventory review system.

   a. What is the *EOQ*? What would be the average time between orders (in weeks), using the *EOQ*?
   b. What should R be?
   c. An inventory withdrawal for 10 pairs was just made. Is it time to reorder?
   d. The store currently uses a lot size of 500 units (that is, $Q = 500$). What is the annual holding cost of this policy? Annual ordering cost? Without obtaining the *EOQ*, how can you conclude from these two calculations that the current lot size is too large?
   e. What is the annual cost saved by shifting from the 500-unit lot size to the *EOQ*?

2. Consider again the data in Problem 1.
   a. Suppose that the weekly demand forecast

of 60 pairs is incorrect, that it will actually be only 40 pairs per week. How much higher will total costs be, owing to the distorted *EOQ* caused by this forecast error?

b. Suppose that actual demand of 60 pairs is correct but that ordering costs are cut to only $10 under a blanket order arrangement. (See Chapter 12.) However, the buyer does not tell anyone, and the *EOQ* is not adjusted to reflect this reduction in *S*. How much higher will total costs be, compared to what they could be if the *EOQ* were adjusted?

3. Suppose that the office (see Problem 1) uses a *P* system instead of a *Q* system.
   a. What *P* (in workdays) and *T* should be used to approximate the economics of the *EOQ*?
   b. How much more safety stock (than with a *Q* system) is needed?
   c. It is time for the periodic review. How much should be ordered?

4. Your firm uses a continuous review system (*Q* system), where the inventory position of each item is updated after every transaction. The firm operates 52 weeks per year. One of the items has the following characteristics.

   - Demand (*D*) = 20,000 units/year
   - Ordering cost (*S*) = $40/order
   - Holding cost (*H*) = $2/unit/year
   - Lead time (*L*) = 2 weeks
   - Standard deviation of *weekly* demand = 100 units
   - Cycle-service level = 95 percent
   - Current on-hand inventory is 1040 units, with no scheduled receipts and no back orders.

   a. Calculate the item's *EOQ*. What is the average time, in weeks, between orders?
   b. Find the safety stock *B* and reorder point *R* that provide a 95 percent cycle-service level.
   c. For these policies, what are the annual costs of
      i. holding the cycle inventory?

   ii. placing orders?
   d. A withdrawal of 15 units just occurred. Is it time to reorder? If so, how much should be ordered?

5. Suppose instead that your firm uses a periodic review system (*P* system), but otherwise the data are the same as in Problem 4.
   a. Calculate the *P* that gives approximately the same number of orders per year as the *EOQ*. Round your answer to the nearest week.
   b. Find the safety stock *B* and the target inventory *T* that provide a 95 percent cycle-service level.
   c. How much larger is the safety stock than with a *Q* system?

6. Suppose that you are a recent graduate who majored in operations management. Your boss has just asked you to review the company's current policies for its continuous review system (*Q* system). You begin by checking out the current policies for a sample of items. The following are the characteristics of one item.

   - Demand (*D*) = 15 units/week (Assume 52 weeks per year.)
   - Ordering and setup cost (*S*) = $50/order
   - Holding cost (*H*) = $12/unit/year
   - Lead time (*L*) = 2 weeks
   - Standard deviation of *weekly* demand = 6 units
   - Cycle-service level = 80 percent

   a. What is the *EOQ* for this item?
   b. What is the desired safety stock *B*?
   c. What is the desired reorder point *R*?
   d. Suppose that the current policy is *Q* = 100 and *R* = 150. If this item were typical, what would you recommend to your boss?

7. Using the same information as in Problem 6, develop the best policies for a periodic review system (*P* system).
   a. What value of *P* gives the same approximate number of orders per year as the *EOQ*? Round to the nearest week.

b. What safety stock B and target inventory T provide an 80 percent cycle-service level?

8. Wood County Hospital consumes 500 boxes of bandages per week. The price of bandages is $70 per box, and the hospital operates 52 weeks per year. The cost of processing an order is $60, and the cost of holding one box for a year is 15 percent of the value of the material.

   a. The hospital orders bandages in lot sizes of 900 boxes. What *extra cost* does the hospital incur, which it could have saved by applying the *EOQ* concept?

   b. Demand is normally distributed, with the standard deviation of weekly demand being 100 boxes. The lead time is one-half week. What safety stock is necessary if the hospital uses a continuous review system, and a 97 percent cycle-service level is desired? What should be the reorder point?

   c. If the hospital uses a periodic review system, with $P = 2$ weeks, what should be the target inventory level T?

9. A golf specialty wholesaler operates 50 weeks per year and is trying to determine an inventory policy for its 1-irons. The 1-irons have the following characteristics.

   - Demand (D) = 1000 units/year and is normally distributed
   - Standard deviation of *weekly* demand = 3 units
   - Ordering cost = $20/order
   - Annual holding cost (H) = $2 per unit
   - Desired cycle-service level = 85 percent
   - Lead time (L) = 3 weeks

   a. If the company uses a periodic review system, based on the cost trade-offs captured by the *EOQ*, what should be P and T? Round P to the nearest week.

   b. If the company uses a continuous review system, what should R be?

10. Management estimates the demand during lead time for an important product to be distributed as follows.

D_L (units)	Probability
20	0.20
50	0.40
70	0.20
100	0.10
200	0.10
	1.00

   a. If a continuous review system is used, what reorder point provides an 80 percent cycle-service level?

   b. What would be the safety stock?

11. Club Hardware estimates the following demand-during-lead-time distribution for a particular pocket wrench.

D_L (units)	Probability
0	0.20
20	0.20
50	0.20
70	0.20
100	0.10
130	0.10
	1.00

   a. What reorder point R would result in a 90 percent cycle-service level?

   b. How much safety stock B is provided with this policy?

12. Matt Herron is the chief buyer at Investment Clothiers, a retail store known for excellence in apparel. It is time to order merchandise for the Christmas season. During a recent trip to Hong Kong, Matt spotted a particular men's overcoat that should sell quite well. Based on past experience, Matt expects the demand for such a coat to range from 100 to 400. He estimates the probability distribution as follows.

Season's Demand	Probability
100	0.10
200	0.40
300	0.40
400	0.10
	1.00

The total cost to Investment Clothiers would be $50 per coat, and the retail price would be set at $90. Any coats left over after Christmas would be sold at $40 each. How many coats should Matt buy if he wants to maximize expected profits?

13. Kay's Pastries are freshly baked and sold at several specialty shops throughout New York. When they are a day old, they must be sold at reduced prices. Daily demand is distributed as follows.

Demand (D)	Probability
100	0.30
200	0.40
300	0.30
	1.00

Each pastry sells for $1.00 and costs $0.60. Each one not sold at the end of the day can be sold the next day at $0.30 as day-old merchandise. How many pastries should be baked each day?

14. A plumbing supply company received the following price schedule for a popular valve from its supplier.

Order Quantity	Price per Valve
0–199	$1.60
200–399	1.40
400 or more	1.20

Annual demand is estimated at 6000 valves, and ordering cost at $10 per order. If annual holding cost is 20 percent of the per unit purchase price, what is the best purchase quantity?

15. As inventory manager you must decide on the order quantity for an item that has an annual demand of 2000 units. It costs you $20 each time you place an order. Your holding cost, expressed as a percentage of average inventory value, is 20 percent. Your supplier has provided the following price schedule.

Price per Unit	Minimum Order Quantity
$2.50	1
$2.40	200
$2.25	300
$2.00	1000

What ordering policy do you recommend?

Advanced Problems

Supplement Connections: Problems 16 through 19 require prior reading of Supplement 5 (Simulation Analysis), and Problems 21 and 22 require prior reading of Supplement 2 (Linear Programming). A computer package is required for solving Problems 21 and 22.

16. The Georgia Lighting Center stocks more than 3000 lighting fixtures, including chandeliers, swags, wall lamps, and track lights. The store sells at retail, operates six days per week, and advertises itself as the "brightest spot in town." One expensive fixture is selling at an average rate of 5 units per day. The reorder policy is $Q = 40$ and $R = 15$. The lead time is two full days, and new orders are placed at the end of the day. Thus a new order is available for use at the beginning of the third day after an order is placed.

Simulate the performance of this Q system for the next three weeks (18 work days). Any stockouts result in lost sales (rather than back orders). The beginning inventory is 19 units, and there are no scheduled receipts. Demand is random and is shown for each of the next 18 days in Table 13.3. Fill in the rest of the table.

a. What is the average daily ending inventory over the 18 days?

b. How many stockouts occurred?

17. Simulate Problem 16 again, but this time use a P system with $P = 8$ and $T = 55$. Let the next review period be day 1. As before, the beginning inventory is 19 units and there are no scheduled receipts.

a. What is the average daily ending inventory over the 18 days?

b. How many stockouts occurred?

TABLE 13.3

Work-day	Beginning Inventory	Orders Received	Daily Demand	Ending Inventory	Inventory Position	Amount Ordered
1	19	—	5			
2		—	3			
3		—	4			
4			1			
5			10			
6			9			
7			7			
8			4			
9			2			
10			7			
11			3			
12			6			
13			10			
14			0			
15			5			
16			10			
17			4			
18			7			

18. In Solved Problem 2, a Q system for hand drills was devised, with $Q = 442$ and $R = 373$. Simulate this system for a 21-day period, using the format of Table 13.4. The daily demand is drawn from a normal distribution with a mean of 100 and standard deviation of 30. The on-hand inventory at the start of day 1 is 113 units and one scheduled receipt for 442 units is to arrive on this first day. The lead time for new orders is three full days. Thus if a new order is placed at the *end* of the second workday, it would be available at the *beginning* of the sixth workday.
   a. What is the average daily ending inventory over the 21 days?
   b. How many new orders are placed?

19. In Solved Problem 3, a P system for hand drills was devised, with $P = 4$ days and $T = 811$. Simulate this system for a 21-day period, using the random demand shown in Table 13.4.
   a. What is the average ending inventory over the 21 days?
   b. How many new orders are placed?

20. The fill rate for a certain safety stock level is

$$F = 1 - \frac{n_s}{Q}$$

where

   F = fill rate, expressed as a proportion
   n_s = expected number of units short per cycle for the safety stock level provided
   Q = order quantity

   a. For the probability distribution in Application 13.6, determine the safety stock, cycle-service level, and expected number of units short per cycle for three different reorder points: 40 units, 50 units, and 60 units.
   b. For each of the three reorder points, determine the number of orders placed per year and the fill rate for $Q = 36$, $Q = 78$, and $Q = 234$. What conclusions can you draw from your results about the effect of lot size on customer service?

TABLE 13.4

Work-day	Beginning Inventory	Orders Received	Daily Demand	Ending Inventory	Inventory Position	Amount Ordered
1	113	442	143			
2		—	82			
3		—	103			
4		—	127			
5			85			
6			60			
7			94			
8			87			
9			102			
10			42			
11			123			
12			148			
13			85			
14			67			
15			83			
16			123			
17			108			
18			88			
19			120			
20			138			
21			74			

21. A problem often of concern to managers in the process industry is blending. Consider the task facing Lisa Rankin, procurement manager of a company that manufactures special additives. She must determine the proper amounts of each raw material to purchase for the production of a certain product. Three raw materials are available. Each gallon of the finished product must have a combustion point of at least 220°F. In addition, the gamma content (which causes hydrocarbon pollution) cannot exceed 6 percent of volume. The zeta content (which cleans the internal moving parts of engines) must be at least 12 percent by volume. Each raw material has varying degrees of these characteristics. (See following table.)

Raw material A costs $0.60 per gallon, whereas raw materials B and C cost $0.40 and $0.50 per gallon, respectively. The procurement manager wishes to minimize the

	Raw Material		
Characteristic	A	B	C
Combustion point (°F)	200	180	280
Gamma content (%)	4	3	10
Zeta content (%)	20	10	8

cost of raw materials per gallon of product. Use linear programming to find the optimal proportions of each raw material to use in a gallon of finished product. *Hint:* Express your decision variables in terms of fractions of a gallon. The sum of the fractions must equal 1.00.

22. The Washington Chemical Company produces chemicals and solvents for the glue industry. The production process is divided into several "focus factories," each producing a specific set of products. The time has come to prepare the production plan for one

TABLE 13.5

	Product					Total Resources Available
Resource	1	2	3	4	5	
Reactor (hr/lb)	0.05	0.10	0.80	0.57	0.15	7,500 hr*
Separator (hr/lb)	0.20	0.02	0.20	0.09	0.30	7,500 hr*
Raw material 1 (lb)	0.20	0.50	0.10	0.40	0.18	10,000 lb
Raw material 2 (lb)	—	0.70	—	0.50	—	6,000 lb
Raw material 3 (lb)	0.10	0.20	0.40	—	—	7,000 lb
Profit contribution ($/lb)	4.00	7.00	3.50	4.00	5.70	

*The total time available has been adjusted to account for setups. The five products have a prescribed sequence owing to the cost of changeovers between products. The company has a 35-day cycle (or 10 changeovers per year per product). Consequently, the time for these changeovers has been deducted from the total time available for these machines.

of the focused factories. This particular factory produces five products that must pass through both the reactor and the separator. Each product also requires a certain combination of raw materials. Production data are shown in Table 13.5.

The Washington Chemical Company has a long-term contract with a major glue manufacturer that requires annual production of 3000 pounds of both products 3 and 4. More of these products could be produced because there is a demand for them.

a. Determine the annual production quantities of each product that maximize contribution to profits. Assume that you can sell all you can produce.

b. Specify the lot sizes for each product.

CASE   PARTS EMPORIUM*

It was June 1, Sue McCaskey's first day in the newly created position of materials manager for Parts Emporium. A recent graduate of a prominent business school, Sue was eagerly awaiting her first "real-world" problem. At approximately 8:30 A.M. it arrived in the form of status reports on inventory and orders shipped. On top of the extensive computer printout was a handwritten note from Joe Donnell, the purchasing manager:

Attached you will find the data you requested concerning inventory and customer service performance. Rest assured that the individual inventory levels are accurate because we took a complete physical inventory count at the end of last week. Unfortunately, we do not keep compiled records in these areas as you requested. However, you're welcome to do this yourself. Welcome aboard!

A little upset that the aggregate information she wanted was not available, Sue decided to randomly select a small sample of approximately 100 items and compile inventory and customer service characteristics to get a feel for the "total picture." The results of this little experiment revealed to her why Parts Emporium decided to create the new position she now filled. It seems that the inventory is in all the wrong places. Although there was an *average* of approximately 60 days of inventory, customer service (measured as the fill rate) was *averaging* only 80 percent. Parts Emporium tries to back order the customer orders not immediately filled from stock, but around 10 percent of these orders are lost to competitor distributorships.

*Courtesy of Professor Robert Bregman, Texas A&M University.

The Company

Parts Emporium, Inc., was formed in 1967 as a wholesale distributor of automobile parts by two disenchanted auto mechanics, Dan Block and Ed Spriggs. Originally located in Dan's garage, the firm showed slow but steady growth until 1970, when it relocated to an old, abandoned meat packing warehouse on the south side of Chicago. With increased space for inventory storage, the company was able to begin offering an expanded line of auto parts. This increased selection, combined with the trend toward longer car ownership, led to an explosive growth of the business in the mid- to late 1970s. By 1981 Parts Emporium was the largest independent distributor of auto parts in the north-central region of the midwestern U.S. market.

In 1984 Parts Emporium relocated into a sparkling new office and warehouse complex off Interstate 55 in suburban Chicago. The warehouse space alone was over 100,000 square feet at this facility. Although only a handful of new products have been added since the warehouse was constructed, its utilization has increased from 65 percent to more than 90 percent of capacity. During this same period, however, sales growth has stagnated. These conditions motivated Dan Block and Ed Spriggs to hire the first manager from outside the company in the firm's history.

The Situation

Sue McCaskey has no illusions concerning her new job. She knows that, although her influence to initiate changes will be limited, she must produce positive results immediately. Thus she has decided to concentrate her initial efforts on two sample products from the extensive product line: the EG151 exhaust gasket and the DB032 drive belt. If she can demonstrate significant gains from the proper management of just two products, then perhaps Dan Block and Ed Spriggs will provide her with the backing to change the inventory management methods for the total product line.

The EG151 exhaust gasket is purchased from an overseas supplier, Haipei, Inc. The data available concerning forecasted versus actual demand are given in Exhibit 1. A quick review of past orders, shown in another document, indicates that a lot size of 150 units is being used and that the lead time from Haipei is fairly constant at two weeks.

The DB032 drive belt is purchased from the Bendox Corporation of Grand Rapids, Michigan. Data concerning forecasted versus actual demand are listed in Exhibit 2. Because this is a new product, data are available only since its introduction in week 11 of this year. There is no current back order for this product. A lot size of 1000 units is being used, with the lead time being fairly constant at three weeks.

The wholesale prices that Parts Emporium charges its customers are $12.99 for the EG151 exhaust gasket and $8.89 for the DB032 drive belt. Because no quantity discounts are offered on these two highly profitable items, gross margins based on current purchasing practices run at 32 percent of the wholesale price for

---

EXHIBIT 1 / EG151 Exhaust Gasket: Forecasted Versus Actual Demand

Week	Forecasted Demand	Actual Demand	Week	Forecasted Demand	Actual Demand
1	99	104	16	102	103
2	104	103	17	100	101
3	107	102	18	101	101
4	105	99	19	103	104
5	102	101	20	107	108
6	102	99	21	104	97
7	101	99	22	101	100
8	103	104	23	101	
9	102	100	24	107	
10	100	100	25	109	
11	101	103	26	107	
12	100	97	27	103	
13	100	99	28	105	
14	99	102	29	102	
15	98	99	30	100	

Note: Inventory on hand (end of week 22) = 0.   Back orders (end of week 22) = 11.

EXHIBIT 2 / *DB032 Drive Belt: Forecasted Versus Actual Demand*

Week	Forecasted Demand	Actual Demand	Week	Forecasted Demand	Actual Demand
11	10	18	21	51	52
12	22	33	22	52	50
13	48	53	23	50	
14	67	54	24	51	
15	62	51	25	53	
16	55	53	26	55	
17	54	50	27	54	
18	51	53	28	56	
19	54	54	29	57	
20	54	49	30	59	

Note: Inventory on hand (end of week 22) = 324.

the exhaust gasket and 48 percent of the wholesale price for the drive belt.

Parts Emporium currently can borrow funds at an interest rate of 13 percent and is achieving an annual return on assets of 21 percent. The 100,000 square foot warehouse was originally built for $1.2 million, but an additional $120,000 was needed later to upgrade the sprinkler system to meet a new, stricter federal code. The annual report for last year noted other warehousing expenditures as follows: $132,000 for utilities, $58,000 for insurance, and $83,000 for maintenance.

Out-of-pocket costs for Parts Emporium to place an order are estimated to be $20 per order for exhaust gaskets and $10 per order for drive belts. On the outbound side, there can be delivery charges. Although most customers pick up their orders at Parts Emporium, 32 percent of all orders involve a delivery to the customer. To provide this service, Parts Emporium contracts with a local company for a flat fee of $21.40 per order, which is added to the customer's bill. The average number of items per order last year was 121.

1. Put yourself in the position of Sue McCaskey and prepare a report to Dan Block and Ed Spriggs detailing an appropriate strategy for managing the inventory of the EG151 exhaust gasket and the DB032 drive belt. Be sure to include a discussion of the proper lot-sizing methodology and the associated benefits.

SELECTED REFERENCES

Bragg, Daniel Jay. "The Impact of Inventory Record Inaccuracy on Material Requirements Planning Systems." Unpublished dissertation, Ohio State University, 1984.

Buffa, Elwood S., and Jeffrey G. Miller. *Production-Inventory Systems: Planning and Control,* 3rd ed. Homewood, Ill.: Richard D. Irwin, 1979.

"Factors That Make or Break Season Sales." *Wall Street Journal,* December 9, 1991.

Fogerty, Donald W., and Thomas R. Hoffman. *Production and Inventory Management.* Cincinnati: South-Western, 1983.

Greene, James H. *Production and Inventory Control Handbook.* New York: McGraw-Hill, 1970.

International Business Machines Corporation. *Basic Principles of Wholesale IMPACT.* Publication E20-8105-1.

Johnson, Lynwood A., and Douglas C. Montgomery. *Operations Research in Production Planning, Scheduling and Inventory Control.* New York: John Wiley & Sons, 1979.

Love, Stephen F. *Inventory Control.* New York: McGraw-Hill, 1979.

Ronen, David. "Inventory Service Measures—A Comparison of Measures." *International Journal of Operations and Production Management,* vol. 3, no. 2 (1983), pp. 37–45.

Silver, Edward A. "Operations Research in Inventory Management: A Review and Critique." *Operations Research,* vol. 9, no. 4 (July–August 1981).

Silver, Edward A., and Rein Peterson. *Decision Systems for Inventory Management and Production Planning.* New York: John Wiley & Sons, 1985.

Chapter 14

AGGREGATE PLANNING

What is the relationship between our positioning strategy and production plan?

Should we use a level work-force strategy or some variable work-force strategy?

How can we adjust the demand pattern to reduce operating costs?

Should we use subcontracting to achieve short-term capacity increases or some combination of inventory accumulation and overtime?

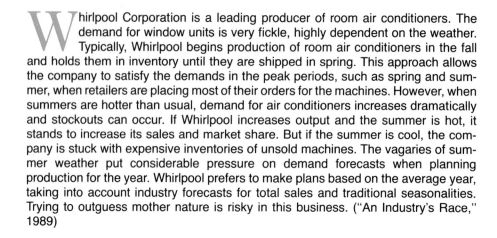

Whirlpool Corporation is a leading producer of room air conditioners. The demand for window units is very fickle, highly dependent on the weather. Typically, Whirlpool begins production of room air conditioners in the fall and holds them in inventory until they are shipped in spring. This approach allows the company to satisfy the demands in the peak periods, such as spring and summer, when retailers are placing most of their orders for the machines. However, when summers are hotter than usual, demand for air conditioners increases dramatically and stockouts can occur. If Whirlpool increases output and the summer is hot, it stands to increase its sales and market share. But if the summer is cool, the company is stuck with expensive inventories of unsold machines. The vagaries of summer weather put considerable pressure on demand forecasts when planning production for the year. Whirlpool prefers to make plans based on the average year, taking into account industry forecasts for total sales and traditional seasonalities. Trying to outguess mother nature is risky in this business. ("An Industry's Race," 1989)

Whirlpool's plan for coping with seasonal demands for room air conditioners is called an **aggregate plan.** There are two types of aggregate plans. The first, called a **production plan,** is a managerial statement of time-phased production rates, work-force levels, and inventory investment that considers customer requirements and capacity limitations. The plan balances the typically conflicting objectives of maximizing customer service, minimizing inventory investment, maintaining a stable work force, minimizing production cost, and maximizing profit. This is the type of aggregate plan Whirlpool uses.

The other form of aggregate plan is the **staffing plan,** a time-phased statement of work-force sizes and labor-related decisions (such as overtime and vacation schedules) that considers customer requirements and machine capacities. This form of aggregate plan is useful for service firms, which do not plan in terms of production rates and inventories. The plan also must balance conflicting objectives involving customer service, work-force stability, cost, and profit.

The aggregate plan links the overall strategy of a firm and its detailed operating plans. For manufacturing companies the production plan links strategic goals and objectives with the master production schedule. We shall see in the next several chapters how this is done. For service firms the staffing plan links strategic goals with detailed work-force schedules. Chapter 18 discusses this linkage. In this chapter we focus on the aggregate plan and its relationship to the hierarchy of plans in manufacturing and service firms.

THE NATURE OF AGGREGATE PLANS

In this section we explain the aspects of aggregation associated with aggregate plans and discuss the relationships of this plan to other important plans in a firm.

Aggregation

The aggregate plan is useful because it is general. The planner can devise a course of action, consistent with strategic goals and objectives, without having to deal with a lot of detail. For example, having to schedule each of the thousands of products and employees at Whirlpool just to find out whether the plan would satisfy budget guidelines would be a hopeless task. Managerial Practice 14.1 shows some aggregate planning problems encountered in practice. Even if a planner could prepare such a detailed plan, the time and effort required to update its details would make it virtually worthless. For this reason, production and staffing plans should be based on aggregate quantities, hence the term *aggregate plan*. The aggregations most often used are products or services, labor,

---

Managerial Practice 14.1

Typical Aggregate Planning Problems

Automobile Industry

- In 1990 General Motors wanted to add a third shift to some of its U.S. automobile assembly plants. The added shift would allow GM to boost a factory's output by as much as 50 percent without having to pay overtime or build additional facilities. However, United Auto Workers' leaders were concerned that three-shift schemes would enable GM to shift production from its underutilized plants. The union was concerned about the number of jobs that would be lost at those underutilized plants.
- In October 1990 the Big Three automakers announced modifications to their production plans due to changes in sales for some product lines. Ford said it would close a truck plant in Louisville, Kentucky, for one week and extend the shutdown of a plant producing Econoline vans in Lorain, Ohio, for another week. Chrysler said it would close a St. Louis plant producing Chrysler LeBarons and Dodge Daytonas for a week in October and permanently close it in seven months. General Motors extended by one week the shutdown of its Willow Run, Michigan, plant producing Chevrolet Caprices. In addition, Ford and GM announced Saturday overtime in plants experiencing increased sales.

Delivery Services

- The United Parcel Service hires a large number of employees for its package-sorting hub. The work

is hard and routine, and the hours are long. UPS demands high levels of productivity, which occasionally generates complaints from Teamsters union members. When faced with the alternatives of hiring full-time or part-time employees in their staffing plans, UPS managers prefer full-time employees so they can train them and, through thoroughly researched process and job designs, instill a strong sense of teamwork and job satisfaction. Although the work is demanding, UPS typically has many more applications than openings when they recruit more employees.

- Federal Express also requires large numbers of employees for their package-sorting facilities; managers, however, prefer part-time employees. To enable next-day delivery, the facilities are designed and staffed to sort more than a million pieces of freight and express mail in only four hours during the middle of the night. A full complement of full-time employees could not be effectively utilized all day long, whereas the part-timers, with high energy levels, can be used to meet daily peak demands. College students are a good source of labor for these sorting facilities.

Sources: "GM Pushes for Three-Shift Production at Some Auto Plants: UAW Is Balking," *Wall Street Journal*, February 26, 1990; "Big Three Auto Firms Set Plant Shutdowns Due to Lagging Sales," *Wall Street Journal*, October 19, 1990; James Heskett, W. Earl Sasser, Jr., and Christopher Hart, *Service Breakthroughs: Changing the Rules of the Game* (New York: The Free Press, 1990), pp. 197–198.

and time. Figure 14.1 shows how a manufacturer of bicycles might aggregate products, labor, and time.

Product Families. A group of products or services that have similar demand requirements and common processing, labor, and materials requirements is called a product family (see Chapter 11). Sometimes, product families relate to market groupings or, in the case of production plans, to specific manufacturing processes. A firm's products or services can be aggregated into a set of relatively broad families, avoiding too much detail at this stage of the planning process. Common and relevant measurements, such as units, dollars, standard hours, gallons, or pounds, should be used. In Fig. 14.1 the bicycle manufacturer has aggregated all products into two families: 20-inch wheel diameter and 26-inch

Product

Work force

(a) Before aggregation

Jan	Feb	March
68,000	68,000	75,000

Hours of labor

Product family

Jan	Feb	March
10,000	15,000	20,000

20-inch wheel

Numbers of bicycles

Product family

Jan	Feb	March
30,000	30,000	30,000

26-inch wheel

Numbers of bicycles

(b) Aggregation

FIGURE 14.1 The Concept of Aggregation

An operator controls the flow of
packages at a Federal Express
package sorting hub.

wheel diameter. This facilitates production planning of the assembly lines in
the plant.

Labor. A company can aggregate labor in various ways, depending on work-
force flexibility. For example, if management uses all its workers to produce
every product family, for planning purposes it considers its work force to be a
single aggregate group. Although the workers have different skills, they are
considered a single group because all types are needed to produce each product
family. The bicycle manufacturer in Figure 14.1 takes this approach.

Alternatively, management can aggregate labor along product family lines
by splitting the work force into subgroups and assigning a different group to
the production of each product family. An automobile manufacturer, such as
Chrysler, would find this approach useful since, under the concept of focused
facilities, operations devotes groups of production lines and even entire plants
to separate product families. (See Chapter 8.) To illustrate aggregation along

TABLE 14.1 / *Types of Employees Typically Included in a Staffing Plan*

Service	Employee Type	Service	Employee Type
Airline	Flight attendants	Health care	Nurses
	Pilots		
Airport operations	Baggage handlers	Municipal sanitation	Refuse collectors
	Skycaps		Truck drivers
Banking	Tellers	Municipal transportation	Bus mechanics
	Encoding clerks		Bus drivers
Defense	New enlistees	Telephone	Installers
Emergency	Police offices		Line workers
	Fire fighters		Operators

product lines, Table 14.1 shows several types of employees that management must include in a staffing plan for services.

Companies that aggregate labor along product lines must plan for changes in economic conditions and/or consumer demand that may cause cutbacks in production of some product families and increases in production of others. The American auto industry faced such a situation in the late 1970s when gasoline prices rose substantially, and consumer preference shifted from full-sized cars to small, fuel-efficient vehicles. Then in the late 1980s, preferences shifted again—this time to high performance and a sporty image. When such shifts occur, labor may not be interchangeable, particularly in automobile assembly, when production of different product families takes place in scattered locations. In such cases, companies will find it more practical to plan for changes in work-force levels and the use of overtime by aggregating labor around product families.

Time. A **planning horizon** is the length of time covered by an aggregate plan. Typically, the planning horizon is one year, although it can differ in various situations. Decisions must be made about output rates for each product family, labor levels for each work-force group, and other factors. But how often should these decisions be made during the planning horizon? Daily is too frequent because of the expense and disruptive effect on output rates and the work force. Yearly is not frequent enough to allow for adjustments to reflect seasonal demand or updated forecasts. Thus such decisions are usually made monthly or quarterly. Some companies use monthly planning periods for the near portion of the planning horizon and quarterly periods for the later portion. In practice, planning periods reflect a balance between the needs for (1) a limited number of decision points to reduce planning complexity and (2) flexibility to adjust output rates and work-force levels when demand forecasts exhibit seasonal variations. The bicycle manufacturer in Fig. 14.1 has chosen monthly planning periods so that adjustments to inventory levels can be made on a timely basis. The labor hours are held steady in January and February to avoid disruptive changes to the work force.

Relationship to Other Plans

Top management needs a financial assessment of the organization's near future, that is, for one or two years ahead. This assessment is called either a business plan (in manufacturing) or an annual plan (in nonprofit services). A **business plan** is a projected statement of income, costs, and profits. It is usually accompanied by budgets, a projected (pro forma) balance sheet, and a projected cash flow statement, showing sources and allocations of funds. The business plan brings together into one coherent package the plans and expectations of a firm's operations, finance, and marketing managers. In particular, it reflects plans for market penetration, new product introduction, and capital investments. A for-profit service organization, such as a retail store, firm of attorneys, or hospital, also prepares such a plan. A nonprofit service organization, such as the United Way or a municipal government, prepares a different type of plan, which we call an **annual plan.** This term is not used universally; others commonly used are the *financial plan* or *budget.*

Figure 14.2 illustrates the relationships among the production (or staffing) plan, the business (or annual) plan, and more detailed plans. In the manufacturing sector, top management sets the company's strategic objectives for at least the next year in the business plan. It provides the overall framework of demand projections, functional area inputs, and capital budget from which the production plan and the master production schedule (MPS) are developed. The production plan specifies corresponding product family production rates, inventory levels, and work-force levels. The master production schedule, in turn, specifies the timing and size of production quantities for each product in the product families (Chapter 15). Thus the production plan plays a key role in translating the strategies of the business plan into an operational plan for the manufacturing process.

In the service sector, top management sets the organization's direction and objectives in the business plan (for-profit organization) or annual plan (non-profit organization). In either case the plan provides the framework for the staffing plan and work-force schedule. The staffing plan presents the number and types of employees needed to meet the objectives of the business or annual plan. The **work-force schedule,** in turn, details the specific work schedule for each category of employee. For example, a staffing plan might allocate ten police officers for the day shift in a particular district; the work-force schedule might assign five of them to work Monday through Friday and the other five to work Wednesday through Sunday to meet the varying daily needs for police protection in that district. Thus the work-force schedule implements the staffing plan in much the same way that the master production schedule implements the production plan. (A more complete discussion of work-force scheduling is presented in Chapter 18.)

Besides this top-down (broad to detailed) planning process, information flows from lower level to higher level planning (detailed to broad). If a produc-

FIGURE 14.2

Relationship of Production and Staffing Plans to Other Plans

Business or annual plan

Production or staffing plan

MPS or work-force schedule

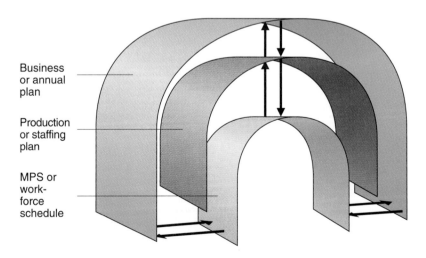

tion plan cannot be developed to satisfy the objectives of the business plan, the business plan might have to be adjusted. Similarly, if a feasible master production schedule cannot be developed, the production plan or the business plan might need adjustment. A similar situation exists for the business or annual plan, staffing plan, and work-force schedule. The planning process is dynamic, and plans—in particular the aggregate plan—are based on two-way information flows. Based on these information flows, plans are periodically revised or adjusted. We present the details of these information flows in the remainder of this chapter and in the following chapters.

MANAGERIAL IMPORTANCE OF AGGREGATE PLANS

Aggregate plans play an important role in achieving organizational objectives. In this section we concentrate on the managerial inputs, objectives, alternatives, and strategies associated with aggregate plans.

Managerial Inputs

Table 14.2 shows the various functional areas that supply managerial inputs to aggregate plans. Because of the plan's importance, a high-ranking manager in each area should provide the inputs. One way of ensuring this participation is to create a committee of functional-area representatives, chaired by a general manager with overall responsibility to see that company policies are followed, conflicts are resolved, and a final plan is approved. Each representative furnishes information essential to the development of the plan.

TABLE 14.2 / Managerial Inputs to Aggregate Plans

Area	Typical Inputs
Engineering	New product development
	Major product changes and their impact on resources
	Labor and machine standards
Finance	Cost data
	Financial condition of firm
Human resources	Labor market conditions
	Capacity of training programs
Manufacturing (or operations)	Current machine capacities
	Work-force productivities
	Current work-force staff levels
	New equipment plans
Marketing	Forecasts
	Economic conditions
	Competitor behavior
Materials	Raw materials availability
	Current inventory levels
	Subcontractor capabilities
	Storage capacities

Typical Objectives

The many and varied inputs from the functional areas in an organization make the aggregate plan an organization plan, not a functional-area plan. Typically, however, the various functional areas have conflicting objectives for the use of the organization's resources.

Table 14.3 shows six objectives commonly considered during development of a production or staffing plan. A little reflection on these six objectives reveals their conflicting nature. For example, maximizing customer service with fast, on-time delivery can be improved by increasing, not minimizing, the stock of finished goods in a production plan. At the Internal Revenue Service, which has a seasonal demand for its services, a staffing plan that minimizes costs may not minimize changes in work-force levels or maximize customer service. Also, a manufacturing firm that uses a stable production rate will necessarily build inventories of finished goods in the face of seasonal demand for its products.

These objectives actually are cost minimization objectives, assuming the level of demand volume is given. However, the weight given to each one in the plan involves cost trade-offs and consideration of nonquantifiable factors. Balancing these various objectives to arrive at an acceptable aggregate plan involves consideration of various decision alternatives. The two basic types of decision alternatives are reactive and aggressive. Operations managers tend to control the reactive alternatives, and marketing managers typically address the

TABLE 14.3 / Typical Objectives in Aggregate Plans

Objective	Comments
Minimize costs/maximize profits	If customer demand is not affected by the plan, minimizing costs will also maximize profits. Many service organizations are nonprofit and seek to minimize costs.
Maximize customer service	As discussed in Chapter 2, delivery time and on-time delivery are two dimensions of time as a competitive priority. Improving these dimensions requires additional work-force, machine capacity, or inventory resources.
Minimize inventory investment	Large accumulations in inventory are expensive because the money could be used for more productive investments.
Minimize changes in production rates	Frequent changes in production rates can cause difficulties in coordinating the supplying of materials and require production line rebalances.
Minimize changes in work-force levels	Fluctuating work-force levels may cause lower productivity because the new employees typically need time to become fully productive.
Maximize utilization of plant and equipment	Firms with a product focus require uniformly high utilization of plant and equipment.

Clerks at the Internal Revenue
Service process tax returns.
During the busy tax season, the
IRS increases the size of its staff
to handle the increased load.

aggressive alternatives. It is important that operations managers and marketing
managers coordinate objectives because aggressive alternatives adjust demand
patterns and reactive alternatives react to them.

Reactive Alternatives

Reactive alternatives are actions that can be taken to cope with demand requirements. That is, the operations manager accepts forecasted demand as a
given and modifies work-force levels, overtime, vacation schedules, inventory
levels, subcontracting, and planned backlogs.

Work-Force Adjustment. Management can adjust work-force levels by hiring or
laying off employees. The use of this alternative can be attractive if the work
force is largely unskilled or semiskilled and the labor pool is large. However,
for a particular company, the size of the qualified labor pool can limit the number of new employees that can be hired at any one time. Also, new employees
must be trained, and the training facilities themselves might limit the number
of new hires at any one time. In some industries, laying off employees is difficult or unusual because of contractual reasons (unions) or societal expectations
(people expect to work year-round in certain industries). In other industries,
such as tourism and agriculture, frequent layoffs and hirings are the norm.

Overtime and Undertime. An alternative to work-force adjustment is the use of overtime and undertime. Overtime can be used to satisfy output requirements that cannot be completed on regular time. However, overtime is expensive (typically 150 percent of the regular-time pay rate), and it is common for operations managers to be restricted in overtime use for this reason. In many cases, moreover, workers do not want to work a lot of overtime for an extended period of time, and excessive overtime may cause poor quality and productivity.

Undertime is used when labor capacity exceeds demand requirements. Workers are kept on the payroll, rather than being laid off. This option is used by companies, such as firms with a process focus, that have highly skilled, hard-to-replace employees. Most often, however, undertime is a consequence of the contractural difficulty in laying off workers. In this case, undertime can cause inefficiency and higher unit costs.

Vacation Schedules. A firm can shut down during an annual lull in sales, leaving a skeleton crew to cover operations and perform maintenance. Depending on the duration of the shutdown, employees would take all, or part, of their allowed vacation time during this period. Automakers, such as General Motors, sometimes use this alternative during the Christmas holiday period, not only to do maintenance or install equipment, but also to reduce inventory. Use of this alternative depends on the extent that the employer can mandate the vacation schedules of its employees. If this authority is limited (say, by union contract) and if part-time or seasonal labor can be substituted for full-time personnel, employees could be encouraged to take vacations during periods when these sources of labor are most abundant. In any case, employees may be strongly discouraged from taking vacations during peak periods.

Anticipation Inventory. In Chapter 12, we pointed out that a plant facing seasonal demand can stock anticipation inventory during light demand periods and use it during heavy demand periods. Although this approach stabilizes production rates and work-force levels, it can be very costly. As we have also noted, stocking finished goods is the most expensive form of inventory investment because the value of the product is greatest in its finished state. Plans to stock components and subassemblies that can be assembled quickly when customer orders come in might be preferable to stocking finished goods.

Recall also that service providers generally cannot use anticipation inventory because services cannot be stocked. In some instances, however, services can be performed prior to actual need. For example, telephone company workers usually lay cables for service to a new subdivision before housing construction begins. They can do this work during a period when the workload for scheduled services is low.

Subcontractors. A short-term capacity source that can be used to overcome capacity shortages is subcontracting. Subcontractors can supply services and build components, assemblies, or even an entire product in some cases. Arrangements with subcontractors can be more permanent if the subcontractor can supply equal or better-quality components or assemblies less expensively than the company can produce them itself. Such is the case with the major automakers, which typically subcontract for underbody frames, steering linkage components, and other items. (See the discussion on vertical integration in Chapter 5.)

Backlogs, Back Orders, and Stockouts. Another way to cope with a given demand forecast is to plan for order backlogs. A **backlog** is an accumulation of customer orders that have been promised for delivery at some future date. Having a sizable backlog is good, provided on-time delivery and quality are not sacrificed. Delivery lead times typically increase during seasonal peaks in demand. Firms with a process focus often use this method. The customer places an order for a customized product or service, and the firm promises it for later delivery. Job shops, TV repair shops, and automobile repair shops work to varying degrees to backlogs. Examples of backlogs in services are tickets for a concert or appointments to see a dentist.

Back orders and stockouts are used by firms with a product focus. Recall that a back order is a customer order that is not ready for the customer when promised or demanded, and a stockout is an inability to satisfy the demand for a stock item when it occurs. In the former case, the customer has not canceled the order, so the net effect is to push demand requirements to later periods. However, in the latter case, the customer may go to a competitor, resulting in a lost sale. Generally, back orders and stockouts are to be avoided. Planned stockouts would be used only when the expected loss in sales and customer goodwill is less than the cost of adding the capacity needed to satisfy demand. University bookstores sometimes use this ploy. Students needing textbooks can get them only in the bookstore. Planned shortages keep book inventories low but do nothing for student goodwill.

In conclusion, it is clear that the reactive alternatives collectively define the output rate. Once decisions have been made regarding how to use each of these methods for each period of the planning horizon, the output rate for each period has been specified. In other words, the output rate is a function of the factors addressed by these alternatives.

Aggressive Alternatives

Attempting to cope with seasonal or volatile demand patterns by using reactive alternatives can be costly. Another approach is to attempt to adjust the demand pattern to achieve efficiency and reduce costs. **Aggressive alternatives** are actions that attempt to modify demand and, consequently, resource requirements. Marketing managers are typically responsible for specifying these actions in the marketing plan.

Complementary Products. One way to even out the load on resources is to produce **complementary products** or services having similar resource requirements but different demand cycles. For example, a company producing garden tractors can also produce snowmobiles, making requirements for major components, such as engines, reasonably uniform year round. In the service sector, city parks and recreation departments can counterbalance seasonal staffing requirements for summer activities by offering indoor activities during the winter. The key is to find products and services that can be produced with existing resources and can level off the need for resources over the year.

Creative Pricing. Promotional campaigns often increase sales with creative pricing. Discounts can be offered to customers if they buy products outside traditional peak sales periods. Automobile rebate programs, price reductions for winter clothing in the late summer months, reduced prices on airline tickets for travel during off-peak periods, and "two for the price of one" automobile tire sales—all are examples of creative pricing alternatives.

Planning Strategies

The alternatives that we have discussed are combined in various ways to arrive at an acceptable aggregate plan. For the remainder of this chapter, let's assume that the expected results of the aggressive alternatives have already been incorporated into the demand forecasts of product families or services. This assumption allows us to focus on the reactive alternatives that serve to define output rates and work-force levels. In this regard a planning strategy amounts to selecting the particular alternatives to be used. There are two pure strategies: the chase strategy and the level strategy.

A **chase strategy** adjusts output rates or work-force levels to match the demand requirements over the planning horizon. The key point is that anticipation inventory or undertime is not used. This strategy can be accomplished in many ways. For example, workers can be hired or laid off, or overtime and subcontracting can be used during peak periods. Thus the chase strategy has the advantage of low inventory investment and backlogs, but a major drawback is the expense of adjusting output rates or work-force levels for every period of the planning horizon. Other major drawbacks include the potential alienation of the work force and the loss of productivity and lower quality because of the constant churn in the work force.

A **level strategy** maintains a constant output rate or work-force level over the planning horizon. The distinguishing feature of a level strategy is that anticipation inventory and/or undertime is used to help maintain constant output. In manufacturing firms a constant production rate is often accomplished by maintaining a stable work force and building anticipation inventory to satisfy peak seasonal demands. Hiring, overtime, or subcontracting can be used if the work force is subject to attrition, but the production rate remains constant. In service firms a level strategy usually involves maintaining a stable work force and using undertime, overtime, and backlogs. The advantages are level output rates and a stable work force at the expense of increased inventory investment, undertime, overtime, or backlogs. Managerial Practice 14.2 shows how Hallmark uses a level strategy for competitive advantage.

Obviously, a range of strategies lies between the chase strategy at one extreme and the level strategy at the other. The best strategy for a company may be a *mixed strategy* of anticipation inventory buildup during slack periods, only

Hallmark's Level Strategy to Compete as a Low-Cost Producer

Hallmark, a $2 billion-a-year producer of greeting cards, spends considerable sums to improve efficiency and has made significant gains—all without imposing layoffs. Hallmark has never used layoffs to adjust production rates of greeting cards, even though the business is highly competitive, exhibits little growth, and is very seasonal. Employee flexibility is the key to this strategy. The company's four plants produce more than 11 million cards a day, along with gift wrapping paper and other party goods. Even though technology in the industry has made production processes increasingly more labor efficient, Hallmark's philosophy has been to retrain its employees continually to make them more flexible. For example, a cutting machine operator might also be a custom card imprinter, a painter, or a modular office assembler as needed. To keep workers buys, Hallmark will shift production from its Kansas City plant to branch plants in Topeka, Leavenworth, and Lawrence, Kansas, to keep those plants fully utilized. It uses the Kansas City plant as its "swing facility"—when demand is down these employees may take jobs in clerical positions, all at factory pay rates. They might also be in classrooms learning new skills.

Hallmark CEO Irvine O. Hockaday believes that being a low-cost producer is compatible with maintaining a stable work force. According to Hockaday, Hallmark must manage for the long term and protect its employees from cyclical markets and other unexpected happenings out of their control. The added job security, however, carries the expectation that the employees will perform commensurate with their compensation package. The philosophy has paid dividends. For example, reducing setup times to support short production runs is critical to keeping inventories and costs low. Employees have suggested ways to cut setup times significantly. A stable work-force policy has ben a major factor in Hallmark's success in the competitive greeting card business.

Source: "Cutting Costs Without Cutting People," *Fortune,* May 25, 1987, pp. 26–31.

*A*t Hallmark's Kansas City plant, holiday wrapping paper passes an inspector en route to packaging.

a few work-force level changes, and overtime. Regardless of whether a company chooses a pure strategy or some mix, that strategy must reflect its planning objectives. The aggregate plan not only is a product of managerial inputs from the various functional areas, but it also has an impact on the activities of these persons and the operations of the functional areas they represent. Thus aggregate plans affect the direction of the firm over the near and intermediate future and are significant managerial tools.

In some situations the best planning strategies are fairly obvious. Table 14.4 shows how certain strategies can be fitted to an organization's environment. These strategies are reasonable in the broad sense, even though the extent of their application in any specific situation must still be analyzed. In general, firms that have a process focus can adapt to volume flexibility rather easily and tend to meet variable demand with overtime, subcontracting, or work-force

TABLE 14.4 / Examples of Fitting Strategy to Environment

Organization	Environment	Possible Strategy
City street repair	Labor intensive Unskilled workers Seasonal requirements Ample labor supply	Variable work-force levels Low overtime No subcontracting
Outboard motor company	Costly equipment Skilled labor Costly inventory	Complementary products Off-season promotions Level production rate Limited hires/layoffs Low inventory investment
TV repair service	Steady, increasing demand Skilled employees Tight labor market	Overtime Gradual hires Increase backlog for short-term demand surges
Men's shoe manufacturer	Labor in short supply Low inventory holding cost	Level work force Build up anticipation inventories Low overtime Subcontracting

level changes, unless highly skilled, hard-to-find labor is involved. However, firms that have a product focus find volume flexibility difficult to handle and tend to meet fluctuating demand with anticipation inventory, scheduled vacations, or plant shutdowns.

THE PLANNING PROCESS

Figure 14.3 shows the planning process for aggregate plans. The overall process is dynamic and continuing; aspects of the plan are updated periodically as new information becomes available and new opportunities emerge.

Determine Demand Requirements

The first step in the planning process is to determine the demand requirements for each period of the planning horizon. The planner can estimate these requirements in various ways (many of which we have already discussed). For staffing plans, the planner bases forecasts of staff requirements for each work-force group on historical demands or managerial judgment and existing backlogs for services. For example, a director of nursing in a hospital can develop a direct-care index for a nursing staff and translate a projection of the patient census into an equivalent total amount of time—and thus number of nurses—required (Wolfe and Young, 1965). Also, a formula developed for police patrol staffing accounts for such factors as the number of calls for service by type, the number of street miles patrolled, and the number of businesses in the community, to determine workload and thus the number of police officers or vehicles required (Chaiken and Larson, 1972).

For production plans, however, the requirements could represent the demand for finished goods, as well as external demand for components or parts.

FIGURE 14.3

The Planning Process
for Aggregate Plans

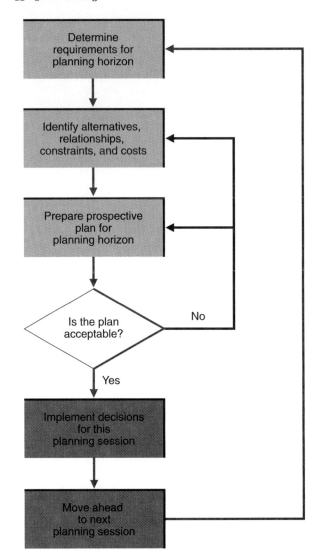

The planner can derive future requirements for finished goods from backlogs (for a process focus) or from forecasts for product families made to stock (for a product focus). Sometimes, distributors or dealers indicate their requirements for finished goods in advance of actual orders. These commitments to purchase various quantities of goods in the future provide a reliable forecast of requirements from those sources.

Identify Alternatives, Relationships, Constraints, and Costs

The second step is to identify the alternatives, relationships, constraints, and costs for the plan. We presented the reactive alternatives used in aggregate plans when we discussed the managerial importance of these plans. We now focus on the basic relationships, constraints, and costs.

Basic Relationships. Two relationships are basic to evaluating and comparing prospective aggregate plans: (1) the equation for the number of workers on the payroll in a given time period, and (2) the equation for the inventory level in production plans. The equation for the number of workers is

$$
\begin{array}{ccccccc}
\text{Workers} & & \text{Workers at} & & \text{Hires at} & & \text{Layoffs at} \\
\text{in current} & = & \text{end of last} & + & \text{start of} & - & \text{start of} \\
\text{period} & & \text{period} & & \text{current period} & & \text{current period}
\end{array}
$$

Any decisions made about hiring or laying off employees during the current period will affect the number of workers on hand. For example, if the director of a post office has 10 part-time clerks at the end of the third period and decides to hire 5 new part-timers at the start of the fourth period, the total number of part-time employees for the fourth period would be 15 clerks. In general, such an equation is needed for each work-force group in the aggregate plan.

Sometimes the equation for the number of workers must be adjusted to reflect the attrition of the work force. Attrition is the loss of workers due to unplanned circumstances, such as quits, illnesses, or disciplinary firings. If attrition is a significant factor, the number of workers at the end of the last period must be reduced by the attrition expected to take place during the current period.

The equation for the inventory level is

$$
\begin{array}{ccccccc}
\text{Inventory} & & \text{Inventory} & & \text{Production} & & \text{Demand} \\
\text{at end of} & = & \text{at end of} & + & \text{in current} & - & \text{requirements in} \\
\text{current period} & & \text{last period} & & \text{period} & & \text{current period}
\end{array}
$$

The production decision for the current period affects the inventory level at the end of the current period. For example, suppose that a paint manufacturer has an inventory level of 600,000 gallons of paint at the end of January, has a forecasted demand for 100,000 gallons in February, and has decided to produce 250,000 gallons in February. The expected inventory at the end of February would be 600,000 + 250,000 − 100,000 = 750,000 gallons. As with the equation for the work force, an inventory equation is needed for each product family in the production plan.

Physical and Policy Constraints. Constraints can represent physical limitations or managerial policies associated with the aggregate plan. For example, a company's training center might be capable of handling only so many new hires at a time, machine capacities may limit maximum output, or inventory storage space may be inadequate. Policy constraints might include limitations on the amount of back ordering, the use of subcontracting or overtime, and the minimum inventory levels to achieve desired safety stocks.

Physical and policy constraints must be satisfied before an aggregate plan can be considered acceptable. Unfortunately, merely choosing alternatives that satisfy the constraints does not ensure that the *best* plan will result. Typically, many plans can satisfy a specific set of constraints.

Costs. In addition to identifying reasonable alternatives and relevant constraints, the planner must gather data on applicable costs. The planner usually considers several types of costs when preparing aggregate plans:

1. **Regular-time costs.** These costs include regular-time wages paid to employees plus fringe-benefit contributions. Fringe benefits typically include health insurance (hospital, surgical, eye care, dental care); Social Security and retirement funds; and paid vacations, holidays, and certain other types of absence.

2. **Overtime costs.** Overtime wages are typically 150 percent of regular-time wages, exclusive of fringe benefits. Some companies offer a 200 percent rate for working overtime on Sundays and holidays.

3. **Hiring and layoff costs.** Hiring costs include the costs of advertising jobs, interviews, training programs for new employees, scrap from new employees, loss of productivity, and initial paperwork. Layoff costs include the costs of exit interviews and severance pay. In some companies, when the work force is reduced, senior employees whose jobs have been eliminated have the right to "bump" less senior employees from their jobs. In the process, many employees may change jobs, with the least senior persons actually getting laid off. In this case, layoff costs should also include all costs of training and lost productivity caused by bumping.

4. **Inventory holding costs.** Inventory holding costs include the costs of capital tied up in inventory, variable storage and warehousing costs, pilferage and obsolescence costs, insurance costs, and taxes. Only costs that vary with the *level* of inventory investment should be included. (See Chapter 12.)

5. **Back-order and stockout costs.** The cost of not satisfying customer demand is difficult to assess. In the case of a back order, costs are incurred for expediting the past-due order, and there is the potential cost of losing the customer's sales to competitors in the future (sometimes called loss of goodwill). In some cases, back orders are not possible; the customer is not identified with a specific order that is past due. For example, when someone goes to a supermarket to buy bananas and they are out of stock, the likely behavior is to go elsewhere (lost sale) rather than to place a name on a waiting list. In these situations, the stockout cost is essentially a lost sales cost consisting of lost profit from the sales plus the loss of goodwill.

Prepare an Acceptable Plan

The third step is to prepare the aggregate plan. Developing an acceptable plan is an iterative process (refer to Fig. 14.3). First, a prospective, or tentative, plan is developed. A production plan with monthly periods, for example, must specify monthly production rates, inventory and backlog accumulations, subcontracted production, and monthly work-force levels (including hires, layoffs, and overtime). The plan is prospective at this point because it has not yet been checked against constraints or evaluated in terms of strategic objectives. If the prospective plan is not acceptable for either of those reasons, a new prospective plan must be developed. It may include new alternatives or proposed changes in physical or policy constraints. When management judges the plan acceptable, implementation can begin.

Implement and Update

The final step is implementing and updating the aggregate plan. Implementing an aggregate plan requires the commitment of top management. This commitment begins with the creation of a planning committee, as we suggested earlier, which makes inputs into, develops, and updates the prospective plan. The committee may recommend changes to better balance conflicting objectives. Acceptance of the plan does not necessarily mean that everyone is in total agreement, but it does imply that everyone will work toward achieving it.

In the remainder of this chapter we demonstrate the preparation of aggregate plans for service and manufacturing firms.

AGGREGATE PLANNING FOR SERVICES

In Application 14.1, we demonstrate the development of two staffing plans, one based on a level strategy and the other on a chase strategy. We term the approach used *trial-and-error* because it first requires stating a strategy, then developing a plan, comparing the developed plan to other plans, and finally modifying the plan and/or strategy as necessary. We continue this process until we are satisfied with the results.

Application 14.1   *Developing a Staffing Plan by Trial-and-Error*

The director of the Clearwater Post Office needs a staffing plan for his part-time work force. Part-time employees fill in for absent full-time clerks and help move mail from sorting station to sorting station. The director must determine how many part-time clerks to maintain on the payroll for each of the 13 accounting periods next year. Each part-time employee can work a maximum of 20 hours per week on regular time, but the actual hours can be different than that. Once on the payroll for an accounting period, they are used each day but may work only a few hours or up to 5 hours on overtime. The director wants us to develop staffing plans consistent with two alternative strategies:

1. *Level strategy.* Determine a stable part-time work-force level without using backlogs or subcontractors, but minimize the amount of undertime (that is, the number of part-time employees working less than 20 hours per week). Overtime can be used to the maximum in peak periods. The resultant plan is called Plan 1. An advantage of the level strategy in this case is that the employees have the security of knowing they have a job from period to period, thereby raising morale. Also, if more employees are on hand than needed at the maximum 20 regular-time hours per week, each employee can work fewer hours per week.

							Accounting Period							
	1	2	3	4	5	6	7	8	9	10	11	12	13	Total
Requirement	5	6	8	15	17	20	15	15	10	16	14	14	12	167
Staff level	16	16	16	16	16	16	16	16	16	16	16	16	16	208
Equivalent staff†	5	6	8	15	16	16	15	15	10	16	14	14	12	162
Hires	6	—	—	—	—	—	—	—	—	—	—	—	—	6
Layoffs	—	—	—	—	—	—	—	—	—	—	—	—	—	0
Overtime	—	—	—	—	1	4	—	—	—	—	—	—	—	5

†Equivalent staff is the equivalent number of employees working the maximum 20 hours per week.

2. *Chase strategy.* Adjust work-force levels as needed to achieve requirements. Do not use overtime, undertime, or subcontractors. The resultant plan is called Plan 2. An advantage of the chase strategy is that costly overtime is avoided. In addition, many part-time employees are college students who cannot work year-round and prefer holiday-period employment.

Data for the staffing problem follow.

Requirements

Work-force requirements are shown as the number of part-time employees required for each accounting period at the maximum regular time of 20 hours per week. The fiscal year begins on July 1 and ends on June 30. For example, in accounting period 6, it is estimated that 20 part-time employees working 20 hours per week on regular time will be needed to help the full-time work force during the Christmas holiday season.

						Accounting Period							
	1	2	3	4	5	6	7	8	9	10	11	12	13	Total
Requirement	5	6	8	15	17	20	15	15	10	16	14	14	12	167

Ten part-time clerks are currently employed. They have not been subtracted from the requirements shown.

Constraints

1. *Physical*:
   No more than 10 new hires in any period because of limited training facilities.
2. *Policy*:
   No backlogs of mail; demand must be met each period.
   Overtime cannot exceed 25 percent of the regular-time capacity in any period. That is, the maximum any part-time employee can work is 25 hours per week [1.25(20)].

Costs

Regular-time wage rate	$500 per accounting period at 20 hours per week
Overtime wages	150% of the regular-time rate
Hires	$600 per person
Layoffs	$100 per person

Plan 2: Chase Strategy for the Clearwater Post Office Staffing Problem

	Accounting Period													
	1	2	3	4	5	6	7	8	9	10	11	12	13	Total
Requirement	5	6	8	15	17	20	15	15	10	16	14	14	12	167
Staff level	5	6	8	15	17	20	15	15	10	16	14	14	12	167
Equivalent staff†	5	6	8	15	17	20	15	15	10	16	14	14	12	167
Hires	—	1	2	7	2	3	—	—	—	6	—	—	—	21
Layoffs	5	—	—	—	—	—	5	—	5	—	2	—	2	19
Overtime	—	—	—	—	—	—	—	—	—	—	—	—	—	0

†Equivalent staff is the equivalent number of employees working the maximum 20 hours per week.

Solution

1. *Level strategy.* We cannot use backlogs or subcontractors, so we must satisfy demand as it occurs in each period. One way to satisfy work-force requirements is to find the number of part-time employees that, when utilized for 25 hours per week (20×1.25), meets the peak requirement. The most overtime that we can use is 25 percent of the regular-time capacity (w), so we have

$$1.25w = 20 \text{ employees required in peak period}$$

$$w = \frac{20}{1.25} = 16 \text{ employees}$$

This staff size minimizes the resulting amount of undertime. As there already are 10 part-time employees, the director should immediately hire 6 more. In periods 1 through 4, and 7 through 13, the employees would be working less than the maximum 20 hours per week because the requirements are less than 16 employees in those periods. For example, in period 1, 16 employees are on the payroll, but only 100 hours [5(20)] per week are needed. Consequently, each employee might work only 6.25 hours per week. Alternatively, management could assign 7 employees 4 hours per week and 9 employees 8 hours per week. Plan 1 shows the resulting hires and overtime.

2. *Chase strategy.* This strategy simply involves adjusting the work force as needed to meet demand. The director should plan to lay off 5 part-time employees immediately, then steadily build the work force to 20 by period 6. After that, we find that the work force can be reduced except for the secondary peak in period 10, when the director should hire 6 more employees. Plan 2 shows the staff level along with the hires and layoffs.

Table 14.5 compares the costs of each plan in Application 14.1. You shouldn't be surprised to see that Plan 1—the level strategy—is less expensive for this situation. Plan 2—the chase strategy—calls for a lot of hiring and laying off. If we weren't staffing part-time employees with flexible work hours, the level strategy would have been more expensive. Intuitively, use of the level strategy in this situation makes sense—and the economics of the case verify it.

TABLE 14.5 / Cost Comparisons for the Clearwater Post Office Staffing Plans

Cost	Plan 1: Level Strategy	Plan 2: Chase Strategy
Regular time†	162 Worker periods @ $500 = $81,000	167 Worker periods @ $500 = $83,500
Overtime	5 Worker periods @ $750 = 3,750	0 Worker periods @ $750 = 0
Hire	6 Workers @ $600 = 3,600	21 Workers @ $600 = 12,600
Layoff	0 Workers @ $100 = 0	19 Workers @ $100 = 1,900
Total	$88,350	$98,000

†Regular-time wages based on the equivalent staff available.

AGGREGATE PLANNING FOR MANUFACTURING

The major advantage of the trial-and-error approach is its simplicity; however, the key to using it lies in the ingenuity of the planner. For production plans, even if a staffing plan has been prepared, the planner still must make many choices for each period of the planning horizon. These decisions relate to the amount of anticipation inventory to produce, the amount of overtime to use, the number of units to subcontract, and other factors.

Tableau Method of Production Planning

In this section we present and demonstrate the **tableau method** of production planning. This approach, often called the *transportation method* for production planning, was first proposed by E.H. Bowman (1956). The method is based on the assumptions that the planner has a capacity plan specifying the maximum capacities of regular time, overtime, and subcontractor production each period; a demand forecast for each period; and that all costs are linearly related to the amount of product produced. Given these assumptions, the tableau method yields the optimal mixed strategy production plan over the planning horizon. Large problems can be solved by computer using standard transportation method programs (see Supplement 3).

Although the transportation method can accommodate the back-order alternative, we address the simpler case in which back orders are not a viable alternative to demonstrate the tableau method, which is a manual approach.

Production Planning Without Back Orders. We begin with a tabulation—called a tableau—of capacity plan and demand forecast quantities, beginning inventory level, and costs for each period of the planning horizon. Figure 14.4 shows such a tableau for a four-period production plan, where

$$h = \text{holding cost per unit per period}$$
$$r = \text{cost per unit to produce on regular time}$$
$$c = \text{cost per unit to produce on overtime}$$
$$s = \text{cost per unit to subcontract}$$
$$I_0 = \text{beginning inventory level}$$
$$I_4 = \text{desired inventory level at the end of period 4}$$

$$R_t = \text{regular-time capacity in period } t$$
$$OT_t = \text{overtime capacity in period } t$$
$$S_t = \text{subcontracting capacity in period } t$$
$$D_t = \text{forecasted demand for period } t$$

FIGURE 14.4

Production Planning
Tableau

	Alternatives	Time period 1	Time period 2	Time period 3	Time period 4	Unused capacity	Total capacity
Period — Beginning inventory	Beginning inventory	0	h	$2h$	$3h$		I_0
1	Regular time	r	$r+h$	$r+2h$	$r+3h$		R_1
1	Overtime	c	$c+h$	$c+2h$	$c+3h$		OT_1
1	Subcontract	s	$s+h$	$s+2h$	$s+3h$		S_1
2	Regular time		r	$r+h$	$r+2h$		R_2
2	Overtime		c	$c+h$	$c+2h$		OT_2
2	Subcontract		s	$s+h$	$s+2h$		S_2
3	Regular time			r	$r+h$		R_3
3	Overtime			c	$c+h$		OT_3
3	Subcontract			s	$s+h$		S_3
4	Regular time				r		R_4
4	Overtime				c		OT_4
4	Subcontract				s		S_4
Requirements		D_1	D_2	D_3	$D_4 + I_4$		

Some elements of the tableau need explanation. First, each row represents an alternative for supplying output. For example, the first row is for beginning inventory (the amount currently on hand), which can be used to satisfy demands in any of the four periods. The second row is for regular-time production in period 1, which can also be used to satisfy demands in any of the four periods the plan will cover. There are rows for overtime and subcontracting as well.

Second, the columns represent the periods the plan must cover, plus the unused and total capacities available. Third, costs are shown in the upper right-hand corner of each cell. They reflect the cost of producing a unit in one period and carrying the unit in inventory for sale in a future period. For example, in period 1 the regular-time cost to produce one unit is r (column 1). To produce the unit in period 1 for sale in period 2, the cost is $r + h$ (column 2) because we must hold the unit in inventory for one period. Satisfying a unit of demand in period 3 by producing in period 1 on regular time and carrying the unit for two periods costs $r + 2h$ (column 3), and so on. The large Xs indicate that back orders (or producing in a period to satisfy demand in a past period) are not allowed.

Fourth, it is obvious that the cheapest alternatives are those in which the output is produced and sold in the same period. However, we may not always be able to use those alternatives exclusively because of capacity restrictions. Finally, the per unit holding cost for the beginning inventory in period 1 is 0 because it is a function of previous production planning decisions. Similarly, the target inventory at the end of the planning horizon is added to the forecasted demand for the last period. No holding cost is charged because we have already decided to have a specified ending inventory; in this regard it is a sunk cost.*

Because no back orders are allowed, a simple manual method for finding the optimal solution is as follows:

1. Put all capacities from the total capacity column into the unused capacity column.
2. In column 1 (period 1) find the cell with the lowest cost.
3. Allocate as much production as you can to that cell but do not exceed the unused capacity in that row or the demand in that column.
4. Subtract your allocation from the unused capacity for that row. This quantity must never be negative.† If there is still some demand left, repeat steps 2–4 until the demand is satisfied.
5. Repeat steps 2 through 4 for periods 2 and beyond. Take each column separately before proceeding to the next. Be sure to check all cells with unused capacity (but without Xs) for the cell with the lowest cost in a column.

---

*If we were analyzing the implications of different ending inventory levels, the holding cost of the ending inventory would have to be added to the costs because ending inventory level would be a decision variable.

†If negative unused capacities cannot be avoided, the solution is infeasible for that capacity plan. More capacity is needed.

There is one guiding principle to keep in mind while using this method: At the end of the procedure, the sum of all entries in a row must equal the total capacity for that row, and the sum of all entries in a column must equal the requirements for that column. Following this principle ensures that capacities are not exceeded and all demands are met.

Application 14.2 Preparing a Production Plan Using the Tableau Method

The Tru-Rainbow Company produces a wide variety of paint products for both commercial and private use. The demand for paint is highly seasonal, peaking in the third quarter. The manufacturing manager needs a prospective production plan for the next budget meeting. The relevant demand requirements, constraints, and costs are as follows:

Requirements

Demand is expressed in thousands of gallons of paint.

	Quarter				
	1	2	3	4	Total
Demand	300	850	1500	350	3000

Current inventory is 250,000 gallons. The desired ending inventory is 300,000 gallons.

Constraints

The maximum allowable overtime in any quarter is 20 percent of the regular-time capacity in that quarter.

Costs

Regular-time cost per unit	$1.00
Overtime cost per unit	$1.50
Subcontracting cost per unit	$1.90
Inventory holding cost	$0.30 per gallon per quarter

Tru-Rainbow's manufacturing manager wants to determine the best production plan using the following capacity plan (expressed in thousands of gallons):

	Quarter			
Capacity Factor	1	2	3	4
Regular time	450	450	750	450
Overtime	90	90	150	90
Subcontracting	200	200	200	200

The subcontractor can supply a maximum of 200 thousand gallons in any quarter. Production can be subcontracted in one period and the excess held in inventory for a future period if that will avoid a stockout. No back orders or stockouts are permitted.

Solution Figure 14.5 contains the tableau solution to the problem. The first step is to transfer all capacities from the total capacity column to the unused capacity column. We note that the total requirements are 270,000 gallons less than total capacity. Therefore we know that at the end of the solution process we will have 270,000 gallons of unused capacity. Next we proceed through steps 2 to 5 for each quarter, starting with quarter 1. The least expensive alternative in quarter 1 is to use the inventory on hand, so we allocate as

FIGURE 14.5

The Tableau Solution
for the Tru-Rainbow
Problem

	Alternatives	Quarter 1	Quarter 2	Quarter 3	Quarter 4	Unused capacity	Total capacity
Quarter	Beginning inventory	0.00 250	0.30	0.60	0.90	250 0	250
1	Regular time	1.00 50	1.30 400	1.60	1.90	450 400 0	450
1	Overtime	1.50	1.80	2.10 90	2.40	90 0	90
1	Subcontract	1.90	2.20	2.50 20	2.80	200 180	200
2	Regular time	✕	1.00 450	1.30	1.60	450 0	450
2	Overtime	✕	1.50	1.80 90	2.10	90 0	90
2	Subcontract	✕	1.90	2.20 200	2.50	200 0	200
3	Regular time	✕	✕	1.00 750	1.30	750 0	750
3	Overtime	✕	✕	1.50 150	1.80	150 0	150
3	Subcontract	✕	✕	1.90 200	2.20	200 0	200
4	Regular time	✕	✕	✕	1.00 450	450 0	450
4	Overtime	✕	✕	✕	1.50 90	90 0	90
4	Subcontract	✕	✕	✕	1.90 110	200 90	200
	Requirements	300	850	1500	650	270	3570

much as we can, 250,000. That leaves a demand of 50,000 gallons to satisfy, so we allocate 50,000 gallons of quarter 1 regular-time capacity (the next least costly alternative) to satisfy demand in quarter 1 and reduce the unused capacity by 50,000. Since quarter 1 demand has now been satisfied, we proceed to quarter 2.

In quarter 2, the least expensive option is to allocate all regular-time production in quarter 2 to satisfy demand in that quarter. As we are still short 400,000 gallons, the next least-costly option is to allocate 400,000 gallons of quarter 1 regular-time production. These allocations satisfy quarter 2 demand, but now there is no more regular-time capacity left in quarters 1 and 2.

For quarter 3 we note that the only capacities we have available in addition to the quarter 3 capacities are overtime and subcontracting in quarters 1 and 2. We begin by allocating the maximum amount of quarter 3 regular-time capacity, the least-costly alternative. Then, in order, we allocate as much as we can of quarter 3 overtime, quarter 2 overtime, quarter 3 subcontracting, quarter 1 overtime, and quarter 2 subcontracting. Finally, we allocate 20,000 gallons of quarter 1 subcontracting capacity to meet quarter 3 demand. These allocations imply that we must produce anticipation inventories in quarters 1 and 2 to meet the peak demand in quarter 3. We update the unused capacities to account for the new allocations. We do the same for quarter 4. A quick check indicates that we have a feasible plan: No unused capacities are negative, the sum of the allocations in each row (including the unused capacity) equals the total capacity for that row, and the sum of the allocations for each quarter equals the demand for that quarter.

The total cost of this prospective production plan is equal to the sum of the allocation in each cell multiplied by the cost per unit in that cell, or \$4,010,000. The plan itself must be reconstructed from the tableau. Based on Fig. 14.5, the plan (expressed in thousands of gallons) is:

Quarter	Regular-Time Production	Overtime Production	Subcontracting	Anticipation Inventory
1	450	90	20	510
2	450	90	200	400
3	750	150	200	0
4	450	90	110	300

Anticipated inventories accumulate whenever production plus subcontracting exceeds quarterly demand. For example, as indicated in quarter 1 of the tableau, operations produces 450,000 gallons on regular time, allocating 50,000 gallons for sale in quarter 1 and 400,000 gallons for sale in quarter 2. The company also produces another 90,000 gallons on overtime and purchases an additional 20,000 gallons from subcontractors for sale in quarter 3, for a total of 560,000 gallons. Thus, as Fig. 14.6 shows, total inventory contains 510,000 gallons in excess of quarter 1's requirements. Conversely, anticipation inventories are consumed when production plus subcontracting is less than quarterly demand. Figure 14.6 illustrates this scenario in quarter 2 when total production plus subcontracting is only 740,000 gallons, but requirements are for 850,000 gallons, calling for consumption of 110,000 gallons from inventory. As the graph indicates, anticipation inventory goes from 510,000 gallons in quarter 1 to 400,000 gallons in quarter 2, all of which is consumed in quarter 3.

FIGURE 14.6

Prospective
Tru-Rainbow
Production Plan

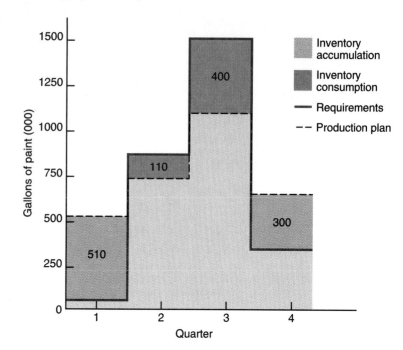

Additional Capacity Plans. The plan we offered to the manufacturing manager in Application 14.2 used a lot of overtime and subcontracting. A better capacity plan—with increases in the work force to boost regular-time production capacity—might result in lower production costs, perhaps even low enough to offset the added capacity costs. A series of capacity plans can be tried and compared to find the best plan. Even though this process in itself involves trial and error, the tableau method finds the best mix of regular time, overtime, and subcontracting for each capacity plan.

Incorporating Back Orders. Back orders can also be considered. For example, in Application 14.2, regular-time production in quarter 3 could be used to satisfy demand from quarter 2 by replacing the X in the quarter 2 cell for regular-time production in quarter 3 with some appropriate penalty cost. In effect, the Xs in the Tru-Rainbow tableau represent very large costs—large enough that we would not consider back orders. We recommend using a computer with a routine for the transportation method (see Supplement 3) for large problems, problems involving trial-and-error analysis of the capacity plan or demand forecasts, and problems involving back orders.

Linear Programming for Production Planning

The tableau method for production planning we just discussed is actually a specialized form of linear programming. Linear programming models for production planning seek to find the optimal production plan given a linear objective function and a set of linear constraints; that is, there can be no cross products or powers of decision variables or other types of nonlinear terms in the problem formulation. Supplement 2 discusses this technique in more detail; however, linear programming models are capable of handling a large number of variables and constraints and are not limited to using a given capacity plan as is the tableau method. Linear programming models can determine optimal inventory levels, back orders, subcontractor quantities, production quantities, overtime production hires, and layoffs. The major drawbacks are that all relationships between variables must be linear and the optimal values of the decision variables may be fractional. The assumption of linearity is violated when certain costs, for example, setup costs, are incurred only when two specific product families are to be produced in the same time period. Also, fractional values of the decision variables may be troublesome when the variables represent discrete items, such as workers, tables, or trucks.

Suppose that you must plan the production of a certain product family and do not want to use back orders. Each worker can produce 5000 units per month. Subcontracting and overtime production are possible options to supplement regular-time production, although overtime is limited to 15 percent of the regular-time production in any month. Let

D_t = demand in month t (presumed known; not a variable)
W_t = workers on hand at the start of month t
H_t = hires at the start of month t
L_t = layoffs at the start of month t
I_t = inventory at the start of month t
S_t = subcontracted production in month t
O_t = overtime production in month t

Then for each month, the following constraints are required:

$W_t = W_{t-1} + H_t - L_t$ (relationship for the number of workers)

$I_t = I_{t-1} + 5000W_t + O_t + S_t - D_t$ (relationship for the inventory level)

$O_t \leq 0.15(5000W_t)$ (relationship for the overtime limit)

There are six variables (D_t is not a decision variable) and three constraints for each month. If the production plan is to cover 12 months, you would need 72 decision variables and 36 constraints. In addition you would need to specify an objective function for minimizing costs or maximizing profits. For example, let:

c_w = regular-time wages per worker per month
c_h = cost to hire one worker
c_L = cost to lay off one worker
c_I = cost to hold one unit of product for one month
c_s = cost to subcontract one unit of product
c_o = cost to produce one unit of product on overtime

An objective function for minimizing costs would be

$$TC = \sum_{t=1}^{12}(c_w W_t + c_h H_t + c_L L_t + c_I I_t + c_s S_t + c_o O_t)$$

It is easy to see that even for simple problems this approach requires a considerable number of variables and constraints. Obviously, a computer is mandatory for production planning applications of linear programming. Nonetheless, the method is very versatile in its ability to handle a wide variety and large number of variables and constraints.

Managerial Considerations

Although trial-and-error approaches or mathematical techniques can be useful in evaluating aggregate planning alternatives, they are only aids to the planning process. You have seen in this chapter that the planning process is dynamic and often complicated by conflicting objectives. Analytic techniques can help managers evaluate plans and resolve conflicting objectives, but managers—not techniques—make the decisions.

After arriving at an acceptable production plan, management must implement it. However, the aggregate plan is stated in aggregate terms. The first step in implementation therefore is to disaggregate the plan to specific products, work centers, and dates by master production scheduling, the topic of Chapter 15. Staffing plans must also be decomposed to work-force schedules for implementation. We discuss work-force scheduling in Chapter 18.

SOLVED PROBLEMS

1. The Cranston Telephone Company employs workers who lay telephone cables and perform a number of other construction tasks. The company prides itself on good service and strives to meet all commitments on time. Company policy is to complete all service orders within the quarter during which they are placed. Each worker puts in 600 hours per quarter regular time and can work an additional 100 hours overtime. The operations department has estimated that the following work-force requirements for such services will be needed next year.

Quarter	1	2	3	4
Hours	12,000	24,000	30,000	6,000

Wages are $6000 per quarter, with an overtime pay rate of $15 per hour. It costs $8000 to hire, train, and outfit a new employee. Layoff costs are $2000 per employee. Currently, 40 employees work for Cranston in this capacity.
  a. Find a level work-force plan that allows for no delay in service and minimizes undertime. What is the total cost of the plan? How many hours in undertime does your plan call for?
  b. Use a chase strategy without overtime. What is the total cost of this plan?
  c. Propose a mixed-strategy plan and evaluate its total cost.

Solution a. The peak demand is 30,000 hours in quarter 3. As each employee can work 700 hours per quarter (600 on regular time and 100 on overtime), the level work force that minimizes undertime is 30,000/700 = 42.86, or 43, employees.

Cost		Amount
Regular wages	($6000 per quarter)(43)(4 quarters)	$1,032,000
Overtime wages*	(4200 hrs in quarter 3)($15 per hour)	63,000
Hire costs	($8000 per hire)(3 hires)	24,000
Total		$1,119,000

*The 43 employees can produce (43)(600) = 25,800 hours of regular time in any quarter. The 30,000-hour requirement in quarter 3 exceeds this amount by 4200 hours.

b. The chase strategy:

Quarter	Demand (hr)	Work Force*	Hires	Layoffs
1	12,000	20	—	20
2	24,000	40	20	—
3	30,000	50	10	—
4	6,000	10	—	40
Total		120	30	60

*Work force is calculated by dividing the demand for each quarter by 600 hours, or the amount one employee can produce in one quarter.

Cost		Amount
Regular wages	($6000 per quarter)(120)	$ 720,000
Hire costs	($8000 per hire)(30 hires)	240,000
Layoff costs	($2000 per layoff)(60 layoffs)	120,000
Total		$1,080,000

c. The following mixed-strategy plan uses hires and layoffs along with overtime to cut costs from the plans in parts (a) and (b). This plan was developed by trial and error.

Quarter	Demand (hr)	Work Force	Hires	Layoffs	Overtime (hr)
1	12,000	20	—	20	—
2	24,000	40	20	—	—
3	30,000	43	3	—	4,200
4	6,000	10	—	33	—
Total		113	23	53	4,200

Cost		Amount
Regular wages	($6000 per quarter)(113)	$ 678,000
Hire costs	($8000 per hire)(23 hires)	184,000
Layoff costs	($2000 per layoff)(53 layoffs)	106,000
Overtime	($15 per hour)(4200 hours)	63,000
Total		$1,031,000

2. The Arctic Air Co. produces residential air conditioners. The manufacturing manager would like to develop a production plan for the next year based on the following demand and capacity data (in hundreds of units).

	Period					
	Jan–Feb (1)	Mar–Apr (2)	May–Jun (3)	Jul–Aug (4)	Sep–Oct (5)	Nov–Dec (6)
Demand (D)	50	60	90	120	70	40
Regular time (R)	65	65	65	80	80	65
Overtime (OT)	13	13	13	16	16	13
Subcontractor (S)	10	10	10	10	10	10

Producing a unit on regular time costs $1000, including $300 for labor. Producing a unit on overtime costs $1150. A subcontractor can produce a unit to Arctic Air specifications for $1250. Holding an air conditioner in stock for one two-month period costs $60, and 200 air conditioners are currently in stock. The plan calls for 400 units in stock at the end of period 6. No back orders are allowed.

Find a plan that minimizes costs.

Solution   Figure 14.7 contains the production plan obtained by the tableau method. It can be summarized as follows:

Period	Regular-Time Production	Overtime Production	Subcontracting	Anticipation Inventory
1	6500	0	0	1700
2	6500	400	0	2600
3	6500	1300	0	1400
4	8000	1600	1000	0
5	7000	0	0	0
6	4400	0	0	400

The cost of this plan is $44,287,000, assuming that workers are not paid for unused capacity in regular-time production or are productively put to work elsewhere in the organization.

FORMULA REVIEW

1. Number of workers in the work force:

Workers in current period	=	Workers at end of last period	+	Hires at start of current period	−	Layoffs at start of current period

2. Inventory level:

Inventory at end of current period	=	Inventory at end of last period	+	Production in current period	−	Demand requirements in current period

FIGURE 14.7

	Alternatives	Period 1	2	3	4	5	6	Unused capacity	Total capacity
Period	I_0	0 / 2	60	120	180	240	300	~~2~~ 0	2
1	R_1	1000 / 48	1060	1120 / 17	1180	1240	1300	~~65~~ ~~17~~ 0	65
	OT_1	1150	1210	1270	1330	1390	1450	13	13
	S_1	1250	1310	1370	1430	1490	1550	10	10
2	R_2	✕	1000 / 60	1060 / 5	1120	1180	1240	~~65~~ ~~5~~ 0	65
	OT_2	✕	1150	1210	1270 / 4	1330	1390	~~13~~ 9	13
	S_2	✕	1250	1310	1370	1430	1490	10	10
3	R_3	✕	✕	1000 / 65	1060	1120	1180	~~65~~ 0	65
	OT_3	✕	✕	1150 / 3	1210 / 10	1270	1330	~~13~~ ~~10~~ 0	13
	S_3	✕	✕	1250	1310	1370	1430	10	10
4	R_4	✕	✕	✕	1000 / 80	1060	1120	~~80~~ 0	80
	OT_4	✕	✕	✕	1150 / 16	1210	1270	~~16~~ 0	16
	S_4	✕	✕	✕	1250 / 10	1310	1370	~~10~~ 0	10
5	R_5	✕	✕	✕	✕	1000 / 70	1060	~~80~~ 10	80
	OT_5	✕	✕	✕	✕	1150	1210	16	16
	S_5	✕	✕	✕	✕	1250	1310	10	10
6	R_6	✕	✕	✕	✕	✕	1000 / 44	~~65~~ 21	65
	OT_6	✕	✕	✕	✕	✕	1150	13	13
	S_6	✕	✕	✕	✕	✕	1250	10	10
	D	50	60	90	120	70	44	132	566

CHAPTER HIGHLIGHTS

● In manufacturing organizations, the production plan links the business plan and the master production schedule. In service organizations, the staffing plan links the annual plan and the work-force schedule.

● Aggregate plans are managerial statements of time-phased production or service rates, labor requirements, and, in manufacturing, inventory investment that considers customer demand and physical capacity limitations.

● Products or services, labor, and time are aggregated to reduce the level of detail in the planning process.

● Managerial inputs are required from the various functional areas in the organization. This approach typically raises conflicting objectives, which must be reconciled in the plan. One of the typical manufacturing objectives not considered in a service organization is to minimize investment in finished goods inventory.

● The two basic types of decision alternatives are reactive and aggressive. Reactive alternatives take customer demand as a given quantity. Aggressive alternatives attempt to change customer demand to achieve efficiency in providing goods or services.

● Two pure planning strategies are the level strategy, which maintains a constant work-force size or production rate, and the chase strategy, which allows work-force levels and production rates to vary according to customer demand.

● Developing aggregate plans is an iterative process of determining requirements; identifying relevant constraints, alternatives, and costs; preparing a prospective plan; checking for acceptability to top management; and implementing the plan.

● Managers must remember that trial-and-error approaches and mathematical techniques are only aids to the planning process. Managers, not techniques, make the decisions.

KEY TERMS

aggregate plan **574**
aggressive alternatives **584**
annual plan **579**
backlog **584**
business plan **578**

chase strategy **585**
complementary products **584**
level strategy **585**
planning horizon **578**
production plan **574**

reactive alternatives **582**
staffing plan **574**
tableau method **594**
work-force schedule **579**

STUDY QUESTIONS

1. What is an aggregate plan? Why must quantities be aggregated?

2. How does the aggregate plan relate to other organizational plans?

3. Consider the statement: "Production planning is the responsibility of our manufacturing personnel because it deals with the resources they are responsible for." Comment on that statement in light of the strategic importance of production planning.

4. Give reasons why executives representing the following areas should be interested in production planning.
   a. Marketing
   b. Manufacturing
   c. Materials
   d. Finance
   e. Human resources
   f. Engineering

5. What are the typical objectives to be consid-

ered in aggregate planning? Comment on the conflicting nature of these objectives.

6. What is the difference between *reactive* and *aggressive* alternatives in aggregate planning? Provide several examples of each.

7. The *chase* strategy and the *level* strategy represent two extremes in aggregate planning. Define each one and describe the type of environment in which each would work best.

8. Briefly describe the aggregate planning process and explain how inputs from functional areas in the organization are solicited and incorporated into production and staffing plans.

9. Compare and contrast the staffing plan in a service organization with a production plan in a manufacturing organization. In what ways are the objectives, alternatives, and planning processes different?

10. The Hometown Bank currently employs eight tellers to staff lobby stations for customer transactions. Customer demand for banking services is variable, with peaks coinciding with the end of the week, end of the month, and holiday seasons. Because of this variability the tellers are idle much of the time; during rush periods, however, customers experience lengthy delays. Suppose that you are the operations manager of this bank.

   a. What staffing plan alternatives would you consider?

   b. What data would you need?

   c. What objectives would you consider?

PROBLEMS

Review Problems

1. The Crop-Chemical Company produces chemical fertilizers. The projected manufacturing requirements (in thousands of gallons) for the next four quarters are 80, 50, 80, and 130, respectively. Stockouts and back orders are to be avoided. A level production strategy is desired.

   a. Determine the quarterly production rate required to meet total demand for the year. Beginning inventory is zero.

   b. Specify the anticipation inventories that will be produced.

   c. Suppose that the requirements for the next four quarters are 80, 130, 50, and 80, respectively. Total demand is the same, but would the production rate in part (a) have to be changed? If so, what rate would be needed now?

2. The Barberton Municipal Division of Road Maintenance is charged with road repair in the city of Barberton and surrounding area. Cindy Kramer, road maintenance director, must submit a staffing plan for the next year based on a set schedule for repairs and city budget. Roads cannot be repaired ahead of schedule because funds will not be available to pay the workers. Delaying the repair of roads is equally infeasible because the state will not match city funds if repairs fall behind schedule.

   Kramer estimates that the labor hours required for the next four quarters are 6000, 12,000, 19,000, and 9000 respectively. Each of the 11 workers on the work force can contribute 520 hours per quarter. It costs $6240 in regular-time wages per worker for a quarter and $18 for each overtime hour. Overtime is limited to 20 percent of the regular-time capacity in any quarter. Workers can be hired for $3000 and fired for $2000. Subcontracting is not considered because of the poor reputation of local subcontractors.

   a. Find a level work-force plan that allows no delay in road repair and minimizes undertime. Overtime can be used to its limits in any quarter. What is the total cost of the plan and how many undertime hours does it call for?

b. Use a chase strategy without overtime. What is the total cost of this plan?

c. Propose a plan of your own. Compare your plan with those in parts (a) and (b) and discuss its comparative merits.

3. Management at the Ross Corporation has determined the following demand schedule.

Month	Demand (units)
1	500
2	800
3	1000
4	1400
5	2000
6	1600
7	1400
8	1200
9	1000
10	2400
11	3000
12	1000

An employee can produce an average of 10 units per month. Workers earn $2000 per month but will not work overtime according to the labor contract in force. It costs Ross $1000 to hire and train a new employee and $500 to lay one off. Inventory costs $8 per unit on hand at the end of each month. Presently there are 100 employees on the payroll.

a. Prepare a production plan with a level strategy. The plan may call for a one-time adjustment of the work force before month 1.

b. Prepare a production plan with a chase strategy.

c. Compare and contrast the two "pure strategy" plans from the aspect of annual costs and other factors you feel are important.

d. Propose a mixed-strategy plan that is better than the two pure-strategy plans. Explain why you believe your plan is better.

4. The Flying Frisbee Company has forecasted the following staffing requirements. It has a seasonal demand and would like two alternative staffing plans developed.

Month	1	2	3	4	5	6	7	8	9	10	11	12
Requirement	2	2	4	6	18	20	20	18	7	3	2	1

Presently there are ten employees on hand. No more than ten new hires can be accommodated in any month because of limited training facilities. No back orders are allowed, and overtime cannot exceed 25 percent of regular-time capacity in any month.

Regular-time wages are $1500 per month and overtime wages are 150 percent of regular-time wages. The hiring cost is $2500 per person, and the layoff costs are $2000.

a. Prepare a staffing plan utilizing a level strategy.

b. Prepare a plan using a chase strategy.

c. Which strategy is more cost effective? What are the advantages and disadvantages of each plan?

5. The Little Shoe Company makes sandals for children. Management has just prepared a forecast of sales (in pairs of sandals) for next year and now must prepare a production plan. The company has traditionally maintained a level work-force strategy. Currently there are 8 workers who have been with the company for a number of years. Each employee can produce 2000 pairs of sandals in a two-month period, the planning period used by Little Shoe. Every year management authorizes overtime in periods 1, 5, and 6, up to a maximum of 20 percent of regular-time capacity. Management wants to avoid stockouts and back orders and will not accept any plan that calls for such shortages. At present there are 12,000 pairs of sandals in finished goods inventory. The demand forecast is

Period	1	2	3	4	5	6
Sales	25,000	6,500	15,000	19,000	32,000	29,000

a. Is the level work-force strategy with the current work force feasible, assuming that overtime is used in periods 1, 5, and 6? Explain.

b. Find two alternative plans that would satisfy management's concern over stockouts and back orders, disregarding costs.

What are the trade-offs between these two plans that must be considered?

6. The Bull Grin Company produces a feed supplement for animal foods produced by a number of companies. Sales are seasonal, but Bull Grin's customers refuse to stockpile the supplement during slack sales periods. In other words, the customers want to minimize their inventory investments, insist on shipments according to their schedules, and won't accept back orders.

Bull Grin employs manual, unskilled labor, who require little or no training. Producing 1000 pounds of supplement costs $830 on regular time and $910 on overtime. These figures include materials, which account for 80 percent of the cost. Overtime is limited to production of a total of 20,000 pounds per quarter. In addition, subcontractors can be hired at $1000 per thousand pounds, but only 30,000 pounds per quarter can be produced this way.

The current level of inventory is 40,000 pounds, and management wants to end the year at that level. Holding 1000 pounds of feed supplement in inventory per quarter costs $100. The latest annual forecast is:

Quarter	Demand (lb)
1	130,000
2	400,000
3	800,000
4	470,000
Total	1,800,000

The following regular-time capacity plan has been proposed:

Quarter	Production Capacity (lb)
1	390,000
2	400,000
3	460,000
4	380,000

Find the optimal production plan and calculate its cost.

7. Consider the Bull Grin Company described

in Problem 6. Suppose that the regular-time capacity plan were:

Quarter	Production Capacity (lb)
1	440,000
2	440,000
3	440,000
4	440,000

a. Find the optimal production plan and calculate its cost.

b. Compare the plan you developed in Problem 6 with this plan. How are the strategies different? What are the cost implications, considering hirings and layoffs? Use the following information:

- Hiring 1000 pounds of regular-time capacity costs $450.

- Laying off 1000 pounds of regular-time capacity costs $350.

- Currently, there are 370,000 pounds of regular-time capacity. At the end of quarter 4 (or start of quarter 5), management wants to have 370,000 pounds of regular-time capacity again.

- Idle workers representing regular-time capacity can be sent home without pay. Therefore, there is no cost for these underutilized resources.

8. Waverly Scale Company produces industrial scales for a variety of applications. It costs Waverly $1500 to hire a semi-skilled worker for its assembly plant and $1000 to lay one off. The plant averages an output of 36,000 scales per quarter with its current work force of 72 employees. Overtime is limited to a maximum of 3000 scales per quarter, and subcontracting is limited to 1000 per quarter. It costs $2430 to assemble one scale on regular time (including materials), $2700 on overtime, and $3300 to subcontract the assembly. The current level of inventory is 4000 scales, and management wants to end the year at that level. Holding a scale in inventory per quarter costs $300.

The demand for scales this coming year is:

Quarter	Demand
1	10,000
2	41,000
3	77,000
4	44,000
	172,000

Customers do not tolerate back orders.

Two work-force plans have been proposed, and management is uncertain as to which one to use.

	Number of Employees	
Quarter	Plan 1	Plan 2
1	72	86
2	78	86
3	92	86
4	72	86

a. Which plan would you recommend to management? Explain, supporting your recommendation with analysis.
b. Suppose management can use creative pricing to get customers to buy scales in nontraditional time periods. The following demand schedule would result.

Quarter	Demand
1	20,000
2	54,000
3	54,000
4	44,000
	172,000

Which work-force plan would you recommend? Since price incentives reduce revenues, is the new demand schedule worth it?

Advanced Problems

Supplement Connections: Problems 9 and 10 require prior reading of Supplement 2 (Linear Programming). A computer package is required for Problems 9 and 10.

9. The Warwick Manufacturing Company produces shovels for industrial and home use. Sales of the shovels are seasonal, but Warwick's customers refuse to stockpile them during slack periods. In other words, the customers want to minimize their inventory investments, insist on shipments according to their schedules, and won't accept back orders.

Warwick employs manual, unskilled labor, who require only very basic training. Producing 1000 shovels costs $3500 on regular time and $3700 on overtime. These figures include materials, which account for over 85 percent of the cost. Overtime is limited to production of a total of 15,000 shovels per quarter. In addition, subcontractors can be hired at $4200 per thousand shovels, but Warwick's labor contract restricts this amount to 5000 shovels per quarter.

The current level of inventory is 30,000 shovels, and management wants to end the year at that level. Holding 1000 shovels in inventory per quarter costs $280. The latest annual demand forecast is:

Quarter	Demand
1	70,000
2	150,000
3	320,000
4	100,000
Total	640,000

Find the *best* regular-time capacity plan, assuming:

- The firm has 30 workers now, and management wants to have the same number in quarter 4. Each worker can produce 4000 shovels per quarter.
- Hiring one worker costs $1000, and laying off a worker costs $600.

You could use a trial-and-error approach on a computer to evaluate various capacity plans until you find the best one. Alternatively, you could use Supplement 2 and build a linear programming model to find the optimal solution.

10. The management of Warwick Company (Problem 9) is willing to give volume price breaks to its customers as an incentive to purchase shovels in advance of the traditional seasons. Warwick's sales and marketing staff estimates that the demand for shovels resulting from the price breaks would be:

Quarter	Demand	Original Demand
1	120,000	70,000
2	180,000	150,000
3	180,000	320,000
4	160,000	100,000
Total	640,000	640,000

a. Compute the optimal production plan (including the work-force staffing plan) for the new demand schedule. Compare it to the optimal production plan under the original demand schedule.

b. What can you say about the effects of demand management in this situation?

11. The manager of Gretchen's Hamburger Paradise must prepare an annual staffing plan. The Hamburger Paradise shop is a fast-food shop located in an ideal spot near the local high school. The only products the shop sells are hamburgers, chili, soft drinks, shakes, and french fries. A sample of 1000 customers taken at random revealed that they purchased 2100 hamburgers, 200 pints of chili, 1000 soft drinks and shakes, and 1000 bags of french fries. Thus for purposes of estimating staffing requirements, the manager assumes that each customer purchases 2.1 hamburgers, 0.2 pint of chili, 1 soft drink or shake, and 1 bag of french fries. Each hamburger requires 4 minutes of labor. A pint of chili requires 3 minutes, while a soft drink/shake and a bag of fries each take 2 minutes of labor.

Gretchen's Hamburger Paradise currently has ten employees who work 80 hours a month. They are high school students who work part time on staggered shifts. Wages are $400 per month for regular time and $7.50 per hour for overtime. It costs $250 to hire and train a new employee and $50 to fire an employee.

The manager realizes that building up seasonal inventories of hamburgers (or any of the products) would not be wise because of customer taste preferences. Also, any demand not satisfied is a lost sale and must be avoided. Three strategies come to mind.

- Level work force and use of up to 20 percent of regular-time capacity on overtime in any month
- Maintain a base of 10 employees, hiring and firing as needed to avoid any overtime.
- Chase strategy, hiring and firing employees as demand changes to avoid overtime

When performing her calculations the manager always rounds to the next highest integer for the number of employees. She also follows a policy of not using an employee more than 80 hours per month, except when overtime is needed. The projected demand by month (number of customers) for next year is:

Jan	3200	July	4800
Feb	2600	Aug	4200
Mar	3300	Sept	3800
Apr	3900	Oct	3600
May	3600	Nov	3500
June	4200	Dec	3000

a. Develop the schedule of service requirements for the next year.

b. Which of the strategies is most effective?

c. Suppose that an arrangement with the high school enables the manager to identify good prospective employees without having to advertise in the local newspaper. This reduces the hiring cost to $50, which is mainly the cost of charred hamburgers during training. Will this change the manager's strategy on a cost basis? *Should* the manager change strategies, considering other objectives that may be appropriate?

Supplement 2 (Linear Programming) and a computer package are required for this case.

Howard Susdorf, president of Sun Manufacturing, studied the reports on his desk. The reports indicated that the company had record inventory levels and labor costs last month. In addition, the shipments to customers fell short of the goal for last month. Susdorf glanced at the stack of phone messages from irate customers and winced at the thought of returning their calls. He felt that it was about time to find out what was going on.

Sun Manufacturing produces engine bearings for use in a wide variety of engines and motors. In just ten years sales have grown to $30 million dollars. In the past two years, however, sales have been steady. When the company started operations it produced only a limited line of bearings. Today the company produces two major product lines representing 3000 individual products. Some of the products are seasonal since they are used as replacement parts for engines used during particular seasons of the year. The facility mostly has a product focus, but it also has several machine shop operations for special customer requests. Most of the employees are skilled workers and belong to one of a number of trade unions.

Howard Susdorf decided that the best thing to do would be to bring in a consultant to provide an independent evaluation of the problems at Sun Manufacturing. He chose Martha Jones, who had a respectable background as a production manager before becoming a professor at the state university. He asked her to meet with anybody she wanted and to use the company records as needed to prepare her report.

Jones's first meeting was with Bill Schmidt, the materials manager. Schmidt is responsible for authorizing work-force changes, overtime, and contracts with suppliers of raw materials and components. The person who develops the master production schedule also reports to him. Schmidt explained the procedure for production planning to Jones:

> The process starts with the forecasts we get from distribution. Each month they give us the forecasts for the two product families for the following two months plus any actual orders that have already been booked. We need the forecasts two months ahead because our manufacturing lead time for finished products is 5 weeks. From these forecasts and estimates of past de-

mands, the master scheduler develops the schedule of production for each of the finished products for the next two months. Based on this schedule we estimate the amount of labor, overtime, and subcontracting we will need. For example, if we estimate we need 130,000 hours of labor and we only have 110,000 hours, we may use overtime or try to hire the labor we need if we have the machine capacity. If this fails, we will subcontract some of the work. The last resort is to change the master schedule. All of this has to be done quickly because we do not have much time. Quite frankly, the process is mind-boggling when you consider the number of products we have. Here's where experience pays off.

Since the process began with the forecasts, Jones decided to talk to Victor Johnson, the vice president of marketing.

> My forecasting group does a pretty good job of estimating future demands, although I multiply their estimates by a certain percentage just to make sure we have enough on hand. However, the way things have been going recently, we may lose some customers. We can't ship our orders on time, and this has caused some bad feelings for all involved.

Jones next wanted to see what John Worthington, vice president of manufacturing, thought about all of this. John was quite candid.

> Some days I hate to come to work. Our work force is not very content. We experience a high degree of turnover, which in turn results in low worker morale and poor productivity. Ten years ago, when we started, our work force was loyal and pleasant to work with. With the expansion that has taken place since then something has gone wrong. Steve Conners, from the human resources department, says it's tough to find good people these days, particularly with the high turnover we have. He feels that we should stop trying to match seasonal demands by hires and layoffs. On top of all this, the labor union representatives are telling me that the next time we talk about a new contract they are going to demand more job security. How can we keep costs down if we lose flexibility in adjusting our labor levels?

Jones felt she had one more stop to make, although she thought that she already knew what she would hear there. She walked into Walter Coyne's office.

Walter was comptroller of Sun Manufacturing and had nothing good to say about the current state of affairs.

These expenditures for overtime and subcontracting are way out of bounds for the past several months. If this continues, the production budget will be used up before the year is half over. Another thing I can't understand is the inventory investment we're making. Perhaps you manufacturing types can explain to me how we can have so much inventory with such poor customer service. All of this puts a severe strain on our cash reserves. I have half a mind to cut the production budget by 20 percent next year and see what falls out. I hope you can help these other people get their act in order.

Jones felt she had heard enough for one day. The following day she spent gathering data about the Sun production planning problem. (See Exhibits 1 through 4.) Her next meeting with Howard Susdorf was next week, and she knew that she had better have some recommendations by then.

QUESTIONS

1. Martha Jones interviewed employees from the areas of materials, marketing, manufacturing, and finance. Comment on the philosophies expressed by these persons. Are there any you disagree with?
2. What changes to the production planning process at Sun Manufacturing would you recommend?
3. Using the data in the exhibits, specify a linear programming model that will determine the minimum-cost production plan for Sun for the next year. (See Supplement 2.)
4. Use your linear programming model and a computer to find a minimum-cost production plan. How should your model be used in Sun's production planning process, as revised by you in Question 2?

EXHIBIT 1 / Production Planning Assumptions

Sun uses two-month planning periods.

All employees can work on both product groups and can be hired into a common labor pool. However, the plan must specify how many employees should be assigned to each product group each planning period.

The effect of work experience on productivity and wages is negligible.

Management can request overtime on any product group at any time.

The number of units worked on overtime on any product group in any planning period cannot exceed 20 percent of the regular-time production on that product group in that planning period.

No back orders are allowed.

For planning purposes, zero levels of inventory in any period are acceptable.

There are no limits on the amount of subcontracting that can be used.

Material costs are the same regardless of whether the products are produced in-house or are subcontracted. It is safe to ignore these costs when comparing alternatives.

EXHIBIT 2 / Demand Forecasts*

	Planning Period					
Product Group	1	2	3	4	5	6
Large engine (L)	500	500	1500	600	500	400
Small engine (S)	350	1500	300	1000	750	500

*Forecasts are expressed in thousands of engine bearings. Data supplied by Victor Johnson from actual customer orders promised for delivery in each of last year's planning periods. Sales are expected to be about the same next year.

EXHIBIT 3 / Cost Data

Hiring cost	$4000 per employee, including training and search costs
Layoff cost	$2800 per employee, including severance pay and paperwork
Wages	$4800 per employee per two-month period
Overtime cost	$7.20 per unit for group L $2.88 per unit for group S
Inventory cost	$1.70 per unit per period for group L $0.90 per unit per period for group S
Subcontracting cost	$8.50 per unit for group L $3.50 per unit for group S

EXHIBIT 4 / Miscellaneous Data

Beginning work-force level*	800 employees
Productivity	1000 units per employee per planning period for group L 2500 units per employee per planning period for group S
Beginning inventories*	25,000 units of group L 50,000 units of group S

*Data supplied by John Worthington. These figures were valid just prior to planning period 1, shown in Exhibit 2.

SELECTED REFERENCES

Bowman, E.H. "Production Planning by the Transportation Method of Linear Programming." *Journal of the Operations Research Society*, vol. 4 (February 1956), pp. 100–103.

Chaiken, J.M., and R.C. Larson. "Methods for Allocating Urban Emergency Units: A Survey." *Management Science*, vol. 19, no. 4 (December, Part 2, 1972), pp. 110–130.

Hanssman, F., and S.W. Hess. "A Linear Programming Approach to Production and Employment Scheduling." *Management Technology*, vol. 1 (January 1960), pp. 46–51.

Holt, C., C.F. Modigliani, and H. Simon. "A Linear Decision Rule for Production and Employment Scheduling." *Management Science*, vol. 2, no. 2 (October 1955), pp. 1–30.

"An Industry's Race with Summer." *New York Times*, February 23, 1989.

Jones, C.H. "Parametric Production Planning." *Management Science*, vol. 15, no. 11 (July 1967), pp. 843–866.

Kinsey, John W. "Master Production Planning—The Key to Successful Master Scheduling." *Proceedings of the 24th Annual APICS Conference*, Boston (October 1981), pp. 81–85.

Krajewski, L., and H. Thompson. "Efficient Employment Planning in Public Utilities." *Bell Journal of Economics and Management Science*, vol. 6, no. 1 (Spring 1975), pp. 314–326.

Lee, S.M., and L.J. Moore. "A Practical Approach to Production Scheduling." *Production and Inventory Management* (1st Quarter 1974), pp. 79–92.

Lee, W.B., and B.M. Khumawala. "Simulation Testing of Aggregate Production Planning Models in an Implementation Methodology." *Management Science*, vol. 20, no. 6 (February 1974), pp. 903–911.

McClain, J.D., and L.J. Thomas. "Horizon Effects in Aggregate Production Planning with Seasonal Demand." *Management Science*, vol. 23, no. 7 (March 1977), pp. 728–736.

Mellichamp, J., and R. Love. "Production Heuristics for the Aggregate Planning Problem." *Management Science*, vol. 24, no. 12 (August 1978), pp. 1242–1251.

Silver, E.A. "A Tutorial on Production Smoothing and Work-force Balancing." *Operations Research* (November–December 1967), pp. 985–1010.

Smith, Linda M. "Marketing's Role in a Manufacturing Environment." *Proceedings of the 23rd Annual APICS Conference*, Los Angeles (October 1980), pp. 248–251.

Taubert, W.H. "A Search Decision Rule for the Aggregate Scheduling Problem." *Management Science*, vol. 14, no. 6 (February 1968), pp. 343–359.

Vollmann, Thomas E. "Capacity Planning: The Missing Link." *Production and Inventory Management* (First Quarter 1973), pp. 61–73.

Wolfe, H., and J.P. Young. "Staffing the Nursing Unit—Part 1: Controlled Variable Staffing." *Nursing Research*, vol. 14, no. 3 (Summer 1965), pp. 236–243.

Chapter 15

MASTER PRODUCTION SCHEDULING

How do our competitive priorities affect our approach to master production scheduling?

How should our master production schedule relate to our production plan?

How can we provide accurate shipping dates to our customers?

How can we get better estimates of cash flows and capacity requirements?

E than Allen Furniture Company produces more than 1400 wood furniture products in 14 geographically dispersed factories. The Ethan Allen production plan determines the desired aggregate production output of each assembly line. Ultimately, however, the company must develop a more detailed plan, one that determines the production quantities and sequence of specific products on the lines. A typical assembly line manufactures from 15 to 100 different products, so care must be taken to produce a schedule that does not exceed the lines' capacities. Otherwise, the strategic objectives of the production plan will not be met. The need to determine such a schedule is common in the world of manufacturing.

In this chapter we show how such a detailed plan, called the master production schedule, disaggregates the production plan into specific product schedules. We also discuss how competitive strategies affect a firm's approach to master production scheduling.

THE MASTER PRODUCTION SCHEDULING PROCESS

The master production scheduling process begins where we left off in Chapter 14. Using the authorized production plan as a basis, operations develops a prospective master production schedule. A **master production schedule (MPS)** details how many end items will be produced within specified periods of time. End items are either finished products or the highest-level assemblies from which shippable products are built (see Chapter 12). Time periods are usually measured in weeks, although hours, days, or even months are sometimes used.

Figure 15.1 shows the master production scheduling process. Think of the prospective MPS as a trial of whether operations can meet the schedule with the resources (such as machine capacities, labor, overtime, and subcontractors) estimated in the production plan. Operations revises the MPS until it either finds a schedule that satisfies all resource limitations or determines that no feasible schedule can be found. In the latter event, the production plan must be revised to adjust production requirements or increase authorized resources. Ultimately, an acceptable prospective MPS emerges for plant management authorization. Operations then uses the authorized MPS as input to material requirements planning, which, as you will see in Chapter 16, determines specific schedules for part, component, and assembly production.

A master production scheduler is responsible for developing an MPS that satisfies the intent of the production plan. Other responsibilities typically include those in Table 15.1. The MPS process may differ from company to company, depending on whether the firm has a process or product focus. Thus the specific procedures and record formats presented later in this chapter illustrate *types of procedures* and may not apply to specific firms. In summary, as Fig. 15.1 illustrates, the MPS process is linked to the authorized production plan and therefore requires feedback from the functional areas involved in production planning. In this way, the master production schedule sets in motion the operations to achieve the production plan's objectives.

FIGURE 15.1

Master Production
Scheduling Process

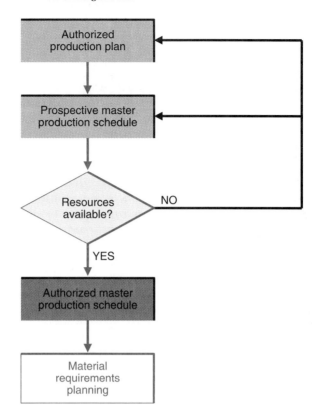

The Master Production Schedule

To give you a clearer idea of master production scheduling, let's consider the MPS of a bicycle manufacturer, first introduced in Chapter 14, Fig. 14.1. The company doesn't accept orders for custom designed bicycles; rather, it produces to stock. For production planning purposes, the firm has grouped its entire line of products into several families, based on wheel diameter. One family of bicycles, based on a 20-inch wheel, includes three different styles: Alpha, which comes with training wheels, is designed for children just learning

TABLE 15.1 / *Typical Responsibilities of a Master Production Scheduler*

Specify delivery promise dates on incoming orders and match actual requirements with the master production schedule.

Evaluate the impact of "top-down" inputs, such as introducing new products, or promising an order, in less than normal lead time.

Evaluate the impact of "bottom-up" inputs, such as anticipated shortage reports from manufacturing or purchasing, indicating that certain components will not be available as scheduled or that planned production rates are not being attained.

Review the master production schedule when necessary for lack of materials or capacity.

Bring basic conflicts to the attention of management for resolution.

Source: Oliver Wight, *Production and Inventory Management in the Computer Age* (Boston: Cahners Books, 1974), p. 69.

to ride. Dirty Dan is a dirt bike with racing decals and rugged tires. And Roadster has hand-caliper brakes, polished aluminum fenders, and a rearview mirror. All three styles are basically the same bicycle, with minor variations in color and accessories.

The production plan for the 20-inch family calls for a steady increase in output to satisfy anticipated increases in sales over the next several months. Presently, the company has excess capacity, which it plans to use up before resorting to overtime to reach peak production in March. This approach keeps costly inventory to a minimum. Consequently, the production plan schedules 10,000 units in January, 15,000 units in February, and 20,000 units in March.

One possible MPS for this family is shown in Fig. 15.2. Note that Dirty Dan is a high-volume product made continuously, while Alpha and Roadster are produced on an intermittent basis. In all cases the batch sizes reflect considerations for assembly capacity, product demands, setup costs, inventory holding costs, and requirements for good customer service. This example, just one of many possible lot size combinations, demonstrates a basic purpose of the MPS: setting due dates for production orders. For example, Fig. 15.2 shows that in January, production is scheduled to complete 400 units of Roadster in week 1 and 400 units in week 3.

Another purpose of the MPS is to provide an accurate picture of the resources and materials needed to support the production plan. Recall that the production plan estimates resource requirements, but it states resource quantities in aggregate terms. Because it specifies the production quantities of specific products, the MPS provides a more accurate picture of resource needs. Also, by specifying the number of end items to be produced during each time period, the MPS determines requirements for all intermediate and purchased items as well. This is the point at which the bill of materials (see Chapter 12) is important. For example, in Fig. 15.2 the MPS shows 1600 units of Alpha scheduled for completion in week 2. This means that by week 2, to complete the 1600 bicycles on schedule, operations must have available 1600 Alpha main frames, 3200 20-inch wheels, 1600 sets of training wheels, and specific quantities of other parts contained in the bill of materials. Thus a good MPS enables a company to make efficient use of its most valuable resources—labor, capital, capacity, and materials.

FIGURE 15.2

Weekly Master
Production Schedule

	January				February				March			
	Week				Week				Week			
Product	1	2	3	4	5	6	7	8	9	10	11	12
Alpha	–	1600	–	1600	–	2400	–	2400	–	3200	–	3200
Dirty Dan	1500	1500	1500	1500	2250	2250	2250	2250	3000	3000	3000	3000
Roadster	400	–	400	–	600	–	600	–	800	–	800	–
Monthly total	10,000				15,000				20,000			

Typical Constraints

A master production schedule must satisfy several constraints. First, the sum of the quantities in the MPS must equal those in the production plan. Figure 15.2 demonstrates two aspects of this constraint. Note that each month the total quantity for all three styles equals the total quantity of bicycles specified in the production plan (see Fig. 14.1). If the production plan specified quantities in dollars or labor hours, the scheduler would have to convert the MPS quantities to the same unit of measure. Master production schedules should specify units of *product*, however, for inventory control purposes.

The second aspect of the constraint is that total requirements for a product, as determined in the production plan, must be allocated over time in an efficient manner. For example, in January the plan calls for operations to produce 3200 units of Alpha, 6000 units of Dirty Dan, and 800 units of Roadster, or a total of 10,000 units. The specific mix is based on historical demand and marketing and promotional considerations. The bicycle company's MPS states production quantities in weekly time periods, although they could be in days or months. The scheduler for the 20-inch bicycle family must select weekly lot sizes for each product, taking into account economic factors such as production setup costs and inventory carrying costs.

The decision that determines lot size and timing is subject to a second constraint: capacity limitations. Typically, several key resources limit production volume. For example, work stations that are usually short on labor capacity, storage space for components and finished products, or working capital can limit the output a company can produce. The scheduler must acknowledge these limitations and recognize that some products require more critical resources than others.

MANAGERIAL ISSUES

The master production schedule is important because it links the firm's broad strategies, as expressed in the production plan, to more specific tactical plans that will enable a firm to achieve its objectives. The relationship of the MPS to competitive priorities, functional area interfaces, and the influence of computers on the MPS are important managerial issues.

The Master Production Schedule and Competitive Priorities

In Chapter 2 you learned that firms structure themselves to gain distinctive advantages over other firms by emphasizing one or more competitive priorities. With respect to the MPS, three basic strategies enable a firm to manage inventories in support of these priorities. The strategy chosen will determine the operations manager's approach to master production scheduling. Choosing among these strategies is related to the issues of inventory placement. (See Chapter 12.)

Make-to-Stock Strategy. Product-focused firms tend to use a **make-to-stock strategy,** an approach in which the firm holds items in stock for immediate delivery. The main advantage of placing most inventory toward the finished-goods level is that customer delivery times are minimized. This strategy is feasible because most product-focused firms produce relatively few standardized products, for which they can make reasonably accurate forecasts. Examples of products produced with a make-to-stock strategy include garden tools, electronic components, and chemicals. Thus these firms develop master production schedules for end items. Figure 15.3 demonstrates that make-to-stock operations typically produce a small number of finished products from a large number of different raw materials. Scheduling production of end items is easier from the standpoint of numbers alone.

Assemble-to-Order Strategy. The **assemble-to-order strategy** is an approach for producing end items with many options from relatively few major assemblies and components, after customer orders are received. This strategy addresses the two competitive priorities, customization and fast delivery time. Operations holds the major assemblies and components in stock until a specific order comes in. Stocking end items would be economically prohibitive because forecasts are relatively inaccurate and options are numerous. For example, an automobile manufacturer can literally produce millions of cars, no two alike, to meet the mix of options and accessories demanded by customers. Other examples include farm tractors, upholstered furniture, and automatic teller machines.

As Fig. 15.3 shows, the number of different items produced and purchased under an assemble-to-order strategy assumes an hourglass shape, emphasizing the relatively small number of major assemblies and components. For example, suppose you were manufacturing an automobile with the following limited number of customer options: 3 engine sizes, 4 transmission types, 2 drive trains, 3 steering options, 3 tire sizes, 3 body styles, 2 trim options, 4 interior options, and 2 brake systems. The body frame and certain other parts are common to every car you produce. Based on these customer choices, you can produce 10,368 different cars ($3 \times 4 \times 2 \cdots$). However, there are only 26 major assemblies and components ($3 + 4 + 2 \cdots$), plus a common assembly of parts needed for every car—a far smaller number than the total number of cars that

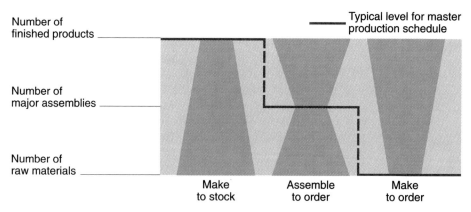

FIGURE 15.3

Relationship of the MPS to Competitive Priorities

Number of finished products

Number of major assemblies

Number of raw materials

—— Typical level for master production schedule

Make to stock   Assemble to order   Make to order

(a) Make-to stock

(b) Assemble to order

(c) Make to order

*H*ewlett-Packard uses a make-to-stock strategy in the manufacture of electronic equipment (a). Prefabricated homes are an example of an assemble-to-order process (b). American Iron and Steel Corporation follows a make-to-order strategy in its steel casting plant (c).

could be produced. Demand for these major assemblies and components is much easier to forecast than that for any completely assembled product. Consequently, operations bases master production scheduling on the major assemblies and components, rather than on the end items.

Make-to-Order Strategy. Many process-focused firms use a **make-to-order strategy,** whereby operations produces end items to customer specifications. This strategy provides a high degree of customization. Because most end items, components, and assemblies are custom-made, their number usually exceeds the number of raw materials used to produce them, as illustrated in Fig. 15.3. Examples include specialized medical equipment, castings, and plastic bottles for a particular brand of shampoo. Because a few raw materials are common to many products, an organization can more easily forecast demand for them than for end items or major assemblies. In such situations, operations generally schedules raw-material utilization only. However, end-item scheduling is feasible if customer orders allow sufficiently long delivery times.

Functional Interfaces

The master production scheduling process involves all of a firm's functional areas. As in the development of a production plan, operations needs inputs from various areas to develop an MPS that achieves production plan objectives and organizational goals. However, interaction with various functional areas doesn't end with the inputs they provide.

Sometimes the way a firm competes prompts interaction through the MPS. For example, operations can create a master production schedule that maintains a stable work force and high utilization of critical work centers. Such a strategy reduces the firm's flexibility to respond to changes in customer demand, however. Reducing flexibility in this way may not be in the best interests of the firm from a marketing perspective. Trade-offs must be made in responding to customer-desired shipping dates, reducing inventory levels, and minimizing the costs of revising production schedules. Such situations require cooperation between marketing and manufacturing. Some companies require the vice presidents of marketing and manufacturing to jointly authorize major MPS changes to ensure mutual resolution of these issues. Managerial Practice 15.1 discusses how these functional interfaces were resolved in developing master production schedules at Hyundai.

The MPS can also be used as a basis for more routine planning functions. Finance uses the MPS to estimate budgets and cash flows. Marketing uses it to project the impact of product mix changes on the firm's ability to satisfy customer demand and manage delivery schedules. Using rough-cut capacity planning, which we discuss later in the chapter, manufacturing can estimate the effects of MPS changes on loads at critical work stations. In general, all the firm's functional areas need the MPS.

Computer-Assisted Master Production Scheduling

The applications of the techniques for master production scheduling and rough-cut capacity planning that we discuss in this chapter require the use of computers. When thousands of items are involved, developing the MPS manually is an enormous, if not impossible, task. Most major computer suppliers and many companies specializing in software for manufacturing systems have developed software packages that perform the types of calculations we will present. These programs also provide managers with detailed reports that are useful for analyzing the MPS. Personal computers, with their excellent graphic capabilities, give managers access to many MPS-related reports, such as load profiles, in readable and useful formats. Interfacing a personal computer with

Managerial Practice 15.1

Master Production Scheduling at Hyundai Motor Company

In 1989 the Hyundai Motor Company produced 780,000 automobiles at a rate of 137 units per hour. The company offers approximately 4000 combinations of model, options, and interior color. Hyundai develops an annual business plan that is expressed in monthly sales volumes by model types and by engine and transmission types. This plan becomes the basis for the master production schedule, which is the responsibility of the production/sales control department. Each month, representatives from the sales, production planning, and materials departments meet to develop monthly production schedules.

Prior to 1986, when the production/sales control department was formed, the MPS was the responsibility of the production planning department, which only considered ''requests'' from the sales department. As capacity utilization increased between 1984 and 1986, the conflicts between sales and production intensified. The sales department wanted to maintain a maximum amount of flexibility in production schedules to satisfy customer orders, whereas the production department preferred to have stability in the schedules. The production/sales control department, which reports to the vice president of manufacturing, was created to mediate the conflicts.

The MPS is developed on an eight-month rolling horizon basis; that is, each month the MPS is updated for the next eight months. During each meeting the schedule for the next month is confirmed and the following month's schedule is developed for the purpose of production planning and buying locally purchased parts. The rest of the monthly schedules are used as forecasts to provide the purchasing department and suppliers enough lead time to acquire imported raw materials and parts.

A separate MPS is prepared for passenger and commercial vehicles. Each is further broken down by model, engine and transmission type, and interior color. For each of its five models—Pony, Stellar, Sonata, Grandeur, and Excel—Hyundai develops a separate master schedule, which is further broken down by destination and trim. These schedules are used to plan the production of different assembly lines dedicated to each model. Next, the MPS for each model is broken down by engine size and transmission type. This schedule is used as the primary input to the engine and transmission plant schedules. Finally, the MPS for each model is converted into a schedule that shows the monthly production volume requirements for the model (such as Excel 5 door) by trim levels (such as L, GL, and GLS) and by interior color (such as chestnut red or dark sapphire). This schedule is of primary importance to suppliers that deliver various parts and interior furnishings.

The production planning department uses the monthly schedules to develop weekly schedules specifying daily volumes by model and sequence. The materials department uses the schedules to calculate parts and materials requirements.

Source: Chan Hahn and Kee Young Kim, *Hyundai Motor Company: Manufacturing Strategies and Production Planning and Control Systems*, Bowling Green State University, 1989, pp. 53–68.

---

a mainframe computer allows managers to ask "what–if" questions about master production schedules and to estimate MPS effects using the data provided.

The techniques that we present in this chapter are descriptive in the sense that modifications to the schedule are left to the discretion of the master production scheduler. The techniques project only what may happen *if* the prospective MPS is implemented. They do not prescribe what *should* be done. Various prescriptive approaches have been proposed, and, if you are interested, you can pursue them in Hax and Meal (1975), Newson (1975), and other publications referenced at the end of this chapter.

DEVELOPING A PROSPECTIVE MASTER PRODUCTION SCHEDULE

In this section we show how a firm that produces to stock develops a master production schedule. This process includes calculating the projected on-hand inventory, determining the timing and size of MPS quantities (the production quantities of specific products), and calculating available-to-promise quantities. Our discussion introduces some basic terminology of master production scheduling and illustrates the trial-and-error aspect of actual scheduling. For simplicity, we assume that our imaginary firm doesn't utilize safety stocks for end items, even though real firms usually do. (Later, in Chapter 16, we address the mechanics of incorporating safety stocks in material requirements planning.) The section concludes with discussions of linking the production plan and the MPS and freezing the MPS. You can find details of how eight specific firms develop MPSs in Berry, Vollmann, and Whybark (1979).

Calculating Projected On-Hand Inventories

The first step is to calculate the **projected on-hand inventory,** which is an estimate of the amount of inventory available each week after demand has been satisfied. It equals the on-hand balance for the previous week, plus the MPS quantity for the current week, minus the forecast *or* actual orders booked for the current week—whichever quantity is greater. Mathematically, we express this relationship as

$$I_t = I_{t-1} + MPS_t - \max(F_t \quad \text{or} \quad CO_t)$$

where

$$I_t = \text{projected on-hand inventory balance at the end of week } t$$
$$MPS_t = \text{MPS quantity due in week } t$$
$$F_t = \text{forecast of orders in week } t$$
$$CO_t = \text{customer orders booked for shipment in week } t$$

MPS_t indicates a quantity that management expects to be completed and ready to ship in week t. The scheduler subtracts the greater quantity, F_t or CO_t, recognizing that the forecast is subject to error. If actual booked orders exceed the forecast, the projection will be more accurate if the scheduler uses CO_t. Conversely, if the forecast exceeds booked orders, F_t will provide the best estimate of requirements for week t.

Let's consider a valve manufacturer of a limited range of products: valves of varying types and sizes, all made to stock. Management needs to develop a master production schedule for its 3-inch gate valve. Marketing has forecast a demand of 80 units for April and 160 units for May. The MPS should be expressed in weekly time periods to enable operations to closely control production of components.

Figure 15.4 shows a partial MPS record, to which we'll later add one row. The quantity on hand (in inventory) is 45. The forecast row shows marketing's forecast of total sales allocated evenly over the eight weeks in April and May. Keep in mind that these forecasts may not reflect actual sales. The customer

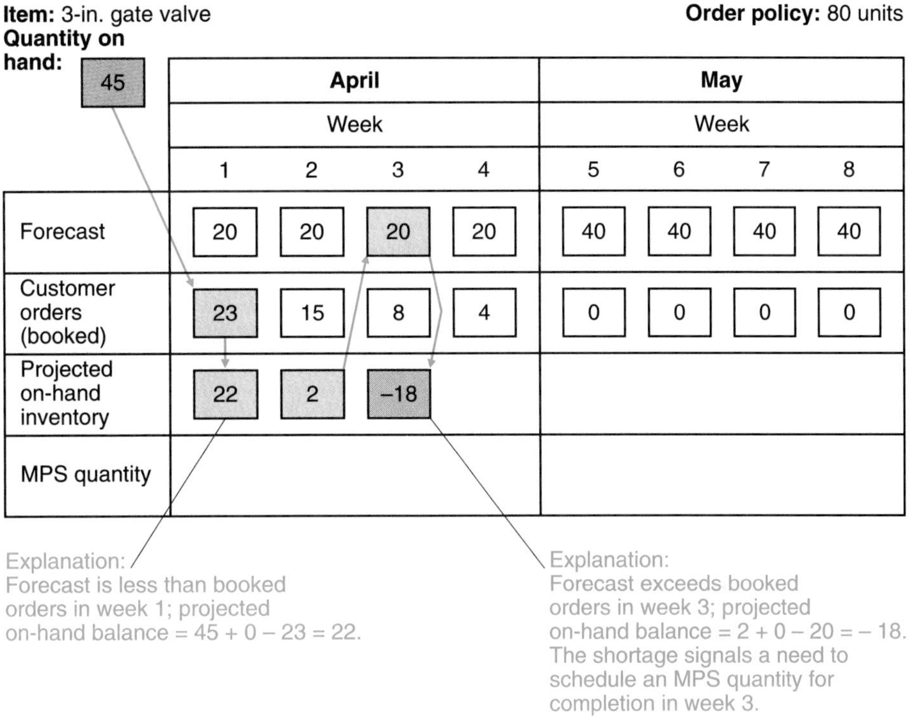

FIGURE 15.4

Projected On-Hand
Inventory for 3-inch
Gate Valve

Item: 3-in. gate valve **Order policy:** 80 units

Quantity on hand: 45

	April				May			
	Week				Week			
	1	2	3	4	5	6	7	8
Forecast	20	20	20	20	40	40	40	40
Customer orders (booked)	23	15	8	4	0	0	0	0
Projected on-hand inventory	22	2	−18					
MPS quantity								

Explanation:
Forecast is less than booked
orders in week 1; projected
on-hand balance = 45 + 0 − 23 = 22.

Explanation:
Forecast exceeds booked
orders in week 3; projected
on-hand balance = 2 + 0 − 20 = − 18.
The shortage signals a need to
schedule an MPS quantity for
completion in week 3.

orders row shows the number of actual customer orders promised for shipment each week. Note that customer orders for 23 valves exceed the forecast of 20 valves for week 1. Using the formula $I_t = I_{t-1} + MPS_t - \max(F_t \text{ or } CO_t)$, the customer orders figure (CO_t), rather than the forecast (F_t), is therefore used to determine the projected on-hand inventory for week 1: 22 (45 + 0 − 23). Although customer orders exceed the forecast for week 1, total booked orders (50) for April are still within that month's forecast (80). The projected on-hand inventory row shows a stockout in week 3; the projected on-hand balance is − 18 (2 + 0 − 20). The shortage signals a need for more valves in that week. At this stage, the MPS row is still blank.

Determining the Timing and Size of MPS Quantities

The second step is to determine the timing and size of MPS quantities. The goal to keep in mind when developing a master production schedule is to maintain a nonnegative projected on-hand inventory balance. As the scheduler projects shortages in inventory, MPS quantities are scheduled to cover them. The following is a simplified procedure for developing a prospective MPS. Schedule completion of the first MPS quantity for the first week when you expect inventory of the product to run out. You can determine this week by calculating the projected on-hand inventory for each week until a shortage (a negative balance, such as − 18 in Fig. 15.4) occurs. The addition of the newly scheduled MPS quantity will keep the projected on-hand inventory balance positive or zero. Continue calculating the projected on-hand inventory until you reach the next period when a shortage occurs. This shortage signals a need for a second MPS quantity. Repeat the process until you reach the end of the planning horizon. In this way, you proceed column by column through the MPS record, filling in the MPS quantities needed to avoid shortages.

Application 15.1	*Determining MPS Quantities*

Using Fig. 15.4, specify the timing and size of MPS quantities for the 3-inch gate valve for a lot size of 80 units. (We present other lot-sizing techniques in Chapter 16.)

Solution   Determine which weeks will experience shortages. In week 1, when beginning inventory is 45 and requirements are 23, there is no shortage. There is also no shortage in week 2, as beginning inventory is 22 and requirements are only 20. The first shortage occurs in week 3, as Fig. 15.4 shows, when the forecast (20) exceeds the projected on-hand inventory (2). The firm will be 18 units short unless it schedules an MPS quantity for that period. Calculations for all 8 weeks are shown in the following table.

Calculations for 3-Inch Valve Prospective MPS

Week	Beginning Inventory		Require- ments	Shortage?		MPS Quantity		Projected On-Hand Inventory
1	45	–	23	No	+	0	=	22
2	22	–	20	No	+	0	=	2
3	2	–	20	Yes	+	80	=	62
4	62	–	20	No	+	0	=	42
5	42	–	40	No	+	0	=	2
6	2	–	40	Yes	+	80	=	42
7	42	–	40	No	+	0	=	2
8	2	–	40	Yes	+	80	=	42

As the table shows, the 80 units scheduled in week 3 will last until week 6, when another 80-lot unit must be scheduled. The second lot lasts until week 8, when a third lot must be scheduled. Figure 15.5 shows the prospective MPS.

Calculating Available-to-Promise Quantities

The third step in developing a prospective master production schedule is to calculate the **available-to-promise (ATP) inventory,** that is, the quantities of end items that marketing can promise to deliver on specified dates. Marketing can also use this information to set shipping dates for new customer orders. The general rule for calculating available-to-promise information is slightly different for the first (current) week of the schedule than for other weeks.

- **The first week:** The ATP inventory for the first week equals current on-hand inventory *plus* the MPS quantity for the first week, *minus* the cumulative total of booked orders, up to (but not including) the week in which the next MPS quantity arrives.

FIGURE 15.5

A Prospective Master
Production Schedule

Item: 3-in. gate valve   **Order policy:** 80 units
Quantity on hand: 45

	April				May			
	Week				Week			
	1	2	3	4	5	6	7	8
Forecast	20	20	20	20	40	40	40	40
Customer orders (booked)	23	15	8	4	0	0	0	0
Projected on-hand inventory	22	2	62	42	2	42	2	42
MPS quantity	0	0	80	0	0	80	0	80

- **Subsequent weeks:** For each week in which an MPS quantity is scheduled for completion, the ATP inventory equals that week's MPS quantity *minus* the cumulative total of booked orders from that week up to (but not including) the week in which the next MPS quantity arrives. Projected on-hand inventory isn't used in this calculation because on-hand inventory was used to calculate the first week's ATP inventory.

Application 15.2   *Using ATP Information to Make Order-Acceptance Decisions*

Suppose that you have received the following orders for the 3-inch gate valve (shown in order of arrival). As they arrive you must decide whether to accept or reject them. Which orders can you accept for shipment, and what would your updated MPS record look like?

Order	Amount (units)	Week Requested
1	5	2
2	38	5
3	24	3
4	15	4

Solution   First, you must determine the ATP inventories for the 3-inch gate valve. Refer to Fig. 15.6 on the next page. The ATP in the first week is 7, [45 (current on-hand inventory) + 0 (MPS quantity) − 23 (booked orders) + 15 (booked orders)] units. The on-hand inventory of 45 units can satisfy all booked orders until week 3, when the first MPS quantity arrives. This leaves 7 extra units for new orders to be shipped in weeks 1 and 2 and beyond. The ATP inventory in week 3 is 68 [80 − (8 + 4 + 0)] units. These 68 units can be promised for shipment in weeks 3, 4, and 5. As there are no booked orders in May, ATP inventories for weeks 6 and 8 equal 80, the respective MPS quantities. Thus 80 units are available for new orders in weeks 6, 7, and 8.

FIGURE 15.6

Available-to-Promise
Calculations

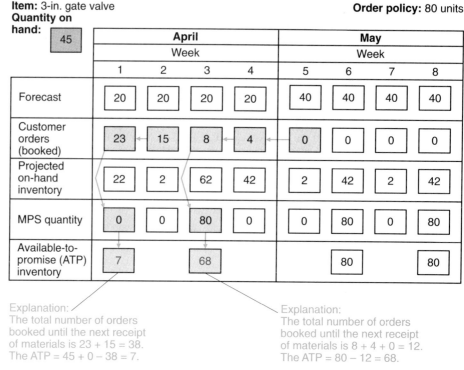

Item: 3-in. gate valve   **Order policy:** 80 units
Quantity on hand: 45

	April				May			
	Week				Week			
	1	2	3	4	5	6	7	8
Forecast	20	20	20	20	40	40	40	40
Customer orders (booked)	23	15	8	4	0	0	0	0
Projected on-hand inventory	22	2	62	42	2	42	2	42
MPS quantity	0	0	80	0	0	80	0	80
Available-to-promise (ATP) inventory	7		68			80		80

Explanation:
The total number of orders booked until the next receipt of materials is 23 + 15 = 38. The ATP = 45 + 0 − 38 = 7.

Explanation:
The total number of orders booked until the next receipt of materials is 8 + 4 + 0 = 12. The ATP = 80 − 12 = 68.

You can now take action on the orders as follows:

Order	Action	Reason
1	Accept	The amount requested (5) is less than the ATP (7) for weeks 1 and 2. The adjusted ATP inventory for week 1 is 2 units.
2	Accept	The new ATP inventory for week 3 would be 68 − 38 = 30 units.
3	Accept	The new ATP for week 3 is 30 − 24 = 6 units.
4	Reject	The ATP for weeks 1 and 3 totals only 8 (2 + 6) units, which is less than the quantity requested. Try to reschedule shipment for week 6 or later.

Figure 15.7 shows the updated MPS record.

Note in Fig. 15.7 that only the customer orders booked, projected on-hand inventory, and ATP inventory rows have been adjusted. Do the negative projected on-hand inventory balances in weeks 5 and 7 pose a problem? Maybe. The forecast is for a total demand of 120 units through week 5, but only 117 units have currently been booked. The 45 units on hand plus the 80 units scheduled to arrive in week 3 will give a total supply of 125 units, leaving 8 units available to promise. If customers demand no more than 8 additional units in new bookings before week 5, there is no problem. However, if customers were to request 16 more (20 − 4) units for shipment in week 4 and 2

FIGURE 15.7

Updated Master
Production Schedule
Record

Item: 3-in. gate valve   **Order policy:** 80 units

Quantity on hand: 45	April				May			
	Week				Week			
	1	2	3	4	5	6	7	8
Forecast	20	20	20	20	40	40	40	40
Customer orders (booked)	23	20	32	4	38	0	0	0
Projected on-hand inventory	22	2	50	30	−10	30	−10	30
MPS quantity	0	0	80	0	0	80	0	80
Available-to-promise (ATP) inventory	2		6			80		80

more (40 − 38) units in week 5—for a total of 18 units—the firm would be 10 units short in week 5.

There are two important lessons here. First, operations will never miss customer order due dates if marketing doesn't promise orders in excess of the ATP inventories *and* if the MPS quantities arrive on time, because ATP inventories are based on actual booked customer orders, not forecasts. Problems arise when orders are booked without planning adequate production in the MPS. Second, the projected on-hand inventory balance gives a "worst case" estimate of inventory balance. The reason is that the demand estimate is the greater of two quantities—either the forecast or actual customer orders booked. If projected on-hand inventory is negative, management should assess the situation before changing the MPS. Negative inventory projections might be the result of a mismatch in timing between forecasts and actual booked orders. In any case, once management revises the MPS, it determines the timing and size of revised MPS quantities in the same manner.

Linking the Production Plan and the MPS

In Applications 15.1 and 15.2, we didn't consider trade-offs associated with leveling production rates or the work force. Nor did we allow for anticipation inventories. Whenever the firm ran out of inventory or released production quantities, the MPS simply became an accumulation of forecasts. As you saw in Chapter 14, however, production planning *does* consider these trade-offs. The key to developing an acceptable MPS, therefore, is to link it *and* the production plan. One way to do so is to use production requirements, rather than forecasts, to determine MPS quantities. **Production requirements** are desired production quantities for a specific end item. To derive them, the scheduler must *disaggregate*, or break down, aggregate product family production quantities, taking into account the desired product mix within each family, current on-hand inventory, and booked customer orders. The resulting requirements then replace the forecasts used in the MPS.

The projected on-hand inventory row also undergoes a significant change. The scheduler does not include the current on-hand inventory and the booked customer orders to date because they are already part of the production requirements.

Consequently, the resulting MPS responds directly to the needs of the production plan. When management links the MPS and the production plan in this way, the MPS for any given item becomes part of an orchestrated plan to achieve company objectives.

Freezing the MPS

The master production schedule is the basis of all assembly, component, and material schedules. For this reason, changes to the MPS can be costly, particularly if they are made to MPS quantities soon to be completed. Increases in an MPS quantity may cause delays in shipments to customers or excessive expediting costs because of material shortages. Decreases in MPS quantities can result in unused materials or assemblies (at least until another need for them arises) and valuable capacities consumed for something not needed. Similar costs occur when forecasted need dates for MPS quantities are changed. For these reasons many firms "freeze" a portion of the master production schedule. Freezing can be accomplished by specifying a **demand time fence,** the number of periods (beginning with the current period) during which no changes can be made to the MPS without special authorization from management. The Ethan Allen Furniture Company uses a demand time fence of 8 weeks. If the current period is period 1, the MPS is frozen for periods 1 through 8. Neither the master scheduler nor the computer can reschedule MPS quantities for this period without management approval.

Freezing the master production schedule is really a matter of degree. The demand time fence specifies a period when very few, if any, changes will occur. Other time fences can be specified that allow varying amounts of change. For example, another commonly used time fence is the **planning time fence,** which is the number of time periods (beginning with the current period) during which the computer will not reschedule MPS quantities. The planning time fence is greater than the demand time fence. Consequently, the master scheduler—but not the computer—can make changes to the MPS quantities between the demand time fence and the planning time fence. Beyond the planning time fence the computer is free to schedule the MPS quantities, using the approved ordering policy. The use of time fences in this way provides varying levels of control over the creation and execution of the master production schedule.

Black and Decker uses a slightly different scheme. It uses three time fences: 8, 13, and 26 weeks. The 8-week fence is essentially a demand time fence. From 8 to 13 weeks the MPS is quite rigid, but minor changes to model series can be made if components are available. From 13 to 26 weeks, substitutions of one end item for another are permitted as long as the production plan is not violated and components are available. Beyond 26 weeks, marketing can make changes as long as they are compatible with the production plan (Vollmann, Berry, and Whybark, 1992).

The length of time fences should be reviewed periodically and should not become fixed for all time. Although freezing the MPS reduces manufacturing costs and makes life easier for those responsible for scheduling components and materials, it tends to make the MPS less responsive to changes in customer demands. The costs of not being able to satisfy customers who place unexpected orders for delivery in the demand time fence must be weighed against the savings in production costs. Freezing should be considered only when the costs of flexibility in meeting customer demands are prohibitive.

ROUGH-CUT CAPACITY PLANNING

After developing a prospective master production schedule, operations must determine whether the MPS is feasible in terms of the firm's available resources. It does so by performing feasibility checks of the MPS with **rough-cut capacity planning,** so called because it gives only a rough approximation of actual resource requirements. Several approaches are used today. **Capacity bills** are analogous to bills of material for an end item except that they specify capacity requirements instead of material requirements. **Resource profiles** use capacity bills to specify capacity requirements for critical resources for each period of the item's total manufacturing lead time.

In this section we describe the method of overall factors. We choose that method because it provides a simple illustration of rough-cut capacity planning. (See Berry, Schmitt, and Vollmann, 1982, for the capacity bills and resource profiles approaches.)

Method of Overall Factors

The **method of overall factors** begins by multiplying each MPS quantity by its direct labor factor (such as direct labor hours per unit) for work performed at critical work stations. Then, the total direct labor hours for all critical work stations in a period is multiplied by each critical work station's load factor (the percentage of total direct labor hours at critical work stations typically spent at the work station) to arrive at an estimate of total hours for that work center. This estimate is called a load profile. The load profile is calculated for all future periods covered by the prospective MPS. Management can compare the resulting load profile for each critical work station to its capacity and then decide whether to keep the proposed schedule or modify it.

To illustrate the method of overall factors, let's consider a company that produces three items, A, B, and C, to stock. Figure 15.8 shows a prospective MPS for those items. To develop the load profile for the schedule in Fig. 15.3, the scheduler needs to (1) identify the critical work stations, (2) estimate direct labor factors for each item, and (3) develop load factors for each critical work station.

FIGURE 15.8

Prospective Master
Production Schedule

| Item | Week | | | | | | | | Total Units |
	1	2	3	4	5	6	7	8	
A	25	25	25	25	35	35	35	35	240
B	–	50	–	50	–	50	–	50	200
C	72	–	75	–	56	–	68	–	271

Critical work stations are operations that limit output because the need to use them frequently exceeds their capacity. The hours scheduled for work at these stations are called **critical hours** because they determine the feasibility of a prospective MPS. Management tries to schedule time at critical work stations as efficiently as possible to maximize output. Thus if a critical work station has 200 hours of capacity per week and for some reason has used only 150 hours this week, the lost 50 hours cannot be used next week should 250 hours be required then.

The method of overall factors uses time standards (or gross estimates if standards aren't available) to estimate the number of direct labor hours required at each work station to produce one unit of each item. The scheduler then aggregates the hours for critical stations to obtain one direct labor factor and aggregates the hours for noncritical stations to obtain a second direct labor factor. Table 15.2 shows both factors for production of items A, B, and C. The scheduler has identified two critical work stations: 0810A and 0820B.

To determine the percentage of total labor hours each critical work station requires for a prospective MPS, the scheduler must consult past records. First, the scheduler determines the total number of direct labor hours that each critical station required over a specific time period. The time period chosen should be long enough to get a representative total. Next, the scheduler calculates the percentage of total critical hours this quantity represents. The result is a load factor for each critical work station that can be used to estimate labor requirements.

The Composite Load Profile. Using the prospective MPS, direct labor factors, and load factors, the scheduler can develop a **composite load profile,** which is an estimate of the direct labor hours for each critical work station, the total for all critical work stations, and the total for the plant. The procedure follows:

> **Step 1:** For each time period multiply each item's MPS quantity by its corresponding critical work station's direct labor factor. Calculate a total

TABLE 15.2 / Direct Labor Factors

Item	Critical Work Stations (hr)	Noncritical Work Stations (hr)	Total (hr)
A	1.60	0.00	1.60
B	6.07	8.00	14.07
C	5.04	4.00	9.04

critical direct labor requirement for each period. Do the same for the total (critical plus noncritical) work station requirements.

Step 2: For each time period multiply each critical work station's load factor by the total critical direct labor hours estimated in step 1.

Developing a Load Profile for a Prospective MPS

Develop a load profile for the MPS in Fig. 15.8.

Solution First, you must develop the load factors for the critical work stations: 0810A and 0820B. The accompanying table shows that the 4900 hours reported for work station 0810A during the past year represent 34 percent of total direct labor hours for all critical work stations that year. Thus the load factor for 0810A is 34 percent. Assume that station 0810A will continue to get 34 percent of the load on all critical stations. Similar reasoning yields a load factor of 66 percent for station 0820B.

Direct Labor Hours and Load Factors

Work Station	Quarter 1	Quarter 2	Quarter 3	Quarter 4	Total	Load Factor (%)
0810A	1,140	1,285	1,175	1,300	4,900	34
0820B	2,430	2,540	2,100	2,380	9,450	66
Total critical hours	3,570	3,825	3,275	3,680	14,350	100
Total noncritical hours	5,200	5,150	5,000	5,300	20,650	

Using the direct labor factors in Table 15.2 and the load factors just calculated, you can develop a composite load profile for the prospective MPS. In the first week the MPS calls for production of 25 units of A and 72 units of C. Use the critical work station labor factors for items A and C to obtain a combined critical direct labor requirement of 402.88 [25(1.60) + 72(5.04)] hours. The total direct labor requirement is 690.88 [25(1.60) + 72(5.04 + 4.00)] hours. You calculate labor requirements for other weeks in a similar manner. The results (rounded to the nearest whole number) are shown in the following table. You can then estimate that in the first week work station 0810A will need 137.02 [0.34(403)] hours and that work station 0820B will need 265.98 [0.66(403)] hours.

Load Profile Using Method of Overall Factors

Work Station	Week 1	2	3	4	5	6	7	8	Total
0810A (34%)	137	117	142	117	115	122	136	122	1008
0820B (66%)	266	227	276	227	223	238	263	238	1958
Total critical hours	403	344	418	344	338	360	399	360	2966
Total non-critical hours	288	400	300	400	224	400	272	400	2684
Total labor hours	691	744	718	744	562	760	671	760	5650

Load Profiles and the Authorization Decision. By comparing load profiles to labor capacities approved in the production plan, the scheduler can determine whether the prospective MPS is feasible. If total direct labor requirements fall within authorized limits of regular time plus overtime—and if the schedule meets other considerations, such as shipping promises and financial requirements—management would likely authorize the prospective MPS. If not, the master production scheduler would have to create a better schedule.

Evaluating the Method of Overall Factors

The method of overall factors is one of the simplest available for rough-cut capacity planning. The direct labor hours per unit used to calculate the load profiles can be a gross estimate based on accounting system data. Alternatively, it can be a more precise estimate based on detailed records of time standards and item routings.

Operations managers generally use gross estimates more often than precise estimates when using this technique. Further, labor requirements usually are proportioned to each work station solely on the basis of historical labor requirements. The assumption that historical requirements represent future requirements implies that the product mix doesn't change. If the mix changes, the capacity bills approach would be preferred. Also, the method of overall factors will not reflect a specific work station's large swings in capacity requirements on a week-to-week basis because its assigned hours represent a fixed percentage of the total critical hours for a week. The method of resource profiles works better in this case. Nonetheless, the method of overall factors works reasonably well in situations where the MPS is fairly stable with respect to product mix on a week-to-week basis. It also works well when the MPS is specified in monthly time periods and only a rough estimate of labor requirements is needed.

SOLVED PROBLEMS

1. You have the data shown in Fig. 15.9 for a particular end item. Your company's order policy is to produce in lots of 50 units.

FIGURE 15.9

		Week									
Quantity on Hand: 5		1	2	3	4	5	6	7	8	9	10
Forecast		20	10	40	10	0	0	40	20	30	10
Customer orders (booked)		30	20	5	8	0	0	0	0	0	0
Projected on-hand inventory		25	5	−35							
MPS quantity		50									
Available-to-promise (ATP) inventory		5									

a. Develop a prospective MPS and calculate the available-to-promise inventory quantities.

b. Decide which of the following customer orders you would accept. What would the updated MPS look like? The three orders arrived in the following sequence:

Order	Quantity	Week Due
1	15	6
2	4	2
3	32	3

Solution

a. Figure 15.10(a) shows the prospective MPS, including ATP quantities. As indicated, we will need the first MPS quantity in week 1, another order in week 3, a third in week 7, and a fourth in week 8. For the indicated ATP inventories and assuming that we have to commit to the orders in their sequence of arrival, we would accept the first two customer orders and reject the third.

FIGURE 15.10

Quantity on Hand: 5	**Week**									
	1	2	3	4	5	6	7	8	9	10
Forecast	20	10	40	10	0	0	40	20	30	10
Customer orders (booked)	30	20	5	8	0	0	0	0	0	0
Projected on-hand inventory	25	5	15	5	5	5	15	45	15	5
MPS quantity	50		50				50	50		
Available-to-promise (ATP) inventory	5		37				50	50		

(a) Prospective MPS

Quantity on Hand: 5	**Week**									
	1	2	3	4	5	6	7	8	9	10
Forecast	20	10	40	10	0	0	40	20	30	10
Customer orders (booked)	30	24	5	8	0	15	0	0	0	0
Projected on-hand inventory	25	1	11	1	1	−14	−4	26	−4	−14
MPS quantity	50		50				50	50		
Available-to-promise (ATP) inventory	1		22				50	50		

(b) Updated MPS

We could ask the third customer if she would accept a shipment of 23 (1 from week 1 ATP and 22 from week 3 ATP) in week 3, with another 9 units following in week 7. The updated MPS record, reflecting the two accepted orders, is shown in Fig. 15.10(b).

b. The latter part of the schedule shows negative projected inventory balances, so we should verify the forecasts. If the forecasts remain valid, we could revise the MPS starting in week 6. However, our ATP quantities show that 123 (1 + 22 + 50 + 50) units will be available for delivery over the next 10 weeks.

2. The Acme Rocket Company produces two products for crafty coyotes interested in a road-runner dinner. The harness rocket (HR) is designed for quick acceleration and low-level flying in the pursuit of fleeing road runners. The shoe rocket (SR) is useful for high-speed chases over long, straight Arizona roads. The prospective MPS shown in Fig. 15.11 has been proposed.

The Acme Rocket Company has two critical work stations: powder packing (PP) and wick setting (WS). Historically, PP has had 70 percent, and WS 30 percent, of the critical work station hours. The direct labor hours per unit follow.

Item	Critical Work Stations (hr)	Noncritical Work Stations (hr)	Total (hr)
HR	10.0	6.0	16.0
SR	7.2	3.5	10.7

a. Create a load profile for weeks 1–5 based on the prospective MPS, using the method of overall factors.

b. Suppose that the production plan specified a total of 680 labor hours per week, including 420 hours at the critical work stations. Do you see any potential problems with the prospective MPS? If so, what changes to the schedule do you propose?

Solution

a. Table 15.3 shows the load profile for weeks 1–5.

b. Note that the suggested schedule results in an uneven load on the factory. In particular, the week 5 load exceeds available resources by 281 (961 − 680) total labor hours, including 196 (616 − 420) hours at the critical work stations.

A change that would ease the MPS is to shift 30 units of SR production from week 5 to week 2, as shown in Table 15.4. This change increases the inventory holding cost of SR but satisfies the capacity constraints. (The profile for weeks 1, 3, and 4 doesn't change.) This change results in approximately 640 labor hours per week.

FIGURE 15.11

Item	Week 1	Week 2	Week 3	Week 4	Week 5	Total Units
HR	20	20	20	40	40	140
SR	30	–	30	–	30	90

TABLE 15.3

	Week					
Work Station	**1**	**2**	**3**	**4**	**5**	**Total**
PP (70%)	291	140	291	280	431	1433
WS (30%)	125	60	125	120	185	615
Total critical hours*	416	200	416	400	616	2048
Total noncritical hours†	225	120	225	240	345	1155
Total labor hours	641	320	641	640	961	3203

*MPS quantity for HR $\times$ 10.00 hr/unit + MPS quantity for SR $\times$ 7.2 hr/unit.

†MPS quantity for HR $\times$ 6.0 hr/unit + MPS quantity for SR $\times$ 3.5 hr/unit.

TABLE 15.4

Work Station	**Week 2**	**Week 5**
PP (70%)	291	280
WS (30%)	125	120
Total critical hours	416	400
Total noncritical hours	225	240
Total labor hours	641	640

FORMULA REVIEW

1. Projected on-hand inventory balance for MPS record:

$$I_t = I_{t-1} + MPS_t - \max(F_t \quad \text{or} \quad CO_t)$$

2. Available-to-promise inventory (ATP) quantities:

First week = Current on-hand inventory *plus* MPS quantity due in first week *minus* cumulative total booked orders until (but not including) the week of arrival of the next MPS quantity.

Subsequent weeks (having an MPS quantity due) = MPS quantity *minus* cumulative total booked orders from that week until (but not including) the week of arrival of the next MPS quantity.

CHAPTER HIGHLIGHTS

● A master production schedule (MPS) expresses operations' plan of production for a specific period of time. It is stated in terms of end items, which may be either shippable products or the highest level assemblies used to make them.

● The master production scheduling process is iterative. A prospective MPS is developed within the overall guidelines of the production plan. If the resources are available, the prospective schedule is authorized for implementation. If not, the prospective MPS or the production plan has to be changed.

• The primary duty of the master production scheduler is to prepare the master production schedule. Other duties include specifying promise dates for incoming customer orders, evaluating the impact of changes in the MPS, revising the MPS as necessary, and communicating with managers when conflicts arise.

• The techniques used for master production scheduling depend on the competitive priorities of the firm. Firms using a make-to-stock strategy typically schedule production of end items, whereas firms using a make-to-order strategy schedule purchased items. Firms using an assemble-to-order strategy schedule major components or assemblies to capitalize on commonality of parts for various end-item parents.

• The MPS is a useful input to the plans developed by finance, marketing, and manufacturing.

• Most major computer companies and many software companies have developed software packages for various MPS techniques.

• A master production schedule record for an item typically contains information on ordering policy as well as forecast (or production) requirements, booked customer orders, on-hand inventory balances, available-to-promise inventory quantities, and MPS quantities for future periods. The available-to-promise inventory information helps to provide valid promise dates for new customer orders.

• In the overall factor method of rough-cut capacity planning, all direct labor hours for an item are accumulated. This figure multiplied by the MPS quantity for the item yields an estimate of overall plant load. The overall load is subdivided into critical and noncritical work station loads. Individual station loads are estimated using historically based percentages.

KEY TERMS

assemble-to-order
  strategy **620**
available-to-promise (ATP)
  inventory **626**
capacity bills **631**
composite load profile **632**
critical hours **632**
critical work stations **632**

demand time fence **630**
make-to-order strategy **621**
make-to-stock strategy **619**
master production schedule
  (MPS) **616**
method of overall factors **631**

planning time fence **630**
production requirements **629**
projected on-hand
  inventory **624**
resource profiles **631**
rough-cut capacity
  planning **631**

STUDY QUESTIONS

1. How does a master production schedule (MPS) differ from a production plan?

2. What is the purpose of the MPS?

3. Briefly explain master production scheduling to your boss, who has not heard of it before. Why are the alternative schedules called "prospective"?

4. How can the available-to-promise (ATP) inventory information in an MPS record be used?

5. Why is the on-hand balance different from the ATP inventory at any particular time?

6. What are the advantages of linking the MPS and the production plan?

7. If you were a master production scheduler in a company using an assemble-to-order strategy, would you prepare a schedule for end items or some group of intermediate level items? Explain.

8. Why is it important to do rough-cut capacity planning?

9. What are the underlying assumptions of the method of overall factors?

10. Why are competitive priorities important

considerations for master production scheduling?

PROBLEMS

Review Problems

1. Complete the MPS record in Fig. 15.12 for a single item. At present there are 35 units of the item in inventory. Each order is for 60 units.

2. Complete the MPS record shown in Fig. 15.13 for a single item. There are currently 75 units of the item in inventory. Each order is for 100 units.

3. The following data apply to an end item.

- The forecasts for the next 10 weeks are 30, 20, 35, 50, 25, 25, 0, 40, 0, and 50 units.
- The current on-hand inventory is 70 units.
- The order policy is to produce in lots of 75.

- The booked customer orders for the item, starting with week 1, are 22, 30, 15, 9, 0, 0, 5, 3, 7, and 0 units.
- At present, there are no MPS quantities for this item.

a. Develop a prospective MPS and calculate the available-to-promise inventory quantities.

b. A customer needs 100 units of this item. What is the earliest shipping date for the entire order that you could give the customer?

4. You have the following information for a particular end item.

- The forecasts for the next 10 weeks are 50, 100, 100, 75, 75, 0, 0, 50, 50, and 75 units.
- The current on-hand inventory is 25 units.
- The order policy is to produce in lots of 100 units. There is an MPS quantity of 100 units scheduled for completion in week 1.

FIGURE 15.12

Quantity on Hand: 35	Week							
	1	2	3	4	5	6	7	8
Forecast	17	15	25	25	20	27	30	35
Customer orders (booked)	15	16	5	11	9	0	5	0
Projected on-hand inventory								
MPS quantity								

FIGURE 15.13

Quantity on Hand: 75	January				February			
	1	2	3	4	5	6	7	8
Forecast	75	65	50	45	65	65	75	75
Customer orders (booked)	40	10	55	0	35	70	0	0
Projected on-hand inventory								
MPS quantity								

- The booked customer orders, starting with week 1, are 60, 45, 20, 15, 0, 0, 0, 0, 0, and 0 units.

a. Develop a prospective MPS and calculate the available-to-promise inventory quantities.

b. Three customer orders have arrived in the following sequence.

Order	Quantity	Week Desired
1	50	2
2	70	3
3	30	4

Which of the orders would you accept? (Assume that you must commit to them in sequence and that you cannot change the desired shipping dates or the MPS.) What would the updated MPS look like?

5. Complete the MPS record in Fig. 15.14 for a single item. At present, there are 50 units of the item in inventory. Each order is for 125 units.

6. You have the partially completed MPS record for orange peelers in Fig. 15.15.
   a. Develop the MPS and calculate the ATP inventory quantities if the current quantity on hand is 400 peelers and the policy is to order 500 each time.
   b. Four customer orders arrived in the following sequence.

Order	Quantity	Week Desired
1	500	4
2	100	5
3	300	1
4	350	7

Assuming you must commit to the orders in the sequence of arrival and you cannot change the desired shipping dates or your MPS, which orders would you accept?

7. Morrison Electronics has forecasted the following demand for one of its products for the next eight weeks: 70, 70, 65, 60, 55, 85, 75, and 85. The booked customer orders for this product, starting in week 1, are 50, 60, 55, 40, 35, 0, 0, and 0 units. The current on-hand inventory is 100 units, and the order quantity is 150 units.
   a. Develop a prospective MPS (including ATP quantities) for this product.
   b. The marketing department at Morrison has revised its forecasts. Starting with week 1, the new forecasts are 70, 70, 75, 70, 70, 100, 100, and 110 units. Prepare a revised MPS record, assuming that the prospective MPS you developed in part (a) doesn't change. Comment on the situation that Morrison now faces.

8. a. Complete the MPS in Fig. 15.16 for a single end item. Currently 500 units are in inventory; Each order is for 800 units.

FIGURE 15.14

	Week									
Quantity on Hand: 50	1	2	3	4	5	6	7	8	9	10
Forecast	10	15	20	30	40	60	80	120	120	120
Customer orders (booked)	12	9	11	5	2	0	4	0	0	0
Projected on-hand inventory										
MPS quantity										
Available-to-promise (ATP) inventory										

FIGURE 15.15

Quantity on Hand: 400	Week									
	1	2	3	4	5	6	7	8	9	10
Forecast	550	300	400	450	300	350	200	300	450	400
Customer orders (booked)	300	350	250	250	200	150	100	100	100	100
Projected on-hand inventory										
MPS quantity										
Available-to-promise (ATP) inventory										

b. Three customer orders have arrived in the following sequence.

Order	Quantity	Week Desired
1	600	6
2	400	4
3	425	5

Assuming that you must commit to the orders in sequence, which orders would you accept (rather than attempt to reschedule)?

c. Suppose that management wishes to fulfill *all* the customer orders by the desired shipping dates. Revise the MPS to accomplish this task. What other factors must you consider when making this revision?

9. The Conestoga Wagon Company produces a single product, a motorized child-sized version of the original Conestoga wagon. The following prospective MPS has been proposed.

Week	1	2	3	4	5	6
Units	50	50	40	30	30	50

There is one critical work station in the shop: the frame-building station. Each wagon requires three direct labor hours at this critical work station. The total direct labor requirement per unit is 18 hours.

a. Using the method of overall factors, determine the direct labor requirements at the frame-building work station.

FIGURE 15.16

Quantity on Hand: 500	Week									
	1	2	3	4	5	6	7	8	9	10
Forecast	300	100	400	600	600	800	600	800	500	600
Customer orders (booked)	150		225	200	300			275		
Projected on-hand inventory										
MPS quantity										
Available-to-promise (ATP) inventory										

b. Assume that the MPS was designed to meet exactly forecasted requirements each period and that there are no available on-hand inventories. Suppose that the available labor hours at the frame-building work station are 150 hours per week for weeks 1 and 2, and 120 hours per week for weeks 3–6. Revise the MPS to ensure that no stockouts occur, capacity constraints are satisfied, and inventory is minimized.

10. Marshall Fans produces a lightweight desktop fan. A prospective MPS for the fan has been proposed.

Month	Jan	Feb	Mar	Apr	May	Jun
Units	300	400	200	400	500	750

Two critical work stations are involved in the production of the fan: 401A and 401B. Historically, 401A has had 80 percent and 401B has had 20 percent of the total critical work station hours.

The direct labor hours per unit are as follows: critical work stations, 2.0; noncritical work stations, 3.0; and total, 5. Using the method of overall factors, determine the direct labor requirements for each individual critical work station and for the entire plant.

11. The Karry Kart Company produces two products, a deluxe kart (DK) and a standard kart (SK). The following prospective MPS has been proposed for the two products.

			Week				
Item	1	2	3	4	5	6	Total
DK	50	50	30	30	30	30	220
SK	60	—	60	—	60	—	180

The direct labor hours per unit are

Item	Critical Work Stations (hr)	Noncritical Work Stations (hr)	Total (hr)
DK	11.0	4.0	15.0
SK	6.0	4.0	10.0

There are three critical work stations: Z101, Z105, and Z107. Historically, Z101, Z105, and Z107 have accounted for 40 percent, 30

percent, and 30 percent of the direct labor hours, respectively.

a. Create a load profile based on the prospective MPS, using the method of overall factors.

b. Suppose that the production plan specified a total of 1100 direct labor hours of which 750 hours are at the critical work stations. Do you see any potential problems with the prospective schedule? If so, propose a better MPS.

Advanced Problems

A computer package is recommended for Problems 12, 15, 16, and 17.

12. The marketing department of NEVED Home-help Products has forecasted the following for the company's two products.

	Month		
Product	Mar	Apr	May
Home energy controller (HEC)	1000	1200	600
Home personal robot (HPR)	200	160	180

The company has 450 units of HEC and 150 units of HPR on hand. The company orders HEC in lots of 400 units and HPR in lots of 80 units. One lot of HEC is scheduled to be received in the second week of March. The company has received the following orders.

	Shipping Dates							
	Mar				Apr			
	1	2	3	4	5	6	7	8
HEC	150	—	—	160	150	—	145	100
HPR	50	—	40	—	20	—	50	—

Management likes to have the MPS expressed in weekly time periods and typically allocates monthly forecasts evenly over the weeks of the month. (Assume 4 weeks per month.)

a. Develop a prospective MPS for each product.

b. A potential customer is interested in buying 900 units of HEC and 150 units of

FIGURE 15.17

Quantity on Hand: 10	Week							
	1	2	3	4	5	6	7	8
Production requirements	40	40	40	40	30	30	50	50
Customer orders (booked)	60	45	30	35	10	5	5	0
Projected on-hand inventory								
MPS quantity	75	75						
Available-to-promise (ATP) inventory								

HPR. What is the earliest realistic date for which marketing can promise delivery of the HEC units? The HPR units?

c. The customer has decided to take delivery of the two products at the same time. What is the earliest date on which marketing could deliver 900 units of HEC and 150 units of HPR to the customer?

13. Complete the MPS record in Fig. 15.17. This partial record shows the *production requirements* for a single end item. There are currently 10 units on hand, and the order policy is to produce in lots of 75. Lots are scheduled for completion in weeks 1 and 2.

14. The *production requirements* for an electric screwdriver for the next six weeks are 20, 30, 15, 20, 50, and 60 units. Marketing has booked orders totaling 25 units in the first (current) week and 10 units in the third week. Currently, 50 screwdrivers are on hand. The policy is to order the exact quantity required to meet production requirements each week.
a. Develop the MPS record for the screwdriver.
b. A distributor of the screwdriver places an order for 45 units. What is the appropriate shipping date for the entire order?

15. Production of 240 units in January, 320 units in February, and 240 units in March has been approved for the seismic-sensory prod-

uct family manufactured at the Hilliard facility of Sloan Automated, Inc. There are three products in this family. The product mix ratio for products A, B, and C for the past two years has been 35 percent, 40 percent, and 25 percent, respectively. There are 60 units of product C on hand. The company orders product C in lots of 40 units and has accepted orders of 25, 12, 8, 10, 2, and 3 of product C in weeks 1–6, respectively. Prepare a prospective MPS for product C and calculate the available-to-promise inventory quantities. Management wishes to allocate the monthly production requirements evenly over the month. Assume that each month has 4 weeks.

16. The master production scheduler at your company has developed the prospective MPS shown in Fig. 15.18 for the three items your company produces. There are two critical work stations in the shop: WSA, which

	Month						Total
Item	Jan	Feb	Mar	Apr	May	Jun	Units
A	30	70	30	75	40	110	355
B	50	–	90	–	50	–	190
C	–	70	–	50	–	70	190

FIGURE 15.18

has recorded 30 percent of the hours at the critical work stations, and WSB, which has recorded the rest. Your production plan has a constant work force size that yields 900 hours per month, of which 300 hours total are at the critical work stations. Work station WSA has been allocated 90 hours per month, and WSB has been allocated 210 hours. Direct labor hours per unit are

Item	Critical Work Stations	Noncritical Work Stations	Total
A	2	4	6
B	1	6	7
C	3	5	8

a. Prepare a load profile for the prospective MPS using the method of overall factors. Comment on the feasibility of this schedule.

b. Prepare an alternative MPS to the one proposed by the master production scheduler

that satisfies the labor budget specified in the production plan. Assume that the master production scheduler adhered to the following guidelines.

Cumulative Production Required by End of Month

Month	A	B	C
Jan	0	50	0
Feb	100	50	70
Mar	100	140	70
Apr	210	140	130
May	210	190	130
Jun	355	190	190

For example, you need no units of A in January, but you do need 100 by the end of February. Also, you need no units of A in March, but by the end of April the cumulative production of A most be 210 units because you need 110 units in April.

SELECTED REFERENCES

Bahl, H.C., and L.P. Ritzman. "An Empirical Investigation of Different Strategies for Material Requirements Planning." *Journal of Operations Management*, vol. 3, no. 2 (1983), pp. 67–77.

Berry, W.L., T.G. Schmitt, and T.E. Vollmann. "Capacity Planning Techniques for Manufacturing Control Systems: Information Requirements and Operational Features." *Journal of Operations Management*, vol. 3, no. 1 (November 1982), pp. 13–25.

Berry, W.L., T.E. Vollmann, and D.C. Whybark. *Master Production Scheduling: Principles and Practices*. Falls Church, Va.: American Production and Inventory Control Society, Inc., 1979.

Bitran, G.R., and A.C. Hax. "On the Design of Hierarchical Production Planning Systems." *Decision Sciences*, vol. 8, no. 1 (January 1977), pp. 28–55.

Bruggeman, J.J., and S. Haythornthwaite. "The Master Schedule." *APICS—The Performance Advantage* (October 1991), pp. 44–46.

Chung, C.H., and L. Krajewski. "Planning Horizons for Master Production Scheduling." *Journal of Operations Management*, vol. 4, no. 4 (August 1984).

Everdell, R., and W. Chamberlain. "Master Scheduling in a Multi-Plant Environment." *Proceedings of the 23rd Annual American Production and Inventory Control Society Conference.* Los Angeles (October 14–17, 1980), pp. 421–429.

Hax, A.C., and H.C. Meal. "Hierarchical Integration of Production Planning and Scheduling." In M. A. Geisler, ed., *Studies in Management Sciences*, vol. 1, *Logistics*. New York: North Holland-American Elsevier, 1975, pp. 53–69.

Ling R. "Master Scheduling in a Make-to-Order Environment." *Inventories and Production*, vol. 1, no. 3 (July–August 1981), pp. 17–21.

Mangiameli, P., and L. Krajewski. "The Effects of Workforce Strategies on Manufacturing Operations." *Journal of Operations Management*, vol. 3, no. 4 (August 1983), pp. 183–196.

Newson, E.P. "Multi-Item Lot Size Scheduling by Heuristic, Part I: With Fixed Resources; Part II: With Variable Resources." *Management Science*, vol. 21, no. 10 (June 1975), pp. 1186–1203.

Orlicky, J. *Material Requirements Planning*. New York: McGraw-Hill, 1975.

Proud, J.F. "Controlling the Master Schedule." *Production and Inventory Management*, vol. 22, no. 2 (Second Quarter 1981), pp. 78–90.

Vollmann, T.E., W.L. Berry, and D.C. Whybark. *Manufacturing Planning and Control Systems*. Homewood, Ill.: Irwin, 1992.

Wight, O. *Production and Inventory Management in the Computer Age*. Boston: Cahners Books, 1974.

Chapter 16

MATERIAL REQUIREMENTS PLANNING

What information is available from MRP systems that will help us to manage materials better?

How important is our choice of lot-sizing rule?

How can we couple MRP with other decision areas?

What prerequisites do we have to meet to implement MRP successfully?

Is MRP appropriate for our firm? Who benefits the most from MRP systems?

Can we use MRP principles for distribution inventories?

ominion Automotive Industries manufactures exterior side-view mirrors for General Motors and Chrysler vans and trucks. The largest plant, located in Sevierville, Tennessee, produces more than 120 products, each with an average of 50 components. Twenty of the 50 parts are fabricated, and the remainder are purchased. Prior to installing a computerized material requirements planning system, the company manually determined its component production requirements. Under the old system the company had a six-month supply of some parts in inventory and shortages of other parts. The company spent $500,000 per year on air freight costs because it could not ship the mirrors to customers on time. Dominion also paid $150,000 a year on premium freight charges for purchased parts as a result of poor planning. Profits were on a downhill slide. After the computerized system was installed, inventories were reduced 54 percent, air shipments were eliminated, labor costs were cut 28 percent, and profit margins rose 10 percent. Today, Dominion is one of the most efficient and profitable companies in the automotive industry.

As the experiences of Dominion Automotive demonstrate, the company that successfully balances customer service with inventory management and investment gains a competitive edge. Thus the ability to maintain an efficient flow of materials from suppliers and to effectively manage internal activities relating to materials is essential to a profitable operation. After developing a realistic master production schedule, operations tries to ensure that all materials and other resources needed to produce finished products will be available at the right time. This is easier said than done because a manufacturer may have to keep track of thousands of components, assemblies, and raw materials.

We begin this chapter with the benefits of material requirements planning (MRP), including a brief comparison of an MRP system and a traditional reorder point system. After noting the problems associated with applying independent-demand inventory methods to dependent-demand items, we illustrate the process of calculating an MRP inventory record. We then show the implications that choice of lot-sizing rules has on inventory management and how MRP helps managers cope with production capacity limitations. Finally, we explore MRP as an information system and the issues concerning implementation of an MRP system.

BENEFITS OF MATERIAL REQUIREMENTS PLANNING

Recall that in Chapter 13 we discussed independent-demand inventory control systems. However, component items that are produced to meet production plan requirements for parent items have *dependent demand*. Such parent–component dependent relationships, which are expressed in bills of materials (see Chapter 12), greatly increase the complexity of inventory management. The complexity comes from interdependencies between items: Production cannot complete an order for a parent if even one of its components is missing.

For years, many companies tried to manage production and delivery of dependent-demand components with independent-demand systems, but the outcome was seldom satisfactory. As a result, **material requirements planning (MRP)**—a computerized information system—was developed specifically to aid in managing dependent-demand inventory and scheduling replenishment orders. The MRP system has allowed many businesses to reduce inventory levels, better utilize labor and facilities, and increase customer service.

Shortcomings of Independent-Demand Systems

To understand better the benefits of MRP, let's begin by examining the shortcomings of independent-demand inventory systems when applied to dependent-demand items. Consider a company that makes office furniture. Two of its many products are desk chairs A and B. These end items (parents) experience fairly constant demand rates: Chair A averages 30 units per week, and chair B 20 units per week. One of the components needed in assembling both items is a pedestal assembly, item C. Each chair requires one unit of item C. As it is used only in these chairs, item C experiences an average demand of 50 (30 + 20) units per week.

Assembly lead times for items A and B are one week, assuming that their components are available when needed. To manage all three items, the company uses a continuous review system. Operations calculates lot sizes (Q) and reorder points (R) according to the concepts discussed in Chapter 13. Suppose that $Q = 150$ and $R = 60$ for chair A, $Q = 120$ and $R = 40$ for chair B, and $Q = 230$ and $R = 150$ for item C. Figure 16.1 on the next page shows what happens whenever an item's inventory level reaches its reorder point.*

Inventory levels for chairs A and B deplete at a uniform, predictable rate. Note, however, that the demand pattern for the pedestal assembly C appears in chunks of 120 (week 1), 150 (week 2), or 270 (week 7) units at a time. The *average* is 50 units per week, but in many weeks (such as weeks 3 through 6) there is no actual demand. Consequently, the pedestal assembly doesn't approach the reorder point gradually. In week 7, the quantity of item C falls precipitously from an inventory balance of 240 units to a stockout of 30 units. The lead time for C is two weeks, so production of chair A is delayed until week 9. Producing 150 units of A takes another week. Thus chair A also suffers a stockout.

What went wrong? First, the assumption of a uniform, continuous demand rate was unrealistic. Typically, component demand is lumpy because of production lot-size decisions made for parent items. Forecasting lumpy demand using statistical methods results in large forecasting errors. Compensating for such errors by increasing safety stock is costly, and even then there is no guarantee that stockouts can be avoided.

Second, assuming that demand for the inventory items was independent was wrong. In fact, the parents and component were linked through bills of

---

*Because the lead time for stock replenishment is so short, on-hand inventory equals the inventory position (except during the lead time) in this example. No scheduled receipts are outstanding when an order is placed.

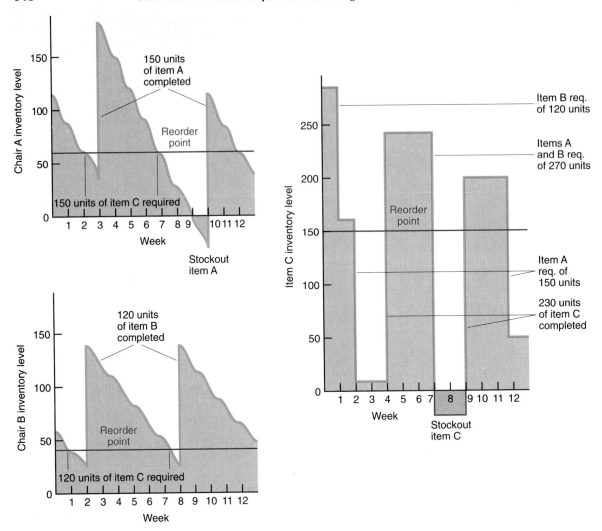

materials. The reorder point system failed to recognize that requirement schedules for components, assemblies, and raw materials needed to make parent items are based on the production schedules of the parents. For example, item C demand is based on the production schedules of chairs A and B. In reorder point systems, analysts don't use information from parent–item schedules to manage the inventories of components or subassemblies.

Finally, the reorder point system provided no forward visibility for planning purposes. Instead, operations assumed that it could rely on past demand patterns to establish reasonable reorder points and safety stocks. Actually, if demand for the pedestal assembly were uniform and predictable, there would be no need to look beyond the present. This condition, however, is often not the case for dependent-demand items. If the analyst had known the schedules for chairs A and B, he or she could have predicted in week 1 that trouble would arise in week 7. Knowing that the lead time for item C is two weeks, the analyst would have arranged to produce enough C to avoid the stockout.

To correct for these problems, a better way is needed to integrate and use the information already available to estimate future requirements for dependent-demand items more accurately. Material requirements planning provides one such approach.

Principles of MRP

During the past two decades, many manufacturing firms have switched from traditional reorder point systems to MRP systems. Impetus for change came from the American Production and Inventory Control Society (APICS), led by such pioneers as Joseph Orlicky (1975), George Plossl (1973), and Oliver Wight (1979). The computer program logic built into an MRP system is based on two principles that set it apart from a reorder point system:

1. MRP *derives* dependent demand for components, subassemblies, and raw materials from the production schedules of their parents. By contrast, in reorder point systems, analysts use statistical forecasting methods to set reorder points.

2. MRP *offsets* replenishment orders (such as production schedules and purchase orders) relative to the date they are needed. That is, if operations needs to replenish an item in week 5 to avoid a stockout, and if the lead time is 3 weeks, the system issues a notice to order in week 2. By contrast, in reorder point systems, items aren't reordered until a reorder point is reached.

The key ingredients of MRP are master production schedules, bills of materials, and inventory records. Using information from these sources, the MRP system identifies actions that operations must take to stay on schedule, such as releasing new production orders, adjusting order quantities, and expediting late orders. An MRP system can improve operations in many ways. For example, when American Sterilizer Company introduced MRP at its Hospital Products and Systems Group, it increased on-time customer deliveries from 70 percent to 95 percent. It also cut overtime by at least 50 percent, reduced component shortages by more than 80 percent, lowered indirect labor by 24 percent, and reduced direct labor by 7 percent. A survey of industrial firms showed that although such benefits are not always realized, neither are they unusual (see Cerveny and Scott, 1989). The average MRP user increased inventory turns from 4.6 to 5.5 and cut delivery lead times from 17.5 to 13.5 weeks. Research conducted by Greene (1988) indicated that about 34,000 manufacturing sites in the United States now use MRP. In the next section we'll demonstrate how the system computes an item's MRP inventory record.

THE MATERIAL REQUIREMENTS PLANNING INVENTORY RECORD

The **MRP inventory record** shows an item's planning factors, gross requirements, scheduled receipts, projected on-hand inventory, planned order receipts, and planned order releases. In many ways it resembles an MPS record (see Chapter 15). The body of the record divides the future into time periods called *time buckets.* These time periods normally represent weeks, but they can be expressed in days or months. Figure 16.2 shows a partially completed MRP inventory record for item C, the pedestal assembly, as well as the MPSs for its parents, chairs A and B.

Although the MRP inventory record has no standard format, the item number and description typically appear at the top of the record. Three planning factors—the planning lead time, lot-sizing rule, and safety stock—usually appear in the upper right-hand corner. In our example, item C's lot size is 230 units, its lead time is two weeks, and safety stock is 50 units. Management must select these quantities in advance. An inventory planner updates these

FIGURE 16.2

Partially Completed
MRP Inventory
Record for Item C

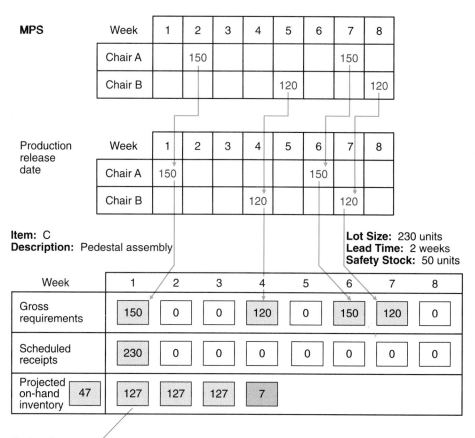

factors whenever conditions, such as lead time, change. We will discuss the planning factors in more detail later. The following paragraphs describe the major elements of a standard MRP inventory record.

Gross Requirements

Figure 16.2 shows item C's gross requirements for the next 8 weeks. The pedestal assembly's requirements exhibit lumpy demand: Operations will withdraw inventory in only four of the eight weeks. These **gross requirements** are the total demand derived from *all* parent production plans. They also include demand not otherwise accounted for, such as replacement parts for units already sold. Because parents A and B are end items, their production plans are found in the master production schedules (MPSs).

Recall from Chapter 15 that in an item's MPS a scheduler states the date by which production of a particular quantity must be completed. The *production release date* is the completion date specified in the MPS, adjusted for the item's lead time. For example, we need 150 units of A completed in week 2 (MPS), but we must release the order in week 1 (production release date) to allow time to assemble the chairs. The MRP system works with release dates to properly schedule production and delivery for components and assemblies. Its program logic anticipates the removal of all materials required by a parent's production order from inventory at the *beginning* of that item's lead time—when the scheduler first releases the order to the shop.* Note that in Fig. 16.2 item C's gross requirements are derived one-for-one from the MPS quantities of A and B, offset by their one-week lead times.† These one-for-one relationships come from the usage quantities specified in the bills of materials (see Chapter 12).

Scheduled Receipts

As defined in Chapter 12, scheduled receipts (sometimes called *open orders*) are orders that have been placed but not yet completed. For a purchased item, the scheduled receipt could be in one of several stages: being ordered by a buyer, being processed by a supplier, being transported to the purchaser, or being inspected by the purchaser's receiving department. If production is making the item in-house, the order could be on the shop floor being processed, waiting for components, waiting in queue, or waiting to be moved to its next operation. According to Fig. 16.2, one 230-unit order of item C is due in week 1. Based on the two-week lead time, the inventory planner probably released the order two weeks ago. Such orders normally don't show up on a record further into the future than the item's lead time.‡

---

*As you will soon see, the production plan for a parent that is *not* an end item comes from the planned order release row in its MRP record. This row has already been offset for the lead time.

†If B's lead time were 4 weeks, and if it were made from two units of C, then C's gross requirements in the first week would equal A's MPS quantity in week 2 (as before), plus double the MPS quantity of B in week 5.

‡Exceptions are possible. For example, the planner might discover that a scheduled receipt is not needed as soon as expected and delay its due date further into the future. Last-minute MPS changes or recently discovered errors in current on-hand inventory are but two possible reasons for delaying orders after their release.

Projected On-Hand Inventory

The first entry in Fig. 16.2, 47 units, indicates on-hand inventory available at the time the record was computed. It is also called *beginning inventory*. As with scheduled receipts, each actual withdrawal and receipt must be entered into the MRP database. Then, when the MRP system produces the revised record (typically once per week), the correct inventory will appear.

Other entries in the row show inventory expected in future weeks. The record takes into account inventory left over from the prior week, scheduled receipts, planned receipts, and gross requirements. Mathematically, we express this relationship as

$$I_t = I_{t-1} + SR_t + PR_t - GR_t$$

where

I_t = projected on-hand inventory balance at the end of week t

SR_t = scheduled receipt (open order) due in week t

PR_t = planned receipt in week t

GR_t = gross requirements in week t

Figure 16.2 shows on-hand inventory projected only through week 4. During that week, the balance drops to 7 units, or substantially below the desired safety stock of 50 units. This condition signals the need for a new planned receipt.

Planned Receipts

A **planned receipt** is a new order—not yet released to the shop or the supplier, as the case may be—for an item. Planning for receipt of these new orders will keep the projected on-hand balance from dropping below the desired safety stock level.* If no safety stock is called for, which is often the case for intermediate items, the purpose of these new orders is to avoid a negative projected on-hand balance in the inventory record. The planned receipt row for a dependent-demand item is equivalent to the MPS row for an end item (see Chapter 15). The record shows when order quantities should be received in both cases.

Let's look at a simplified procedure for developing the planned receipt row and finishing the rest of the projected on-hand inventory row:

1. Schedule completion of the initial planned receipt in the week when inventory would otherwise drop below the safety stock by projecting weekly on-hand inventory until it shows a shortage. The addition of the newly planned receipt should raise the projected on-hand balance to equal or exceed the safety stock.
2. Continue to project on-hand inventory until the next shortage occurs. This signals the need for the second planned receipt.

---

*There is one exception: If a shortage can be eliminated by expediting a scheduled receipt already released (but coming in late), there is no need for a new order.

Repeat this process until the end of the planning horizon, proceeding column by column through the MRP record—filling in planned receipts as needed and completing the projected on-hand inventory row.

Planned Order Releases

A **planned order release** indicates when an order for a specified quantity of an item is to be issued. The release date is the receipt date minus the lead time. For uniformity, we always use the *midpoint convention* to offset for lead time. The midpoint convention assumes that withdrawals and receipts occur at the middle of the week.* The planned order release row makes it easier to derive gross requirements for an item's components that are farther down the bill of materials. These gross requirements come directly from the planned order release row: No additional time offsets are needed.

Application 16.1	Calculating Planned Receipts, Projected On-Hand Inventory, and Planned Order Releases

Calculate planned receipts, projected on-hand inventory, and planned order releases for item C for all 8 weeks. Display your results as a completed MRP inventory record (see table below).

Solution The first inventory shortage occurs in week 4, depleting the on-hand inventory below the safety stock of 50 units. With the receipt of 230 units, the inventory projection rises to 237 units. The 230-unit order will last until week 7, when another lot must be received. Because this second planned receipt will last through week 8, we need to plan only two new orders, releasing them in weeks 2 and 5. The completed MRP inventory record is shown in Fig. 16.3.

Planned Receipts and Projected On-hand Inventory for Item C

Week	Beginning Inventory		Scheduled Receipts		Gross Require-ments	Shortage?	Planned Receipts	Projected On-hand Inventory
1	47	+	230	−	150	No	0	127
2	127	+	0	−	0	No	0	127
3	127	+	0	−	0	No	0	127
4	127	+	0	−	120	Yes	230	237
5	237	+	0	−	0	No	0	237
6	237	+	0	−	150	No	0	87
7	87	+	0	−	120	Yes	230	197
8	197	+	0	−	0	No	0	197

---

*If receipts tend to occur at the end of the week and withdrawals at the beginning—and this difference isn't reflected in the lead-time estimate—a different convention should be used and the planned order releases moved back one more week.

FIGURE 16.3

Completed MRP
Inventory Record for
Item C

Item: C
Description: Pedestal assembly

Lot Size: 230 units
Lead Time: 2 weeks
Safety Stock: 50 units

Week	1	2	3	4	5	6	7	8
Gross requirements	150	0	0	120	0	150	120	0
Scheduled receipts	230	0	0	0	0	0	0	0
Projected on-hand inventory 47	127	127	127	237	237	87	197	197
Planned receipts				230			230	
Planned order releases		230			230			

Explanation:
Without a new order in week 4,
inventory will drop below the
50-unit safety stock to
127 + 0 + 0 − 120 = 7 units.
Adding the planned receipt
brings the balance to
127 + 0 + 230 − 120 = 237 units.
Offsetting for a 2-week lead time
puts the corresponding planned
order release back to week 2.

Explanation:
The first planned order lasts
until week 7, when projected
inventory would drop to
87 + 0 + 0 − 120 = −33 units.
Adding the second planned
receipt brings the balance to
87 + 0 + 230 − 120 = 197 units.
The corresponding planned order
release is for week 5 (or week
7 − 2 weeks).

PLANNING FACTORS

The planning factors in an MRP record play an important role in the overall performance of the MRP system. By manipulating these factors, managers can fine-tune inventory operations. In this section we discuss the planning lead time, the lot-sizing rule, and safety stock.

Planning Lead Time

The specification of an item's planning lead time determines the amount of time allowed to get the item into stock once the order is issued. If the planning lead time is longer than necessary, the item may arrive in inventory sooner than needed, thereby increasing inventory holding costs. If lead time is too short, stockouts, excessive expediting, or both may occur. If the item is purchased, the planning lead time is the time allowed to receive a shipment from the supplier once the order has been sent. Often the purchasing contract stipulates the delivery date.

If the item is manufactured in-house, the planning lead time consists of estimates for the following time elements:

- Setup time
- Process time
- Material handling move time between operations
- Waiting time in queue

Each of these time elements must be estimated for every operation along the item's routing. While setup, processing, and move time may be relatively easy to estimate, the waiting time for material handling equipment or a machine to perform a particular operation may be more difficult. In a process-focused facility, such as a job shop, the load on the shop varies considerably over time, causing actual waiting times for a particular order also to fluctuate widely. Good estimates for waiting times are difficult to come by. Because jobs spend much time in queues in these environments, estimated waiting time is typically a large proportion of the planning lead time. However, in a product-focused facility, such as an assembly plant, product routings are more standard and the waiting time is more predictable. Waiting time is typically less significant as a proportion of planning lead times.

Lot-Sizing Rules

The computer logic for MRP requires that a lot-sizing rule be preassigned to each item before the system can compute planned receipts and planned order releases. A lot-sizing rule determines the timing and size of order quantities. Although many types of rules may be used, we can categorize them as either *static* or *dynamic*.

Static Lot Sizing. **Static lot-sizing rules** are procedures that maintain the same order quantity each time an order is issued. The **fixed order quantity (FOQ)** is a typical lot-sizing rule under which the lot size is a predetermined, fixed quantity. For example, the lot size might be the size dictated by upper equipment capacity limits, such as when a full lot must be loaded into a furnace at one time. For purchased items the FOQ could be set at the quantity discount level, truckload capacity, or minimum purchase quantity. Alternatively, the lot size could be predetermined by the economic order (*EOQ*) formula (see Chapter 13). Figure 16.3 illustrates the FOQ rule. If an item's gross requirement within a week is particularly large, the FOQ might be insufficient to restore even the desired safety stock. In such unusual cases, the inventory planner must increase the lot size beyond the FOQ, typically to a size large enough to bring the projected on-hand inventory just up to the desired safety stock level.*

Dynamic Lot Sizing. **Dynamic lot-sizing rules** are procedures that allow a different order quantity for each order issued. Whatever its size, each planned order must be large enough to prevent shortages (falling below the desired

---

*Another option is to make the order quantity an integer multiple of the FOQ. This option is appropriate when capacity constraints limit production to FOQ sizes (at most) and setup costs are high.

safety stock)—but no larger—over a specified number of weeks. The **periodic order quantity (POQ)** is a lot-sizing rule that does just that. The lot size equals the total of the gross requirements for P weeks (beginning with the week of the receipt), plus any desired safety stock, minus the projected on-hand balance from the previous week. This amount restores the safety stock and exactly covers P weeks' worth of gross requirements. That is, the projected on-hand inventory should equal the desired safety stock in the Pth week.

The POQ rule does *not* mean that operations should issue a new order every P weeks. Rather, when an order *is* planned, its lot size must be enough to cover P weeks. One way to select a P value is to divide the average lot size desired (such as the *EOQ*) by the average weekly demand.* That is, express the target lot size as weeks of supply and round to the nearest integer.

A special case of the POQ rule is the **lot for lot (L4L)** rule, under which the lot size ordered covers the gross requirements of a single week. Thus $P = 1$. This rule ensures that the planned order is just large enough to prevent a shortage in the single week it covers. The goal is to minimize inventory levels. The lot size equals the gross requirement for the week, plus any desired safety stock, minus the projected on-hand balance from the previous week. The projected on-hand inventory combined with the new order will equal the desired safety stock (0 if none is required). Following the first planned order, there will be an additional planned order to match each subsequent gross requirement.

Application 16.2	*Calculating Planned Order Releases Using the POQ and L4L Rules*

Modify the MRP inventory record for item C, as shown in Fig. 16.3, using (a) the POQ rule with $P = 3$ and (b) the L4L rule.

Solution

a. The stockroom must receive the first planned order in week 4, and this inventory must cover weeks 4, 5, and 6. The lot size is 193 [(120 + 0 + 150) + 50 − 127] units. The second order must arrive in week 7, with a lot size of 120 units [(120 + 0) + 50 − 50]. This second order reflects only two weeks' worth of gross requirements—to the end of the planning horizon. The completed record is shown in Fig. 16.4.

b. The first planned order in week 4 is only 43 (120 + 50 − 127) units. The stockroom must receive additional planned orders in weeks 6 and 7 to satisfy each of the subsequent gross requirements. The complete record is shown in Fig. 16.5.

Comparison of Lot-Sizing Rules. Choosing a lot-sizing rule can have important implications for inventory management. For example, applying the FOQ rule to Fig. 16.3 yields an *average* projected on-hand inventory of 167 units over eight weeks [(127 + 127 + $\cdots$ + 197)/8]. For the POQ rule (see Fig. 16.4), the average inventory is only 116 units, even though there are still only two planned orders over the same time period. Finally, using the L4L rule (see Fig. 16.5) drops average inventory to only 79 units.† This further cut in inven-

---

*The reasons and methods for selecting P in this context are similar to some of those discussed in Chapter 13 regarding periodic review systems.

†Safety stock usually is not associated with an L4L item, but we retain it in Application 16.2 to maintain consistency.

Item: C Description: Pedestal assembly							Lot Size: $P = 3$ Lead Time: 2 weeks Safety Stock: 50 units			
Week		1	2	3	4	5	6	7	8
Gross requirements		150			120		150	120	
Scheduled receipts		230							
Projected on hand	47	127	127	127	200	200	50	50	50
Planned receipts					193			120	
Planned order releases			193		120				

tory adds one more planned order and its accompanying setup time and cost.
We can draw three conclusions from this comparison:

1. The FOQ rule generates a higher level of average inventory because it creates inventory *remnants*. A remnant is inventory that is carried into a week but is too small to prevent a shortage. Remnants occur because the FOQ doesn't match requirements exactly. For example, according to Fig. 16.3, the stockroom must receive a planned order in week 7, even though that week begins with 87 units on hand. The remnant is the 37 ($87 - 50$) units in excess of the required safety stock that the stockroom will carry for three weeks beginning with receipt of the first planned order in week 4.

2. The POQ reduces the amount of on-hand inventory because it does a better job of matching order quantity to requirements. It adjusts lot sizes as requirements increase or decrease. Figure 16.4 shows that in week 7, when the POQ rule has fully taken effect, the projected on-hand inventory is the minimum allowed by the safety stock requirement. There are no remnants.

3. The L4L rule minimizes inventory investment, but it also maximizes the number of orders placed. This rule is most applicable to expensive items or items with small ordering or setup costs. It is the only rule possible for a *special*, an item made to order rather than made to stock.

Item: C Description: Pedestal assembly							Lot Size: L4L Lead Time: 2 weeks Safety Stock: 50 units			
Week		1	2	3	4	5	6	7	8
Gross requirements		150			120		150	120	
Scheduled receipts		230							
Projected on hand	47	127	127	127	50	50	50	50	50
Planned receipts					43		150	120	
Planned order releases			43		150	120			

In general, static lot-sizing rules create inventory remnants that, in turn, introduce greater stability into the production process. Inventory remnants can buffer unexpected scrap losses, capacity bottlenecks, inaccurate inventory records, or unstable gross requirements. Dynamic rules, in contrast, reduce inventory levels by avoiding remnants, but they may introduce instability by tying the lot-size decision so closely to requirements. If any requirement changes, so must the lot size, which can cause trouble at the component level. If component plans were based on lower expectations of gross requirements, inventory may not be able to respond quickly enough. Thus last-minute increases in parent orders may be hindered by missing components.

Safety Stock

An important managerial issue is the quantity of safety stock to require. This issue is more complex for dependent-demand items than for independent-demand items (see Chapter 13). Excessive safety stock for dependent-demand items, particularly for those with lumpy demand (gross requirements), is of little value. Safety stock is more valuable when there is considerable uncertainty about future gross requirements or the timing or size of scheduled receipts. Consequently, the usual policy is to maintain safety stock for end items (at the master production scheduling level) and purchased items. This approach protects against fluctuating customer orders at the top of the bills of materials and unreliable suppliers at the bottom.

MATERIAL REQUIREMENTS PLANNING AS AN INFORMATION SYSTEM

From the basic concepts of MRP, we can now turn to its larger context: MRP as a computerized information system. Figure 16.6 shows that MRP computer logic translates four basic inputs into several outputs that aid decision making in a variety of materials management areas.

Inputs

The first input is the authorized master production schedule, which is the driving force of MRP. Material requirements planning provides the information needed to release new orders, adjust priorities, and revise capacities to implement the MPS. The MPS, in turn, is linked to strategic plans for marketing and production.

Inventory records are the second input. The basic building blocks of up-to-date records are inventory transactions. Planners make transactions when they release new orders, adjust due dates for scheduled receipts, withdraw inventory, cancel orders, correct inventory errors, reject shipments, and verify scrap losses and stock returns. Recording such transactions is essential for maintaining accurate records, particularly of on-hand inventory balances and the status of scheduled receipts. Without an accurate and current database, an MRP system will be ineffective.

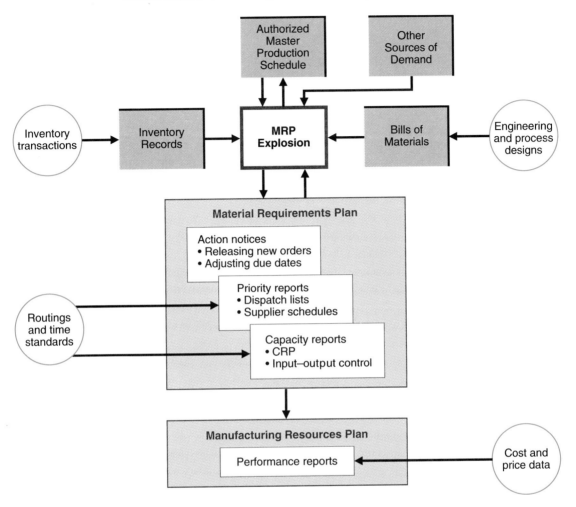

FIGURE 16.6 Overview of MRP Systems

Bills of materials, the third input, are derived from engineering and process designs. Material requirements planning derives an item's gross requirements from the planned order releases of its parents, so BOM information about the item's parents and their usage quantities must be known.

Other sources of demand not reflected in the MPS are the final input. Examples include demand for replacement parts, external orders from other company plants or warehouses, or units needed for quality control purposes (such as destructive testing). Independent demands for end items are already accounted for in the authorized MPS. However, when these demands are for components rather than end items, the MRP computer logic adds them to components' gross requirements to complete the material requirements plan.

Material Requirements Planning Explosion

An MRP system acts like an engine, transforming inputs into usable outputs. It translates the master production schedule and other sources of demand into the requirements for all components, assemblies, and raw materials needed to produce the required parent items. This process, sometimes called an **MRP explosion,** generates the material requirements plan.

Types of MRP Systems. There are two types of MRP systems. A **regenerative MRP system** periodically performs the explosion process, typically on a weekly basis, and completely recomputes all inventory records. After a week, the material requirements plan becomes outdated. The system then performs a new explosion based on the latest MPS, bills of materials, and information on scheduled receipts and on-hand balances. A **net change MRP system** recomputes records as needed. With each change in the MPS and with each transaction, the system executes a partial explosion to update the affected records. Net change systems tend to be preferred in more dynamic manufacturing situations. However, they may take more computer time and generate too many action notices (sometimes called "system nervousness"). Most new MRP system users begin with a regenerative system.

Level-by-Level Processing. An item's gross requirements are derived from three sources: the MPS for immediate parents that are end items, the planned order releases for parents below the MPS level, and any other requirements not originating in the MPS. MRP computer logic offsets requirements from MPS items for their lead times. However, requirements from planned order releases need no additional offset; planned order releases are already expressed by release dates. To accumulate the gross requirements for a particular component, the computer starts with the MPS and works downward through the bills of materials, calculating the planned order releases of all items as it goes. This procedure is called **level-by-level processing.**

To accomplish this procedure on a computer, a *level code* is permanently assigned to each item. Levels are denoted by a number; the lowest number represents the highest level. Level 0 is the highest level an item can be assigned. By convention, all MPS items are assigned level 0. Those components having only an MPS item as an immediate parent are assigned level 1. Their components are assigned level 2, and so on. Sometimes an item is found at different levels in various bills of materials because it has more than one immediate parent or because its only immediate parent has more than one parent. In that case the item is assigned the lowest level at which it appears in any bill of materials. For example, Fig. 16.7 shows the bills of materials for two end items, F1 and G2. Both items are assigned level 0. Intermediate item R1 only has one immediate parent, which happens to be an MPS item, and so is assigned level 1. Item A4, however, has two immediate parents: R1 and G2. The *lowest* level at which A4 appears in any bill of materials in our example is level 2; it is therefore assigned level 2. When updating the inventory records in an MRP system, the

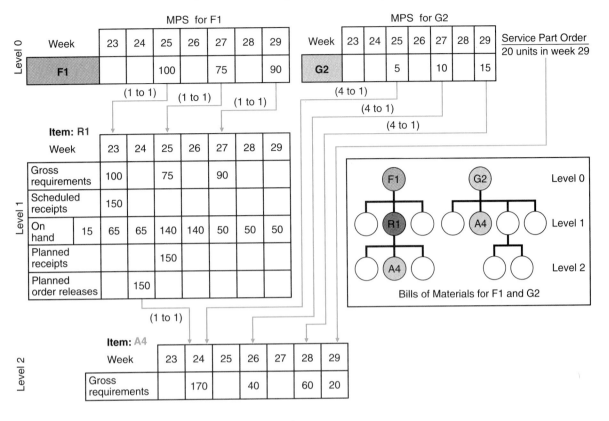

FIGURE 16.7 Deriving Gross Requirements for A4

computer proceeds with level-by-level processing, each time checking to ensure that all items with lower code numbers (higher assigned levels) have been processed before accumulating the gross requirements for an item. The basic computer logic is simple: An item cannot be processed until all its parents have been processed.

Figure 16.7 shows an example of level-by-level processing. The computer begins by determining the MPS for items F1 and G2 at level 0. It then proceeds to scan all the immediate components of F1 and G2 to find those with a level 1 code. R1 satisfies the requirement (there may be others, but we have not shown them). All the necessary information for accumulating the gross requirements for R1 is known, so we can proceed to update the MRP record for R1. There is a two-week lead time for the assembly of F1, so the F1 MPS for week 25 becomes a gross requirement for R1 in week 23, and so on. The scheduled receipts, on-hand inventory projection, planned receipts, and planned order releases for R1 can be calculated. The computer continues to process all items with a level 1 code, bypassing A4 because it has a lower level code.

When the processing gets to level 2, A4's MRP record can be updated. At that time, the planned order releases from R1 can be combined with the MPS for G2 to arrive at the gross requirements for A4. Note that G2 has a one-week assembly lead time and 4 units of A4 are needed for each unit of G2. In addition, A4 is needed as a replacement part for products already in use. Consequently, the service order of 20 units in week 29 must be added to A4's gross requirements in that week.

Action Notices

Inventory records for material requirements planning are computed for each item appearing in the bills of materials. These records together represent the current *material requirements plan*, which can be printed in hard copy or displayed on a computer video screen. Inventory planners use the computer-generated plan to make decisions about releasing new orders, expediting open orders, and the like. Actually, planners need to be alerted only to items that need their attention. They can then view the full records for those items and make the necessary decisions. This management-by-exception approach depends on the issuance of action notices.

An **action notice** is a computer-generated memo indicating the need to release an order or adjust the due date of a scheduled receipt. An action notice can simply be a list of part numbers for items needing attention. Or it can be the full record for such items, with a note at the bottom identifying the action needed. The general rule for releasing a new order differs from the rule for adjusting the due date of a scheduled receipt.

Releasing New Orders. If there is a nonzero quantity in the first week's entry of the planned order release row, sometimes called the **action bucket,** the computer issues an action notice. An order in the action bucket is the call to release the planned order. When an order is released, paperwork is issued to the shop, authorizing the withdrawal of all required materials from the inventory storeroom and the start of production. The date actual production begins depends on the amount of work already in the shop. Delaying the release one week will provide *less* than the planned lead time for producing the item. Releasing an order before it gets to the action bucket allows *more* than the planned lead time for production.

Making Decisions. Although the computer generates action notices, *decisions* based on them are made by the inventory planner. The planner reviews the item's complete MRP inventory record, along with those of its components. If component inventory is available to support the order, the planner usually decides to release the order as planned. The planner would input an *inventory transaction* to change the computer record file by adding the quantity and due date of a new scheduled receipt. This new order would show up in the scheduled receipts row the next time the system generates the material requirements plan, and it drops out of the planned order receipt row. When releasing a new order, the planner can also prepare documentation for tool requisitions, routings, or parts lists. For purchased items, a requisition is sent to the appropriate buyer, who in turn places the order with a supplier. These purchasing activities are often computer assisted. At times the planner may deviate from the lot size or timing specified in an item's planned order release. We demonstrate how this can be done when we discuss priority planning in the next section.

Priority Planning with MRP

Priority reports, as shown in Fig. 16.6, are important because they provide the link between materials planning and the actual execution of the materials plan on the shop floor. They inform supervisors and buyers as to what particular orders should be given priority. The key to effective priority reports is a good priority planning system. This involves recognizing priority dependencies, using the information provided by the MRP system, and linking to the shop floor with a shop floor control system.

Valid Priorities. Maintaining valid priorities, which involves recognizing the priority dependency of jobs, is the key to effective priority planning. An order has a **valid priority** if its due date matches its need date. The due date could be a delivery date promised to a customer or a shop due date that identifies the scheduled start time of a parent item for an order. At the time an order is issued, the due date and the need date are the same. However, as time passes, either the due date or the need date may change for a variety of reasons. For example, customers cancel orders, new customer orders are put into the schedule, machines fail and delay components, supplier shipments arrive later, or changes are made to the bill of materials for a product. Companies often try to cope with disturbances such as these by using expediters, persons charged with the responsibility to usher specific orders through the system on a priority basis. However, not all schedule changes are communicated quickly enough, leaving many scheduling decisions to machine operators, who have to work with limited, often faulty information.

Priority Dependency. To maintain valid priorities, managers must recognize the **priority dependency** of jobs in a manufacturing system in which the bills of materials have several levels. In vertical priority dependency, the priority of a component order depends on the priority of the parent order. For example, consider the gear and pinion sets that the Eaton Corporation produces for truck axles. A gear and a pinion (the components) must each be manufactured and matched to become a completed gear and pinion set (the parent). If an order is canceled for a particular gear and pinion set, the due dates for processing the gear order and the pinion order for that set should be updated to reflect their new need dates.

In horizontal dependency, the priority of a component order depends on the priority of another component order. For example, if the production order for the gears is delayed because of raw material shortages, the due date for the pinions should be revised to reflect the new date for gear availability. In that way, valuable machine time will not be spent on the order for pinions, only to have them wait in stock until the gears finally arrive. A formal system for priority planning should allow for such dependencies, so that the priorities make sense to the persons who must process the orders. Otherwise, an informal system will develop and management will lose control of an important activity.

A Formal System. Figure 16.8 shows how material requirements planning can be used in priority planning. Based on an authorized master production schedule, the system generates a detailed plan, complete with planned order releases for all purchased materials, components, and assemblies. If an unanticipated disturbance leads to a shortage of materials, the MRP system issues action notices, identifying problems that must be solved. Management can then determine the extent to which the original due dates for the affected open orders have diverged from their need dates. If capacity is sufficient, adjustments can be made accordingly. We will discuss the capacity reports later in the chapter.

Schedule adjustment is facilitated by two features of MRP. Consider the gear and pinion set and its components in Fig. 16.9. Below each component inventory status record is a **peg record,** which indicates for each week the quantity needed of each parent item. The gear has several parents and the gross requirements of 22 units in week 8 are split between two different parent items. The peg record provides the *upward visibility* needed to determine whether schedule adjustments are necessary and, if so, how to make them.

FIGURE 16.8

A Formal Scheduling System

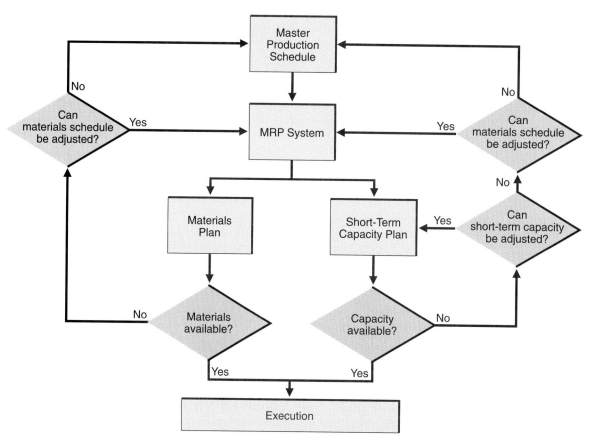

FIGURE 16.9

Data for Priority
Planning

Item: GP502
Description: Gear and pinion set

Lot Size: POQ–2 weeks
Lead Time: 4 weeks
Safety Stock: 0 units

Week		1	2	3	4	5	6	7	8	9	10
Gross requirements		20	45	13	31	10	48	52	37	18	63
Scheduled receipts		60		57							
Projected on hand	8	48	3	47	16	6	52	0	18	0	0
Planned receipts							94		55		63
Planned order releases			94		55		63				

Item: G500
Description: Gear

Lot Size: 100
Lead Time: 7 weeks
Safety Stock: 0 units

Week		1	2	3	4	5	6	7	8	9	10
Gross requirements			94		55		63		22	30	
Scheduled receipts			100				100				
Projected on hand	50	50	56	56	1	1	38	38	16	86	86
Planned receipts										100	
Planned order releases			100								

Item: P002
Description: Pinion

Lot Size: 100
Lead Time: 3 weeks
Safety Stock: 0 units

Week		1	2	3	4	5	6	7	8	9	10
Gross requirements			94		55		63				
Scheduled receipts			100		100						
Projected on hand	0	0	6	6	51	51	88	88	88	88	88
Planned receipts							100				
Planned order releases				100							

Peg Record G500				Peg Record P002		
Week	Quantity	Parent		Week	Quantity	Parent
2	94	GP502		2	94	GP502
4	55	GP502		4	55	GP502
6	63	GP502		6	63	GP502
8	12	GP507				
8	10	GP509				
9	30	GP504				

Another useful device is called a **firm planned order.** This technique enables the planner to override the fixed parameters of the MRP system on an exception basis. The planner can change lead times and/or lot sizes and adjust schedules to validate the priorities on the shop floor. Subsequent replanning with the MRP system will not change the timing or size of the firm planned orders.

| *Application 16.3* | *Revising Priorities with an MRP System* |

Refer to the data for the gear and pinion set in Fig. 16.9. For each of the four disturbances in the following table—taken independently of the others—suggest a schedule change that will avoid shortages of materials.

Solution   The suggested schedule changes are also shown in the table. The results become apparent only after the records have been recomputed. The first two disturbances are caused by changes in parent–item plans, and the component schedule changes amount to realigning the due dates and need dates of certain scheduled receipts. The third disturbance, an unavoidable delay in G500, originates at the component level and affects parent–item plans. The peg record is used to determine which parent item(s) will be affected—in this case, GP502 only. The inventory record for GP502 indicates that its gross requirements still could be met if the planned order release in week 2 is reduced to 42. A subsequent planned order of 52 can be scheduled for week 3, when the component order is to be available. This lot-size change for GP502 can be accomplished using firm planned orders. Note that as P002 has no on-hand inventory, the due date for its scheduled receipt in week 2 has not diverged from its need date.

The last disturbance shown in the table also requires the use of peg records and firm planned orders. In this case, the lead time for the planned order of GP502 in week 4 is shortened to three weeks. A subsequent replanning session with MRP will move the gross requirements of 55 units to week 5 for both components, thus avoiding any unplanned shortages of materials.

Revising Priorities with an MRP System

Disturbance	Resulting Schedule Change	
1. Customer cancelation of gross requirement of 52 units of GP502 in week 7. (This change reduces the planned order release in week 2 to only 42 units.)	G500: Delay the scheduled receipt in week 2 until week 4. Remove the planned order release in week 2.	P002: Delay the scheduled receipt in week 4 until week 6. Remove the planned order release in week 3.
2. Increase in customer order for GP502 in week 9 by 15 units. (The planned order release in week 4 now becomes 70 units.)	G500: Expedite scheduled receipt in week 6 to week 4.	P002: No change.
3. Machine failures delay the open order for G500 in week 2. (It is now expected to be completed in week 3.)	GP502: Change the planned order release in week 2 to 42 units. Create a new planned order release for 52 units in week 3.	P002: No change.
4. Temporary labor shortages delay the scheduled receipt for P002 in week 4. (It is now expected to be completed in week 5.)	G500: No change.	GP502: Compress the lead time of the planned order release in week 4 to three weeks. This moves the planned order release to week 5.

Shop Floor Control Systems. Priority planning using MRP is of no use unless the planner transmits the changes in scheduled receipt due dates to the shop floor. The planner can do so with a **shop floor control system.** Figure 16.10 shows the typical inputs and functions of such a system. The input files used here are similar to those used in MRP. The order file contains the details of all planned order releases and scheduled receipts. The scheduled receipts data enable the user to track the progress of any open order and are updated by the shop floor control system as status changes are recorded.

Four major functions can be performed with shop floor control systems. The order release function adjusts the released date of planned orders to correspond to any capacity constraints and component availability. Orders are released only if components are available, unless the check is overridden. As part of this function, the planner also initiates all the paperwork that authorizes the start of the order, requisitions materials, and specifies moves between operations and routings.

The scheduled receipt maintenance function provides an accurate database for each order. The primary source of information is the report of daily shop floor transactions giving the status of the scheduled receipts. This function also covers order splitting, which involves breaking up a lot size once production has begun to accommodate capacity problems or the need to expedite portions of the original lot, and adding more operations to a routing because of rework.

The dispatching function generates a dispatch list, as identified in Fig. 16.6. It specifies the status of jobs in each work center and ranks them in order of priority based on their due dates. The planner can revise the dispatch list daily to reflect the latest changes in priorities of scheduled receipts.

From the database the status reporting function generates a variety of reports needed in the shop floor control system. For example, the planner can

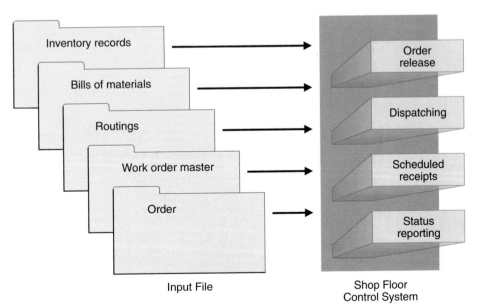

FIGURE 16.10

Typical Shop Floor
Control System

Inventory records

Bills of materials

Routings

Work order master

Order

Order release

Dispatching

Scheduled receipts

Status reporting

Input File

Shop Floor
Control System

generate reports detailing the status of scheduled receipts for a specific customer order or the status of any work center showing the orders currently being processed there and the load expressed in standard hours.

Thus the shop floor control system can translate realignment of due dates and need dates into action. This method is useful for converting various operations plans and schedules into production that will effectively achieve the firm's overall goals.

Capacity Reports

The MRP computer logic itself does not recognize capacity limitations when computing the planned orders. *Managers* must monitor the capacity requirements of material requirements plans, making adjustments as needed. Let's look at two important sources of information for the crucial short-term decisions that materials managers continually make: capacity requirements planning reports and input–output reports.

Capacity Requirements Planning. Capacity requirements planning (CRP) is a technique for projecting time-phased labor requirements for critical work stations. The goal of CRP is to match the MPS with the plant's production capacity. The technique is used to calculate workload according to work required to complete the scheduled receipts already in the shop and to complete the planned order releases yet to be released. Capacity requirements planning is a more detailed and accurate version of the method of overall factors used for master production scheduling (see Chapter 15). A key difference is that CRP uses the scheduled receipts and planned orders for *all* produced items in the bills of materials, not just the end items, to estimate capacity requirements.

Figure 16.11 shows a capacity requirements report for a lathe station that turns wooden legs used in tables. There are 4 lathes, each scheduled for two shifts per day. The lathe station has a maximum capacity of 320 hours per week. The *planned* hours represent labor requirements for all planned orders to be routed through the lathe station. Work projected beyond actual lead times is only in the planning stage. The *actual* hours represent the backlog of work visible on the shop floor, that is, scheduled receipts. Combining requirements

FIGURE 16.11

Capacity
Requirements Report

Date: 07/28/92			**Week 32**
Plant 01 Dept. 03: Lathe Station			
Capacity: 320 hours per week			
Week	Planned Hours	Actual Hours	Total Hours
32	90	210	300
33	156	104	260
34	349	41	390
35	210	0	210
36	360	0	360
37	280	0	280

from both sources gives *total* hours. Comparing total hours to actual capacity constraints can give advance warning of potential problems. The planner must resolve any capacity problems uncovered.

Application 16.4   *Identifying Capacity Problems with CRP*

Does the CRP report in Fig. 16.11 reveal any problems at the lathe station? If so, what should be done?

Solution   The report should arouse the planner's concern. Unless something is done, the current capacity of 320 hours per week will be exceeded in week 34 and week 36. Requirements for all other time periods are well below the capacity limit. Perhaps the best choice is to release some orders earlier than called for in weeks 32, 33, and 35. This adjustment will help smooth capacity and alleviate projected bottlenecks. Other options might be to change the lot sizes of some items, use overtime, subcontract, off-load to another work station, or simply let the bottlenecks occur.

The forward visibility of CRP reports is a capability unique to modern MRP systems. Computing these reports requires more than a list of scheduled receipts and planned orders. Routings (see Chapter 12) are needed to identify which orders will be processed at each work station. Time standards (see Chapter 7) are needed for the setup and processing times of the orders. Information on lead times and the current status of scheduled receipts helps estimate when each order will reach a work station.

Input–Output Control. An **input–output control report** compares planned input (from prior CRP reports) with actual input, and planned output with actual output. Inputs and outputs are expressed in common units, usually hours. Information in the report indicates whether work stations have been performing as expected and helps management pinpoint the source of capacity problems. Actual outputs can fall behind planned outputs for two reasons:

1. **Insufficient inputs.** Output may lag when inputs are insufficient to support the planned output rates. The problem can lie upstream at a prior operation, or it may be caused by missing purchased parts. In effect, not enough work arrives to keep the operation busy.
2. **Insufficient capacity.** Output may lag at the station itself. Even though input rates keep pace, output may slip below expected levels because of absenteeism, equipment failures, inadequate staffing levels, or low productivity rates.

Application 16.5   *Identifying Problems Using Input–Output Control*

The input–output report in Fig. 16.12 has been prepared for a rough mill work station where desk chair components are machined. Management established a tolerance of ±25 hours of cumulative deviations from plans. As long as cumulative deviations do not exceed this threshold, there is no cause for concern. Is there a problem? If so, what is the cause?

FIGURE 16.12

Input–Output Report

Work Station: Rough Mill Tolerance: ± 25 hours					Week 32
Week Ending	28	29	30	31	32
Inputs Planned Actual Cumulative deviation	160 145 −15	155 160 −10	170 168 −12	160 177 +5	165
Outputs Planned Actual Cumulative deviation	170 165 −5	170 165 −10	160 150 −20	160 148 −32	160

Solution In week 31 actual outputs fell behind planned outputs by a total of 32 hours. This cumulative deviation exceeds the 25-hour tolerance, so there is a problem. Actual inputs are keeping pace with planned inputs, so the lag results from insufficient capacity at the rough mill itself. Temporary use of overtime may be necessary to increase the output rate.

MRP II: A Comprehensive Information System

To this point we have emphasized the attributes of MRP as an information system for manufacturing. However, the databases created and maintained by MRP can be used to generate valuable reports for other functional areas of the firm.

It is now possible to enhance MRP systems with simulation possibilities that create "what-if" scenarios. Management can receive performance reports that project the dollar value of shipments, product costs, overhead allocations, inventories, backlogs, and profits. Time-phased information from the MPS, scheduled receipts, and planned orders can be converted into cash flow projections, broken down by product families. For example, the projected on-hand quantities in MRP inventory records allow the computation of future levels of inventory investment. These levels are obtained simply by multiplying the quantities by the per unit value of each item and adding these amounts for all items belonging to the same product family. Similar computations are possible for other performance measures of interest to management.

When the full range of these outputs is added to a basic MRP system—tying it to the company's financial system—the result is **manufacturing resource planning (MRP II)** (see Wight, 1979). The original material requirements planning system is sometimes referred to as *mrp* or *little MRP* because it was limited only to aiding order-launching decisions. Information from MRP II is used by key managers of the firm representing manufacturing, purchasing, marketing, finance, and engineering. MRP II reports help these managers develop and monitor the overall business plan and recognize sales objectives, manufacturing capabilities, and cash flow constraints.

The Colorado Springs Division of Hewlett-Packard provides an example of the successful use of MRP II. This division, which makes a variety of complex electronic instruments, modified its MRP system to provide financial reports in step with its operational plans. Predictions are quite good, with production costs coming within 1 percent of predictions. Managerial Practice 16.1 explains how MRP II is used by a manufacturer of syringes and miniature valves.

IMPLEMENTATION ISSUES

Although thousands of firms have tried MRP, not all have succeeded. A company can easily invest $500,000 in an MRP system, only to still be plagued by high inventories and late customer deliveries. What goes wrong? One possibility is that the MRP system is poorly implemented. Success is not automatic but is achieved only through the dedicated efforts of those involved in making the system function as intended. A second possibility, which we discuss later, is that the company's manufacturing environment does not give MRP a distinct advantage over other systems.

Prerequisites

There are four main prerequisites to successful implementation of an MRP system: computer support, accurate and realistic input, management support, and user knowledge and acceptance.

Computer Support. It is unrealistic to think of using MRP without a computer. Successful implementation of MRP requires a careful assessment of computer requirements, such as the size of random access memory, the capacity of external data storage devices, the processing speeds of the central processing unit (CPU), and the number and type of individual work stations. Some systems can be completely installed on personal computers, depending on the number

At Hewlett-Packard, the manufacturing of printed circuit boards is controlled through the use of a touch terminal.

Managerial Practice 16.1

MRP II Implementation at Kloehn

Kloehn is one of five manufacturers specializing in syringes, miniature valves, and computer-driven syringe assemblies found in scientific and medical instrumentation. Eighty percent of its production is specially produced for such customers as Abbott Labs and Hewlett-Packard. Kloehn employs about 100 people and has sales in the $10–$15 million range. Although sales volume today is rapidly expanding and the future looks bright, it has not always been that way. To provide good customer service in the mid-1980s, Kloehn built up large inventories of raw materials and finished goods to meet anticipated customer demands. In 1987 customer demand fell off and Kloehn was left with a costly situation that could have put it out of business.

CEO Garth Kloehn decided that the company had to develop the capability to identify and track all costs and to design controls to keep costs in line with sales. Kevin Fox was hired as manager of production control and manufacturing information systems to implement an integrated manufacturing system. After extensive study, Fox selected IBM's Manufacturing Accounting Production and Inventory Control System (MAPICS). Within 60 days of completing the first phase of implementation, manufacturing lead time had been cut 20 percent, largely by integrating marketing and manufacturing using the Order Entry & Invoicing and Inventory Manage-

ment modules. In addition, inventory turns increased from 1.2 to 4 and profitability rose 10 percent from 1989 to 1990.

With MRP II every department in the company is in some way integrated with the system. Here are some of the ways this was done at Kloehn:

Engineering: The system automatically updates revisions as it generates new blueprints, ensuring that each job package contains the latest customer specs. The time to create a new product was reduced 33 percent.

Research and Development: The system tracks existing product costs and holds information on the history of similar products.

Shop Floor: The system provides an accurate and efficient way to track labor hours and costs.

Marketing: The system checks the product status, stock availability, stock locations, and routings and can verify engineering drawings.

Accounting: The system provides financial analysis for budgeting and forecasting, departmentalization of costs, automatic journal entries, and financial ratio analysis.

Source: Jim Barnes, "For Kloehn, Good Customer Service Meant Controlling Its Own Growth," *APICS—The Performance Advantage* (August 1991), pp. 26–29.

*K*loehn uses IBM's MAPICS system in its integrated approach to manufacturing management.

of stock items to be controlled. Processing speed can be a major consideration because completely exploding a master schedule with thousands of components and assemblies can take many hours of computer time. The system generates numerous reports, thus requiring adequate printing capabilities. Additional processing requirements might be imposed if the firm adopts a net change system to frequently update the data in the system.

Another consideration linked to computer support is the choice of software. Many companies sell MRP software for main frame, mini-computer, and personal computer applications; Haddock and Hubicki (1989) published a list of 65 such companies. In addition to MRP itself, each software package contains a number of modules, ranging from accounting applications and production costing to capacity requirements planning. Software packages can cost anywhere from several thousands of dollars for a PC-based system to $500,000 or more for a mainframe system.

Accurate and Realistic Input. Any decision support system such as MRP rests on valid input data. You saw in Fig. 16.6 that MRP relies on many data inputs, the three principal ones being the master production schedule, bills of materials, and inventory records. When MRP fails to live up to expectations, management should look first at these inputs. Are they accurate and realistic? If not, little progress can be made. Data accuracy makes a major difference in whether MRP implementation is successful (see White et al., 1982).

As we discussed in Chapter 13, cycle counting is one of several ways to improve record accuracy. With this approach, inventory items are checked on a periodic basis, the more expensive ones being checked more frequently. MRP inventory records are checked against the actual counts, and corrections are made to the inventory record file in the MRP system. But this activity can keep a group of cycle counters busy full time, depending on the number of items in stock, and can be tedious and time consuming. Consider the problem of counting thousands of transistors or resistors in a plant producing electronics products. In such cases, sensitive scales can be used to estimate the number of items in stock. Based on the weight of one or a small number of parts, and the weight of their container, the scale can estimate the total number of parts in the container. These scales can be very accurate, with errors less than 1 percent.

Management Support. Converting to a new system challenges long-established habits and prerogatives of those involved, whether they are managers, planners, buyers, marketing specialists, or shop supervisors. Resistance to change is normal and predictable. Overcoming such resistance begins with top management, who should convey to others the importance of success. Through active involvement in implementing and using MRP, top management can motivate others.

User Knowledge and Acceptance. Users at all levels of the company must be knowledgeable in MRP. They must understand how they will be affected and what is required of them to make the system work. Such understanding helps replace resistance with enthusiasm. Training programs often involve employees throughout the organization. The Tennant Company, an $80 million producer of industrial maintenance equipment, gave 525 of its 575 employees at least some MRP training. Usually, a personnel problem—such as lack of training, inadequate management support, or resistance to change—is the single most important impediment to MRP success (see White et al., 1982). Managerial Practice 16.2 shows how another company addressed the four prerequisites for successful implementation of MRP II.

Favorable Environments for Material Requirements Planning

Some companies do not adopt an MRP system, or are disappointed with its results, because their manufacturing environment does not give MRP a distinct advantage over other systems. Cerveny and Scott (1989) reported that 40 percent of the firms they surveyed had not adopted an MRP system and, of those that did, 67 percent said the system was a success and 16 percent said it was a failure. Four environmental characteristics are particularly important:

1. Number of BOM levels
2. Magnitude of lot sizes
3. Volatility
4. Manufacturing's positioning strategy

You have seen that one of MRP's unique advantages is its management of lumpy demand for dependent-demand items. Dependent-demand items are most numerous when there are many levels in the bills of materials. Thus the greatest numbers of MRP users are in the fabricated metals, machinery, and electric and electronic industries, which tend to have many BOM levels. It is no coincidence that the average user of MRP has more than six BOM levels (see Schroeder et al., 1981). Even with many levels, though, dependent-demand patterns need not be lumpy. The other variable is the magnitude of lot sizes. Our own simulation studies bear out these conditions: The relative superiority of MRP is greatest with more BOM levels and larger lot sizes. When a firm works with extremely small lot sizes, as do some Japanese manufacturers, changing over to MRP is less beneficial.

A highly volatile manufacturing environment that management cannot stabilize is also less likely to achieve large MRP savings. A basic assumption underlying MRP systems is that projections of gross requirements, scheduled receipts, and planned order releases are realistic. This assumption is not valid when there are high scrap rates, capacity bottlenecks, last-minute rush jobs, and unreliable suppliers.

Finally, MRP seems to be most attractive for firms that have positioned themselves with an intermediate strategy. (See Fig. 2.6 in Chapter 2.) They produce in batches, experience low to medium demand volumes, tend to offer a number of product options, and make products that have relatively short life

Managerial Practice 16.2

A Successful MRP II Implementation at the Henry L. Hanson Company

For more than 30 years the Henry L. Hanson Company of Worcester, Massachusetts, has dominated the hardware industry with exclusive production of threading tools, taps, dies, and drill bits. The company employs 250 people. Recently competition began eroding its foothold and forced the company to look at automating its manufacturing systems. The company addressed each of the four prerequisites for successful implementation.

1. Computer support. The original system was only partially automated, and handwritten inventory counts and routing information were often carried around in employees' back pockets. The company decided to purchase an IBM System 38. After 10 months of study, a management team selected the Business Planning and Control System (BPCS) software from System Software Associates, Inc.

2. Accurate and reliable data. Before the MRP II system was installed, only 30 to 40 percent of the inventory records were accurate. Management instituted a program for periodically reviewing inventory levels and thereby increased accuracy to 95 percent. Similar accuracy problems existed with the bills of materials and engineering standards. Both accuracies were dramatically increased before the system was fully operational.

3. Management support. A management committee consisting of the CEO, vice president, director of distribution, production control manager, data processing manager, and MRP II project leader oversaw the selection of software and the implementation's progress. It is important to note that top management was actively involved.

4. User knowledge and acceptance. The year prior to implementation the employees were educated in basic MRP II principles. Just prior to implementation, they were given intensive in-house training on the features and functionality of the software modules. By the time the system was turned on, all reservations had been removed. Presently, an average of 40 employees access the system regularly, and 10 use it on a daily basis.

The MRP II system has benefited the Hanson Company in many ways. Overtime has been drastically reduced. The company now fills orders with 95 percent delivery accuracy, a 35 percent improvement. The company can now exchange information with its remote manufacturing sites in Maine, Wisconsin, and Rhode Island. In total, inventory and manufacturing performance are so improved that the company is presently producing products at lower costs and regaining control of the hardware market.

Source: Dick Pelligrini and Mike La Flamme, "Hardware Manufacturer Benefits from 'Class A' Status," *P&IM Review with APICS News* (April 1988), pp. 46–48.

cycles. These characteristics are not necessary for successful MRP system utilization, but they give you an idea of the sort of environment in which MRP can be best utilized. Firms at the extreme points of the diagonal in Fig. 2.6, with a process focus or product focus, find that MRP is less valuable. In process-focused firms, annual demand for specific items is small, and the number of customized products is large. Products are often expensive and require substantial engineering, which makes lead times long and uncertain. Maintaining files on bills of materials is complicated by the customization, and lot sizes are small. In product-focused firms using continuous processes (such as a paper mill), there tend to be few BOM levels, high capital intensity, and tight constraints on equipment capacity. Here the focus of managerial concern is with the master production schedule. Only 3 percent of MRP system users operate continuous manufacturing processes (see Cerveny and Scott, 1989).

DISTRIBUTION REQUIREMENTS PLANNING

The principles of MRP can also be applied to distribution inventories. Consider the distribution system in Fig. 16.13. The top echelon represents retail stores at various locations throughout the country. At the middle level are regional distribution centers (DCs) that replenish retail store inventories on request. The bottom level consists of one or more plants that supply the DCs. In the past, plants tended to schedule production to meet the forecasted demand patterns of the DCs. These forecasts were likely to be based on past usage, as is done for independent-demand items. The DCs, in turn, replenished their inventories based on past demand patterns of the retail stores. In short, reorder-point logic was used at all three levels.

To illustrate the shortcomings of this approach, let's suppose that customer demand for a product suddenly increases by 10 percent. What will happen? Because the retailers carry some inventory, there will be some delay before the DCs feel the full 10 percent increase. Still more time passes before the plants feel the effect of the full increase, reflected as higher demand from the DCs. This means that for months the plants could continue underproducing at a 10 percent rate. When the deficiency finally becomes apparent, the plants must increase their output by much more than 10 percent to replenish inventory levels. Thus a small change is gradually magnified into a much larger change.

Distribution requirements planning (DRP) is an inventory control and scheduling technique that applies MRP principles to distribution inventories. It helps avoid self-induced swings in demand. An inventory record is maintained for each item at each location. The planned order releases projected at the retail level are used to derive the gross requirements for each item at the DC level, using standard MRP logic and bills of materials. Next, planned order releases at the DC level are computed, from which the gross requirements for the plant level can be derived. This information provides the basis for updating the master production schedule at the plant.

Use of DRP requires an integrated information system. If the manufacturer operates its own DCs and retail stores (forward integration), this poses no particular problem. If operations in each echelon are owned by different firms, all must agree to convey planned order releases from one level to the next. Open

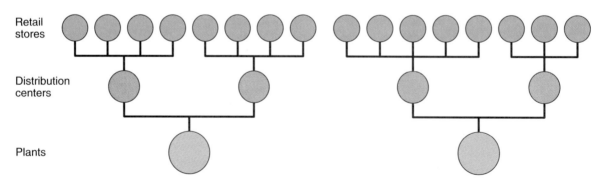

FIGURE 16.13   A Multi-Echelon Distribution System

communication between firms need not stop at the plant level. More and more manufacturers are conveying planned order release data to their suppliers, giving them a better idea of future demand. Reducing demand uncertainty pays off either in lower inventories or in better service.

SOLVED PROBLEMS

1. The MRP inventory record in Fig. 16.14 has been partially completed, showing gross requirements, scheduled receipts, and current on-hand inventory. Parameters for lead time and safety stock are also given. Item H10-A is produced in the plant (not purchased).
   a. Fill in the last three rows of the record, using an FOQ of 80 units.
      i. Will there by any action notices?
      ii. If there are action notices, what factors would you consider in reacting to them?
   b. Revise the last two rows using the L4L rule.
   c. Revise the last two rows again, this time using the POQ rule and a value of *P* that will give an average lot size of 80 units. Assume that *average* weekly demand will be 20 units for the foreseeable future when computing *P*.

   Solution   a. See Fig. 16.15.

FIGURE 16.14

Item: H10–A Description: Chair seat assembly								Lot Size: 80 units Lead Time: 4 weeks Safety Stock: 10 units		
Week	31	32	33	34	35	36	37	38	39	40
Gross requirements		60				35		45		60
Scheduled receipts			80							
Projected on hand	20									
Planned receipts										
Planned order releases										

FIGURE 16.15

Item: H10–A Description: Chair seat assembly								Lot Size: 80 units Lead Time: 4 weeks Safety Stock: 10 units		
Week	31	32	33	34	35	36	37	38	39	40
Gross requirements		60				35		45		60
Scheduled receipts			80							
Projected on hand	20	20	-40	40	40	40	85	85	40	40	60
Planned receipts						80				80
Planned order releases		80				80				

FIGURE 16.16

Week	31	32	33	34	35	36	37	38	39	40
Planned receipts						5		45		60
Planned order releases		5		45		60				

(a)

Week	31	32	33	34	35	36	37	38	39	40
Planned receipts						50				60
Planned order releases		50				60				

(b)

    i. There will be an action notice to expedite the scheduled receipt in week 33 to week 32.

    ii. The capacity must be checked to see whether the order can be expedited.

  b. The last two rows—based on use of the L4L rule—are shown in Fig. 16.16(a).

  c. The last two rows—based on use of $P = 4$ weeks—are shown in Fig. 16.16(b).

2. The MPS for product A calls for completion of a 50-unit order in week 4 and a 60-unit order in week 8. The MPS for product B calls for the completion of a 200-unit order received in week 5. The lead times are 2 weeks for A and 1 week for B. Develop a material requirements plan for the next six weeks for items C, D, E, and F, identifying any action notices that would be provided. The BOMs are shown in Fig. 16.17, and data from the inventory records are shown in Table 16.1.

FIGURE 16.17

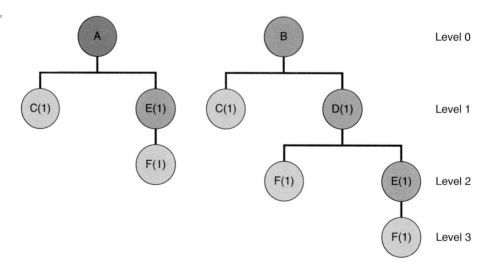

TABLE 16.1

Data Category	Item			
	C	D	E	F
Lot-size rule	FOQ = 250	FOQ = 400	L4L	POQ ($P = 2$)
Lead time	3	2	3	2
Safety stock	50	0	0	0
Scheduled receipts	250 (week 2)	None	50 (week 1)	None
Beginning (on-hand) inventory	60	300	0	0

Solution   The lowest level code for each component is as follows: item C—level 1; item D—level 1; item E—level 2; and item F—level 3 (see Fig. 16.17). Therefore, we begin with item C, then go to D, E, and F in that order (see Fig. 16.18). We find that item D does not have any planned order releases, so it doesn't add to the requirements for E and F. Item A *does* add requirements for E. Item E's planned order release becomes a gross requirement for item F in week 3.

An action notice would call for delaying the scheduled receipt for item E from week 1 to week 2. A second action notice would notify the planner that item F has a planned order release in the action bucket.

FIGURE 16.18

Item: C
Description:

Lot Size: 250 units
Lead Time: 3 weeks
Safety Stock: 50 units

Week	1	2	3	4	5	6	7	8
Gross requirements		50		200		60		
Scheduled receipts		250						
Projected on hand	60	60	260	260	60	60	250	250	250
Planned receipts						250		
Planned order releases			250					

(a) Item C

Item: D
Description:

Lot Size: 400 units
Lead Time: 2 weeks
Safety Stock: 0 units

Week	1	2	3	4	5	6	7	8
Gross requirements				200				
Scheduled receipts								
Projected on hand	300	300	300	300	100	100	100	100	100
Planned receipts								
Planned order releases								

(b) Item D

FIGURE 16.18

(Continued)

Item: E Description:						Lot Size: L4L Lead Time: 3 weeks Safety Stock: 0 units		
Week	1	2	3	4	5	6	7	8
Gross requirements		50				60		
Scheduled receipts	50 →							
Projected on hand 0	50	0	0	0	0	0	0	0
Planned receipts						60		
Planned order releases			60					

(c) Item E

Item: F Description:						Lot Size: POQ ($P = 2$) Lead Time: 2 weeks Safety Stock: 0 units		
Week	1	2	3	4	5	6	7	8
Gross requirements			60					
Scheduled receipts								
Projected on hand 0	0	0	0	0	0	0	0	0
Planned receipts			60					
Planned order releases	60							

(d) Item F   Action bucket

FORMULA REVIEW

Projected on-hand inventory balance for MRP record: $I_t = I_{t-1} + SR_t + PR_t - GR_t$

CHAPTER HIGHLIGHTS

- Material requirements planning (MRP) is a computerized scheduling and information system useful in managing dependent-demand inventories.

- The shortcomings of reorder point systems in a dependent-demand environment are as follows: (1) the assumption of a uniform, continuous demand rate is unrealistic; (2) the assumption that items are independent of each other when, in reality, they are not; and (3) no provision of forward visibility for planning purposes.

- The basic principles of MRP are (1) dependent demands should be derived, not forecasted, and (2) replenishment orders should be offset for required production and delivery lead times.

- The material requirements plan is prepared from the most recent inventory records of all items. The basic elements in each record are gross requirements, scheduled receipts, on-hand inventory, planned receipts, and planned order releases.

- Several parameters must be preassigned to each inventory record, including lot size, planning lead time, and safety stock. Various static and dynamic lot-sizing rules can be used.

- The planned order releases of a parent, modified by usage quantities, become the gross requirements of its components. This procedure involves level-by-level processing, starting at the MPS level.

- As a computerized information system, MRP has three basic inputs: the master production schedule, inventory records, and bills of materials. A fourth input, demand from sources other than the MPS, is also a possibility.

- Action notices allow management by exception, bringing to a planner's attention only those items for which new orders need to be released or that have open orders with misaligned due dates. Decisions based on the notices are normally made by the planner.

- MRP systems can provide outputs such as the material requirements plan, action notices, priority reports, and performance reports. The most advanced system is MRP II, which allows management to integrate and monitor production, marketing, and financial plans.

- The key to effective priority planning in manufacturing is to maintain valid priorities by ensuring that order due dates correspond to order need dates. Horizontal and vertical priority dependencies need to be recognized. Priority planning with an MRP system is aided by the use of peg records and firm planned orders.

- Shop floor control systems transmit the changes in open-order due dates to the shop floor and make use of priority rules to control the scheduling process. These systems also involve the functions of order release, scheduled receipt maintenance, and status reporting.

- Implementation of MRP systems is widespread. Significant inventory, customer service, and productivity benefits have been reported by many firms. Prerequisites to successful implementation are adequate computer support, accurate databases, management support, and user knowledge and acceptance.

- The relative benefits of MRP depend on the number of BOM levels, the magnitude of lot sizes, environmental volatility, and positioning strategy.

- The principles of MRP can be used to manage distribution inventory with a system called distribution requirements planning (DRP).

KEY TERMS

action bucket **662**
action notice **662**
capacity requirements planning (CRP) **668**
distribution requirements planning (DRP) **676**
dynamic lot-sizing rules **655**
firm planned order **666**
fixed order quantity (FOQ) **655**
gross requirements **651**

input–output control report **669**
level-by-level processing **660**
lot for lot (L4L) **656**
manufacturing resource planning (MRP II) **670**
material requirements planning (MRP) **647**
MRP explosion **660**
MRP inventory record **650**
net change MRP system **660**

peg record **664**
periodic order quantity (POQ) **656**
planned order release **653**
planned receipt **652**
priority dependency **663**
regenerative MRP system **660**
shop floor control system **667**
static lot-sizing rules **655**
valid priority **663**

STUDY QUESTIONS

1. How does independent demand differ from dependent demand?

2. How does reorder point logic account for lead times and demand forecasts? How does MRP logic account for them?

3. Define *gross requirements*, *scheduled receipts*, *planned receipts*, and *planned order releases*.

4. Calculating planned order releases when using a POQ rule is less complicated after the first one. For each subsequent planned re-

ceipt, the lot size is simply the gross requirements sum for the next P weeks. Safety
stock and the previous week's projected on-
hand balance can be ignored. Why?

5. MRP logic derives a component's gross requirements from the planned order releases
of all its parents. Why does this necessitate a
top-down processing of records?

6. How is safety stock handled by MRP? How
much should be carried? At what levels?

7. Why do priority and capacity reports help to
close the loop? Why isn't it always wise to
implement the material requirements plan
without change?

8. Your company is considering the use of its
MRP system for priority planning. Briefly
explain to your boss the advantages and uses
of peg records and firmed planned orders.

9. What potential problem do you detect from
the data in the input–output control report in
Fig. 16.19? What is the source of the problem, and what can be done to resolve it?

10. Comment on the statement, "It is impossible to put together realistic marketing and
financial plans without being able to set and
achieve production plans."

11. How can MRP users report *simultaneous* improvements in inventory, customer service,
and productivity? Isn't there a fundamental
trade-off, where improvement in one comes
at the expense of another? Explain.

12. Why do some companies fail to achieve any
measurable improvements from MRP?

13. Suppose that a manufacturer decides to
share planned order release information with
its suppliers. What benefits can accrue to
both parties? Can there be disadvantages?

14. Why can the reliability of time-phased gross
requirements be decreased by the following shocks: last-minute changes in the MPS,
unexpected scrap losses, late supplier shipments, unexpected capacity bottlenecks, or
inaccurate inventory records.

15. The relative advantage of MRP over a reorder point system does not hold for small lot
sizes and short lead times. Do you agree?
Disagree? Why?

PROBLEMS

Review Problems

1. The inventory record shown in Fig. 16.20
has been partially completed, showing
gross requirements, scheduled receipts, and
current on-hand inventory. Lead-time and
safety stock factors are shown.
a. Complete the last three rows of the record
using an FOQ of 110 units.
b. Complete the last three rows of the record using the POQ lot-sizing rule, with
$P = 2$.

FIGURE 16.19

| Work Station: Chair Assembly | | | | | Week 49 |
Tolerance: ± 50 hours					
Week Ending	45	46	47	48	49
Inputs					
Planned	300	300	300	300	310
Actual	305	275	280	260	
Cumulative deviation	+5	−20	−40	−80	
Outputs					
Planned	300	300	300	300	320
Actual	310	290	270	260	
Cumulative deviation	+10	0	−30	−70	

FIGURE 16.20

Item: M405–X Description: Table top assembly		Lot Size: Lead Time: 2 weeks Safety Stock: 0 units									
Week		1	2	3	4	5	6	7	8	9	10
Gross requirements		90		85		80		45	90		
Scheduled receipts		110									
Projected on hand	40										
Planned receipts											
Planned order releases											

c. Complete the last three rows of the record using the L4L lot-sizing rule.

2. Figure 16.21 shows a partially completed inventory record. Gross requirements, scheduled receipts, and current on-hand inventory, as well as lead-time and safety stock parameters, are shown.
   a. Complete the record using an FOQ of 220 units.

b. Complete the record using the POQ rule, with $P = 3$.

c. Complete the record using the L4L rule.

3. The inventory record in Fig. 16.22 has been partially completed, showing gross requirements, scheduled receipts, and current on-hand inventory. Lead-time and safety stock parameters are also given. Item K12-Q is produced in the plant (not purchased).

FIGURE 16.21

Item: MQ–09 Description: Rear wheel assembly		Lot Size: Lead Time: 1 week Safety Stock: 50 units									
Week		1	2	3	4	5	6	7	8	9	10
Gross requirements		205		130	85		70	60	95		
Scheduled receipts		220									
Projected on hand	100										
Planned receipts											
Planned order releases											

FIGURE 16.22

Item: K12–Q Description: Chair seat assembly		Lot Size: Lead Time: 3 weeks Safety Stock: 0 units									
Week		31	32	33	34	35	36	37	38	39	40
Gross requirements			90		45		20		50		75
Scheduled receipts		75									
Projected on hand	30										
Planned receipts											
Planned order releases											

	Week	1	2	3	4	5	6	7	8	9	10	11	12
Gross requirements			50		35		55		30		10		25
Scheduled receipts				60									
Projected on hand	40												
Planned receipts													
Planned order releases													

Item: GF–4
Description: Motor assembly

Lot Size:
Lead Time: 3 weeks
Safety Stock: 30 units

FIGURE 16.23

a. What is the source of the information already shown for gross requirements and scheduled receipts?
b. Fill in the last three rows of the record, using an FOQ of 75 units.
   i. Will there be any action notices?
   ii. If there are action notices, what factors would you consider in responding to them?
c. Revise the planned order release row using the L4L rule.
d. Revise the planned order release row again, this time using the POQ rule and a value of *P* that should (in the long run) yield an average lot size of 75 units. When computing *P*, assume that the average weekly demand will be 25 units for the foreseeable future.

4. The inventory record in Fig. 16.23 has been partially completed.

a. Complete the last three rows of the record using an FOQ of 60 units.
   i. Will there by any action notices?
   ii. If there are action notices, what factors would you consider in responding to them?
b. Revise the planned order release row using the L4L rule.
c. Revise the planned order release row using the POQ rule. Find the value of *P* that should (in the long run) yield an average lot size of 60 units. Assume that the average weekly demand for the foreseeable future is 15 units.

5. A partially completed inventory record is shown in Fig. 16.24.
a. Complete the record using an FOQ of 85 units. Will there by any action notices?
b. Revise the planned order release row using the L4L rule.

FIGURE 16.24

Item: 34–IJ
Description: Nozzle

Lot Size:
Lead Time: 4 weeks
Safety Stock: 35 units

	Week	1	2	3	4	5	6	7	8	9	10
Gross requirements		45		50		75			55		60
Scheduled receipts			85								
Projected on hand	45										
Planned receipts											
Planned order releases											

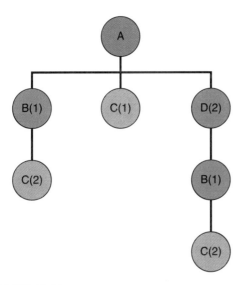

FIGURE 16.25

c. Review the planned order release row using the POQ rule. The average weekly demand is 25 units. Use the value of *P* that should (in the long run) result in an average lot size of 75 units.

6. In the master production schedule for product A, the MPS quantity row (showing *completion* dates) calls for 250 units in week 8. The lead time for production of A is 2 weeks. Develop the material requirements plan for the next six weeks for items B, C, and D. The BOM is shown in Fig. 16.25, and data from the inventory records are shown in Table 16.2. The numbers in parentheses in the BOM are usage quantities. For example, two units of C are needed for each unit of parent B. In deriving C's gross re-

quirements, double the planned order releases from B. Assume that next week is week 1.

After completing the plan, identify any action notices that would be issued. *Hint:* The record for item D must be completed first, followed by the records for B and C. An item's gross requirements cannot be derived without knowing the planned order releases of all its parents.

7. The MPS for product A calls for 85 units to be completed in week 4 and 100 units in week 7 (the lead time is 1 week). The MPS for product B calls for 180 units to be completed in week 7 (the lead time is 2 weeks). Develop the material requirements plan for the next six weeks for items C, D, E, and F. Identify any action notices that will be provided. The BOMs are shown in Fig. 16.26. Data from inventory records are shown in Table 16.3.

8. Product A is made from one unit of B and two units of C. Item B is assembled from two units of D and one unit of E. Item C is fabricated from one unit of D. Lead time for items B and D is 2 weeks each, whereas it is one week each for items C and E. To minimize inventory, items B, C, and E have L4L lot-sizing rules. Purchased item D must be ordered in lots of 300 because of transportation costs. Item B has a scheduled receipt of 45 units due in this week. On-hand inventory is 0 for items B, C, and E and 130 units for D. No item has a safety stock requirement.
   a. Draw the bill of materials for item A.

TABLE 16.2

Data Category	Item		
	B	C	D
Lot-size rule	L4L	FOQ = 1000	L4L
Lead time	2	1	3
Safety stock	0	100	0
Scheduled receipts	None	1000 (week 1)	None
Beginning (on-hand) inventory	0	200	0

FIGURE 16.26

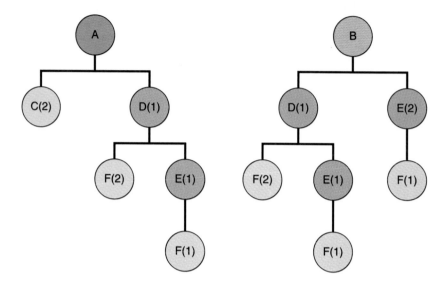

TABLE 16.3

Data Category	Item			
	C	D	E	F
Lot-size rule	FOQ = 220	L4L	FOQ = 300	POQ ($P = 2$)
Lead time	3	2	3	2
Safety stock	20	0	0	80
Scheduled receipts	280 (week 1)	None	300 (week 3)	None
Beginning (on-hand) inventory	25	0	150	600

b. The MPS calls for orders of 45 units of A to be finished in weeks 3, 6, and 7. The assembly lead time for A is one week. Develop a material requirements plan for the next six weeks for items B, C, D, and E.

c. Will any action notices be generated? If so, what are they?

9. Figure 16.27 illustrates the BOM of product A.

- The master production schedule calls for 50 units of A in week 4, 65 units in week 7, and 80 units in week 10. The lead time for A is two weeks.
- Item C is not produced just to make A. It is also produced to meet the forecasted demand for replacement parts. Past replacement part demand has been 20 units per week (add 20 units to C's gross requirements).
- The lead times for items F and C are one week, and for the other items the lead time is two weeks.

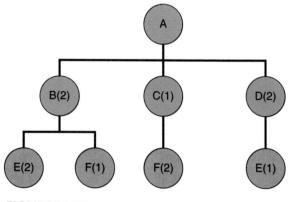

FIGURE 16.27

- A safety stock of 30 units is required for item C. No safety stock is required for items B, D, and F.
- The L4L lot-sizing rule is used for items B and F; the POQ lot-sizing rule ($P = 3$) is used for C. Item E has an FOQ of 600 units, and D has an FOQ of 250 units.
- On-hand inventories are 50 units for B, 50 for C, 120 for D, 70 for E, and 250 for F.
- Item B has a scheduled receipt of 50 units in week 2.

Develop a material requirements plan for the next eight weeks for items B, C, D, E and F. What action notices will be generated?

10. The following information is available about three MPS items.

    Item A: An 80-unit order is to be received in week 4. A 55-unit order is to be received in week 7.
    Item B: A 125-unit order is to be received in week 7.

Item C: A 60-unit order is to be received in week 7.

The lead times are 1 week for A, 2 weeks for B, and 3 weeks for C. Develop the material requirements plan for the next six weeks for items D, E, and F, identifying any action notices that would be provided. The BOMs are shown in Fig. 16.28, and data from the inventory records are shown in Table 16.4.

11. Your company uses an MRP system to do priority planning. Consider the information presented in Fig. 16.29 concerning three items the company manufactures. Item X1 has two components, Y1 and Y2; both Y1 and Y2 have more than one parent. Your job is to have materials in the right place at the right time. You are interested in maintaining valid priorities and satisfying customer demand, as evidenced by the gross requirements for item X1.

    State why situations (a) and (b), taken independently of each other, would (or would

FIGURE 16.28

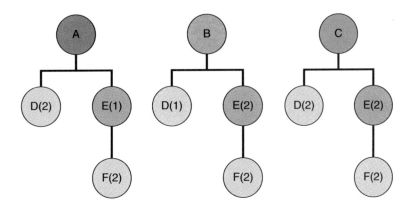

TABLE 16.4

	Item		
Data Category	D	E	F
Lot-size rule	FOQ = 150	L4L	POQ ($P = 2$)
Lead time	3 weeks	1 week	2 weeks
Safety stock	40	0	30 units
Scheduled receipts	250 (week 1)	120 (week 2)	None
Beginning (on-hand) inventory	150	0	100

FIGURE 16.29

Item: X1
Description: Rotor

Lot Size: 100
Lead Time: 2 weeks
Safety Stock: 0 units

Week		1	2	3	4	5	6	7	8	9	10
Gross requirements		50		33			82	70	40		52
Scheduled receipts		100									
Projected on hand	22	72	72	39	39	39	57	87	47	47	95
Planned receipts							100	100			100
Planned order releases					100	100			100		

Item: Y1
Description: Armature

Lot Size: 150
Lead Time: 3 weeks
Safety Stock: 0 units

Week		1	2	3	4	5	6	7	8	9	10
Gross requirements		25		18	133	110		40	100		20
Scheduled receipts		150			150						
Projected on hand	10	135	135	117	134	24	24	134	34	34	14
Planned receipts								150			
Planned order releases					150						

Item: Y2
Description: Rotor housing

Lot Size: 120
Lead Time: 5 weeks
Safety Stock: 0 units

Week		1	2	3	4	5	6	7	8	9	10
Gross requirements			30		133	110			100		20
Scheduled receipts			120			120					
Projected on hand	50	50	140	140	7	17	17	17	37	37	17
Planned receipts									120		
Planned order releases				120							

Peg Record Y1				Peg Record Y2		
Week	Quantity	Parent		Week	Quantity	Parent
1	25	Z3		2	30	Z4
3	18	Z3		4	33	Z8
4	33	Z8		4	100	X1
4	100	X1		5	10	Z8
5	10	Z8		5	100	X1
5	100	X1		8	100	X1
7	40	Z3		10	20	Z8
8	100	X1				
10	20	Z8				

not) cause a problem in priority validity for the components. If there is a problem, how would you resolve it, assuming sufficient capacity?

a. A customer cancels an order for X1, causing its gross requirement in week 6 to become 28 units instead of 82 units.

b. A good customer asks you to ship an unplanned order of 100 units of X1 in week 5. This increases the gross requirement of X1 in week 5 to 100 units. Top management agrees to make the shipment but does not compensate for it by adjusting the gross requirements of X1 in other weeks.

12. Again use the MRP information in Problem 11. State why situations (a)–(d), taken independently, would (or would not) cause a problem in priority validity or materials coverage for X1, Y1, or Y2. If there is a problem, how would you resolve it, assuming sufficient capacity? If more than one approach seems reasonable to you, discuss each one in terms of its relative advantages and disadvantages.

a. Suppose that Y1 is a purchased item and the supplier tells you that the scheduled receipt you expected in week 4 will now arrive in week 5. There is no way to expedite the scheduled receipt to have it arrive as previously planned. There are no other suppliers who can get Y1 to you by week 4. You must now accept the fact that the order will arrive in week 5.

b. Suppose instead that Y1 is a manufactured part. The gross requirement of 25 units in week 1 has been canceled.

c. The requirement for item Z8 has increased in week 4 from 33 to 43.

d. A new machinist working on the order for Y2 scheduled for week 5 irrevocably damaged 50 percent of the lot. The quantity now expected in week 5 is 60 units.

Advanced Problems

Problem 13 is based on information contained in Chapters 11 and 13. A computer package is useful for Problem 16.

13. The dependent demand for a standard item has averaged 30 units per week during the last year. Suppose that the actual dependent demand for the next five weeks is that shown in Table 16.5.

a. Complete Table 16.5. Begin by making three sets of forecasts for weeks 2–5. The first forecasting technique uses the past average of 30 units for all future weeks. The last two update the forecast weekly with simple exponential smoothing, using smoothing parameter α (see Chapter 11) of either 0.10 or 0.20. Finally, calculate the mean absolute deviation (MAD) for each forecasting technique.

b. Judging from the MAD values obtained:

TABLE 16.5

		Three Forecasts			Forecast Errors		
			Exponential Smoothing			Exponential Smoothing	
Week	**Actual Dependent Demand**	Simple Average	$\alpha = 0.10$	$\alpha = 0.20$	Simple Average	$\alpha = 0.10$	$\alpha = 0.20$
1	0	30	30	30	−30	−30	−30
2	90						
3	0						
4	0						
5	60						
				$MAD =$			

i. Does the adaptiveness of exponential smoothing help with forecasting dependent demand?

ii. Would you say that the *MAD* value is small or large, relative to an average weekly demand of 30 units?

iii. How can such forecasting errors be eliminated?

c. Suppose that 80 units of this item are on hand, desired safety stock is 10 units, lead time is two weeks, and there are no scheduled receipts or back orders.

i. If demand is forecast at 30 units per week, would a new order be released this week using reorder point logic?

ii. Using the actual dependent-demand schedule in Table 16.5, would a new order be released using MRP logic? Assume L4L lot sizing.

14. Items A and B are dependent-demand items. Item B's only parent is A. Three units of B are needed to make one unit of A. The current material requirements plan for A is shown in Fig. 16.30 and that for B is shown in Fig. 16.31.

a. Today the planner responsible for items A and B learned some good news and some bad news. Although the scheduled receipt of 90 units of A has been finished (the good news), only 45 units were put in the storeroom; the other 45 were scrapped (the bad news). Recalculate the two inventory records, reflecting this event. *Hint:* A scheduled receipt should no longer be shown for A, but its on-hand balance now is 65 units.

b. Would any action notices relative to the new material requirements plan be issued? If so, what are they?

FIGURE 16.30

Item: A Description:		Week						Lot Size: 90 units Lead Time: 1 week Safety Stock: 0 units		

		Week	1	2	3	4	5	6	7
Gross requirements			85		50			110	60
Scheduled receipts			90						
Projected on hand	20		25	25	65	65	65	45	75
Planned receipts					90			90	90
Planned order releases				90			90	90	

FIGURE 16.31

Item: B Description:							Lot Size: L4L Lead Time: 3 weeks Safety Stock: 0 units

		Week	1	2	3	4	5	6
Gross requirements				270			270	270
Scheduled receipts				270				
Projected on hand	0		0	0	0	0	0	0
Planned receipts							270	270
Planned order releases				270	270			

FIGURE 16.32

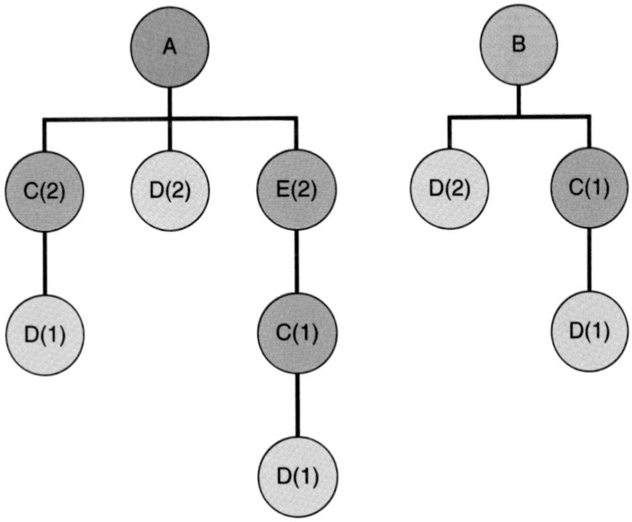

15. Figure 16.32 shows the BOMs for two end items, A and B. Table 16.6 shows the MPS quantity *release* dates (already offset for lead time) for each one. Table 16.7 contains data from inventory records for items C, D, and E. Determine the material requirements plan for items C, D, and E for the next eight weeks. Identify any action notices that would be provided.

TABLE 16.6

	Date							
Product	1	2	3	4	5	6	7	8
A		125		95		150		130
B			80			70		

TABLE 16.7

	Item		
Data Category	C	D	E
Lot-size rule	POQ (P = 3)	FOQ = 800	L4L
Lead time	2	1	3
Safety stock	75	120	0
Scheduled receipts	None	800 (week 1)	200 (week 2)
Beginning (on-hand) inventory	625	350	85

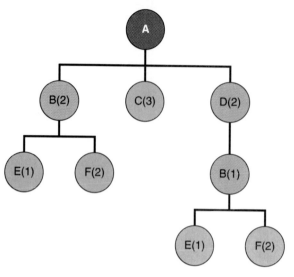

16. The BOM for product A is shown in Fig. 16.33. The MPS for product A calls for 120 units to be *released* (already offset for lead times) in weeks 2, 4, 5, and 8. Table 16.8 shows data from the inventory records. Develop the material requirements plan for the next eight weeks for each item. Would any action notices be issued?

17. Items A and B are dependent-demand items. Four units of B are needed to make one unit of A. Item B's only parent is A. The current material requirements plans for A and B are shown in Fig. 16.34. If 110 units of A are on hand, rather than 80 units, what is the new material requirements plan? Would there by any action notices?

FIGURE 16.33

FIGURE 16.34

Item: A Description:								Lot Size: 90 units Lead Time: 2 weeks Safety Stock: 10 units			
Week		1	2	3	4	5	6	7	8	9	10
Gross requirements		120			70			85	90		
Scheduled receipts		90									
Projected on hand	80	50	50	50	70	70	70	75	75		
Planned receipts					90			90	90		
Planned order releases			90			90	90				

Item: B Description:								Lot Size: L4L Lead Time: 4 weeks Safety Stock: 0 units			
Week		1	2	3	4	5	6	7	8	9	10
Gross requirements			360			360	360				
Scheduled receipts			360								
Projected on hand	0	0	0	0	0	0	0	0	0		
Planned receipts						360	360				
Planned order releases		360	360								

TABLE 16.8

Data Category	Item				
	B	C	D	E	F
Lot-size rule	FOQ = 700	FOQ = 700	L4L	L4L	L4L
Lead time	4	3	3	2	1
Safety stock	50	100	0	100	0
Scheduled receipts	700 (week 1)	450 (week 2)	150 (week 2)	None	1400 (week 1)
Beginning (on-hand) inventory	215	105	125	750	0

CASE   WHERE IS THE POT OF GOLD?

Last year a new MRP system was installed at King Manufacturing. Fred Neff, the vice president of operations, worked closely with the task force created to bring MRP "on line." He frequently attended the training sessions for selected employees, emphasizing how MRP should help King Manufacturing secure a better competitive edge. On the day when the system "went up" there was an aura of tranquility and goodwill. As a symbolic gesture, King's complete supply of red tags was discarded. The days of the informal system of fire fighting were over!

One year later, Neff's mood now is quite different. Inventory and overtime levels have not dropped as much as expected. Customer service is as bad as ever, and complaints of late shipments are too numerous. Convinced that this shouldn't happen with MRP, Neff is having a new round of discussions with key members of the operations department. After all, "a problem well stated is one half solved."

Barbara Jones

Barbara Jones, the P&IM manager, assured Neff that inventory records and BOM files are now being faithfully maintained. "With our regenerative system, there is a new explosion each week. This gives us an updated materials requirements plan and action notices for launching new orders. Some of my group do think we should extend our outputs to get priority and capacity reports. As you know, we decided to get the order-launching capability well established before worrying about such refinements. Besides, most of our problems rest with the purchasing and marketing departments. We experience too many stockouts of purchased parts, even though we have worked closely with I.M. Beyer's group to get realistic lead-time estimates. As for marketing, they keep taking last-minute orders from favorite customers. This plays havoc with our master production schedule."

Bill Hardy

Neff's conversation with Bill Hardy, the shop superintendent, suggested that the informal system is still alive and well. "I'm starting to wonder about this MRP system, even though it looks great on paper. Last week we had hardly any work, and I was forced to overproduce on several orders just to keep everyone busy. This week is just the opposite. So many new orders were released with short fuses that almost everyone will need to work overtime. It's either feast or famine. Why couldn't Jones's group have released some of these orders a couple of weeks ago?

"Another thing is the due dates assigned to each order. They never get updated, but things change pretty quickly around here. Morale is slipping. The only chuckle we get is when I.M. Beyer walks through the plant. Everyone knows that purchasing isn't doing the job. He should come down more frequently. Incidentally, we could use more expediters. We want to start using red tags again."

I. M. Beyer

Neff's conversation with the purchasing manager, I.M. Beyer, was equally disconcerting. "Our buyers are really getting frustrated with this new system. There is no time for creative buying. Almost all of their time is spent following up on late orders. For example, yesterday we received an action notice to bring in 200 units of C130-A in just two weeks. We need three months of lead time for this item! We tried both possible suppliers, but they said that a delivery in two weeks was impossible. What are Jones's planners doing? The perplexing thing is that the planned lead time in the inventory record for C130-A is correctly stated as 12 weeks. Doesn't MRP offset for lead time?

"It is getting to the point that I avoid trips to the plant. Everyone out there seems to think that we are the cause of their problems."

QUESTIONS

1. Discuss what is wrong at King Manufacturing. Is the problem with the system itself or how it is being used?
2. What steps should Neff and others take to find the pot of gold at the end of the rainbow?

SELECTED REFERENCES

Aquilano, Nicholas J., and Dwight E. Smith. "A Formal Set of Algorithms for Project Scheduling with Critical Path Scheduling/Material Requirements Planning." *Journal of Operations Management*, vol. 1, no. 2 (November 1980), pp. 57–67.

Benton, W.C., and D. Clay Whybark. "Material Requirements Planning (MRP) and Purchase Discounts." *Journal of Operations Management*, vol. 2, no. 2 (February 1982), pp. 137–143.

Biggs, Joseph R., Chan K. Hahn, and Peter A. Pinto. "Performance of Lot-Sizing Rules in an MRP System with Different Operating Conditions." *Academy of Management Review*, vol. 5, no. 1 (1980), pp. 89–96.

Blackburn, J., and R. Millen. "Improved Heuristics for Multi-Stage Requirements Planning Systems." *Management Science*, vol. 28, no. 1 (January 1982).

Carlson, J.M. "The Control of Change in a Net Change MRP Environment." *Proceedings of the 23rd Annual Conference*, American Production & Inventory Control Society, Falls Church, Va., October 1980, pp. 177–181.

Cerveny, Robert P., and Lawrence W. Scott. "A Survey of MRP Implementation." *Production and Inventory Management Journal*, vol. 30, no. 3 (1989), pp. 31–34.

Graves, S.C. "Multi-Stage Lot Sizing: An Iterative Procedure." In L. Schwarz, ed., *Multi-level Production/Inventory Systems: Theory and Practice*. New York: North-Holland, 1981.

Greene, Alice H. "MRP 96—Getting Another Perspective." *P&IM Review with APICS News* (November 1988), pp. 26–27.

Haddock, Jorge, and Donald E. Hubicki. "Which Lot-Sizing Techniques Are Used in Material Requirements Planning?" *Production and Inventory Management Journal*, vol. 30, no. 3 (1989), pp. 53–56.

Harl, Johannes E., and Larry P. Ritzman. "A Heuristic Algorithm for Capacity Sensitive Lot Sizing." *Journal of Operations Management*, vol. 5, no. 3 (May 1985), pp. 309–326.

Honeywell, Inc. *Manufacturing IMS/66 (Extended) Systems Handbook*, DE80, rev. 1, June 1977.

International Business Machines Corporation. *Communications Oriented Production Information and Control Systems*, Publications G320-1974–G320-1981.

Jacobs, F.R. "The OPT Scheduling System: A Review of a New Production Scheduling System." *Production and Inventory Management*, vol. 24, no. 3 (1983).

Miller, Jeffrey G., and Linda G. Sprague. "Behind the Growth in Material Requirements Planning." *Harvard Business Review* (September–October 1975), pp. 83–91.

Orlicky, Joseph. *Material Requirements Planning*. New York: McGraw-Hill, 1975.

Plossl, George W. *Manufacturing Controls—The Last Frontier for Profits*. Reston, Va.: Reston Publishing Company, 1973.

Ritzman, Larry P., Barry E. King, and Lee J. Krajewski. "Manufacturing Performance—Pulling the Right Levers." *Harvard Business Review* (March–April 1984), pp. 143–152.

Ritzman, Larry P., and Lee J. Krajewski. "Comparison of Material Requirements Planning and Reorder Point Systems." In Haluk Bekiroglu, ed., *Simulation for Production and Inventory Control*. La Jolla, Calif.: Society for Computer Simulation, 1983.

Schroeder, Roger G., John C. Anderson, Sharon E. Tupy, and Edna M. White. "A Study of MRP Benefits and Costs." *Journal of Operations Management*, vol. 2, no. 1 (October 1981), pp. 1–9.

Steinberg, Earle E., Basheer Khumawala, and Richard Scamell. "Requirements Planning Systems in the Health Care Environment." *Journal of Operations Management*, vol. 2, no. 4 (August 1982), pp. 251–259.

Steinberg, Earle E., William B. Lee, and Basheer Khumawala. "A Requirements Planning System for the Space Shuttle Operations Schedule." *Journal of Operations Management*, vol. 1, no. 2 (November 1980), pp. 69–76.

"The Trick of Material Requirements Planning." *Business Week*, June 4, 1979.

White, Edna M., John C. Anderson, Roger G. Schroeder, and Sharon E. Tupy. "A Study of the MRP Implementation Process." *Journal of Operations Management*, vol. 2, no. 3 (May 1982), pp. 145–153.

Whybark, D. Clay. "MRP: A Profitable Concept for Distribution." *Research Issues in Logistics*, 1975, pp. 82–93.

Wight, Oliver W. "MRP II: Manufacturing Resource Planning." *Modern Materials Handling* (September 1979).

Chapter 17

JUST-IN-TIME SYSTEMS

Key Questions from Managers

CHAPTER OUTLINE

Under what circumstances could we use a just-in-time system effectively?

What service environment is best suited for the implementation of JIT?

What can we do to make employees more receptive to the changes associated with JIT?

Can we make all types of production and inventory management systems work equally well in a given environment?

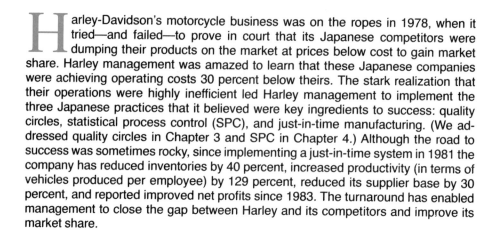

H arley-Davidson's motorcycle business was on the ropes in 1978, when it tried—and failed—to prove in court that its Japanese competitors were dumping their products on the market at prices below cost to gain market share. Harley management was amazed to learn that these Japanese companies were achieving operating costs 30 percent below theirs. The stark realization that their operations were highly inefficient led Harley management to implement the three Japanese practices that it believed were key ingredients to success: quality circles, statistical process control (SPC), and just-in-time manufacturing. (We addressed quality circles in Chapter 3 and SPC in Chapter 4.) Although the road to success was sometimes rocky, since implementing a just-in-time system in 1981 the company has reduced inventories by 40 percent, increased productivity (in terms of vehicles produced per employee) by 129 percent, reduced its supplier base by 30 percent, and reported improved net profits since 1983. The turnaround has enabled management to close the gap between Harley and its competitors and improve its market share.

The Harley-Davidson story is not unusual. Just-in-time systems require major changes to a company's traditional operating practices, and often it is a major emotional event (such as being faced with going out of business or closing a plant) that galvanizes management and labor to work together and effect the needed changes. Just-in-time systems are more than inventory control systems; they involve process design issues as well as inventory and scheduling issues. In this chapter we will identify the key elements of just-in-time systems and discuss how they are employed in manufacturing as well as service operations. We will also address the strategic implications of such systems and some of the implementation issues of which companies should be aware. Finally, we will discuss the issue of choosing the appropriate production and inventory management system for a given environment.

ELEMENTS OF JUST-IN-TIME SYSTEMS

Just-in-time (JIT) systems are designed to produce or deliver goods or services as needed, using minimal inventories. JIT is actually a philosophy that focuses on reducing inefficiencies and unproductive time in the production process. Embodied in the JIT system are the concepts of continuous improvement and total quality control, as well as employee involvement and inventory reduction. JIT is clearly a comprehensive system, one known by many different names, such as "zero inventory," "stockless production" (Hewlett-Packard), "material as needed" (Harley-Davidson), or "continuous flow manufacturing" (IBM). In this section we will discuss the following elements of JIT systems: material flow discipline, small lot sizes, short setup times, the uniform master production schedule, standardization of components and work methods, consistent high quality, close supplier ties, flexible work force, product focus, preventive maintenance, and continuous improvement.

Material Flow Discipline

Two basic disciplines govern the flow of materials: the pull method and the push method. To differentiate between these two systems, consider the production system at a McDonald's restaurant. Let's focus on one particular product, the Quarter Pounder. One person is responsible for producing this burger. Burger patties must be fried; buns toasted and then dressed with ketchup, pickles, mayonnaise, lettuce, and cheese; and the patties inserted into buns and put on a tray. Another person takes the tray and places the burgers into containers and restocks the inventory. Inventories must be kept low because any burgers left unsold after seven minutes must be destroyed.

The system we just described consists of two work stations: the burger maker and the final assembler. The flow of materials is from the burger maker to the final assembler. One way to manage this flow is by using the **push method.** With this method, management schedules the receipt of all raw materials (such as meat, buns, and condiments) and authorizes the start of production, all in advance of Quarter Pounder needs. The burger maker might start production of 24 burgers (the size of the griddle) and, when completed, push them along to the final assembler, where they might have to wait until she is ready for them. She may have to assemble several other products as well.

The other way to manage the flow between the burger maker and the final assembler is to use the **pull method.** This is the method used by just-in-time systems. With the pull method, the final assembler checks the inventory level of burgers and, when they are almost depleted, orders six more. The burger maker produces the six burgers and gives the tray to the final assembler, who completes the assembly and places the burgers in the inventory for sale. Of the two methods, the pull method is better for the production of burgers. The two workers must coordinate the two work stations closely to keep inventory low, primarily because of the seven-minute time limit. The final assembler asks for burgers only as needed. The production of burgers is a highly repetitive process, setup times and process times are low, and the flow of materials is well defined. There is no need to produce to anticipated needs more than a few minutes ahead.

In manufacturing, both methods of material flow are prevalent. Firms utilizing just-in-time systems use the pull method because it enables closer control between inventory needs and production at the work stations. These firms tend to have highly repetitive manufacturing processes and well-defined material flows. Other firms use a push method, such as material requirements planning (MRP). For example, job shops producing products in low volumes with low repeatability in the production process tend to use the push method. In this environment a customer order is promised for delivery on some future date. Production is started at the first work station, and pushed ahead to the next one, in anticipation of shipping the completed order on the promised date. MRP works well in such a situation.

Small Lot Sizes

Users of JIT systems maintain inventory in lot sizes as small as possible. Small lot sizes are important for three reasons. First, small lot sizes reduce cycle inventory. Recall from our discussion in Chapter 12 that the average cycle inventory equals $Q/2$, where Q is the lot size. As Q gets smaller, so does cycle inventory. Figure 17.1 shows the effect on cycle inventory of reducing the lot size from 100 to 50, assuming a uniform demand of 10 units per hour; cycle inventory is cut in half. Second, small lot sizes help cut lead times, which in turn cut pipeline (WIP) inventory because the total processing time at each work station for large lots is greater. Also, a large lot often has to wait longer to be processed because the work station it needs is working on another large lot. In addition, for rework of defective lots, large lots require more time.

Finally, small lots help achieve a uniform workload on the operating system. Whereas large lots tend to represent large chunks of processing time and therefore hinder scheduling uniform loads on the work stations, small lots can be juggled more effectively and thereby enable schedulers to utilize capacities more efficiently. In addition, work stations can more effectively accommodate mixed-model production (more than one item) by reducing queue times for production. We will return to this point when we discuss uniform master production schedules.

Short Setup Times

Despite the many advantages of small lot sizes, none will be realized unless setup times are minimal. Reduced lot sizes bring the disadvantage of increased setup frequency. In operations where the setup times are normally low, as in the McDonald's example, it is common sense to use small lots. However, in fabrication operations with sizable setup times, increasing the frequency of setups carries the potential penalty of increased underutilization of human and

FIGURE 17.1

Comparison of Small and Large Lot Sizes

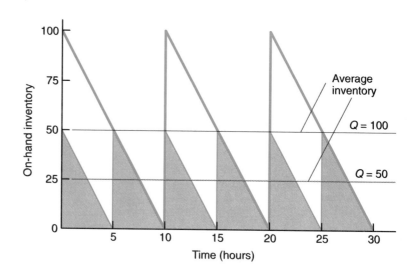

*E*xterior and interior body panels for the Accord are produced on this press line at Honda's Marysville, Ohio, plant, where single-digit changeover times for the dies are achieved.

capital resources. These operations must reduce setup times to realize the benefits of small-lot production.

Achieving low setup times often requires close cooperation among engineering, management, and labor. For example, changing dies on large presses to form sheet metal automobile parts can take three to four hours. Not so at the Honda automobile plant in Marysville, Ohio, where four stamping lines—two tandem press lines and two state-of-the-art transfer presses—stamp all the exterior and major interior body panels for Accord production. The Honda team members in the stamping department worked on ways to reduce the changeover time for the massive dies. The result was impressive: A complete change of dies now takes less than eight minutes, even for the giant 2400-ton press. But nobody is satisfied yet. The teams that actually set up the presses continue to seek improvement and, in fact, compete as teams to reduce changeover time. This same sort of competition carries over to other machines in the plant as well. The Japanese have a term (or goal) for setup time reduction called **single-digit setup,** which means to have setup times less than 10 minutes. It utilizes a variety of techniques, including conveyors for die storage, cranes for moving large dies, simpler dies, machine controls, microcomputers to automatically feed and position work, and changeover preparation while the current job is being processed.

The Uniform Master Production Schedule

As with MRP, the master production schedule drives the system. That is, the requirements and policies established at the MPS level have a direct impact on the daily requirements for the JIT system. The JIT system works best, however, if the load on individual work stations is relatively uniform on a daily basis. Uniform loads can be achieved by assembling the same type and number of units each day, thus creating a uniform daily demand at all work stations. Capacity planning, which recognizes capacity constraints at critical work stations, and line balancing are used to develop the monthly assembly schedule.

For example, at Toyota there may be a need to produce 4500 Corollas per week for the next month, requiring two full shifts, five days per week. This means that 900 Corollas, or 450 per shift, must be produced each day. Three models of Corollas are produced: four-door sedans (S), two-door coupes (C), and wagons (W). Suppose that Toyota needs 200 sedans, 150 coupes, and 100 wagons to satisfy market demand. To produce 450 units in one shift of 480 minutes, the line must produce a Corolla every 480/450 = 1.067 minutes.

There are many ways to devise the master production schedule for the Corollas. Table 17.1 shows three options. First, with big-lot production, all daily requirements of a model are produced in one batch. The sequence of 200 S's, 150 C's, and 100 W's would be repeated once per shift. Not only would these big lots increase the average cycle inventory level, they would also cause lumpy requirements on all the work stations feeding the assembly line.

The second option uses **mixed-model assembly** in smaller lot sizes. Note that the production requirements are in the ratio of 4 sedans to 3 coupes to 2 wagons, found by dividing the model production requirements by the greatest common divisor, 50. If the Toyota planner develops a production cycle consisting of 9 units, 4 of which are sedans, 3 are coupes, and 2 are wagons, the cycle would have to be completed in 9(1.067) = 9.60 minutes. In addition, the cycle would have to be repeated 50 times per shift [50(9.60 min) = 480 min]. Consequently, with these requirements per shift for each model and adequate capacity, Toyota's planner can balance the mixed-model assembly line for the month's production schedule. The smaller lots, moreover, impose smaller, more frequent requirements on the work stations feeding the final assembly line and therefore smooth the load on these work stations.

The ultimate option uses lot sizes of one unit. Table 17.1 shows a sequence that, if repeated 50 times per shift, would achieve the same total output as the other options. This option is feasible only if the setup times are very short. The sequence generates a steady rate of component requirements for the various models and allows the use of small lot sizes at the feeder work stations. Consequently, the capacity requirements at those stations are greatly

TABLE 17.1 / Lot Size Options for a JIT Master Production Schedule

Option	Comment
Big-Lot Production	
S = 200 W = 100 C = 150	Do once per shift; high cycle inventories; lumpy requirements on feeder work stations
Small-Lot Production	
S = 4 C = 3 W = 2	Do 50 times per shift; low cycle inventories
Single-Unit Lot Sizes	
S–W–S–C–S–C–S–W–C	Do 50 times per shift; lowest cycle inventory; most uniform load on feeder work stations

smoothed. These requirements can be compared to actual capacities during the planning phase, and modifications to the production cycle, production requirements, or capacities can be made as necessary.

Standardization of Components and Work Methods

In Chapter 12 we discussed how the standardization of components, or part commonality, increases repeatability. For example, a firm producing 10 products from 1000 different components could design its products so they consist of only 100 different components. The daily requirements for each of the 100 components would be greater than for each of the 1000 components. Because the requirements per component increase, so does repeatability; that is, each worker performs a given standardized task or work method more often each day. Productivity tends to increase because, with increased repetition, the workers learn to do the task more efficiently. Standardization of components and work methods is important to the high-productivity, low-inventory objectives of JIT systems.

Consistent, High Quality

Scrap and rework are inconsistent with the uniform flow of materials that JIT strives to maintain. JIT systems control quality at the source, with workers acting as their own quality inspectors. All the techniques of total quality control (TQC) are appropriate for JIT systems (see Chapters 3 and 4). On discovery, defective units are returned immediately to the worker responsible for them. And workers are encouraged to stop the entire assembly line if a quality problem arises.

Stopping the line, however, is a costly action that brings a problem to everyone's attention. Management must realize the enormous responsibility this places on the hourly workers and must prepare them properly, as one GM division soon learned. When Buick City began using JIT in 1985 management

*T*he Le Sabre production line at Buick City is an example of successful implementation of JIT.

authorized its workers to stop the production line at their stations by pulling a cord—a practice the Japanese call *andon*. GM also eliminated production line inspectors and cut the number of supervisors in half. The workers were not prepared for that responsibility; productivity and quality took a nosedive. The paint on Le Sabres wasn't shiny enough. The seams weren't straight. The top of the dashboard had a wave that was not planned. Management, labor, and engineering formed a team to correct the problems. Work methods were changed, and the *andon* system was modified to include a yellow warning cord so that workers could call for help without stopping the line. Today, the Buick Le Sabre exemplifies top-notch quality. According to surveys by J.D. Power & Associates of problems reported in the first three months, the Le Sabre placed sixth out of 120 domestic and foreign models in 1990.

Close Supplier Ties

Because JIT systems operate with very low levels of inventory, stock shipments are more numerous and must arrive in a timely fashion. A contract might require a supplier to deliver goods to a factory as often as several times per day. The supplier of automobile seats to the Honda of America plant in Marysville, Ohio, makes up to 50 deliveries per day, for example. When a specific model (Accord or Civic), color, and trim option begins assembly, the information is transmitted via electronic data interchange (EDI) to the supplier, who then has two hours to get the correct seat to the assembly line. Early shipments cause added inventory costs. Late shipments, poor quality, or short shipments cause stockouts. Each minute an automobile assembly plant is stopped because of material shortages costs as much as $20,000. Because JIT systems are so dependent on good supplier performance, it is no wonder that world-class JIT users work very closely with their suppliers. Manufacturers' relationships with suppliers focus on three areas: reducing the number of suppliers, using suppliers that are geographically closer, and improving relations with suppliers.

Typically, one of the first actions undertaken when implementing a JIT system is to pare the number of suppliers. Xerox, for example, reduced its number of suppliers from 5000 to just 300. This puts a lot of pressure on these suppliers to deliver high-quality components on time. To compensate, world-class JIT users extend their contracts with these suppliers and give them firm advance-order information. In addition, they include their suppliers in the early phases of product design, to avoid problems with purchased components and parts after production has begun. They also work with their suppliers' vendors, trying to achieve JIT inventory flows throughout the entire supplier chain.

Manufacturers using JIT generally find themselves using suppliers close at hand. For years the Big Three automakers have been pushing suppliers to relocate their plants closer to the auto assembly plants, but only with moderate success. When GM located its Saturn complex in Tennessee, many suppliers were clustered nearby. Harley-Davidson, when reducing its number of suppliers, gave preference to those closer to its plants—for example, three fourths of the suppliers for the Milwaukee engine plant are located within a 175-mile radius. As such, the company has reduced the need for safety stocks. However, not all companies luxuriate in having their suppliers close by. These companies must have a finely tuned distribution system. For example, New United Motor Manufacturing Incorporated (NUMMI), the joint venture between GM and Toyota located in California, has suppliers in Indiana, Ohio, and Michigan. Through a carefully coordinated system involving trains and piggyback truck trailers, each day enough parts for exactly one day's production are delivered to the company's doorstep.

JIT users also find that improving supplier relations is essential. Perhaps the biggest mistake companies make when implementing JIT is to treat this system as a way of getting their suppliers to hold the inventories. This attitude strains whatever good relations the company has with its suppliers. The JIT philosophy is to look for ways to improve efficiency and reduce inventories throughout the supplier chain. If a company insists that a supplier hold large amounts of inventory to satisfy JIT schedules, one of three things typically happens—all of them bad: The price of the purchased item increases, quality decreases so the supplier can afford to hold the inventory, or the supplier declines to renew the contract. The long-term effects of pushing inventory on suppliers are detrimental to everyone in the supplier chain.

Flexible Work Force

A work force is flexible if its workers can perform more than one job. When the skill levels required to perform most tasks are low—at a McDonald's restaurant, for instance—there is a high degree of flexibility in the work force, particularly after a little training. As skill levels increase, however, it becomes more and more difficult to shift workers to other jobs without extensive, costly training. Nevertheless, flexibility can be very beneficial. It can help a firm absorb shocks without resorting to inventory buffers—an aspect important to the uniform flow of JIT systems. Workers can be shifted from various work stations to help relieve bottlenecks as they arise. Or they can step in and do the job for those on vacation. As you might imagine, assigning workers to tasks they don't usually perform decreases efficiency. Consequently, frequent rotation of workers is not typically a good idea. Nonetheless, some rotation is desirable to relieve boredom and to refresh worker flexibility.

Product Focus

A product focus can reduce the frequency of setups. If volumes are high enough, groups of machines and workers can be organized into a product layout (see Chapter 10) to eliminate setups entirely. By processing a small number of very similar products on the same dedicated equipment, machines can be preset to the proper specifications. If volume is insufficient to keep a line of similar products busy, group technology can be used. This technique manufactures components with common attributes and enough collective volume on what is essentially a small production line. Changeovers from components in one product family to the next in the same family are minimal.

Another tactic is to use the one-worker, multiple machines (OWMM) approach, which is essentially a one-person line. One worker operates several machines, with each machine advancing the process a step at a time. Because the same product is made repeatably, setups are eliminated. For example, in a McDonald's restaurant the person preparing fish sandwiches uses the OWMM approach. When the signal is given to produce more fish sandwiches, the employee puts the fish patties into the fish fryer and sets the timer. Then while the fish are frying, he puts the buns into the steamer. When the buns are finished, he puts them on a tray and dresses them with condiments. When the fish patties are ready, he inserts them into the buns. The completed sandwiches are placed on the shelf for the final assembler to package for the customer. Then the cycle repeats itself.

A final comment: Automation plays a big role in JIT systems and is a key to low-cost production. Sakichi Toyoda, the founder of Toyota, once said, "Whenever there is money, invest it into machinery." Money freed up because of JIT inventory reductions can be invested in automation to further reduce costs. The benefits, of course, are greater profits or greater market share (because prices can be reduced), or both. Automation should be planned carefully, however. Many companies believed that if some automation is good, more is better. That is not always the case. When GM initiated Buick City, for example, it installed 250 robots, some with vision systems to install windshields. The robots, unfortunately, skipped black cars because they could not see them; but new software eventually solved the problem. All told, 30 of the plant's robots were mothballed either because humans performed better or Buick purchased too many robots.

Preventive Maintenance

Because automation is a big factor in JIT systems, preventive maintenance is very important. Any unplanned machine downtime can be very disruptive because JIT emphasizes finely tuned material flows and very little buffer inventory between work stations. Preventive maintenance can reduce the frequency and duration of machine downtime. One tactic allows several hours between shifts for routine maintenance activities. Then, once the technician has the machine apart and has replaced normal maintenance items and lubricated as needed, tests can be taken on other parts that might need replacement. At this stage, replacement is easier and quicker than if the machine fails during production. Of course, each machine need not go through a complete maintenance teardown every day. The machines are put on a schedule that balances the cost of the preventive maintenance program against the risks and costs of machine failure.

Another tactic is to make workers responsible for routinely maintaining their own equipment. The goal is to develop employee pride in keeping their machines in top condition. This tactic, however, is typically limited to general housekeeping chores, minor lubrication, and adjustments. High-tech machines need trained specialists. Nonetheless, even these simple duties go a long way toward improving the performance of machines.

Continuous Improvement

One of the hallmarks of world-class manufacturing is continuous improvement. Management should always be searching for ways to get better, and JIT systems spotlight areas that need improvement. However, the road to world-class manufacturing can be long and arduous.

Companies such as Toyota have spent as many as ten years perfecting their systems. The companies worked at reducing inventory levels on a trial-and-error basis. Figure 17.2 characterizes the philosophy behind continuous improvement with JIT systems. The water level represents the inventory level, including cycle, safety stock, and work-in-process inventories. When the water level is high enough, the ship passes over the rocks, symbolizing good customer service. To a manager of a JIT system, clear sailing implies the possibility of too much inventory and waste, so the manager gives the order to reduce the inventory. Lowering the water level ultimately means that the ship will hit a rock, which represents one of the many problems encountered in manufacturing. This step is intentional because the problem becomes obvious, and workers, supervisors, engineers, and analysts make every effort to demolish the exposed rock.

The methods for demolishing the rocks involve improvements in the elements of JIT we have discussed in this section. Referring to Fig. 17.2, too much scrap might require improving work methods, quality training for employees, and supplier quality. Capacity imbalances might focus attention on the master production schedule and the flexibility of the work force. Unreliable deliveries suggest improvement is needed in the relationships with suppliers

FIGURE 17.2

Continuous Improvement with JIT Systems

through more cooperation and exchanges of information. Alternatively, it might mean that those suppliers should be replaced. Although there are many other rocks companies could encounter, the procedure of periodically stressing the system to identify the rocks and focusing on the elements of the JIT system is at the heart of continuous improvement.

For example, the Kawasaki plant in Nebraska periodically cuts safety stocks to almost zero. Problems are exposed, recorded, and later assigned as improvement projects. After the tops of the rocks are shaved off, inventories are permanently cut. This is the trial-and-error process that the Japanese, for example, have used to shape their manufacturing environment to provide more efficient manufacturing operations. JIT is an excellent tool to expose inefficient practices. Managerial Practice 17.1 describes how one U.S. company used JIT to gain continuous improvements in operations.

THE KANBAN SYSTEM

One of the most publicized JIT systems is kanban, developed by Toyota. **Kanban,** meaning card or visible record in Japanese, refers to cards used to control the flow of production through a factory. The most basic kanban system uses single cards. In this system users attach a card to each container of items that have been produced. This card represents a percentage of the daily requirements for an item. When the user of the parts empties a container, the card is removed from the container and put on a receiving post. The empty container is taken to the storage area. The card is ultimately sequenced on a production-ordering post with the cards for other items to be fabricated. The card is put back on a container when production commences at the fabrication cell. Then containers filled with parts are returned to a storage area. The user of the parts retrieves the container with the card still attached, and so on.

Toyota uses a two-card system, which permits more control over withdrawal quantities. Although there are many types of cards, the two main ones used by Toyota are the withdrawal card and the production-order card. The withdrawal card specifies the item and quantity the user of the item should withdraw from the producer of the item, as well as the stocking locations for both the user and producer. The production-order card specifies the item and production quantity to be produced, the materials required and where to find them, and where to store the finished item. Material cannot be withdrawn without a withdrawal card, and production cannot begin without a production-order card. The cards are attached to containers when production commences. Each container holds approximately 10 percent of the daily requirements for the item. Figure 17.3 illustrates the two-card system. To simplify our discussion, we will refer to a fabrication process that feeds an assembly line. Keep in mind, though, that the system works for any process that feeds another process. In all, seven steps are required, involving two loops—one for each type of card:

> *Step 1.* Accumulated empty containers, with withdrawal cards attached, are taken from the assembly line to the storage area. Withdrawal cards are detached from the containers.

Continuous Improvement at
Northern Telecom

Northern Telecom, which began operations only eight years after Alexander Graham Bell invented the telephone, produces central office switching equipment, transmission equipment, and private business exchanges (PBX) for the telephone industry. In the late 1970s Northern Telecom entered an extended, vigorous growth period when it introduced the first fully digital switch. By 1984 sales were $2.5 billion, an increase of 1200 percent from eight years before. The work force increased by 1500 employees, and for three consecutive years, output doubled. Then, in 1985, competitors introduced fully digital switches of their own and pressure increased to produce high-quality, more-sophisticated products at low cost. Although Northern Telecom was coping with the new competitive environment and had already implemented a JIT production philosophy in some plants, management decided that long-term success required a complete reexamination of the production process. Continuous improvements were needed along many dimensions. Three of the areas the company addressed first were manufacturing process improvement, new product introduction and change, and procurement.

Manufacturing process improvement. As its first step Northern Telecom introduced total quality control (TQC), which involved training in quality control for supervisors and line employees and empowering employees to shut down the line when quality problems surfaced (*andon* system). Manufacturing lot sizes were reduced, and the line was instructed to pull material as needed, with a target lot size of one unit, rather than push a week's worth of inventory to the line.

New product introduction and change. By introducing cross-functional product teams, Northern Telecom reduced the time required to bring a new product to market in some divisions by as much as 50 percent. The teams consisted of representatives of various functions, including design, manufacturing, and marketing. While a product was still in the design phase, the team shared ideas about what is commercially important or difficult to manufacture. Consequently, problems were resolved earlier than before. The teams helped smooth the normally rocky process involved in making design changes.

Procurement. Northern Telecom reduced its suppliers from 9400 in 1984 to 2500 in 1988. To accomplish this, one division designed a certification program whereby suppliers had to prove they could meet very ambitious certification standards. Today the entire company uses the program. Some suppliers had to make significant changes to their operations to win Northern Telecom's business. In addition, the company worked closely with its suppliers to ensure that quality standards were met and would then pull materials directly from successful suppliers to the assembly line. This effort reduced the receiving cycle time from three weeks to just four hours, the incoming inspection staff from 47 to 24, and problems on the shop floor caused by defective materials by 97 percent.

The following table shows how continuous improvement efforts at Northern Telecom resulted in significant operational benefits. The data are percentages relative to the year the first measure was taken. For example, the manufacturing cycle time for central office equipment in 1989 was only 25 percent of that in 1986. All percentages are approximate.

Performance Measure	Percentage				
	1985	1986	1987	1988	1989
Manufacturing cycle time:					
Central office switches		100%	48%	27%	25%
Transmission equipment		100	50	37	30
PBX		100	49	33	30
Aggregate inventory	100	100	73	72	70
Operations overhead	100	80	75	75	65

Source: Roy Merrills, "How Northern Telecom Competes on Time," *Harvard Business Review* (July–August 1989), pp. 108–114.

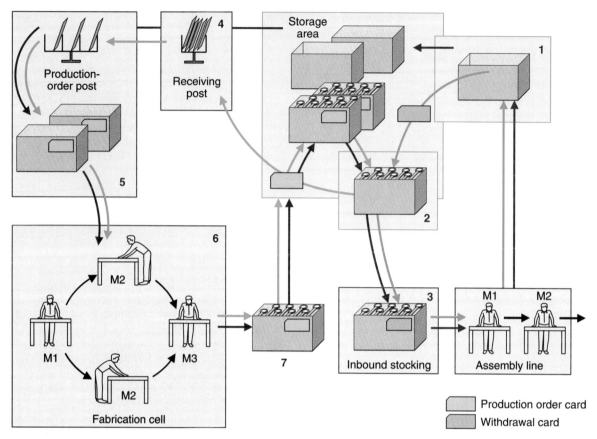

FIGURE 17.3   Two-Card Kanban System

Step 2. The empty containers are exchanged for full ones. The production-order card on each full container is detached and placed on the receiving post.

Step 3. The contents of the full containers are checked against the specifications on the withdrawal card, and if satisfactory, a withdrawal card is attached to each full container. The containers are moved to the inbound stocking location of the assembly line. This step completes the loop for the withdrawal card.

Step 4. The production sequence at the fabrication cell begins with the removal of the production-order cards from the receiving post. They are reviewed and sorted before being placed on the production-order post.

Step 5. The parts are produced in the sequence of the production-order cards on the post. Production-order cards are attached to empty containers and taken to the fabrication cell.

Step 6. The production-order card and the container move as a pair through the fabrication process.

Step 7. In the last step the finished units are transported to the storage area to support the production requirements of the assembly line. This completes the loop for the production-order card.

All work stations and suppliers are coordinated in a similar way to provide just-in-time quantities of materials.

General Operating Rules

The operating rules for the two-card system are simple and are designed to facilitate the flow of materials, while maintaining control of inventory levels:

1. Each container must have a card.
2. The assembly line always withdraws materials from the fabrication cell. The fabrication cell never pushes parts to the assembly line because, sooner or later, parts will be supplied that are not yet needed for production.
3. Containers of parts must never be removed from a storage area without an authorizing withdrawal card.
4. The containers should always contain the same number of good parts. The use of nonstandard containers or irregularly filled containers disrupts the production flow of the assembly line.
5. Defective parts should never be passed along to the assembly line. This act would waste not only material but also the time of workers at the downstream work stations who process the defective parts.
6. Total production should not exceed the total amount authorized on the production-order cards in the system. Similarly, the quantity of parts withdrawn by the assembly line should not exceed the total amount authorized on the withdrawal cards in the system.

Determining the Number of Containers (Kanban Card Sets)

The number of authorized containers in a JIT system determines the amount of authorized inventory. Management must make two determinations: (1) the size of the containers and (2) the number of containers flowing back and forth between the supplier station and the user station. The first decision amounts to determining the lot size and may be compared to calculating the economic order quantity (*EOQ*) (see Chapter 13). Some simplified rules can be applied, however. For example, Toyota uses 10 percent of daily demand.

The number of containers flowing back and forth between two stations directly impacts the work-in-process inventory and safety stock. The containers spend some time in production, waiting in a queue, waiting in a storage location, or in transit. Therefore, at any one moment, one container may be in use at the user station, another may be being refilled at the supplier station waiting to be processed, and others may be in transit, in storage, or waiting to be moved around. The key to determining the number of required containers is estimating the average lead time needed to produce a container of parts. The lead time is a function of the processing time per container at the supplier station and the waiting time at the production process and for materials handling. The number of containers needed to support the user station equals the average demand during the lead time plus some safety stock to account for unexpected circumstances, divided by the size of one container. Because a container cannot be withdrawn from storage without a withdrawal card, and its replacement cannot be produced without a production-order card, determining the number of containers amounts to determining the number of kanban card sets (one of each type per container). Therefore, the number of kanban card sets is

$$k = \frac{\text{Average demand during lead time plus safety stock}}{\text{Size of container}}$$

$$= \frac{d(\bar{w} + \bar{p})(1 + \alpha)}{c}$$

where
k = number of production-order/withdrawal card sets for a given part

d = expected daily demand for the part, in units

$\bar{w}$ = average waiting time during the production process plus materials handling time per container in fractions of a day

$\bar{p}$ = average processing time per container in fractions of a day

c = quantity in a standard container of the part

α = a policy variable that reflects the efficiency of the work stations producing and using the part (Toyota uses a value no more than 10 percent)

The kanban system allows management to fine-tune the flow of materials in the system in a straightforward way. For example, removing card sets from the system reduces the number of authorized containers of the part, which results in reducing the inventory of the part.

The container quantity c and the efficiency factor α are also variables that management can use to control inventory. Adjusting c changes the lot sizes, and adjusting α changes the amount of safety stock. The kanban system is actually a special form of the base-stock system that we described in Chapter 13. In this case, the stocking level is $d(\bar{w} + \bar{p})(1 + \alpha)$ and the order quantity is fixed at c units. Each time a container of parts is removed from the base stock, authorization is given to replace it.

Application 17.1   Determining the Appropriate Number of Kanban Card Sets

The Westerville Auto Parts Company produces rocker-arm assemblies for use in the steering and suspension systems of four-wheel drive trucks. A typical container of parts spends 0.02 day in processing and 0.08 day in materials handling and waiting during its manufacturing cycle. The daily demand for the part is 2000 units. Management feels that demand for the rocker-arm assembly is uncertain enough to warrant a safety stock equivalent of 10 percent of its authorized inventory.

1. If there are 22 parts in each container, how many kanban card sets (production-order and withdrawal cards) should be authorized?
2. Suppose that a proposal to revise the plant layout would cut materials handling and waiting time per container to 0.06 day. How many card sets would be needed?

Solution The two calculations are as follows:

1. If d = 2000 units/day, $\bar{p}$ = 0.02 day, α = 0.10, $\bar{w}$ = 0.08 day, and c = 22 units, then

$$k = \frac{2000(0.08 + 0.02)(1.10)}{22} = \frac{220}{22} = 10 \text{ card sets}$$

2. If d = 2000 units/day, $\bar{p}$ = 0.02 day, α = 0.10, $\bar{w}$ = 0.06 day, and c = 22 units, then

$$k = \frac{2000(0.06 + 0.02)(1.10)}{22} = \frac{176}{22} = 8 \text{ card sets}$$

The average lead time per container is given as ($\bar{w} + \bar{p}$). With a lead time of 0.10 day, 10 card sets are needed. However, if the improved facility layout reduces the materials handling time and waiting time ($\bar{w}$) to 0.06 day, only 8 card sets are needed. The maximum authorized inventory of the rocker-arm assembly is kc units. Thus in calculation (1) the maximum authorized inventory is 220 units but in calculation (2) only 176 units. Reducing $\bar{w}$ by 25 percent has reduced the inventory of the part by 20 percent.

Other Kanban Signals

Cards are not the only way to signal the need for more production of a part. Other, less formal, methods are possible.

Container System. Sometimes it is possible to use the container itself as a signal device: An empty container signals the need to fill it. The amount of inventory of the part is adjusted by adding or removing containers. This system works well when the container is specially designed for a part and no other parts could accidentally be put in it. Such would be the case when the container is actually a pallet or fixture used to position the part during precision processing.

Containerless Systems. Systems requiring no containers have been devised. In assembly line operations, operators having their own workbench areas put completed units on painted squares, one unit per square. Each painted square represents a container, and the number of painted squares on each operator's bench is calculated to balance the line flow. When the subsequent user removes a unit from one of the producer's squares, the empty square signals the need to produce another unit.

McDonald's also uses a containerless system. A command from the manager or the final assembler starts production, or the number of hamburgers in the ramp itself signals the need. Either way, the customer dictates production.

JIT IN SERVICES

The just-in-time philosophy can be applied to the production of services just as it can to manufacturing. We have already discussed some of the elements of JIT used in a McDonald's restaurant. What service environments are most amenable to the use of JIT? Generally, service environments are likely candidates for JIT if their operations are repetitive, have reasonably high volume, and deal with tangible items such as sandwiches, mail, checks, bills, or letters. In other words, the services must involve "manufacturing-like" operations. That isn't to say that other services such as haircutting, which involves a high degree of customization, cannot use one or more JIT elements in their operations. We would be stretching the point, however, if we claimed they use JIT in a significant way. Nonetheless, many service environments can take advantage of JIT.

One service environment particularly amenable to the application of JIT is that of administration (Billesbach and Schniederjans, 1989). Administrative activities, including scheduling, billing, order taking, accounting, and financial tasks, are applicable to many of the elements of JIT we have already discussed. However, one administrative element, continuous improvement, takes a slightly different approach here than in a manufacturing environment. While it is true that continuous improvement means that employees and managers continue to seek ways to improve operations just as they would in a manufacturing setting, the mechanics differ for highlighting the areas needing improvement. In manufacturing, for example, managers reduce in-process inventory levels by removing kanban cards, thereby stressing the system by exposing the "rocks" (see Fig. 17.2). In an administrative setting, a common approach used by managers to place stress on the system is reducing the number of employees doing a particular operation or series of operations until the process begins to slow or come to a halt. The "rocks" can be identified, and ways for overcoming the problems can be explored. Managerial Practice 17.2 shows how the JIT philosophy was implemented at a bank.

STRATEGIC IMPLICATIONS OF JIT

An effective operations strategy links major operations decisions to produce a consistent whole. When corporate strategy centers on dramatic improvements in inventory turnover and labor productivity, just-in-time systems can be the solution. JIT is also an integral part of strategies based on time-based competition because it focuses on cutting throughput times (see Chapter 2). Nonetheless, the implementation of JIT systems results in decision linkages such as those summarized in Table 17.2. We have already discussed most of the decision areas depicted in the table, so in this section we will focus on competitive priorities and positioning strategy, as well as the overall benefits of JIT.

TABLE 17.2 / Typical Decision Linkages in JIT Systems

Decision Area	Choice
Inventory	Minimize lot sizes and safety stock.
Competitive priorities	Emphasize low cost and consistent quality.
Positioning strategy	Have a product focus.
Process design	Minimize setup times. Reduce the frequency of setups through product layouts, group technology, and one worker, multiple machines. Automate as much as possible.
Work-force management	Seek a flexible, cooperative work force through job enlargement, consensus management, and training.
Maintenance	Minimize the frequency and duration of breakdowns.
Materials management	Have a cooperative orientation with suppliers.
Master production scheduling	Maintain the same daily output rate for a whole month.
Quality	Put quality control at the source.

Competitive Priorities

Low cost and consistent quality are the priorities emphasized most often under JIT. Superior features (Rolls-Royce quality) or volume flexibility is emphasized less. The ability to provide product variety depends on the degree of flexibility designed into the production system. For example, mixed-model automobile assembly lines allow variety in output from the standpoint of color, options, and even body style. Production to customized, individual orders, however, is usually not attempted with a JIT system. Generally, end items are standards rather than specials, preproduced to inventory in support of a shipping schedule. The erratic demand and last-minute rush jobs of customized orders do not link well with a system designed to produce at a constant daily rate utilizing low inventory buffers.

Positioning Strategy

A product focus is chosen to achieve high-volume, low-cost production. Workers and machines are organized around product flows, arranged to conform to the necessary sequence of work operations. With line flows, a unit finished at one station goes almost immediately to the next station, thereby reducing manufacturing lead time and inventory. Process repetition makes opportunities for methods improvement more visible.

Operational Benefits

Table 17.3 lists some of the operational benefits of JIT systems. One goal is to drive setup times so low that production of one unit or a part becomes economical. Although this goal is rarely achieved, its focus is still on small-lot production. In addition, constant attention is given to cutting safety stock and WIP

TABLE 17.3 / Operational Benefits of Just-In-Time Systems

• Reduce space requirements.	• Increase equipment utilization.
• Reduce inventory investment in purchased parts, raw materials, work in process, and finished goods.	• Reduce paperwork and require only simple planning systems.
• Reduce manufacturing lead times.	• Set valid priorities for production scheduling.
• Increase the productivity of direct labor employees, indirect support employees, and clerical staff.	• Encourage participation by the work force.
	• Increase product quality.

Managerial Practice 17.2

Implementing JIT at Security Pacific

The External Mail Services section of the Security Pacific Corporation processes approximately 5 million customer statements, notices, and other mailings monthly. Seven million checks must be sorted, enclosed in envelopes with statements, and mailed to 190,000 customers. Of this total, 30,000 customer statements have so many checks that they must be prepared manually. In the spring of 1989 management decided to reduce the processing time and improve the accuracy of the 30,000 manually prepared month-end statements. They decided not to take the traditional approach of adding employees and quality inspectors because costs would increase. Instead, they decided to redesign the system, taking into account the JIT philosophy.

Figure 17.4 shows the manual system design in 1989. Each check passes through four work stations:

1. *Marp (mismatch account report) table and check-filing area.* When the automatic sorter rejects checks because the magnetic ink encoding is unreadable, a report is generated that alerts a staff member to hand-sort the checks and file them in the correct customer account. They are then carted to the setup table.

2. *Setup table.* A clerk places the corresponding printed statements for each batch of checks at the back of the tray. One tray, or lot size, could have thousands of items. The trays are moved to the statement stuffing cubicles.

3. *Statement cubicles.* Clerks match checks with statements and insert them into envelopes for mailing. The envelopes are moved to the metering area.

4. *Electronic scales and metering area.* The envelopes are weighed on electronic scales (e-scales) and posted.

There were several problems with the original system. Statements had to travel 240 feet from first handling to final metering. Processing clerks had to walk from 10 to 30 feet to get more work or to deposit their output at the next station. In addition, several bottlenecks existed. Typically, 10,000 statements were in queue at the marp/file area and 7500 customer accounts at the setup area. Metering commonly had 13,500 statements waiting for processing. Clearly, a better way had to be found.

Figure 17.5 shows the system design after JIT implementation. A product layout is the core of the system. With the setup table placed near the marp and file area, carts now travel only 3 to 10 feet to the setup station, whereas in the past they had to travel 120 feet. Lot sizes were reduced to 250 statements per tray. This design facilitated a balanced staff plan—two setup staff keep pace with five to six stuffing staff, who keep pace with two electronic scale operators. Work flows without a large buildup since it goes from station to station, usually by handoff from one worker to the next.

Security Pacific realized the following benefits from implementing JIT:

- Mail processing time was reduced by 33 percent.
- Mismatches were reduced by 94 percent.
- Staff salaries were reduced by $32,400 annually.
- Floor space was reduced by 50 percent.
- In-process queues were reduced by 75–90 percent.

Source: Paul Jackson, "White Collar JIT at Security Pacific," *Target,* vol. 7, no. 1 (Spring 1991), pp. 32–37.

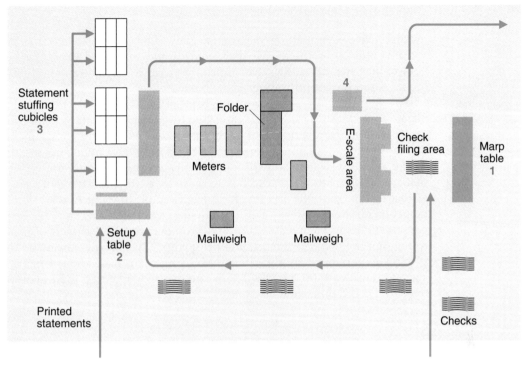

FIGURE 17.4   Manual Statement Stuffing—Security Pacific, 1989

Paul Jackson, "White Collar JIT at Security Pacific," TARGET, Vol. 7, No. 1 (Spring 1991), pp. 34 & 35. Reprinted with permission of the Association for Manufacturing Excellence, Wheeling, IL.

FIGURE 17.5

Manual Statement Stuffing—Post JIT Implementation

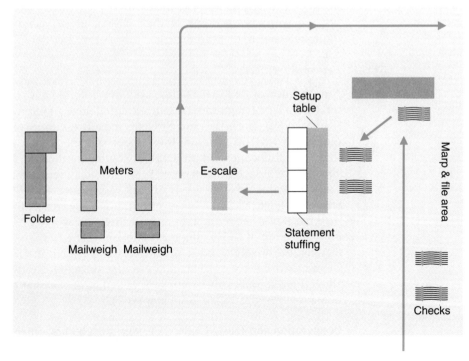

Paul Jackson, "White Collar JIT at Security Pacific," TARGET, Vol. 7, No. 1 (Spring 1991), pp. 34 & 35. Reprinted with permission of the Association for Manufacturing Excellence, Wheeling, IL.

inventory between manufacturing processes. The result is less storage space and inventory investment. Smaller lot sizes and smoothed flows of materials help reduce manufacturing lead times, increase work-force productivity, and improve equipment utilization.

The kanban system is simplicity itself. Product mix or volume changes planned by the MPS can be accomplished by adjusting the number of card sets in the system. The priority of each production order is reflected in the sequence of the production-order cards on the post. The sequence is determined by the stock levels of each part in the storage area: Production orders for parts that are running low are placed before those for parts that have more supply.

Just-in-time systems also involve a considerable amount of work-force participation on the shop floor. Small-group interaction sessions encourage worker participation and have resulted in improvements in many aspects of manufacturing, not the least of which is product quality. Overall, the advantages of JIT systems experienced by the companies using them have caused many managers to reevaluate their own systems and consider adapting their plant operations to the JIT philosophy.

IMPLEMENTATION ISSUES

The benefits of JIT systems seem to be outstanding, yet their implementation can lead to much different results for the unwary. Problems can arise even after JIT has long been operational. Even the Japanese, who pioneered JIT practices in the automobile industry, are not immune: Tokyo is experiencing monumental traffic jams owing in large measure to truck deliveries to JIT manufacturers—small trucks make up 47 percent of Tokyo's traffic. In this section we will address some of the issues managers should be aware of when implementing a JIT system.

Organizational Considerations

Human Costs of JIT. Just-in-time systems, coupled with statistical process control (SPC) (see Chapter 4), require a high degree of regimentation to work well (Klein, 1989). Both JIT and SPC are meant to eliminate all variations in production. With JIT, workers must meet specified cycle times, and with SPC they must follow prescribed problem-solving methods. Such systems might not allow enough slack time to relax, so workers may feel pushed. Stress may build, causing productivity losses or quality reductions. In addition, workers might feel they have lost any sense of autonomy because of the close linkages in material flows between stations with little or no safety stocks. Managers can mitigate some of these effects by allowing slack in the system through the judicious use of safety stock inventories and by emphasizing material flow instead of worker pace. Managers can also promote the use of work teams and allow them to determine their task assignments or rotations within the team's domain of responsibility (see Chapter 7).

Cooperation and Trust. Under JIT, workers and first-line supervisors must take on responsibilities formerly assigned to middle managers and support staff. Activities such as scheduling, expediting, and productivity improvements become part of the duties of lower-level personnel. Consequently, organizational relationships must be reoriented to build close cooperation and mutual trust between the work force and management. Such cooperation and trust may be difficult to achieve, particularly in light of the typical adversarial positions taken by labor and management in the past. For example, the Mazda plant in Flat Rock, Michigan, was experiencing quality problems in August 1988. Absenteeism greater than the Japanese expected and inexperience of the work force were cited as major contributors. Some people felt that the real problem was a lack of understanding of the American culture by Japanese managers. As the president of UAW Local 3000 put it, "To the Japanese, work is the most important part of life, and they expect everybody to be as dedicated as they are. But to Americans, the job is there to support your life on the outside" (Lupo and Lippert, 1988).

Reward Systems and Labor Classifications. In some instances the reward system must be revamped when implementing JIT. At General Motors, for example, a plan to reduce stock at one plant ran into trouble because the production superintendent refused to cut back production of unneeded parts; his salary was based on his plant's production volume.

The realignment of reward systems isn't the only hurdle. Labor contracts traditionally have reduced management's flexibility in reassigning workers as the need arises. As a result, a typical automobile plant in the United States has several unions and dozens of labor classifications. To gain more flexibility, management in some cases has obtained union concessions by granting other types of benefits. In other cases management has relocated plants to take advantage of nonunion or foreign labor. In contrast, at Toyota, management deals with only one company union, and there are only eight different labor classifications in a typical plant.

Process Considerations

Firms using JIT typically have a product focus or at least some dominant material flows. To take advantage of JIT, firms might have to change their existing layout. Certain work stations would be moved closer together, and cells of machines devoted to particular families of components would be designed. Rearranging a plant to conform to JIT practices can be costly, however. For example, although many plants now receive raw materials and purchased parts by rail, to facilitate smaller, more frequent shipments under JIT, truck deliveries would be preferable. Loading docks might have to be reconstructed or expanded and certain operations relocated to accommodate the change in transportation mode and quantities of arriving materials.

Inventory and Scheduling

MPS Stability. Daily production schedules must be stable for extended periods. At Toyota, the master production schedule is stated in fractions of days over a three-month period and is revised only once a month. The first month of the schedule is frozen to avoid disruptive changes in the daily production schedule for each work station; that is, the work stations execute the same work schedule each day of the month. At the beginning of each month, card sets are reissued for the new daily production rate. Stable schedules are needed, so that production lines can be balanced and new assignments found for employees who would otherwise be underutilized. The JIT system cannot respond quickly to scheduling changes because there is little slack inventory or capacity to absorb these changes.

Setups. If the inventory advantages of JIT are to be realized, small container sizes must be used. Because small containers require a large number of setups, however, companies must achieve significant reductions in setup times. Some companies will not be able to achieve short setup times and will therefore have to use large-lot production, negating some of the advantages of JIT.

Purchasing. If frequent, small shipments of purchased items cannot be arranged with suppliers, large inventory savings for these items cannot be realized. In the United States such arrangements may prove difficult because of the geographic dispersion of suppliers.

Another JIT implementation issue related to purchasing is the need to pare the number of suppliers. This is no easy task; it requires close working relationships with surviving suppliers to ensure high levels of quality and timely deliveries.

CHOOSING A PRODUCTION AND INVENTORY MANAGEMENT SYSTEM

Earlier we presented the reorder point (ROP) system (see Chapter 13) and the material requirements planning (MRP) system (see Chapter 16). In this chapter we discussed just-in-time systems. Obviously, management has several systems from which to choose—and many more will become available in the future. Do all of these systems work equally well in a given environment? To this question we respond: Absolutely not. In this section we briefly compare these production and inventory systems and share some insights from our research in this area (see references at the end of the chapter).

ROP, MRP, or JIT?

ROP and MRP. In our research of these systems we found that MRP outperforms ROP in discrete-item manufacturing environments producing to stock, an advantage that increases as the number of levels in the bills of materials increases. Since the gross requirements of a component are the planned order releases of its parents, component gross requirements tend to become very lumpy, thereby deviating from the assumptions of the ROP system. The more levels in a system, the lumpier are the requirements at the bottom of the bills of materials because lot sizes tend to increase. Also, even when comparing the two systems for the same number of levels in the bills of materials, MRP's advantages over ROP increase as lot sizes increase. In general, MRP is the obvious choice unless lot sizes are small, there are few BOM levels, and demand requirements are stable.

MRP and JIT. Is it necessary to choose between a push and a pull system? Actually, these methods are not mutually exclusive, and the best solution is often a hybrid of the strengths of both approaches (Karmarkar, 1989). MRP II systems are good at overall materials planning and data management and can be used to support the informational needs of various functional areas in the firm. MRP systems can be used effectively to understand the implications of lot-sizing decisions and master scheduling changes on overall inventories and capacity. JIT systems, on the other hand, are a less expensive, more effective way to control material flows on the shop floor. A kanban system can be used to maintain low levels of inventory and to adjust production rates over time.

The nature of the production process determines the appropriate system. For line flows, order releases do not change from week to week, so a rate-based system such as JIT works well. While MRP is an effective technique to schedule production on a weekly basis, scheduling of the daily requirements within each specific week is left to the production supervisors. At this level, the shop floor level, a pull system is all that is needed. MRP is not very useful here. But in a repetitive manufacturing environment with reasonably stable but varying schedules, a hybrid system may be appropriate. MRP could be used for order release, as schedules change, or for coordinating with suppliers on long lead time items. Pull methods could be used for actual material flows on the shop floor. Names such as "synchro-MRP," "rate-based MRP II," and "JIT-MRP" have been used to describe these hybrid systems.

In job shop environments, where material flows are complex and demands are highly variable, MRP is the system of choice. The material flows are too complex for JIT, and pull techniques cannot cope with the demand and lead time variability. In addition, the shop floor requires sophisticated tracking and scheduling capability.

In general, although the ROP, MRP, and JIT systems work well in certain environments, they may not work well in others. The choice of a system can affect inventory levels and customer service. High inventory levels strain a company's financial resources and can limit its capability to invest in needed capital improvements. Poor customer service affects market share and the company's ability to compete in the marketplace. An inappropriate system can be an expensive mistake.

Shaping the Manufacturing Environment

Which specific aspects of manufacturing affect system performance? We have identified several factors that affect inventory investment, productivity, and customer service, but by and large, the production and inventory management system by itself does not have an overriding impact on any of these factors. From our studies we concluded that reduced lot sizes and setup times have the greatest impact, followed by reduced yield losses and increased worker flexibility. Firms can improve on these factors regardless of the system. Other aspects of manufacturing, such as capacity slack or safety stock, bills of materials, facility design, and supplier performance, had less impact on performance. Nonetheless, our philosophy is that firms should "get their house in order" by working to improve these environmental factors for whatever production and inventory system in use. For example, reducing lot sizes and setup times will decrease investment and improve customer service, regardless of the system being used. The point is that any production and inventory system will not by itself set things right but that significant improvements in performance *can* be achieved by shaping the manufacturing environments properly. A focus on continuous improvement is a key to shaping a manufacturing environment.

SOLVED PROBLEM

A company using a kanban system has an inefficient machine group. For example, the daily demand for part L105A is 3000 units. The average waiting time for a container of parts is 0.8 day. The processing time for a container of L105A is 0.2 day, and a container holds 270 units. There are presently 20 kanban card sets for this item.

    a. What is the implicit value of the policy variable?
    b. What is the total planned inventory (work in process and finished goods) for item L105A?
    c. Suppose that the policy variable α were 0. How many card sets would be needed now? What is the effect of the policy variable in this example?

Solution   a. We use the equation for the number of card sets to find α.

$$k = \frac{d(\bar{w} + \bar{p})(1 + \alpha)}{c}$$

$$= \frac{3000(0.8 + 0.2)(1 + \alpha)}{270} = 20$$

$$1 + \alpha = \frac{20(270)}{3000(0.8 + 0.2)} = 1.8$$

$$\alpha = 1.8 - 1 = 0.8$$

    b. With 20 card sets in the system and each container holding 270 units, the total planned inventory would be 5400 [20(270)] units.
    c. If $\alpha = 0$,

$$k = \frac{3000(0.8 + 0.2)}{270} = 11.11 \quad \text{or} \quad 12 \text{ card sets}$$

The policy variable adjusts the number of card sets. In this case it is quite dramatic because $(\bar{w} + \bar{p})$ is relatively large and the container size is small relative to daily demand.

FORMULA REVIEW

Number of kanban card sets:

$$k = \frac{d(\bar{w} + \bar{p})(1 + \alpha)}{c}$$

CHAPTER HIGHLIGHTS

● The purpose of JIT systems is to produce or deliver the right items in the quantities needed by subsequent production processes or customers at the time needed. The intent is to coordinate production flows to reduce the need for inventories. JIT is a pull system.

● Some of the key elements of JIT systems are small lot sizes, short setup times, uniform master production schedules, standardized components and work methods, consistent high quality, close supplier ties, flexible work force, product focus, preventive maintenance, and continuous improvement.

● Toyota's kanban system uses withdrawal and production-order card sets to control production flow. The withdrawal card specifies the item and quantity that the user should withdraw from the producer and where to find the item. The production-order card specifies the item and quantity that the producer process must produce each time, where to store the finished item and input materials, and where to find them.

● Material cannot be withdrawn without a withdrawal card. Production cannot begin without a production-order card. The produced items are placed in containers, which should always hold the same standard number of parts. The author-ized inventory of a part is a function of the number of authorized cards for that item. The number of cards depends on average demand during manufacturing lead time, the container size, and a policy variable to adjust for unexpected occurrences.

● JIT has been applied to the production of services. Likely candidates include service environments that have repetitive operations, in reasonably high volume, and deal with some tangible item.

● Just-in-time systems have many advantages, including reductions in inventory, space requirements, and paperwork, and increases in productivity, worker participation, machine utilization, and quality. However, JIT systems also pose implementation problems revolving around organizational, process, and inventory/scheduling considerations.

● For a given manufacturing environment, the choice of a production and inventory system can make a difference. MRP and JIT can be used together in a hybrid system under certain conditions. Also, improving certain environmental factors can significantly reduce inventory investment, improve customer service, and increase productivity, regardless of the system in use.

KEY TERMS

just-in-time (JIT) systems **696**
kanban **706**
mixed-model assembly **700**
pull method **697**
push method **697**
single-digit setup **699**

STUDY QUESTIONS

1. Explain the purpose of just-in-time systems. Why is JIT considered a *pull system*?

2. Toyota's kanban system utilizes two main types of cards that authorize certain actions. Explain the purposes of these cards and describe how they are used.

3. Consider the formula for determining the number of kanban card sets for an item. If the process for that item is *inefficient*, which parameters in the equation might be larger than desirable? Why? Suppose that a supervisor wanted to increase the safety stock. Which parameter would be adjusted?

4. Why do you suppose it took Toyota ten years to perfect its kanban system? How can the system be used to identify areas for improvement?

5. Why is the master production schedule critical to the Toyota kanban system? What characteristics must the schedule have?

6. Consider the statement, "The just-in-time system is a total managerial concept, whereas the kanban system and systems like it are merely information systems designed to provide the basis for the timing and lot-sizing decisions of production quantities." Do you agree or disagree? Why?

7. What factors should management consider when deciding whether to use a JIT system in a given manufacturing environment?

8. Which elements of JIT systems, in your opinion, would be the most troublesome for U.S. manufacturers to implement? Why?

9. What are the similarities and dissimilarities of JIT applications in service firms relative to manufacturing firms?

10. JIT has been described as a system based on team work. The implication is that employees feel more involved, and therefore productivity and quality increase. Yet one of the problems in implementing JIT has been the loss of autonomy of these teams. Comment.

11. Why does the choice of a production and inventory system have implications for the firm as a whole?

12. What does "shaping the environment" mean?

PROBLEMS

Review Problems

1. A certain Japanese automaker operates an assembly plant in the United States. The plant uses a kanban system to control production and inventory. You have been put in charge of a certain machine group that manufactures a tie-rod assembly. The daily demand rate for tie-rods is 1000 units. The average waiting time for parts in your machine group is 0.40 day, and the average processing time per container is 0.30 day. Each container holds 50 tie-rods. You have decided to allow 10 percent of the average waiting and processing time per container for unexpected contingencies. How many card sets would you suggest for controlling production of the tie-rods?

2. A fabrication cell supplies gears to an assembly line using a pull approach. The assembly line requires 500 gears per day. Containers typically wait 0.20 day in the fabrication cell. Each container holds 20 gears, and one gear requires 0.09 day in machine time. Setup times are negligible. If the policy variable for unforeseen contingencies is set at 5 percent, how many card sets should be in the system?

3. You have been asked to analyze the operations of a company using the kanban system. One of the work stations feeding the assembly line produces part K669B. The daily demand for K669B is 2000 units. The average processing time per unit is 0.001 day. Com-

pany records show that the average container spends 1.10 days waiting at the feeder work station. The container for K669B can hold 270 units. Eleven card sets are authorized for the part.

   a. Find the value of the policy variable (α) that expresses the amount of implied safety stock in this system.

   b. Using the implied value of α from (a), determine the required reduction in waiting time if one card set were removed. Assume that all other parameters remain fixed.

4. An assembly line requires two components: A and B. A is produced by center 1 and B by center 2. Each unit the assembly line produces requires 3 units of A and 2 units of B. The daily production on the assembly line is 800 units.

   The container for part A holds 75 units. The policy variable for center 1 is set at 0.06. The average waiting time for a container of A is 0.10 day, and it takes 0.07 day to produce a container.

   The container for part B holds 50 units, and the policy variable for center 2 is 0.08. The average waiting time per container of B

is 0.15 day, and the time to process a container is 0.20 day.

   a. How many card sets are needed for part A?

   b. How many card sets are needed for part B?

5. A production facility uses a kanban system and operates eight hours per day. Suppose that a certain part requires 150 seconds of processing at machine cell 33B and averages 2.4 hours of waiting time there. Management has allowed a 10 percent buffer for unexpected occurrences. Each container holds 20 parts, and 10 card sets are authorized. How much daily demand can be satisfied with this system?

6. The average daily demand for a component is 4000 units. The policy variable (α) for the work center producing the component is 0.10, and it takes 0.50 day to produce a container of 200 parts. However, the waiting time per container is too high because of a lack of capacity. Presently it is at 2.0 days. Show management what effect reductions in waiting time have on the required number of card sets. Plot the number of card sets needed for each reduction of 0.10 day in waiting time. Round up fractional values of k.

SELECTED REFERENCES

Billesbach, T.J., and M.J. Schniederjans. "Applicability of Just-in-Time Techniques in Administration." *Production and Inventory Management Journal* (Third Quarter 1989), pp. 40–44.

Hahn, Chan K., Peter Pinto, and Daniel Bragg. "Just-in-Time Production and Purchasing." *Journal of Purchasing and Materials Management* (Fall 1983), pp. 2–10.

Hall, R.W. *Driving the Productivity Machine.* Falls Church, Va.: The American Production and Inventory Control Society, 1981.

Hutchins, D. "Having a Hard Time with Just-in-Time." *Fortune* (June 1986), pp. 64–66.

Karmarkar, U. "Getting Control of Just-in-Time." *Harvard Business Review* (September–October 1989), pp. 123–131.

Klein, J.A. "The Human Costs of Manufacturing Reform." *Harvard Business Review* (March–April 1989), pp. 60–66.

Krajewski, L.J., B. King, L.P. Ritzman, and D.S. Wong.

"Kanban, MRP and Shaping the Manufacturing Environment." *Management Science*, vol. 33, no. 1 (January 1987), pp. 57–75.

Lupo, Nunzio, and John Lippert. "Mazda's Michigan Plant Produces Many Problems." Knight-Ridder Newspapers, *Columbus Dispatch*, August 27, 1988.

Melynk, S., and P. Carter. "Viewing Kanban as an (s,Q) System: Developing New Insights into a Japanese Method of Production and Inventory Control." In Sang M. Lee and Gary Schwendimen, eds., *Management by Japanese Systems.* New York: Praeger, 1982.

Monden, Y. "Adaptable Kanban System Helps Toyota Maintain Just-in-Time Production." *Journal of Industrial Engineering* (May 1981), pp. 29–46.

Monden, Y. "What Makes the Toyota Production System Really Tick?" *Journal of Industrial Engineering* (January 1981), pp. 36–46.

Nelleman, D.O., and L. Smith. "Just-in-Time vs. Just-in-

Case Production/Inventory Systems Concepts Borrowed Back from Japan." *Production and Inventory Management* (Second Quarter 1982), pp. 12–20.

Rice, J.W., and T. Yoshikawa. "A Comparison of Kanban and MRP Concepts for the Control of Repetitive Manufacturing Systems." *Production and Inventory Management* (First Quarter 1982), pp. 1–13.

Ritzman, L.P., B.E. King, and L.J. Krajewski. "Manufacturing Performance—Pulling the Right Levers." *Harvard Business Review* (March–April 1984), pp. 143–152.

Ritzman, L.P., and L.J. Krajewski. "Performance Comparisons Between MRP and Reorder Point Systems." In H. Berkiroglu, ed., *Simulation and Inventory Control*. La Jolla, Calif.: Society for Computer Simulation, 1983.

Schonberger, R.J. *Japanese Manufacturing Techniques*. New York: The Free Press, 1982.

Chapter 18

SCHEDULING

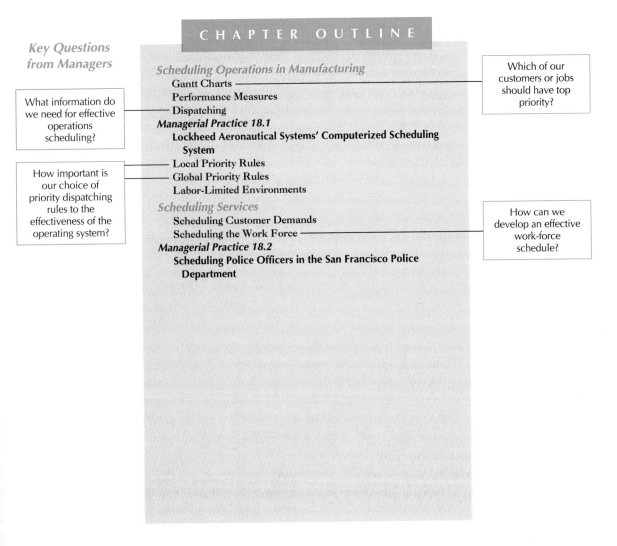

CHAPTER OUTLINE

What information do we need for effective operations scheduling?

How important is our choice of priority dispatching rules to the effectiveness of the operating system?

Which of our customers or jobs should have top priority?

How can we develop an effective work-force schedule?

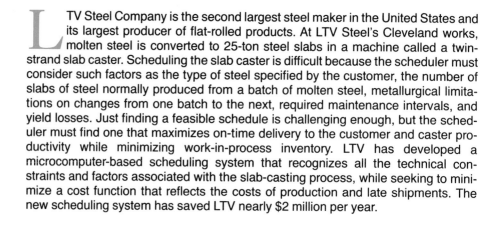

L TV Steel Company is the second largest steel maker in the United States and its largest producer of flat-rolled products. At LTV Steel's Cleveland works, molten steel is converted to 25-ton steel slabs in a machine called a twin-strand slab caster. Scheduling the slab caster is difficult because the scheduler must consider such factors as the type of steel specified by the customer, the number of slabs of steel normally produced from a batch of molten steel, metallurgical limitations on changes from one batch to the next, required maintenance intervals, and yield losses. Just finding a feasible schedule is challenging enough, but the scheduler must find one that maximizes on-time delivery to the customer and caster productivity while minimizing work-in-process inventory. LTV has developed a microcomputer-based scheduling system that recognizes all the technical constraints and factors associated with the slab-casting process, while seeking to minimize a cost function that reflects the costs of production and late shipments. The new scheduling system has saved LTV nearly $2 million per year.

As the LTV example demonstrates, effective scheduling systems can give a significant boost to a firm's competitiveness. Scheduling allocates resources over time to accomplish specific tasks. Normally, scheduling is done after a number of other managerial decisions have already been made. Managers must make decisions about products or services and competitive priorities, choose an appropriate process design and layout, and commit the level of capital and labor required—all before designing a system to schedule the various tasks to be performed. For example, planning emergency services such as fire protection first requires an analysis of the best location for fire stations, decisions about the type and quantity of fire-fighting equipment at each location, and a staffing plan for each station before decisions such as specific work schedules for each employee can be determined. Nonetheless, the ability to generate good schedules can be extremely important for achieving strategic goals. Although generally true for manufacturing, good scheduling is a must for service providers—especially for those services where the customer comes into close contact with the delivery system.

In this chapter we discuss the issues associated with scheduling in both manufacturing and service organizations, and some useful techniques for generating schedules. There are two basic types of scheduling: **work-force scheduling,** which determines when employees work; and **operations scheduling,** which assigns jobs to machines or workers to jobs. While both types of scheduling can be found in manufacturing and service firms, there are dominant patterns that we will focus on. In manufacturing, operations scheduling is of primary importance because the "job," represented by a production lot, is the focus of attention. Many performance measures, such as on-time delivery, inventory levels, the manufacturing cycle time, cost, and quality, relate directly to that production lot. Work-force scheduling is less of an issue unless the firm employs a significant number of part-time workers or operates seven days a

*I*n Harley-Davidson's operations schedule, the operator at this work station attaches a gear assembly to the tire rim. The completed assemblies are then carted to the next work station in their routing.

week. In services, however, work-force scheduling is crucial because it is the availability of servers that is often a dominant factor in a firm's competitiveness. Important measures of performance such as customer waiting time, waiting-line length, utilization, cost, and quality are related to the availability of the servers. Operations scheduling is usually less important. Nonetheless, examples can be found that run against these dominant patterns, and it should be kept in mind during our discussion that both types of scheduling are prevalent in practice.

SCHEDULING OPERATIONS IN MANUFACTURING

Operations schedules are short-term plans designed to implement the master production schedule. While dealing with technical constraints that relate directly to production, operations scheduling begins with a known capacity and focuses on how to best use that capacity. Our discussion of operations scheduling focuses on situations in which a number of jobs—such as component production orders—must be processed at one or more work stations, at which machines such as lathes or workers might be stationed. Typically, each work station can perform a variety of tasks, and there is the potential for queues (or waiting lines) to develop. Each work station performs one operation of the production process. In this section we present several approaches to operations scheduling and discuss their managerial implications.

Gantt Charts

A traditional device used for sequencing work on machines and monitoring progress is the **Gantt chart,** first devised by Henry L. Gantt in 1917. There are two basic forms of the chart: the job or activity progress chart and the machine chart. The *progress chart* graphically displays the current status of each job relative to its due date and its scheduled completion date. For example, suppose that an automobile parts manufacturer has three jobs underway, one each for Ford, Plymouth, and Pontiac. The status of these orders is shown in Fig. 18.1.

For the current date—April 21 denoted by the caret—this Gantt chart shows that the Ford order is behind schedule, the Plymouth order is exactly on schedule, and the Pontiac order is actually ahead of schedule. Now suppose that the Ford plant will have to shut down its assembly line if it does not receive its order by April 26. This situation calls for a more detailed chart and a new schedule. Suppose that the three jobs are all waiting to be processed at the Watterson grinder, after which they must be polished before shipment. Figure 18.2 shows one of several possible schedules the plant manager could use. This form of Gantt chart, called a *machine chart,* depicts the sequence of work for each machine and also can be used to monitor progress. The chart notation shown in Fig. 18.1 is also used here. On April 23, the chart shows that the Ford job is on schedule (the new schedule), because the actual progress coincides with the current date, and that the polisher is idle. However, comparing actual progress to the originally planned due dates in Fig. 18.1 shows that all three jobs will be past due but that the Ford plant will not have to shut down. Thus the plant manager can easily see from the Gantt machine chart the consequence of juggling the schedules. The usual approach is to juggle the schedules by trial and error until a satisfactory one is found.

Performance Measures

Technically, there were 36 schedules to consider for the two machines at the automobile parts company. For each of the 3! (that is, $3 \times 2 \times 1$) ways to sequence the Watterson grinder, there were 3! ways to sequence the polisher.

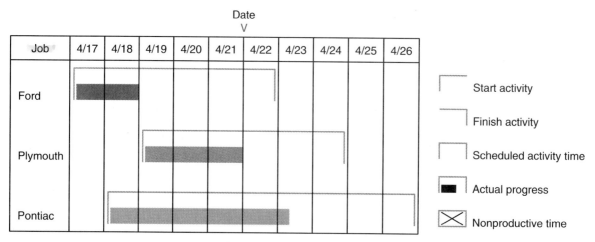

FIGURE 18.1   Gantt Chart of Job Progress for an Auto Parts Company

FIGURE 18.2

Gantt Chart for
Machines at an Auto
Parts Company

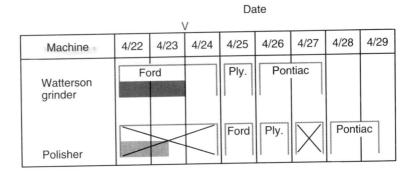

FIGURE 18.2

Gantt Chart for
Machines at an Auto
Parts Company

In general, for *n* jobs, each requiring *m* machines, there are $(n!)^m$ possible schedules. Some might not be feasible because of individual job routings or because scheduling some jobs might depend on the completion of others. Even so, there are typically thousands of ways to schedule a number of jobs on a particular set of machines, and in a job shop, for example, hundreds of scheduling decisions are made every day. Thus from the manager's perspective, identifying the performance measures to be used in selecting a schedule is important. If the overall goals of the organization are to be achieved, the schedules should reflect managerially acceptable performance measures.

Many different performance measures could be used in operations scheduling. The following list identifies and describes the more commonly used measures, some of which will be familiar to you already. Others are derivatives, or variants, of these measures.

- **Job flow time.** The amount of shop time for the job is called **job flow time.** It is the sum of the moving time between operations, waiting time for machines or work orders, process time (including setups), and delays resulting from machine breakdowns, component unavailability, and the like. Job flow time is the difference between the time of completion and the time the job was available for its first processing operation, not necessarily when the job began its first operation.
- **Makespan.** The total amount of time required to complete a *group* of jobs is called **makespan.** It is the difference between the start of the first job and completion of the last job.
- **Past due.** The measure **past due** can be expressed as the *amount of time* by which a job missed its due date or as the *percentage of total jobs* processed over some period of time that missed their due dates.
- **Work-in-process inventory.** Any job in a queue, moving from one operation to the next, being delayed for some reason, being processed, or residing in component or subassembly inventories is considered to be **work-in-process (WIP) inventory.** It is an example of *pipeline inventory*, in which the item is produced rather than purchased. This measure can be expressed in units (individual items only), number of jobs, dollar value for the entire system, or weeks of supply.
- **Total inventory.** The sum of scheduled receipts and on-hand inventories

is the **total inventory.** This measure could be expressed in weeks of supply, dollars, or units (individual items only).

- **Utilization.** The percentage of work time productively spent by a machine or worker is called **utilization.** It can be aggregated for more than one machine or worker. If there are fewer workers than machines, utilization can be calculated separately for each resource.

Each of these measures can be expressed as a statistical distribution having a mean and a variance, but the performance measures are not entirely independent of each other. For example, minimizing the mean job flow time tends to reduce work-in-process inventory and increase utilization. In a flow shop (a production system in which all products follow a linear routing pattern), minimizing the makespan for a group of jobs also tends to increase facility utilization.

We present examples of these interactions later in this chapter. We mention them here to point out that working with criteria such as job flow time, makespan, and past due—provided that their relationships to inventory and utilization are understood—can make scheduling easier.

Dispatching

Just as there are many feasible schedules for a specific group of jobs on a particular set of machines, there are also many ways to generate schedules. They range from straightforward manual methods, such as manipulating Gantt charts, to sophisticated computer models for developing optimal schedules. We limit our discussion here to one class of schedule-generating procedures called **dispatching procedures.** Simply stated, these procedures allow the schedule for a given work station to evolve over a period of time because the decision about which job to process next (or to let the station remain idle) is made when the work station becomes available for further processing. One advantage of this method of generating schedules over others is that last-minute information on operating conditions can be incorporated into the schedule as it evolves.

Typically, the decision about which job to process next is made with the help of **priority sequencing rules.** When several jobs are waiting in line at a work station, priority rules specify the job processing sequence. A worker can apply these rules to select the next job. These rules can also be incorporated into a computerized scheduling system that generates a dispatch list of jobs and priorities that a supervisor uses to assign jobs to work stations. The following priority sequencing rules are commonly used in practice:

- **First come, first served (FCFS).** The job that arrived at the work station first has the highest priority.
- **Earliest due date (EDD).** The job with the earliest due date is scheduled next.
- **Shortest processing time (SPT).** The job requiring the shortest processing time at the work station is processed next.
- **Critical ratio (CR).** Job priorities are calculated by dividing the time

remaining to a job's due date by the total shop time remaining. The latter includes the setup, processing, move, and planned queuing times of all remaining operations, including the operation being scheduled. A ratio less than 1.0 implies that the job is behind schedule, and a ratio greater than 1.0 implies that the job is ahead of schedule. The job with the lowest CR is scheduled next.

- **Slack per remaining operation (S/RO).** Slack is the difference between the time remaining to a job's due date and the total shop time remaining, including the operation being scheduled. A job's priority is determined by dividing the slack by the number of operations that remain, including the one being scheduled. The job with the lowest S/RO is scheduled next.

Even though there are many ways to break ties, in our discussion if one or more jobs have the same top priority, we will arbitrarily choose one of them to process next.

The simplicity of the priority sequencing rules belies the complexity of the scheduling task. Tracking hundreds of jobs through hundreds of work stations requires intensive data gathering and manipulation. For each job the scheduler needs to use information on its processing requirements as well as information on its current status. For example, processing information might include the job's due date; its routing; the standard setup, processing, and planned queue times at each operation; alternate machines that could be used at each operation; and the components and raw materials needed at each operation. Current-status information—such as the job's location (in queue for a machine or material-handling device or being processed on a machine), how much of the operation is completed (if currently being processed), the actual arrival and departure times at each operation or queue, the actual processing and setup times, the amount of scrap generated at each operation (which may determine the need to perform rework operations), and many other bits of information—can be important in a given environment. The priority sequencing rules utilize some of this information to determine the processing sequence of jobs at a given work station. The remaining information is useful for estimating job arrival times at the next work station in their routing, whether an alternate machine should be used when the primary one is busy, and the need for material-handling equipment. Much of this information changes throughout the day, making manual data-gathering methods ineffective. Computers are a necessary tool for maintaining valid priorities. Managerial Practice 18.1 discusses the computerized system used by an aircraft manufacturer.

Priority rules can be classified as local or global. **Local priority rules** base a job's priority assignment only on information represented by the jobs in the individual work station queue. For example, EDD, FCFS, and SPT are local rules. By contrast, **global priority rules** base a job's priority assignment on information from other work stations, in addition to the one being scheduled. Examples of global rules are CR and S/RO. Global rules might be viewed as always the best choice. However, they might not provide enough benefit in a

Managerial Practice 18.1

Lockheed Aeronautical Systems' Computerized Scheduling System

The defense industry faces reduced levels of government spending for major defense projects and greater competitive pressures to secure the few projects that will be authorized. The Lockheed Aeronautical Systems Company is responding to these competitive pressures by designing production systems to cope with the problems of aircraft production in the twenty-first century. The company has developed a pilot paperless shop floor control system that provides factory workers with current, accurate electronic data and support documentation—in both text and graphics—needed to perform their jobs. The system tracks job progress and time at each operation and recommends the next job to process at a given work station.

The system works as follows. When a worker arrives at his work station, he logs into the system and passes his identification badge through a magnetic reader. The system verifies the ID and displays, in order of priority, the current orders that must be processed that day at that work station. The work queue is continually updated as work is completed and new work arrives. The worker can select the first order on the list merely by touching it on the screen, or if so authorized, he can override the system and select a different one. Once the job is selected, the system displays all pertinent work information for that job. The worker then gets the parts and verifies that he has the correct ones by wanding a bar code label on the attached tag. When the worker completes the job, the work is automatically dispatched to the next work station.

Although the project is still in its infancy, Lockheed management believes that the successes to date demonstrate the potential benefits, including increased shop floor control, improved scheduling, improved cost and quality performance, integration of other factory systems, increased learning rates for new shop floor workers, and rapid delivery of up-to-date data to the shop floor. Time will tell whether the system will live up to its potential, but it certainly is a step toward improving Lockheed's competitive position in an exceedingly competitive market.

Source: Michael Sheehan, "Paperless Systems Boosting Performance, Reduce Costs," *Production and Inventory Management* (September 1991), pp. 37–40.

given situation to outweigh the cost of the added information requirements. In the next two sections we will see how local and global rules can be used.

Local Priority Rules

Local priority rules can be used to schedule any number of work stations. For the purpose of introducing the concepts of dispatching, we will focus on the scheduling of a single operation at a work station.

Application 18.1   *Comparing Local Priority Rules*

The Taylor Machine Shop rebores engine blocks, among other things. Currently, five engine blocks are waiting for processing. At any time, the company has only one engine expert on duty who can do this type of work. The engine problems have been diagnosed, and standard times for each job have been estimated. The customers have said when they expect the work to be completed. The accompanying table shows the situation as of Monday morning. Since Taylor is open from 8 A.M. to 5 P.M. each weekday, plus overtime on weekends as needed, the customer pickup times are measured in business hours from Monday morning. Use the SPT and EDD rules to schedule the engine expert and calculate the average hours early, hours past due, work-in-process, and total inventory for each rule.

Engine Block	Standard Time, Including Setup (hr)	Scheduled Customer Pickup Time (business hrs from now)
Ranger	8	10
LTD Wagon	6	12
Bronco	15	20
Econoline 150	3	18
Thunderbird	12	22

Solution   The following table shows the schedule if the SPT rule is used. The flow time for each job equals the waiting time plus the processing time. For example, the Ranger block had to wait 9 hours before the engine expert started to work on it. Since the standard time for the job is 8 hours, its flow time is 17 hours.

Shortest Processing-Time Schedule for Engine Block Jobs

Vehicle Sequence	Begin Work	Process Time (hr)	End Work	Flow Time (hr)	Scheduled Customer Pickup Time	Actual Customer Pickup Time*	Hours Early	Hours Past Due
Econoline 150	0	3	3	3	18	18	15	
LTD wagon	3	6	9	9	12	12	3	
Ranger	9	8	17	17	10	17		7
Thunderbird	17	12	29	29	22	29		7
Bronco	29	15	44	44	20	44		24
Total				102		120	18	38
Average				20.4			3.6	7.6

Average work-in-process $= \dfrac{102}{44} = 2.32$ blocks.   Average total inventory $= \dfrac{120}{44} = 2.73$ blocks.

*Based on the assumption that customers will never pick up their engine blocks before the scheduled pickup time and, if there is a delay, they will pick up their blocks immediately upon completion.

We calculate the average work-in-process inventory by dividing the sum of the individual job flow times by the total elapsed time (or makespan). You might think of the sum as the total *job-hours* spent by the engine blocks waiting for the engine expert and being processed. (In this application there are no component or subassembly inventories, so WIP consists only of those engine blocks waiting in queue or being processed.) Dividing this sum by the total elapsed time required to complete work on all the engine blocks provides the average work-in-process inventory.

We calculate the average total inventory similarly. Total inventory is the sum of the work-in-process inventory and the completed jobs waiting to be picked up by customers. The average total inventory is equal to the sum of the *actual* pickup times divided by the makespan. The sum is the total job-hours spent waiting for the engine expert, being processed, and waiting for pickup. For example, the first job to be picked up is the LTD wagon block, which spent 12 hours in the system. Then the Ranger block is picked up after spending 17 job-hours in the system. The time spent by any job in the system is merely its actual customer pickup time because all jobs were available for processing at time zero. When we divide this sum by the total elapsed time, we get the average total inventory. In this case, the averages are 2.32 engine blocks in work-in-process and 2.73 engine blocks in total inventory. This implies an average of 0.41 (2.73 − 2.32) blocks in finished inventory, waiting for customer pickup. The following table shows the schedule and performance criteria derived from the EDD priority rule.

Earliest Due Date Schedule for Engine Block Jobs

Vehicle Sequence	Begin Work	Process Time (hr)	End Work	Flow Time (hr)	Scheduled Customer Pickup Time	Actual Customer Pickup Time*	Hours Early	Hours Past Due
Ranger	0	8	8	8	10	10	2	
LTD wagon	8	6	14	14	12	14		2
Econoline 150	14	3	17	17	18	18	1	
Bronco	17	15	32	32	20	32		12
Thunderbird	32	12	44	44	22	44		22
Total				115		118	3	36
Average				23.0			0.6	7.2

Average work-in-process = $\dfrac{115}{44}$ = 2.61 blocks.   Average total inventory = $\dfrac{118}{44}$ = 2.68 blocks.

*Based on the assumption that customers will never pick up their engine blocks before the scheduled pickup time and, if there is a delay, they will pick up their blocks immediately upon completion.

Comparing the two tables in the solution of Application 18.1, you can see that the SPT schedule provided a lower average flow time and lower work-in-process inventory. The EDD schedule gave better customer service, as measured by the average hours past due, and a lower maximum hours past due (22 versus 24). It also provided a lower total inventory because fewer job-hours were spent waiting for customers to pick up their engine blocks after they had been completed. The SPT priority rule will push jobs through the system to completion more quickly than will the other rules. Speed can be an advantage—but only if jobs can be delivered sooner than promised and revenue collected earlier. If they cannot, the completed job must stay in finished inventory, canceling the advantage of minimizing the average work-in-process inventory. Consequently, the priority rule, and the production schedule, affects criteria that may be of concern to management. In Application 18.1, SPT and EDD provided schedules that resulted in different values for the criteria. Interestingly, both schedules have the same makespan: 44 hours. This result will always occur in single-operation scheduling for a *fixed number* of jobs available for processing, regardless of the priority rule used (because there are no idle work station times between any two jobs).

Local priority rules can also be used to schedule more than one operation. Each operation is treated independently of the others. When the work station becomes idle, the priority rule is applied to the jobs waiting for that operation and the one with the highest priority is selected. When that operation is finished, the job is moved to the next operation in its routing, where it waits until it again has the highest priority. At any work station, the jobs in the waiting line change over a period of time, so the choice of a priority rule can make quite a difference in processing sequence.

Using simulation models of job-shop systems, researchers have studied the implications of various priority rules for various performance measures. In most of these studies, all jobs were considered independent, and the assumption was made that sufficient capacity was generally available. Some generalizations about the performance of three local priority rules are stated in Table 18.1.

Global Priority Rules

Global rules consider information about succeeding operations before setting the priority of a job in a particular waiting line. Therefore these rules apply to the scheduling of two or more work stations (or operations). Before discussing the more general case, let's look at a special case.

Two–Work Station Flow Shop. Suppose that we have a situation in which a number of jobs are ready for processing on two work stations and that the routings of all jobs are identical. In situations like this, the makespan criterion becomes important. Recall that the makespan for a group of jobs in a single-operation scheduling problem is the same, regardless of the sequence chosen. This is no longer true for scheduling two or more operations. Minimizing the makespan for a group of jobs to be processed on two work stations in a flow shop has the advantage of minimizing the idle time of the *second* work station because the first work station will be utilized continuously until it processes the last job.

TABLE 18.1 / *Generalizations About the Performance of Selected Local Rules*

Rule	Comments
Earliest due date (EDD)	Performs well with respect to the percentages of jobs past due and the variance of hours past due. For a given set of jobs to be processed on a single machine, it minimizes the maximum of the past due hours of any job in the set. It is popular with firms that are sensitive to due date changes, although it does not perform very well with respect to flow time, work-in-process inventory, or utilization.
First come, first served (FCFS)	Even though this rule is considered fair to the jobs (or customers), it performs poorly with respect to all performance measures. It is actually a random rule with respect to operating performance measures.
Shortest processing time (SPT)	Often referred to as the "world champion," it tends to minimize mean flow time, work-in-process inventory, and percentage of jobs past due and to maximize shop utilization. However, it could increase total inventory value because it tends to push all work to the finished state. In addition, it tends to produce a large variance in past due hours because the larger jobs might have to wait a long time for processing. Also, it provides no opportunity to adjust schedules when due dates change. The advantage of this rule over others diminishes as the load on the shop increases.

Johnson (1954) developed a procedure to minimize makespan in scheduling a group of jobs on two work stations. He showed that the sequence of jobs at the two work stations should be identical, and so the priority assigned to a job should be the same at both work stations. His procedure assumes there is a known set of jobs, all available to begin processing on the first work station. In this sense it is not a dispatching procedure, but it does assign priorities to jobs based on their operation times at both work stations.

For known processing times for each job at both work stations, the procedure is as follows:

1. Scan the process times at each work station and find the shortest process time among those jobs not yet scheduled. If there is a tie, choose one job arbitrarily.
2. If the shortest process time is on work station 1, schedule the corresponding job as early as possible. If the shortest process time is on work station 2, schedule the corresponding job as late as possible.
3. Eliminate the last job scheduled from further consideration. Repeat steps 1 and 2 until all jobs are scheduled.

Application 18.2   *Scheduling a Group of Jobs on Two Work Stations*

A recent fire in one of the Morris Machine Company's shops damaged five machines. The machines will be recovered at two work stations in the following manner.

Operation 1: Unbolt the machine from the floor, move it to the repair shop, and dismantle it.

Operation 2: Clean or replace parts, test the machine, make adjustments, and reinstall it in the shop.

The estimated time for repairing each machine is shown in the accompanying table. Each operation will be performed by a separate crew of maintenance and engineering personnel. The shop will be inoperable until all the machines are back in place, so the plant manager is interested in finding a schedule that minimizes the makespan and has authorized round-the-clock operations until the machines have been repaired.

	Time (hr)	
Machine	Operation 1	Operation 2
M1	12	22
M2	4	5
M3	5	3
M4	15	16
M5	10	8

Solution   The optimal sequence is shown in the following table. Machine 2 is the first to be processed by the crew assigned to operation 1. Machine 1 is next, followed by machines 4, 5, and 3. Even though the choice of the next machine was unique for each step, ties that occur can be broken arbitrarily. No other sequence of machines will produce a lower makespan. To determine the makespan, we have to draw a Gantt chart, as shown in Fig. 18.3. In this case, it will take 65 hours to refurbish and reinstall all five machines.

Application of Johnson's Procedure to Morris Machine Company Repairs

Iteration	Job Sequence	Comments
1	[ ][ ][ ][ ][3]	Shortest process time is three hours for M3 on the second operation.
2	[2][ ][ ][ ][3]	Eliminate M3's times from the table of estimated times. The next shortest process time is four hours for M2 on operation 1.
3–5	[2][ ][ ][5][3]	Repeat the procedure for M5, M1, and M4.
	[2][1][ ][5][3]	
	[2][1][4][5][3]	

Multiple–Work Station Scheduling. We can also use global rules to schedule multiple work stations when using the dispatching procedure. Although many global rules have been devised, we present only the critical ratio (CR) and slack per remaining operation (S/RO) as examples of global priority rules. Consider Table 18.2 on the next page, which contains information about a set of four jobs presently waiting in queue at an engine lathe. Several operations, including the one at the engine lathe, remain to be done on each job.

Using CR to schedule the machine, we divide the time remaining to the due date by the shop time remaining (measured in days for our example) to get the priority index for each job. For job 1, this is $15/6.1 = 2.46$. The sequence of jobs to be processed by the engine lathe is 4–2–3–1, assuming that no other jobs arrive in the meantime. Using S/RO, we divide the difference between the time remaining to the due date and the shop time remaining by the number

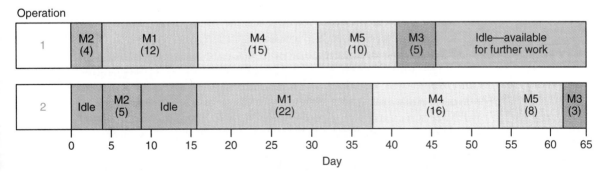

FIGURE 18.3   Gantt Chart of the Morris Machine Company Repair Schedule

TABLE 18.2 / *Operating Data and the Resulting Schedules Based on CR and S/RO*

Job	Operation Time at Engine Lathe (hr)	Time Remaining to Due Date (days)	Number of Operations Remaining, Including Engine Lathe	Shop Time Remaining, Including Engine Lathe (days)
1	2.3	15	10	6.1
2	10.5	10	2	7.8
3	6.2	20	12	14.5
4	15.6	8	5	10.2

Critical Ratio		Slack/Remaining Operation			
Job	Priority Index	Sequence on Engine Lathe	Job	Priority Index	Sequence on Engine Lathe
1	2.46	Fourth	1	0.89	Third
2	1.28	Second	2	1.10	Fourth
3	1.38	Third	3	0.46	Second
4	0.78	First	4	−0.44	First

of remaining operations. For job 1, this is $(15 − 6.1)/10 = 0.89$. The sequence of jobs is 4–3–1–2. Note that the two priority rules yield two different schedules. By way of comparison, the SPT schedule, using the operation times (measured in hours) at the engine lathe only, is 1–3–2–4. No preference is given to job 4 in the SPT schedule, even though it may not be finished by its due date.

Labor-Limited Environments

Two basic types of environments affect the complexity of operations scheduling. In a **machine-limited environment** the limiting resource is the number of machines or work stations available. The assumption—which we made for local and global priority rules—is that a job never has to wait for lack of a worker. Perhaps more typically, however, the number of workers is less than the number of machines or work stations. In this case, workers are trained to work on a variety of machines or tasks, increasing the flexibility of operations. Thus in a **labor-limited environment,** the resource constraint is the amount of labor available, not the number of machines or work stations.

Labor-limited environments add another dimension to operations scheduling. Along with deciding which job to process next at a particular work station, the scheduler must also assign a worker to his or her next work station. The scheduler can use a dispatching procedure to make these decisions as the situation arises, similar to the scheduling of engine blocks in Application 18.1. In labor-limited environments, the labor-assignment policies, as well as the dispatching priority rules, affect performance. Table 18.3 contains some examples of labor-assignment rules.

TABLE 18.3 / *Examples of Labor Assignment Rules*

Assign personnel to the work station having the job in queue that has been in the system longest.

Assign personnel to the work station having the most jobs in queue.

Assign personnel to the work station having the largest standard work content in its queue.

Assign personnel to the work station having the job in queue that has the earliest due date.

SCHEDULING SERVICES

In Chapter 1 we discussed the differences between manufacturing and services. Whether a firm is more like a goods producer (produces a physical product, has low customer contact, is capital intensive) or more like a services producer (produces an intangible product, has high customer contact, is labor intensive), one major distinction affecting the scheduling task is that services cannot be preproduced. Without inventories to buffer demand uncertainties, managing capacities becomes very important. In this section we will discuss various ways that scheduling systems can facilitate the capacity management of service providers.

Scheduling Customer Demands

One way to manage capacity is to schedule customers for time periods with available capacity. With this approach, capacity remains fixed and demand is leveled to provide timely service and utilize capacity. Three methods are commonly used: appointments, reservations, and backlogs.

Appointments. An appointment system assigns to customers specific times for service. The advantages of this method are timely customer service and high utilization of servers. Doctors, dentists, lawyers, and automobile repair shops are examples of service providers that use appointment systems. Doctors can use the system to schedule parts of their day to visit hospital patients, and lawyers can set aside time to prepare cases. To provide timely service, however, care must be taken when making appointments. Scheduled customers will become peeved if they find that the "schedule has slipped" and a long wait is in store. This problem can be avoided by scheduling adequate time to the individual customer rather than merely scheduling customers on equal time intervals. In addition, appointment systems can backfire if there are a significant number of late arrivals or no-shows.

Reservations. Reservation systems, although very similar to appointment systems, are used when the customer actually occupies or uses facilities associated with the service. For example, customers reserve hotel rooms, automobiles, or airline seats. And buying tickets for a concert is actually a reservation system. The major advantage of reservation systems is the lead time they give the service manager to plan the efficient use of facilities. Often reservations require some form of down payment to reduce the problem of no-shows. Many hotels require one night's payment when the reservation is made, and conferences usually have a deadline for registration cancellations.

Backlogs. A less precise way to schedule customers is to allow backlogs to develop. For this reason, customers never know exactly when service will commence. They present their service request to an order taker, who adds it to the queue of orders already in the system. Various priority rules can be used to determine which order to process next. The usual rule is first-come, first-served, but if the order involves rework on a previous order, it may get a higher priority. TV repair shops, restaurants, banks, grocery stores, and barber shops are examples of the many businesses that use this system.

Scheduling the Work Force

Another way to manage capacity with a scheduling system is to specify the on-duty and off-duty periods for each employee over a certain time period. This approach is used when customers demand quick responses and total demands can be forecasted with reasonable accuracy. In these instances, capacity is adjusted to meet the expected loads on the service system. Typical situations involving work-force scheduling include assigning postal clerks, nurses, or police officers to specific workdays and shifts; clerks in a store in a mall open 7 days a week, 14 hours a day; drivers for a bus company with many routes, operating 20 hours a day, 365 days a year, and with highly variable demands; and airline crews on different routes and mandatory layovers.

Purpose of the Work-Force Schedule. Work-force schedules translate the staffing plan (see Chapter 14) into specific schedules of work for each employee. Consider the work-force schedule posted by the managers of the Amalgamated Parcel Service (APS) shown in Table 18.4. The APS processing center is open

TABLE 18.4 / *Posted APS Work-Force Schedule*

Employee	M	T	W	Th	F	S	Su	
Chen	X	Off	X	X	X	Off	X	
Smith	X	Off	X	X	X	Off	X	
Carter	X	X	X	X	X	Off	Off	
Johnson	X	X	X	X	X	Off	Off	
Kramer	X	X	X	X	X	Off	Off	
Griffin	Off	X	X	X	X	X	Off	
Whitcomb	Off	X	X	X	X	X	Off	
Hernandez	X	Off	X	X	X	X	Off	
Booth	X	X	Off	X	X	X	Off	
Bell	X	Off	X	X	X	X	Off	
								Total
Capacity (*C*)	8	6	9	10	10	5	2	50
Requirements (*R*)	6	4	8	9	10	3	2	42
Slack (*C* − *R*)	2	2	1	1	0	2	0	8

*E*ffective scheduling of the on-duty and off-duty periods for air traffic controllers is critical to the safety of air travelers. Here an air traffic controller monitors the progress of aircraft under his jurisdiction.

seven days a week and can be operated by a small number of employees. The staffing plan for APS calls for ten employees in the time period covered. The work-force schedule must specify the days of the week that each employee is to be on duty. Scheduling wouldn't be a problem if the company worked only one eight-hour shift, five days a week—but that isn't the case at APS. In Table 18.4 the Xs denote workdays for the employees. For example, Chen has Tuesday and Saturday off each week.

Determining the workdays for each employee in itself doesn't make the staffing plan operational. Daily work-force requirements, stated in the aggregate in the staffing plan, must be satisfied. Thus for an APS staffing plan calling for 168 employee-days per month, or 42 employee-days per week, Table 18.4 shows the daily requirements. The work-force capacity available each day must meet or exceed daily work-force requirements. If it does not, the scheduler must try to rearrange days off until the requirements are met. If no such schedule can be found, management might have to change the staffing plan and authorize more employees, overtime hours, or larger backlogs.

Finally, the work-force schedule reallocates employees as requirements change. Suppose that the manager at the APS center learns that some special shipments will arrive on Sunday, requiring two more employees than usual. In the schedule in Table 18.4, three days have a slack capacity of two employees. Thus the manager could ask Carter and Johnson, for example, to work Sunday in exchange for Monday off.

Constraints. The technical constraints imposed on the work-force schedule are the resources provided by the staffing plan and the requirements placed on the operating system. However, other constraints, including legal and behavioral considerations, can also be imposed. For example, a hospital may be required to have at least a minimum number of registered nurses on duty on each floor at all times. Similarly, a minimum number of fire and safety personnel must be on duty at a fire station at all times. Such constraints limit management's flexibility in developing work-force schedules, but the constraints imposed by the psychological needs of workers complicate scheduling even more. Some of these constraints are written into labor agreements. For example, an employer may agree to give employees a certain number of consecutive days off per week or limit employees' consecutive workdays to a certain maximum. Other provisions might govern the allocation of vacation, days off for holidays, or rotating shift assignments. In addition, the preferences of the employees themselves need to be considered.

One way that managers deal with certain undesirable aspects of scheduling is to use a **rotating schedule,** which rotates employees through a series of workdays and/or hours. Thus over a period of time, each person has the same opportunity to have weekends and holidays off and to work days, as well as evenings and nights. For example, the schedules in Table 18.4 could be rotated by giving each employee the next employee's schedule the following week. For example, Chen takes Smith's schedule, Smith takes Carter's, and so forth. After ten weeks, Chen would have the first schedule again. In contrast, a **fixed schedule** calls for each employee to work the same days and hours each week. A fixed schedule at APS would always require Chen, Smith, Hernandez, Booth, and Bell to have split, rather than consecutive, days off.

Developing a Work-Force Schedule. Let's take a closer look at the APS work-force schedule shown in Table 18.4. Five employees did not get two consecutive days off. Obviously, the scheduler did not consider this constraint. In this section we demonstrate a method that recognizes this constraint.*

The objective is to identify the two consecutive days off for each employee that will minimize the amount of total slack capacity. The work schedule for each employee is simply the five days that remain after the two days off have been determined. The scheduler follows these steps:

1. From the schedule of net requirements for the week, find all the pairs of consecutive days that include the minimum daily requirements. Select the unique pair that has the lowest total requirements for the two days. For example, if the requirements are as follows:

Monday:	8	Friday:	7
Tuesday:	9	Saturday:	4
Wednesday:	2	Sunday:	2
Thursday:	12		

    the minimum capacity requirement is 2, occurring on Wednesday and Sunday. The pairs that contain the minimum requirement are Saturday–Sunday, Sunday–Monday, Tuesday–Wednesday, and Wednesday–Thursday. The pair having the lowest total requirements is Saturday–Sunday, with 4 and 2.

---

*The method demonstrated here is similar to one developed by Tibrewala, Philippe, and Browne (1972). Their method ensures a work-force schedule that minimizes total slack capacity.

2. If a tie occurs, choose one of the tied pairs consistent with provisions written into the labor agreement, if any. Alternatively, the tie could be broken by asking the employee being scheduled to make the choice. As a last resort, the tie could be broken arbitrarily. For example, preference could be given to Saturday–Sunday pairs.

3. Assign the employee the selected pair of days off. Subtract the requirements satisfied by the employee from the net requirements for each day the employee is to work. In our example, the employee is assigned Saturday and Sunday off. After requirements are subtracted, Monday's requirement is 7, Tuesday's is 8, Wednesday's is 1, Thursday's is 11, and Friday's is 6. Saturday's and Sunday's requirements don't change because no employee is yet scheduled to work those days.

4. Repeat steps 1–3 until all requirements are satisfied or a given number of employees have been scheduled.

This method reduces the amount of slack capacity assigned to days having low requirements and forces scheduling first the days having high requirements. It also recognizes some of the behavioral and contractual aspects of work-force scheduling in the tie-breaking rules. However, the schedules produced might *not* minimize total slack capacity. Different rules for finding the days-off pair and breaking ties are needed to ensure minimal total slack capacity.

Application 18.3	*Developing a Work-Force Schedule*

For the data in Table 18.4, find a work schedule for each employee that provides two consecutive days off and minimizes the amount of total slack capacity. To break ties in the selection of off days, give preference to Saturday–Sunday if it is one of the tied pairs. If not, select one of the tied pairs arbitrarily.

Solution   The schedule of requirements is

M	T	W	Th	F	S	Su	Employee
6	4	8	9	10	3	2	Chen

Although both S–Su and Su–M contain the minimum requirements, S–Su has the lowest total requirements. Therefore, the unique pair of minimum requirements is S–Su and Chen is scheduled to work Monday–Friday.

We reduce the requirements for M–F to recognize that Chen will be on duty. Note that the requirements for S–Su are carried forward because these were employee days off in the last step. This results in the following net requirements.

M	T	W	Th	F	S	Su	Employee
5	3	7	8	9	3	2	Smith

The unique minimum again is on S–Su, so we assign Smith to a M–F schedule. The day-off assignments for the remainder of the employees are shown in the table on the following page.

Day-Off Assignments for the Remainder of the APS Employees

M	T	W	Th	F	S	Su	Employee	Comments
			Net Requirements					
4	2	6	7	8	3	2	Carter	S–Su has the lowest total net requirements.
3	1	5	6	7	3	2	Johnson	M–T has the lowest total net requirements.
3	1	4	5	6	2	1	Kramer	S–Su has the lowest total net requirements.
2	0	3	4	5	2	1	Griffin	M–T has the lowest total net requirements.
2	0	2	3	4	1	0	Whitcomb	S–Su has the lowest total net requirements.
1	0	1	2	3	1	0	Hernandez	S–Su is chosen according to the tie-breaking rule.
0	0	0	1	2	1	0	Booth	Su–M is arbitrarily chosen because S–Su does not have the lowest total requirements.
0	0	0	0	1	0	0	Bell	S–Su is chosen according to the tie-breaking rule.

The schedule for all the APS employees is shown in Table 18.5. With its substantial amount of slack capacity, the schedule is not unique. Booth, for example, could have Su–M, M–T, or T–W off without causing a capacity shortage. Indeed, APS might be able to get by with one less employee because of the total of eight slack days of capacity. However, APS needs all ten employees on Fridays. If the manager were willing to get by with only nine employees on Fridays, or if someone could work one day of overtime on a rotating basis, he would not need Bell. As you can see in the table above, the net requirements left for Bell to satisfy amount to only one day, Friday. As it is, Bell can be used to fill in for vacationing or sick employees.

Scheduling Telephone Operators. Work-force scheduling in practice often entails a myriad of constraints and concerns. Such is the case with telephone operator scheduling. In some firms, such as telephone companies and mail-order catalogue houses, operators must be on duty 24 hours a day, seven days a week. Sometimes a portion of the staff is part time, allowing management a great deal of flexibility in developing schedules but adding considerable complexity to the requirements. The flexibility comes from the opportunity to match anticipated loads closely by using overlapping shifts or odd shift lengths; the complexity comes from evaluating the numerous possible alternatives. Management must also consider the timing of lunch breaks and rest periods, the number and starting times of shift schedules, and the days off for each em-

TABLE 18.5 / *APS Work-Force Schedule, Imposing the Two Consecutive Days Off Constraint*

Employee	M	T	W	Th	F	S	Su
Chen	X	X	X	X	X	Off	Off
Smith	X	X	X	X	X	Off	Off
Carter	X	X	X	X	X	Off	Off
Johnson	Off	Off	X	X	X	X	X
Kramer	X	X	X	X	X	Off	Off
Griffin	Off	Off	X	X	X	X	X
Whitcomb	X	X	X	X	X	Off	Off
Hernandez	X	X	X	X	X	Off	Off
Booth	Off	X	X	X	X	X	Off
Bell	X	X	X	X	X	Off	Off

	M	T	W	Th	F	S	Su	Total
Capacity (*C*)	7	7	10	10	10	3	3	50
Requirements (*R*)	6	4	8	9	10	3	2	42
Slack (*C* − *R*)	1	3	2	1	0	0	1	8

ployee. An additional, typical concern is that the number of operators on duty at any given time be sufficient to answer calls within a reasonable amount of time. At General Telephone and Electronics (GTE) operators must answer calls within ten seconds 90 percent of the time.

Computerized scheduling systems are available to cope with the complexity of the operator scheduling problem. At GTE, computer programs have been developed to schedule operators on a weekly basis (Buffa, Cosgrove, and Luce, 1976). First, the daily requirements for the week, expressed in operator-hours, are estimated. Then, shifts are designed that conform to state and federal laws and union agreements, while matching the pattern of daily requirements as closely as possible. Day-off assignments are made for each operator, and based on seniority, operators select their work shift. In the first year after implementing the system, GTE realized a net annual savings of $170,000 in clerical and supervisory costs and a 6 percent increase in productivity.

Scheduling Police Officers. Police departments face requirements for police services that vary considerably throughout the day. Needs can be as much as eight times greater from 10 to 11 P.M. than from 5 to 6 A.M. A patrol car allocation model (PCAM) has been designed to allocate a certain number of cars to shifts, where a shift is defined as a specific eight-hour block of time on a particular day for a specific precinct (see Chaiken and Dormont, 1978). The model can also handle overlay shifts, which begin during one normal shift and end during the following shift.

This model has proven to be quite versatile. It can be used during budget preparation to determine the total number of patrol officers a department needs to meet stated performance standards. It can also be used to allocate officers to precincts and shifts and to study the effects of changes in performance standards or service-call priorities. Police departments that have used PCAM include those in Los Angeles, San Diego, Virginia Beach, Seattle, Atlanta, Toledo, Minneapolis, Wilmington, and New Brunswick, New Jersey. Managerial Practice 18.2 describes the San Francisco Police Department's experience in developing a new work-force scheduling system.

Managerial Practice 18.2

Scheduling Police Officers in the San Francisco Police Department

The San Francisco Police Department (SFPD) serves a population of 700,000 with about 850 officers on regular patrol duty. The city is divided into nine police precincts, with each staffing as many as 120 officers. In 1986 the SFPD was using a manual system to generate officer schedules, and there was no way to determine if the trial-and-error schedules were close to optimal with respect to serving the needs of the community. More importantly, the manual system was too cumbersome to evaluate alternative policies for scheduling and deploying officers.

A task force, after extensive study, decided that a new system was needed. The system had to be easy to use and capable of generating optimal and realistic schedules in less than 30 minutes on a microcomputer. It also had to use existing data sources and allow adjustments to suggested schedules in less than 60 seconds. An extensive review of the literature revealed that no such approach existed, so a new one had to be built. In addition to the technical requirements just mentioned, the system had to be capable of addressing a number of other issues:

- *A 10-hour day, 4-day week (4/10) versus an 8-hour day, 5-day week (5/8).* The Police Officers Association was very interested in the 4/10 option, but police management didn't know how that would affect coverage.
- *One officer per car versus two officers per car.* Many officers preferred the two-per-car option, but that too would affect coverage.
- *Fixed versus rotating schedules.* The rotating schedules, particularly when combined with the 4/10 option, were popular with the officers. However, rotating schedules tend to require more officers to achieve the same coverage because officers usually move in groups and group sizes must be approximately the same size. This constraint poses problems in covering peak days because there

would be either more or fewer officers than needed, relative to the fixed schedule approach.

- *Number of start times.* Technically, a shift could start on any one of the 168 (24 × 7) hours of the week, but that would cause a nightmare for administrators. The more shift starting times that are available, however, the closer officer capacity can match the anticipated load. Some balance was needed, and the new system had to enable an evaluation of the alternatives.
- *Minimum number of officers on duty.* The system had to allow for constraints imposing a minimum number of officers on duty at certain selected times of the day and week.
- *Nonpatrol duties.* Training and station duties had to be accounted for in the workload.

The new system had three major components. First, it made use of an existing forecasting system. For each of the 168 hours of the week, the forecasting component translated the number of calls for service into the number of officers required, modified for the proportion of two-officer car teams. It also added in the nonpatrol duties. Second, a mathematical model determined the best schedule, given the number of officers available. Finally, the last component allowed police personnel to modify the suggested schedules in an interactive mode.

The benefits accruing from the system are substantial. The SFPD now has 25 percent more patrol units available in time of need, the equivalent of adding 200 officers to the force at a cost of $11 million. In addition, response times have improved 20 percent. Even traffic citations have increased, by $3 million annually.

Source: Phillip Taylor and Stephen Huxley, "A Break from Tradition for the San Francisco Police: Patrol Officer Scheduling Using an Optimization-Based Decision Support System," *Interfaces* (January–February 1989), pp. 4–24.

SOLVED PROBLEMS

1. The Neptune's Den Machine Shop specializes in overhauling outboard marine motors. Some motors require replacement of broken parts, whereas others need a complete overhaul. Currently, five motors with varying problems are awaiting service. The best estimates for the labor times involved and the promise dates (the number of days from today) are shown in the following table. Customers usually do not pick up their motors early.

Motor	Estimated Labor Time (days)	Promise Date (days from now)
50-hp Evinrude	5	8
7-hp Chrysler	4	15
100-hp Mercury	10	12
4-hp Sportsman	1	20
75-hp Nautique	3	10

a. Develop separate schedules using the SPT and EDD rules.
   i. What is the average flow time for each schedule?
   ii. What is the percentage of past due jobs for each schedule?
   iii. Which schedule minimizes the maximum past due days for any motor?
b. For each schedule in part (a), calculate
   i. average work-in-process inventory (in motors).
   ii. average total inventory (in motors).

Solution a. Shortest processing time (SPT):

Repair Sequence	Process Time	Flow Time	Promise Date	Actual Pickup Date	Days Early	Days Past Due
4-hp Sportsman	1	1	20	20	19	
75-hp Nautique	3	4	10	10	6	
7-hp Chrysler	4	8	15	15	7	
50-hp Evinrude	5	13	8	13		5
100-hp Mercury	10	23	12	23		11
Total		49		81		

Earliest due date (EDD):

Repair Sequence	Process Time	Flow Time	Promise Date	Actual Pickup Date	Days Early	Days Past Due
50-hp Evinrude	5	5	8	8	3	
75-hp Nautique	3	8	10	10	2	
100-hp Mercury	10	18	12	18		6
7-hp Chrysler	4	22	15	22		7
4-hp Sportsman	1	23	20	23		3
Total		76		81		

  i. Average flow time for SPT is 9.8 (49/5) days. For EDD it is 15.2 (76/5) days.
  ii. Percentage of past due jobs for SPT is 40 (2/5) percent. For EDD it is 60 (3/5) percent.
  iii. The EDD schedule minimizes the maximum days past due but has a greater flow time and causes more jobs to be past due.

b. SPT:

$$\text{Average WIP} = \frac{\text{Total flow time}}{\text{Makespan}}$$

$$= \frac{49}{23} = 2.13 \text{ motors}$$

$$\text{Average total inventory} = \frac{\text{Total actual pickup times}}{\text{Makespan}}$$

$$= \frac{81}{23} = 3.52 \text{ motors}$$

EDD: $\text{Average WIP} = \dfrac{76}{23} = 3.30 \text{ motors}$

$$\text{Average total inventory} = \frac{81}{23} = 3.52 \text{ motors}$$

2. The following data were reported by the shop floor control system for order processing at the edge grinder. The current date is week 150. The number of remaining operations and the total work remaining include the operation at the edge grinder. All orders are available for processing, and none have been started yet.

Current Order	Process Time (hr)	Due Date (wk)	Remaining Operations	Total Work Remaining (wks)
A101	10	162	10	9
B272	7	158	9	6
C105	15	152	1	1
D707	4	170	8	18
E555	8	154	5	8

a. Specify the priorities for each job if the shop-floor control system uses
  i. slack per remaining operation (S/RO).
  ii. critical ratio (CR).
b. For each priority rule, calculate the average flow time per job at the edge grinder.

Solution   a. Specify the priorities for each job using the two dispatching rules.
  i. S/RO: The priority of a job equals the time remaining to its due date minus the total work remaining divided by the number of remaining operations. The sequence of production (priority in parentheses)

would be

$$\text{E555:} \quad \left(\frac{154 - 150 - 8}{5} = -0.80 \right)$$

$$\text{B272:} \quad \left(\frac{158 - 150 - 6}{9} = 0.22 \right)$$

$$\text{D707:} \quad \left(\frac{170 - 150 - 18}{8} = 0.25 \right)$$

$$\text{A101:} \quad \left(\frac{162 - 150 - 9}{10} = 0.30 \right)$$

$$\text{C105:} \quad \left(\frac{152 - 150 - 1}{1} = 1.00 \right)$$

ii. CR: The priority of a job equals the time remaining to its due date divided by the total work remaining. The sequence of production (priority in parentheses) would be

$$\text{E555:} \quad \left(\frac{154 - 150}{8} = 0.50 \right)$$

$$\text{D707:} \quad \left(\frac{170 - 150}{18} = 1.11 \right)$$

$$\text{A101:} \quad \left(\frac{162 - 150}{9} = 1.33 \right)$$

$$\text{B272:} \quad \left(\frac{158 - 150}{6} = 1.33 \right)$$

$$\text{C105:} \quad \left(\frac{152 - 150}{1} = 2.00 \right)$$

b. We are looking for the flow time of a given set of jobs at a single machine, so each job's flow time equals the flow time of the job just prior to it in sequence plus its own processing time. Consequently, the average flow times are

$$\text{S/RO:} \quad \frac{8 + 15 + 19 + 29 + 44}{5} = 23.0 \text{ hours}$$

$$\text{CR:} \quad \frac{8 + 12 + 22 + 29 + 44}{5} = 23.0 \text{ hours}$$

Thus the average flow time per job is the same for each rule. This result will not always be the case.

3. Treetop Airlines needs to schedule 10 aircraft of various designs for maintenance. For scheduling, it is convenient to think of two maintenance operations for each plane in the following sequence.

Operation 1: Engine and flight systems ground checks, replacing worn or damaged parts where necessary.
Operation 2: Flight tests and final safety checks.

Based on flight records and the specific design of each aircraft, management has estimated that each operation will require the following amount of time (in days):

Aircraft	Operation 1	Operation 2
1	3	1
2	4	4
3	3	2
4	6	1
5	1	2
6	3	6
7	2	4
8	4	8
9	8	2
10	1	1

Suppose that one of management's objectives is to minimize the total time that all 10 aircraft go without maintenance. This objective can be translated as minimizing the makespan of the 10-aircraft fleet. First, find a schedule that minimizes the makespan. Then calculate the average job flow time on an aircraft through the two operations, assuming that all 10 aircraft are available for maintenance now. What is the total elapsed time for maintaining all 10 aircraft?

Solution

Johnson's rule can be used to find the schedule that minimizes the total makespan. Four jobs are tied for the shortest process time: 1, 4, 5, and 10. We arbitrarily chose to start with job 5, the first on the list for operation 1. The 10 steps used to arrive at a sequence are as follows.

Select job 5 first.	5 – – – – – – – – –
Select job 10 next. Arbitrarily put toward front.	5–10 – – – – – – –
Select job 1 next. Put at end.	5–10 – – – – – – – –1
Put job 4 toward the end.	5–10 – – – – – – 4–1
Put job 7 toward the front.	5–10–7 – – – – – 4–1
Put job 3 toward the end.	5–10–7 – – – – 3–4–1
Put job 9 toward the end.	5–10–7 – – – 9–3–4–1
Put job 6 toward the front.	5–10–7–6 – – 9–3–4–1
Put job 2 toward the front.	5–10–7–6–2 – 9–3–4–1
Put job 8 in remaining space.	5–10–7–6–2–8–9–3–4–1

There are several optimal solutions to this problem because of the ties at the start of the scheduling procedure. All have the same makespan, however.

The schedule would be as follows.

Aircraft	Operation 1		Operation 2	
	Start	Finish	Start	Finish
5	0	1	1	3
10	1	2	3	4
7	2	4	4	8
6	4	7	8	14
2	7	11	14	18
8	11	15	18	26
9	15	23	26	28
3	23	26	28	30
4	26	32	32	33
1	32	35	35	36
Total				200

The makespan is 36 days. The average flow time is the sum of operation 2 finish times divided by 10, or 200/10 = 20 days.

4. The Food Bin grocery store operates 24 hours per day, 7 days per week. Fred Bulger, the store manager, has been analyzing the efficiency and productivity of store operations recently. For example, at present there are 10 checkout clerks on the first shift, from 8:00 A.M. to 5:00 P.M. However, Bulger has noticed a considerable amount of slack capacity on certain days of the week. These clerks could be used to bag groceries, but their wages are higher than those of the bagging clerks who should be doing that task. Consequently, Bulger decided to observe the need for checkout clerks on the first shift for a one-month period. Each time the queue in front of a cash register exceeded three customers, he recorded the need for another register to open. At the end of the month, he calculated the average number of checkout registers that should be open during the first shift each day. His results showed peak needs on Saturdays and Sundays.

Day	M	T	W	Th	F	S	Su
Requirements	3	4	4	3	4	7	8

Bulger now had to come up with a work-force schedule that guaranteed each checkout clerk two consecutive days off but still covered all requirements.

a. Develop a work-force schedule that covers all requirements while giving two consecutive days off to each clerk. How many clerks are needed? Assume that the clerks have no preference regarding which days they have off.

b. Specify the work schedule for each checkout clerk.

Solution   a. Use the method demonstrated in Application 18.3 to determine the number of clerks needed.

Clerk	M	T	W	Th	F	S	Su
1	3	4	4	3	4	7	8
2	3	4	3	2	3	6	7
3	2	3	2	2	3	5	6
4	1	2	2	2	2	4	5
5	1	2	1	1	1	3	4
6	0	1	0	1	1	2	3
7	0	1	0	0	0	1	2
8	0	0	0	0	0	0	1

The minimum number of clerks is 8.

b. One of many possible work schedules, based on the results in part (a), is:

Employee	M	T	W	Th	F	S	Su
1	Off	Off	X	X	X	X	X
2	X	X	X	Off	Off	X	X
3	X	X	Off	Off	X	X	X
4	Off	Off	X	X	X	X	X
5	X	X	X	Off	Off	X	X
6	Off	Off	X	X	X	X	X
7	X	X	X	Off	Off	X	X
8	X	X	X	X	Off	Off	X
No. on duty	5	5	7	4	4	7	8
Requirements	3	4	4	3	4	7	8
Slack	2	1	3	1	0	0	0

The slack in this schedule Monday–Thursday would indicate to Bulger the number of employees he might ask to work part time (fewer than 5 days per week). For example, clerk 2 might only work Saturdays and Sundays; clerk 5 only Tuesdays, Saturdays, and Sundays; and clerk 6 only Fridays, Saturdays, and Sundays. There would be no slack in that revised schedule.

FORMULA REVIEW

1. Critical ratio:

$$CR = \text{Time remaining to due date} \\ \text{divided by the total work time remaining}$$

2. Slack per remaining operation:

$$S/RO = \text{Time remaining to due date} \\ \text{minus total work time remaining} \\ \text{divided by the number of remaining operations}$$

CHAPTER HIGHLIGHTS

- Scheduling is the allocation of resources over a period of time to accomplish a specific set of tasks.

- Gantt charts are useful for depicting the sequence of work at a particular work station, as well as monitoring the progress of jobs in the system.

- There are many ways to schedule multiple jobs on multiple work stations. Performance measures that can be used to develop an acceptable schedule include average job flow time, makespan, percentage of jobs past due, average amount of time past due per job, average work-in-process inventory, average investment in total inventory, and utilization of equipment and workers.

- Dispatching procedures allow a schedule to evolve because the decision about which job to process next at a work station (or for the station to remain idle) is made when the work station becomes available for further processing. Priority rules are used to make these decisions. Local priority rules assign priorities on the basis of information concerning only the jobs in the individual work station queue. Examples of these rules are EDD, FCFS, and SPT. Global priority rules assign priorities on the basis of information from other machines or work stations, in addition to the one being scheduled. Examples of these rules are CR and S/RO. The choice of priority rule can affect the schedule performance measures that are of concern to management.

- Labor-limited systems add another dimension to operations scheduling. Not only must a decision be made about which job to process next at a work station but also about which work station an operator should work at next.

- Capacity considerations are important for scheduling services. If the capacity of the operating system is fixed, loads can be leveled by using approaches such as appointments, reservations, and backlogs. If service is determined by labor availability, work-force scheduling may be appropriate.

- A work-force schedule translates a staffing plan into a specific work schedule for each employee. Typical work-force scheduling considerations include capacity limits, service targets, consecutive days off, maximum number of workdays in a row, type of schedule (fixed or rotating), and vacation and holiday time.

KEY TERMS

dispatching procedures **730**
fixed schedule **742**
Gantt chart **727**
global priority rules **731**
job flow time **729**
labor-limited environment **738**
local priority rules **731**

machine-limited
  environment **738**
makespan **729**
operations scheduling **726**
past due **729**
priority sequencing rules **730**

rotating schedule **742**
total inventory **730**
utilization **730**
work-force scheduling **726**
work-in-process (WIP)
  inventory **729**

STUDY QUESTIONS

1. How does scheduling in general fit into overall operations management?

2. In the automobile parts example, we sequenced the jobs on the Watterson grinder in the order Ford–Plymouth–Pontiac. We used trial and error with Gantt charts. Specify a simple priority rule that would have yielded the same schedule. Use the information in Fig. 18.1.

3. What is the difference between the job flow-time measure and the makespan measure? When does makespan become relevant?

4. Suppose that you have two alternative approaches for determining machine schedules. One is an optimizing approach that can be run once a week on the computer. The other is a dispatching approach that utilizes priority rules to determine the schedule as it evolves. Discuss the advantages and disadvantages of each approach and the conditions under which each approach is likely to be better.

5. On what basis would you make a choice between local priority rules and global priority rules?

6. The shortest processing time (SPT) rule has been criticized because it tends to produce schedules having a large variance in past-due hours. That is, some jobs get through the production system quickly, whereas others (the ones that have long processing times) must spend considerable time in queue. Suggest a modification to the SPT rule to overcome this criticism.

7. It has been pointed out that there is a problem with S/RO when more than one job in queue has negative slack. For example, if job 1 has a slack of -1 with 1 operation remaining and job 2 has a slack of -2 with 10 operations remaining, S/RO would choose job 1 first because it has the smallest (most negative) ratio. Yet job 2 seems to be the one that should be processed next. Suggest a simple modification to the S/RO rule to overcome this difficulty.

8. Explain why management should be concerned about priority systems in manufacturing and service organizations.

9. Work-force schedules have a number of uses. Discuss these uses within the context of a service operation familiar to you.

10. Compare and contrast work-force scheduling with operations scheduling. Are they related in any way? If so, how?

PROBLEMS

Review Problems

1. The following second-shift schedule was developed for the boring mill and turret lathe operations at 2 P.M.

	Boring Mill		Turret Lathe	
Job	Setup	Process	Setup	Process
1			3:00–3:30	3:30–5:00
2	3:00–3:45	3:45–4:30	6:15–6:45	6:45–7:30
3	7:00–7:30	7:30–8:00	8:30–9:00	9:00–9:30
4	10:00–10:15	10:15–11:00		

a. Draw a Gantt chart for each machine.
b. Suppose a new job arrives at 2:30 P.M. requiring 45 minutes of setup and 45 minutes of processing on the boring mill first, then 30 minutes of setup and 1 hour of processing on the turret lathe. The job needs to be complete by 9:00 P.M. for final assembly. Based on the following assumptions, insert this job into the schedule.
   i. Each operator must have a dinner break from 5:00 to 5:30 P.M.
   ii. Interrupting a job already being processed with another job is too costly. However, dinner breaks in the middle of a job are permitted.
   iii. Jobs 2 and 3 can be processed in any order—that is, boring mill first or turret lathe first.
   iv. Job 3 must be completed by 9:30 P.M. to meet a subassembly schedule. The other jobs are not needed until the next day.

Draw revised Gantt charts for each machine.

2. The machine shop at Blackwell Industries

operates 24 hours a day and uses a numerically controlled welding machine. The load on the machine is monitored, and no more than 24 hours of work is released to the welding operator in one day. The data for a typical set of jobs are shown in Table 18.6. Management has been investigating scheduling procedures that would focus on reducing inventory and increasing customer service levels inside the shop. Assume that at 8:00 A.M. on Tuesday the NC welding machine was idle.

a. Develop a schedule using each of the following priority rules and draw a Gantt machine chart for each schedule.
   i. FCFS
   ii. SPT
   iii. EDD

b. For each schedule in part (a), calculate the average past due hours per job and the average flow time per job. Keep in mind that the jobs are available for processing at different times.

c. Comment on the customer-service and inventory performance of the three rules. What trade-offs should management consider in selecting rules for scheduling the welding machine in the future?

3. The Studywell Company manufactures modern wooden desks for ambitious college and high school students. Every weekend, management schedules overtime to reduce the backlog on their most popular models. The automatic routing machine is used to cut certain types of edges on the desk tops. The following orders need to be scheduled for the routing machine.

Order	Estimated Machine Time (hr)	Due Date (hr from now)
AZ135	14	14
DM246	8	20
SX435	10	6
PC088	3	18

The due dates reflect the need for the order to be at its next operation.

a. Develop separate schedules using the SPT and EDD rules.
   i. What is the average flow time for each schedule?
   ii. What is the percentage of past due jobs for each schedule?
   iii. Which schedule minimizes the maximum past due hours for any order?

b. For each schedule in part (a), calculate
   i. average work-in-process inventory (in orders).
   ii. average total inventory (in orders).

c. Comment on the performance of the two rules relative to these measures.

4. The drill press is a bottleneck operation in a production system. Currently, five jobs are waiting to be processed. The following are the available operations data. Assume that the current date is week 5 and that the number of remaining operations and the total work remaining include the operation at the drill press.

Job	Process Time	Due Date	Operations Remaining	Total Work Remaining (wks)
AA	4	10	3	4
BB	8	16	4	6
CC	13	21	10	9
DD	6	23	3	12
EE	2	12	5	3

TABLE 18.6

Job	Release Time	Lot #	Process	Setup Time (hr)	Due
1	8:00 A.M. Tuesday	80	.10 hr	1	3:00 A.M. Wednesday
2	8:45 A.M. Tuesday	100	.05 hr	2	11:00 P.M. Tuesday
3	9:00 A.M. Tuesday	160	.08 hr	2	10:00 P.M. Tuesday
4	9:15 A.M. Tuesday	300	.02 hr	4	6:00 P.M. Tuesday

a. Specify the priority for each job if the shop floor control system uses the following priority rules.
   i.   SPT
   ii. S/RO
   iii. EDD
   iv. CR

b. For each priority rule, calculate the average flow time per job at the furnace.

c. Which of these priority rules would work best for priority planning with an MRP system? Why?

5. Refer to the Gantt machine chart in Fig. 18.4.

a. Suppose that a routing requirement is that each job must be processed on machine A first. Can the makespan be improved? If so, draw a Gantt chart with the improved schedule. If not, state the reason for your answer.

b. Suppose there is no routing restriction on machine sequence. Jobs can be processed in any sequence on the machines. Can the makespan in the chart be improved in this case? If so, draw a Gantt chart with your schedule. If not, state the reason for your answer.

6. A manufacturer of small-boat sails has a group of custom sails awaiting the last two processing operations prior to sending the sails to their valued customers. Operation 1 must be performed prior to operation 2, and the jobs have different time requirements for each operation. The hours required are as follows:

Job	Operation 1	Operation 2
1	1	8
2	5	3
3	8	1
4	3	2
5	9	8
6	4	6
7	7	7
8	2	2
9	4	4
10	9	1

a. Determine the optimal sequence using Johnson's rule.

b. Draw a Gantt chart for each operation.

7. Mighty Metal Company is under tremendous pressure to complete a government contract for 6 orders in 20 working days. The orders are for spare parts for highway maintenance equipment. According to the government contract, a late penalty of $500 is imposed each day the order is late. Due to a nationwide increase in highway construction, Mighty Metal has received many orders for spare part replacement and the shop has been very busy. To complete the government contract, the parts must be deburred and heat treated. The production control manager has suggested the following schedule.

FIGURE 18.4   Machine

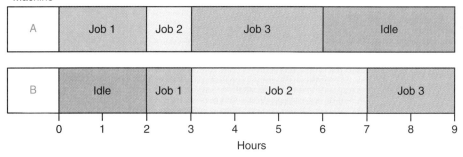

	Deburr		Heat Treat	
Job	Start	Finish	Start	Finish
1	0	2	2	5
2	2	5	5	9
3	5	11	11	12
4	11	14	14	20
5	14	15	20	23
6	15	18	23	25

Is there a better schedule to avoid the late penalties? If so, show it.

8. Sharon Tepper is the operations manager of the machine shop of Universal Manufacturing. She has to schedule eight jobs that are to be sent to final assembly for a very important customer order. Currently, all eight jobs are in department 12 and must be routed to department 22 next. Eric Koval, supervisor for department 12, is very concerned about keeping his work-in-process inventory low and is adamant about processing the jobs through his department on the basis of shortest processing time. Pat Mooney, supervisor for department 22, pointed out that if Koval wouldn't be so selfish, the orders could be finished and shipped earlier. Tepper realizes that the eight jobs have top priority and are very important to the operating profits of Universal. The processing times for each job in each department follow.

Process Time (days)

Job	Department 12	Department 22
1	2	3
2	4	6
3	7	3
4	5	8
5	4	2
6	10	6
7	8	6
8	2	5

   a. Determine a schedule for the operation in each department. Use SPT for department 12 and the same sequence for department 22.
      i. What is the average job flow time for department 12?

   ii. What is the makespan through both departments?
   b. Find a schedule that will minimize the makespan through both departments and then calculate the average job flow time for department 12.
   c. Discuss the trade-offs represented by these two schedules. What implications do they have for centralized scheduling?

9. Return to Solved Problem 3 and the Treetop Airlines' need to schedule ten aircraft for maintenance.
   a. Suppose that one of management's objectives is to maximize the number of aircraft in service that have received maintenance. This can be translated as minimizing the average job flow time of the ten aircraft through the two operations, assuming that once the plane has completed the second operation it immediately returns to service. First, devise a schedule using SPT. This can be accomplished by adding the two operation times for each aircraft and scheduling the aircraft as if there were only one operation. The resulting sequence is used for both operations. Then calculate the average flow time per aircraft. What is the total elapsed time to maintain all ten aircraft with your schedule?
   b. Compare the original solution to Solved Problem 3 and your solution in part (a). Discuss the trade-offs that must be made between the schedule and other factors that must be considered in scheduling the aircraft for maintenance.

10. John Mathews manages the Richland Distribution Center. After careful examination of his database information, he has determined the daily requirements for part-time loading dock personnel. The distribution center operates seven days a week, and the daily part-time staffing requirements are:

Day	M	T	W	Th	F	S	Su
Requirements	8	3	5	3	9	2	3

Find the minimum number of workers Mathews must hire. Prepare a work-force schedule for these individuals so that each will have two consecutive days off per week and all staffing requirements are satisfied. Give preference to the pair Saturday–Sunday in case of a tie.

11. Arthur Tumble manages a ski school in a large resort and is trying to develop a schedule for instructors. The instructors receive little salary and work just enough to earn room and board. They do receive free skiing, spending most of their free time tackling the resort's notorious double black diamond slopes. As a consequence, the instructors work only four days a week. One of the lesson packages offered at the resort is a four-day beginner package. Tumble likes to keep the same instructor with a group over the four-day period, so he schedules the instructors for four consecutive days and then three days off. Tumble uses years of experience with demand forecasts provided by management to formulate his instructor requirements for the upcoming month.

Day	M	T	W	Th	F	S	Su
Requirements	5	4	4	5	5	7	6

a. Determine how many instructors Tumble needs to employ. Give preference to Saturday and Sunday off.

b. Specify the work schedule for each employee. How much slack does your schedule generate for each day?

12. The mayor of Massilon, Ohio, wanting to be environmentally progressive, recently decided to implement a recycling plan. All residents of the city would receive a special three-part bin to separate their glass, plastic, and aluminum, and the city would be responsible for picking up the materials. A young city and regional planning graduate, Keith Raker, was hired to manage the recycling program. After careful study of the city's population density, Raker decided that the following number of recycling collectors

would be needed.

Day	M	T	W	Th	F	S	Su
Requirements	12	7	9	9	5	3	6

The requirements were based on the populations of the various housing developments and subdivisions in the city and surrounding communities. To motivate some areas to have their pickups scheduled on weekends, a special tax break would be given.

a. Find the minimum number of recycling collectors required if each employee works five days a week and has two consecutive days off. Give preference to S–Su when that pair is involved in a tie.

b. Specify the work schedule for each employee. How much slack does your schedule generate for each day?

c. Suppose Raker can smooth the requirements further through greater tax incentives. The requirements would be 8 on Monday and 7 on the other days of the week.

   i. How many employees would be needed now?

   ii. Giving preference to S–Su when that pair is involved in a tie doesn't yield the optimal solution. Find a better solution than the one in part (i) in terms of minimal total slack capacity.

   iii. Does smoothing of requirements have implications for capital investment in this business? If so, what are they?

Advanced Problems

Supplement Connection: Problem 14 requires prior reading of Supplement 3 (Transportation Method). A computer package is recommended for solving this problem.

13. Eight jobs must be processed on three machines in the sequence M1–M2–M3. The processing times (in hours) are:

Job	M1	M2	M3
1	2	4	6
2	5	1	4
3	2	3	5
4	3	5	2
5	1	5	3
6	2	6	2
7	4	2	6
8	2	1	2

Machine M2 is a bottleneck and management wants to maximize its use. Consequently, the schedule for the eight jobs, through the three machines, was based on the SPT rule on M2. The proposed schedule is 2–8–7–3–1–4–5–6.

a. It is now 4 P.M. on Monday. Suppose that processing on M2 is to begin at 7 A.M. on Tuesday. Using the proposed schedule, determine the schedules for M1 and M3 so that job 2 begins processing on M2 at 7:00 A.M. on Tuesday. Draw Gantt charts for M1, M2, and M3. What is the makespan for the eight jobs?

b. Find a schedule that better utilizes M2 and yields a shorter makespan.

14. A special case of the transportation problem (see Supplement 3) is the assignment problem. That is, each capacity source has only one unit of supply, each destination has only one unit of demand, and the number of sources equals the number of destinations. This would be the situation in operations scheduling when a scheduler needs to assign n workers to n tasks or n jobs to n machines. Apply the method in Supplement 3 to the following situation.

The operations manager of the Rapid Rental auto rental company has recognized the need for some kind of centralized scheduling. The company operates in eight cities in the Midwest. On several Fridays recently, it was obvious that four of the locations would each be one car short for the following Monday, while each of the other four locations would have one excess car. The driving distances between each of the locations

follow.

Locations Having 1 Extra Car	Locations Needing One More Car			
	Dayton	Columbus	Toledo	Indianapolis
Cincinnati	56	99	206	114
Cleveland	215	142	115	305
Sandusky	167	115	61	292
Akron	144	91	127	287

Last Friday when the Dayton manager realized the need for another car, she called the Cincinnati office, the closest agency with one, and had it send a car. The same thing occurred at the Columbus office, and Akron sent a car. The Toledo manager contacted the Sandusky office and received a car. By the time the Indianapolis manager began calling for a car, he was forced to take the only one left, which was in Cleveland, the farthest location from Indianapolis.

The operations manager realized that the managers were trying to reduce their own costs and get the closest car they could. However, the total distance traveled in obtaining these cars was 513 miles. Find an assignment of cars to locations that minimizes the number of miles driven.

15. The last few steps of a production process require two operations. Some jobs require processing on M1 before processing on M3. Other jobs require processing on M2 before M3. Currently, six jobs are waiting at M1 and four jobs are waiting at M2. The following data have been supplied by the shop-floor control system.

Job	Process Time (hr)			Due Date (hr)
	M1	M2	M3	
1	6	—	4	13
2	2	—	1	18
3	4	—	7	22
4	5	—	3	16
5	7	—	4	30
6	3	—	1	29
7	—	4	6	42
8	—	2	10	31
9	—	6	9	48
10	—	8	2	40

The due dates are expressed in hours from now.

a. Schedule this shop using the following rules.

 i. SPT   ii. EDD
 iii. S/RO   iv. CR

b. Discuss the operating implications of each of the schedules you developed in part (a).

16. Return to Problem 10 and the work-force schedule for part-time dock workers. Suppose that each part-time worker can work only three days, but the days must be consecutive. Devise an approach to this workforce scheduling problem. Your objective is to minimize total slack capacity. What is the minimum number of clerks needed now and what would their schedules be?

SELECTED REFERENCES

Andrews, B.H., and H.L. Parsons. "L.L. Bean Chooses a Telephone Agent Scheduling System." *Interfaces* (November–December 1989), pp. 1–9.

Baker, K.R. *Introduction to Sequencing and Scheduling.* New York: John Wiley & Sons, 1984.

Berry, W.L., and V. Rao. "Critical Ratio Scheduling: An Experimental Analysis." *Management Science*, vol. 22, no. 1 (October 1975), pp. 192–201.

Browne, J.J. "Simplified Scheduling of Routine Work Hours and Days Off." *Industrial Engineering* (December 1979), pp. 27–29.

Browne, J.J., and J. Prop. "Supplement to Scheduling Routine Work Hours." *Industrial Engineering* (July 1989), p. 12.

Browne, J.J., and R.K. Tibrewala. "Manpower Scheduling." *Industrial Engineering* (August 1975), pp. 22–23.

Buffa, E.S., M.J. Cosgrove, and B.J. Luce. "An Integrated Work Shift Scheduling System." *Decision Sciences*, vol. 7, no. 4 (October 1976), pp. 620–630.

Chaiken, J.M., and P. Dormont. "A Patrol Car Allocation Model: Capabilities and Algorithms." *Management Science*, vol. 24, no. 12 (August 1978), pp. 1291–1300.

Conway, R.W. "Priority Dispatching and Job Lateness in a Job Shop." *Journal of Industrial Engineering*, vol. 16, no. 4 (July 1965).

Day, James E., and Michael P. Hottenstein. "Review of Sequencing Research." *Naval Research Logistics Quarterly*, vol. 27, no. 1 (March 1970), pp. 11–39.

Fryer, J.S. "Operating Policies in Multiechelon Dual-Constraint Job Shops." *Management Science*, vol. 19, no. 9 (May 1963), pp. 1001–1012.

Hill, A.D., J.D. Naumann, and N.L. Chervany. "SCAT and SPAT: Large-Scale Computer-Based Optimization Systems for the Personnel Assignment Problem." *Decision Sciences*, vol. 14, no. 2 (April 1983), pp. 207–220.

Johnson, S.M. "Optimal Two Stage and Three Stage Production Schedules with Setup Times Included." *Naval Logistics Quarterly*, vol. 1, no. 1 (March 1954), pp. 61–68.

Kanet, J.K., and J.C. Hayya. "Priority Dispatching with Operation Due Dates in a Job Shop." *Journal of Operations Management*, vol. 2, no. 3 (May 1982), pp. 167–175.

Krajewski, L.J., and L.P. Ritzman. "Shift Scheduling in Banking Operations: A Case Application." *Interfaces*, vol. 10, no. 2 (April 1980), pp. 1–8.

LeGrande, E. "The Development of a Factory Simulation System Using Actual Operating Data." *Management Technology*, vol. 3, no. 1 (May 1963).

Mabert, V.A. "Static vs. Dynamic Priority Rules for Check Processing in Multiple Dispatch–Multiple Branch Banking." *Journal of Operations Management*, vol. 2, no. 1 (May 1982), pp. 187–196.

Marsten, R.E., M.R. Muller, and C.L. Killon. "Crew Planning at Flying Tiger: A Successful Application of Integer Programming." *Management Science*, vol. 25, no. 12 (December 1979), pp. 1175–1196.

Nelson, R.T. "Labor and Machine Limited Production Systems." *Management Science*, vol. 13, no. 9 (May 1967), pp. 648–671.

Saladin, Brooke A. "A Methodology for the Allocation of Police Patrol Vehicles." Unpublished dissertation, Ohio State University, 1980.

Tibrewala, R.K., D. Philippe, and J.J. Browne. "Optimal Scheduling of Two Consecutive Idle Periods." *Management Science*, vol. 19, no. 1 (September 1972), pp. 71–75.

Chapter 19

PROJECT
SCHEDULING AND
CONTROL

What tools are
available to
schedule and control
projects?

Which activities in
our project
determine the
duration of the entire
project?

How can we
incorporate
uncertainty in time
estimates for various
activities into project
planning?

Do network
planning methods
increase our
potential to control
costs and provide
better customer
service?

How do we
determine the effect
of limited resources
on the project
duration?

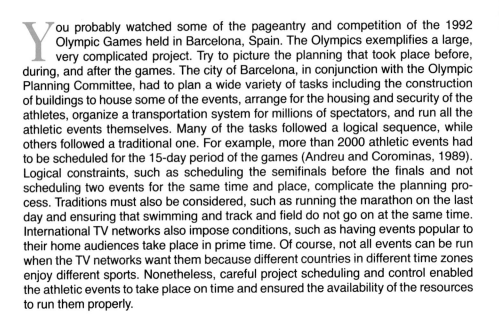

You probably watched some of the pageantry and competition of the 1992 Olympic Games held in Barcelona, Spain. The Olympics exemplifies a large, very complicated project. Try to picture the planning that took place before, during, and after the games. The city of Barcelona, in conjunction with the Olympic Planning Committee, had to plan a wide variety of tasks including the construction of buildings to house some of the events, arrange for the housing and security of the athletes, organize a transportation system for millions of spectators, and run all the athletic events themselves. Many of the tasks followed a logical sequence, while others followed a traditional one. For example, more than 2000 athletic events had to be scheduled for the 15-day period of the games (Andreu and Corominas, 1989). Logical constraints, such as scheduling the semifinals before the finals and not scheduling two events for the same time and place, complicate the planning process. Traditions must also be considered, such as running the marathon on the last day and ensuring that swimming and track and field do not go on at the same time. International TV networks also impose conditions, such as having events popular to their home audiences take place in prime time. Of course, not all events can be run when the TV networks want them because different countries in different time zones enjoy different sports. Nonetheless, careful project scheduling and control enabled the athletic events to take place on time and ensured the availability of the resources to run them properly.

Like the 1992 Summer Olympics, projects are unique operations with a finite life span. Generally, many interrelated activities must be scheduled and monitored within strict time, cost, and performance guidelines. In this chapter we consider methods for managing complex projects. We begin with a general introduction to the basic project management tools and some of the managerial aspects of project scheduling and control. We then explore the use of network models for managing projects, ending with an assessment of their limitations.

MANAGING PROJECTS

As we have noted, the Olympic Committee was responsible for scheduling and controlling a large project. We define **project** as an interrelated set of activities that has a definite starting and ending point and that results in a unique product. Examples of large projects include the following:

- Constructing a building or an amusement park
- Constructing a road, a dam, or an oil pipeline
- Renovating a blighted urban area
- Developing a prototype for a new ocean liner or airplane
- Installing a large computer system
- Introducing a new product
- Organizing a state fair
- Registering eligible recipients for a health-care program
- Redesigning the layout of a plant or office

Many construction projects were required for the 1992 Olympic Games in Barcelona. Shown here is the construction site of a pavillion.

Project Management Tools

As we discussed in Chapter 18, Gantt charts have long been used to schedule and control projects (see Figs. 18.1 and 18.2). For large projects, however, Gantt charts are difficult to work with. First, they don't directly recognize precedence relationships between activities. Second, they don't indicate which activities are crucial to completing the project on time.

Two network planning methods—**program evaluation and review technique (PERT)** and **critical path method (CPM)**—were developed in the 1950s to deal with some of the shortcomings of Gantt charts. As we shall see later, both methods look at a project as a set of interrelated activities that can be visually displayed in a **network diagram,** which consists of nodes (circles) and arcs (arrows) that depict the relationships between activities. Working with a network diagram, an analyst can determine which activities, if delayed, will delay the entire project.

Early differences between PERT and CPM concerned time estimates. PERT was developed for the U.S. Navy's Polaris missile project, which involved 3000 separate contractors and suppliers. Because many of the project's activities had never been performed before, PERT was developed to handle uncertain time estimates. In retrospect, PERT is generally credited with reducing the project's completion time by at least 18 months.

J.E. Kelly of Remington-Rand and M.R. Walker of Du Pont developed CPM as a means of scheduling maintenance shutdowns at chemical processing plants. Because maintenance projects were routine in the chemical industry, reasonably accurate time estimates for activities were available. Thus CPM was based on the assumption that project activity times can be estimated accurately and do not vary.

Today, the differences between PERT and CPM are minor. Basically, either approach can cope with uncertainty. For purposes of our discussion, we don't make arbitrary distinctions between these methods. We simply refer to them collectively as PERT/CPM.

Managerial Aspects

Given the finite nature of projects, project management is very goal oriented. Unlike the manager of a business, the project manager knows that when the team has accomplished its assigned objectives, it could disband. Team members might move on to other projects or return to their regular jobs.

Managing a complex project involving thousands of interrelated activities and personnel with diverse backgrounds and skills is a tremendous challenge. Usually, the activities to be performed are unique. Thus the project manager may have difficulty falling back on prior experience or established procedures. Furthermore, many team members will not be associated with the project for its full duration. They may view the project as disruptive to their regular work relationships and routines. Others will experience conflicts in loyalty or in demands on their time between their projects and department supervisors. But, in spite of these potential difficulties, working on projects also offers substantial rewards—the excitement of dynamic work, the satisfaction of solving challenging problems, the status of membership on an elite team, and the opportunity to work with and learn from other skilled professionals.

Project managers must stay on top of their projects to meet schedules and keep costs within budget. In August 1983 the Florida Power and Light Company accomplished a rare feat: It completed construction of a nuclear power plant in just over six years, only four months beyond a schedule set in 1977. On the average, it takes 10 to 12 years to build such a complex project. However, Florida Power and Light set up teams to handle specific problems, and managers made sure their suppliers upheld contractual commitments. A computer tracked the progress of each of the 20,000 tasks required to finish the plant. For each month that such a plant runs over schedule, nearly 770,000 barrels of oil are consumed in the production of energy at a cost of $23 million to rate payers. In addition, the capital cost of the plant would rise by $13 million, increasing the cost to rate payers by $2.5 million annually over the life of the plant.

However, Murphy's law—"If something can go wrong, it will"—applies to all projects. As Managerial Practice 19.1 illustrates, unexpected problems can cause delays, requiring rescheduling and reallocation of resources—and often resulting in severe financial repercussions. Frequently, managers must make quick decisions on the basis of incomplete information. To maintain control, they need the capability to answer "what-if" questions regarding the timing of project activities and to evaluate the time and cost implications of resource trade-offs. Network planning models are very useful for these purposes.

Software packages are growing in complexity. They must work on networks of PCs, mainframes,

Software Project Management at Lotus Development Corporation

delays had devastating effects on profitability. Sales lagged in 1988 as customers stopped buying the standard 1-2-3 in anticipation of the new version. In addition, costs grew significantly during the Release 3 project, in large part due to a work force increase to speed up the project. After Lotus announced the delivery date postponements, its stock dropped 57 percent.

and work stations, across dozens of different technical standards. Many programs include a graphical interface that make them easier to use but more difficult to produce. Often this complexity causes delivery delays. Such was the case with Lotus Development Corporation's new 1-2-3 spreadsheet program called Release 3. It has three-dimensional displays and can retrieve data from other programs. Lotus took three years to develop the new release—after experiencing several delivery delays—too late to meet the promised market date. These

The project's delays can be attributed to two main causes. First, the product's design was difficult and complex. Whereas Lotus 1-2-3 required only two developers, the Release 3 project required 35. Second, the programmers did not work to a coordinated schedule, and nobody knew how their task fit into the overall scheme of things. Halfway into the project, Lotus management realized that drastic changes had to be made. Management thus required that the programmers submit weekly schedules and progress reports. In addition, a manager personally reviewed the code written each day. Although management could not change the complexity of the program, the new procedures did help the rest of the project run smoothly.

In June 1989 Release 3 was finally ready for delivery. Even though Lotus took a financial beating for a period of time, the experience has taught the company how to better manage complex software projects—which should put it in a better competitive position in the future.

*S*ystems analysts at work at Lotus.

Source: "The Spreadsheet That Nearly Wore Lotus Out," *Business Week* (July 3, 1989), pp. 62–64.

PROJECT MANAGEMENT USING NETWORK MODELS

Managing a project, regardless of its size and complexity, requires identifying every activity to be undertaken and planning when each activity must begin and end to complete the overall project on time. To achieve that goal, the project manager needs an effective method for organizing a network of interrelated activities and personnel. The degree of difficulty in scheduling is a function of the number of activities, their required sequence, and their timing. Typically, all projects managed with network models involve the following steps:

1. Describe the project.
2. Diagram the network.

3. Determine time estimates.
4. Determine the critical path.
5. Develop the project plan.
6. Monitor the project.

Describe the Project

The project manager must first describe the project in terms that everyone involved will understand. This description should include a clear statement of the project's end point—for example, a completed software package. In addition, the project manager must carefully define all project activities and precedence relationships. An **activity** is the smallest unit of work effort consuming both time and resources that the project manager can schedule and control. A **precedence relationship** is a sequencing constraint between related activities; that is, it determines that one activity cannot start until a preceding activity has been completed. For example, brochures announcing a conference for executives cannot be sent out (activity B) until the brochure is designed by the program committee (activity A). In this case, activity A must precede activity B.

Just what constitutes an activity for the purpose of the project description can become an issue. A project manager's list of activities will likely be more general than the activity list of those managing various aspects of the project. For example, the manager of a project to start manufacturing in a foreign country may include on her list of activities "construct the plant." This indicates that completion of construction will have a major bearing on when operations can begin. However, she does not have to list the many activities included in the construction process. That will be the responsibility of the construction supervisor she will employ. In general, a manager's project description should reflect only the level of detail that he or she needs to make scheduling and resource allocation decisions.

Diagram the Network

Diagramming a project as a network first requires establishing the precedence relationships between activities. For complex projects this task can be tedious. Nevertheless, it is essential because incorrect or omitted precedence relationships will result in costly delays. As we have said, a project is represented by a network diagram, consisting of nodes (circles) and arcs (arrows) that depict the relationships between activities. Interpretation of the graphic symbols will differ, depending on the specific modeling technique used, as illustrated in Fig. 19.1. One approach, the **activity-on-arc (AOA) network,** uses arcs to represent activities and nodes to represent events. An **event** is the point at which one or more activities are to be completed and one or more other activities are to begin. An event consumes neither time nor resources. Because the AOA approach emphasizes activity connection points, we say that it is event oriented. As Fig. 19.1(a) shows, precedence relationships require that an event not occur until all preceding activities have been completed.

A second approach is the **activity-on-node (AON) network** in which the nodes represent activities and the arcs indicate the sequence in which they are

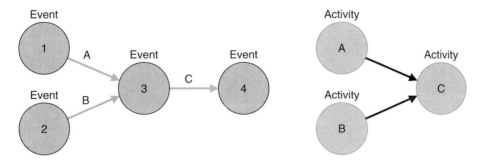

(a) AOA approach: Event 4 cannot take place until activities A, B, and C have been completed.

(b) AON approach: Activity C cannot take place until activities A and B have been completed.

FIGURE 19.1 AOA and AON Approaches to Activity Relationships

performed. This approach is activity oriented. The precedence relationships in Fig. 19.1(b) require than an activity cannot begin until all preceding activities have been completed. We shall use AON networks in all our examples because they are easier to construct than AOA networks. (We used AON networks to describe assembly lines in Chapter 10.) Nonetheless, you could perform all of the analyses we demonstrate with AOA networks as well.

Application 19.1 | *Diagramming an AON Network*

In the interest of better serving the public in Benjamin County, St. Adolf's Hospital has decided to relocate from Christofer to Northville, a large suburb that at present has no major medical facility. The move to Northville would mean constructing a new hospital and making it operational. Judy Kramer, executive director of the board of St. Adolf's, must prepare for a hearing, scheduled for next week, before the Central Ohio Hospital Board (COHB) on the proposed project. Part of the hearing will address the specifics of the total project, including time and cost estimates for its completion.

With the help of her staff, Kramer has identified 11 major project activities. She has also specified the immediate predecessors (those activities that must be completed before a given activity can begin) for each activity. The results are as follows:

Activity	Description	Immediate Predecessor(s)
A	Select administrative and medical staff.	—
B	Select site and do site survey.	—
C	Select equipment.	A
D	Prepare final construction plans and layout.	B
E	Bring utilities to the site.	B
F	Interview applicants and fill positions in nursing, support staff, maintenance, and security.	A
G	Purchase and take delivery of equipment.	C
H	Construct the hospital.	D
I	Develop an information system.	A
J	Install the equipment.	E, G, H
K	Train nurses and staff.	F, I, J

Draw the AON network diagram for this project.

Solution   An AON network for the hospital project, based on Kramer's 11 activities and their precedence relationships, is shown in Fig. 19.2. It depicts activities as circles, with arrows indicating the sequence in which they are to be performed. Activities A and B emanate from the start node because they have no immediate predecessors. The arrows connecting activity A to activities C, F, and I indicate that all three require completion of activity A before they can begin. Similarly, activity B must be completed before activities D and E can begin. The rest of the diagram follows the same logical sequence. Start and finish nodes do not actually represent activities. They merely provide beginning and ending points for the network.

The network diagram provides the basis for project analysis. Thus the diagram must accurately represent all activities and precedence relationships. For example, having a loop in the network where activity B preceded activity D, D preceded E, and E preceded B wouldn't make sense. Modeling a large project as a network is a useful process in itself because, at the very least, it forces management to identify necessary activities and recognize the precedence relationships between them.

Determine Time Estimates

Project managers must decide whether to use probabilistic (uncertain) or deterministic (certain) time estimates for activities. For projects that have been done many times before, a manager would feel safe using deterministic time

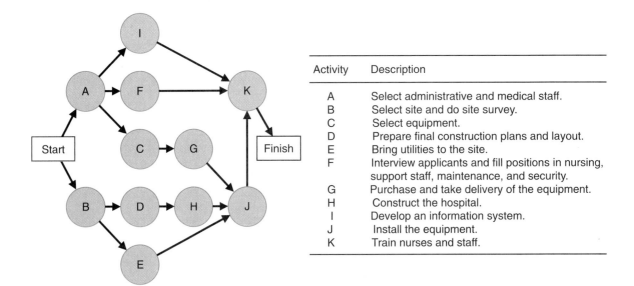

Activity	Description
A	Select administrative and medical staff.
B	Select site and do site survey.
C	Select equipment.
D	Prepare final construction plans and layout.
E	Bring utilities to the site.
F	Interview applicants and fill positions in nursing, support staff, maintenance, and security.
G	Purchase and take delivery of the equipment.
H	Construct the hospital.
I	Develop an information system.
J	Install the equipment.
K	Train nurses and staff.

FIGURE 19.2   AON Network Diagram for the St. Adolf's Hospital Project

FIGURE 19.3

AON Network
Showing Activity
Times

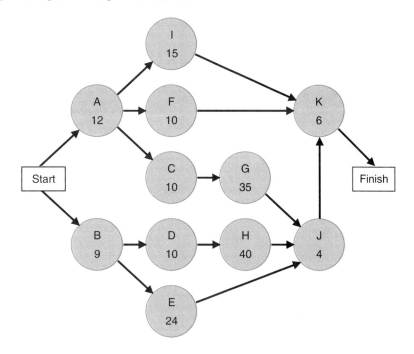

estimates. For now, let's assume that Judy Kramer has extensive experience relocating hospitals and that she feels certain enough of the time each activity will take to use deterministic estimates. (We discuss probabilistic estimates later in the chapter.) Figure 19.3 shows the estimated times for each activity of the St. Adolf's project.

Determine the Critical Path

A crucial aspect of project management is time of completion. The sum of all the times for each activity in Fig. 19.3 is 175 weeks. This estimate reflects strictly sequential work, that is, work proceeding on only one activity at a time. However, PERT/CPM is based on the assumption that the resources are available to proceed on various activities simultaneously. Thus the project manager—at this stage—considers only the precedence relationships and the activity times in scheduling activities. Indeed, Fig. 19.3 indicates that the project can be finished in much less than 175 weeks.

To determine the earliest completion time of a project, the project manager must first find the critical path. A *path* is a sequence of activities through the network between a project's start and finish. As you can see in Fig. 19.3, the network describing the hospital relocation has five paths: A–I–K, A–F–K, A–C–G–J–K, B–D–H–J–K, and B–E–J–K. The **critical path** is the sequence of activities between a project's start and finish that takes the longest time to complete. In other words, the activities along the critical path determine the completion time of the project. The critical path has zero slack time at each activity along the path. **Activity slack** is the maximum time an activity can be delayed without delaying the entire project. We calculate activity slack using four time values for each activity.

1. Earliest start time is the earliest possible beginning time for an activity.
2. Earliest finish time is the earliest start time plus the time needed for an activity.
3. Latest start time is the latest possible beginning time for an activity that will allow the project to be completed on schedule.
4. Latest finish time is the latest possible completion time for an activity that will not delay the entire project completion time.

Earliest Start and Earliest Finish Times. To calculate the earliest start and earliest finish times, we make use of two simple concepts:

1. The **earliest start time (ES_i)** for an activity i is equal to the latest of the earliest finish times of the immediately preceding activities. That is,

$$ES_i = \max [EF \text{ times of all activities immediately preceding activity } i]$$

2. The **earliest finish time (EF_i)** for an activity i is equal to its earliest start time plus its expected duration:

$$EF_i = ES_i + t_e$$

Application 19.2   *Calculating Earliest Start and Earliest Finish Times*

Calculate the earliest start and finish times for the activities in the hospital project. Figure 19.3 contains the activity times.

Solution   We begin at the start node at time zero. Activities A and B have no predecessors, so the earliest start times for these activities are also zero. The earliest finish times for these activities are

$$EF_A = 0 + 12 = 12 \quad \text{and} \quad EF_B = 0 + 9 = 9$$

Thus EF_A becomes the earliest start time for activities I, F, and C; EF_B becomes the earliest start time for activities D and E. Consequently,

$$EF_I = 12 + 15 = 27 \quad EF_D = 9 + 10 = 19$$
$$EF_F = 12 + 10 = 22 \quad EF_E = 9 + 24 = 33$$
$$EF_C = 12 + 10 = 22$$

Similarly, $EF_G = 22 + 35 = 57$ and $EF_H = 19 + 40 = 59$. Activity J has several predecessors, so the earliest time the next activity can begin is the maximum of the finish times of any of the preceding activities: $ES_J = \max [EF_G, EF_H, EF_E] = 59$. Thus $EF_J = 59 + 4 = 63$. Finally, $ES_K = \max [EF_I, EF_F, EF_J] = 63$ and $EF_K = 63 + 6 = 69$. This result implies that the earliest the project can be completed is week 69. (Note that the EF of the last activity is also the project's duration.) The earliest start and finish times for all activities are shown in Fig. 19.4.

Latest Start and Latest Finish Times. To calculate the latest start and latest finish times, we start at the finish node and assume that the project is to be completed

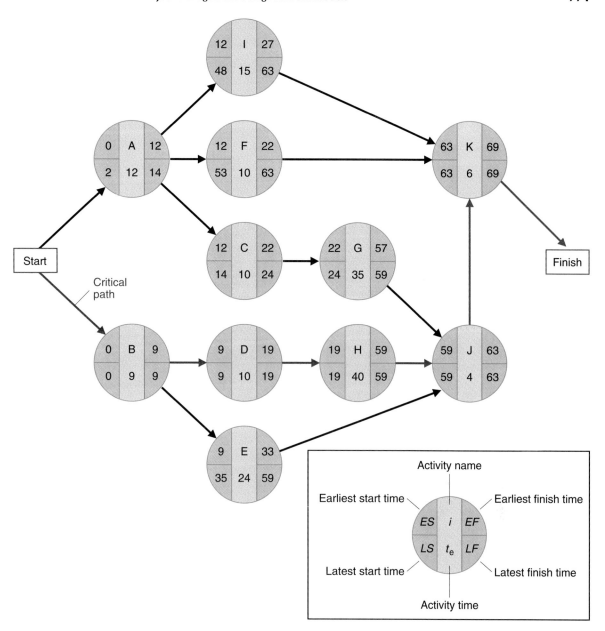

FIGURE 19.4   Network Showing Data Needed for Activity Slacks

at the maximum of the earliest finish times of all activities immediately preceding it.* We use two other concepts.

1. The **latest start time** (LS_i) for an activity i is equal to its latest finish time minus its expected duration:

$$LS_i = LF_i - t_e$$

2. The **latest finish time** (LF_i) for an activity i is equal to the earliest of the latest start times of all activities immediately following it. That is,

$$LF_i = \min\ [LS \text{ times of all activities}$$
$$\text{immediately following activity } i]$$

Application 19.3   *Calculating Latest Start and Latest Finish Times*

For the hospital project, calculate the latest start and latest finish times for each activity using Fig. 19.3.

Solution   We begin by setting the latest finish activity time of activity K at week 69, its earliest finish time calculated in Application 19.2. Thus the latest start time for activity K is

$$LS_K = 69 - 6 = 63$$

If activity K is to start no later than week 63, all its predecessors must finish no later than that time. Consequently,

$$LF_I = LF_F = LF_I = 63$$

The latest start times for these activities are

$$LS_I = 63 - 15 = 48$$
$$LS_F = 63 - 10 = 53$$
$$LS_I = 63 - 4 = 59$$

After we have calculated LS_I, we can calculate the latest start times for the immediate predecessors of activity J:

$$LS_G = 59 - 35 = 24$$
$$LS_H = 59 - 40 = 19$$
$$LS_E = 59 - 24 = 35$$

Similarly, we can now calculate latest start times for activities C and D:

$$LS_C = 24 - 10 = 14 \quad \text{and} \quad LS_D = 19 - 10 = 9$$

Activities A and B each have more than one immediate following activity. $LF_A = \min$ $[LS_I, LS_F, LS_C] = 14$, and $LS_A = 14 - 12 = 2$; $LF_B = \min\ [LS_D, LS_E] = 9$, and $LS_B = 9 - 9 = 0$. This result implies that activity B must be started immediately if the project is to be completed by week 69. The latest start and latest finish times for all activities are shown in Fig. 19.4.

---

*Alternatively, the negotiated contract due date could be used. In that case, the activity slacks on the critical path may not be zero.

Activity Slack. Slack information is useful to project managers because it helps them to make decisions regarding reallocation of resources. Resources could be taken from activities with slack and given to other activities that are behind schedule until the slack is used up. We can calculate activity slack in one of two ways:

$$S_i = LS_i - ES_i \quad \text{or} \quad S_i = LF_i - EF_i$$

Application 19.4	Calculating Activity Slack

Calculate the slack for the activities in the hospital project. Use the data in Fig. 19.4.

Solution — We can use either starting times or finishing times. The accompanying table shows the slack for each activity, calculated by $LS_i - ES_i$ or $LF_i - EF_i$.

Activity Slacks for the St. Adolf's Hospital Project

Node	Duration	Start		Finish		Slack	Critical Path?
		Earliest	Latest	Earliest	Latest		
A	12	0	2	12	14	2	No
B	9	0	0	9	9	0	Yes
C	10	12	14	22	24	2	No
D	10	9	9	19	19	0	Yes
E	24	9	35	33	59	26	No
F	10	12	53	22	63	41	No
G	35	22	24	57	59	2	No
H	40	19	19	59	59	0	Yes
I	15	12	48	27	63	36	No
J	4	59	59	63	63	0	Yes
K	6	63	63	69	69	0	Yes

The slack at an activity depends on the performance of activities leading to it. If the time for activity A proved to be 14 weeks instead of 12 weeks, the slack for activities C and G would be zero. The time for activity A could have increased because of unexpected work delays or because resources were shifted from activity A to some activity that was behind schedule. Slack is shared among all activities on a particular path.

Critical Path. We can now identify the critical path. All activities on the critical path have zero slack. The activity string B–D–H–J–K constitutes the critical path for the hospital project. The red line in Fig. 19.4 denotes the critical path, and the preceding table shows how it can be identified in report form.

The critical path is important because it defines the completion time of the project. Any delays in activities along the critical path delay project completion. Adding the expected times for each activity along the critical path, we determine that the expected time to complete the hospital project is 69 weeks. Thus Judy Kramer should focus more attention on these activities in managing the project, although if activity A or C were to fall behind by two weeks, they and activity G would be on the critical path as well. Using up slack can result in more than one critical path for a project.

Rather than calculating activity slack first, we could have found the critical path by enumerating all the activity paths in the network and identifying the one having the longest cumulative time. Table 19.1 shows this solution, mainly to demonstrate that the path having the minimum slack is also the *longest* path in the network. We emphasize that manually finding the critical path in this way is easy for small projects; however, computers must be used to find it for large, complex projects. Computer routines normally compute activity slack reports giving information as shown in the table in Application 19.4 because project managers want this information anyway. Identification of the critical path is a by-product of that information.

Monitor Project Progress

Even the best laid project plans can go awry. Progress must be monitored so that delays can be readily identified. A slack-sorted report on a weekly basis (or some other suitable schedule) is helpful in this regard. Suppose that in the hospital project, 16 weeks have passed and activity A has just been completed because it was late in getting started. Consequently, activity A was completed 4 weeks late (see Fig. 19.4). Also suppose that activity B took 10 weeks instead of the expected 9 weeks. Table 19.2 shows a slack-sorted report as of the sixteenth week of the project. Activities A and B are not shown because they have already been completed.

Note that activities C, G, J, and K now have negative slack and replace activities D and H on the critical path. Negative slack occurs when the assumptions used to compute the planned slack prove to be invalid. In this example, the start date of activity A was later than anticipated and the activity time of B was longer than expected. Activities that depend on the timely completion of activities A and B show negative slacks because they have been pushed beyond their planned latest start dates. The activities at the top of the report are more critical than those at the bottom. If the original completion target of week 69 is still valid, the project manager would try to make up two weeks of time somewhere along path C–G–J–K. However, to make the deadline, one week will also have to be made up along path D–H. If that time is made up, there will be two critical paths: C–G–J–K and D–H–J–K. Managers can use slack-sorted reports such as this one more conveniently than a network diagram. Most project managers work with this type of computer report.

TABLE 19.1 / *Network Paths for the Hospital Project*

Path	Expected Time (wk)	Path	Expected Time (wk)
A–F–K	28	B–D–H–J–K	69 (critical)
A–I–K	33	B–E–J–K	43
A–C–G–J–K	67		

TABLE 19.2 / *Slack-Sorted Computer Report*

Activity	Duration	Earliest Start	Latest Start	Slack	Critical Path?
C	10	16	14	−2	Yes
G	35	26	24	−2	Yes
J	4	61	59	−2	Yes
K	6	65	63	−2	Yes
D	10	10	9	−1	No
H	40	20	19	−1	No
E	24	10	35	25	No
I	15	16	48	32	No
F	10	16	53	37	No

PROBABILISTIC TIME ESTIMATES

To this point, we have assumed that the time estimates for the project were certain. Many times, however, managers must deal with uncertainty, which can be the result of labor shortages, weather, supply delays, or accidents. In these cases, probabilistic time estimates can be used.

Estimating Activity Times

Suppose that a project manager realizes early in planning that the project will not be quite like others he or she has managed. Consequently, uncertainty must be incorporated into the time estimates for the activities. While there are several ways to accomplish this, we shall discuss the method originally proposed for the PERT method.

In this approach, the manager meets with those responsible for each activity and gets three reasonable time estimates for all activities under their control. The time estimates should be based on the assumption that all the resources needed to complete the activity within its most likely time are available during a normal work period. There are three time estimates:

1. **Most optimistic time (a).** The shortest time in which the activity can be completed, if all goes exceptionally well. The probability of completing the activity sooner is estimated to be only one chance in a hundred.
2. **Most likely time (m).** The best guess of the time required to perform the activity if the activity could be repeated many times under similar circumstances (no learning factor).
3. **Most pessimistic time (b).** The longest estimated time required to perform an activity, assuming that everything that could go wrong does go wrong. The probability that it will take more time to complete the activity is estimated to be only one chance in a hundred.

Calculating Time Statistics

The time estimates give the manager enough information to estimate the mean and variance of a probability distribution for each activity if he or she is willing to make several key statistical assumptions (Littlefield and Randolph, 1991). In PERT/CPM, each activity time is treated as though it were a random variable derived from a beta probability distribution. The primary reason for choosing this distribution is that it can take on a variety of shapes, allowing the most likely time estimates to fall anywhere between the most pessimistic and most optimistic time estimates. This condition is not possible with just any distribution. For example, the normal distribution is symmetrical, requiring the mode to be equidistant from the end points. This condition can be unduly restrictive.

There are two other key assumptions. First, we assume that a, m, and b can be estimated accurately. Of course, accuracy is a difficult attribute to measure in this case. The estimates might best be considered values that define a reasonable time range for the activity duration, negotiated between the manager and the employees responsible for the activities. Second, we assume that the standard deviation of the activity time is one-sixth the range, defined by the difference between b and a. This makes intuitive sense because, for example, 6 standard deviations will span approximately 99.74 percent of the normal distribution. Given these assumptions, the derivation of the mean and variance of each activity's probability distribution is complex, involving approximations to nonlinear equations.

These derivations show that the mean of the beta distribution can be estimated using the following weighted average of the three time estimates. Note that the most likely time is weighted four times greater than the most pessimistic or most optimistic estimates.

$$t_e = \frac{a + 4m + b}{6}$$

The variance of the beta distribution for each activity is

$$\sigma^2 = \left(\frac{b - a}{6}\right)^2$$

The variance increases as the difference between the most pessimistic and most optimistic time estimates increases. This result implies that the less certain a person is in estimating the actual time for an activity, the greater will be the variance.

Application 19.5   *Calculating Means and Variances*

Suppose that Judy Kramer has arrived at the following time estimates for activity B (site selection and survey) of the hospital project:

$$a = 7 \text{ weeks} \qquad m = 8 \text{ weeks} \qquad b = 15 \text{ weeks}$$

Calculate the expected time for activity B and the variance.

Solution   The expected time for activity B is

$$t_e = \frac{7 + 4(8) + 15}{6} = \frac{54}{6} = 9 \text{ weeks}$$

Note that the expected time (9 weeks) does not equal the most likely time (8 weeks) for this activity. These times will be equal only when the most likely time is equidistant from the most optimistic and most pessimistic times. We calculate the variance for activity B as follows:

$$\sigma^2 = \left(\frac{15 - 7}{6}\right)^2 = \left(\frac{8}{6}\right)^2 = 1.78$$

The accompanying table shows expected activity times and variances for the activities listed in Judy Kramer's project description. Note that the greatest uncertainty lies with the time estimate for activity I, followed by the estimates for activities E and G. The expected times for each activity will prove useful in determining the critical path.

Time Estimates and Activity Statistics for the St. Adolf's Hospital Project

	Time Estimates (weeks)			Activity Statistics		
Activity	Most Optimistic (a)	Most Likely (m)	Most Pessimistic (b)	Expected Time (t_e)	Variance (σ^2)	Critical Path?
A	11	12	13	12	0.11	No
B	7	8	15	9	1.78	Yes
C	5	10	15	10	2.78	No
D	8	9	16	10	1.78	Yes
E	14	25	30	24	7.11	No
F	6	9	18	10	4.00	No
G	25	36	41	35	7.11	No
H	35	40	45	40	2.78	Yes
I	10	13	28	15	9.00	No
J	1	2	15	4	5.44	Yes
K	5	6	7	6	0.11	Yes

Analyzing Probabilities

Because the time estimates for activities involve uncertainty, project managers find it useful to know the probability of achieving any activity in a specific amount of time. To obtain it, we must define the probability distribution of achievement dates for an activity. Managers often focus on the project completion date, so we'll use the *finish* node as an example. Before we proceed, however, we must make clear that the analysis relies on the independence of the activities. In this context, activities are independent if the duration time of one activity does not depend on the duration time of any other activity. A dependency could happen, for example, if the same work crew is assigned two activities that can be done at the same time. The more persons assigned to one activity, the longer it takes to do the other activity.

To develop the probability distribution for the project completion time, we assume that the duration times of activities along the critical path will determine the completion time of the project. This assumption is reasonable if no other path in the network has low amounts of slack. Because the activity duration times are independent random variables, we can make use of the central limit theorem, which states that the sum of a group of independent, identically distributed random variables approaches a normal distribution as the number of random variables increases. The mean of the normal distribution is the sum of the expected activity times on the critical path, or the earliest expected finish time for the project. For example, the probability distribution for the completion time of the hospital project is normal with a mean of 69 weeks.

Similarly, because of the assumption of activity time independence, we use the sum of the variances of the activities along the critical path as the variance of the project time distribution. From the table in Application 19.5, we find that the variance of the critical path B–D–H–J–K would be $1.78 + 1.78 + 2.78 + 5.44 + 0.11 = 11.89$.

To analyze probabilities of completing the project by a certain date using the normal distribution, we can use the z-transformation formula as follows:

$$z = \frac{T' - TE}{\sqrt{\Sigma\sigma_{CP}^2}}$$

where T' = due date for the project
TE = earliest expected completion date for the project
$\Sigma\sigma_{CP}^2$ = sum of the variances on the critical path

The procedure for assessing the probability of completing any activity in a project by a given date is similar to the one we just discussed. However, instead of the critical path, we would use the longest time path of activities from the start node to the activity node in question.

Application 19.6 | *Calculating the Probability of Completing a Project by a Given Date*

Calculate the probability that the hospital will become operational in 72 weeks.

Solution   With a critical path length of 69 weeks and a variance of 11.89, we can calculate the z-value as follows:

$$z = \frac{72 - 69}{\sqrt{11.89}} = \frac{3}{3.45} = 0.87$$

Using the normal distribution table in Appendix 3, we find that the probability is about 0.20 that the project will exceed 72 weeks. Thus there is an 80 percent probability that the project will be completed in 72 weeks. This probability is shown graphically in Fig. 19.5.

Thus we can use the uncertainty in activity time estimates to make statements about the chances of completing a project on schedule. The analysis hinges on the identification of the critical path. We calculated the critical path on the basis of the expected times for each activity and disregarded the variances. Conceivably, one or more network paths for a project may be shorter than the critical path but have enough variance in activity time estimates to

FIGURE 19.5

Probability of
Exceeding 72 Weeks

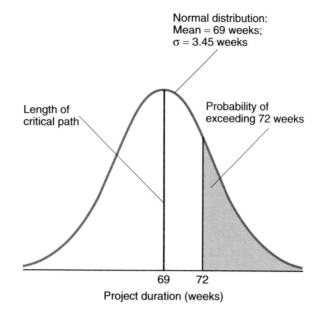

actually become the critical path sometime during the project. Such is the case
in the hospital project. In Table 19.1, you can see that the path A–C–G–J–K
is 67 weeks long, or only two weeks shorter than the critical path. The sum of
the variances along that path is 15.55.

This situation is shown in Fig. 19.6. Path A–C–G–J–K will be the critical
path if its length equals or exceeds 69 weeks *or* if the length of path B–D–H–
J–K equals 67 weeks or less. Figure 19.6 shows there is considerable overlap

FIGURE 19.6

Probability
Distributions for the
Critical Path and
Next Longest Path for
the Hospital Project

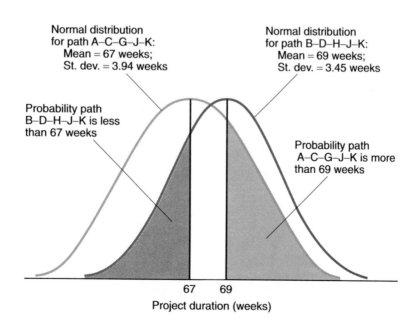

between the probability distributions for these two paths. Computing the probability that path A–C–G–J–K will be critical requires the estimation of the joint probability that path A–C–G–J–K $\geq$ 69 weeks *and* path B–D–H–J–K $\leq$ 67 weeks in addition to the shaded areas in Fig. 19.6. Since the two paths are dependent on each other (share common activities), the calculation of the joint probability requires computer simulation. Nonetheless, close attention to activities A, C, and G, in addition to activities B, D, H, J, and K, seems warranted.

Also, if the project has multiple critical paths, the critical path with the largest variance should be used in the denominator of the z-transformation formula. This approach allows the probability estimate to reflect the correct amount of uncertainty in the project duration.

COST AND RESOURCE CONSIDERATIONS

In this section we discuss the use of PERT/CPM methods to find minimum-cost schedules. We also describe how to incorporate resource constraints in project scheduling.

Analyzing Costs

So far, our discussion has focused on managing project time. The implicit assumption is that if the project can be kept on schedule, total project costs will be acceptable. The reality of project management, however, is that there are always time–cost trade-offs. Total project costs are the sum of direct costs, indirect costs, and penalty costs. Direct costs include labor, materials, and any other costs directly related to project activities. The higher the intensity of effort (through overtime and increased personnel and equipment), the shorter the duration of the activity. Indirect costs include administration, depreciation, financial, and other variable overhead costs that can be avoided by reducing total project time. The shorter the duration of the project, the lower the indirect costs. Penalty costs may be incurred if the project extends beyond some specific date. Conversely, in some cases a bonus may be provided for early completion. Penalties or bonuses, largely a function of legal arrangements, can be very significant. Thus when a project manager considers total project costs, or total profits, the best schedule may require *crashing*, or expediting, some activities to reduce overall project completion time.

Direct Costs and Times. Direct costs can be subdivided into normal costs and crash costs for each activity. Associated with these costs are a normal time and a crash time.

1. **Normal time (NT).** The time to complete the activity under normal conditions. This time is analogous to the expected time, t_e, mentioned earlier.
2. **Normal cost (NC).** The activity cost associated with the normal time.
3. **Crash time (CT).** The shortest possible time to complete the activity.
4. **Crash cost (CC).** The activity cost associated with the crash time.

FIGURE 19.7

Cost-Time
Relationships in Cost
Analysis

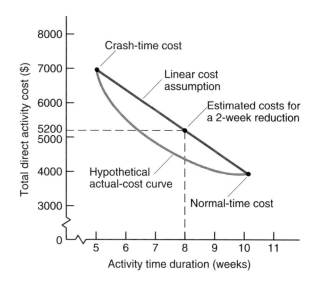

Cost Assumptions. In making a cost analysis, we assume that costs increase linearly as activity time is reduced from its normal time. For example, suppose that the normal time for activity C in the hospital project is 10 weeks at a direct cost of $4000. If the crash time is 5 weeks at a crash cost of $7000, the net time reduction is 5 weeks at a net cost increase of $3000. We assume that it costs $600 ($3000/5) per week to crash activity C. This assumption of linear marginal costs is illustrated in Fig. 19.7. Also shown is a hypothetical actual-cost curve.* Thus if activity C were expedited by two weeks, the estimated direct costs would be $5200 even though actual costs would be approximately $4500, according to Fig. 19.7. Table 19.3 contains direct cost and time data for the hospital project. The amounts in the last column were calculated as follows:

$$\text{Cost to crash per week} = \frac{CC - NC}{NT - CT}$$

Indirect and Penalty Costs. Suppose that project indirect costs are $8000 per week. In addition, suppose that after week 65 St. Adolf's incurs a penalty cost of $20,000 per week if the hospital is not fully operational. With a critical path completion time of 69 weeks, it appears that the hospital faces some major expenses. As the figures in Table 19.3 indicate, any activity in the project could be expedited for a certain increase in direct costs. For every week that the project is shortened—to week 65—the hospital saves one week of penalty *and* indirect costs, or $28,000. For decreases beyond week 65, the savings are only the weekly indirect costs of $8000. The objective is to determine the target project completion time that minimizes total project costs.

---

*PERT/CPM methods do not require the assumption of linear cost increases. Nonlinear relationships can be used, but the linear assumption is usually adequate.

TABLE 19.3 / Direct Cost and Time Data for the Hospital Project

Activity	Normal Time (NT)	Normal Cost (NC)	Crash Time (CT)	Crash Cost (CC)	Maximum Time Reduction (wk)	Cost to Crash per Week
A	12	$ 12,000	11	$ 13,000	1	$ 1,000
B	9	50,000	7	64,000	2	7,000
C	10	4,000	5	7,000	5	600
D	10	16,000	8	20,000	2	2,000
E	24	120,000	14	200,000	10	8,000
F	10	10,000	6	16,000	4	1,500
G	35	500,000	25	530,000	10	3,000
H	40	1,200,000	35	1,260,000	5	12,000
I	15	40,000	10	52,500	5	2,500
J	4	10,000	1	13,000	3	1,000
K	6	30,000	5	34,000	1	4,000
Total		$1,992,000		$2,209,500		

Normal and Minimum-Time Schedules. From the perspective of project completion time, the normal time schedule and the minimum-time schedule provide the limits for the minimum-cost schedule search. Finding the cost for the normal time schedule is straightforward. Table 19.3 shows that total direct cost is $1,992,000. In addition, indirect costs are $8000 per week, or $552,000 for 69 weeks. Four weeks of penalty costs come to $80,000. Thus the total cost for a 69-week project is $2,624,000.

The first step in finding the cost of the minimum-time schedule is to find the minimum project duration by crashing all the activities in the project and finding the length of the critical path. Figure 19.8 shows the CPM network with the crash times (in weeks) for each activity. The critical path is B–D–H–J–K, with a total completion time of 56 weeks. Total direct cost for this expedited schedule, as shown in Table 19.3, is $2,209,500. Indirect costs would be $448,000 [56($8000)]. As there are no penalty costs, the total project cost would be $2,657,500.

The schedule that we just evaluated crashed all activities to their limits. However, the minimum time of 56 weeks can be achieved *without* crashing all the activities. Table 19.4 shows how to derive the **minimum-time schedule** for the hospital project that has the least cost. We begin by finding the activity not on the critical path that is the most expensive to crash. We then relax it as much as possible, without exceeding its normal time or increasing the length of the total project. This activity is E. We can return it to its normal time and save $80,000 relative to the total crash schedule. The next most expensive noncritical activity is G. Its normal time is 35 weeks; however, we can relax it only 9 weeks because, at an adjusted time of 34 weeks, path A–C–G–J–K is also 56 weeks long. Activities I and F can both be returned to their normal times, but all other activities remain at their crash times. The total savings relative to the total crash schedule is $125,500. Consequently, the total project cost for the minimum-time schedule is $2,532,000 ($2,657,500 − $125,500).

FIGURE 19.8

Network Showing
Crash Times and the
Critical Path

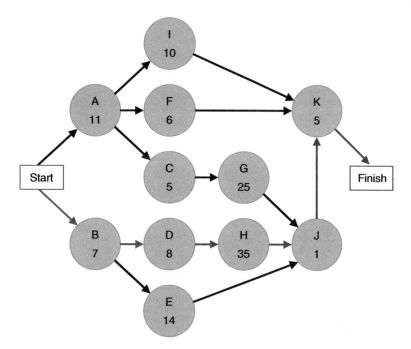

Finding the Minimum-Cost Schedule. So far we have established a total project cost upper limit of $2,532,000 for the minimum-time schedule. Thus Judy Kramer should not accept an intermediate schedule between 56 and 69 weeks that costs more than $2,532,000. In determining the **minimum-cost schedule,** we start with the normal time schedule and crash activities along the critical path in such a way that the added crash costs are less than the savings in indirect and penalty costs. The procedure involves the following steps.

1. Determine the project's critical path(s).
2. Find the activity (activities) on the critical path(s) that is (are) cheapest to crash per week.
3. Reduce the time for this activity until (a) it cannot be further reduced, (b) another path becomes critical, or (c) the increase in direct costs exceeds the savings that result from shortening the project. If more than

TABLE 19.4 / Deriving the Minimum-Time Schedule

Noncritical Activity	Cost to Crash per Week	Crash Time (wk)	Maximum Relax Time (wk)	Adjusted Time (wk)	Savings Relative to Total Crash Schedule
E	$8000	14	10	24	$ 80,000
G	3000	25	9	34	27,000
I	2500	10	5	15	12,500
F	1500	6	4	10	6,000
Total					$125,500

one path is critical, it may be necessary to reduce the time for an activity on each path simultaneously.

4. Go back to step 1 and repeat the procedure, so long as the increase in direct costs is less than the savings generated by shortening the project.

Application 19.7   *Finding a Minimum-Cost Schedule*

Determine the minimum-cost schedule for the hospital project. Use the information in Fig. 19.8 and Table 19.3.

Solution

Trial 1
1. The critical path is B–D–H–J–K.
2. The cheapest activity to crash per week is J at $1000, which is much less than the savings in indirect and penalty costs of $28,000 per week.
3. Crash activity J to its limit of 3 weeks because the critical path remains unchanged. This action affects three paths in the network. The new expected times for each path are

A–I–K	33 weeks	B–D–H–J–K	66 weeks
A–F–K	28 weeks	B–E–J–K	40 weeks
A–C–G–J–K	64 weeks		

Compare these times to those in Table 19.1.

Trial 2
1. The critical path is still B–D–H–J–K.
2. The cheapest activity to crash per week now is D at $2000.
3. The first week of reduction in activity D saves $28,000, but the second saves only $8000. However, these savings still exceed the cost of crashing D by two weeks. After week 65, there are no more penalty costs. Note that after crashing D, we now have two critical paths.

Trial 3
1. The critical paths are B–D–H–J–K and A–C–G–J–K, and both are at 64 weeks. *Both* critical paths must now be shortened to realize any savings in indirect project costs. If one is shortened and the other isn't, the length of the project remains unchanged.
2. Our alternatives are to crash one of the following combinations of activities, (A, B), (A, H), (C, B), (C, H), (G, B), (G, H), or to crash activity K, which is on both critical paths (J has already been crashed). Jointly crashing (A, B) costs $8000; (A, H), $13,000; (C, B), $7600; (C, H), $12,600; (G, B), $10,000; and (G, H), $15,000. The cheapest alternative is activity K at $4000 per week.
3. Crash activity K to its limit of five weeks. The critical paths remain unchanged.

Trial 4
1. The critical paths are B–D–H–J–K and A–C–G–J–K, and both are at 63 weeks.
2. The least expensive alternative at this stage is to simultaneously crash activities B and C at a cost of $7600 per week. This amount is still less than the savings of $8000 per week.
3. Crash activities B and C by two weeks, the limit for activity B.

Any other combination of activities will result in a net increase in total project costs because the crash costs exceed weekly indirect costs. The table on page 785 contains a summary of the cost analysis for the hospital project. As you can see, the minimum-cost schedule is 61 weeks, with a total cost of $2,506,200. To obtain this schedule, we crashed activities B, D, J, and K to their limits and activity C to 8 weeks. The other activ-

Cost Analysis for the St. Adolf's Hospital Project

Trial	Crash Activity	Resulting Critical Path*	Time Reduction (wk)	Project Duration (wk)	Total Project Direct Costs at Last Trial	Crash Costs Added This Trial	Total Indirect Costs	Total Penalty Costs	Total Project Costs
0	—	B–D–H–J–K	—	69	$1,992,000	$ —	$552,000	$80,000	$2,624,000
1	J	B–D–H–[J]–K	3	66	1,992,000	3,000	528,000	20,000	2,543,000
2	D	A–C–G–[J]–K	2	64	1,995,000	4,000	512,000	0	2,511,000
		B–[D]–H–[J]–K							
3	K	A–C–G–[J]–[K]	1	63	1,999,000	4,000	504,000	0	2,507,000
		B–[D]–H–[J]–[K]							
4	B, C	A–C–G–[J]–[K]	2	61	2,003,000	15,200	488,000	0	2,506,200
		[B]–[D]–H–[J]–[K]							

*A ☐ indicates that the activity has been crashed to its limit.

ities remain at their normal times. This schedule costs about $25,800 less than the minimum-time schedule.

Figure 19.9 on the next page shows the cost curves for the hospital project. The curves consist of a series of straight-line segments because of our assumption that marginal costs are linear. We stopped at 61 weeks, but we could have continued crashing more activities (even though total costs would have increased) until week 56 and plotted the costs along the way to get a better approximation of the cost curves in that range.

Resource Limitations

The project management models that we have discussed so far consider only activity times in determining overall project duration and the critical path. Recall that an underlying assumption in the use of PERT/CPM is that sufficient resources will be available when needed to complete all project activities on schedule. However, developing schedules without considering the load placed on resources can result in inefficient resource use and even cause project delays if capacity limitations are exceeded.

For purposes of discussion, consider the project represented by the project diagram in Fig. 19.10. Each of the five activities involves a certain amount of time and has a resource requirement. The critical path is A–B–E, and the total time to complete the project, ignoring resource limitations, is nine days.

Although AON network diagrams are useful for displaying an entire project and showing the precedence relationships between activities, they are not very useful for showing the implications of resource requirements for a schedule of activities. Gantt charts (see Chapter 18) are more useful in this regard.

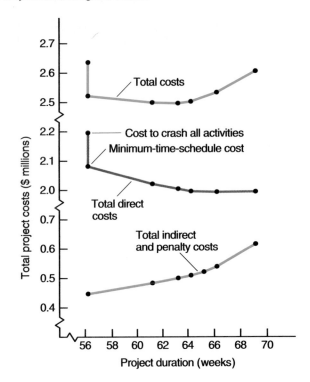

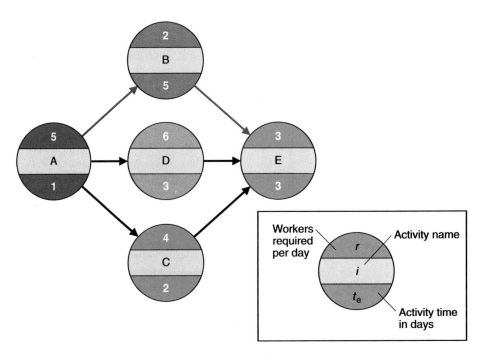

We want to generate a schedule that recognizes resource constraints, as well as the precedence relationships between activities. Let's suppose that we are limited to a small number of workers per day. Although we could use an optimizing approach, such as linear programming (see Supplement 2), to derive a schedule under these conditions, a more useful approach in practice is to use a procedure such as the one developed by Weist (1966):

1. Start with the first day of the project and schedule as many activities as possible, considering precedence relationships and resource limitations. Continue with the second day, and so on, until all activities are scheduled.

2. When several activities compete for the same resources, give preference to the activities with the least slack, as calculated using standard PERT/CPM methods.

3. Reschedule noncritical activities, if possible, to free resources for critical or nonslack activities.

The intent of this procedure is to minimize total project time, subject to resource constraints.

Application 19.8   *Developing a Resource-Constrained Schedule*

Generate a resource-constrained schedule for the project depicted in Fig. 19.10. Assume that we have only six workers per day.

Solution

1. Schedule activity A first because all other activities depend on its completion.
2. The choice is between activities B, C, and D because their predecessor has been scheduled. Activities C and D have slack, but activity B doesn't because it's on the critical path. Thus schedule B next. So far, we have committed five workers on day 1 and two workers on days 2–6.
3. We have a choice between activities C and D, but we must choose C next. It requires only four workers per day, and we can schedule it on days 2 and 3 without violating our resource constraint of six workers per day. Activity D requires six workers per day, but we have already scheduled activity B, which needs two workers.
4. The remaining activities to schedule are D and E. We must schedule D first because of precedence constraints. The resulting schedule is shown in Fig. 19.11 on the next page.

This schedule results in the shortest project time possible under the resource constraints; but, the use of the procedure will not always be so successful. We can only say that it will generally produce solutions close to, but not necessarily, the optimum.

COMPUTERIZED PROJECT SCHEDULING AND CONTROL

Computerized network planning models are used extensively in practice. Applications can be found in government administration as well as the construction, aerospace, pharmaceutical, utility, manufacturing, entertainment, and architectural-engineering industries. Ford Motor Company used computerized

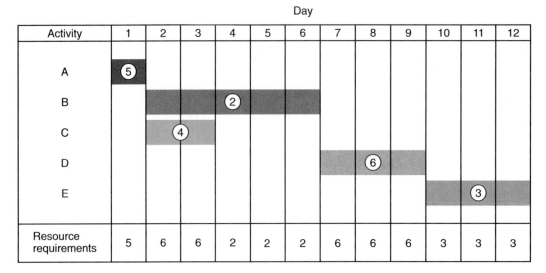

FIGURE 19.11   Resource-Constrained Schedule

network planning models for retooling assembly lines, and the Chrysler Corporation used them for building a new assembly plant. Other users include the San Francisco Opera Association, the Walt Disney Company, and Procter & Gamble. Note the diversity of organizations capitalizing on PERT/CPM methods.

When is a computer needed? The answer is fairly obvious if the project is very large, such as the Olympic Games or the construction of a high-rise office building. However, there are several considerations to make in addition to size (Sullivan, 1986). Generally, a computer should be used if any of the following factors apply:

1. The project has more than 100 activities. Tracking that many activities manually can be difficult.

2. There are frequent updates or major changes to the original project. Using a computer, the project manager can recalculate the critical path and study the effects of resource reallocations.

3. The project manager needs to track resource usage. Computer software packages provide resource reports that facilitate the management of scarce resources.

4. The project manager wants to make actual-versus-planned comparisons for future planning. Such a capability allows the project manager to assess the reasons why the planned and actual performance differed.

With the advent of personal computers, project management software has become accessible to many companies. Software costs have come down, and the user interfaces are less intimidating. Prices range from $500 to $700 for some of the more popular software packages designed for the PC. Their capabilities vary considerably (see *PC Magazine*, 1990, for more information). For example, the maximum number of tasks per project is 280 for Harvard Project Manager® and 16,000 for InstaPlan 500®. Programs also vary with respect to their output reports. These outputs include the following capabilities:

- *Gantt charts and PERT/CPM diagrams.* The graphics capabilities of software packages allow for visual displays of project progress on Gantt charts similar to Fig. 19.11 and PERT/CPM network diagrams such as Figs. 19.4 and 19.10. Most packages allow the user to display portions of the network on the video monitor to analyze specific problems.

- *Project status and summary reports.* These reports include budget variance reports that compare planned to actual expenses at any stage in the project, resource histograms that graphically display the usage of a particular resource over time, status reports for each worker by task performed, and summary reports that indicate project progress to top management.

- *Tracking reports.* These reports identify areas of concern that need attention. The information in these reports includes the percentage of activity completion with respect to time or allocated budget or labor resources and estimated completion dates and costs. Most software packages allow multiple projects to be tracked at the same time. This feature is important when resources must be shared jointly by a number of projects.

Almost any project requiring significant resources will use project management software. Nonetheless, managers should be aware that even today's user-friendly packages can evoke employee resistance. Extensive employee training might be needed to fully benefit from these systems.

CRITIQUE OF PERT/CPM SYSTEMS

So far, we have demonstrated the benefits that PERT/CPM systems offer to project managers. Let's now turn to criticisms of the assumptions and limitations of PERT/CPM.

Network Diagrams

The methods used in PERT/CPM are based on the assumption that project activities having clear beginning and ending points can be identified. A further assumption is that activity sequence relationships can be identified at the start of the project and specified in a network diagram. However, these assumptions often are too restrictive. For example, one activity must be shown to precede the other in the PERT/CPM network diagram. In reality, two activities, where one must precede the other, often can be overlapped and worked on simulta-neously up to a certain point. Also, project content can change, and a network diagram developed at the start of a project may later limit the project manager's flexibility to handle changing situations. At times, actual precedence relation-ships cannot be specified beforehand. That is, the sequencing of some activi-ties is contingent on the result of certain other activities, which can't always be anticipated. In situations such as these, PERT/CPM methods might not be very useful.

Control

The major underlying assumption in PERT/CPM methods is that managers should focus on the activities along the critical path. However, as we pointed out earlier in this chapter, managers should also pay attention to *near-critical* paths. The reason is that these near-critical paths could easily become critical if one or more of the activities along these paths slip relative to their schedule. Project managers who overlook this possibility often complain that using PERT/CPM did not help them complete their projects on time. This short-coming is not that of PERT/CPM itself but rather is the result of an incomplete understanding of the concepts involved.

Time Estimates

When activity times are uncertain, the assumption is that they follow the beta distribution, with the variance of the total project time equaling the sum of the variances along the critical path. This aspect of PERT/CPM has brought a va-riety of criticism. First, the formulas used to calculate the mean and variance of the beta distribution are only approximations and are subject to error. Errors on the order of 10 percent for the mean and 5 percent for the variance can be expected. These errors could give incorrect critical paths. Second, arriving at a single accurate time estimate, let alone three, for an activity that has never been performed before is very difficult. A single time estimate—the most likely time—is preferred by many project managers. They believe that the pessimistic time estimates often are inflated and vary far more from the most likely time estimate than do the optimistic time estimates. They argue that some managers use these pessimistic time estimates as an excuse for failure. Perhaps a more harmful by-product of inflated pessimistic time estimates is the inflation of *expected* activity times, which builds a cushion of slack into the schedule. Finally, the choice of the beta distribution was somewhat arbitrary, and the use of another distribution would result in different expected times and variances for each activity.

Although the application of PERT/CPM to project management has short-comings, managers who recognize the limitations of these methods can use them effectively. In fact, their shortcomings have not precluded widespread use of PERT/CPM. Even though network planning models are not perfect, their skillful use can significantly aid project managers in their work.

COMPUTER SOLVED PROBLEM
Project Scheduling for a Computer-Based Learning System

The new products manager at Weblo Enterprises wishes to evaluate the feasibility of a new computer-based learning system. The manager has decided to use three time estimates because of the general uncertainty in undertaking this effort. The following table presents the project tasks and corresponding time estimates (weeks):

Task	Most Optimistic	Most Likely	Most Pessimistic	Predecessors
A. Market Research	5	7	10	—
B. R&D	12	18	25	—
C. Engineering	6	9	12	B
D. Prototype Design	8	12	15	C
E. Costing	2	3	4	C
F. Testing	3	5	8	D
G. Market Survey	2	4	7	A,D
H. Market Analysis	2	3	4	G
I. Quality Assurance	1	2	3	A,D
J. Financial Analysis	3	3	4	E,F,H
K. Supplier Analysis	2	2	2	E
L. Patent Search	1	3	4	B
M. Internal Assessment	2	2	2	A
N. Reporting	3	3	3	I,J,K,L
O. Decision Making	1	2	3	M,N

a. What is the estimated completion time and standard deviation?

b. Identify the critical path(s).

c. What task has the greatest amount of slack?

d. What is the probability of completing the project in 55 weeks? 60 weeks?

Solution This problem is solved using CMOM (Project Planning and Control module). Your output may look different if you are using another software package.

a. Printout 1 shows the results of the analysis. The expected completion time is approximately 54.33 weeks with a standard deviation of 2.83 weeks.

b. The critical path consists of tasks B, C, D, G, H, J, N, and O.

c. Task M, with a slack of 43.17, has the greatest amount of slack.

d. Printout 2 shows that the probability of completing the project within 55 weeks is approximately 59 percent and that the probability of completing the project within 60 weeks is approximately 98 percent.

CMOM—PROJECT PLANNING & CONTROL
THREE TIME ESTIMATES

SOLUTION

ACTIVITY		START	FINISH	EXPECTED TIME	SLACK	CRITICAL PATH
1–A	EARLIEST:	0	7.167	7.167	31.833	NO
	LATEST:	31.833	39			
2–B	EARLIEST:	0	18.167	18.167	0	YES
	LATEST:	0	18.167			
3–C	EARLIEST:	18.167	27.167	9	0	YES
	LATEST:	18.167	27.167			
4–D	EARLIEST:	27.167	39	11.833	0	YES
	LATEST:	27.167	39			
5–E	EARLIEST:	27.167	30.167	3	16	NO
	LATEST:	43.167	46.167			
6–F	EARLIEST:	39	44.167	5.167	2	NO
	LATEST:	41	46.167			
7–G	EARLIEST:	39	43.167	4.167	0	YES
	LATEST:	39	43.167			
8–H	EARLIEST:	43.167	46.167	4.167	0	YES
	LATEST:	43.167	46.167			
9–I	EARLIEST:	39	41	2	8.333	NO
	LATEST:	47.333	49.333			
10–J	EARLIEST:	46.167	49.333	3.167	0	YES
	LATEST:	46.167	49.333			
11–K	EARLIEST:	30.167	32.167	2	17.167	NO
	LATEST:	47.333	49.333			
12–L	EARLIEST:	18.167	21	2.833	28.333	NO
	LATEST:	46.500	49.333			
13–M	EARLIEST:	7.167	9.167	2	43.167	NO
	LATEST:	50.333	52.333			
14–N	EARLIEST:	49.333	52.333	3	0	YES
	LATEST:	49.333	52.333			
15–O	EARLIEST:	52.333	54.333	2	0	YES
	LATEST:	52.333	54.333			

PROJECT SUMMARY

EXPECTED COMPLETION TIME:	54.333
VARIANCE ON CRITICAL PATH:	8
STANDARD DEVIATION:	2.828

CRITICAL PATH =	2–B	3–C	4–D	7–G	8–H	10–J
	14–N	15–O				

PRINTOUT 2

PROBABILITY ANALYSIS

T'	=	PROJECT DUE DATE	:	55
TE	=	EXPECTED COMPLETION TIME	:	54.333
E::	=	VARIANCE ON CRITICAL PATH	:	8
: E::	=	STANDARD DEVIATION	:	2.828
Z	=	(T' − TE) / : $\overline{E::}$	:	0.236
PROBABILITY OF COMPLETION BY DUE DATE			:	0.594

PROBABILITY ANALYSIS

T'	=	PROJECT DUE DATE	:	60
TE	=	EXPECTED COMPLETION TIME	:	54.333
E::	=	VARIANCE ON CRITICAL PATH	:	8
: $\overline{E::}$	=	STANDARD DEVIATION	:	2.828
Z	=	(T' − TE) / : $\overline{E::}$	:	2.003
PROBABILITY OF COMPLETION BY DUE DATE			:	0.977

SOLVED PROBLEMS

1. An advertising project manager has developed the network diagram shown in Fig. 19.12 for a new advertising campaign. In addition, the manager gathered the time information for each activity, as shown in the accompanying table.
   a. Calculate the expected times and variances for each activity.
   b. Calculate the activity slacks and determine the critical path using the activity expected times.
   c. What is the probability of completing the project within 18 weeks?

	Time Estimates (wk)		
Activity	Most Optimistic	Most Likely	Most Pessimistic
A	1	2	3
B	4	6	8
C	3	3	3
D	2	8	10
E	3	6	9
F	1	8	15
G	4	5	6

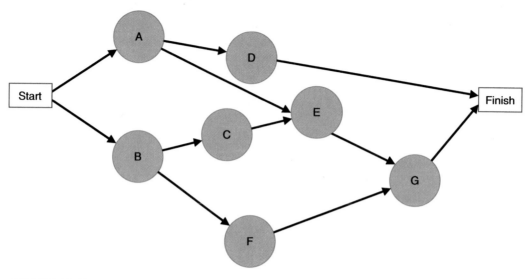

FIGURE 19.12

Solution   a. The expected times and variances for each activity are as follows:

Activity	Expected Time (wk)	Variance
A	2	0.11
B	6	0.44
C	3	0.00
D	7.33	1.78
E	6	1.00
F	8	5.44
G	5	0.11

b. We need to calculate the earliest start, latest start, earliest finish, and latest finish times for each activity. Starting with activities A and B, we proceed from the beginning of the network and move to the end, calculating the earliest start and finish times:

Activity	Earliest Start (wk)	Earliest Finish (wk)	Comments
A	0	0 + 2 = 2	Can start immediately
B	0	0 + 6 = 6	Can start immediately
C	6	6 + 3 = 9	Cannot start until B is finished
D	2	2 + 7.33 = 9.33	Cannot start until A is finished
E	9	9 + 6 = 15	Cannot start until C is finished
F	6	6 + 8 = 14	Cannot start until B is finished
G	15	15 + 5 = 20	Cannot start until E is finished

The earliest the project can be completed is week 20, when activity G is finished. Using that as a target date, we can work backward through the network, calculating the latest start and finish times:

Activity	Latest Start (wk)	Latest Finish (wk)	Comments
G	15	20	Project must be completed in week 20
F	7	15	Keeps G on schedule
E	9	15	Keeps G on schedule
D	12.67	20	No following activities
C	6	9	Keeps E on schedule
B	0	6	Keeps C on schedule
A	7	9	Keeps E on schedule

We can now calculate the activity slacks and determine which activities are on the critical path, as follows:

Activity	Start Earliest	Start Latest	Finish Earliest	Finish Latest	Activity Slack	Critical Path
A	0	7	2	9	7	No
B	0	0	6	6	0	Yes
C	6	6	9	9	0	Yes
D	2	12.67	9.33	20	10.67	No
E	9	9	15	15	0	Yes
F	6	7	14	15	1	No
G	15	15	20	20	0	Yes

The paths, and their total expected times and variances, are:

Path	Total Expected Time (wk)	Total Variance
A–D	2 + 7.33 = 9.33	0.11 + 1.78 = 1.89
A–E–G	2 + 6 + 5 = 13	0.11 + 1.00 + 0.11 = 1.22
B–C–E–G	6 + 3 + 6 + 5 = 20	0.44 + 0.00 + 1.00 + 0.11 = 1.55
B–F–G	6 + 8 + 5 = 19	0.44 + 5.44 + 0.11 = 5.99

The critical path is B–C–E–G, with a total expected time of 20 weeks. However, path B–F–G is 19 weeks and has a large variance.

c. We first calculate the z-value:

$$z = \frac{T' - TE}{\sqrt{\Sigma\sigma_{CP}^2}} = \frac{18 - 20}{\sqrt{1.55}} = -1.61$$

Using Appendix 3 we find that the probability of completing the project in 18 weeks or less is only 0.0537. Because path B–F–G is very close to the length of the critical path and has a large variance, it might well become the critical path during the project.

2. Your company has just received an order for a specially designed electric motor from a good customer. Nonetheless, the contract states that starting on the thirteenth day from now, your firm will experience a penalty of $100 per day if the job is not completed. Indirect project costs amount to $200 per day. The data on direct costs and activity precedence relationships are given in Table 19.5.
   a. Draw the project network diagram.
   b. What completion date would you recommend?

TABLE 19.5

Activity	Normal Time (days)	Normal Cost	Crash Time (days)	Crash Cost	Immediate Predecessor(s)
A	4	$1000	3	$1300	None
B	7	1400	4	2000	None
C	5	2000	4	2700	None
D	6	1200	5	1400	A
E	3	900	2	1100	B
F	11	2500	6	3750	C
G	4	800	3	1450	D, E
H	3	300	1	500	F, G

Solution   a. The AON network diagram, including normal activity times, for this procedure is shown in Fig. 19.13. Keep the following points in mind while constructing a network diagram.

- Always have start and finish nodes.
- Try to avoid crossing paths to keep the diagram simple.
- Use only one arrow to directly connect any two nodes.
- Put the activities with no predecessors at the left and point the arrows from left to right.
- Use scratch paper and be prepared to revise the diagram several times before you come up with a correct and uncluttered diagram.

b. Determining a good completion date requires the use of the minimum-cost schedule procedure. Using the data in Table 19.5, you can determine the crash cost per day and the maximum crash time for each

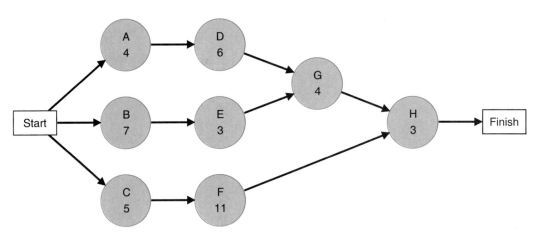

FIGURE 19.13

activity:

Activity	Crash Cost Per Day ($)	Maximum Crash Time (days)
A	300	1
B	200	3
C	700	1
D	200	1
E	200	1
F	250	5
G	650	1
H	100	2

Table 19.6 contains a summary of the analysis and the resultant project duration and total cost. The critical path is C–F–H at 19 days, which you find by searching for the longest path in the network. The cheapest of these activities to crash is H. It costs only an extra $100 per day to crash H, and $300 ($200 + $100) per day in indirect and penalty costs can be saved. We crash this activity two days (the maximum). The lengths of the paths are now

A–D–G–H   15 days
B–E–G–H   15 days
C–F–H   17 days

The critical path is still C–F–H. The next cheapest activity to crash is F at $250 per day. We can crash F only two days because at that point we will have three critical paths. Further reductions in project duration will require simultaneous crashing of more than one activity. The cost to do so exceeds the savings. Consequently, you should stop. Note that every activity is critical. The recommended completion date is day 15.

3. A maintenance crew at the Woody Manufacturing Company must do scheduled machine maintenance in the fabricating department. A series of interrelated activities must be accomplished, requiring a different number of workers each day. Figure 19.14 shows the project network, the workers required, and the activity time. The company can devote a maximum of 6 maintenance workers per day to these activities.
   a. Use Weist's procedure to find a new schedule, and draw a Gantt chart for it.
   b. How long will the project take, and which activities are critical?

TABLE 19.6

Trial	Crash Activity	Resulting Critical Path	Time Reduction (days)	Project Duration (days)	Project Direct Costs, Last Trial	Crash Cost Added	Total Indirect Costs	Total Penalty Costs	Total Project Costs
0	—	C–F–H	—	19	$10,100	—	$3,800	$700	$14,600
1	H	C–F– H	2	17	10,100	200	3,400	500	14,200
2	F	A–D–G– H	2	15	10,300	500	3,000	300	14,100
		B–E–G– H							
		C–F– H							

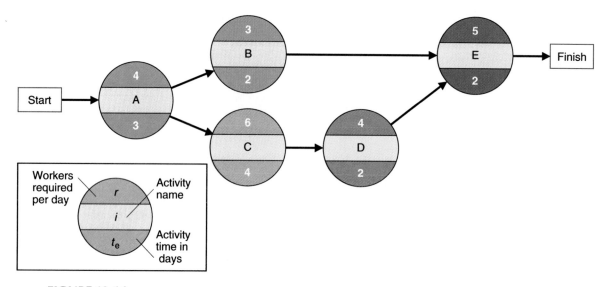

FIGURE 19.14

Solution   a. The critical path of this project (disregarding the resource constraint) is
A–C–D–E at 11 weeks. Consequently, only activity B has slack. Figure
19.15 shows the schedule.
  i. Schedule activity A first on day 1. We cannot schedule any other
  activities until day 4 because of the resource constraint.
  ii. Activities B and C are now tied. We schedule C next because it has
  no slack.
  iii. Activities B and D are tied. We choose D next because it has no
  slack. We must start it on day 8 because of the resource constraint.

FIGURE 19.15

Day

Activity	1	2	3	4	5	6	7	8	9	10	11	12	13
A		④											
B										③			
C						⑥							
D								④					
E												⑤	
Resource requirements	4	4	4	6	6	6	6	4	4	3	3	5	5

iv. Activity B must be scheduled next because of its precedence relationship to activity E.

v. Finally, schedule E for days 12 and 13. It could not be started earlier because of the resource constraint.

b. The project will take 13 days and every activity is critical. No activity can be shifted from its present schedule without violating the maintenance worker capacity limitation.

FORMULA REVIEW

1. Start and finish times:

$ES_i = $ max [EF times of all activities immediately preceding activity i]

$EF_i = ES_i + t_e$

$LS_i = LF_i - t_e$

$LF_i = $ min [LS times of all activities immediately following activity i]

2. Activity slack:

$$S_i = LS_i - ES_i \quad \text{or} \quad LF_i - EF_i$$

3. Activity time statistics:

$$t_e = \frac{a + 4(m) + b}{6} \quad \text{(Expected activity time)}$$

$$\sigma^2 = \left(\frac{b - a}{6}\right)^2 \quad \text{(Variance)}$$

4. z-transformation formula:

$$z = \frac{T' - TE}{\sqrt{\Sigma \sigma^2_{CP}}}$$

5. Project costs:

$$\text{Cost to crash per week} = \frac{CC - NC}{NT - CT}$$

CHAPTER HIGHLIGHTS

• Managing a project involves (1) describing the project, (2) diagramming the network, (3) determining time estimates, (4) determining the critical path, (5) developing the project plan, and (6) monitoring the project.

• PERT and CPM are network modeling methods that are useful in project management.

• Uncertainty in activity times can be recognized by securing three time estimates for each activity. Actual activity times are assumed to follow a beta distribution.

• PERT/CPM methods focus attention on the critical path: the sequence of activities requiring the greatest cumulative amount of time for completion. Delay in any of these activities will delay the entire project.

- PERT/CPM methods can be used to assess the probability of finishing the project by a certain date or to find the minimum-cost schedule with the assumption that marginal costs are linear.

- A slack-sorted report can be used to identify those activities that are behind schedule and those from which resources can be withdrawn and reassigned to activities needing them.

- The Weist procedure can be used to generate a capacity-sensitive project schedule when resource constraints are present.

- A number of criticisms have been leveled at PERT/CPM methods. Although these methods have shortcomings, they are widely used.

KEY TERMS

activity **766**
activity-on-arc (AOA) network **766**
activity-on-node (AON) network **766**
activity slack **769**
crash cost (*CC*) **780**
crash time (*CT*) **780**
critical path **769**
critical path method (CPM) **763**

earliest finish time (*EF$_i$*) **770**
earliest start time (*ES$_i$*) **770**
event **766**
latest finish time (*LF$_i$*) **772**
latest start time (*LS$_i$*) **772**
minimum-cost schedule **783**
minimum-time schedule **782**
most likely time (*m*) **775**
most optimistic time (*a*) **775**

most pessimistic time (*b*) **775**
network diagram **763**
normal cost (*NC*) **780**
normal time (*NT*) **780**
precedence relationship **766**
program evaluation and review technique (PERT) **763**
project **762**

STUDY QUESTIONS

1. What are the steps in effective project management? What are the penalties for mismanaging a large project?

2. What information is needed to construct the network diagram for a project? Can any project be diagrammed as a network?

3. A certain advertising agency is preparing a bid for a promotional campaign of a type never before attempted. The project consists of a large number of interrelated activities. Explain how you would arrive at a single time estimate for each activity, so that you can use a network planning model to assess the chances that the project can be completed when the sponsor wants it.

4. Why was the beta distribution chosen over the normal distribution for PERT/CPM analyses?

5. Why is the critical path of such importance in project management? Can it change during the course of the project? If so, why?

6. When determining the probability of completing a project within a certain amount of time, what assumptions are you making? What role do the lengths and variances of paths other than the critical path play in such an analysis?

7. Explain the usefulness of the slack-sorted report. Is it still useful when the slacks of all project activities are positive?

8. Suppose that your company has accepted a project of a type it has completed many times before. Any activity can be expedited with an increase in costs. There are weekly indirect costs, and there is a weekly penalty if project completion extends beyond a cer-

tain date. Identify the data that you would need and explain the analytic process that you would use to determine a minimum-cost schedule. What assumptions would you make in doing such an analysis?

9. Suppose you are trying to convince management that methods such as PERT/CPM would be useful to them. Some of the managers have voiced the following concerns.
   a. There is a tendency for technicians to handle the operation of PERT/CPM; thus, management will not use it often.
   b. It puts pressure on managers because everyone knows where the critical path is. Managers of activities along the critical path are in the spotlight, and if their activities are delayed, the cost of the delay is on their shoulders.
   c. The introduction of network planning techniques may require new communication channels and systems procedures.
   Comment on each of these concerns.

PROBLEMS

Review Problems

1. Consider the following data for a project.

Activity	Immediate Predecessors	Activity Time (days)
A	—	2
B	A	4
C	A	5
D	B	2
E	B	1
F	B, C	8
G	D, E	3
H	F	5
I	C, F	4
J	G, H, I	7

   a. Draw the AON network diagram.
   b. Compute the critical path for this project.
   c. Is there anything management should be concerned about relative to the critical path?

2. A project has the following precedence relationships and activity times.

Activity	Immediate Predecessors	Activity Time (weeks)
A	—	8
B	—	10
C	A	10
D	B, C	15
E	B	12
F	D	4
G	E	8
H	F, G	7

   a. Draw the AON network diagram.
   b. Compute the activity slacks. Which activities are on the critical path?

3. The following information is available about a project.

Activity	Immediate Predecessors	Activity Time (days)
A	—	3
B	—	4
C	—	5
D	—	4
E	A	7
F	B, C, D	2
G	E, F	4
H	F	6
I	E, G	4
J	G	3
K	H	3

   a. Draw the AON network diagram.
   b. Find the critical path.

4. Recently, you were assigned to manage a project for your company. You have constructed a network diagram depicting the various activities in the project (Fig. 19.16). In addition, you asked various managers and subordinates to estimate the amount of time that they would expect each of the activities to take. Their responses are shown on the following page.

FIGURE 19.16

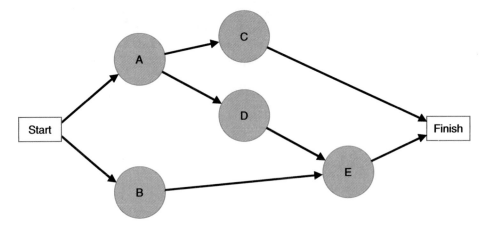

	Time Estimates (days)		
Activity	Most Optimistic	Most Likely	Most Pessimistic
A	5	8	11
B	4	8	11
C	5	6	7
D	2	4	6
E	4	7	10

a. What is the expected completion time of the project?

b. Suppose that the optimistic times prevail during the project. What is the earliest the project could be completed?

c. What is the probability of completing the project in 17 days?

5. The following information has been gathered for a project.

Activity	Time (wk)	Immediate Predecessor(s)
A	6	—
B	9	A
C	3	A
D	7	A, C
E	11	B, C
F	3	E, D

a. Draw the network diagram.

b. Calculate the slack for each activity and determine the critical path. How long will the project take?

6. Consider the following project information.

Activity	Time (wk)	Immediate Predecessor(s)
A	4	—
B	3	—
C	5	—
D	3	A, B
E	6	B
F	4	D, C
G	8	E, C
H	12	F, G

a. Draw the network diagram for this project.

b. Specify the critical path(s).

c. Calculate the total slack for activities A and D.

d. What happens to the slack for D if A takes five days?

7. Consider the following data for a project never before attempted by your company.

Activity	Expected Time, t_e (wk)	Immediate Predecessor(s)
A	5	—
B	3	—
C	2	A
D	5	B
E	4	C, D
F	7	D

a. Draw the network diagram for this project.

b. Identify the critical path and estimate the project's duration.

c. Calculate the slack for each activity.

8. The director of continuing education at Bluebird University has just approved the planning for a sales-training seminar. Her administrative assistant has identified the various activities that must be done and their relationships to each other, as shown in Table 19.7. Because of the uncertainty in planning the new course, the assistant also supplied the following time estimates for each activity.

	Time Estimates (days)		
Activity	Most Optimistic	Most Likely	Most Pessimistic
A	5	7	8
B	6	8	12
C	3	4	5
D	11	17	25
E	8	10	12
F	3	4	5
G	4	8	9
H	5	7	9
I	8	11	17
J	4	4	4

The director wants to conduct the seminar 47 working days from now. What is the probability that everything will be ready in time?

9. Information concerning a project is given in Table 19.8. Indirect project costs amount to $250 per day. The company will experience a $100 per day penalty for each day the project lasts beyond day 14.

a. What is the project's duration, using only normal times?

b. What completion date do you recommend?

c. What is the critical path?

10. Table 19.9 contains information about a project. Shorten the project by two days using the procedure for finding a minimum-cost schedule. Assume that project indirect costs and penalty costs are negligible. Identify activities to crash while minimizing the additional crash costs.

11. Hamilton Berger, district manager for Gumfull Foods, Inc., is in charge of opening a new fast-food outlet in the college town of Senility. His major concern is the hiring of a manager and a cadre of hamburger cooks, assemblers, and dispensers. He also has to coordinate the renovation of a building that previously was owned by a pet supplies re-

TABLE 19.7

Activity	Description	Immediate Predecessor(s)
A	Design brochure and course announcement.	—
B	Identify prospective teachers.	—
C	Prepare detailed outline of course.	—
D	Send brochure and student applications.	A
E	Send teacher applications.	B
F	Select teacher for course.	C, E
G	Accept students.	D
H	Select text for course.	F
I	Order and receive texts.	G, H
J	Prepare room for class.	G

TABLE 19.8

Activity	Normal Time (days)	Normal Cost	Crash Time (days)	Crash Cost	Immediate Predecessor(s)
A	5	$1000	4	$1200	—
B	5	800	3	2000	—
C	2	600	1	900	A, B
D	3	1500	2	2000	B
E	5	900	3	1200	C, D
F	2	1300	1	1400	E
G	3	900	3	900	E
H	5	500	3	900	G

TABLE 19.9

Activity	Time (days)	Immediate Predecessor(s)	Maximum Crash Time (days)	Cost to Crash (per day)
A	7	—	1	$200
B	12	—	3	250
C	7	A	1	250
D	6	A	1	300
E	1	B	1	200
F	1	C, D	0	—
G	3	D, E	2	200
H	3	F	1	350
I	2	G	0	—

tailer. He has gathered the data shown in Table 19.10.

Top management has told Berger that the new outlet is to be opened as soon as possible. Every week that the project can be shortened will save the firm $1200 in lease costs. Hamilton thought about how to save time during the project and came up with two possibilities.

- Employ Amazon, Inc., a local employment agency, to locate some good prospects for the manager's job. This approach would save three weeks in activity A and cost Gumfull Foods $2500.
- By adding a few workers, he could shorten the time for activity B by two weeks at an additional cost of $2700.

Help Ham Berger by answering the following questions.

a. How long is the project expected to take?

b. Suppose that Berger has a personal goal of completing the project in 14 weeks. What is the probability that this can happen?

c. What additional expenditures should be made to reduce the project's duration? Use the expected times for each activity as though they were certain.

12. The diagram in Fig. 19.17 was developed for a project that you are managing. Suppose that you are interested in finding ways to speed up the project at minimal additional cost. Determine the schedule for completing the project in 25 days at minimum cost. Penalty costs and project overhead costs are negligible. Alternative time and cost data for each activity are shown in Table 19.11.

TABLE 19.10

Activity	Description	Immediate Predecessor(s)	Time (wk) a	m	b
A	Interview at college for new manager.	—	2	4	6
B	Renovate building.	—	5	8	11
C	Place ad for employees and interview applicants.	—	7	9	17
D	Visit by new-manager prospects.	A	1	2	3
E	Purchase equipment for new outlet and install.	B	2	4	12
F	Check references for employee applicants and make final selection.	C	4	4	4
G	Check references for new manager and make final selection.	D	1	1	1
H	Hold orientation meetings and do paperwork to get manager and employees on payroll.	E, F, G	2	2	2

FIGURE 19.17

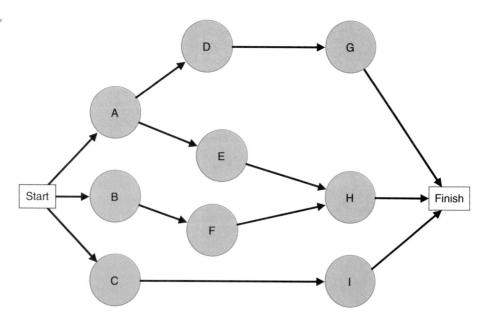

TABLE 19.11

Activity	Alternative 1 Time (days)	Cost	Alternative 2 Time (days)	Cost
A	12	$1,300	11	$ 1,700
B	13	1,150	10	1,500
C	20	3,000	18	4,500
D	9	2,000	5	3,000
E	12	550	9	900
F	10	700	8	1,050
G	8	1,550	6	1,800
H	1	450	2	800
I	5	2,500	2	4,000
Total		$13,200		$19,250

13. The construction crew of Johnson Home-builders must frame in a new house. The following data are available for the project.

Activity	Immediate Predecessor(s)	Time (days)	Workers Required (per day)
A	—	4	2
B	—	1	6
C	A	3	3
D	B	2	3
E	C, D	3	5

a. Draw the network diagram for the project.
b. Disregarding capacity limitations, determine the project's critical path and duration.
c. What is the slack for each activity?
d. Only six construction workers are available each day. Use Weist's procedure to find a new schedule and draw a Gantt chart for it.
   i. What is the critical path in this schedule?
   ii. How long will the project take now?

14. The network shown in Fig. 19.18 includes the number of workers required per day for each activity, the name of each activity, and the time (in days) required. Use Weist's procedure to find a schedule that utilizes a max-

imum of ten workers each day. Draw a Gantt chart for this schedule.
a. How long will this project take?
b. What is the critical path?

15. A line crew for the Alphabet Telephone Company must install some cable in a rural area. The following data are available for the project.

Activity	Immediate Predecessor(s)	Time (days)	Line Crew Required (per day)
A	—	2	10
B	A	3	6
C	A	5	5
D	A	3	5
E	D	3	5
F	B, C, E	1	7

a. Disregarding capacity limitations, determine the critical path and calculate the slack for each activity. How long will the project take?
b. Suppose that there are only ten crew members. Use Weist's procedure to find a schedule that does not exceed ten workers per day on the project. Draw a Gantt chart for your schedule.
   i. What is the critical path now?
   ii. What are the slacks for each activity?
   iii. How long will the project now take?

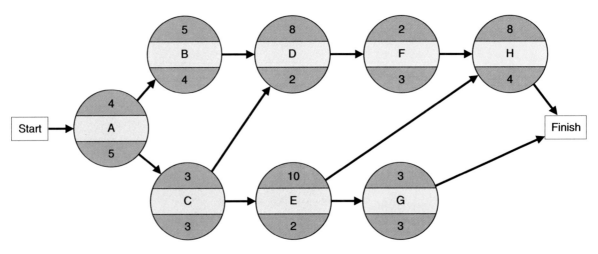

FIGURE 19.18

We suggest that you use a PERT/CPM computer program for Problems 19 and 20.

16. The following information concerns a new project your company is undertaking.

Activity	Immediate Predecessor(s)	Time (days)
A	—	10
B	—	11
C	A, B	9
D	A, B	5
E	A, B	8
F	C, E	13
G	C, D	5
H	G	10
I	F, G	6
J	E, H	9
K	I, J	11

a. Draw the network diagram for this project.
b. Determine the critical path and project completion time.

17. The project manager of Good Public Relations has gathered the data shown in Table 19.12 for a new advertising campaign.

a. How long is the project likely to take?
b. What is the probability that the project will take more than 38 weeks?
c. Consider the path A–E–G–H–J. What is the probability that this path will exceed the expected project duration?

18. The following information is known about a project.

Activity	Immediate Predecessor(s)	Time (days)	Workers Required (per day)
A	—	4	6
B	A	3	3
C	A	1	4
D	C	3	3
E	B, D	4	6
F	E	3	5
G	E	2	2

a. Draw the network diagram for this project.
b. Determine the critical path and project duration.
c. Find a schedule that smooths the workload requirements without delaying project completion. Draw a Gantt chart for your schedule.

TABLE 19.12

		Time Estimates		
Activity	Immediate Predecessor(s)	Most Optimistic	Most Likely	Most Pessimistic
A	—	8	10	12
B	—	5	8	17
C	—	7	8	9
D	B	1	2	3
E	A, C	8	10	12
F	D, E	5	6	7
G	D, E	1	3	5
H	F, G	2	5	8
I	G	2	4	6
J	H	4	5	8
K	H	2	2	2

TABLE 19.13

Activity	Immediate Predecessor(s)	Activity Time (days)	Activity Cost	Activity	Immediate Predecessor(s)	Activity Time (days)	Activity Cost
A	—	3	100	I	E	1	100
B	—	4	150	J	D, E	4	75
C	A	2	125	K	F, G	3	150
D	B	5	175	L	G, H, I	3	150
E	B	3	150	M	I, J	2	100
F	C, D	4	200	N	K, I, M	4	175
G	C	6	75	O	H, M	1	200
H	C, D, E	2	50	P	N, L, O	5	150

19. The information in Table 19.13 is available about a large project.
    a. Determine the critical path and the expected completion time of the project.
    b. Plot the total project cost, starting from day 1 to the expected completion date of the project, assuming the earliest start times for each activity. Compare that result to a similar plot for the latest start times. What implication does the time differential have for cash flows and project scheduling?

20. Consider the project data shown in Table 19.14.
    a. What is the completion time of this project?
    b. What is the critical path?
    c. Suppose that your contract calls for completion of the project within 32 days. What is the probability you will meet that deadline?

TABLE 19.14

Activity	Immediate Predecessor(s)	Time Estimates (wk) Most Optimistic	Most Likely	Most Pessimistic
A	—	1	2	3
B	A	2	4	6
C	—	3	6	12
D	A, C	2	6	10
E	B	2	4	8
F	B, C	3	6	9
G	D, F	1	2	4
H	E	3	5	9
I	D, F	4	6	10
J	G, I, K	1	1	2
K	H	2	3	6
L	G, I	1	2	3
M	J	4	7	10
N	L	5	6	7
O	K, M, N	1	2	5

CASE   THE PERT STUDEBAKER*

You have been the director of service operations for Roberts' Auto Sales and Service (RASAS) since the beginning of the year. It is now mid-February. RASAS consists of three car dealerships that sell and service several makes of American and Japanese cars, two auto parts stores, a large body shop and car painting business, and an auto salvage yard. Your boss, Vikky Roberts, owns RASAS. She grew up around cars and car dealers and went into the car business more than 20 years ago when she inherited a Studebaker dealership from her father. The Studebaker Corporation was on the wane when she obtained the business, but she was able to capitalize on her knowledge and experience to build her business into the diversified and successful "mini-empire" it is today. Her motto, "Sell 'em today, repair 'em tomorrow!" reflects a strategy that she refers to in private as "Get 'em coming and going."

Roberts has always retained a soft spot in her heart for Studebaker automobiles. They were manufactured in South Bend, Indiana, from 1919 to 1966, and many are still operable today because of a vast number of collectors and loyal fans. In fact, Roberts has just acquired a 1963 Studebaker Avanti that is in bad need of restoration. She has also noted the public's growing interest in the restoration of vintage automobiles. These circumstances have led to your meeting with Roberts today.

The Restoration Business

Roberts is quite excited!

I'm thinking of expanding into the vintage car restoration business, and I need your help in assessing the feasibility of such a move. I also want to restore my 1963 Avanti to mint condition, or as close to mint condition as possible. If I do go into the car restoring business, I can use the Avanti as an exhibit in sales and advertising and take it to auto shows to attract business for the new shop.

As you nod in agreement and start to take notes, she continues.

I realize that many people want the thrill of restoring an old car themselves but don't have time to run down

all the old parts. Still others just want to own a vintage auto because it is different, and many of them have plenty of money to pay someone to restore an auto for them.

I'd like our business to appeal to both types of people. We could serve as a parts broker for NOS ("new old stock") for old cars. These are new parts in their original cartons, but they are considered old because they were manufactured many years ago. Frequently they're scattered all over the country, and it can be a time-consuming process to find the right part. With our repair facilities we could also machine our own parts to replicate those that are hard to find or no longer exist.

We'd also assemble a library of parts and body manuals for old cars. No restorer can go far without referring to the appropriate manual for the car he or she is restoring. Our business could serve as an information resource for do-it-yourself restorers. The do-it-yourselfers could come to us for help in compiling their parts lists and we could acquire the parts for them. For others we would take charge of the entire restoration.

Your Assignment

Vikky Roberts now comes to the point of the meeting:

Now here's what I want you to do. I want you to take a good look at my Avanti and see what needs to be done to restore it to the condition it was in when it came from the factory more than 30 years ago. I'd like to have it restored in time to exhibit it at the National Studebaker Meet beginning July 15 in Springfield, Missouri. If this car could win a first prize in its category, it would be a real public relations coup for us—especially if we decide to enter this new venture. Even if we don't, the car will be a showpiece for the rest of the business.

In a week, I want a report from you about what is involved and whether we can get the car done in time to show it at the Springfield meet this summer. As I recall, there is a technique called PERT/CPM that would be appropriate for this. Use that to determine if the July 15 date is feasible. The parts manager, the body shop manager, and the chief mechanic will cer-

*Courtesy of Professor Sue Perrott Siferd, Arizona State University.

tainly assist you in estimating times and tasks that need to be done. They'll help you with cost estimates too. Our accountant assures me that the costs can be treated as advertising, but I want to limit the expenditures on this project to what we could recover by selling the restored car. I've already spent $1500 to acquire the car.

In addition, I'd like a brief report on some of the aspects of the proposed business, such as how it fits in with our other businesses, and what our operations task should be with regard to cost, quality, customer service, and flexibility.

You spend a few days pouring over several issues of *Turning Wheels*, a publication for owners and drivers of Studebakers, and other books on car restoration. You discover that there are categories of restoration. A basic restoration gets the car looking great and running, but a mint condition restoration puts the car back in original condition—as it was "when it rolled off the line." When restored cars compete, a car in mint condition has an advantage over one that is just a basic restoration. As cars are restored, they can also be customized. This means that something is put on the car that couldn't have been on the original. Customized cars compete in separate classes. You understand that your boss wants a mint condition restoration, without customization. (The proposed new business would accept any kind of restoration a customer wanted.)

You also learn that a restored 1963 Avanti can probably be sold for $15,000. You proceed on the assumption that your total budget is not to exceed $13,500

($15,000 minus the $1500 your boss has already spent).

In these same few days you look over the car thoroughly and talk at length with the body shop manager, the parts manager, and the chief mechanic. The four of you come up with a list of tasks, the time these tasks are likely to take, the order in which they must be performed, and their respective cost estimates (see Exhibit 1). (Even though much of the work will be done by Roberts' own employees, you must consider labor and materials costs. All relevant costs have been included in the cost estimates.)

QUESTIONS

1. Using Exhibit 1, prepare your report, assuming that the project will begin in late February of the current year. This gives you 100 working days to complete the project, including transporting the car to Springfield before the meet begins. Your report should briefly discuss the aspects of the proposed new business, such as the competitive priorities (see Chapter 2), that your boss asked about.

2. Compose a table containing the project activities, with a letter assigned to each activity, the time estimates, and the precedence relationships from which you will assemble the network diagram.

3. Draw an AON network diagram of the project similar to Fig. 19.4. Determine the activities on the critical path and the estimated slack for each activity.

4. Prepare a project budget showing the cost of each activity and the total for the project.

EXHIBIT 1

Order all needed material and parts (upholstery, windshield, carburetor, and oil pump). Time: 2 days. Cost (phone calls and labor): $100.

Receive upholstery material for seat covers. Can't be done until order is placed. Time: 30 days. Cost: $250.

Receive windshield. Can't be done until order is placed. Time: 10 days. Cost: $130.

Receive carburetor and oil pump. Can't be done until order is placed. Time: 7 days. Cost: $180.

Remove chrome from body. Can be done immediately. Time: 1 day. Cost: $50.

Remove body (doors, hood, trunk, and fenders) from frame. Can't do until chrome is removed. Time: 1 day. Cost: $150.

Have fenders repaired by body shop. Can't do until body is removed from frame. Time: 4 days. Cost: $200.

Repair doors, trunk, and hood. Can't do until body is removed from frame. Time: 6 days. Cost: $300.

Pull engine from chassis. Do after body is removed from frame. Time: 1 day. Cost: $50.

Remove rust from frame. Do after the engine has been pulled from the chassis. Time: 3 days. Cost: $300.

Regrind engine valves. Have to pull engine from chassis first. Time: 5 days. Cost: $500.

Replace carburetor and oil pump. Do after engine has been pulled from chassis and after carburetor and oil pump have been received. Time: 1 day. Cost: $50.

Rechrome the chrome parts. Chrome must have been removed from the body first. Time: 3 days. Cost: $150.

Reinstall engine. Do after valves are reground and carburetor and oil pump have been installed. Time: 1 day. Cost: $150.

Put doors, hood, and trunk back on frame. The doors, hood, and trunk must have been repaired. The frame also has to have had its rust removed. Time: 1 day. Cost: $80.

Rebuild transmission and replace brakes. Do this after the engine has been reinstalled and the doors, hood, and trunk are back on the frame. Time: 4 days. Cost: $700.

Replace windshield. Windshield must have been received. Time: 1 day. Cost: $70.

Put fenders back on. The fenders must already have been repaired and the transmission rebuilt and the brakes replaced. Time: 1 day. Cost: $60.

Paint car. Can't do this until the fenders are back on and windshield replaced. Time: 4 days. Cost: $1700.

Reupholster interior of car. Must have first received upholstery material. Car must also have been painted. Time: 7 days. Cost: $1200.

Put chrome parts back on. Car has to have been painted and chrome parts rechromed. Time: 1 day. Cost: $50.

Pull car to Studebaker show in Springfield, Missouri. Must have completed reupholstery of interior and have put the chrome parts back on. Time: 2 days. Cost: $500.

SELECTED REFERENCES

Andreu, R., and A. Corominas. "SUCCCES 92: A DSS for Scheduling the Olympic Games." *Interfaces*, vol. 19, no. 5 (September–October 1989), pp. 1–12.

Aquilano, N.J., and D.E. Smith. "A Formal Set of Algorithms for Project Scheduling with Critical Path Scheduling—Material Requirements Planning." *Journal of Operations Management*, vol. 1, no. 2 (November 1980), pp. 57–67.

Britney, R. "Bayesian Point Estimation and the PERT Scheduling of Stochastic Activities." *Management Science*, vol. 22, no. 9 (May 1976), pp. 938–948.

Davis, E.W. "Project Scheduling Under Resource Constraints—Historical Review." *AIIE Transactions*, vol. 5, no. 4 (December 1973), pp. 297–311.

Fawcette, J.E. "Choosing Project Management Software." *Personal Computing*, vol. 8, no. 10 (October 1984), pp. 154–167.

Littlefield, T.K., and P.H. Randolph. "PERT Duration Times: Mathematical or MBO." *Interfaces*, vol. 21, no. 6 (November–December 1991), pp. 92–95.

Martin, C.C. *Project Management: How to Make It Work*. New York: AMACOM, a Division of American Management Associations, 1976.

PC Magazine. September 11, 1990, pp. 338–339.

Sullivan, K.B. "Experts' Advice on Deciding When a PC May Help a Project." *PC Week*, January 21, 1986, p. 135.

Weist, J.D. "Heuristic Programs for Decision Making." *Harvard Business Review* (September–October 1966), pp. 129–143.

Weist, J.D., and F.K. Levy. *A Management Guide to PERT/CPM*, 2nd ed. Englewood Cliffs, N.J.: Prentice-Hall, 1977.

Chapter 20

OPERATIONS AS A COMPETITIVE WEAPON

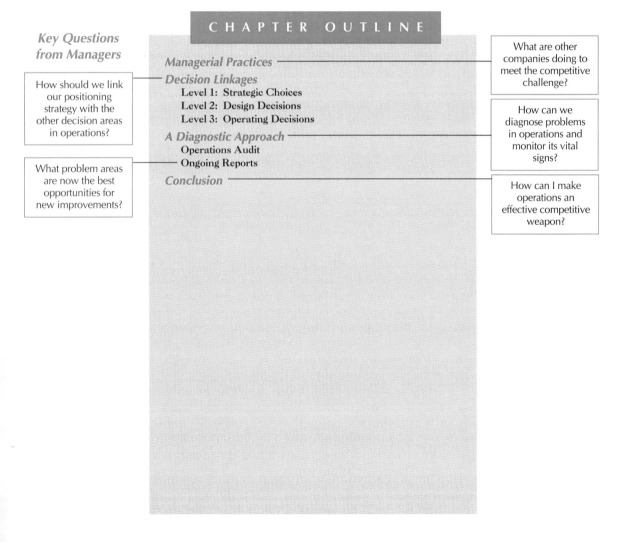

Key Questions from Managers

How should we link our positioning strategy with the other decision areas in operations?

What problem areas are now the best opportunities for new improvements?

CHAPTER OUTLINE

Managerial Practices

Decision Linkages
    Level 1: Strategic Choices
    Level 2: Design Decisions
    Level 3: Operating Decisions

A Diagnostic Approach
    Operations Audit
    Ongoing Reports

Conclusion

What are other companies doing to meet the competitive challenge?

How can we diagnose problems in operations and monitor its vital signs?

How can I make operations an effective competitive weapon?

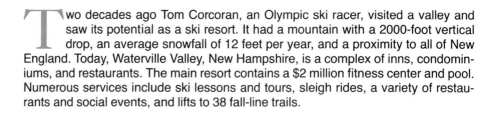

Two decades ago Tom Corcoran, an Olympic ski racer, visited a valley and saw its potential as a ski resort. It had a mountain with a 2000-foot vertical drop, an average snowfall of 12 feet per year, and a proximity to all of New England. Today, Waterville Valley, New Hampshire, is a complex of inns, condominiums, and restaurants. The main resort contains a $2 million fitness center and pool. Numerous services include ski lessons and tours, sleigh rides, a variety of restaurants and social events, and lifts to 38 fall-line trails.

We have tried to convey the key role that operations management plays in the business community. In Chapter 1 we looked at how a ski manufacturer's strategic, design, and operating decisions gave it a competitive advantage. The ski industry, however, includes an equally competitive service sector—numerous resorts that supply the slopes on which beginners and skilled athletes use their equipment. Operations management plays a no less important role in this segment of the ski market.

The service delivery system must recognize the competitive priorities of each service. For example, lifts are designed within safety guidelines for high-volume, low-cost operations. The more elegant restaurants are designed for low-volume, high-quality meals. Scheduled events must begin on time, and careful capacity planning keeps costs down and quality of service high—a difficult task given the seasonal business. Extensive off-season promotions help stabilize demand. Thus effective strategic, design, and operating decisions are three factors that give Waterville Valley Resort the competitive edge.

As is the case with so many real company examples described in this text, operations management is a key weapon in the arsenal of world-class competitors. This is the message of our last chapter.

Having come full circle, we now pull together the various topics covered into a unified view of operations management. At this point we also return to the important trends presented in Chapter 1. Our concern in operations management is to improve productivity and quality in both manufacturing and services. Global competitiveness, time-based competition, technological change, ethics, and the environment all pose important challenges for today's operations managers. It seems to us that improvements across all of these dimensions are mandatory, not optional.

British, Japanese, and U.S. executives agree on one point: Among all the functions in business, operations management is the most important source of productivity improvements (McInnes, 1984). A strategic approach to operations, backed by careful analysis, is fundamental to such improvements. Three points on operations strategy, first stated in Chapter 1, need repeating here:

1. Operations can be a competitive weapon or a millstone.
2. Although management must first address strategic choices, success also depends on tactical choices based on careful analysis of specific alternatives.

A view of the ski lodge at the Waterville Valley Resort.

3. Managers should link decisions in operations.

In this chapter, we address each of these points. We begin by reviewing some of the managerial practices presented in earlier chapters. They are examples of what companies are actually doing to make operations a competitive weapon. They also show that *many* things—ranging from strategic choices such as competitive priorities to tactical choices such as scheduling—must be done well. This information underscores the first two points in the preceding list. We address the third point—consistently linking decisions—by describing how decisions in operations relate to positioning strategy. We conclude with a discussion of a diagnostic approach for gaining a competitive advantage.

MANAGERIAL PRACTICES

What is the best avenue for making operations a competitive weapon? The actual business examples in prior chapters give us considerable insight into how firms meet the competitive challenge.

- Zoom Telephonics, Inc., introduced modems as a new product (*product and service planning*).
- Earl Scheib, Inc., emphasized low price for its car face-lifts (*competitive priorities*).
- The Paul Revere Insurance Company instituted quality teams in its long-term effort to improve total quality (*quality management*).
- Hay and Forage Industries launched a computerized process control system for maintaining the quality of its farm equipment (*quality control*).
- K2 Corporation invested in a triaxial braiding process to make its Alpine skis (*process design*).
- MCI Communications Corporation spent $300 million to update its computer systems and to offer innovative residential calling services (*technology management*).

- AT&T Credit Corporation set up self-managing teams in a high-volume division, with each one prepared to process all aspects of a small business's equipment lease application (*job design*).
- The Limited took on an expansion drive, in terms of both new outlets and on-site expansions, while it was reeling from the women's apparel slump in the late 1980s (*capacity*).
- Nearly 2000 maquiladora plants have sprung up in northern Mexico (*location*).
- Wendy's International, Incorporated poured $40 million into refurbishing more than 500 restaurants to achieve a very contemporary appeal (*layout*).
- La Quinta Inns developed a forecasting model to predict inn operating margin at new location sites (*forecasting*).
- Ethan Allen created a warehouse to hold its inventory more centrally (*materials management*).
- Hallmark uses a level strategy to avoid layoffs in a very seasonal business (*aggregate planning*).
- Hyundai Motor Company updates monthly its master production schedule to find the best compromise between the sales department's desire for flexibility and the production control department's desire for stability (*master production planning*).
- Dominion Automotive Industries installed a computerized system for determining component production requirements leading to lower inventory levels and labor costs (*material requirements planning*).
- Northern Telecom seeks continuous improvement, small-lot production, and close supplier relationships to improve its operations (*just-in-time systems*).
- The San Francisco Police Department now uses an interactive computerized model to schedule and deploy its officers (*scheduling*).
- The Olympic Planning Committee planned and scheduled more than 2000 athletic events for the 1992 Olympic Games in Barcelona (*project scheduling*).

Companies are addressing each decision area in operations to achieve excellence. Some types of approaches are particularly fashionable, such as total quality control, time-based competition, sophisticated technology (including FMS), just-in-time systems, environmental awareness, and work teams. However, there is no single cure or magic formula. Operations managers must deal with all aspects of the production system while attempting to improve productivity and quality.

DECISION LINKAGES

Making operations management a competitive weapon means that strategic, design, and operating decisions should be consistent and linked. Inconsistent or independent decisions can act at cross-purposes and thus decrease overall productivity. Results of surveys suggest that a lack of consistent, linked decisions is a key factor in lagging productivity (Judson, 1982). Unfortunately, most efforts at improving productivity are disjointed reactions to the latest productivity problems. Only one third of the firms surveyed linked their efforts to improve productivity with their competitive priorities and positioning strategy. However, greater agreement between corporate strategy and operations can result in higher profits (Richardson, Taylor, and Gordon, 1985).

We emphasized linking decisions within the operations function in many of the chapters. In the next several sections we summarize the linking process, as depicted in Fig. 20.1, at three decision levels:

- Level 1: Strategic choices
- Level 2: Design decisions
- Level 3: Operating decisions

Figure 20.1 shows that strategic choices are the first decisions that an organization makes and that all other decisions are based on these choices. If management properly links these most strategic choices to other decisions, operations becomes a competitive weapon. For example, a high-volume commodities manufacturer with a process focus and general-purpose equipment will probably not compete successfully on cost. The plant doesn't need the flexibility, and efficiency will be low.

The patterns described in the following sections are *tendencies* rather than unbreakable rules, and you will encounter many exceptions. For example, some assembly lines that have a product focus will also be labor intensive. Some retailers may offer customized services and yet the customers all follow the same service flow. Another example is manufacturing plants that make ad-

FIGURE 20.1

Linking Decisions
Within Operations
Management

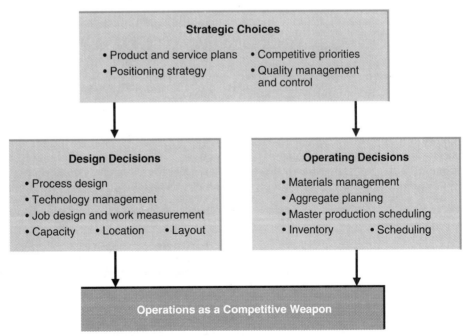

hesives and glues: Only the formula changes from one customized order to the next. In reality relationships are complex, but our purpose is to present general patterns.

Level 1: Strategic Choices

Corporate strategy connects with operations through positioning strategy. A *process focus* strategy means jumbled flows of products (or customers) through the system. Flexibility is maximized by organizing resources around the process (or function performed). A *product focus* strategy is just the opposite, trading off flexibility to achieve standard routings, line flows, and resources organized by product. The best focus for a specific company depends on its product and service plans, competitive priorities, and quality choices, as shown in Table 20.1.

Product and Service Plans and Competitive Priorities. Table 20.1 shows the linkage of positioning strategy to product and service plans and competitive priorities. When *product and service plans* call for more customization, costs will be high and volumes low. Life cycles are shorter, and products and services tend to be in the early stages of their life cycles. Dedicating resources to specific products and services is unwise. A process focus is best because its flexibility handles the changing product and service mix—but at higher unit costs. This means that the *competitive priority* cannot be cost. Customization, superior quality, and volume flexibility are the other choices. They differentiate the product or service from others, preventing head-on cost competition. Fast delivery times are unlikely with a process focus. Products are customized, made from scratch, rather than produced in large volumes and shelved awaiting demand that may never come. The emphasis is on meeting due date promises, rather than giving quick deliveries.

TABLE 20.1 / Linking Positioning Strategy with Other Strategic Choices

	Positioning Strategy	
Decision Area	Process Focus	Product Focus
Product and service planning	More customization, with low volumes Shorter life cycles An entrance–exit strategy favoring early exit	More standardization, with high volumes Longer life cycles An entrance–exit strategy favoring late exit
Competitive priorities	More emphasis on customization and volume flexibility Long delivery times	More emphasis on low cost Short delivery times
Quality management and control	High-performance design quality Stringent process documentation Focus on tooling and fixtures	Consistent quality More automated inspection Statistical process control

Quality Management and Control. Table 20.1 also shows the linkage of positioning strategy to quality. Reliable quality, which means consistently meeting product specifications, is important to all firms because scrap and rework are costly. The most important link with positioning strategy lies with the product and service specifications themselves. A firm choosing high-performance design quality as its competitive priority, as does a five-star restaurant or Rolls-Royce, is likely to have a process focus. Prices must be higher, resulting in lower product volumes. This approach rules out a product focus because resource utilization would be too low. There is another link: Firms choosing customization or volume flexibility as a competitive priority are likely to be small and process focused. Their quality control procedures focus on the control of variables such as tooling and fixtures and on stringent process documentation to ensure replicability of production procedures. Statistical process control is not emphasized because of low-volume production and short runs.

High-volume production systems with a product focus, on the other hand, not only emphasize statistical process control but might even automate much of the inspection process. To ensure consistent quality, these firms have formal procedures for monitoring incoming materials, process yields, and outgoing products. Scrap and rework are particularly disruptive to the line flows in a product-focused facility.

Level 2: Design Decisions

Designing the production system should fit the positioning strategy. Table 20.2 on the next page shows these linkages.

Process Design and Technology Management. A process focus means more general-purpose (and less-efficient) equipment. Operations are more labor intensive, gaining flexibility but giving up rock-bottom costs. We discussed these differences in Chapter 2. A small process-focused machine shop often has an investment in equipment of only $10,000 per employee, while a large product-focused brewery has an investment of $500,000 per employee. A survey of 150 firms showed that the average capital investment for those having more of a process focus was only $17,000 per employee (Taylor, 1980). Those firms having more of a product focus had an average investment almost four times as large. Capital intensity and automation require high production volumes for effective equipment utilization. In the past in the automotive industry, a new automated line was introduced with each model change, at a cost of more than $20 million—quite a disincentive for frequent model changes. Only recently has the relationship between product volumes and capital intensity been broken in certain situations. Group technology, reprogrammable robots, and flexible machining can mean higher capital intensity, even with low volumes and short life cycles.

As a process-focused production system is labor intensive, labor costs are of particular concern in delivering its services or making its products. Managers give continuous attention to efficiency losses caused by setups, materials handling, and component delays. With a product focus, their attention shifts to

TABLE 20.2 / Linking Positioning Strategy with Design Decisions

	Positioning Strategy	
Decision Area	Process Focus	Product Focus
Process design and technology management	General purpose, flexible equipment	Specialized equipment dedicated to a few products or services
	Labor intensive, with less automation	Capital intensive, with more automation
	Attention on labor costs	Attention on facility utilization and overhead costs
	Less vertically integrated	More vertically integrated
Job design	Flexible work force	Specialized work force
	Enlarged jobs	Specialized jobs
	Informal promotion channels	Formal promotion channels
	Frequent two-way communication with supervisors	Less frequent two-way communication with supervisors
	Fewer staff specialists	More staff specialists
Capacity	Large capacity cushion	Small capacity cushion
	Large capacity imbalances	Small capacity imbalances
	Difficult to measure	Easy to measure
	Less of a management concern	More of a management concern
	Small economies of scale	Large economies of scale
Location	Single facility	Multiple facilities
	Expand on site or relocate nearby	Expand by adding new facilities, possibly overseas
	More local or regional markets	More national or international markets
	Transportation costs not a primary location factor	Transportation costs sometimes a primary location factor
Layout	Process layouts	Product layouts
	Flexible	Inflexible
	Variable-path materials handling	Fixed-path, automated materials handling

effective facility utilization, because of the high capital intensity, and controlling various overhead costs.

A final link is with vertical integration. With a process focus, where volumes are low and unit costs are high, a firm tends to rely on outside suppliers to manufacture parts and assemblies for its products. Suppliers can achieve economies of scale by pooling the demand from several process-focused firms. On the other hand, firms with a product focus and high volumes tend to do more part and assembly work in-house, integrating backward (make rather than buy) and forward (toward the customer).

Job Design. A process focus also favors use of a flexible work force. Workers receive more cross-training so that they can help out with the capacity imbalances and frequent shocks (such as rush jobs and scrap losses) at a process-focused facility. This approach creates enlarged, broader jobs, which often serve to motivate workers and to increase wage rates. Small, process-focused firms have less formal promotion channels and are less likely to be unionized than large firms. Until recent innovative contracts, such as that at GM's Saturn facility, unions have favored narrow job boundaries and more formal promotion channels. Filling one opening sets off a chain reaction of bumping under the provisions of most labor contracts.

The unpredictability of day-to-day production requirements of a process focus places great importance on two-way communication between workers and supervisors to identify which work to do next and how to do it. Fewer supervisory tasks are diverted to task specialists. For example, scheduling of equipment very far ahead is less critical (owing to lower capital intensity) and even less possible (owing to unpredictability). When equipment investment reaches $1 million per worker, as is true with some product-focused processes, more staff specialists can be justified for production planning and work design.

Capacity. The most obvious link is the capacity cushion. It must be larger with a process focus because of low capital intensity (which reduces the cushion's cost), shifting product mixes (creating capacity imbalances), increased demand and supply uncertainties, greater scheduling complexity, and more variable demand (peaks and valleys). Because capacity often comes in chunks, expanding by even the minimum increment can create a large cushion with the small volumes of a process focus. One study in particular confirms the link between positioning strategy and the capacity cushion (Taylor, 1980). Firms with more of a process focus averaged 10 shifts per week, whereas those with a product focus averaged 17. The maximum number of shifts possible is 21 per week (or 3 shifts/day, 7 days/week). Product-focused firms must maximize utilization of their capital-intensive facilities, operating them around-the-clock if necessary.

Table 20.2 shows three other links to capacity. First, capacity is particularly difficult to measure with a process focus because multiple products share the same equipment. Changing product mixes creates imbalances and floating bottlenecks. Second, managers of process-focused facilities are less preoccupied with capacity decisions. Equipment costs are low, and lead times to buy new, general-purpose equipment are shorter. Management doesn't need to plan so far ahead for capacity changes, and unit costs depend less on high utilization. Finally, economies of scale are less dramatic. With the facility's smaller size, it benefits less from spreading fixed costs (which are lower anyway) and from avoiding setups by dedicating resources to specific products or services.

Location. The most striking link between positioning strategy and design decisions is simply the number of facilities. Low-volume producers choose a process focus out of necessity. Since they are small, they usually have just one facility. They expand either on-site or by relocating nearby. They appeal to a local or regional market, which makes transportation costs less of a primary location factor. Even for distant customers, the product is not standardized enough to avoid costly direct shipments. High-volume producers create multiple facilities, including a system of warehouses. Each facility can focus on product, market area, or process. Product-focused firms are more likely to consider international expansion as a way of penetrating foreign markets.

Layout. The layout translates positioning strategy into concrete form with either a *process layout* for a process focus or a *product layout* for a product focus.

With a process layout, employees and equipment are grouped by function or process. All grinding is done by the grinding department, all bill processing by the accounts payable section, and all budget-priced apparel displayed in the department store's basement. This approach facilitates supervision, fosters worker flexibility, and improves responses to changing product mixes. The jumbled routings, however, result in less efficient materials-handling methods. Variable-path devices, such as carts, forklifts, and overhead cranes, must be used. Only with the line flows of a product focus can efficient fixed-path devices (such as conveyors) be utilized.

Level 3: Operating Decisions

Positioning strategy must also link with tactical decisions about operating (rather than designing) the facility. These linkages are shown in Table 20.3.

Materials Management. With a process focus, low repeatability and jumbled routings cause complexity. Last-minute changes by customers and suppliers, imprecise time standards, and difficulties in predicting capacities create uncertainty. Because of the complexity and uncertainty, plans cannot be made far in advance. Instead, planning is done at a local, decentralized level to adapt to

TABLE 20.3 / Linking Positioning Strategy with Operating Decisions

	Positioning Strategy	
Decision Area	Process Focus	Product Focus
Materials management	More complexity and uncertainty Shorter-range plans Higher tolerance for cushion of extra workers and inventory Informal supplier and customer relationships Inventory held lower in BOM Information oriented to orders	Less complexity and uncertainty Longer-range plans Lower tolerance for cushion of extra workers and inventory Formal supplier and customer relationships Inventory held higher in BOM Information oriented to forecasts
Aggregate planning	More volume flexibility Relies on overtime, subcontracting, or extra shifts	Less volume flexibility Relies on anticipation inventory and aggressive alternatives
Master production scheduling	Less stable MPS	More stable MPS
Inventory	Short runs Longer cycle times and more WIP Component shortages Lot sizing and sequencing loosely coupled MRP system	Long runs Shorter cycle times and less WIP Capacity shortages Lot sizing and sequencing tightly coupled JIT system
Scheduling	Fluid and changing Planned just a few days ahead Decentralized decisions Labor-limited environment	Stable Planned many days ahead Centralized decisions Machine-limited environment

the latest conditions. Greater work-force and inventory cushions are tolerated because of the dynamic environment. A process focus also involves less formal relationships with suppliers. No long-term contracts are negotiated with key suppliers. Raw-material volumes are low, so the firm has less control over suppliers, who naturally cater to larger customers. On the outbound side, distribution channels are less formal. Markets are likely to be local or regional, and no elaborate network of distribution centers is needed. Products are more likely to be specials, which rules out positioning finished goods inventory at warehouses close to the customer. Direct shipments from the plant to the customer are the norm.

The customized products of a process focus mean that inventory must be created lower in the bills of materials. Inventory is not created by plan at higher levels because of low turnover and fear of obsolescence. More intermediate items are likely to be produced to help increase part commonality, keep customer delivery times at acceptable levels, cut losses owing to setups, and buffer against bottlenecks.

A final link with materials management deals with information requirements. With a process focus, information tends to be oriented to the bidding process and specific customer orders. Output plans are communicated by releasing jobs with detailed routing information. With a product focus, information is oriented to demand forecasts and current inventory positions, rather than individual customer orders. Product-focused firms produce more to stock and less to order.

Aggregate Planning. A process focus allows more volume flexibility and changes in the output rate to meet seasonal or cyclical demand. One study showed that changing the output rate by using overtime, subcontracting, and extra shifts is about twice as common with a process focus (Taylor, 1980). A product focus is accompanied by a *level strategy*, letting anticipation inventory build during the slack season. A firm may even have enough clout to require customers to take early delivery of the inventory. It is also better positioned for aggressive alternatives. The last resort for a product-focused firm is to shut down one of its plants entirely. There are five reasons for these links between a level strategy and a product focus:

1. Overtime and extra shifts tend to be infeasible options, as the plant is more likely to be operating with three shifts already to maximize facility utilization.
2. A product focus implies low variable costs, making the extra cost of subcontracting prohibitive. Too much is lost by going outside to have the work done. It is also unlikely that a subcontractor can be found to supply the necessary volumes when business is booming.
3. Products are more standardized, making it possible to build anticipation inventory without fear of obsolescence.
4. Line processes are more rigid and tend to be set at specific output rates. Rebalancing a line means changing the jobs of many individuals. It is simpler to temporarily shut down a whole line when demand falls.

5. A high-volume producer is more likely to be able to influence the market or add new products as aggressive alternatives to level out the uneven demand pattern.

Master Production Schedule. The master production schedule is less stable with a process focus. There is a greater willingness to change the MPS to satisfy last-minute requests. Products are more likely to be custom-engineered, which raises the possibility of delays before the job is released to production because engineering changes are more frequent. Another cause of unstable schedules is that a small, process-focused firm has much less clout with customers than does a product-focused firm.

Inventory. Positioning strategy also links with inventory decisions. Low volumes mean short runs, and at the extreme, special customer orders are matched with shop orders on a one-for-one basis. The shorter runs do not necessarily mean lower turnover, as demand is also lower. A 100-unit batch may represent a six-months' supply in a job shop but just a one-day's supply with the high volumes of a product focus.

Items at a process-focused facility are routed through many work stations. Each station is a potential bottleneck and has a long waiting line. Lead times (or cycle times) are long and variable, which requires more work-in-process (WIP) inventory and more safety stock. For example, firms with a process focus reported that 36 percent of their inventory is WIP (Taylor, 1980). This level drops to only 18 percent with a product focus.

Table 20.3 shows three other links with inventory. Customization and low-volume production make component availability the key concern of inventory planners at a process-focused facility. With the capital intensity of a product focus, the concern shifts to capacity shortages. Achieving plans that provide for adequate capacity forces inventory and sequencing decisions to be more highly integrated. Finally, product diversity lends itself to an order-based system such as MRP. Its logic is particularly appropriate for ensuring component availability. The repetitiveness of high-volume production indicates the need for a system such as JIT.

Scheduling. Process-focused facilities have fluid and changing schedules because both demand and supply are less certain. Reactive, crisis-oriented scheduling is not as apparent with a product focus. Instead, scheduling and monitoring of day-to-day performance is more elaborate. Because of the high cost of idle resources, schedules are developed further into the future, often on a more centralized basis. When inventory that decouples operations is stripped away, more attention must be given to scheduling to maximize facility utilization and customer service. In some cases, lead times to customers might even have to be extended to get better utilization. At medical facilities, for example, attempts are made to achieve better utilization by an appointment system. Patients are scheduled well in advance of when the service is to be provided, except for emergency cases.

Finally, Table 20.3 shows that a process focus normally means labor-limited scheduling and a more flexible work force. Both labor assignment policies and dispatching priority rules are needed. Machine-limited scheduling for a product focus is simpler in this respect. However, it is not without its challenges. Schedules must recognize capacity constraints and maximize facility utilization.

A DIAGNOSTIC APPROACH

A strategic approach to operations management answers two fundamental questions: (1) What should we be doing? and (2) How are we doing? The first question has a *planning orientation*, which has been our main perspective. We started with corporate strategy and positioning decisions and then linked them to planning in the various functional areas of operations management. The second question has a *control orientation* (see Ruefli and Sarrazin, 1981). The purpose of control is to monitor performance, identify problems, and diagnose causes of problems. Managers can then take corrective actions to restore operations to the desired course. We conclude with a brief description of two control methods: audits and ongoing reports.

Operations Audit

One important diagnostic tool is an **operations audit,** or special study of operations. Checklists for service providers (Chase and Aquilano, 1985) and manufacturers (Skinner, 1978) are available. They contain a variety of dimensions on which to evaluate operations. Two scores are assigned to each dimension, one for current performance and one for the goal. Large negative differences represent planning and/or production problems. An audit begins with competitive priorities and works down through each of the decision areas shown in Fig. 20.1. Starting from the top ties the audit to strategic planning and evaluation of decision consistency. Dimensions for evaluating process design include the following:

- Degree of capital intensity
- Extent of equipment specialization
- Degree of worker flexibility
- Degree of vertical integration
- Degree of customer involvement in the process
- Frequency of process innovations
- Work-force involvement in process design

Similar lists can be developed for the other decision areas in operations, tailoring the choices to the needs of the individual firm.

Ongoing Reports

Another diagnostic tool is **ongoing reports** on multiple measures. Some measures are traditional accounting data on costs (broken into various categories), profits, and return on investment. Over the years, manufacturing management has been evaluated primarily on the basis of direct labor (actual versus time standard) costs. There is growing recognition, however, that such measures are insufficient and can actually restrain production systems. An excessive financial orientation makes efficiency or short-term profits the overriding priority. New technologies, quality improvements, and the quality of work life are ignored because many of their benefits are long-term and difficult to quantify. Although extremely useful, short-term financial measures must be kept in perspective.

Recognizing that no single measure of performance is adequate, the logical approach is to use multiple tracking devices. Those listed in Table 20.4 help managers monitor the *vital signs* of the production system. Such measures are tailored to specific operations and change from time to time. A pyramid approach is used, whereby department managers pick five or ten measures that best fit their operations. Each manager passes a few to his or her supervisor, and so on. Thus a vice president of operations might end up with 20 or 30 indicators.

ABC analysis, which we first introduced for inventory problems (see Chapter 12), is particularly valuable here to focus management's attention on the relatively few key problem areas. Management-by-exception applies equally well to inventory (by type or department), equipment failures (by machine or department), customer goods returned (by product line or department), scrap or rework (by work station), or employee absenteeism (by department).

Finally, managers have to remember that this monitoring is but a means to an end. The end is improving performance and linking operations to corporate strategy. Managers must draw on a knowledge of operations and an awareness of their environment in seeking remedies. If inventory is too high, for example, the cause can be any number of factors. Large lot sizes, high forecast errors, long lead times, uneven or seasonal demand, unstable master production schedules, or inaccurate records are all possible causes. Managers must dig deeply to discover the real problems underlying the symptomatic problems uncovered by ongoing reports—and then remedy them.

TABLE 20.4 / *Some Vital Signs for Operations Management*

Actual-to-forecasted demand (%)	Total inventory (weeks of supply)	Ratio of maintenance hours to direct labor hours (%)
Returned merchandise ($)	WIP inventory (% of total)	
Scrap rate (%)	Transaction volume (number)	Purchase orders (% placed in 3 days)
Nursing hours to patient hours (%)	Capital intensity ($ per worker)	Late deliveries from suppliers (% of orders)
Ratio of sales $ to payroll $ (%)	Training (hours/week)	
Number of grievances	Number of products produced per machine	Overtime ($)
Voluntary quits	Change in sales and profit margins over last year (life cycle position)	On-time delivery (% of orders)
Overhead ($)		Order backlog ($)
Facility utilization (%)	Rework labor (% of direct labor)	Inventory ($)
Leased truck utilization (%)	Materials costs (% of total)	Book-to-cycle count accuracy (%)
Open orders ($)	Direct labor (actual versus standard)	Cycle time (days)
Purchase prices (% of prior prices)	Absenteeism (labor days lost)	Transaction costs ($)
	Tooling cost ($)	Customer return rate (%)
Seasonal inventory ($)	Number of quality circle projects	Variation in monthly production rate
New orders booked ($)	Equipment breakdowns (hours lost)	Number of production orders per month
Stockouts		

CONCLUSION

We have stressed that the operations function, whether in manufacturing or services, can and must be managed better. Operations can definitely be a competitive weapon—not a millstone—as Japanese manufacturers have proved. We also emphasized that each decision in operations can affect efforts to improve productivity and quality. Operations management must be approached strategically, but with careful attention to tactical decisions and techniques.

In making operations a competitive weapon, managers must take more initiative, show greater commitment, be quality conscious, and be ready to act. Rather than blame government regulation or intractable unions for lagging competitiveness, each manager should ask: Am *I* perceived as quality conscious by the work force? Am *I* making sensible decisions and linking them coherently? Am *I* taking the initiative as much as *I* can in my position? Can *I* be more innovative? Am *I* encouraging employees in operations to do what is wanted and needed, rather than just what they are told? Am *I* committed to excellence in operations? As current or future operations managers, your firm's response to the competitive challenge depends on your answers to those questions.

CHAPTER HIGHLIGHTS

● Productivity, quality, global competitiveness, time-based competition, technological change, ethics, and the environment all pose important challenges for operations management.

● Making operations management a competitive weapon depends on doing many things well, rather than seeking a magic solution.

● A strategic approach is needed to improve operations, so that decisions are linked and consistent. Management's positioning strategy is the starting point for making consistent operations decisions. The choice of process focus or product focus must be linked with the other decision areas in the operation.

● At the highest decision levels, a process focus links with customized products and services, low volumes, short life cycles, an entrance–exit strategy favoring early exit, high-performance design quality, and stringent process documentation.

● For design decisions, a process focus links with flexible resources, labor intensity, minimal vertical integration, enlarged jobs, informal promotion channels, frequent two-way communication, large capacity cushions, small economies of scale, single-site locations, local or regional markets, process layouts, and variable-path materials handling.

● For operating decisions, a process focus means complexity and uncertainty, short-range plans, high tolerance for inventory cushions, informal supplier and customer relationships, holding inventory low in the BOM, volume flexibility, short runs, long cycle times, substantial WIP, potential component shortages, and decentralized scheduling.

● An operations audit helps to diagnose problems in operations by systematically evaluating a variety of dimensions. It starts with competitive priorities and works down through the various operating decision areas.

● Ongoing reports are another diagnostic tool for managers. Since there is no single measure of performance, multiple measures should be used. When problems have been identified, managers must draw on their knowledge of operations and awareness of the environment to solve them.

● Operations management needs a strategic orientation, but with full attention to tactical decisions and techniques.

STUDY QUESTIONS

1. "The only real answer to the productivity challenge is relocating facilities to where labor rates are cheap." Do you agree or disagree with this statement? Why?

2. What product and service plans and competitive priorities link well with a process focus? Why?

3. Why is a product-focused facility more likely to be capital intensive? To place more emphasis on equipment utilization? To have a larger staff?

4. Why does the choice of materials handling equipment depend on positioning strategy?

5. Why are inventories stocked at more forward positions with a product focus?

6. "The Japanese have successfully challenged all the traditional thinking and beliefs of U.S. operations managers. We can expect widespread adoption of their approaches in the next decade." Do you agree or disagree with this statement? Why?

7. Comment on the statement: "Annual profits and efficiency are the only true measures of a production system."

8. What dimensions for an operations audit would you suggest for layout? For inventory?

SELECTED REFERENCES

Burnham, John M. "Improving Manufacturing Performance—Management's Vital Challenge." *Production and Inventory Management*, vol. 25, no. 2 (Second Quarter 1984), pp. 1–20.

Chase, Richard B., and Nicholas J. Aquilano. *Production and Operations Management*. Homewood, Ill.: Richard D. Irwin, 1989.

"Deming's Demons." *Wall Street Journal*, June 4, 1990, pp. R39–R41.

Drucker, Peter E. "The Emerging Theory of Manufacturing." *Harvard Business Review* (May–June 1990), pp. 94–102.

Eccles, Robert G. "The Performance Measurement Manifesto." *Harvard Business Review* (January–February 1991), pp. 131–137.

Hayes, Robert H., and Kim B. Clark. "Explaining Observed Productivity Differentials Between Plants: Implications for Operations Research." *Interfaces*, vol. 15, no. 6 (November–December 1985), pp. 3–14.

Janson, Robert L. "Graphic Indicators of Operations." *Harvard Business Review* (November–December 1980), pp. 164–170.

Judson, Arnold S. "The Awkward Truth about Productivity." *Harvard Business Review* (September–October 1982), pp. 93–97.

Kaplan, Robert S., and David P. Norton. "The Balanced Scorecard—Measures That Drive Performance." *Harvard Business Review* (January–February 1992), pp. 71–79.

McDougall, Duncan C. "How to Tell When You've Found an Effective Performance Measurement System for Manufacturing." *Operations Management REVIEW* (Fall 1987 & Winter 1988), pp. 38–48.

McInnes, J. Morris. "Corporate Management of Productivity—An Empirical Study." *Strategic Management Journal*, vol. 5 (1984), pp. 351–365.

Magaziner, Ira C., and Mark Patinkin. *The Silent War*. New York: Random House, 1989.

Miller, Jeffrey G., and Thomas E. Vollmann. "The Hidden Factory." *Harvard Business Review* (September–October 1985), pp. 142–150.

Porter, Michael E. "The Competitive Advantage of Nations." *Harvard Business Review* (March–April 1990), pp. 73–93.

"Productivity and Quality Improvement in the 90s." *Ninth Productivity Survey*. Atlanta, Georgia: Institute of Industrial Engineers, 1990.

Richardson, P.R., A.J. Taylor, and J.R.M. Gordon. "A Strategic Approach to Evaluating Manufacturing Performance." *Interfaces*, vol. 15, no. 6 (November–December 1985), pp. 15–27.

Ritzman, Larry P., Barry E. King, and Lee J. Krajewski. "Manufacturing Performance—Pulling the Right Levers." *Harvard Business Review* (March–April 1984), pp. 143–152.

Ruefli, Timothy, and Jacques Sarrazin. "Strategic Control of Corporate Development Under Ambiguous Circumstances." *Management Science*, vol. 27, no. 10 (October 1981), pp. 1158–1170.

Schmenner, Roger W. "Behind Labor Productivity Gains in the Factory." *Journal of Manufacturing and Operations Management*, vol. 1, no. 4 (Winter 1988a), pp. 323–338.

Skinner, Wickham. *Manufacturing in the Corporate Strategy*. New York: John Wiley & Sons, 1978.

Taylor, Sam G. "Are Process Industries Different?" *23rd Annual Conference Proceedings*. American Production and Inventory Control Society, Los Angeles, October 1980, pp. 94–96.

Wheelwright, Steven C., and Robert H. Hayes. "Competing Through Manufacturing." *Harvard Business Review* (January–February, 1985), pp. 99–109.

FINANCIAL ANALYSIS

Many decisions in operations management involve large capital investments. Automation, vertical integration, capacity expansion, layout revisions, and installing a new MRP system are but some examples. Most of a firm's assets are tied up in the operations function. Therefore the operations manager should seek high-yield capital projects and then assess their costs, benefits, and risks. Such projects typically are subjected to one or more types of financial analysis. In this supplement, we present a brief overview of basic financial analyses.

TIME VALUE OF MONEY

An important concept underlying many financial analysis techniques is that a dollar in hand today is worth more than a dollar to be received in the future. A dollar available today can be invested to earn a return, so that more than one dollar will be available in the future. This concept is known as the **time value of money**.

Future Value of an Investment

If $5000 is invested at 10 percent interest for one year, at the end of the year the $5000 will have earned $500 in interest and the total amount available will be $5500. If the interest earned is allowed to accumulate, it also earns interest and the original investment will grow to $12,970 in ten years. The process by which interest on an investment accumulates, and then earns interest itself for the remainder of the investment period, is known as **compounding interest**. The value of an investment at the end of the period over which interest is compounded is called the **future value of an investment**.

To calculate the future value of an investment, we first express the interest rate and the time period in the same units of time as the interval at which compounding occurs. Let's assume that interest is compounded annually, so we express all time periods in years and use annual interest rates. To find the value of an investment one year in the future, we multiply the amount invested by the sum of 1 plus the interest rate (expressed as a decimal). The value of a $5000 investment at 12 percent per year one year from now is

$$\$5000(1.12) = \$5600$$

If the entire amount remains invested, at the end of two years we have

$$5600(1.12) = \$5000(1.12)^2 = \$6272$$

In general,

$$F = P(1 + r)^n$$

where

F = future value of the investment at the end of n periods

P = amount invested at the beginning, called the principal

r = periodic interest rate

n = number of time periods for which the interest compounds

Present Value of a Future Amount

Let's look at the opposite problem. Suppose that we want to make an investment now that will be worth $10,000 in one year. If the interest rate is 12 percent, and P represents the amount invested now, we can express this problem as

$$F = \$10,000 = P(1 + 0.12)$$

Solving for P gives us:

$$P = \frac{F}{(1 + r)} = \frac{10,000}{(1 + 0.12)} = \$8,929$$

The amount to be invested now to accumulate to a certain amount in the future at a specific interest rate is called the **present value of an investment**. The process of finding the present value of an investment, when the future value and the interest rate are known, is called **discounting** the future value to its present value. If the number of time periods n for which discounting is desired is greater than 1, the present value is determined by dividing the future value by the nth power of the sum of 1 plus the interest rate. The general formula for determining the present value is

$$P = \frac{F}{(1 + r)^n}$$

The interest rate is also called the **discount rate**.

Present Value Factors

Although we can calculate P from its formula in a few steps with most pocket calculators, we can use a table instead. Note that we can write the present value formula another way:

$$P = \frac{F}{(1 + r)^n} = F\left[\frac{1}{(1 + r)^n}\right]$$

Let $[1/(1 + r)^n]$ be the *present value factor*, which we call pf and which can be found in Appendix 1. This table gives you the present value of a future amount of $1 for various time periods and interest rates. To use the table, locate the column for the appropriate interest rate and the row for the appropriate period. The number in the body of the table where this row and column intersect is the pf value. Multiply it by F to get P. For example, suppose that an investment will generate $15,000 in ten years. If the interest rate is 12 percent, we find in Appendix 1 that $pf = 0.3220$. Multiplying it by $15,000 gives us the present value, or

$$P = Fpf = \$15,000(0.3220)$$
$$= \$4830$$

Annuities

An **annuity** is a series of payments of a fixed amount for a specified number of years. We treat all payments as happening at the end of a year. Suppose that we want to invest an amount at an interest rate of 10 percent, so that we may draw out $5000 per year for each of the next four years. We could determine the present value of this $5000 four-year annuity by treating the four payments as single future payments. The present value of an investment needed now, in order to receive these payments for the next four years, is the sum of the present values of each of the four payments. That is,

$$P = \frac{\$5000}{1 + 0.10} + \frac{\$5000}{(1 + 0.10)^2}$$
$$+ \frac{\$5000}{(1 + 0.10)^3} + \frac{\$5000}{(1 + 0.10)^4}$$
$$= \$4545 + \$4132 + \$3757 + \$3415$$
$$= \$15,849$$

A much easier way to calculate this amount is to use Appendix 2. Look for the factor in the table at the intersection of the 10 percent column and the fourth period row and find 3.1699. For annuities, we call this present value factor af, to distinguish it from the present value factor for a single payment. We determine the present value of an annuity by multiplying its amount by af. For our example, we get

$$P = Aaf = \$5000(3.1699)$$
$$= \$15,849$$

where

P = present value of an investment
A = amount of the annuity received each year
af = present value factor for an annuity

TECHNIQUES OF ANALYSIS

We can now apply these concepts to the financial analysis of proposed investments. Two basic financial analysis techniques are

1. the net present value method and
2. the payback method.

Both methods are based on cash flows. Our first step, then, is to calculate the cash flows resulting from the investment (project).

Determining Cash Flows

We have to estimate as accurately as possible the cash that will flow into and out of the organization because of the project. *Cash flow* includes revenues, costs, and changes in assets and liabilities. It is important to remember two points when determining cash flows for any project:

1. Consider only the amounts of cash flows that will change if the project is undertaken. These amounts are called incremental cash flows and

are the difference in the cash flows with the project and without it.

2. Cash flows should be converted to *after-tax* amounts before applying the net present value or payback method to them. This step introduces taxes and depreciation into the calculations.

Depreciation. Depreciation is an allowance for the consumption of capital. In this type of analysis, depreciation is relevant for only one reason: It acts as a tax shield.* Taxes must be paid on before-tax cash inflows *minus* the depreciation associated with the proposed investment. We will use the *straight-line method* of calculating annual depreciation, since it is simplest and is usually adequate for internal planning purposes.† First, subtract the estimated salvage value from the amount of investment required at the beginning of the project, then divide by the number of years of life. If the item can be sold for cash at the end of its life, it has a salvage value greater than zero. The general expression for annual depreciation is

$$D = \frac{(I - S)}{n}$$

where

D = annual depreciation

I = amount of the investment

S = salvage value

n = number of years of project life

Tax Considerations. The income-tax rate varies from one state or country to another. We will use an income-tax rate of 50 percent, assuming that all relevant federal, state, and local income taxes are included in this rate. When you are doing a financial analysis, you may want to use an average income-tax rate based on the firm's historical tax rate over the past several years, or you may want to base the tax rate on the highest tax bracket that applies to the taxpaying unit. The one thing you should never do is ignore taxes in your analysis.

After-Tax Cash Inflows. We are now ready to determine the after-tax cash flows for each year of the project's life. We calculate the amount of taxes in four steps:

1. Contribution margin = Revenue − Variable cost.

2. Before-tax cash inflow = Contribution margin − Fixed costs.

3. Taxable cash inflow = Before-tax cash inflow − Depreciation.

4. Additional taxes = Taxable cash inflow × Tax rate.

In some investment projects, revenues are unaffected. The before-tax cash inflow is really a cost savings, such as might come from an automation project. It is the equivalent of the before-tax cash inflow of step 2. In such cases we would begin with step 3.

Now, we simply subtract the additional taxes (step 4) from the before-tax cash inflow (step 2), or

$$\text{After-tax cash inflow} = \text{Before-tax cash inflow} - \text{Additional taxes}$$

Salvage Values. The cash flow from the sale or disposal of plant and equipment at the end of a project's life is known as **salvage value**. Adding it to the after-tax cash flow, you arrive at the total cash flow for the year. If an item has a negative salvage value, which can happen if you must pay to dispose of something, you subtract this amount from the after-tax cash flow to obtain the net cash flow for the year. Gains or losses on disposition of property must be carefully evaluated for tax effects in order to determine the cash flow actually resulting from them. Only the after-tax values are relevant to cash-flow determination.* We will assume that all salvage values are net of their tax effects in this textbook.

---

*Depreciation is not a legitimate cash flow because it is not cash that is actually paid out each year. On the other hand, depreciation does affect how an accountant calculates net income, against which the income-tax rate is applied. Therefore, depreciation enters into the calculation, as a tax shield, only when we have to figure our tax liability.

†For tax purposes, permissible depreciation methods change from time to time. Since 1986 the only acceptable accelerated depreciation method is known as the *Modified Accelerated Cost Recovery System (MACRS)*. The MACRS shortens the lives of investments, giving firms larger tax deductions. For more discussion on depreciation methods, see Brigham and Gapenski (1991) or any current accounting or finance textbook.

---

*Disposal of property often results in an accounting gain or loss that can increase or decrease income tax and affect cash flows. These tax effects should be considered in determining the actual cash inflow or outflow from disposal of property.

Application   S1.1   *Calculating After-Tax Flows*

A local restaurant is considering adding a salad bar. The investment required to remodel the dining area and add the salad bar will be $16,000. Other information about the project is as follows:

1. The price and variable cost per salad are $3.50 and $2.00, respectively.
2. Annual demand should be about 11,000 salads.
3. Fixed costs, other than depreciation, will be $8000, which covers the energy to operate the refrigerated unit and another part-time employee to stock the salad bar during peak business hours.
4. The project is expected to last four years and have no salvage value at the end of that time. The straight-line depreciation method is used.

5. The tax rate is 50 percent.
6. Management wants to earn a return of at least 14 percent on the project.

Determine the after-tax cash flows for the life of this project.

Solution

The annual depreciation is

$$D = \frac{(I - S)}{n} = \frac{\$16,000 - \$0}{4} = \$4000$$

The cash flows through 1996 are shown in Table S1.1. The after-tax cash inflow is $6250 per year through 1996.

TABLE S1.1 / Cash Flows for the Salad Bar Project

		Year			
Item	1992	1993	1994	1995	1996
Initial Information					
Annual demand (salads)		11,000	11,000	11,000	11,000
Investment	$16,000				
Interest (discount) rate	0.14				
Cash flows					
Revenue		$38,500	$38,500	$38,500	$38,500
Minus variable cost		−22,000	−22,000	−22,000	−22,000
Contribution margin		16,500	16,500	16,500	16,500
Minus fixed cost		− 8,000	− 8,000	− 8,000	− 8,000
Before-tax cash inflow		8,500	8,500	8,500	8,500
Minus depreciation		− 4,000	− 4,000	− 4,000	− 4,000
Taxable cash inflow		4,500	4,500	4,500	4,500
Taxes @ 50%		2,250	2,250	2,250	2,250
Before-tax cash inflow		8,500	8,500	8,500	8,500
Minus taxes		− 2,250	− 2,250	− 2,250	− 2,250
After-tax cash inflow		$ 6,250	$ 6,250	$ 6,250	$ 6,250

Application   S1.2   *Calculating NPV*

Refer again to the salad bar cash flows in Table S1.1. What is the net present value of the project?

Solution

Table S1.1 shows the calculations for the salad bar project, with after-tax cash inflows of $6250 per year. While the $16,000 cash outflow for the initial investment is already a present value, the four $6250 inflows are not. They are equivalent to a four-year annuity. As management wants to earn a return of at least 14 percent on its investment, we use that rate to find the *af* value in Appendix 2 to be 2.9137. The net present value of the inflows minus outflows is

$$NPV = \$6250(2.9137) - \$16,000$$

$$= \$2211$$

We can obtain the same result by discounting each year's after-tax cash flow to its present value and adding all the present values. This method is shown in the following equations.

1993:	$6250(0.8772) = $5482
1994:	$6250(0.7695) = $4809
1995:	$6250(0.6750) = $4219
1996:	$6250(0.5921) = $3701

$$
\begin{aligned}
NPV \text{ of project} &= (\$5482 + \$4809 \\
&\quad + \$4219 + \$3701) \\
&\quad - \$16,000 \\
&= \$2211
\end{aligned}
$$

Because the NPV is positive, the recommendation would be to approve the project.

Net Present Value Method

The **net present value (NPV) method** evaluates an investment by calculating the present value of all after-tax cash inflows and then subtracting the original investment amount from their total. The difference is the net present value. If it is positive for the discount rate used, the investment earns a rate of return higher than the discount rate. If the net present value is negative, the investment earns a rate of return lower than the discount rate. Most firms set the discount rate equal to the *overall weighted average cost of capital*, which becomes the lowest desired return on investment. If a negative net present value results, the project is not approved. The discount rate that represents the lowest desired return on investment is thought of as a hurdle over which the investment must pass and is often referred to as the **hurdle rate.***

Payback Method

The other commonly used method of evaluating projects is the **payback method**, which determines how much time will elapse before the total of *after-tax* cash flows will equal or pay back the initial investment.

The payback method continues to be widely used, particularly at lower management levels, even though it is scorned by many academics. Its advantages are its quick and easy application. It also gives decision makers some idea of how long it will be until investment funds are recovered. Uncertainty surrounds every investment project. The costs and revenues on which analyses are based are really best estimates, not actual values. An investment project with a quick payback is not considered as risky as one with a long payback. The payback method also has drawbacks. A major criticism is that it encourages managers to focus on the short run. A project that takes a long time to develop but generates excellent cash flows later in its life is usually rejected by the payback method. The payback method has also been criticized for its failure to consider the time value of money. For these reasons, we recommend that payback analysis be combined with a more sophisticated method such as NPV in analyzing the financial implications of a project.

Managing by the Numbers

The precision and analytical detachment that come from using the NPV or payback method can be deceiving. American business has been accused of *managing by the numbers*, with a preference for short-term results from low-risk projects (see Hayes and Abernathy, 1980, and Skinner, 1984). Part of the problem lies with managers who are on the fast track to the top

---

*A related technique is called the *internal rate of return* (IROR). Using trial and error, we find the discount rate that makes the present value of the after-tax inflows equal to the outflows. The IROR makes the NPV of a project equal to zero. Multiple projects can be ranked from best to worst using IROR.

Application   S1.3   *Calculating the Payback Period*

What is the payback period for the salad bar project?

Solution
Using the after-tax cash flows from Table S1.1, we add the cash flows for each year until we get as close as possible to $16,000 without exceeding it. For the years

1993 and 1994 cash flows are $6250 + $6250 = $12,500. The payback method assumes that cash flows come in evenly throughout the year, so that in 1995 only $3500 must flow in before the payback point is reached. Since $3500/$6250 is 0.56, the payback period is 2.56 years.

of their organizations. They occupy a rung on the ladder for a short time and then move up and so perceive it to be in their career interests to favor investments that give quick results. They establish short paybacks and high hurdle rates. They ignore or forgo long-term benefits from technological advances, innovative product plans, and strategic capacity additions. Over the long haul, this narrow vision jeopardizes the firm's competitive advantage—and even survival.

Managing by the numbers has a second cause. Projects with the greatest strategic impact are also likely to be riskier and have more qualitative benefits, which cannot be easily quantified. Consider an investment in some of the newer types of flexible automation. (See Chapter 6.) Benefits can include better quality, quicker delivery times, higher sales, and lower inventory. The equipment might be reprogrammed to handle new products not yet conceived of by the firm. Enough might be learned with the new technology that subsequent investments will pay off at an even higher rate of return. The mistake is to ignore these benefits simply because they cannot be easily quantified. It is far better to bring in the risks and qualitative factors as part of the analysis, rather than to ignore them. The proliferation of micro-computers and the corresponding use of computer spreadsheets to perform financial analyses have made possible the rapid evaluation of many different alternatives relating to a project. These are referred to as "what if" analyses and allow an analyst to look at what would happen to cash flows if certain events, or combinations of events, were to occur. Using a preference matrix may also help recognize qualitative factors more explicitly.

The message is clear. Financial analysis is a valu-able tool for evaluating investment projects. However, it never replaces the insight that comes from hands-on experience. Managers must use their judgment, taking into account not only NPV or payback data but also how the project fits operations and corporate strategy.

Review Problems

Supplement Connections: The financial analysis techniques presented in this supplement are applied in Chapter 2 (Problems 16–20 and 26), Chapter 5 (Problems 11–17), Chapter 6 (Problems 1–6), Chapter 7 (Problem 16), Chapter 8 (Problems 15–21), and Chapter 9 (Problem 25).

Selected References

Brigham, Eugene F., and Louis C. Gapenski. *Financial Management: Theory and Practice*, 6th ed. Orlando, Fla.: Dryden, 1991.

Hayes, Robert H., and William J. Abernathy. "Managing Our Way to Economic Decline." *Harvard Business Review* (July–August 1980), pp. 67–77.

Hodder, James E., and Henry E. Riggs. "Pitfalls in Evaluating Risky Projects." *Harvard Business Review* (January–February 1985), pp. 128–135.

Kieso, Donald E., and Jerry J. Weygandt. *Intermediate Accounting*, 4th ed. New York: John Wiley & Sons, 1983.

Skinner, Wickham. "Operations Technology: Blind Spot in Strategic Management." *Interfaces*, vol. 14, no. 1 (January–February 1984), pp. 116–125.

Weston, J. Fred, and Thomas E. Copeland. *Managerial Finance*, 8th ed. Chicago: Dryden, 1986.

Woodward, Herbert N. "Management Strategies for Small Companies." *Harvard Business Review* (January–February 1976), pp. 113–121.

Supplement 2

LINEAR PROGRAMMING

This supplement addresses a technique that is useful for allocating scarce resources among competing demands. **Linear programming (LP)** seeks to optimize a linear objective function subject to a set of linear constraints. The product-mix problem, along with a number of others, can be analyzed with this method.

BASIC CONCEPTS IN LINEAR PROGRAMMING

Linear programming has been applied to a wide variety of operations management problems, some of which are shown in Table S2.1. Linear programming is a powerful tool for solving complex resource allocation problems and can provide much information about the implicit values of various resources. We must emphasize, however, that it is *only a tool* for decision makers. Linear programming does not make decisions—decision makers do. Linear programming is a method for solving a linear model that specifies the objectives and constraints for a particular type of problem. In the model, linearity in all relationships must be assumed. At best, in most applications this assumption yields only a good approximation to the real relationships. Consequently, the solution of the model can be regarded only as a good starting point for the overall solution of the problem. As you will see, the supplementary information generated, such as shadow prices of critical resources or right-hand-

side ranges, could be more important than the solution itself.

The General Linear Programming Method

Linear programming is an optimizing process that seeks values for decision variables that satisfy linear constraints of a problem and optimize a linear objective function. The general linear programming method is

Maximize: $c_1x_1 + c_2x_2 + \cdots + c_nx_n$

Subject to: $a_{11}x_1 + a_{12}x_2 + \cdots + a_{1n}x_n \leq b_1$

$a_{21}x_1 + a_{22}x_2 + \cdots + a_{2n}x_n \leq b_2$

$$\vdots$$

$a_{m1}x_1 + a_{m2}x_2 + \cdots + a_{mn}x_n \leq b_m$

$x_1, x_2, \ldots, x_n \geq 0$

The last set of constraints, $x_1, x_2, \ldots, x_n \geq 0$, are called nonnegativity restrictions because they force the decision variables to values of zero or greater. In this problem there are *n* decision variables and *m* constraints (exclusive of the nonnegativity restrictions). Some of the constraints could be written as *greater than or equal to* ($\geq$) or *equals* ($=$), depending on the problem statement. The c_j, a_{ij}, and b_i values are given constants. Linear programming can also be used to *minimize* the value of the objective function.

TABLE S2.1 / *Typical Applications of Linear Programming to Resource Allocation Problems*

Problem Type	Description
Production planning	*Production:* Find the minimum-cost production schedule for a given work-force plan, taking into account inventory carrying and subcontracting costs.
	Production and work force: Find the minimum-cost production schedule, taking into account hiring and layoff costs as well as inventory carrying, overtime, and subcontracting costs, subject to various capacity and policy constraints.
	Staffing: Find the optimal staffing plan for various categories of workers, subject to various demand and policy constraints.
Distribution	*Shipping plans:* Find the optimal shipping assignments from factories to distribution centers or from warehouses to retailers.
Inventory planning	*Stock control:* Determine the optimal mix of products to hold in inventory in a warehouse.
	Supplier selection: Find the optimal combination of suppliers to minimize the amount of unwanted inventory.
Location planning	*Plants or warehouses:* Determine the optimal location of a plant or warehouse with respect to total transportation costs between various alternative locations and existing supply and demand sources.
Process control	*Stock cutting:* Given the dimensions of a roll or sheet of raw material, find the cutting pattern that minimizes the amount of scrap material.
Product planning	*Mixes:* Find the optimal production quantities of a group of products, subject to resource capacity and market demand constraints.
	Blends: Find the optimal proportions of various ingredients of products such as gasoline, paints, and foods, subject to certain minimal requirements.
Scheduling	*Shifts:* Determine the minimum-cost assignment of workers to shifts, subject to varying demand.
	Vehicles: Assign *m* vehicles to *n* products or jobs and determine the number of trips to make, subject to vehicle size, vehicle availability, and demand constraints.
	Routing: Find the optimal routing of a product through a number of sequential processes, each with their own capacities and characteristics.

Application   S2.1   *Developing a Linear Programming Model*

The Stratton Company produces plastic pipe, couplings, and fittings for the construction industry. To increase the efficiency of its operations, the company has focused its resources by major product lines. The couplings and fittings require specialized equipment and are often produced to satisfy specific needs of the customer. The plastic pipe, however, is more standard, and general-purpose equipment can be used. Two basic types of plastic pipe are produced, differing in diameter, wall thickness, and strength.

John Fisher, the plant manager, recently received an updated demand forecast for the two types of pipe. Based on an examination of the resources needed to manufacture the two pipe products, it was obvious that the plant could not satisfy the demand. Three resources are critical to the output of pipe: extrusion hours, pack-

aging hours, and a special additive to the plastic raw material to control strength and flexibility. Fisher gathered the following data, which represent the situation for next week. All data are expressed in units of 100 feet of pipe.

	Product		Resource
Resource	Type 1	Type 2	Availability
Extrusion	4 hr	6 hr	48 hr
Packaging	2 hr	2 hr	18 hr
Additive mix	2 lb	1 lb	16 lb

The contribution to profits and overhead per 100 feet of pipe is $34 for type 1 and $40 for type 2. Develop a linear programming model to determine how much of each type of pipe should be produced to maximize contribution to profits and overhead.

Solution

Because the company's operations are focused and product lines do not share critical resources, the product-mix decision regarding the two types of pipe can be made independently of decisions about the other product lines. Even though there are other operations in the manufacturing of plastic pipe, this company only has three resources that are considered critical to the output of the pipe. The product-mix decision should be made in light of these limitations.

Let's begin construction of the mathematical model by letting

x_1 = amount of type 1 pipe to be produced, measured in 100-foot increments (for example, x_1 = 2 means 200 feet of type 1 pipe)

x_2 = amount of type 2 pipe to be produced, measured in 100-foot increments

These are the decision variables to be determined by solution of the model. The values of these variables determine the product mix that the Stratton Company should implement. However, each unit of x_1 and x_2 produced consumes some of the critical resources. In the extrusion department, a unit of x_1 requires 4 hours and a unit of x_2 requires 6 hours. For specific values of x_1 and x_2, we find the total amount of extrusion resources consumed by multiplying the number of units of each product produced by the resources consumed per unit and adding them. The total must not exceed the 48 hours of resources available. Thus we have the first constraint for our model:

$$4x_1 + 6x_2 \leq 48 \qquad \text{(extrusion)}$$

Similarly, we can formulate the constraints imposed by the packaging resource and the supply of additive mix:

$$2x_1 + 2x_2 \leq 18 \qquad \text{(packaging)}$$

$$2x_1 + 1x_2 \leq 16 \qquad \text{(additive mix)}$$

These three constraints impose restrictions on our choice of values for the decision variables. The values we choose for x_1 and x_2 must satisfy all the constraints, but an infinite number of values for x_1 and x_2 will satisfy these constraints. For example, x_1 = 1, x_2 = 1; x_1 = 2.01, x_2 = 4.03; and x_1 = -4, x_2 = -10 all satisfy the constraints in our problem. The negative values for x_1 and x_2 do not make sense, so we add nonnegativity restrictions to the model as follows:

$$x_1 \geq 0 \quad \text{and} \quad x_2 \geq 0 \quad \text{(nonnegativity restrictions)}$$

However, we are still left with an infinite number of possible solutions. To select the best values for x_1 and x_2, we need an objective function. The Stratton Company wants to maximize the contribution to profits and overhead. Since each unit of x_1 yields \$34 and each unit of x_2 yields \$40, we want to maximize \$34x_1 + \$40x_2, subject to the various constraints.

We can now state the entire model for the product-mix problem at the Stratton Company.

Objective: Maximize \$34x_1 + \$40x_2

Subject to: $4x_1 + 6x_2 \leq 48$

$$2x_1 + 2x_2 \leq 18$$

$$2x_1 + 1x_2 \leq 16$$

$$x_1 \geq 0 \quad \text{and} \quad x_2 \geq 0$$

The methods we will discuss can be used to solve this model for those values of x_1 and x_2 that maximize the contribution to profits and overhead.

Three important assumptions are implicit in the formulation of linear programming problems:

1. The objective function and constraint equations must be linear. Thus we can have no cross-products of decision variables, powers of x_j, or other types of nonlinear terms in the problem formulation. For the Stratton Company, this implies that one unit of x_1 contributes \$34 to profits and overhead and two units contribute \$68, regardless of how much x_2 is produced.

Similarly, one unit of x_2 consumes 6 hours of extrusion time and two units consume 12 hours. Production of x_1 does not affect the per unit consumption of x_2 of any of the resources.

2. The decision variables can have fractional values. For example, x_1 = 3.2 in the Stratton Company example poses no problem, since it means 320 feet of pipe. However, in other problems the decision variables may be expressed in units such as workers, tables, or trucks that are

not divisible. We can use a more advanced technique, called *integer programming,* in these situations if simply rounding off the linear programming solution, subject to satisfying the constraints, is unacceptable.

3. The constants are known with certainty. For example, each unit of x_1 requires 2 pounds of additive—no more, no less. The values of the constants cannot be satistical averages. They must be deterministic values that will not change when the solution to the problem is implemented.

Although these assumptions are quite restrictive, linear programming can provide a means to analyze complex resource allocation problems and several other benefits that are worth considering. First, the process of building the model forces managers to identify the important decision variables and constraints, a useful step in its own right. Identifying the nature and scope of the problem represents a big step toward solving it. Second, even though we assume that we know all the constants with certainty, we can use our best guess about their proper values and perform a *sensitivity analysis* of the constants that we suspect of violating our assumptions. Sensitivity analysis is a method whereby we systematically modify the value of critical constants to determine how the optimal solution is affected. For example, suppose that John Fisher at the Stratton Company was not sure about the number of packaging hours available next week; it could vary from 16 to 20 hours. Fisher could use the linear programming model and first try 16 hours, then 20 hours.* If there is no significant difference in the resulting product mixes, the value for available resources in the packaging department is not critical in the range of 16 to 20 hours. A reasonable value, such as 18 hours, would do for planning purposes. However, if the product mix is sensitive to the amount of packaging resources in this range, Fisher should try to estimate the amount of resources he will have next week. If the best he can do is specify a range of possible values, he may have to use a more sophisticated technique, such as *chance-constrained programming* or *stochastic programming* (see Wagner, 1975).

---

*Certain information about the range of values for c_j and b_i for which the optimal solution will not change can be derived by analyzing the algebraic information associated with the optimal solution itself without recalculating the entire solution each time. However, this analysis holds only for changes in the constants taken one at a time and not in combination with others.

Finally, the solution to a linear programming problem is not necessarily the solution that management will actually use. Often, various nonquantitative factors must be considered. Nonetheless, the linear programming solution can be a good starting point for the final decision.

Graphic Analysis

Solutions to practical linear programming problems involve algebraic methods. However, considerable insight into linear programming concepts can be provided through the analysis of a simple two-variable problem using the **graphical method of linear programming**. We will continue to use the Stratton Company product-mix problem in Application S2.1 as our example.

We begin by plotting the constraint equations, disregarding the inequality portion of the constraints ($<$) and assuming that each constraint is an equality ($=$). We let one variable equal zero and plot the axis intercept of the other variable. For the extrusion department, we have $4x_1 + 6x_2 = 48$. If $x_1 = 0$, then $x_2 = 8$. Similarly, if $x_2 = 0$, then $x_1 = 12$. We can connect the points (0, 8) and (12, 0) with a straight line, as shown in Fig. S2.1. All points on the line *and* to the left of the line will satisfy the extrusion constraint be-

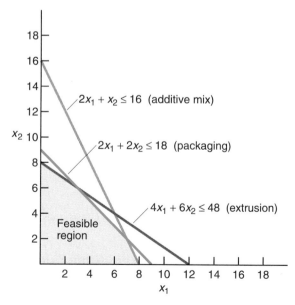

FIGURE S2.1   Feasible Region for the Product-Mix Problem

cause the original constraint was an inequality. We can plot the two other constraints in a similar manner.

Each constraint helps to define the region of feasible solutions to the problem. The **feasible region**, shown as the shaded portion of Fig. S2.1, contains the solutions that satisfy all the constraints simultaneously, including the nonnegativity restrictions. In our product-mix example, all the constraints were of the *less-than-or-equal-to* variety. Consequently, only the values of x_1 and x_2 in the lower left portion of the graph are feasible. In general, this condition is not always the case. For example, suppose that a linear programming model had the constraints

$$2x_1 + x_2 \geq 10$$

$$2x_1 + 3x_2 \geq 18$$

$$x_1 \leq 7$$

$$x_2 \leq 5$$

$$x_1, x_2 \geq 0$$

Figure S2.2 shows the feasible region in this case. The two *greater-than-or-equal-to* constraints provide lower limits that must be met or exceeded. Only the points on the line and to the right are feasible for these constraints.

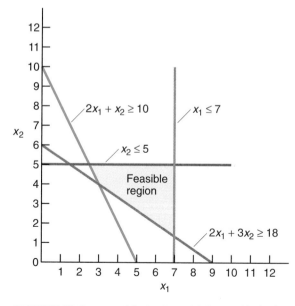

After we have defined the feasible region for the Stratton Company, the problem becomes one of finding the solution that maximizes the contribution to profits and overhead. The optimal solution to a linear programming problem will be an extreme point (corner point) of the feasible region. In Fig. S2.1 there are four corner points, excluding the origin, which would obviously be a poor solution. We could try each of these corner points in the objective function and select the one that maximizes its value. We may not be able to read these points from the graph accurately enough in some cases, and algebraically solving for all the corner points is inefficient when we have to calculate a large number of points.

The best approach is to plot the objective function on the graph of the feasible region for some arbitrary value of total contribution to profits and overhead. The line is called an *iso-profit* line because every point on that line will yield the same contribution. We can then draw a series of other iso-profit lines parallel to that line until we find the one farthest from the origin but still touching the feasible region. This point identifies the optimal solution to the problem.

We can use a similar procedure when we want to minimize the objective function. In this case we would draw an *iso-cost* line for an arbitrary value on the graph of the feasible region. We would then draw parallel iso-cost lines until we found the one *closest* to the origin but still touching the feasible region.

Suppose that we plot the objective function of our product-mix problem for an arbitrary value of $170 in the same manner as the constraint equations. This line is shown in Fig. S2.3, along with two other iso-profit lines. It is obvious that the optimal solution to the problem occurs at the corner point represented by the intersection of the extrusion and packaging constraints. Simultaneously solving the two equations representing these constraints yields $x_1 = 3$ and $x_2 = 6$. This is the optimal product mix, which can be verified by looking at the graph. The Stratton Company should produce 300 feet of type 1 pipe and 600 feet of type 2 pipe next week.

There can be more than one optimal solution to a linear programming problem. This situation occurs when the objective function is parallel to one of the faces of the feasible region and would be the case if our objective function were $38x_1 + $38x_2. Both $x_1 = 3$, $x_2 = 6$ and $x_1 = 7$, $x_2 = 2$, as well as any other point on the line connecting these two corner points, would be optimal. When this situation occurs, management would probably base a final decision on nonquantifiable factors. The important point here, however, is that

FIGURE S2.2   Feasible Region with Lower Limits for the Product-Mix Problem

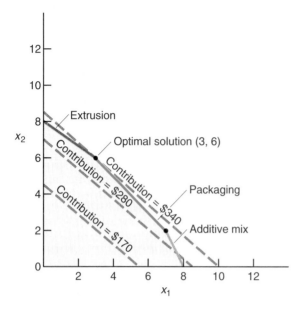

$$2x_1 + 2x_2 \leq 18$$
$$2x_1 + 1x_2 \leq 16$$
$$x_1,\ x_2 \geq 0$$

The simplex method involves the solution of linear equations,. but the constraints in our model are expressed as inequalities. To use the simplex method, we have to transform the original model and express all constraints as equalities. We can do this by augmenting the model with *slack variables*, that is,

Maximize: $\$34x_1 + \$40x_2 + \$0s_1 + \$0s_2 + \$0s_3$

Subject to: $4x_1 + 6x_2 + 1s_1 + 0s_2 + 0s_3 = 48$

$2x_1 + 2x_2 + 0s_1 + 1s_2 + 0s_3 = 18$

$2x_1 + 1x_2 + 0s_1 + 0s_2 + 1s_3 = 16$

$x_1,\ x_2,\ s_1,\ s_2,\ s_3 \geq 0$

FIGURE S2.3   Iso-Profit Lines and Solution to the Product-Mix Problem

A slack variable for a given constraint takes up the difference between the total resource consumption implied by specific values of x_1 and x_2 and the total amount of the resource available. For example, consider the extrusion constraint for which s_1 is the slack variable and actually represents the amount of idle time in the extrusion department. If $x_1 = 2$ and $x_2 = 5$, s_1 would be 10 hours ($48 - 38$). Alternatively, if $x_1 = 3$ and $x_2 = 6$, s_1 would be zero. Slack variables must be nonnegative to ensure that they accurately measure the slack resources for a particular constraint. Also, since slack resources do not generate contributions to profits and overhead, they have coefficients of zero in the objective function. Insofar as the decision variables x_1 and x_2 are concerned, an optimal solution to the augmented model will also be an optimal solution to the original model.

we only need to consider the corner points of the feasible region when optimizing an objective function. Even when there are multiple optimal solutions, there will always be a corner point that is the optimum. This feature enables us to use a technique capable of solving complex linear programming problems efficiently.

THE SIMPLEX METHOD

The **simplex method** is an iterative algebraic procedure for solving linear programming problems. Starting with an initial solution, the procedure systematically evaluates corner points of the feasible region in such a way that the objective function improves (or at worst stays the same) at each iteration. In practice, these problems are solved on computers, but we will solve manually the Stratton Company product-mix problem to demonstrate the logic of the approach.

Problem Formulation and Initial Tableau
Recall the model we developed for the Stratton Company product-mix problem:

Maximize: $\$34x_1 + \$40x_2$

Subject to: $4x_1 + 6x_2 \leq 48$

The most convenient way to summarize the information needed to solve a linear programming problem using the simplex method is to use a *tableau*. Table S2.2 shows the initial tableau for our product-mix problem. Most of it merely duplicates the c_j, a_{ij}, and b_i constants row by row from our augmented model. The first row of the tableau contains the objective function coefficients for each variable, including slack variables. This is the only row that does not change in subsequent tableaus. The first column shows the objective function coefficients for the variables in the current solution to the problem.

TABLE S2.2 / Initial Tableau for the Product-Mix Problem

c_j		$34	$40	$0	$0	$0	
	Solution Variables	x_1	x_2	s_1	s_2	s_3	Quantity
$0	s_1	4	6	1	0	0	48 ←
$0	s_2	2	2	0	1	0	18
$0	s_3	2	1	0	0	1	16
	z_j	$0	$0	$0	$0	$0	$0
	$c_j - z_j$	$34	$40	$0	$0	$0	

The variables (one for each constraint) chosen for the current solution are listed under *solution variables*. In the initial tableau the slack variables are chosen for the initial solution to the problem. In our example, we have three constraints; consequently, we list s_1, s_2, and s_3. The column labeled *quantity* shows the current value of the solution variables. In the initial tableau these values are merely the quantities on the right-hand side of the constraint equations. The initial tableau for our product-mix problem indicates that $s_1 = 48$, $s_2 = 18$, and $s_3 = 16$. By convention, the variables that are not in the current solution have values of zero. Thus $x_1 = 0$ and $x_2 = 0$. This solution corresponds to the origin (0, 0) in the graph of the feasible region shown in Figure S2.3.

All the variables in the problem are listed to the right of the solution variables column. In the initial tableau, the coefficients of a particular variable in each constraint of the augmented model are listed under the variable name. These coefficients in the initial and subsequent tableaus have a special meaning. They indicate the *substitution rates* for a particular variable not in the solution, relative to those variables in the solution. For example, the 6, 2, and 1 in the x_2 column mean that for each unit of x_2 introduced into the solution, s_1 will be reduced by 6 units, s_2 will be reduced by 2 units, and s_3 will be reduced by 1 unit. In subsequent tableaus, these substitution rates will change. This information will be useful in determining how to improve the current solution at any iteration.

The final two rows of the tableau provide summary information about the trade-offs in introducing a variable into the solution. The z_j row shows the *profit forgone* by introducing 1 unit of variable j into the solution. To calculate the value of z_j, we need the substitution rates for variable j (in the column for variable

j) and the profit contributions of the variables in the solution (the coefficients in the column labeled c_j on the far left). Consider variable x_1. If we introduce 1 unit of variable x_1 into the solution, we must give up 4 units of s_1, 2 units of s_2, and 2 units of s_3. However, since slack variables provide no contribution to profits, the total profit forgone by the introduction of 1 unit of x_1 is $z_1 = \$0(4) + \$0(2) + \$0(2) = \$0$. All we are doing is giving up slack resources at this stage of the solution process. Similarly, $z_2 = \$0(6) + \$0(2) + \$0(1) = \$0$. The value for z_j in the *quantity* column shows the current value of the objective function. Since $s_1 = 48$, $s_2 = 18$, and $s_3 = 16$, we have $\$0(48) + \$0(18) + \$0(16) = \$0$.

The $c_j - z_j$ row shows the *net contribution* effect of introducing 1 unit of variable j into the solution. It is the difference between the profit contribution of variable j and the profit forgone by the introduction of 1 unit of variable j. For x_1 we have $c_1 - z_1 = \$34$ ($\$34 - \$0$), and for x_2 we have $c_2 - z_2 = \$40$ ($\$40 - \$0$). The net contribution for any variable already in the solution will always be $0 because the introduction of one more unit into the solution must be accompanied by the removal of 1 unit of the same variable to avoid violating one of the constraints.

It is apparent from the initial tableau that no resources are being used in production because only slack variables are in the solution. In addition, it also shows that the current solution can be improved. This is evident in the $c_j - z_j$ row where the net contributions by x_1 and x_2 are greater than zero.

Selecting the Entering Variable

In linear programming, we select one variable to enter the solution and one variable to leave the solution at each iteration until we find the optimal solution. The $c_j - z_j$ row tells us whether an improved solution is possible. In our problem, there is a positive net contribution of \$34 per unit of x_1 and \$40 per unit of x_2. As we are interested in maximizing the contribution to profits and overhead, it would make sense to choose the variable that has the largest net contribution as the new variable to enter into the solution. This variable is x_2 in our product-mix problem. The column associated with the entering variable is designated with a vertical arrow in Table S2.2.

Determining the Exiting Variable

Now that we have decided to introduce x_2 into the solution, we must determine the variable it is to replace. Consider Fig. S2.1 again and the current solution, which is at the origin. To introduce x_2 into the solution, we proceed vertically along the x_2 axis. We want to have as much x_2 in the solution as possible without violating any constraints, so our choices are 8, 9, and 16, as denoted by the intercepts of the equations for the constraints. It is obvious that if we want to satisfy *all* the constraints by our choice of x_2, we must be limited to the *smallest* increase, or $x_2 = 8$.

We can come to the same conclusion without the graph by using the substitution rates for the entering variable and the values in the quantity column of the tableau. We can find the value that the entering variable will have in the next solution and the variable in the current solution that will be replaced. For example,

$$s_1 \text{ row (extrusion):} \quad \frac{48}{6} = 8$$

$$s_2 \text{ row (packaging):} \quad \frac{18}{2} = 9$$

$$s_3 \text{ row (additive mix):} \quad \frac{16}{1} = 16$$

As we increase x_1 from zero, the first limitation that we encounter is the extrusion capacity, when $x_2 = 8$. If we go beyond that value we will violate the constraint. Also, since s_1 is associated with the first row, it will be at zero when $x_2 = 8$. This result makes intuitive sense because s_1 is the amount of idle resources in the extrusion department. When $x_2 = 8$, we are using all the extrusion capacity for the production of type 2 pipe because each unit of that product consumes 6 hours of extrusion time. Consequently, s_1 is the variable that exits the solution, and the row associated

with s_1 is designated by a horizontal arrow, as shown in Table S2.2.

To summarize the simplex method to this point, we have used two rules.

1. **Entering rule.** Select the variable with the largest value of $c_j - z_j$ to introduce into the solution in a *maximization* problem. In a *minimization* problem, select the variable with the largest *negative* value of $c_j - z_j$ because the objective function is to be as small as possible.
2. **Exiting rule.** Divide the substitution rates for the entering variable into the corresponding values in the quantity column. Consider only *positive* values for the substitution rates and select the row variable with the lowest ratio to be removed from the solution. This procedure is the same regardless of whether the objective function is to be minimized or maximized.

Transforming the Tableau

As we mentioned earlier, we use the simplex method to systematically evaluate corner points of a feasible region. Because the corner points are formed by the intersection of lines representing linear equations, we need to solve a system of linear equations. We will use a procedure called *Gaussian elimination* to transform the tableau to reflect a new solution to our problem. In the tableau, the coefficients in the column of a variable currently in the solution consist of a 1 in the row associated with that variable and 0s in all the other rows. For s_1, our exiting variable, we have 1, 0, 0. The values in the column for x_2, our entering variable, are 6, 2, 1. The Gaussian elimination procedure will transform the column for x_2 into 1, 0, 0, thereby entering x_2 into the solution and replacing s_1. We make this transformation by performing various mathematical operations on the rows of the tableau. In a system of linear equations, we can multiply an entire equation by a constant and not change the nature of the relationship. We can also add two equations to form a third equation to replace one of them and not change the solution to the original set of equations. We now apply Gaussian elimination to transform our initial tableau.

Calculating the New Row for the Entering Variable. At the intersection of the entering variable column and the exiting variable row is a value called the *pivot element*. (See the circled value in Table S2.2.) We replace the old s_1 row with a new row having a value of 1 for the pivot element. That is, we divide

TABLE S2.3 / Transforming the s_2 and s_3 Rows in the Product-Mix Problem

			s_2 Row							s_3 Row			
Column	Old s_2 Row	+	$\left(\begin{array}{c}\text{Constant} \\ \text{for } s_2\end{array}\right.$	×	$\left.\begin{array}{c}\text{New } x_2 \\ \text{Row}\end{array}\right)$	=	New s_2 Row	Old s_3 Row	+	$\left(\begin{array}{c}\text{Constant} \\ \text{for } s_3\end{array}\right.$	×	$\left.\begin{array}{c}\text{New } x_2 \\ \text{Row}\end{array}\right)$	= New s_3 Row
x_1	2	+	(−2	×	2/3)	=	2/3	2	+	(−1	×	2/3)	= 4/3
x_2	2	+	(−2	×	1)	=	0	1	+	(−1	×	1)	= 0
s_1	0	+	(−2	×	1/6)	=	−1/3	0	+	(−1	×	1/6)	= −1/6
s_2	1	+	(−2	×	0)	=	1	0	+	(−1	×	0)	= 0
s_3	0	+	(−2	×	0)	=	0	1	+	(−1	×	0)	= 1
Quantity	18	+	(−2	×	8)	=	2	16	+	(−1	×	8)	= 8

the values in the old s_1 row by the pivot element 6 to create a new row for our next tableau:

	x_1	x_2	s_1	s_2	s_3	Quantity
Old s_1 row	4	6	1	0	0	48
New x_2 row	2/3	1	1/6	0	0	8

The new x_2 row replaces the first row in our tableau. Note that the new value for x_2 (in the quantity column) will be 8 in our next solution.

Transforming the Other Rows. We transform each of the other rows by selecting an appropriate constant, multiplying each element of the new x_2 row by this constant, and adding the result, element by element, to the row to be changed in such a way that we have a 0 in the x_2 column. The appropriate constant in each case is the element in the x_2 column for the row to be transformed, multiplied by −1. For the s_2 row, the constant is −2, and for the s_3 row it is −1. Table S2.3 shows the calculations for the transformed s_2 and s_3 rows.

The new tableau is shown in Table S2.4. We calculated values for the z_j and $c_j - z_j$ rows as before, except that now some of the z_j values are greater than zero. At the end of this first iteration it is obvious that we can make further improvements in the solution, since $c_1 - z_1 = \$22/3$.

Criterion of Optimality and the Solution to the Product-Mix Problem

The criterion for optimality in a linear programming problem can be stated as follows for

Maximization problems: If every entry in the $c_j - z_j$ row is zero or negative, the current solution is optimal.

Minimization problems: If every entry in the $c_j - z_j$ is zero or positive, the current solution is optimal.

Because our product-mix problem is a maximization problem, we have not met the criterion of optimality. Consequently, we must perform another

TABLE S2.4 / Second Tableau for the Product-Mix Problem

c_j		$34	$40	$0	$0	$0	
	Solution Variables	x_1	x_2	s_1	s_2	s_3	Quantity
$40	x_2	2/3	1	1/6	0	0	8
$0	s_2	(2/3)	0	−1/3	1	0	2 ←
$0	s_3	4/3	0	−1/6	0	1	8
	z_j	$80/3*	$40	$20/3†	$0	$0	$320
	$c_j - z_j$	$22/3 ↑	$0	−$20/3	$0	$0	

*$z_1 = \$40(2/3) + \$0(2/3) + \$0(4/3) = \$80/3$.
†$z_3 = \$40(1/6) - \$0(1/3) - \$0(1/6) = \$40/6 = \$20/3$.

iteration of the tableau. The entering variable is x_1, as it has the largest positive $c_j - z_j$ value. The exiting variable is s_2 because it has the lowest value when we divide the substitution rates in the x_1 column into the values in the quantity column:

$$x_2 \text{ row:} \quad 8/(2/3) = 12$$

$$s_2 \text{ row:} \quad 2/(2/3) = 3$$

$$s_3 \text{ row:} \quad 8/(4/3) = 6$$

Consequently, x_1 will enter the solution and replace s_2. The pivot element for this iteration is 2/3. Dividing the values in the old s_2 row in Table S2.4 by 2/3 yields the new x_1 row:

	x_1	x_2	s_1	s_2	s_3	Quantity
New x_1 row	1	0	$-1/2$	3/2	0	3

The calculations for transforming the x_2 and s_3 rows are shown in Table S2.5 and the new tableau is shown in Table S2.6. We have now satisfied the criterion for optimality. The Stratton Company should produce 300 feet of type 1 pipe and 600 feet of type 2 pipe. In so doing, the company will use all the available time for the extrusion and packaging ($s_1 = s_2 = 0$) and will have an extra 4 pounds of additive mix ($s_3 = 4$). You can verify the latter result by substituting $x_1 = 3$ and $x_2 = 6$ into the constraint for the additive mix.

The simplex process started at the origin and moved to the corner point $x_1 = 0$, $x_2 = 8$ because x_2 contributed the most to profits and overhead. It then moved to the intersection of the extrusion and packaging constraints (Fig. S2.1), which is the optimal solution. Note that the value of x_2 was reduced from 8 to 6 in the final iteration. By introducing 3 units of x_1, we were able to better utilize the available resources and generate more contribution to profits and overhead, even though we gave up 2 units of x_2.

Sensitivity Analysis

The simplex method provides more useful information than just the optimal solution to a linear programming problem. From the optimal tableau we can determine the value of each resource in terms of its contribution to profits and overhead. We can also determine the net benefit (or cost) of adjusting the amount of resources we have (the b_i quantities on the right-hand side of the constraint equations). This information can be useful in making policy decisions about resource acquisition. Alternatively, if the b_i quantities must be forecasts, the information can be useful in determining the consequences of inaccurate forecasting. In this section we discuss the sensitivity analysis concepts of shadow prices and right-hand-side ranging.

Shadow Prices. The relative value of a resource with respect to the objective function in a linear programming problem is called its **shadow price**. It is the amount of change in the objective function per unit change in its right-hand-side value. Since the slack variables measure the amount of idle resources, the shadow prices for the resources are found in the $c_j - z_j$ row for the slack variables (disregarding the negative signs). Thus, in Table S2.6, the shadow price for extrusion capacity is $3 per hour and is found in the s_1 column. Similarly, the shadow prices for packaging and the additive mix are $11 per hour and $0 per pound, respectively.

We can use the shadow prices for our product-mix problem in the following way. If we had an additional hour of packaging capacity next week, we could generate $11 more in contribution to profits and overhead. If the added hour would cost less than $11 to obtain, it would pay for us to add an hour to the packaging capacity. For example, if the additional hour cost $7,

TABLE S2.5 / Transforming the x_2 and s_3 Rows in the Product-Mix Problem

		s_2 Row						s_3 Row			
Column	Old x_2 Row	+	(Constant for x_2 | × | New x_1 Row)	=	New x_2 Row	Old s_3 Row	+	(Constant for s_3 | × | New x_1 Row)	=	New s_3 Row

Column	Old x_2 Row	+	(Constant for x_2 × New x_1 Row)	=	New x_2 Row	Old s_3 Row	+	(Constant for s_3 × New x_1 Row)	=	New s_3 Row
x_1	2/3	+	$(-2/3 \times 1\ )$	=	0	4/3	+	$(-4/3 \times 1\ )$	=	0
x_2	1	+	$(-2/3 \times 0\ )$	=	1	0	+	$(-4/3 \times 0\ )$	=	0
s_1	1/6	+	$(-2/3 \times -1/2)$	=	1/2	$-1/6$	+	$(-4/3 \times -1/2)$	=	1/2
s_2	0	+	$(-2/3 \times 3/2)$	=	-1	0	+	$(-4/3 \times 3/2)$	=	-2
s_3	0	+	$(-2/3 \times 0\ )$	=	0	1	+	$(-4/3 \times 0\ )$	=	1
Quantity	8	+	$(-2/3 \times 3\ )$	=	6	8	+	$(-4/3 \times 3\ )$	=	4

TABLE S2.6 / Optimal Tableau for the Product-Mix Problem

c_j		$34	$40	$0	$0	$0	
	Solution Variables	x_1	x_2	s_1	s_2	s_3	Quantity
$40	x_2	0	1	1/2	−1	0	6
$34	x_1	1	0	−1/2	3/2	0	3
$0	s_3	0	0	1/2	−2	1	4
	z_j	$34	$40	$3	$11	$0	$342
	$c_j - z_j$	$0	$0	−$3	−$11	$0	

the contribution to profits and overhead would increase by $4. Similarly, if we had one *less* hour of packaging capacity next week, it would cost $11 in lost contribution to profits and overhead. The trade-offs for extrusion capacity are similar, but the impact on profits and overhead per hour of capacity is much less. The shadow price of zero for the additive mix makes sense because we already have an extra 4 pounds that we cannot use. Adjusting the availability of that resource by a pound would have no effect on the value of the objective function.

Right-Hand-Side Ranging. Knowing that the shadow price is greater than the cost of acquiring a given resource or less than the price we could obtain from selling it has only limited usefulness. We need to know *how much* resource we can buy or sell and retain an advantage. Put another way, we need the range of right-hand-side quantities (b_i's) over which the shadow price is valid for a given resource. This procedure is called **right-hand-side ranging**, and we start with the information in the optimal tableau.

For illustrative purposes consider packaging capacity, for which s_2 is the slack variable. The optimal tableau in Table S2.6 shows that if we add one hour of s_2 into the solution, we will increase the production of x_2 by 1 unit (because the substitution rate is −1), decrease the production of x_1 by 3/2 units, and increase the slack amount of additive mix by 2 pounds (the substitution rate is −2).* The profits and overhead contribution forgone would be $11. However, *adding* one hour of s_2 is analogous to reducing the number of packaging hours (b_2) by one hour because it restricts the amount of resources available for x_1 and x_2. We can determine how many hours of packaging capacity we would be willing to sell (that is, how much s_2 we can introduce into the solution), provided that the price exceeds $11, in the same way that we determined the

*A negative substitution rate means that the row variable actually increases as the entering variable increases. Therefore the exiting variable cannot be one that has a negative substitution rate with the entering variable.

John Fisher of the Stratton Company needs the answers to two important questions. If more funds were made available to expand capacity in the extrusion or packaging areas, would it pay to increase capacities there if it costs $8 per hour to increase extrusion capacity and $6 per hour to increase packaging capacity? Also, would it pay to buy more additive mix?

Solution
Since it costs $8 per hour to expand extrusion capacity, Fisher should not do it because the shadow price for that capacity is only $3 per hour. However, expanding packaging hours costs only $6 per hour and the shadow price is $11 per hour. Therefore he should increase packaging capacity. Finally, buying more additive mix would not pay because there is already a surplus of 4 pounds; the shadow price is zero for that resource.

exiting variable in the simplex procedure:

x_2 row: $6/(-1) = -6$ (negative, disregard)

x_1 row: $3/(3/2) = 2$

s_3 row: $4/(-2) = -2$ (negative, disregard)

Consequently, we can introduce two hours of s_2 (or equivalently, reduce packaging hours by 2, to 16 hours) before we will replace x_1 in the solution. The solution would then be $x_1 = 0$ and $x_2 = 8$, as shown in Fig. S2.4. Every hour that we reduce capacity over this range will cost us $11 in contribution to profits and overhead.

Now, we need to determine how much we can expand packaging capacity and still obtain a benefit of $11 per hour. Again, we work with slack variable s_2 in the optimal tableau, but this time we reverse the signs of the substitution rates. Intuitively, adding negative s_2 to the solution is analogous to adding packaging capacity. Proceeding as we did before, we have

x_2 row: $6/(1)$ $= 6$

x_1 row: $3/(-3/2) = -2$ (negative, disregard)

s_3 row: $4/(2)$ $= 2$

As we increase packaging capacity we will ultimately run out of additive mix because s_3 will become the exiting variable. We can add only 2 hours before this will happen, making total packaging capacity 20 hours. The new solution would be $x_1 = 6$ and $x_2 = 4$ in Fig. S2.4. The new value of the objective function would be $364, or $22 more than in our current solution, as we would expect. Consequently, the range in packaging hours over which the shadow price of $11 would be valid is $16 \le b_2 \le 20$.

Similarly, we can find the range for extrusion capacity: $40 \le b_1 \le 54$. With respect to the additive mix, the shadow price of $0 will hold for any increase in supply. It will also hold for any reductions of up to 4 pounds because that is the amount of slack resource we have. Therefore the range for the additive mix is $12 \le b_3 \le \infty$.

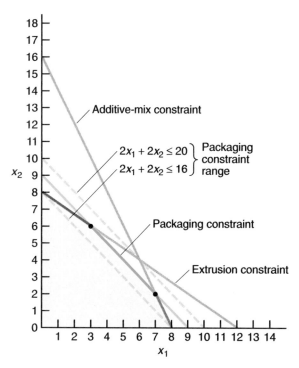

FIGURE S2.4   Right-Hand-Side Ranging for the Packaging Constraint

Problem Formulation with Equality or Greater-Than-or-Equal-To Constraints

Suppose that our product mix problem had the requirement that all the additive mix be used in the production of x_1 and x_2. The constraint would now be

$$2x_1 + 1x_2 = 16$$

Before, when the constraint was $2x_1 + 1x_2 \le 16$, we added a slack variable to make the constraint an equality and to provide us with an initial solution to the problem. Now, the constraint does not allow slack, and we have no convenient initial solution. To overcome this difficulty we can add an *artificial variable* to the constraint equation, as follows:

$$2x_1 + 1x_2 + 1a_1 = 16$$

Insofar as it gives us an initial solution, an artificial variable acts like a slack variable. However, unlike a slack variable, an artificial variable should not appear in the final solution to the problem. If a_1 has a positive value in the end, it would mean that $2x_1 + 1x_2 < 16$, which violates the constraint. To safeguard against this result, we insert a very large negative coefficient in the objective function for a_1. The objective function for our problem would then be

Maximize: $\$34x_1 + \$40x_2 + \$0s_1 + \$0s_2 - \$Ma_1$

where M is a number such as \$1 million.* As it has a negative sign, the simplex method will remove it from the solution before we find the optimal solution.

We also need to modify each greater-than-or-equal-to constraint. Suppose that we must use *at least* 16 pounds of additive mix. The constraint would become $2x_1 + 1x_2 \geq 16$. Adding a slack variable to make the constraint an equality will not work here. We have to subtract something from the left-hand side of the constraint to make it an equality, as follows:

$$2x_1 + 1x_2 - 1s_3 = 16$$

The variable, s_3, which must be nonnegative, is called a *surplus variable* and measures the amount by which the left-hand side exceeds the right-hand side of the constraint. Unfortunately, even though we now have an equality, we do not have an initial solution. We would have $s_3 = -16$, which violates the nonnegativity restriction.

We can use an artificial variable to provide an initial solution here, as we did for the previous constraint equation. We write the constraint as follows:

$$2x_1 + 1x_2 - 1s_3 + 1a_1 = 16$$

The objective function would now be

Maximize: $\$34x_1 + \$40x_2 + \$0s_1$
$+ \$0s_2 + \$0s_3 - \$Ma_1$

Note that the surplus variable has a coefficient of zero in the objective function, just like a slack variable. Procedurally, the simplex method treats slack, surplus, and artificial variables identically; however, artificial variables have no economic meaning and must have a value of zero in the final solution.

Summary of the Simplex Method

Using the simplex method involves the following steps:

1. Formulate the problem in terms of a linear objective function and a set of linear constraints. Augment the formulation with slack, surplus, or artificial variables, as needed.
2. Set up the initial tableau with slack or artificial variables as the solution variables and calculate the z_j and $c_j - z_j$ quantities.
3. Determine the entering variable with the largest $c_j - z_j$ value in maximization problems or the smallest $c_j - z_j$ value for minimization problems.
4. Determine the exiting variable by finding the ratio of the value in the quantity column to the corresponding substitution rate in the entering variable column for each row and selecting the smallest positive ratio.
5. Create a new tableau. Calculate the new row for the entering variable by dividing the old row for the exiting variable by the pivot element and placing it in the new tableau. Use Gaussian elimination to transform the values in the remaining rows and place them in the new array. Calculate the new z_j and $c_j - z_j$ values for the new tableau.
6. In maximization problems, if all $c_j - z_j$ values are zero or negative, the optimal solution has been found. In minimization problems, stop when all $c_j - z_j$ values are zero or positive. If these conditions do not hold, repeat steps 3–6.

Practical applications of linear programming are carried out with the help of a computer. Most major computer suppliers have general-purpose software packages that solve complex linear programming problems. Although the concepts we have presented in this supplement could be used for large-scale applications, the advanced procedures of computer programs and the computational speed of the computer dramatically reduce the amount of time required to solve problems. In addition, a complete sensitivity analysis of objective function coefficients and right-hand-side values is provided along with the solution. See the Computer Solved Problem for an example. If a particular application, such as product mix or blending, must be repeated frequently, special-purpose programs can be developed. They have input generator routines that simplify the input of data and generate the objective function and constraints for the problem. These special-purpose programs also have output routines that prepare specially designed managerial reports.

---

*In a minimization problem, an artificial variable has a large *positive* coefficient, M, in the objective function to ensure that it will not appear in the final solution.

COMPUTER SOLVED PROBLEM
Determining an Optimal Product Mix

The product planning manager at Westlake Electronics wishes to determine the optimal television product mix for the next quarter. The production and storage capacities for the firm's three plants are given:

Plant	Production Capacity (hours)	Storage Area (square feet)
1	50,000	10,000
2	60,000	15,000
3	35,000	5,000

The manager has three types of TVs under consideration: black and white, regular color, and large-screen color. The gross profit, storage, and production utilization requirements are as follows:

Product	Gross Profit ($)	Storage Requirements (square feet)	Manpower Requirements (Hours/unit)
1. B-W TV	75	3	9
2. Color TV	125	4	12
3. Large-screen TV	200	7	16

a. What is the optimal product mix that maximizes gross profit?

b. What is the impact on the product mix if the production capacities for all three plants are increased by 10%? Decreased by 10%?

c. What is the impact on the product mix if the company has an order for a minimum of 1500 black and white TVs and 500 large-screen TVs?

d. How would the product mix change if the management required (1) equal utilization of capacity in all three plants and (2) the market demand given in part (c)?

Solution

This problem is solved using CMOM (Linear Programming module). Your output may look different if you are using another software package.

a. Let P_{ij} serve as the production decision variables, where i represents the plant and j the product. For example, P_{12} represents the pro-

duction at plant 1 of regular color TVs. Printout 1 shows the basic linear programming model. The base model consists of nine decision variables (3 plants × 3 types of TVs) and six constraints (3 plant production capacities and 3 plant storage capacities). The optimal product mix for part (a) is given in Printout 2. These results show that producing only the regular color TV sets maximizes gross profit. More specifically, the optimal product mix is to produce 2500 regular color sets in plant 1, 3750 sets in plant 2, and 1250 sets in plant 3. These values are highlighted in blue. The value of the objective function, shown in gray, is $937,500.

b. The proposed changes in production capacities will have no effect on the optimal production mix or value of the objective function, because the remaining production capacities (or slack) for each plant greatly exceed the proposed changes. See Printout 2 and the constraints highlighted in red.

c. The incorporation of the two demand constraints—black and white TVs ≥ 1500 and large-screen TVs ≥ 500—significantly alters the original production mix. These constraints are

$$P_{11} + P_{21} + P_{31} \geq 1500$$

$$P_{13} + P_{23} + P_{33} \geq 500$$

Printout 3 presents the revised optimal mix, highlighted in blue, which includes the two new demand constraints (one for black and white TVs, the other for large-screen TVs). Notice that the value of the objective function has decreased with respect to the value obtained in part (a). It is now $900,000, as shown in gray. This should not be surprising since the requirement to produce the other two types of TVs reduces the capacities available for making regular color TVs.

d. To solve the management requirement of equal utilization of plant capacity requires the incorporation of two additional constraints. Basically, the idea is to ensure that the relative utilizations for all three plants are the same, that is, that the number of TVs produced divided by the total plant production capacity are equal. To illustrate, consider the following constraint for

NUMBER OF VARIABLES	:	9
NUMBER OF <= CONSTRAINTS	:	6

MODEL

	P11	P12	P13	P21	P22	P23
MAX-Z	75	125	200	75	125	200
C1	9	12	16	0	0	0
C2	0	0	0	9	12	16
C3	0	0	0	0	0	0
C4	3	4	7	0	0	0
C5	0	0	0	3	4	7
C6	0	0	0	0	0	0

	P31	P32	P33	RHV
MAX-Z	75	125	200	
C1	0	0	0	<= 50000
C2	0	0	0	<= 60000
C3	9	12	16	<= 35000
C4	0	0	0	<= 10000
C5	0	0	0	<= 15000
C6	3	4	7	<= 5000

SOLUTION

VARIABLE LABEL	VARIABLE VALUE	ORIGINAL COEFFICIENT	COEFFICIENT SENSITIVITY
P11	0	75	18.7500
P12	2500	125	0
P13	0	200	18.7500
P21	0	75	18.7500
P22	3749.9998	125	0
P23	0	200	18.7500
P31	0	75	18.7500
P32	1250	125	0
P33	0	200	18.7500

CONSTRAINT LABEL	ORIGINAL RHV	SLACK OR SURPLUS	SHADOW PRICE
C1	50000	20000	0
C2	60000	15000.0020	0
C3	35000	20000	0
C4	10000	0	31.2500
C5	15000	0	31.2500
C6	5000	0	31.2500

OBJECTIVE FUNCTION VALUE: 937500

PRINTOUT 3

SOLUTION

VARIABLE LABEL	VARIABLE VALUE	ORIGINAL COEFFICIENT	COEFFICIENT SENSITIVITY
P11	1500	75	0
P12	1374.9999	125	0
P13	0	200	0
P21	0	75	0
P22	3749.9998	125	0
P23	0	200	0
P31	0	75	0
P32	375.0003	125	0
P33	499.9999	200	0

CONSTRAINT LABEL	ORIGINAL RHV	SLACK OR SURPLUS	SHADOW PRICE
C1	50000	20000	0
C2	60000	15000.0020	0
C3	35000	22499.9980	0
C4	10000	0	31.2500
C5	15000	0	31.2500
C6	5000	0	31.2500
C7	1500	0	18.7500
C8	500	0	18.7500

OBJECTIVE FUNCTION VALUE: 900000

---

equating utilizations between plant 1 and plant 2:

$$\frac{P_{11} + P_{12} + P_{13}}{50,000} = \frac{P_{21} + P_{22} + P_{23}}{60,000}$$

The rearrangement of this equality constraint yields the following expression:

$$1.2P_{11} + 1.2P_{12} + 1.2P_{13} - P_{21} - P_{22} - P_{23} = 0$$

A similar relationship is required to link either plant 1 or plant 2 with plant 3. The one we will use is:

$$0.7P_{11} + 0.7P_{12} + 0.7P_{13} - P_{31} - P_{32} - P_{33} = 0$$

The optimal production mix that includes these two constraints along with the two from part (c)

is given in Printout 4, highlighted in blue. These results show a completely different production mix with a lower objective function value ($880,952, shown in gray). Again, a smaller value of the objective function should not be surprising since these added constraints further reduce the ability to produce the most profitable product mix.

Review Problems

Supplement Connections: The simplex method of linear programming presented in this supplement is applied in Chapter 2 (Problems 16–26), Chapter 5 (Problems 18 and 19), Chapter 8 (Problem 22), Chapter 13 (Problems 21 and 22), and Chapter 14 (Problems 9 and 10 and the Sun Manufacturing Case).

PRINTOUT 4

SOLUTION

VARIABLE LABEL	VARIABLE VALUE	ORIGINAL COEFFICIENT	COEFFICIENT SENSITIVITY
P11	0	75	25.0000
P12	2222.2222	125	0
P13	158.7302	200	0
P21	0	75	25.0000
P22	1666.6671	125	0
P23	1190.4758	200	0
P31	1666.6668	75	0
P32	0	125	1.1905
P33	0	200	79.7620

CONSTRAINT LABEL	ORIGINAL RHV	SLACK OR SURPLUS	SHADOW PRICE
C1	50000	20793.6465	0
C2	60000	20952.3828	0
C3	30000	15000	0
C4	10000	0	25
C5	15000	0	25
C6	5000	0	51.1905
C7	0	0	25
C8	0	0	78.5714
C9	1500	166.6664	0
C10	500	849.2057	0

OBJECTIVE FUNCTION VALUE: 880952.3800

Selected References

Asim, R., E. De Falomir, and L. Lasdon. "An Optimization-Based Decision Support System for a Product-Mix Problem." *Interfaces*, vol. 12, no. 2 (April 1982), pp. 26–33.

Hadley, G. *Linear Programming*. Reading, Mass.: Addison-Wesley, 1962.

Hillier, F.S., and G.J. Lieberman. *Introduction to Operations Research*, 2nd ed. San Francisco: Holden-Day, 1974.

Krajewski, L.J., and H.E. Thompson. *Management Science: Quantitative Methods in Context*. New York: John Wiley & Sons, 1981.

Markland, R.E. *Topics in Management Science*. New York: John Wiley & Sons, 1979.

Perry, C., and K.C. Crellin. "The Precise Management Meaning of a Shadow Price." *Interfaces*, vol. 12, no. 2 (April 1982), pp. 61–63.

Wagner, H.M. *Principles of Operations Research*, 2nd ed. Englewood Cliffs, N.J.: Prentice-Hall, 1975.

Zeleny, M. "On the Squandering of Resources and Profits via Linear Programming." *Interfaces*, vol. 11, no. 5 (October 1981), pp. 101–107.

TRANSPORTATION METHOD OF LINEAR PROGRAMMING

Supplement 2 showed that the simplex method is an efficient procedure for solving linear programming problems. Efficiency, however, is relative and is directly related to the computational effort required to solve the problem. In this supplement we discuss a method for solving a class of linear programming problems that is more efficient than the simplex method.

SOLVING TRANSPORTATION PROBLEMS

The transportation method is an iterative procedure for solving problems when we want to minimize the cost of shipping products from m plants or sources of supply to n destinations. (The same approach can be used for a profit maximization problem.) We can also use this method to analyze alternative plant or warehouse locations or to find an optimal production plan (see Chapters 9 and 14). Here we illustrate the transportation method for the plant location problem, where the sources are plants and the destinations are warehouses. There are four basic steps to the transportation method:

1. Translate the problem description into an initial tableau, which represents the plants as rows and the warehouses as columns. Each cell in the tableau represents a shipping route from a plant to a warehouse. Add cost, demand, and capacity data.
2. Generate an initial feasible solution.
3. Incrementally improve on the initial solution until no further improvements are possible, which means that the final solution is optimal. At each iteration an entering route and an exit-

ing route must be identified before moving from one solution to the next.
4. Identify and evaluate the final solution.

Steps 2 and 3 are now usually solved with a computer package, due to the massive amount of data processing for realistically large problems. However, the analyst must still perform the first step, which can require considerable creativity, and also the last step. Here we examine all four steps so that you more fully understand the logic that goes into the computer program. This coverage helps you understand what the computer does, and doesn't do, in finding the "optimal" solution.

The Initial Tableau

We begin by putting the problem in the format of a standard matrix, sometimes called a *tableau*. The rows in the tableau (except the last one) represent plants, either existing ones or proposals for new locations. The columns (except the last one) represent warehouses. The last row shows each warehouse's demand, and the last column each plant's capacity. Each cell in the tableau is a decision variable in the problem: How much the plant in the cell's row should ship to the warehouse in its column. The cost to ship one unit from a plant to a warehouse is shown in the upper-right hand corner of the corresponding cell. In the transportation method, the sum of the allocations to a row must equal the capacity of that row; similarly, the sum of the allocations to a column must equal the requirements for that column. These two sets of constraints are called **rim conditions**. The sum of the capacities must always equal the sum of the requirements when we use the transportation method.

Formulating the Initial Tableau

The Giant Farmer Company processes and cans vegetables and fruits for sale in discount food stores. Presently the company has two plants: one in Chicago and one in Houston. The company also owns and operates four warehouses, located in Miami, Denver, Lincoln, and Jackson. A recent forecast of demand at the warehouses indicated that it will exceed supply in the near future. In particular, a new plant with a capacity of 8000 cases per week is needed. The decision has been made to build a new plant, but the location still has to be selected.

An important factor in the location decision will be the cost of transportation from the plants to the warehouses. Two potential sites for the new plant have been identified: Buffalo and Atlanta. The following data on capacities, forecasted demand, and shipping costs have been gathered.

Plant	Capacity in Cases per Week (00)	Warehouse	Demand in Cases per Week (00)
Chicago	100	Miami	70
Houston	75	Denver	90
New Plant	80	Lincoln	45
Total	255	Jackson	50
		Total	255

Shipping Cost to Warehouse (per case)

Plant	Miami	Denver	Lincoln	Jackson
Chicago	$7	$ 2	$4	$5
Houston	3	1	5	2
Buffalo (alternative 1)	6	9	7	4
Atlanta (alternative 2)	2	10	8	3

The shipping cost data reflect the best arrangements that can be made from each plant to each warehouse, considering both the cost and the quality of service provided by the shipper. Management would like to determine the location for the new plant that minimizes shipping costs.

Set up the initial tableau, using the Buffalo option for the new plant's location.

Solution

The initial tableau is shown in Fig. S3.1. There is a row for each plant and a column for each warehouse. Note that in this case the total capacity (255 units per week) equals the total requirements.

Plant	Warehouse				Capacity
	Miami	Denver	Lincoln	Jackson	
Chicago	7	2	4	5	100
Houston	3	1	5	2	75
Buffalo	6	9	7	4	80
Requirements	70	90	45	50	255 / 255

FIGURE S3.2

Initial Tableau with
Dummy Warehouse
for the Giant Farmer
Company Problem

Plant	Warehouse					Capacity
	Miami	Denver	Lincoln	Jackson	Dummy	
Chicago	7	2	4	5	0	100
Houston	3	1	5	2	0	75
Buffalo	6	9	7	4	0	100
Requirements	70	90	45	50	20	275 / 275

In many real problems, capacity may exceed requirements or vice versa. If so, we can easily adjust the model to satisfy the rim conditions for the transportation method. If capacity exceeds requirements by *r* units, we create an additional *column* in the tableau representing a dummy warehouse with a demand for *r* units and make the shipping costs in the newly created cells $0. This approach is analogous to adding slack variables in a simplex linear programming solution. Similarly, if requirements exceed capacity by *r* units, we create a new *row* representing a dummy plant with a capacity of *r* units. We assign shipping costs of $0 per unit in the new cells to reflect the addition of slack variables to the problem. Figure S3.2 shows the initial tableau for the Giant Farmer Company in Application S3.1, when the Buffalo plant's capacity is expanded to 100 units. In this case a dummy warehouse is added with a 20-unit capacity to maintain the rim conditions. In the final solution at least one plant will be shown to be shipping to the dummy warehouse. These shipments will not really be made, which is why the unit costs are shown to be $0. The amount of the plant's shipment is equal to the capacity that is unused.

Generating an Initial Solution

Like the simplex method, the transportation method requires an initial solution. This step amounts to allocating quantities to cells so that we meet the rim conditions. We will present two procedures for specifying an initial solution: the northwest-corner approach and Vogel's approximation method (VAM).

The Northwest-Corner Approach.   The quickest way to arrive at an initial solution to a transportation problem is to use the *northwest-corner approach*. As you may surmise from the name, the procedure starts in the northwest (upper left-hand) corner of the tableau and allocates as many units as possible to that cell without exceeding (this is important to note) the row capacity or the column requirement. This allocation will completely satisfy either the row or the column constraint. In our example (we restore Buffalo's capacity to 80 units for the rest of the supplement) we can allocate 70 units to the Chicago–Miami route, which eliminates Miami from further allocations, as shown in Fig. S3.3.

We continue to make allocations to satisfy each row or column quantity but do not exceed any of the rim conditions. Thus the sequence of our allocations would be to Chicago–Denver (eliminating the first row), Houston–Denver (eliminating the second column), Houston–Lincoln (eliminating the second row), and so on.

The total cost for this initial solution is $1095, as calculated at the bottom of Fig. S3.3. In general, the northwest-corner approach does not yield low-cost initial solutions. This result is to be expected since costs were not considered in the allocation process. Consequently, we usually must trade off quickness in arriving at an initial solution with added work later in finding the optimal solution.

Vogel's Approximation Method (VAM).   Although **Vogel's approximation method (VAM)** re-

Plant	Warehouse				Capacity
	Miami	Denver	Lincoln	Jackson	
Chicago	7 / 70	2 / 30	4	5	100
Houston	3	1 / 60	5 / 15	2	75
Buffalo	6	9	7 / 30	4 / 50	80
Requirements	70	90	45	50	255 / 255

Total cost = 70($7) + 30($2) + 60($1) + 15($5) + 30($7) + 50($4) = $1095

quires more work than the northwest-corner approach, it normally provides an initial solution that is much closer to the optimal solution. The more useful initial solution results from inclusion of the objective function in making the allocations. Application of VAM to our problem is shown in Fig. S3.4.

We begin by calculating a penalty cost for each row and column. The penalty cost for each row is the difference between the lowest cost element in a row and

the *next largest* cost element in that row. We obtain the penalty cost for each column in the same manner. For example, in our problem the penalty cost for the first row is $2 ($4 − $2), and the penalty cost for the first column is $3 ($6 − $3).

In making our first allocation, we choose the row or column having the largest penalty cost because it is like an opportunity cost. That is, if we do not allocate as many units as possible now to the cell with lowest

Plant	Warehouse				Capacity	VAM Costs
	Miami	Denver	Lincoln	Jackson		
Chicago	7	2	4	5	100	$2
Houston	3 / 70	1	5	2	75	$1
Buffalo	6	9	7	4	80	$2
Requirements	70	90	45	50	255 / 255	
VAM Costs	$3	$1	$1	$2		

(a) Iteration 1

(continued)

Plant	Warehouse				Capacity	VAM Costs
	Miami	Denver	Lincoln	Jackson		
Chicago	7	2	4	5	100	$2
Houston	3 70	1	5	2	75	$1
Buffalo	6	9	7	4 50	80	$3
Requirements	70	90	45	50	255 255	
VAM Costs	–	$1	$1	$2		

(b) Iteration 2

Plant	Warehouse				Capacity	VAM Costs
	Miami	Denver	Lincoln	Jackson		
Chicago	7	2	4	5	100	$2
Houston	3 70	1 5	5	2	75	$4
Buffalo	6	9	7	4 50	80	$2
Requirements	70	90	45	50	255 255	
VAM Costs	–	$1	$1	–		

(c) Iteration 3

cost in that row or column, we may have to allocate units later to the cell with the next largest cost in that row or column. The largest cost penalty is $3, for column 1, so we allocate as many units as we can to the lowest-cost cell in the first column. This is the Houston–Miami route, the allocation is for 70 units, and this allocation satisfies the Miami requirements. If we have a tie in penalty costs, we can arbitrarily choose from the tied rows or columns.

In the second iteration (and thereafter), we have to recalculate the penalty costs to determine whether any have changed because of the last allocation. In this case, only the third-row penalty cost changed because we have eliminated column 1. The $3 penalty cost for the third row is now the largest, so we allocate 50 units to the lowest-cost cell. Even though 80 units of capacity are available in row 3 (Buffalo), the requirement in column 4 (Jackson) is only 50 units.

The rest of the iterations are straightforward. In iteration 3, row 2 has the highest penalty cost. How-

FIGURE S3.4   (continued)

Plant	Warehouse				Capacity	VAM Costs
	Miami	Denver	Lincoln	Jackson		
Chicago	7	2 85	4	5	100	$2
Houston	3 70	1 5	5	2	75	—
Buffalo	6	9	7	4 50	80	$2
Requirements	70	90	45	50	255 / 255	

VAM Costs   — $7 $3   —

(d) Iteration 4

Plant	Warehouse				Capacity
	Miami	Denver	Lincoln	Jackson	
Chicago	7	2 85	4 15	5	100
Houston	3 70	1 5	5	2	75
Buffalo	6	9	7 30	4 50	80
Requirements	70	90	45	50	255 / 255

Total cost = 70($3) + 85($2) + 5($1) + 15($4) + 30($7) + 50($4) = $855

(e) Final Allocation

ever, we can allocate only 5 units to the lowest-cost cell because we had previously allocated 70 units to that row and the capacity is 75 units. We can eliminate column 2 in the fourth iteration by allocating 85 units to the Chicago–Denver route. The final allocation is obvious at this point. Two cells need allocations, and their values are prescribed by the rim conditions. The total cost of this initial solution is $855, which is $240 less than the cost generated by the northwest-corner approach.*

Improving the Solution, Iteration by Iteration
Now that we have a feasible solution, we must find a way to improve it. This improvement process takes place through a series of iterations. With each itera-

*Regardless of the method used for determining an initial solution, the number of allocated cells must equal $m + n - 1$, where m = number of rows and n = number of columns. If we have more than that number, it means that we did not allocate as much as we could to each cell at each step. If we have less than that number, we have a case called *degeneracy*, which we discuss later.

tion, a new solution is found that is at least as good as the solution found in the prior iteration. The process we use assures that a solution is finally reached that cannot be improved upon and therefore is optimal. Three steps are involved at each iteration:

1. Select an **entering route**, which is a nonallocated cell (or route) in the prior iteration that will be introduced in the new solution.
2. Select an **exiting route**, which is an allocated cell (or route) in the prior iteration that will be removed in the new solution to make way for the entering route.
3. Transform the tableau to reflect the impact of this change to all cells, including the cells representing the entering and exiting routes.

Select the Entering Route.   Although there are other approaches to selecting the entering route in a transportation problem, we will discuss the so-called *stepping-stone method* because it is the most intuitive of those available.* The method is named for the procedure utilized. In general terms, we begin by selecting a nonallocated cell for evaluation. We hypothetically allocate one unit to the cell, then adjust the currently allocated cells to balance the affected row capacities and column requirements alternately, without violating the rim conditions. In this respect, the tableau is like a shallow pond of water, with the allocated cells serving as stepping stones. Starting with the nonallocated cell, we move from allocated cell to allocated cell, each time moving at a right angle to the last move, alternately subtracting one unit from and adding one unit to the allocated cells, until we end up at the nonallocated cell again. In so doing, we create a *loop* and satisfy all rim conditions. Fortunately, there is only one loop for each nonallocated cell. We can calculate the net cost advantage from this loop.

Consider Fig. S3.5, which contains the initial solution derived from VAM in Fig. S3.4. An asterisk (*) indicates an allocated cell, and the □ indicates the nonallocated cell that we will evaluate first. The dashed line shows the loop for this cell. The cost of shipping one unit from Chicago to Jackson is $5, but, since Jackson requires only 50 units, we must decrease the shipment from Buffalo to Jackson by one unit at a *savings* of $4. This leaves Buffalo one unit short of its

Net contribution to total cost/unit = $5 − $4 + $7 − $4 = $4

FIGURE S3.5   Loop for the Chicago–Jackson Route

capacity of 80 units, but we know that all of its capacity will be needed because the total requirement from all warehouses equals the total capacity of the plants. Consequently, we added one unit to the Buffalo–Lincoln route, *increasing* costs by $7. In so doing, we have allocated to Lincoln one more unit than it requires, so we reduce the shipment from Chicago to Lincoln by one unit at a *savings* of $4. This completes the loop and the net contribution to total costs is $4 ($5 − $4 + $7 − $4). Since the net contribution is positive, opening a route from Chicago to Jackson is not profitable at this time. It would add $4 to the total cost for each unit shipped.

Figure S3.6 shows the loops for the remaining nonallocated cells, and Table S3.1 shows the calculation of the net contributions for each one. Note that some loops are more complicated than others. The Houston–Jackson loop crosses itself, which is permissible as long as the intersection is at a right angle. The Buffalo–Denver loop passes over the Houston–Denver cell because if we had stopped there, the only right-angle move would have been Houston–Miami. From that position, there is no right-angle move to an allocated cell. Finally, we should mention that loops can be traversed in two directions.

We can now identify the entering route for our problem. From Table S3.1, it is obvious that the only route that would reduce costs is Buffalo–Miami. In general, we would pick the route with the largest negative net contribution.

Select the Exiting Route.   After we have determined the entering route, we allocate as many units to that route as possible. To maintain the same number of shipments (allocated cells) as before, this step im-

---

*Another approach, called the *modified-distribution* (MODI) *method*, actually requires less work but is based on concepts beyond the scope of this supplement. This approach is discussed in Krajewski and Thompson (1981).

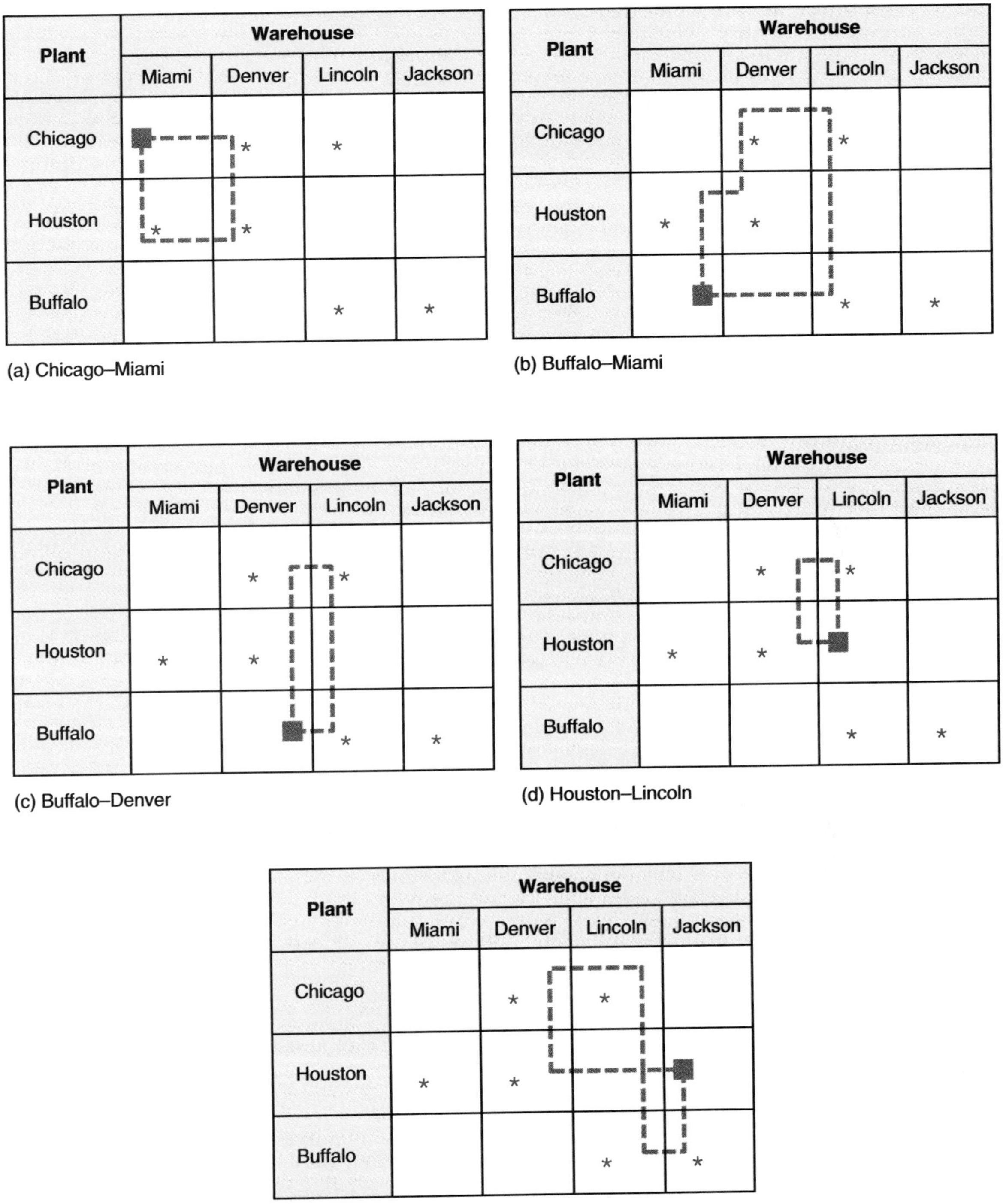

Plant	Warehouse			
	Miami	Denver	Lincoln	Jackson
Chicago	■	*	*	
Houston	*	*		
Buffalo			*	*

(a) Chicago–Miami

Plant	Warehouse			
	Miami	Denver	Lincoln	Jackson
Chicago		*	*	
Houston	*	*		
Buffalo	■		*	*

(b) Buffalo–Miami

Plant	Warehouse			
	Miami	Denver	Lincoln	Jackson
Chicago		*	*	
Houston	*	*		
Buffalo		■	*	*

(c) Buffalo–Denver

Plant	Warehouse			
	Miami	Denver	Lincoln	Jackson
Chicago		*	*	
Houston	*	*	■	
Buffalo			*	*

(d) Houston–Lincoln

Plant	Warehouse			
	Miami	Denver	Lincoln	Jackson
Chicago		*	*	
Houston	*	*		■
Buffalo			*	*

(e) Houston–Jackson

FIGURE S3.6   Loops for the Remaining Nonallocated Cells

TABLE S3.1 / Net Contributions for the Remaining Nonallocated Cells

Shipment Change		Cost Change	Shipment Change		Cost Change
Chicago–Miami			**Houston–Lincoln**		
Add 1 unit	Chicago–Miami	+ $7	Add 1 unit	Houston–Lincoln	+ $5
Subtract 1 unit	Houston–Miami	− $3	Subtract 1 unit	Chicago–Lincoln	− $4
Add 1 unit	Houston–Denver	+ $1	Add 1 unit	Chicago–Denver	+ $2
Subtract 1 unit	Chicago–Denver	− $2	Subtract 1 unit	Houston–Denver	− $1
Net contribution		+ $3	Net contribution		+ $2
Buffalo–Miami			**Houston–Jackson**		
Add 1 unit	Buffalo–Miami	+ $6	Add 1 unit	Houston–Jackson	+ $2
Subtract 1 unit	Houston–Miami	− $3	Subtract 1 unit	Buffalo–Jackson	− $4
Add 1 unit	Houston–Denver	+ $1	Add 1 unit	Buffalo–Lincoln	+ $7
Subtract 1 unit	Chicago–Denver	− $2	Subtract 1 unit	Chicago–Lincoln	− $4
Add 1 unit	Chicago–Lincoln	+ $4	Add 1 unit	Chicago–Denver	+ $2
Subtract 1 unit	Buffalo–Lincoln	− $7	Subtract 1 unit	Houston–Denver	− $1
Net contribution		− $1	Net contribution		+ $2
Buffalo–Denver					
Add 1 unit	Buffalo–Denver	+ $9			
Subtract 1 unit	Chicago–Denver	− $2			
Add 1 unit	Chicago–Lincoln	+ $4			
Subtract 1 unit	Buffalo–Lincoln	− $7			
Net contribution		+ $4			

plies that one of the current shipments must be reduced to zero. (When more than one shipment is reduced to zero, degeneracy results.) We determine the maximum shipping quantity for the entering route and the route that will be removed from the solution by analyzing the loop for the entering route.

Figure S3.7 shows the tableau for the initial solution that we developed using VAM and the loop for the Buffalo–Miami route. The (+) or (−) in the circle of each cell in the loop indicates that we must add or subtract a unit from that cell to satisfy the rim conditions. Note that each row and column affected has one positive cell and one negative cell. To determine the maximum quantity that can be shipped from Buffalo to Miami, we examine the negative cells because these are the cells for which shipping quantities will be reduced. In this example, they are Houston–Miami (70 units), Chicago–Denver (85 units), and Buffalo–Lincoln (30 units). Consequently, the maximum quantity that we can ship along the Buffalo–Miami route is the *minimum* of (70, 85, 30), or 30

units. To ship any more than 30 units would result in a negative quantity in the Buffalo–Lincoln cell and would violate the nonnegativity restriction. Since Buffalo–Lincoln has the minimum allocation of the negative cells in the loop, we remove it from the solution.

Transform the Tableau.   Figure S3.8 shows the new solution to the problem after 30 units have been added to each positive cell and subtracted from each negative cell. The values in the circles are the net contributions for each nonallocated cell of Fig. S3.8 and are calculated in the same manner as those in Table S3.1.

Identifying and Evaluating the Final Solution
The criteria for optimality in transportation problems can be stated as follows:

> *Minimization problems:*   If the net contributions of all nonallocated cells are zero or *positive*, the current solution is optimal.

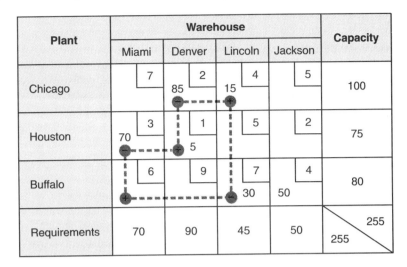

Plant	Warehouse				Capacity
	Miami	Denver	Lincoln	Jackson	
Chicago	7	2 ⊖ 85	4 ⊕ 15	5	100
Houston	3 ⊖ 70	1 ⊕ 5	5	2	75
Buffalo	6 ⊕	9	7 ⊖ 30	4 50	80
Requirements	70	90	45	50	255 / 255

Maximization problems: If the net contributions of all nonallocated cells are zero or *negative*, the current solution is optimal.

Because the net contributions of all six nonallocated cells in Fig. S3.8 are positive, and because this is a minimization problem, the solution shown is optimal—provided that we locate a new plant in Buffalo with an 80-unit capacity. If one or more of the net contributions were still negative, we would have to do another iteration of the tableau. The solution process took only one iteration beyond the initial one. The best distribution plan, with the total transportation cost of $825, is for Chicago to serve Denver and Lincoln with 55 and 45 units, respectively. Houston supplies Miami with 40 units and Denver with 35 units. Finally, Buffalo ships 30 units to Miami and fully satisfies Jackson's demand for 50 units.

Turning to alternative 2, locating the new plant in Atlanta, the solution to the transportation problem results in a total transportation cost of $575. We leave the solution of this problem to you. If transportation cost is the overriding consideration, the new plant should be located in Atlanta. However, management usually considers many other factors before making a final plant location decision. (See Chapter 9.)

Plant	Warehouse				Capacity
	Miami	Denver	Lincoln	Jackson	
Chicago	7 +$3	2 55	4 45	5 +$3	100
Houston	3 40	1 35	5 +$2	2 +$1	75
Buffalo	6 30	9 +$5	7 +$1	4 50	80
Requirements	70	90	45	50	255 / 255

Total cost = 40($3) + 30($6) + 55($2) + 35($1) + 45($4) + 50($4) = $825

DEGENERACY

An optimal solution need never be more than $m + n - 1$ allocated cells, and so the transportation method restricts its search to such solutions. For example, the final solution in Fig. S3.8 has 6 $(3 + 4 - 1)$ plant–warehouse shipments. It is possible, however, to have fewer than $m + n - 1$ allocated cells, a situation called degeneracy. **Degeneracy** can occur in the derivation of an initial solution when we satisfy a row constraint and a column constraint simultaneously

with one allocation, or when we introduce a new route into the solution and more than one negative cell in the loop has the same minimum allocation. Degeneracy is troublesome because without $m + n - 1$ allocated cells, we cannot create loops for each nonallocated cell.

The procedure for dealing with degeneracy involves the allocation of an infinitesimal quantity, ε, to as many nonallocated cells as necessary to bring the total number of allocated cells to $m + n - 1$. It is important that we choose only those nonallocated cells

FIGURE S3.9

Identifying and Dealing with Degeneracy

Plant	Warehouse				Capacity
	Miami	Denver	Lincoln	Jackson	
Chicago	7 / 100	2	4	5	100
Houston	3	1 / 60	5 / 15	2	75
Buffalo	6	9	7 / 30	4 / 50	80
Requirements	100	60	45	50	255 / 255

(a) Tableau with degeneracy using northwest-corner approach

Plant	Warehouse				Capacity
	Miami	Denver	Lincoln	Jackson	
Chicago	7 / 100	2 / ε	4	5	100
Houston	3	1 / 60	5 / 15	2	75
Buffalo	6	9	7 / 30	4 / 50	80
Requirements	100	60	45	50	255 / 255

(b) Tableau with added allocation

having loops that cannot be formed without the ε allocation. Since the value of ε is so small, it does not enter into the total cost of the solution or the shipping quantity for a given route; its only use is in calculating the loops for nonallocated cells. We treat the cell with ε as a typical allocated cell in our calculations, and we continue with the stepping-stone method until we reach the condition of optimality.

Figure S3.9(a) revises the Miami and Denver demand requirements so that degeneracy occurs when applying the northwest-corner approach to find an initial solution (compare with Fig. S3.3). Figure S3.9(b) shows one way of dealing with it, positioning ε in the Chicago–Denver route. This placement allows all of the remaining six nonallocated cells to be evaluated. Some experimentation may be needed to find an acceptable spot for ε because not every placement will allow you to evaluate all six nonallocated cells. For example, you can instead put ε in the Chicago–Lincoln cell but not in the Houston–Jackson cell. For the latter case the Buffalo–Miami route cannot be evaluated.

Review Problems

Supplement Connections: The transportation method of linear programming presented in this supplement is applied in Chapter 9 (Problems 20–25) and Chapter 18 (Problem 14).

Selected References

Hadley, G. *Linear Programming.* Reading, Mass.: Addison-Wesley, 1962.

Hillier, F.S., and G.J. Lieberman. *Introduction to Operations Research,* 2nd ed. San Francisco: Holden-Day, 1974.

Krajewski, L.J., and H.E. Thompson. *Management Science: Quantitative Methods in Context.* New York: John Wiley & Sons, 1981.

Markland, R.E., and J.R. Sweigart. *Quantitative Methods: Applications to Managerial Decision Making.* New York: John Wiley & Sons, 1987.

Taylor, Bernard W., III. *Introduction to Management Science.* Boston: Allyn and Bacon, 1990.

Wagner, H.M. *Principles of Operations Research,* 2nd ed. Englewood Cliffs, N.J.: Prentice-Hall, 1975.

QUEUING MODELS

This supplement discusses simple models that have been derived from queuing theory. Although useful, these models are based on stringent assumptions about the operating environment. More complex queuing problems and many nonqueuing problems, can be analyzed by *simulation*. (See Supplement 5.)

STRUCTURE OF QUEUING PROBLEMS

Analysis of queuing problems begins with a description of the basic elements of the queuing phenomenon as they relate to the specific situation to be analyzed. Figure S4.1 shows these basic elements, which are common to all queuing problems. An **input source** generates potential customers for the **service system**, which consists of one or more queues, a priority discipline, and some service facilities. Some cus-

tomers may decide not to enter the system (*balking* customers). Other customers enter a queue or waiting line. Some of these customers may elect to leave the system before being served (*reneging* customers). A **priority discipline** selects the next customer to be served by the **service facilities**. The system can include one or more facilities, each consisting of a person (or crew), a machine (or group of machines), or both. After the service has been performed, the served customers leave the system.

Besides describing the basic elements of a queuing problem, we must also identify relevant *decision variables* and the *operating characteristics*. We need this information to determine whether to use an appropriate queuing theory model or to develop a simulation model. In this section we discuss the basic elements, operating characteristics, and decision variables.

FIGURE S4.1

Basic Elements of Queuing Problems

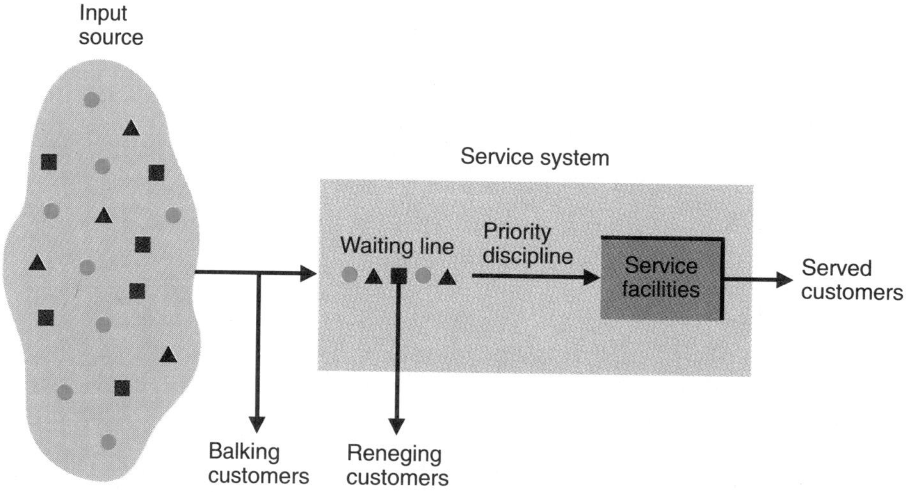

Input Source

An input source is the population of potential customers for the service system. This source can be described by its size, the distribution of customer arrivals, and the disposition of customers.

Size. The input source can be either a *finite* or an *infinite* population of potential customers. This distinction is based on the relative proportion of the input source that can be in the service system at any one time. If the rate (customers per unit of time) at which the input source generates new customers for the service system is appreciably affected by the number of customers already in the system, the input source is said to be finite. Alternatively, an infinite input source is one in which the number of customers in the system does not affect the rate at which the input source generates new customers.

Arrival Distribution. The distribution of customer arrivals is a probability distribution that describes either the number of arrivals per unit of time or the time between successive arrivals, called the **interarrival time**. A Poisson distribution is often used to describe customer arrivals per unit of time. Let A_T be the number of customers arriving during an interval of time, 0, T. If λ is the mean number of customer arrivals per unit of time, the probability that there will be exactly n arrivals during the time interval 0, T is

$$P(A_T = n) = \frac{(\lambda T)^n}{n!} e^{-\lambda T} \qquad \text{for } n = 0, 1, 2, \ldots$$

The mean of the Poisson distribution is λT, and the variance also equals λT.

The Poisson distribution is a discrete distribution; that is, the probabilities are for a specific number of arrivals per unit of time. For example, suppose that customers arrive at a complaint desk in a large department store at the rate of two customers per hour ($\lambda = 2$). The probability that four customers will arrive in the next hour ($n = 4$, $T = 1$) is

$$P(A_1 = 4) = \frac{[2(1)]^4}{4!} e^{-2(1)} = \frac{16}{24} e^{-2} = 0.090$$

It may be more convenient to specify the arrival distribution in terms of customer interarrival times. If the input source generates customers according to a Poisson distribution, we can use the *exponential distribution* to describe the probability that the next customer will arrive in the time interval (0, T). The mean of the distribution is $1/\lambda$, and the variance is $(1/\lambda)^2$. We will defer further discussion of the exponential distribution until we address the service time distribution.

Customer Disposition. Customers in queuing situations can be either *patient* or *impatient*. In this regard, patience has nothing to do with the colorful language a customer may use while waiting in line for a long time on a hot day. A patient customer is one who enters the system and remains there until being served. An impatient customer is one who either estimates the waiting time and decides not to enter the system (balking) or enters the queue but leaves the system before being served (reneging). For the models in this supplement, we make the simplifying assumption that all customers are patient.

Queues

Queues may be described by their size limitations and the number of lines.

Size Limitations. The queue size can be *limited* or *unlimited*. A limited queue is constrained to be no larger than some finite number of customers. Unlimited queues are found in those situations where space or other resource limitations do not impose a limitation on queue length.

Number of Lines. Queues can be designed to be a *single line* or *multiple lines*. Figure S4.2 shows an example of each arrangement. When multiple servers are available and each one can handle general transactions, the single-line arrangement has the advantage of maintaining server utilization at a high level and giving the customer a sense of fairness. Customers believe that they are being served on the basis of when they arrived, not on how well they guessed their waiting time when selecting a particular line, as in the multiple-line arrangement. The multiple-line design is best when some of the servers provide a limited set of services.

Sometimes, queues are not organized neatly into "lines." Machines that need repair on the production floor of a factory remain right where they are when they fail and wait for the maintenance crew to come to them. Nonetheless, we can think of the machines as forming a single line or multiple lines, depending on the number of repair crews and their specialties.

Priority Discipline

When a waiting line forms, the question becomes one of which customer to serve next. Most service systems

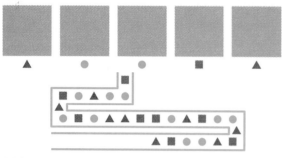

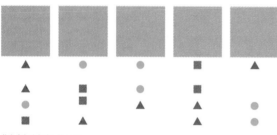

(a) Single line

(b) Multiple lines

FIGURE S4.2   Waiting-Line Arrangements

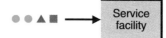

(a) Single channel,
single phase

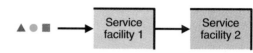

(b) Single channel,
multiple phase

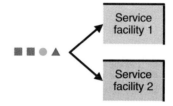

(c) Multiple channel,
single phase

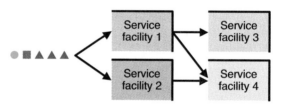

(d) Multiple channel,
multiple phase

that the average person encounters in daily life use the first-come, first-served (FCFS) rule. The customer at the head of the waiting line has the highest priority, and so on, to the customer who last arrived. However, this rule is only one of many priority disciplines used in queuing systems.

The service system may even invoke a **preemptive discipline**. Preemption takes place when a customer of higher priority interrupts the service of another customer. Modeling queuing systems having complex priority disciplines is difficult, and most often in practice simulation is used to analyze these situations (see Supplement 5).

Service Facilities

Service facilities consist of the personnel and/or equipment necessary to perform the service for the customer. They can be characterized by their arrangement and service-time distribution.

Arrangement.   Figure S4.3 shows examples of the five basic types of service facility arrangements. The choice of arrangement is a function of customer volume and the nature of services performed. Some ser-

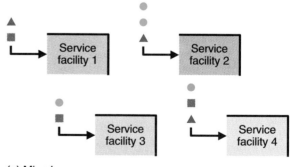

(e) Mixed

Routing for ▲ : 1–2–4
Routing for ● : 2–4–3
Routing for ■ : 3–2–1–4

FIGURE S4.3   Examples of Service Facility Arrangements

vices require a sequence of steps, whereas others require only a single step.

The *single-channel, single-phase* system is based on the assumption that all services demanded by a customer can be performed by a single-server facility. The *single-channel, multiple-phase* arrangement is used when the services are best performed in sequence by more than one facility, yet customer volume or other constraints limit the design to one channel.

The *multiple-channel, single-phase* arrangement is used when demand is large enough to warrant providing the same service at more than one facility or when the services offered by the facilities are different. Figure S4.3 shows a single-line queue for the multiple-channel arrangements. The *multiple-channel, multiple-phase* arrangement is just an extension of the preceding arrangement. In some cases, customers cannot switch channels after service has begun, while in others they can.

However, the most general (and complex) facility arrangement is the *mixed* arrangement. In this situation, each customer has a specific routing between service facilities; consequently, service cannot be neatly described in phases. Queues can develop in front of each facility. The arrival times at each facility are a complex function of variations in processing times and move times between facilities, as well as the priority disciplines and capacities of the other facilities.

Service-Time Distribution. The service-time distribution describes the probability that the service time of the customer at a particular facility will be no more than T time periods. A distribution found to be useful in practice is the *exponential distribution:*

$$P(t \le T) = 1 - e^{-\mu T}$$

where μ is the mean number of customers completing service per unit of time t. The mean of the service-time distribution is $1/\mu$, and the variance is $(1/\mu)^2$. For example, suppose that the clerk at a customer complaint desk can serve an average of three customers per hour. Thus the mean of the service distribution is 1/3 hour (20 minutes). The probability that a customer will require less than 10 minutes ($T = 10/60 = 0.167$ hour) is

$$P(t \le T) = 1 - e^{-3(0.167)}$$

$$= 0.39$$

As T increases, the probability that the customer's service time will be less than T approaches 1.0.

Some characteristics of the exponential distribution do not always conform to an actual situation. An underlying assumption is that each service time is independent of those that preceded it. Consequently, it does not allow for any learning about the work performed and resulting productivity improvements. Another underlying assumption is that very small, as well as very large, service times are possible. This assumption does not hold in situations for which start-up time is fixed, there is some cutoff on total service time, or the service time is constant, or nearly so.

Although we presented these decision areas as though they are independent, they are obviously interrelated. Adjusting the customer arrival rate λ might have to be accompanied by an increase in the service rate μ in some way. Decisions about the number of facilities, the number of phases, and queue arrangements also are related.

Operating Characteristics

Queuing models enable the analyst to study the effects of manipulating decision variables on the operating characteristics of a service system. Some of the more common operating characteristics considered include the following:

1. **Queue length.** The number of customers in the waiting line reflects one of two conditions. Short queues could mean either good customer service or too much capacity. Similarly, long queues could indicate either low server efficiency or the need to increase capacity.
2. **Number of customers in system.** The number of customers in queue and being served also relates to service efficiency and capacity. Large values imply congestion, potential customer dissatisfaction, and a need for more capacity.
3. **Waiting time in queue.** Long lines do not reflect long waiting times if the service rate is fast. However, when waiting time seems long to customers, they perceive that the quality of service is poor. Long waiting times may indicate a need to adjust the service rate of the system or change the arrival rate of customers.
4. **Total time in system.** The total elapsed time from entry into the system until exit from the system may indicate problems with customers, server efficiency, or capacity. If some customers are spending too much time in the service system, there may be a need to change the priority discipline, increase productivity, or adjust capacity in some way.

5. **Service facility utilization.** The collective utilization of the service facilities reflects the percentage of time the facilities are busy. Management is interested in maintaining high utilization, but this objective may adversely impact the other operating characteristics.

The effect of various alternatives to be analyzed for a queuing problem can be expressed in terms of the operating characteristics. If operating characteristics and alternatives can be related to dollars, the effects of an alternative can be expressed in dollars. However, it is difficult to place a dollar figure on certain characteristics (such as the waiting time of a shopper in a grocery store). In such cases, an analyst must weigh the cost of implementing the alternative under consideration against a subjective effect on operating characteristics.

Decision Variables

The analysis of queuing problems involves making decisions in one or more of the following areas:

1. **Arrival rates.** Management often can affect the rate of customer arrivals (λ). Advertising or differential pricing, such as that used by a telephone company for long-distance calls after 5:30 P.M., can affect the rate of demand for services.
2. **Number of service facilities.** The number of service facilities, such as tool cribs, toll booths, or bank tellers, has to be determined. Whether some facilities in a phase should perform a unique set of services has to be decided. These decisions relate to the number of facilities in a particular phase of the service system and, consequently, to the capacity of the system.
3. **Number of phases.** This decision involves the allocation of service tasks to sequential phases of the facility arrangement. At some point, two sequential service facilities may be more efficient than one. In the assembly-line problem discussed in Chapter 10, the decision concerned the number of phases needed along the assembly line. Determining the number of workers needed on the line also involves assigning a certain set of work elements to each one. In addition to affecting the facility arrangement, this decision also affects the service rate (μ) of each facility and the capacity of the system.
4. **Number of servers per facility.** Sometimes, a

service facility is operated by more than one person. Such would be the case when a single facility is defined as a work crew or group of workers (such as the number of workers assigned to a telephone line repair crew). This decision is reflected in the service rate (μ) of the service facility.

5. **Server efficiency.** By adjusting the capital-to-labor ratio, devising improved work methods, or instituting incentive programs, management can affect the efficiency of servers assigned to a service facility. Decisions in this area are reflected in μ, the service rate of the service facility.
6. **Priority discipline.** The priority rule to be used and whether to have a different priority rule for each service facility are important decisions. Whether to allow preemption and, if so, under what conditions is equally important.
7. **Queue arrangement.** Whether to have a single-line queue or a line for each facility in a given phase of service has to be decided.

APPLICATION OF QUEUING MODELS TO OPERATIONS MANAGEMENT

We now turn to some examples of the application of queuing theory models to operations management. To simplify the presentation, we will use the following notation.

λ = mean arrival rate (customers per unit of time)

μ = mean service rate per server (customers per unit of time)

$\dfrac{1}{\lambda}$ = mean time between arrivals

$\dfrac{1}{\lambda_0}$ = mean time between arrivals for a finite input source

$\dfrac{1}{\mu}$ = mean time per customer served

ρ = average utilization of the service facility; sometimes called the traffic density (defined as λ/μ or $\lambda/s\mu$)

L = average number of customers in the service system

L_q = average number of customers in the waiting line

W = average time spent in the system (including service)

W_q = average waiting time in line

n = number of customers in the service system

P_n = probability that there are n customers in the system

N = number of customers in the input source (for the finite input-source case)

s = number of servers

In this section, we analyze problems requiring the single-server, multiple-server, and finite input-source models, all of which are single phase. More advanced models can be found in the references at the end of this supplement.

Application S4.1   *Calculating the Operating Characteristics of a Single-Channel, Single-Phase System*

The manager of a grocery store in Sunnyville is interested in providing good service to the senior citizens who shop in his store. Presently, the store has a separate checkout counter for senior citizens. The senior citizens arrive at the counter at an average of 30 per hour, according to a Poisson distribution, and are served at an average rate of 35 customers per hour, with exponential service times. Find the following averages:

1. Utilization of the checkout clerk
2. Number of customers in the system
3. Number of customers in line
4. Time spent in the system
5. Waiting time in line

Solution

The checkout counter can be modeled as a single-channel, single-phase system. Using the equations for the operating characteristics of the *single-server model* in Table S4.1, we can calculate the average characteristics as follows:

1. The average utilization of the checkout clerk is

$$\rho = \frac{\lambda}{\mu} = \frac{30}{35} = 0.857 \quad \text{or} \quad 85.7\%$$

2. The average number of customers in the system is

$$L = \frac{\lambda}{\mu - \lambda} = \frac{30}{35 - 30} = 6 \text{ customers}$$

3. The average number of customers in line is

$$L_q = \rho L = 0.857(6) = 5.14 \text{ customers}$$

4. The average time spent in the system is

$$W = \frac{1}{\mu - \lambda} = \frac{1}{35 - 30}$$
$$= 0.20 \text{ hour or 12 minutes}$$

5. The average time spent waiting in line is

$$W_q = \rho W = 0.857(0.20)$$
$$= 0.17 \text{ hour or 10.28 minutes}$$

TABLE S4.1 / Single-Server Model

Assumptions	Operating Characteristics
Input source: infinite; no balking or reneging	$\rho = \dfrac{\lambda}{\mu}$
Arrival distribution: Poisson; mean arrival rate = λ	
Service distribution: exponential; mean service time = $1/\mu$	$P_n = (1 - \rho)\rho^n$
Queue: unlimited length; single line	$L = \dfrac{\lambda}{\mu - \lambda}$
Priority discipline: FCFS	$L_q = \rho L$
Number of servers: 1	
Number of phases: 1	$W = \dfrac{1}{\mu - \lambda}$
	$W_q = \rho W$

Consider the Sunnyville grocery in Application S4.1. The manager would like to address the following questions:

1. What service rate would be required to have customers average only 8 minutes in the system?
2. For that service rate, what is the probability of having more than 4 customers in the system?
3. What service rate would be required to have only a 10 percent chance of exceeding 4 customers in the system?

Solution

1. We need to use the equation for the average time in the system and solve for μ.

$$W = \frac{1}{\mu - \lambda}$$

$$8 \text{ minutes} = 0.133 \text{ hour} = \frac{1}{\mu - 30}$$

$$0.133\mu - 0.133(30) = 1$$

$$\mu = 37.52 \text{ customers/hour}$$

2. The probability that there will be more than 4 customers in the system is equal to 1 minus the probability that there are 4 or fewer customers in the system.

$$P = 1 - \sum_{n=0}^{4} P_n$$

$$= 1 - \sum_{n=0}^{4} (1 - \rho)\rho^n,$$

where $\rho = \dfrac{30}{37.52} = 0.80$

$$= 1 - 0.2(1 + 0.8 + 0.8^2 + 0.8^3 + 0.8^4)$$

$$= 1 - 0.672$$

$$= 0.328$$

Therefore there is a nearly 33 percent chance that more than 4 customers will be in the system.

3. We use the same logic as in (2), except that μ is now a decision variable. It is easier first to find the correct average utilization by trial and error and then to solve for the service rate.

$$P = 1 - (1 - \rho)(1 + \rho + \rho^2 + \rho^3 + \rho^4)$$

Try $\rho = 0.7$:

$$0.10 \stackrel{?}{=} 1 - (0.3)(1 + 0.7 + 0.49 + 0.343 + 0.240)$$

$$0.10 \neq 0.168$$

Try $\rho = 0.6$:

$$0.10 \stackrel{?}{=} 1 - (0.4)(1 + 0.6 + 0.36 + 0.216 + 0.1296)$$

$$0.10 \neq 0.078$$

Try $\rho = 0.63$:

$$0.10 \stackrel{?}{=} 1 - (0.37)(1 + 0.63 + 0.3969 + 0.2500 + 0.1575)$$

$$0.10 \approx 0.099$$

Therefore, for a utilization rate of 63 percent, the probability of more than 4 customers in the system is 10 percent. For $\lambda = 30$, the service rate must be

$$\frac{30}{\mu} = 0.63$$

$$\mu = 47.62 \text{ customers/hour}$$

The manager must now find a way to increase the service rate from 35 per hour to approximately 48 per hour. He can increase the service rate in a number of different ways, ranging from employing a high school student to help bag the groceries to incorporating electronic point-of-sale equipment that reads the prices from bar-coded information on each item.

The management of the American Parcel Service terminal in Verona, Wisconsin, is concerned about the amount of time the company's trucks are idle, waiting to be unloaded. The terminal operates with four unloading bays. Each bay requires a crew of two employees, and each crew costs $30 per hour. The estimated cost of an idle truck is $50 per hour. Trucks arrive at an average rate of three per hour, according to a Poisson distribution. A crew can unload a semitrailer rig in an average of one hour, with exponential service times. What is the total hourly cost of operating the system?

The *multiple-server model* in Table S4.2 is appropriate. To find the total cost of labor and idle trucks, we must calculate the average waiting time in the system and the average number of trucks in the system. However, we first need to calculate the average number of trucks in queue and the average waiting time in queue.

The average utilization of the four bays is

$$\rho = \frac{\lambda}{\mu s} = \frac{3}{1(4)} = 0.75 \quad \text{or} \quad 75\%$$

For this level of utilization, we can now compute the probability of no trucks in the system.

$$P_0 = \left[\sum_{n=0}^{s-1} \frac{(\lambda/\mu)^n}{n!} + \frac{(\lambda/\mu)^s}{s!}\left(\frac{1}{1-\rho}\right) \right]^{-1}$$

$$= \frac{1}{\left[1 + 3 + \frac{9}{2} + \frac{27}{6} + \frac{81}{24}\left(\frac{1}{1-0.75}\right) \right]} = 0.0377$$

The average number of trucks in queue is

$$L_q = \frac{P_0(\lambda/\mu)^s \rho}{s!(1-\rho)^2} = \frac{0.0377(3/1)^4(0.75)}{4!(1-0.75)^2} = 1.53 \text{ trucks}$$

The average waiting time in queue is

$$W_q = \frac{L_q}{\lambda} = \frac{1.53}{3} = 0.51 \text{ hour}$$

The average time spent in the system is

$$W = W_q + \frac{1}{\mu} = 0.51 + \frac{1}{1} = 1.51 \text{ hours}$$

Finally, the average number of trucks in the system is

$$L = \lambda W = 3(1.51) = 4.53 \text{ trucks}$$

Consequently, the number of trucks in the system averages 4.53 at all times. We can now calculate the hourly costs of labor and idle trucks as follows:

Labor cost = $30(s)$ = $30(4)	=	$120.00
Idle truck cost = $50(L)$ = $50(4.53)	=	226.50
	Total hourly cost =	$346.50

The Worthington Gear Company had installed a bank of 10 robots about three years ago. The robots have greatly increased the labor productivity of the firm. However, recent attention has been directed to the maintenance function. The firm does no preventive maintenance on the robots because of the high variability in the breakdown distribution. Each machine has an exponential breakdown (or interarrival) distribution with an average time between failures of 200 hours ($\lambda_0 = 0.005$ breakdown per hour). Each machine-hour lost to downtime costs $30, which means that the firm has to react quickly to machine failure. The firm employs one maintenance person, who takes an average

of 10 hours to fix a robot ($\mu = 0.10$). Actual maintenance times have been observed to be exponentially distributed. The wage rate is $10 per hour for the maintenance person, who can be productively put to work elsewhere when not fixing robots. Determine the daily cost of labor and robot downtime.

Solution

The *finite-source model* in Table S4.3 is appropriate for this analysis because there are only 10 machines in the input source and the other assumptions are satisfied. To calculate the cost of labor and robot downtime, we need only to estimate L, the average number of ma-

TABLE S4.2 / Multiple-Server Model

Assumptions	Operating Characteristics
Input source: infinite; no balking or reneging	$\rho = \dfrac{\lambda}{s\mu}$
Arrival distribution: Poisson; mean arrival rate $= \lambda$	$P_0 = \left[\displaystyle\sum_{n=0}^{s-1} \dfrac{(\lambda/\mu)^n}{n!} + \dfrac{(\lambda/\mu)^s}{s!}\left(\dfrac{1}{1-\rho}\right)\right]^{-1}$
Service distribution: exponential; mean service time $= 1/\mu$	$P_n = \begin{cases} \dfrac{(\lambda/\mu)^n}{n!}P_0 & 0 < n < s \\[2mm] \dfrac{(\lambda/\mu)^n}{s!s^{n-s}}P_0 & n \geq s \end{cases}$
Queue: unlimited length; single line	
Priority discipline: FCFS	
Number of servers: s	
Number of phases: 1	$L_q = \dfrac{P_0(\lambda/\mu)^s \rho}{s!(1-\rho)^2}$
	$W_q = \dfrac{L_q}{\lambda}$
	$W = W_q + \dfrac{1}{\mu}$
	$L = \lambda W$

chines in the maintenance system. However, to demonstrate the use of the finite-source model, we will compute all the operating statistics.

The probability that the maintenance system is empty is

$$P_0 = \left[\sum_{n=0}^{N} \frac{N!}{(N-n)!}\left(\frac{\lambda_0}{\mu}\right)^n \right]^{-1}$$

$$= \frac{1}{\displaystyle\sum_{n=0}^{10} \frac{10!}{(10-n)!}\left(\frac{0.005}{0.10}\right)^n} = 0.538$$

The average utilization of the maintenance person is

$$\rho = 1 - P_0$$

$$= 1 - 0.538 = 0.462 \quad\text{or}\quad 46\%$$

The average number of robots waiting to be repaired is

$$L_q = N - \frac{\lambda_0 + \mu}{\lambda_0}(1 - P_0)$$

$$= 10 - \frac{0.005 + 0.10}{0.005}(1 - 0.538)$$

$$= 0.30 \text{ robot}$$

The average number of robots in queue and being re-paired is

$$L = N - \frac{\mu}{\lambda_0}(1 - P_0) = 10 - \frac{0.10}{0.005}(1 - 0.538)$$

$$= 0.76 \text{ robot}$$

The average waiting time of robots for the maintenance person is

$$W_q = L_q[(N - L)\lambda_0]^{-1} = \frac{0.30}{(10 - 0.76)(0.005)}$$

$$= 6.49 \text{ hours}$$

Finally, the average time that a failed robot spends waiting for service and being repaired is

$$W = L[(N - L)\lambda_0]^{-1} = \frac{0.76}{(10 - 0.76)(0.005)}$$

$$= 16.45 \text{ hours}$$

The daily cost of labor and robot downtime is

Labor cost = ($10/hour)(8 hours/day)	= $ 80.00
Idle robot cost = (0.76 robot)($30/robot-hour)(8 hours/day)	= 182.40
Total daily cost	= $262.40

TABLE S4.3 / Finite Source Model

Assumptions	Operating Characteristics
Input source: finite; equals N customers	$P_0 = \left[\sum\limits_{n=0}^{N} \dfrac{N!}{(N-n)!} \left(\dfrac{\lambda_0}{\mu} \right)^n \right]^{-1}$
Arrival distribution: exponential interarrival times; mean $= 1/\lambda_0$	$\rho = 1 - P_0$
Service distribution: exponential; mean service time $= 1/\mu$	$L_q = N - \dfrac{\lambda_0 + \mu}{\lambda_0}(1 - P_0)$
Queue: no more than $N - 1$; single line	$L = N - \dfrac{\mu}{\lambda_0}(1 - P_0)$
Priority discipline: FCFS	$W_q = L_q[(N-L)\lambda_0]^{-1}$
Number of servers: 1	$W = L[(N-L)\lambda_0]^{-1}$
Number of phases: 1	

For the problems we analyzed with the use of queuing theory models in this supplement, we were fortunate that the arrivals had a Poisson distribution (or exponential interarrival times), that the service times had an exponential distribution, that the service facilities had a simple arrangement, and that the priority discipline was first come, first served. Many more models have been developed with queuing theory (see, for example, Cooper, 1980; and Saaty, 1961). However, they get very complex as they deviate from our earlier simplifying assumptions. Many times, the nature of the input source, the constraints on the queue, the priority discipline, the service-time distribution, and the arrangement of the facilities are such that the queuing theory is no longer useful. In these cases, simulation is often used.

COMPUTER SOLVED PROBLEM
Process Design Using Queuing Analysis

The assistant manager at Essex Department Store is considering the possibility of consolidating gift-wrapping into a single station located in the basement. Currently, gift-wrapping is provided on each of the store's three floors. The average arrival rate is 4 customers per hour, and the average time required to wrap a package is 6 minutes. Each attendant is paid $5 per hour. The cost of customer waiting is estimated at $10 per hour. The proposed consolidation would require each customer to spend, on average, an additional 2 minutes to reach the new facility.

a. How many servers should be assigned to the proposed facility to minimize total cost?
b. Is the proposed facility more economically attractive than the current system?
c. Is the total customer waiting time more or less with the proposed system?

d. What are the implications of the final decision if the current attendants can be replaced with senior attendants with a service rate of 13 customers per hour and a wage of $8 per hour?

Solution

This problem is solved using CMOM. Your output may look different if you are using another software package.

a. For the current system, there are 3 separate service facilities, each with a customer arrival rate of 4 customers per hour and a service rate of 10 customers per hour. Using CMOM, the cost for one facility is $11.67; for 3 it is $35.00 per hour. For the new system, the additional 2 minutes to reach the facility reduces the service rate to only 7.5 customers per hour [60/(6 + 2)]. The arrival

PRINTOUT 1

CMOM—QUEUING & WAITING LINES
MULTIPLE SERVER

DATA ENTERED

ARRIVAL RATE	:	12 ◄──────── TOTAL ARRIVAL RATE (3×4)
SERVICE RATE	:	7.5000
COST OF SERVICE	:	5
COST OF WAITING	:	10
LOWER SERVER LIMIT	:	2
UPPER SERVER LIMIT	:	5

CMOM—QUEUING & WAITING LINES
MULTIPLE SERVER

SOLUTION

MULTIPLE SERVER PARAMETRIC ANALYSIS

NO. SERVERS	SYSTEM WAIT	SYSTEM LENGTH	TOTAL COSTS
2	0.3704	4.4444	54.4444
3	0.1594	1.9129	34.1291
4	0.1384	1.6605	36.6047
5	0.1343	1.6122	41.1218

rate is three times that of one of the current facilities. The printout for the current system is not shown.

b. Yes; $34.13 per hour (proposed) versus $35.00 per hour (current). Printout 1 provides the necessary information.

c. Slightly less: 0.1594 per hour (proposed) versus 0.1667 (current). The printout for the current system is not shown.

d. Using senior attendants cannot be justified ($47.76 per hour). The printout for this analysis is not shown.

Review Problems

Supplement Connections: The queuing models presented in this supplement are applied in Chapter 5 (Problems 20–25) and Chapter 8 (Problems 23–26).

Selected References

Cooper, Robert B. *Introduction to Queuing Theory*, 2nd ed. New York: Elsevier-North Holland, 1980.

Hillier, F.S., and G.S. Lieberman. *Introduction to Operations Research*, 2nd ed. San Francisco: Holden-Day, 1975.

Moore, P.M. *Queues, Inventories and Maintenance*. New York: John Wiley & Sons, 1958.

Saaty, T.L. *Elements of Queuing Theory with Applications*. New York: McGraw-Hill, 1961.

Supplement 5

SIMULATION ANALYSIS

Simulation is the act of reproducing the behavior of a system. A **descriptive model** of the system is developed, and certain variables are manipulated to measure their effects on the operating characteristics of interest. A descriptive model, unlike a linear programming model, for example (see Supplement 2), merely describes the system and cannot prescribe what should be done about the problem. It can be used to estimate the operating characteristics of the system under study for alternative solutions to the problem. The alternatives are systematically used in the model and the relevant operating characteristics are recorded. After all the alternatives are tried, the best one is selected, based on the simulation.

The queuing theory models presented in Supplement 4 are actually descriptive models because they describe the operating characteristics of the queuing situation. The difference with simulation is that we do not know the equations for the operating characteristics. We must actually generate customer arrivals, put customers in queues, select the next customer to be served using some priority discipline, serve that customer, and so on. We actually keep track of the number in queue, waiting time, and the like during the simulation and calculate the averages and variances at the end.

Simulation can also be used in analyzing nonqueuing problems. Consider a flight simulator for a major airline. Pilots are tested on the flight simulator periodically. The cockpit of the simulator is identical to that of a real plane. Through the use of computer graphics and other visual and mechanical effects, the pilot feels as though he or she is actually flying the plane. However, the entire process takes place inside a large laboratory.

REASONS FOR USING SIMULATION

We have already said that we would use simulation in queuing situations for which queuing theory models become too complex or are not available. There are also other reasons for using simulation for analyzing operations management problems. First, many practical problems cannot be solved with optimizing methods. The relationship between the variables may be nonlinear and very complex. In addition, there may be too many variables and/or constraints to handle with current optimizing approaches. A simulation model may be the only way to estimate the operating characteristics or objective function values and analyze the problem.

Second, simulation models can be used to conduct experiments without disrupting real systems. Experimenting with a real system can be very costly. It would be unreasonable to go through the expense of purchasing and installing a new flexible manufacturing system without first estimating its benefits in detail from an operating perspective. A simulation model can be used to conduct experiments for a fraction of the cost of installing such a system. Also, the model could be used to evaluate different configurations or processing decision rules. To try any of these methods while attempting to maintain a production schedule would be virtually impossible.

Third, simulation models can be used to obtain operating characteristic estimates in much less time than required to gather the same operating data from a real system. This feature of simulation is called **time compression**. For example, a simulation model of airport operations can generate statistics for a year on airplane arrivals, landing delays, and terminal delays in a

875

matter of minutes on a computer. Alternative airport designs can be analyzed and decisions made quickly.

Finally, simulation is useful in sharpening managerial decision-making skills through gaming. A descriptive model that relates managerial decisions to important operating characteristics (such as profits, market share, and so on) can be developed. From a set of starting conditions, the participants make periodic decisions with the intention of improving one or more operating characteristics. In such an exercise a few hours "play" can simulate a year's time. Gaming also enables managers to experiment with new ideas without disrupting normal operations.

Despite these reasons for using simulation, many practitioners still think of simulation as the method of last resort. Mathematical analysis is still preferred by management scientists because it provides the "best" solution for the problem, whereas simulation requires the analyst to try various alternatives. If the "best" alternative is not on the list of alternatives, only a suboptimal solution will be obtained. In addition, simulation modeling is usually very expensive because of the detail required in the computer model. It is not uncommon for thousands of hours to be spent on programming and debugging complex models. Optimizing approaches, if they apply, are usually less expensive. Nonetheless, simulation is used extensively in practice. Christy and Watson (1983) surveyed non-academic members of the Institute of Management Sciences and the Operations Research Society of America and found that 89 percent of the firms responding used simulation. Of those, the largest category of use was in production (59 percent), followed by corporate planning (53 percent) and engineering (46 percent). It would seem that the so-called last resort is an option often used in practice.

THE SIMULATION PROCESS

The simulation process includes data collection, random-number assignment, model formulation and analysis. This process is known as **Monte Carlo simulation** because of the random numbers used to generate the simulation events.

Data Collection
Simulation is typically a data-intensive approach. Data may be required for costs, productivities, capacities, and probability distributions. There are two typical approaches to data collection. Statistical sampling procedures are used when the data are not readily available from published sources or when the cost of searching for and collecting the data is high. Historical search is used when the data are available in company records, governmental and industry reports, professional and scientific journals, or newspapers.

Application   S5.1   *Data Collection for a Simulation*

The Specialty Steel Products Company produces items such as machine tools, gears, automobile parts, and other specialty items in small quantities to customer order. Because the products are so diverse, demand is measured in machine-hours. Whenever an order for a certain quantity of product comes in, it is translated into required machine-hours, based on time standards for each operation. Management is concerned about capacity in the lathe department. Assemble the data necessary to analyze the addition of one more lathe machine and operator.

Weekly Production Requirements (hr)	Relative Frequency
200	0.05
250	0.06
300	0.17
350	0.05
400	0.30
450	0.15
500	0.06
550	0.14
600	0.02
	1.00

Solution

Historical records indicate that lathe department demand varies from week to week as follows.

To gather these data, all weeks with requirements of 175.00–224.99 hours were grouped in the 200-hour category; all weeks with 225.00–274.99 hours, in the 250-hour category; and so. The average weekly production requirements for the lathe department are

$$200(0.05) + 250(0.06) + 300(0.17) + \cdots + 600(0.02) = 400 \text{ hours}$$

Employees in the lathe department work 40 hours per week on 10 machines. However, the number of machines that are actually operating during any week may be less than 10. Machines may need repair, or a worker may not show up for work. Historical records indicate that actual machine-hours were distributed as follows.

Regular Capacity (hr)	Relative Frequency
320 (8 machines)	0.30
360 (9 machines)	0.40
400 (10 machines)	0.30

The average number of operating machine-hours in a week is 320(0.30) + 360(0.40) + 400(0.30) = 360 hours.

The company has a policy of completing each week's workload on schedule, using overtime and sub-contracting if necessary. The maximum amount of overtime authorized in any week is 100 hours, and any excess requirements over 100 hours are subcontracted to a small machine shop in town. Lathe operators receive $10 per hour for regular time. However, management estimates that it costs $25 per hour per employee for overtime work, which includes premium-wage, variable overhead, and supervision costs. Subcontracting costs $35 per hour, exclusive of materials costs.

Management is considering adding another machine and a worker to the lathe department. To justify the new machine, management estimates that weekly savings in overtime and subcontracting costs should be at least $650. These savings would cover the cost of the additional worker and provide for a reasonable return on machine investment. Prior experience with the uncertainty in available capacity each week is reflected in the estimated distribution of weekly capacity hours with 11 machines.

Regular Capacity (hr)	Relative Frequency
360 (9 machines)	0.30
400 (10 machines)	0.40
440 (11 machines)	0.30

Random-Number Assignment

Before we can begin to analyze this problem with simulation, we must specify a way to generate demand and capacity each week. Suppose that we want to simulate 100 weeks of lathe operations with 10 machines. We would expect that 5 percent of the time (five weeks of the 100) we would have a demand for 200 hours. Similarly, we would expect that 30 percent of the time (30 weeks of the 100) we would have 320 hours of capacity. What about starting our simulation with a demand of 200 hours for the first five weeks, 250 hours for the next six weeks, and so on? Or, using a capacity of 320 hours for the first 30 weeks? The reason for not doing our simulation in this manner is that the real system does not operate that way. Demand may be 200 hours one week but 550 hours the next. However, we certainly want our simulation to generate a demand of 200 hours for 5 percent of the time, as stated in the demand distribution. Similarly, we want to generate a capacity of 320 hours for 30 percent of the time, but not sequentially.

We can obtain the effect we want by using a random-number table to determine the amount of de-mand and capacity each week. A **random number** is a number that has the same probability of being selected as any other number. Appendix 5 at the back of the book contains five-digit random numbers for our use.

The events in the simulation can be generated in an unbiased way if random numbers are assigned to the events in the same proportion as their probability of occurrence. We expect a demand of 200 hours for 5 percent of the time. If we have 100 random numbers (00–99), we can assign 5 numbers (or 5 percent of them) to the event "200 hours demanded." Thus we can assign the numbers 00–04 to that event. If we randomly choose numbers in the range 00–99 enough times, we would expect that 5 percent of the time they would fall in the range of 00–04. Similarly, we can assign the numbers 05–10 to the event "250 hours demanded." In Table S5.1, we show the allocation of the 100 random numbers to the demand events in the same proportion as the probability of their occurrence. We similarly assigned random numbers to the *capacity* events for 10 machines. The capacity events for the 11-machine simulation would have the same random

TABLE S5.1 / Random-Number Assignments to Simulation Events

Event: Weekly Demand (hr)	Probability	Random Numbers	Event: Existing Weekly Capacity (hr)	Probability	Random Numbers
200	0.05	00–04	320	0.30	00–29
250	0.06	05–10	360	0.40	30–69
300	0.17	11–27	400	0.30	70–99
350	0.05	28–32			
400	0.30	33–62			
450	0.15	63–77			
500	0.06	78–83			
550	0.14	84–97			
600	0.02	98–99			

number assignments, except that the events would be 360, 400, and 440 hours, respectively.

Model Formulation

Formulating a simulation model entails specifying the relationships among the variables. Simulation models consist of decision variables, uncontrollable variables, and dependent variables. Decision variables are controlled by the decision maker and will change from one run to the next as different decisions are simulated. For example, the number of lathe machines is the decision variable in the Specialty Steel Products problem in Application S5.1. Uncontrollable variables, however, are random events and not in the control of the decision maker. At Specialty Steel Products, the weekly production requirements and the *actual* number of machine-hours available are un-

controllable variables for the simulation analysis. Dependent variables are dependent on the values of the decision variables and the uncontrollable variables. At Specialty Steel Products, operating characteristics such as idle time, overtime, and subcontracting hours are dependent variables.

The relationships among the variables are expressed in mathematical terms so that the dependent variables can be computed for any values of the decision variables and uncontrollable variables. For example, the simulation model for Specialty Steel Products must specify how weekly production requirements and actual capacity availability will be determined, and then how idle-time hours, overtime hours, and subcontracting hours will be computed given the values for production requirements and capacity hours.

Application S5.2 Formulating a Simulation Model

Formulate a simulation model for Specialty Steel Products that will estimate ide-time hours, overtime hours, and subcontracting hours for a given number of lathes. Design the simulation model to terminate after 20 weeks of simulated lathe department operations.

Solution

We will use the first two rows of random numbers in Appendix 5 for the demand events and the third and fourth rows for the capacity events. Since these are five-digit numbers, we will use only the first two digits of each number for our random numbers. The choice of

the rows in the random number table was arbitrary. The important point is that we must be consistent in drawing random numbers and should not repeat the use of numbers in any one simulation.

To simulate a particular capacity level, we proceed as follows:

1. Draw a random number from Appendix 5 from the first two rows. Start with the first number in the first row, then go to the second number in the first row, and so on.
2. Find the random-number interval for produc-

tion requirements associated with the random number.

3. Record the production hours (PROD) required for the current week.

4. Draw another random number from Appendix 5 from row 3 or row 4. Start with the first number in row 3, then go to the second number in row 3, and so on.

5. Find the random-number interval for capacity (CAP) associated with the random number.

6. Record the capacity hours available for the current week.

7. IF CAP ≥ PROD, then IDLE HR = CAP − PROD.

8. IF CAP < PROD, then SHORT = PROD − CAP. IF SHORT ≤ 100, then OVERTIME HR = SHORT and SUBCONTRACT HR = 0. IF SHORT > 100, then OVERTIME HR = 100 and SUBCONTRACT HR = SHORT − 100.

9. Repeat steps 1–8 until you have simulated 20 weeks.

Analysis

Table S5.2 contains the simulations for the two capacity alternatives at Specialty Steel Products. We used a unique random-number sequence for weekly production requirements for each capacity alternative and another one for the existing weekly capacity to make a direct comparison between the capacity alternatives.

Based on the 20-week simulations, we would expect average weekly overtime hours to be reduced by 12 hours (41.5 − 29.5, highlighted in red) and subcontracting hours to be reduced by 8 hours (18 − 10, highlighted in gray) per week. The average weekly savings would be

$$\text{Overtime} = (12 \text{ hours})(\$25/\text{hour}) = \$300$$

$$\text{Subcontracting} = (8 \text{ hours})(\$35/\text{hour}) = \underline{280}$$

$$\text{Total savings per week} = \underline{\underline{\$580}}$$

This amount falls short of the minimum required savings of $650 per week. Does this mean that we should not add the machine and worker? Before we answer that question, let's look at Table S5.3 (p. 881), which shows the results of a *1000-week* simulation for each alternative. These results are quite different from those of the 20-week simulations. Now the savings are estimated to be $692 ($1851.50 − $1159.50, highlighted in blue) and exceed the minimum required savings for the additional investment. This result emphasizes the importance of selecting the proper run length for a simulation analysis. We must run the simulation long enough to achieve stable results before we begin calculating operating characteristics. Typically, operating characteristics fluctuate widely for short run lengths and stabilize for longer run lengths. We can use statistical tests to check for stability.

Simulation analysis can be viewed as a form of hypothesis testing, whereby the results of a simulation run provide sample data that can be analyzed statistically. When the simulation has achieved stability, data can be recorded and compared with the results from other simulation runs. Statistical tests can also be made to determine whether differences in the alternative operating characteristics are statistically significant. Commonly used statistical methods include *analysis of variance, t-tests,* and *regression analysis.* These techniques require replication of each simulation experiment. For example, if we wanted to test the null hypothesis that the difference between the total weekly costs is zero, we would have to run the simulation model several times for each capacity alternative. Each time, we would use a different set of random numbers to generate weekly production requirements and weekly existing capacity. The number of replications is analogous to the sample size in statistical terminology. If we can show that the weekly cost for 11 machines is significantly different (in a statistical sense) from the weekly cost for 10 machines, we can be more confident in the estimate of the difference between the two.

Even though a difference between simulation experiments may be statistically significant, it may not be *managerially* significant. For example, suppose that we developed a simulation model of a car-wash operation. We may find, by changing the speed of the car wash from 3 minutes per car to 2.75 minutes per car, that we can reduce the average waiting time per customer by 0.20 minute. Even though this may be a statistically significant difference in the average waiting time, the difference is so small that it may not even be noticeable by the customers. What is managerially significant is often a judgment decision.

TABLE S5.2 / 20-Week Simulations of Alternatives

Week	Demand RN	Weekly Prod (hr)	Capacity RN	10 Machines — Existing Weekly Capacity (hr)	Idle Hours	Overtime Hours	Sub-contract Hours	11 Machines — Existing Weekly Capacity (hr)	Idle Hours	Overtime Hours	Sub-contract Hours
1	71	450	50	360		90		400		50	
2	68	450	54	360		90		400		50	
3	48	400	11	320		80		360		40	
4	99	600	36	360		100	140	400		100	100
5	64	450	82	400		50		440		10	
6	13	300	87	400	100			440	140		
7	36	400	41	360		40		400			
8	58	400	71	400				440	40		
9	13	300	00	320	20			360	60		
10	93	550	60	360		100	90	400		100	50
11	21	300	47	360	60			400	100		
12	30	350	76	400	50			440	90		
13	23	300	09	320	20			360	60		
14	89	550	54	360		100	90	400		100	50
15	58	400	87	400				440	40		
16	46	400	82	400				440	40		
17	00	200	17	320	120			360	160		
18	82	500	52	360		100	40	400		100	
19	02	200	17	320	120			360	160		
20	37	400	19	320		80		360		40	
Total					490	830	360		890	590	200
Weekly average					24.5	41.5	18.0		44.5	29.5	10.0

TABLE S5.3 / Comparison of 1000-Week Simulations

	10 Machines	11 Machines
Idle hours	26.0	42.2
Overtime hours	48.3	34.2
Subcontract hours	18.4	8.7
Cost	$1851.50	$1159.50

COMPUTERS AND SIMULATION

It doesn't take much imagination to recognize that analyzing simulation models requires a computer for virtually all real problems. Simulation programming can be done in a variety of computer languages. General-purpose programming languages such as BASIC, FORTRAN, or Pascal can be used. The advantage of general-purpose programming languages is that they are available on most computer systems. Special simulation languages, such as GPSS, SIMSCRIPT, and SLAM, are also available. These languages have the advantage of simplifying programming because they have macro instructions for the commonly used elements of simulation models. These macro statements automatically generate a series of computer instructions needed to accomplish certain tasks. For example, generating arrivals, keeping track of queues, and calculating the statistics on the operating characteristics of a queuing problem is relatively simple with these special languages.

Review Problems

Supplement Connections: The simulation analysis presented in this supplement is applied in Chapter 5 (Problem 26), Chapter 6 (Problem 7), Chapter 7 (Problem 13), Chapter 8 (Problems 27, 28, and 29), and Chapter 13 (Problems 16–19).

Selected References

Christy, David P., and Hugh J. Watson. "The Application of Simulation: A Survey of Industry Practice." *Interfaces*, vol. 13, no. 5 (October 1983), pp. 47–52.

Ernshoff, J.R., and R.L. Serson. *Design and Use of Computer Simulation Models.* New York: Macmillan, 1970.

Hillier, F.S., and G.S. Lieberman. *Introduction to Operations Research*, 2nd ed. San Francisco: Holden-Day, 1975.

Law, Averill M., and W. David Kelton. *Simulation Modeling and Analysis*, 2nd ed. New York: McGraw-Hill, 1991.

Meier, R.C., W.T. Newell, and H.L. Pazer. *Simulation in Business and Economics.* Englewood Cliffs, N.J.: Prentice-Hall, 1969.

Naylor, T.H., et al. *Computer Simulation Techniques.* New York: John Wiley & Sons, 1966.

Solomon, Susan L. *Simulation of Waiting Lines.* Englewood Cliffs, N.J.: Prentice-Hall, 1983.

Watson, Hugh J. *Computer Simulation in Business.* New York: John Wiley & Sons, 1981.

FINANCIAL
AND
STATISTICAL AIDS

APPENDIX 1   PRESENT VALUE FACTORS FOR A SINGLE PAYMENT

Number of Periods (n)	Interest Rate (r)																	
	0.01	0.02	0.03	0.04	0.05	0.06	0.08	0.10	0.12	0.14	0.16	0.18	0.20	0.22	0.24	0.26	0.28	0.30
1	9901	9804	9709	9615	9524	9434	9259	9091	8929	8772	8621	8475	8333	8197	8065	7937	7812	7692
2	9803	9612	9426	9246	9070	8900	8573	8264	7972	7695	7432	7182	6944	6719	6504	6299	6104	5917
3	9706	9423	9151	8890	8638	8396	7938	7513	7118	6750	6407	6086	5787	5507	5245	4999	4768	4552
4	9610	9238	8885	8548	8227	7921	7350	6830	6355	5921	5523	5158	4823	4514	4230	3968	3725	3501
5	9515	9057	8626	8219	7835	7473	6806	6209	5674	5194	4761	4371	4019	3700	3411	3149	2910	2693
6	9420	8880	8375	7903	7462	7050	6302	5645	5066	4556	4104	3704	3349	3033	2751	2499	2274	2072
7	9327	8706	8131	7599	7107	6651	5835	5132	4523	3996	3538	3139	2791	2486	2218	1983	1776	1594
8	9235	8535	7894	7307	6768	6274	5403	4665	4039	3506	3050	2660	2326	2038	1789	1574	1388	1226
9	9143	8368	7664	7026	6446	5919	5002	4241	3606	3075	2630	2255	1938	1670	1443	1249	1084	0943
10	9053	8203	7441	6756	6139	5584	4632	3855	3220	2697	2267	1911	1615	1369	1164	0922	0847	0725
11	8963	8043	7224	6496	5847	5268	4289	3505	2875	2366	1954	1619	1346	1122	0938	0787	0662	0558
12	8874	7885	7014	6246	5568	4970	3971	3186	2567	2076	1685	1372	1122	0920	0757	0625	0517	0429
13	8787	7730	6810	6006	5303	4688	3677	2897	2292	1821	1452	1163	0935	0754	0610	0496	0404	0330
14	8700	7579	6611	5775	5051	4423	3405	2633	2046	1597	1252	0985	0779	0618	0492	0393	0316	0254
15	8613	7430	6419	5553	4810	4173	3152	2394	1827	1401	1079	0835	0649	0507	0397	0312	0247	0195
16	8528	7284	6232	5339	4581	3936	2919	2176	1631	1229	0930	0708	0541	0415	0320	0248	0193	0150
17	8444	7142	6050	5134	4363	3714	2703	1978	1456	1078	0802	0600	0451	0340	0258	0197	0150	0116
18	8360	7002	5874	4936	4155	3503	2502	1799	1300	0946	0691	0508	0376	0279	0208	0156	0118	0089
19	8277	6864	5703	4746	3957	3305	2317	1635	1161	0829	0596	0431	0313	0229	0168	0124	0092	0068
20	8195	6730	5537	4564	3769	3118	2145	1486	1037	0728	0514	0365	0261	0187	0135	0098	0072	0053
21	8114	6598	5375	4388	3589	2942	1987	1351	0926	0638	0443	0309	0217	0154	0109	0078	0056	0040
22	8034	6468	5219	4220	3418	2775	1839	1228	0826	0560	0382	0262	0181	0126	0088	0062	0044	0031
23	7954	6342	5067	4057	3256	2618	1703	1117	0738	0491	0329	0222	0151	0103	0071	0049	0034	0024
24	7876	6217	4919	3901	3101	2470	1577	1015	0659	0431	0284	0188	0126	0085	0057	0039	0027	0018
25	7798	6095	4776	3751	2953	2330	1460	0923	0588	0378	0245	0160	0105	0069	0046	0031	0021	0014
26	7720	5976	4637	3607	2812	2198	1352	0839	0525	0331	0211	0135	0087	0057	0037	0025	0016	0011
27	7644	5859	4502	3468	2678	2074	1252	0763	0469	0291	0182	0115	0073	0047	0030	0019	0013	0008
28	7568	5744	4371	3335	2551	1956	1159	0693	0419	0255	0157	0097	0061	0038	0024	0015	0010	0006
29	7493	5631	4243	3207	2429	1846	1073	0630	0374	0224	0135	0082	0051	0031	0020	0012	0008	0005
30	7419	5521	4120	3083	2314	1741	0994	0573	0334	0196	0116	0070	0042	0026	0016	0010	0006	0004
35	7059	5000	3554	2534	1813	1301	0676	0356	0189	0102	0055	0030	0017	0009	0005	0003	0002	0001
40	6717	4529	3066	2083	1420	0972	0460	0221	0107	0053	0026	0013	0007	0004	0002	0001	0001	0000

$$P = \frac{F}{(1 + r)^n} = Fpf,$$

where

P = Present value of a single investment;
F = Future value of a single payment;
n = Number of periods for which P is to be invested;
r = The periodic interest rate; and
pf = The present value factor for \$1 = $1/(1 + r)^n$.

Number of Periods (n)	Interest Rate (r)																	
	0.01	0.02	0.03	0.04	0.05	0.06	0.08	0.10	0.12	0.14	0.16	0.18	0.20	0.22	0.24	0.26	0.28	0.30
1	0.9901	0.9804	0.9709	0.9615	0.9524	0.9434	0.9259	0.9091	0.8929	0.8772	0.8621	0.8475	0.8333	0.8197	0.8065	0.7937	0.7812	0.7692
2	1.9704	1.9416	1.9135	1.8861	1.8594	1.8334	1.7833	1.7355	1.6901	1.6467	1.6052	1.5656	1.5278	1.4915	1.4568	1.4235	1.3916	1.3609
3	2.9410	2.8839	2.8286	2.7751	2.7232	2.6730	2.5771	2.4869	2.4018	2.3216	2.2459	2.1743	2.1065	2.0422	1.9813	1.9234	1.8684	1.8161
4	3.9020	3.8077	3.7171	3.6299	3.5460	3.4651	3.3121	3.1699	3.0373	2.9137	2.7982	2.6901	2.5887	2.4936	2.4043	2.3202	2.2410	2.1662
5	4.8534	4.7135	4.5797	4.4518	4.3295	4.2124	3.9927	3.7908	3.6048	3.4331	3.2743	3.1272	2.9906	2.8636	2.7454	2.6351	2.5320	2.4356
6	5.7955	5.6014	5.4172	5.2421	5.0757	4.9173	4.6229	4.3553	4.1114	3.8887	3.6847	3.4976	3.3255	3.1669	3.0205	2.8850	2.7594	2.6427
7	6.7282	6.4720	6.2303	6.0021	5.7864	5.5824	5.2064	4.8684	4.5638	4.2883	4.0386	3.8115	3.6046	3.4155	3.2423	3.0833	2.9370	2.8021
8	7.6517	7.3255	7.0197	6.7327	6.4632	6.2098	5.7466	5.3349	4.9676	4.6389	4.3436	4.0776	3.8372	3.6193	3.4212	3.2407	3.0758	2.9247
9	8.5660	8.1622	7.7861	7.4353	7.1078	6.8017	6.2469	5.7590	5.3282	4.9464	4.6065	4.3030	4.0310	3.7863	3.5655	3.3657	3.1842	3.0190
10	9.4713	8.9826	8.5302	8.1109	7.7217	7.3601	6.7101	6.1446	5.6502	5.2161	4.8332	4.4941	4.1925	3.9232	3.6819	3.4648	3.2689	3.0915
11	10.3676	9.7868	9.2526	8.7605	8.3064	7.8869	7.1390	6.4951	5.9377	5.4527	5.0286	4.6560	4.3271	4.0354	3.7757	3.5435	3.3351	3.1473
12	11.2551	10.5753	9.9540	9.3851	8.8633	8.3838	7.5361	6.8137	6.1944	5.6603	5.1971	4.7932	4.4392	4.1274	3.8514	3.6059	3.3868	3.1903
13	12.1337	11.3484	10.6350	9.9856	9.3936	8.8527	7.9038	7.1034	6.4235	5.8424	5.3423	4.9095	4.5327	4.2028	3.9124	3.6555	3.4272	3.2233
14	13.0037	12.1062	11.2961	10.5631	9.8986	9.2950	8.2442	7.3667	6.6282	6.0021	5.4675	5.0081	4.6106	4.2646	3.9616	3.6949	3.4587	3.2487
15	13.8651	12.8493	11.9379	11.1184	10.3797	9.7122	8.5595	7.6061	6.8109	6.1422	5.5755	5.0916	4.6755	4.3152	4.0013	3.7261	3.4834	3.2682
16	14.7179	13.5777	12.5611	11.6523	10.8378	10.1059	8.8514	7.8237	6.9740	6.2651	5.6685	5.1624	4.7296	4.3567	4.0333	3.7509	3.5026	3.2832
17	15.5623	14.2919	13.1661	12.1657	11.2741	10.4773	9.1216	8.0216	7.1196	6.3729	5.7487	5.2223	4.7746	4.3908	4.0591	3.7705	3.5177	3.2948
18	16.3983	14.9920	13.7535	12.6593	11.6896	10.8276	9.3719	8.2014	7.2497	6.4674	5.8178	5.2732	4.8122	4.4187	4.0799	3.7861	3.5294	3.3037
19	17.2260	15.6785	14.3238	13.1339	12.0853	11.1581	9.6036	8.3649	7.3658	6.5504	5.8775	5.3162	4.8435	4.4415	4.0967	3.7985	3.5386	3.3105
20	18.0456	16.3514	14.8775	13.5903	12.4622	11.4699	9.8181	8.5136	7.4694	6.6231	5.9288	5.3527	4.8696	4.4603	4.1103	3.8083	3.5458	3.3158
21	18.8570	17.0112	15.4150	14.0292	12.8212	11.7641	10.0168	8.6487	7.5620	6.6870	5.9731	5.3837	4.8913	4.4756	4.1212	3.8161	3.5514	3.3198
22	19.6604	17.6580	15.9369	14.4511	13.1630	12.0416	10.2007	8.7715	7.6446	6.7429	6.0113	5.4099	4.9094	4.4882	4.1300	3.8223	3.5558	3.3230
23	20.4558	18.2922	16.4436	14.8568	13.4886	12.3034	10.3711	8.8832	7.7184	6.7921	6.0442	5.4321	4.9245	4.4985	4.1371	3.8273	3.5592	3.3254
24	21.2434	18.9139	16.9355	15.2470	13.7986	12.5504	10.5288	8.9847	7.7843	6.8351	6.0726	5.4509	4.9371	4.5070	4.1428	3.8312	3.5619	3.3272
25	22.0232	19.5235	17.4131	15.6221	14.0939	12.7834	10.6748	9.0770	7.8431	6.8729	6.0971	5.4669	4.9476	4.5139	4.1474	3.8342	3.5640	3.3286
26	22.7952	20.1210	17.8768	15.9828	14.3752	13.0032	10.8100	9.1609	7.8957	6.9061	6.1182	5.4804	4.9563	4.5196	4.1511	3.8367	3.5656	3.3297
27	23.5596	20.7069	18.3270	16.3296	14.6430	13.2105	10.9352	9.2372	7.9426	6.9352	6.1364	5.4919	4.9636	4.5243	4.1542	3.8387	3.5669	3.3305
28	24.3164	21.2813	18.7641	16.6631	14.8981	13.4062	11.0511	9.3066	7.9844	6.9607	6.1520	5.5016	4.9697	4.5281	4.1566	3.8402	3.5679	3.3312
29	25.0658	21.8444	19.1885	16.9837	15.1411	13.5907	11.1584	9.3696	8.0218	6.9830	6.1656	5.5098	4.9747	4.5312	4.1585	3.8414	3.5687	3.3317
30	25.8077	22.3965	19.6004	17.2920	15.3725	13.7648	11.2578	9.4269	8.0552	7.0027	6.1772	5.5168	4.9789	4.5338	4.1601	3.8424	3.5693	3.3321
35	29.4086	24.9986	21.4872	18.6646	16.3742	14.4982	11.6546	9.6442	8.1755	7.0700	6.2153	5.5386	4.9915	4.5411	4.1644	3.8450	3.5708	3.3330
40	32.8347	27.3555	23.1148	19.7928	17.1591	15.0463	11.9246	9.7791	8.2438	7.1050	6.2335	5.5482	4.9966	4.5439	4.1659	3.8458	3.5712	3.3332

$$P = \frac{A}{(1+r)} + \frac{A}{(1+r)^2} + \cdots + \frac{A}{(1+r)^n} = A\sum_{j=1}^{n} 1/(1+r)^j = Aaf,$$

where

P = Present value of a single investment;

A = Amount of annuity to be received at the end of each period;

n = Number of periods for which the annuity is received.

r = The periodic interest rate; and

af = The annuity factor for an annuity of $1 =

$$\sum_{j=1}^{n} 1/(1+r)^j.$$

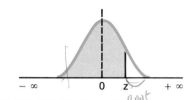

	.00	.01	.02	.03	.04	.05	.06	.07	.08	.09
.0	.5000	.5040	.5080	.5120	.5160	.5199	.5239	.5279	.5319	.5359
.1	.5398	.5438	.5478	.5517	.5557	.5596	.5636	.5675	.5714	.5753
.2	.5793	.5832	.5871	.5910	.5948	.5987	.6026	.6064	.6103	.6141
.3	.6179	.6217	.6255	.6293	.6331	.6368	.6406	.6443	.6480	.6517
.4	.6554	.6591	.6628	.6664	.6700	.6736	.6772	.6808	.6844	.6879
.5	.6915	.6950	.6985	.7019	.7054	.7088	.7123	.7157	.7190	.7224
.6	.7257	.7291	.7324	.7357	.7389	.7422	.7454	.7486	.7517	.7549
.7	.7580	.7611	.7642	.7673	.7704	.7734	.7764	.7794	.7823	.7852
.8	.7881	.7910	.7939	.7967	.7995	.8023	.8051	.8078	.8106	.8133
.9	.8159	.8186	.8212	.8238	.8264	.8289	.8315	.8340	.8365	.8389
1.0	.8413	.8438	.8461	.8485	.8508	.8531	.8554	.8577	.8599	.8621
1.1	.8643	.8665	.8686	.8708	.8729	.8749	.8770	.8790	.8810	.8830
1.2	.8849	.8869	.8888	.8907	.8925	.8944	.8962	.8980	.8997	.9015
1.3	.9032	.9049	.9066	.9082	.9099	.9115	.9131	.9147	.9162	.9177
1.4	.9192	.9207	.9222	.9236	.9251	.9265	.9279	.9292	.9306	.9319
1.5	.9332	.9345	.9357	.9370	.9382	.9394	.9406	.9418	.9429	.9441
1.6	.9452	.9463	.9474	.9484	.9495	.9505	.9515	.9525	.9535	.9545
1.7	.9554	.9564	.9573	.9582	.9591	.9599	.9608	.9616	.9625	.9633
1.8	.9641	.9649	.9656	.9664	.9671	.9678	.9686	.9693	.9699	.9706
1.9	.9713	.9719	.9726	.9732	.9738	.9744	.9750	.9756	.9761	.9767
2.0	.9772	.9778	.9783	.9788	.9793	.9798	.9803	.9808	.9812	.9817
2.1	.9821	.9826	.9830	.9834	.9838	.9842	.9846	.9850	.9854	.9857
2.2	.9861	.9864	.9868	.9871	.9875	.9878	.9881	.9884	.9887	.9890
2.3	.9893	.9896	.9898	.9901	.9904	.9906	.9909	.9911	.9913	.9916
2.4	.9918	.9920	.9922	.9925	.9927	.9929	.9931	.9932	.9934	.9936
2.5	.9938	.9940	.9941	.9943	.9945	.9946	.9948	.9949	.9951	.9952
2.6	.9953	.9955	.9956	.9957	.9959	.9960	.9961	.9962	.9963	.9964
2.7	.9965	.9966	.9967	.9968	.9969	.9970	.9971	.9972	.9973	.9974
2.8	.9974	.9975	.9976	.9977	.9977	.9978	.9979	.9979	.9980	.9981
2.9	.9981	.9982	.9982	.9983	.9984	.9984	.9985	.9985	.9986	.9986
3.0	.9987	.9987	.9987	.9988	.9988	.9989	.9989	.9989	.9990	.9990
3.1	.9990	.9991	.9991	.9991	.9992	.9992	.9992	.9992	.9993	.9993
3.2	.9993	.9993	.9994	.9994	.9994	.9994	.9994	.9995	.9995	.9995
3.3	.9995	.9995	.9995	.9996	.9996	.9996	.9996	.9996	.9996	.9997
3.4	.9997	.9997	.9997	.9997	.9997	.9997	.9997	.9997	.9997	.9998

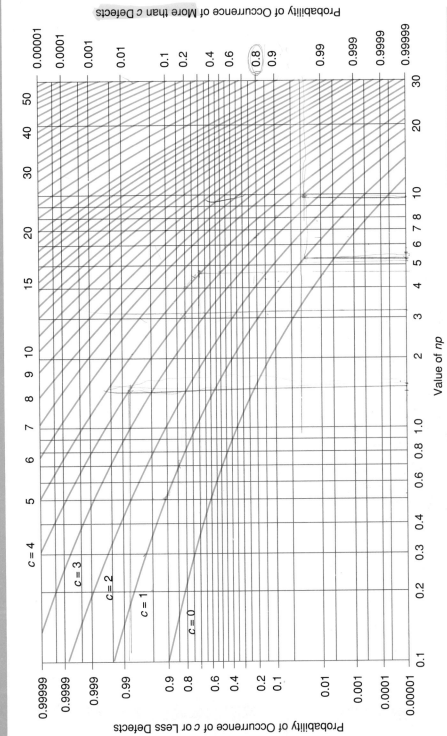

Probability of Occurrence of More than c Defects

Value of np

Probability of Occurrence of c or Less Defects

Source: Harold F. Dodge and Harry G. Romig, *Sampling Inspection Tables*, 2d ed., copyright © 1959, New York: John Wiley & Sons and copyright © 1959, Bell Telephone Laboratories, Inc. Reprinted with permission.

71509	68310	48213	99928	64650	13229	36921	58732	13459	93487
21949	30920	23287	89514	58502	46185	00368	82613	02668	37444
50639	54968	11409	36148	82090	87298	41396	71111	00076	60029
47837	76716	09653	54466	87987	82362	17933	52793	17641	19502
31735	36901	92295	19293	57582	86043	69502	12601	00535	82697
04174	32342	66532	07875	54445	08795	63563	42295	74646	73120
96980	68728	21154	56181	71843	66134	52396	89723	96435	17871
21823	04027	76402	04655	87276	32593	17097	06913	05136	05115
25922	07122	31485	52166	07645	85122	20945	06369	70254	22806
32530	98882	19105	01769	20276	59401	60426	03316	41438	22012
00159	08461	51810	14650	45119	97920	08063	70819	01832	53295
66574	21384	75357	55888	83429	96916	73977	87883	13249	28870
00995	28829	15048	49573	65277	61493	44031	88719	73057	66010
55114	79226	27929	23392	06432	50200	39054	15528	53483	33972
10614	25190	52647	62580	51183	31338	60008	66595	64357	14985
31359	77469	58126	59192	23371	25190	37841	44386	92420	42965
09736	51873	94595	61367	82091	63835	86858	10677	58209	59820
24709	23224	45788	21426	63353	29874	51058	29958	61220	61199
79957	67598	74102	49824	39305	15069	56327	26905	34453	53964
66616	22137	72805	64420	58711	68435	60301	28620	91919	96080
01413	27281	19397	36231	05010	42003	99865	20924	76151	54089
88238	80731	20777	45725	41480	48277	45704	96457	13918	52375
57457	87883	64273	26236	61095	01309	48632	00431	63730	18917
21614	06412	71007	20255	39890	75336	89451	88091	61011	38072
26466	03735	39891	26361	86816	48193	33492	70484	77322	01016
97314	03944	04509	46143	88908	55261	73433	62538	63187	57352
91207	33555	75942	41668	64650	38741	86189	38197	99112	59694
46791	78974	01999	78891	16177	95746	78076	75001	51309	18791
34161	32258	05345	79267	75607	29916	37005	09213	10991	50451
02376	40372	45077	73705	56076	01853	83512	81567	55951	27156
33994	56809	58377	45976	01581	78389	18268	90057	93382	28494
92588	92024	15048	87841	38008	80689	73098	39201	10907	88092
73767	61534	66197	47147	22994	38197	60844	86962	27595	49907
51517	39870	94094	77092	94595	37904	27553	02229	44993	10468
33910	05156	60844	89012	21154	68937	96477	05867	95809	72827
09444	93069	61764	99301	55826	78849	26131	28201	91417	98172
96896	43760	72890	78682	78243	24061	55449	53587	77574	51580
97523	54633	99656	08503	52563	12099	52479	74374	79581	57143
42568	30794	32613	21802	73809	60237	70087	36650	54487	43718
45453	33136	90246	61953	17724	42421	87611	95369	42108	95369
52814	26445	73516	24897	90622	35018	70087	60112	09025	05324
87318	33345	14546	15445	81588	75461	12246	47858	08983	18205
08063	83575	25294	93027	09988	04487	88364	31087	22200	91019
53400	62078	52103	25650	75315	18916	06809	88217	12245	33053
90789	60614	20862	34475	11744	24437	55198	55219	74730	59820
73684	25859	86858	48946	30941	79017	53776	72534	83638	44680
82007	12183	89326	53713	77782	50368	01748	39033	47042	65758
80208	30920	97774	41417	79038	60531	32990	57770	53441	58732
62434	96122	63019	58439	89702	38657	60049	88761	22785	66093
04718	83199	65863	58857	49886	70275	27511	99426	53985	84077

AUTHOR INDEX

SUBJECT INDEX

Elemental standard data approach, 265
e-mail (electronic mail) system, 223
Employee(s). *See also* Work force
  compensation plans and, 279–280
  JIT systems and, 716
  quality improvement and, 107–108
  technological change and, 220–221
Employee empowerment, 254–255
Employee involvement, 254–256
End effector, 235
End item, 502–503
Engineering, 14
  concurrent, 41
  quality, 118–119
Entering route, selecting,
    transportation method and, 857
Entering variables, simplex method
    and, 841, 842–843
Entrance-exit strategies, 36–37
Environmental scanning, 18–19
Equality, simplex method and, 846–
    847
Equipment
  owning versus leasing, 191
  utilization of, 508
Error, forecast. *See* Forecast error
Euclidean distance, 352
European Community (EC),
    globalization in, 340–341
Exception reports, inventory
    management and, 558
Executive judgment, forecasting and,
    463–464
Exiting route, selecting,
    transportation method and, 857–
    860
Exiting variables, simplex method
    and, 841–842
Exit strategies, 36–37
Expansion, on-site, 348
Expansionist strategy, 305
Expected payoff, 553–554
Experience curve, 273
Exponential distribution, queuing
    models and, 864, 866
Exponential smoothing, 443–445
  trend-adjusted, 446–447
External failure costs, 97, 101–103
  litigation and, 102–103
  warranty costs and, 101–102

Facility location, 344. *See also*
    Location
Facsimile (fax) machine, 224
Failure costs
  external, 97, 101–103
  internal, 97–101
Fast delivery time, 48
Fax (facsimile) machine, 224
Feasible region, 839
Final design, in product and service
    planning, 42
Finance, 14

Financial analysis, 829–834
  cash flow determination and, 830–
    832
  managing by the numbers and,
    833–834
  net present value method and, 833
  payback method and, 833
  time value of money and, 829–830
Financial criteria, in screening ideas
    for new products and services,
    38, 40
Financial planning
  aggregate plans and, 579
  learning curves and, 278
Financial services, technology in,
    225–226
Firm planned order, 666
First-come, first-served (FCFS) rule,
    730, 865
Fishbone diagram, 113
Fixed automation, 230–231
Fixed costs, 44
  capacity planning and, 301
Fixed order quantity (FOQ), 655
Fixed order quantity system. *See*
    Continuous review system
Fixed-position layout, 382
Flexibility
  as competitive priority, 49
  layout, 384
  resource, 181, 183–185
  volume, 49
  of work force, JIT system and,
    703
Flexible automation, 231–232
Flexible manufacturing systems
    (FMS), 237, 239–240
Flow(s)
  cash, determining, 830–832
  process-focused strategy and, 64
  product-focused strategy and, 69,
    72
Flow diagrams, process analysis and,
    196
Flow shop, 56
Focused facilities, construction, 302–
    303
Focus forecasting, 450–451
Follow-the-leader strategy, 306
Forecast, 430
Forecast error, 452–456
Forecasting, 429–476, 815
  causal methods for, 436, 459–462
  choosing technique for, 436–438
  with computers, 438
  demand characteristics and, 430–
    435
  designing system for, 435–438
  error and, 452–456
  focus, 450–451
  level of aggregation and, 435
  linear regression and, 459–462
  long term, 437–438
  medium term, 437

qualitative methods for, 436, 462–
    466
  short term, 436
  technological, 465–466
  time series analysis and. *See* Time
    series analysis
  units of measurement and, 435–436
Forward integration, 188
From-to matrix, 390–391
Functional interfaces, master
    production schedule and, 622
Future value of an investment, 829

Gantt charts, 727–728
  computers and, 789
General-purpose plant, 357
Geographic diversity, location
    decisions and, 337
Global firms, 344
Globalization, 339–344
Global priority rules, 731, 735–738
  multiple-work station scheduling
    and, 737–738
  two-work station flow shop and,
    735–736
Goods, 5
Graphical method of linear
    programming, 838–840
Graphics, 226
Greater-than-or-equal-to constraints,
    simplex method and, 846–847
Group technology (GT), 387–389
Growth stage, in product life cycle,
    33
Guassian elimination, 842

Hardware quality, 92
Heuristics, location analysis and, 361–
    362
High-performance design, 48
Hiring costs, aggregate planning and,
    590
Holding costs
  aggregate planning and, 590
  of inventory, 506–507
Hollow corporation, 190
Homogeneity, statistical process
    control and, 147
Human resources, 14
Hybrid inventory control systems,
    549–550
Hybrid layout, 382, 385–389
  group technology and, 387–389
  one worker, multiple machines,
    385–386

Idea generation, in product and
    service planning, 38
Idle time, line balancing and, 405
Imaging machines, 228
Immediate processors, 401
Incentive plans, individual, 280
Independent demand, 504–505

Order(s) (*continued*)
economic order quantity and, 533–538
firm planned order and, 666
new, releasing, 662
open, 510
periodic order quantity and, 656
placing, 493
planned order releases and, 653
receiving, 493
time between, 537
tracking, 493
Ordering cost, 507
Organizational barriers, to quality improvement, 106–107
Organizational strategy. *See* Corporate strategy
Organizational structure
inventory management and, 518
restructuring and, 255
Original-equipment manufacturer (OEM), 188
Output measures, capacity planning and, 298–299
Output rate, line balancing and, 403
Overlapped operations, 385
Overtime, aggregate plans and, 583
Overtime costs, aggregate planning and, 590

Pacing, layout and, 408
Parent, 502
Parent company, proximity to, location decisions and, 346
Part commonality, 503
Past due measure, 729
Payback method, 833
Payoff matrix, 553
p-Charts, 139–141
$\bar{x}$-charts versus, 146
Penalty costs, 781
Performance criteria, layout and, 383–384
Performance measures, operations scheduling and, 728–730
Performance rating factor (RF), 262
Periodic order quantity (POQ), 656
Periodic review system, 545–549
comparative advantages of, 547–548, 549
selecting reorder interval and, 546
selecting target inventory level and, 546–547
Perpetual inventory system, 548
Physical arrangement, 378–379. *See also* Layout
Physical constraints, identifying for aggregate planning, 589–590
Piece rate plans, 280
Pilot study, 259
Pipeline inventory, 510–511
reduction of, 516
Pivot element, simplex method and, 842–843

Planned order releases, MRP inventory record and, 653
Planned receipts, MRP inventory record and, 652–653
Planning. *See also* Material requirements planning
financial, 278, 579
hybrid, 385–389
layout, 378–379
long-range. *See* Corporate strategy
for new products and services. *See* Product and service planning process. *See* Process layouts
sequential-sampling plan and, 158–159
strategic issues in, 379–384
strategy versus tactics and, 21–22
technological change and, 220
Planning horizons
aggregate plans and, 578
inventory management and, 518
Planning orientation, 825
Planning stage, in product life cycle, 32–33
Planning strategies, for aggregate plans, 585–587
Planning time fence, 630
Plant charters, 356–357
Plants within plants (PWP), 302
Police officers, scheduling, 745–746
Policy constraints, identifying for aggregate planning, 589–590
Pooling effect, 497
Positioning strategies, 54–73
intermediate, 56
JIT systems and, 713
process focus and, 54–55, 56, 58–65
product focus and, 55, 56–57, 65–73
for services, 57
Precedence diagram, 401
Precedence relationship, 766
Predetermined data approach, 265–267
Preemptive discipline, queuing models and, 865
Preemptive pricing, 37
Preference matrix, 42–44
Present value factors, 830
Present value of an investment, 829–830
Prevention costs, 96–97
Preventive maintenance, JIT system and, 704
Price
shadow, 844–845
supplier selection and, 493
Price break, 551
Pricing
aggregate plans and, 585
preemptive, 37
Priority dependency, 663–664
Priority discipline, queuing models and, 863, 864–865, 867
Priority planning, with material requirements planning, 663–668

Priority sequencing rules, 730–738
global, 731, 735–738
local, 731, 732–735
Privacy, office layouts and, 399
Private carrier, 500
Probabilities, analyzing, 777–780
Problem-solving work teams, 254
Process, JIT systems and, 717
Process advantages, capacity planning and, 302
Process analysis, 195–201
flow diagrams and, 196
multiple activity charts and, 200–201
process charts and, 197–200
Process capability, variation and, 133
Process charts, 197–200
Process control. *See also* Statistical process control
variation and, 133
Process design, 179–206, 815, 819–820. *See also* Process analysis
capital budgeting and, 194–195
capital intensity and, 181, 182–183
customer involvement and, 181, 192–193
definition of, 180–181
linking product or service design to, 112–113
process-focused strategy and, 60
product-focused strategy and, 67–68
quality improvement and, 109–113
queuing models and, 872
relationship between facets of, 193–194
resource flexibility and, 181, 183–185
vertical integration and, 181, 188–191
Process-focused strategy, 54–55, 56, 58–65, 818
capacity and location and, 61
layout and flow and, 61, 64
materials management, staffing plans, inventory, and scheduling and, 64–65
process design, technology, and job design and, 60–61
service plans, competitive priorities, and quality and, 60
Process layouts, 381, 389–400, 822
decision tools for, 394–395
designing, 389–395
for offices, 398–400
for warehouses, 395–397
Process plant, 357
Producer's risk (α), 149
Product(s). *See also* New products and services
complementary, 584–585
manufacturing versus services and, 5
Product and service planning, 31–46, 815, 818